Fourth Edition

STATICS AND STRENGTH OF MATERIALS FOR ARCHITECTURE AND BUILDING CONSTRUCTION

Barry S. Onouye

Kevin Kane

Pearson

Original edition, entitled *Statistics and Strength of Materials for Architecture and Building Construction: Pearson New International Edition*, 4th Edition, by Onouye Barry S, Kane Kevin published by Pearson Education, Inc, Publishing as Personal International, Copyright © 2013 by Pearson Education, Inc.

ISBN 978-93-325-4501-4

First Impression, 2015
Second Impression, 2017

Published by Pearson India Education Services Pvt. Ltd, CIN: U72200TN2005PTC057128, formerly known as TutorVista Global Pvt. Ltd, licensee of Pearson Education in South Asia.

Head Office: 15th Floor, Tower-B, World Trade Tower, Plot No. 1, Block-C, Sector-16, Noida 201 301, Uttar Pradesh, India.

Registered Office: 4th Floor, Software Block, Elnet Software City, TS-140, Block 2 & 9, Rajiv Gandhi Salai, Taramani, Chennai 600 113, Tamil Nadu, India.
Fax: 080-30461003, Phone: 080-30461060
www.pearson.co.in, Email: companysecretary.india@pearson.com

Printed in India by Rahul Print O Pack

Table of Contents

Introduction

Figure 1 Radial, spiral pattern of the spider web.

1 DEFINITION OF STRUCTURE

Structure is defined as something made up of interdependent parts in a definite pattern of organization (Figures 1 and 2)—an interrelation of parts as determined by the general character of the whole. Structure, particularly in the natural world, is a way of achieving the most strength from the least material through the most appropriate arrangement of elements within a form suitable for its intended use.

The primary function of a building structure is to support and redirect loads and forces safely to the ground. Building structures are constantly withstanding the forces of wind, the effects of gravity, vibrations, and sometimes even earthquakes.

The subject of structure is all-encompassing; everything has its own unique form. A cloud, a seashell, a tree, a grain of sand, the human body—each is a miracle of structural design.

Buildings, like any other physical entity, require structural frameworks to maintain their existence in a recognizable physical form.

To structure also means *to build*—to make use of solid materials (timber, masonry, steel, concrete) in such a way as to assemble an interconnected whole that creates space suitable to a particular function or functions and to protect the internal space from undesirable external elements.

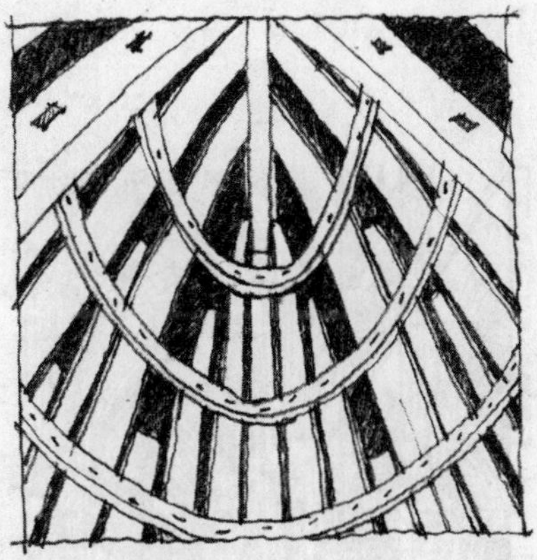

Figure 2 Bow and lattice structure of the currach, an Irish workboat. Stresses on the hull are evenly distributed through the longitudinal stringers, which are held together by steam-bent oak ribs.

A structure, whether large or small, must be stable and durable, must satisfy the intended function(s) for which it was built, and must achieve an economy or efficiency—that is, maximum results with minimum means (Figure 3). As stated in Sir Isaac Newton's *Principia*:

> *Nature does nothing in vain, and more is in vain when less will serve; for Nature is pleased with simplicity, and affects not the pomp of superfluous causes.*

Figure 3 Metacarpal bone from a vulture wing and an open-web steel truss with web members in the configuration of a Warren Truss.

Figure 4 Eiffel Tower.

2 STRUCTURAL DESIGN

Structural design is essentially a process that involves balancing between applied forces and the materials that resist these forces. Structurally, a building must never collapse under the action of assumed loads, whatever they may be. Furthermore, tolerable deformation of the structure or its elements should not cause material distress or psychological harm. Good structural design is more related to correct intuitive sense than to sets of complex mathematical equations. Mathematics should be merely a convenient and validating tool by which the designer determines the physical sizes and proportions of the elements to be used in the intended structure.

The general procedure of designing a structural system (called *structural planning*) consists of the following phases:

- Conceiving of the basic structural form.
- Devising the gravity and lateral force resisting strategy.
- Roughly proportioning the component parts.
- Developing a foundation scheme.
- Determining the structural materials to be used.
- Detailed proportioning of the component parts.
- Devising a construction methodology.

Figure 5 Nave of Reims Cathedral (construction begun in 1211).

After all of the separate phases have been examined and modified in an iterative manner, the structural elements within the system are then checked mathematically by the structural consultant to ensure the safety and economy of the structure. The process of conceiving and visualizing a structure is truly an art.

There are no sets of rules one can follow in a linear manner to achieve a so-called "good design." The iterative approach is most often employed to arrive at a design solution. Nowadays, with the design of any large structure involving a team of designers working jointly with specialists and consultants, the architect is required to function as a coordinator and still maintain a leadership role even in the initial structural scheme. The architect needs to have a broad general understanding of the structure with its various problems and a sufficient understanding of the fundamental principles of structural behavior to provide useful approximations of member sizes. The structural principles influence the form of the building, and a logical solution (often an economical one as well) is always based on a correct interpretation of these principles. A responsibility of the builder (constructor) is to have the knowledge, experience, and inventiveness to resolve complex structural and constructional issues without losing sight of the spirit of the design.

A structure need not actually collapse to be lacking in integrity. For example, a structure indiscriminately employing inappropriate materials or an unsuitable size and proportion of elements would reflect disorganization and a sense of chaos. Similarly, a structure carelessly overdesigned would lack truthfulness and reflect a wastefulness that seems highly questionable in our current world situation of rapidly diminishing resources.

> *It can be said that in these works (Gothic Cathedrals, Eiffel Tower, Firth of Forth Bridge), forerunners of the great architecture of tomorrow, the relationship between technology and aesthetics that we found in the great buildings of the past has remained intact. It seems to me that this relationship can be defined in the following manner: the objective data of the problem, technology and* **statics** *(empirical or scientific), suggest the solutions and forms; the aesthetic sensitivity of the designer, who understands the intrinsic beauty and validity, welcomes the suggestion and models it, emphasizes it, proportions it, in a personal manner which constitutes the artistic element in architecture.*

Quote from Pier Luigi Nervi, *Aesthetics and Technology in Architecture*, Harvard University Press; Cambridge, Massachusetts, 1966. (See Figures 4 and 5.)

Figure 6 Tree—a system of cantilevers.

Figure 7 Beehive—cellular structure.

3 PARALLELS IN NATURE

There is a fundamental "rightness" in the structurally correct concept, leading to an economy of means. Two kinds of "economy" are present in buildings. One such economy is based on expediency, availability of materials, cost, and constructability. The other "inherent" economy is dictated by the laws of nature (Figure 6).

In his wonderful book *On Growth and Form*, D'Arcy Wentworth Thompson describes how Nature, as a response to the action of forces, creates a great diversity of forms from an inventory of basic principles. Thompson says that

> *in short, the form of an object is a diagram of forces; in this sense, at least, that from it we can judge of or deduce the forces that are acting or have acted upon it; in this strict and particular sense, it is a diagram.*

The form as a diagram is an important governing idea in the application of the principle of *optimization* (maximum output for minimum energy). Nature is a wonderful venue to observe this principle, because survival of a species depends on it. An example of optimization is the honeycomb of the bee (Figure 7). This system, an arrangement of hexagonal cells, contains the greatest amount of honey with the least amount of beeswax and is the structure that requires the least energy for the bees to construct.

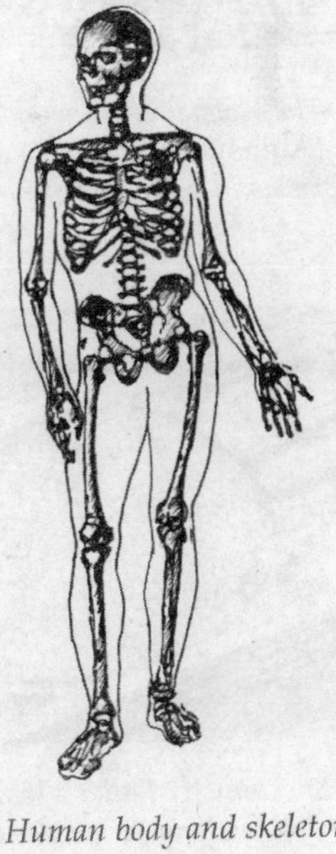

Figure 8 Human body and skeleton.

Galileo Galilei (16th century), in his observation of animals and trees, postulated that growth was maintained within a relatively tight range—that problems with the organism would occur if it were too small or too large. In his *Dialogues Concerning Two New Sciences*, Galileo hypothesizes that

Figure 9 Flying structures—a bat and Otto Lilienthal's hang glider (1896).

> *it would be impossible to build up the bony structures of men, horses, or other animals so as to hold together and perform their normal functions if these animals were to be increased enormously in height; for this increase in height can be accomplished only by employing a material which is harder and stronger than usual, or by enlarging the size of the bones, thus changing their shape until the form and appearance of the animals suggest monstrosity. . . . If the size of a body be diminished, the strength of that body is not diminished in the same proportion; indeed, the smaller the body the greater its relative strength. Thus a small dog could probably carry on its back two or three dogs of his own size; but I believe that a horse could not carry even one of his own size.*

Economy in structure does not just mean frugality. Without the economy of structure, neither a bird nor an airplane could fly, for their sheer weight would crash them to earth. Without economy of materials, the dead weight of a bridge could not be supported. Reduction in dead weight of a structure in nature involves two factors. Nature uses materials of fibrous cellular structure (as in most plants and animals) to create incredible strength-to-weight ratios. In inert granular material such as an eggshell, it is often used with maximum economy in relation to the forces that the structure must resist. Also, structural forms (like a palm leaf, a nautilus shell, or a human skeleton) are designed in cross-section so that the minimum of material is used to develop the maximum resistance to forces (Figure 8).

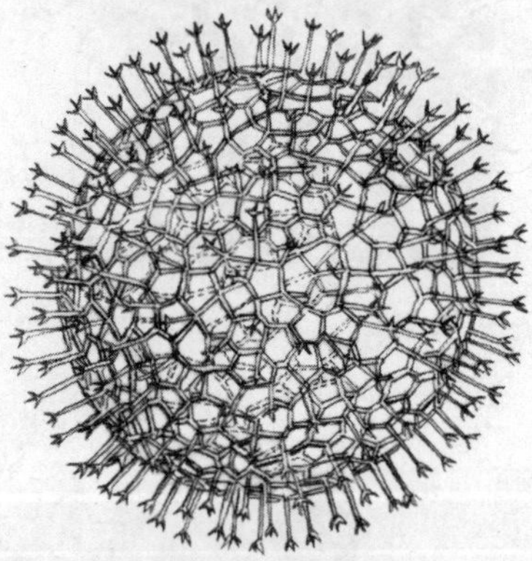

Figure 10 The skeletal latticework of the radiolarian (Aulasyrum triceros) consists of hexagonal prisms in a spherical form.

Nature creates slowly through a process of trial and error. Living organisms respond to problems and a changing environment through adaptations over a long period of time. Those that do not respond appropriately to the environmental changes simply perish.

Historically, human development in the area of structural forms has also been slow (Figure 9). For the most part, limited materials and knowledge restricted the development of new structural elements or systems. Even within the last 150 years or so, new structural materials for buildings have been relatively scarce—steel, reinforced concrete, prestressed concrete, composite wood materials, and aluminum alloys. However, these materials have brought about a revolution in structural design and are currently being tested to their material limit by engineers and architects. Some engineers believe that most of the significant structural systems are known and, therefore, that the future lies in the development of new materials and the exploitation of known materials in new ways.

Figure 11 Buckminster Fuller's Union Tank Car dome, a 384-ft.-diameter geodesic dome.

Advances in structural analysis techniques, especially with the advent of the computer, have enabled designers to explore very complex structures (Figures 10 and 11) under an array of loading conditions much more rapidly and accurately than in the past. However, the computer is still being used as a tool to validate the intent of the designer and is not yet capable of actual "design." A human designer's knowledge, creativity, and understanding of how a building structure is to be configured are still essential for a successful project.

4 LOADS ON STRUCTURES

Structural systems, aside from their form-defining function, essentially exist to resist forces that result from two general classifications of loads:

1. **Static.** This classification refers to gravity-type forces.
2. **Dynamic.** This classification is due to inertia or momentum of the mass of the structure (like earthquakes). The more sudden the starting or stopping of the structure, the greater the force will be.

Note: *Other dynamic forces are produced by wave action, landslides, falling objects, shocks, blasts, vibration from heavy machinery, and so on.*

A light, steel frame building may be very strong in resisting static forces, but a dynamic force may cause large distortions to occur because of the frame's flexible nature. On the other hand, a heavily reinforced concrete building may be as strong as the steel building in carrying static loads but have considerable stiffness and sheer dead weight, which may absorb the energy of dynamic forces with less distortion (*deformation*).

All of the following forces must be considered in the design of a building structure (Figure 12).

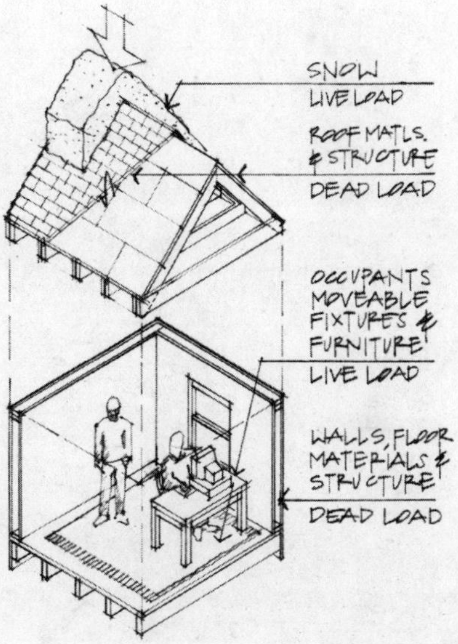

Figure 12 Typical building loads.

- **Dead Loads.** Loads resulting from the self-weight of the building or structure and of any permanently attached components, such as partition walls, flooring, framing elements, and fixed equipment, are classified as dead loads. Standard weights of commonly used materials for building are known, and a complete building's dead weight can be calculated with a high degree of certainty. However, the weight of structural elements must be estimated at the beginning of the design phase of the structure and then refined as the design process proceeds toward completion. A sampling of some standard building material weights used for the initial structural design process is:

  concrete = 150 pounds per cubic foot (pcf)
  timber = 35 pcf
  steel = 490 pcf
  built-up roofing = 6 pounds per square foot (psf)
  half-inch gypsum wallboard = 1.8 psf
  plywood, per inch of thickness = 3 psf
  suspended acoustical ceiling = 1 psf

  When activated by earthquake, static dead loads take on a dynamic nature in the form of horizontal inertial forces. Buildings with heavier dead loads generate higher inertial forces that are applied in a horizontal direction.

- **Live Loads.** Transient and moving loads that include occupancy loads, furnishings, and storage are classified as live loads. Live loads are extremely variable by nature and normally change during a structure's lifetime as occupancy changes. Building codes specify minimum uniform live loads for the design of roof and floor systems based on a history of many buildings and types of occupancy conditions. These codes incorporate safety provisions for overload protection, allowance for construction loads, and serviceability considerations, such as vibration and deflection behavior. Minimum roof live loads include allowance for minor snowfall and construction loads. (See Table 2 for an additional listing of common live loads for buildings.)

- **Snow Loads.** Snow loads represent a special type of live load because of the variability involved. Local building officials or applicable building codes prescribe the design snow for a specific geographical jurisdiction. Generally, snow loads are determined from a zone map reporting 50-year recurrence intervals of an extreme snow depth. Snow weights can vary from approximately 8 pcf for dry powder snow to 12 pcf for wet snow (Figure 13). Design loads can vary from 10 psf on a horizontal surface to 400 psf in some specific mountainous regions. In many areas of the United States, design snow loads can range from 20 to 40 psf.

  The accumulation depth of the snow depends on the slope of the roof. Steeper slopes have smaller accumulations. Special provisions must also be made for potential accumulation of snow at roof valleys, parapets, and other uneven roof configuration.

DB Auer/EPA/Newscom

Figure 13 Failure from snow load.

Except for a building's dead load, which is fixed, the other forces listed above can vary in duration, magnitude, and point of application. A building structure must nevertheless be designed for these possibilities. Unfortunately, a large portion of a building structure exists for loads that will be present at much lower magnitudes—or may never occur at all.

The structural efficiency of a building is often measured by its dead load weight in comparison to the live load carried. Building designers have always strived to reduce the ratio of dead to live load. New methods of design, new and lighter materials, and old materials used in new ways have contributed to the dead/live load reduction.

The size of the structure has an influence on the ratio of dead to live load. A small bridge over a creek, for example, can carry a heavy vehicle—a live load representing a large portion of the dead/live load ratio. The Golden Gate Bridge in San Francisco, on the other hand, spans a long distance, and the material of which it is composed is used chiefly in carrying its own weight. The live load of the vehicular traffic has a relatively small effect on the bridge's internal stresses.

With the use of modern materials and construction methods, it is often the smaller rather than the larger buildings that show a high dead/live load ratio. In a traditional house, the live load is low, and much of the dead load not only supports itself but also serves as weather protection and space-defining systems. This represents a high dead/live load ratio. In contrast, in a large factory building, the dead load is nearly all structurally effective, and the dead/live load ratio is low.

The dead/live load ratio has considerable influence on the choice of structure and especially on the choice of beam types. As spans increase, so do the bending effects caused by dead and live loads; therefore, more material must be introduced into the beam to resist the increased bending effects. This added material weight itself adds further dead load and pronounced bending effects as spans increase. The dead/live load ratio not only increases but may eventually become extremely large.

- **Wind Loads.** Wind is essentially air in motion and creates a loading on buildings that is dynamic in nature. When buildings and structures become obstacles in the path of wind flow, the wind's kinetic energy is converted into potential energy of pressure on various parts of the building. Wind pressures, directions, and duration are constantly changing. However, for calculation purposes, most wind design assumes a static force condition for more conventional, lower rise buildings. The fluctuating pressure caused by a constantly blowing wind is approximated by a *mean pressure* that acts on the windward side (the side facing the wind) and leeward side (the side opposite the windward side) of the structure. The "static" or nonvarying external forces are applied to the building structure and simulate the actual varying wind forces.

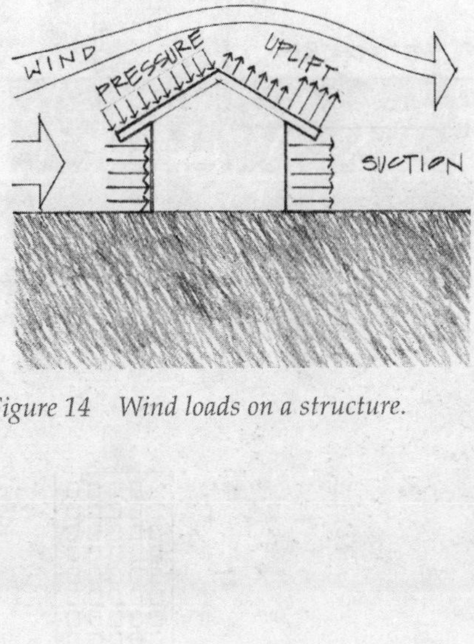

Figure 14 Wind loads on a structure.

Direct wind pressures depend on several variables: wind velocity, height of the wind above ground (wind velocities are lower near the ground), and the nature of the building's surroundings. Wind pressure on a building varies as the square of the velocity (in miles per hour). This pressure is also referred to as the *stagnation pressure.*

Buildings respond to wind forces in a variety of complex and dynamic ways. The wind creates a negative pressure, or suction, on both the leeward side of the building and on the side walls parallel to the wind direction (Figure 14). Uplift pressure occurs on horizontal or sloping roof surfaces. In addition, the corners, edges, and eave overhangs of a building are subjected to complicated forces as the wind passes these obstructions, causing higher localized suction forces than generally encountered on the building as a whole.

Wind is a fluid and acts like other fluids—a rough surface causes friction and slows the wind velocity near the ground. Wind speeds are measured at a standard height of 10 meters (33 feet) above the ground, and adjustments are made when calculating wind pressures at higher elevations. The wind pressure increases with the height of the building. Other buildings, trees, and topography affect how the wind will strike the building. Buildings in vast open areas are subject to larger wind forces than are those in sheltered areas or where a building is surrounded by other buildings. The size, shape, and surface texture of the building also impact the design wind forces. Resulting wind pressures are treated as lateral loading on walls and as downward pressure or uplift forces (suction) on roof planes.

- **Earthquake Loads** (*seismic*). Earthquakes, like wind, produce a dynamic force on a building. During an actual earthquake, there are continuous ground motions that cause the building structure to vibrate. The dynamic forces on the building are a result of the violent shaking of the ground generated by seismic shock waves emanating from the center of the fault (the *focus* or *hypocenter*) (Figure 15). The point directly above the *hypocenter* on the earth's surface is known as the *epicenter*. The rapidity, magnitude, and duration of these shakes depend on the intensity of the earthquake.

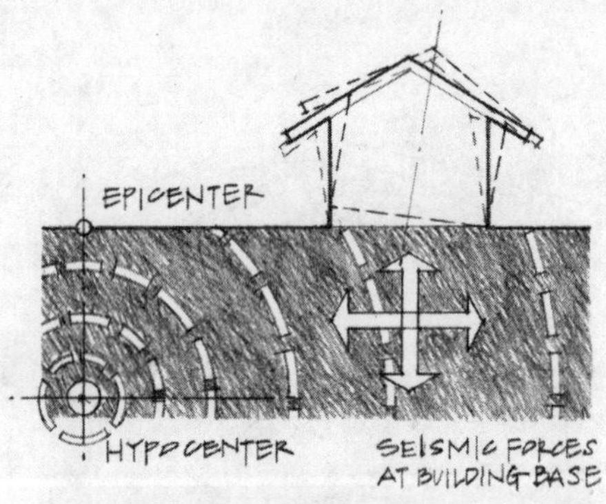

Figure 15 Earthquake loads on a structure.

During an earthquake, the ground mass suddenly moves both vertically and laterally. The lateral movements are of particular concern to building designers. Lateral forces developed in the structure are a function of the building's mass, configuration, building type, height, and geographic location. The force from an earthquake is initially assumed to develop at the base of the building; the force being known as the base shear (V_{base}). This base shear is then redistributed equal and opposite at each of the floor levels where the mass of the building is assumed concentrated.

Figure 16 Approximate building periods of vibration.

All objects, including buildings, have a *natural or fundamental period of vibration*. It represents the time it takes an object or building to vibrate through one cycle of vibration (or sway) when subjected to an applied force. When an earthquake ground motion causes a building to start vibrating, the building begins to displace (sway) back and forth at its natural period of vibration. Shorter, lower buildings have very short periods of vibration (less than one second), while tall high rises can have periods of vibration that last several seconds (Figure 16). Fundamental periods are a function of a building's height. An approximate estimate of a building's period is equal to

$$T = 0.1N$$

where N represents the number of stories and T represents the period of vibration in seconds.

The ground also vibrates at its own natural period of vibration. Many of the soils in the United States have periods of vibration in the range of 0.4 to 1.5 seconds. Short periods are more characteristic of hard soils (rock), while soft ground (some clays) may have periods of up to two seconds.

Many common buildings can have periods within the range of the supporting soils, making it possible for the ground motion to transmit at the same natural frequency as that of the building. This may create a condition of resonance (where the vibrations increase dramatically), in which the inertial forces might become extremely large.

Inertial forces develop in the structure due to its weight, configuration, building type, and geographic location. Inertial forces are the product of mass and acceleration (Newton's second law: $F = m \times a$). Heavy, massive buildings will result in larger inertial forces; hence, there is a distinct advantage in using a lighter weight construction when seismic considerations are a key part of the design strategy.

For some tall buildings or structures with complex configurations or unusual massing, a dynamic structural analysis is required. Computers are used to simulate earthquakes on the building to study how the forces are developed and the response of the structure to these forces. Building codes are intended to safeguard against major failures and loss of life; they are not explicitly for the protection of property.

5 BASIC FUNCTIONAL REQUIREMENTS

The principal functional requirements of a building structure are:

1. Stability and equilibrium.
2. Strength and stiffness.
3. Continuity and redundancy.
4. Economy.
5. Functionality.
6. Aesthetics.

Primarily, structural design is intended to make the building "stand up" (Figure 17). In making a building "stand up,"

Figure 17 Stability and the strength of a structure—the collapse of a portion of the University of Washington Husky stadium during construction (1987) due to lack of adequate bracing to ensure stability. Photo by author.

Figure 18 Equilibrium and Stability?—sculpture by Richard Byer. Photo by author.

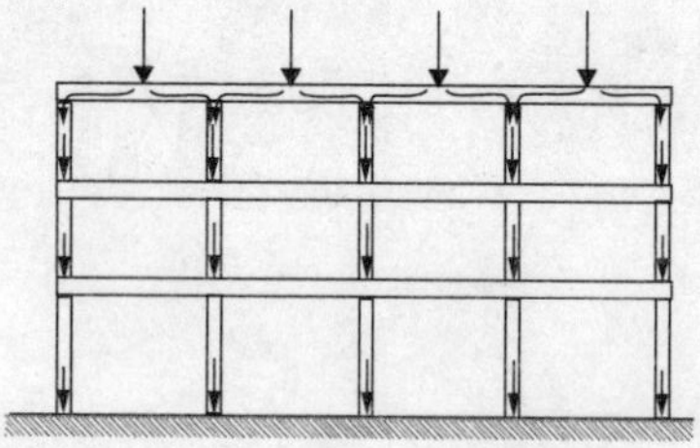

(a) Continuity—loads from the roof beams are redistributed to the roof columns below. A continuous path is provided for the column loads to travel directly to the columns below and then on to the foundation.

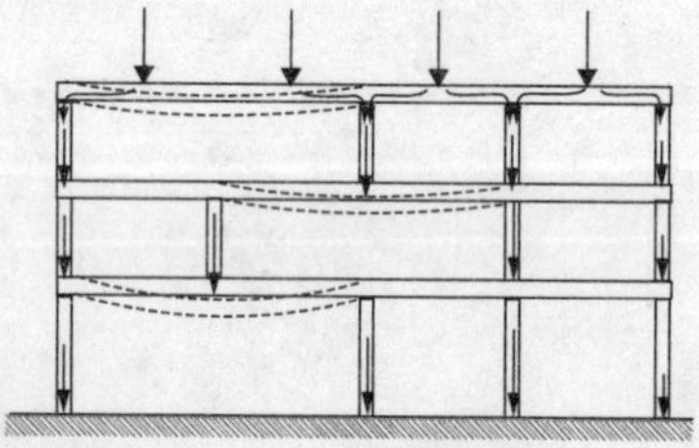

(b) Discontinuity in the vertical elevation can result in very large beam bending moments and deflection. Structural efficiency is enhanced by aligning columns to provide a direct path to the foundation. Beam sizes can thus be reduced significantly. In this example, missing or damaged columns could also represent how structural frameworks can have the ability to redistribute loads to adjacent members without collapse. This is referred to as structural redundancy.

Figure 19 Examples of continuity and redundancy.

the principles governing the stability and equilibrium of buildings form the basis for all structural thinking. *Strength* and *stiffness* of materials are concerned with the stability of a building's component parts (beams, columns, walls), whereas *statics* deals with the theory of general stability. Statics and strength of materials are actually intertwined, because the laws that apply to the stability of the whole structure are also valid for the individual components.

The fundamental concept of *stability* and *equilibrium* is concerned with the balancing of forces to ensure that a building and its components will not move (Figure 18). In reality, all structures undergo some movement under load, but stable structures have deformations that remain relatively small. When loads are removed from the structure (or its components), internal forces restore the structure to its original, unloaded condition. A good structure is one that achieves a condition of equilibrium with a minimum of effort.

Strength of materials requires knowledge about building material properties, member cross-sections, and the ability of the material to resist breaking. Also of concern is that the structural elements resist excessive deflection and/or deformation.

Continuity in a structure refers to a direct, uninterrupted path for loads through the building structure—from the roof level down to the foundation. *Redundancy* is the concept of providing multiple load paths in a structural framework so that one system acts as a backup to another in the event of localized structural failure. Structural redundancy enables loads to seek alternate paths to bypass structural distress. A lack of redundancy is very hazardous when designing buildings in earthquake country (Figure 19).

On 9/11, both of the World Trade Center towers were able to withstand the impact of jetliners crashing into them and continue standing for some time, permitting many people to evacuate. The towers were designed with structural redundancy, which prevented an even larger loss of life. However, the process by which the collapse of the impacted story level led to the progressive collapse of the entire building may have led some investigators to hint that an inadequate degree of structural redundancy existed.

The requirements of *economy, functionality,* and *aesthetics* are usually not covered in a structures course and will not be dealt with in this text. Strength of materials is typically covered upon completion of a statics course.

6 ARCHITECTURAL ISSUES

A technically perfect work can be aesthetically inexpressive but there does not exist, either in the past or in the present, a work of architecture which is accepted and recognized as excellent from an aesthetic point of view which is not also excellent from the technical point of view. Good engineering seems to be a necessary though not sufficient condition for good architecture.

—Pier Luigi Nervi

The geometry and arrangement of the load-bearing members, the use of materials, and the crafting of joints all represent opportunities for buildings to express themselves. The best buildings are not designed by architects who, after resolving the formal and spatial issues, simply ask the structural engineer to make sure it does not fall down.

An Historical Overview

It is possible to trace the evolution of architectural space and form through parallel developments in structural engineering and material technology. Until the 19th century, this history was largely based on stone construction and the capability of this material to resist compressive forces. Less durable wood construction was generally reserved for small buildings or portions of buildings.

Neolithic builders used drystone techniques, such as coursed masonry walling and corbelling, to construct monuments, dwellings, tombs, and fortifications. These structures demonstrate an understanding of the material properties of the various stones employed (Figure 20).

Timber joining and dressed stonework were made possible by iron and bronze tools. Narrow openings in masonry building walls were achieved through corbelling and timber or stone lintels.

The earliest examples of voussoir arches and vaults in both stone and unfired brick construction have been found in Egypt and Greece (Figure 21). These materials and structural innovations were further developed and refined by the Romans. The ancient Roman architect Vitruvius, in his *Ten Books*, described timber trusses with horizontal tie members capable of resisting the outward thrust of sloping rafters.

Roman builders managed to place the semicircular arch atop piers or columns; the larger spans reduced the number of columns required to support the roof. Domes and barrel and groin vaults were improved through the use of modular fired brick, cement mortar, and hydraulic concrete. These innovations enabled Roman architects to create even larger unobstructed spaces (Figure 22).

Figure 20 Stonehenge.

Figure 21 Construction of a Greek peristyle temple.

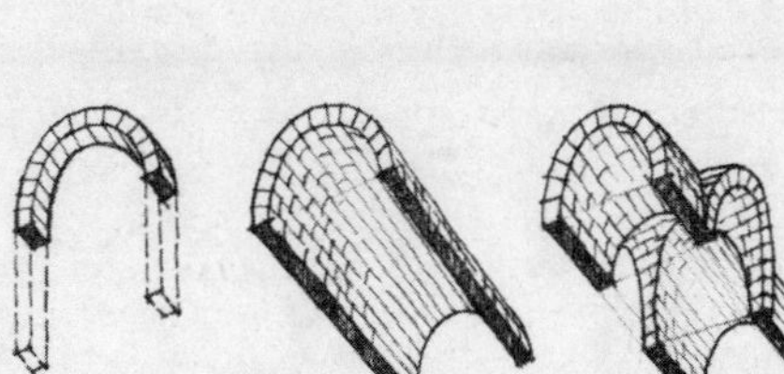

Figure 22 Stone arch, barrel vault, and groin vault.

Figure 23 Construction of a Gothic cathedral.

Gradual refinements of this technology by Romanesque mason builders eventually led to the structurally daring and expressive Gothic cathedrals. The tall, slender nave walls with large stained glass openings, which characterize this architecture, are made possible by improvements in concrete foundation construction; the pointed arch, which reduces lateral forces; flying arches and buttresses, which resist the remaining lateral loads; and the ribbed vault, which reinforces the groin and creates a framework of arches and columns, keeping opaque walls to a minimum (Figure 23).

The medium of drawing allowed Renaissance architects to work on paper, removed from construction and the site. Existing technical developments were employed in the search for a classical ideal of beauty and proportion.

Structural cast iron and larger, stronger sheets of glass became available in the late 18th century. These new materials were first employed in industrial and commercial buildings, train sheds, exhibition halls, and shopping arcades. Interior spaces were transformed by the delicate long-span trusses supported on tall, slender, hollow columns. The elements of structure and cladding were more clearly articulated, with daylight admitted in great quantities. Wrought iron and, later, structural steel provided excellent tensile strength and replaced brittle cast iron. Art Nouveau architects exploited the sculptural potential of iron and glass, while commercial interests capitalized on the long-span capabilities of rolled steel sections.

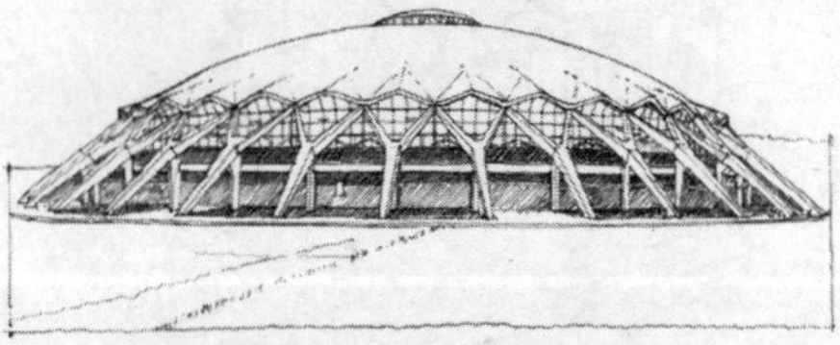

Figure 24 Sports Palace, reinforced concrete arena, by Pier Luigi Nervi.

The tensile properties of steel were combined with the high compressive strength of concrete, making a composite section with excellent weathering and fire-resistive properties that could be formed and cast in almost any shape (Figure 24). Steel and reinforced concrete structural frames enabled builders to make taller structures with more stories. The smaller floor area devoted to structure and the greater spatial flexibility led to the development of the modern skyscraper.

Today, pretensioned and posttensioned concrete, engineered wood products, tensile fabric, and pneumatic structures and other developments continue to expand the architectural and structural possibilities.

The relationship between the form of architectural space and structure is not deterministic. For example, the development of Buckminster Fuller's geodesic dome did not immediately result in a proliferation of domed churches or office buildings. As history has demonstrated, vastly different spatial configurations have been realized with the same materials and structural systems. Conversely, similar forms have been generated utilizing very different structural systems. Architects as well as builders must develop a sense of structure (Figure 25). Creative collaboration between architect, builder, and engineer is necessary to achieve the highest level of formal, spatial, and structural integration.

Criteria for the Selection of Structural Systems

Most building projects begin with a client program outlining the functional and spatial requirements to be accommodated. Architects typically interpret and prioritize this information, coordinating architectural design work with the work of other consultants on the project. The architect and structural engineer must satisfy a wide range of factors in determining the most appropriate structural system. Several of these factors are discussed here.

Nature and magnitude of loads

The weight of most building materials (Table 1) and the self-weight of structural elements (dead loads) can be calculated from reference tables listing the densities of various materials. Building codes establish design values for the weight of the occupants and furnishings—live loads (Table 2)—and other temporary loads, such as snow, wind, and earthquake.

Building use/function

Sports facilities (Figure 26) require long, clear span areas free of columns. Light wood framing is well suited to the relatively small rooms and spans found in residential construction.

Site conditions

Topography and soil conditions often determine the design of the foundation system, which in turn influences the way loads are transmitted though walls and columns. Low soil-bearing capacities or unstable slopes might suggest a series of piers loaded by columns instead of conventional spread footings. Climatic variables, such as wind speed and snowfall, affect design loads. Significant movement (thermal expansion and contraction) can result from extreme temperature fluctuations. Seismic forces, used to calculate building code design loads, vary in different parts of the country.

Building systems integration

All building systems (lighting, heating/cooling, ventilation, plumbing, fire sprinklers, electrical) have a rational basis that governs their arrangement. It is generally more elegant and cost-effective to coordinate these systems to avoid conflict and compromise in their performance. This is especially the case where the structure is exposed and dropped ceiling spaces are not available for duct and pipe runs.

Fire resistance

Building codes require that building components and structural systems meet minimum fire-resistance standards. The combustibility of materials and their ability to carry design loads when subjected to intense heat are tested to ensure that buildings involved in fires can be safely evacuated in a

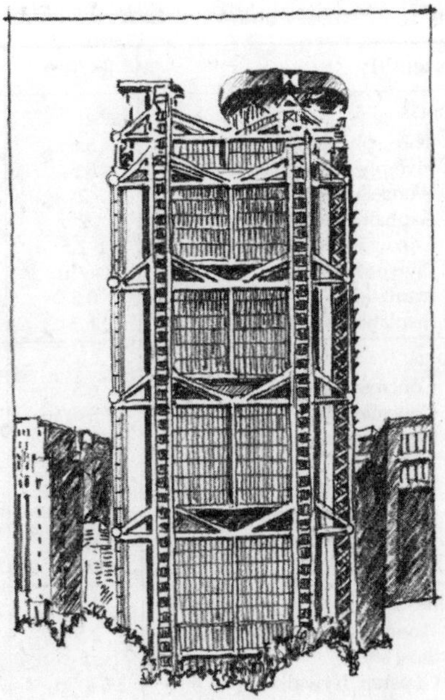

Figure 25 Hong Kong Bank, by Norman Foster.

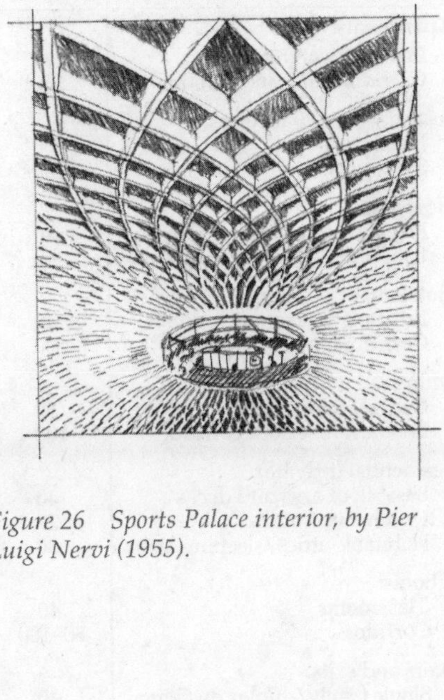

Figure 26 Sports Palace interior, by Pier Luigi Nervi (1955).

Table 1 Selected building material weights.

Assembly	lb./ft.^{2}	kN/m^2
Roofs:		
Three-ply and gravel	5.5	0.26
Five-ply and gravel	6.5	0.31
Wood shingles	2	0.10
Asphalt shingles	2	0.10
Corrugated metal	1–2.5	0.05–0.12
Plywood	3 #/in.	0.0057 kN/mm
Insulation—fiberglass batt	0.5	0.0025
Insulation—rigid	1.5	0.075
Floors:		
Concrete plank	6.5	0.31
Concrete slab	12.5 #/in.	0.59 kN/mm
Steel decking w/concrete	35–45	1.68–2.16
Wood joists	2–3.5	0.10–0.17
Hardwood floors	4 #/in.	0.19 kN/mm
Ceramic tile w/thin set	15	0.71
Lightweight concrete	8 #/in.	0.38 kN/mm
Timber decking	2.5 #/in.	0.08 kN/mm
Walls:		
Wood studs (average)	2.5	0.012
Steel studs	4	0.20
Gypsum drywall	3.6 #/in.	0.17 kN/mm
Partitions (studs w/drywall)	6	0.29

*Table 2 Selected live load requirements.**

Occupancy/Use (Uniform load)	lb./ft.^{2}	kN/m^2
Apartments:		
Private dwellings	40	1.92
Corridors and public rooms	100	4.79
Assembly areas/theaters:		
Fixed seats	60	2.87
Stage area	100	4.79
Hospitals:		
Private rooms and wards	40	1.92
Laboratories/operating rooms	60	2.87
Hotels:		
Private guest rooms	40	1.92
Corridors/public rooms	100	4.79
Offices:		
General floor area	50	2.40
Lobbies/first floor corridor	100	4.79
Residential (private):		
Basic floor area and decks	40	1.92
Uninhabited attics	20	0.96
Habitable attics/sleeping areas	30	1.44
Schools:		
Classrooms	40	1.92
Corridors	80–100	3.83–4.79
Stairs and exits:		
Single family/duplex dwellings	40	1.92
All other	100	4.79

**Loads are adapted from various Code sources and are listed here for illustrative purposes only. Consult the governing Code in your local jurisdiction for actual design values.*

given period of time. Wood is naturally combustible, but heavy timber construction maintains much of its strength for an extended period of time in a fire. Steel can be weakened to the point of failure unless protected by fireproof coverings. Concrete and masonry are considered to be noncombustible and are not significantly weakened in fires. The levels of fire resistance vary from unrated construction to four hours and are based on the type of occupancy and size of a building.

Construction variables

Cost and construction time are almost always relevant issues. Several structural systems will often accommodate the load, span, and fire-resistance requirements for a building. Local availability of materials and skilled construction trades typically affect cost and schedule. The selected system can be refined to achieve the most economical framing arrangement or construction method. The use of heavy equipment, such as cranes or concrete trucks and pumps, may be restricted by availability or site access.

Architectural form and space

Social and cultural factors that influence the architect's conception of form and space extend to the selection and use of appropriate materials. Where structure is exposed, the location, scale, hierarchy, and direction of framing members contribute significantly to the expression of the building.

This text, *Statics and Strengths of Materials for Architecture and Building Construction*, covers the analysis of statically determinate systems using the fundamental principles of free-body diagrams and equations of equilibrium. Although during recent years have seen an incredible emphasis on the use of computers to analyze structures by matrix analysis, it is the author's opinion that a classical approach for a beginning course is necessary. This text aim is to give the student an understanding of physical phenomena before embarking on the application of sophisticated mathematical analysis. Reliance on the computer (sometimes the "black or white box") for answers that one does not fully understand is a risky proposition at best. Application of the basic principles of statics and strength of materials will enable the student to gain a clearer and, it is hoped, more intuitive sense about structure.

Statics

Figure 1 Sir Isaac Newton (1642–1727).

Born on Christmas Day in 1642, Sir Isaac Newton is viewed by many as the greatest scientific intellect who ever lived. Newton said of himself, "I do not know what I may appear to the world, but to myself I seem to have been only like a boy playing on the seashore, and diverting myself in now and then finding a smoother pebble or a prettier shell than ordinary, whilst the great ocean of truth lay all undiscovered before me."

Newton's early schooling found him fascinated with designing and constructing mechanical devices such as water clocks, sundials, and kites. He displayed no unusual signs of being gifted until his later teens. In the 1660s, he attended Cambridge but without any particular distinction. In his last undergraduate year at Cambridge, with no more than basic arithmetic, he began to study mathematics, primarily as an autodidact, deriving his knowledge from reading with little or no outside help. He soon assimilated existing mathematical tradition and began to move beyond it to develop calculus (independent of Leibniz). At his mother's farm, where he had retired to avoid the plague that had hit London in 1666, he watched an apple fall to the ground and wondered if there was a similarity between the forces pulling on the apple and the pull on the moon in its orbit around the Earth. He began to lay the foundation of what was later to become the concept of universal gravitation. In his three laws of motion, he codified Galileo's findings and provided a synthesis of celestial and terrestrial mechanics.

1 CHARACTERISTICS OF A FORCE

Force

What is force? Force may be defined as the action of one body on another that affects the state of motion or rest of the body. In the late 17th century, Sir Isaac Newton (Figure 1) summarized the effects of force in three basic laws:

- **First Law:** Any body at rest will remain at rest, and any body in motion will move uniformly in a straight line, unless acted upon by a force. (Equilibrium)
- **Second Law:** The time rate of change of momentum is equal to the force producing it, and the change takes place in the direction in which the force is acting. ($F = m \times a$)
- **Third Law:** For every force of action, there is a reaction that is equal in magnitude, opposite in direction, and has the same line of action. (Basic concept of force.)

Newton's first law involves the principle of equilibrium of forces, which is the basis of statics. The second law formulates the foundation for analysis involving motion or dynamics. Written in equation form, Newton's second law may be stated as

$$F = m \times a$$

where F represents the resultant unbalanced force acting on a body of mass m with a resultant acceleration a. Examination of this second law implies the same meaning as the first law, because there is no acceleration when the force is zero and the body is at rest or moves with a constant velocity.

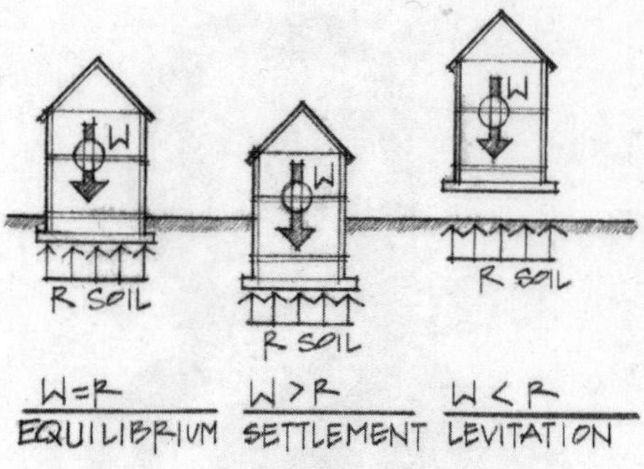

Figure 2 Ground resistance on a building.

The third law introduces us to the basic concept of force. It states that whenever a body A exerts a force on another body B, body B will resist with an equal magnitude but in the opposite direction.

For example, if a building with a weight W is placed on the ground, we can say that the building is exerting a downward force of W on the ground. However, for the building to remain stable on the resisting ground surface without sinking completely, the ground must resist with an upward force of equal magnitude. If the ground resisted with a force less than W, where $R < W$, the building would settle. On the other hand, if the ground exerted an upward force greater than W ($R > W$), the building would rise (levitate) (Figure 2).

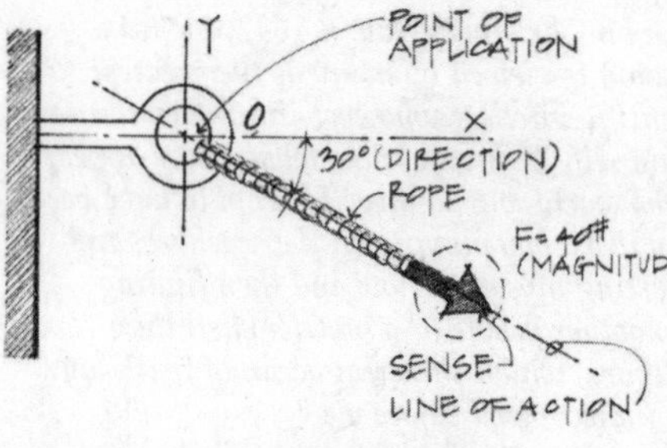

Figure 3 Rope pulling on an eyebolt.

Characteristics of a Force

A force is characterized by its (a) point of application, (b) magnitude, and (c) direction.

The *point of application* defines the point where the force is applied. In statics, the point of application does not imply the exact molecule on which a force is applied but a location that, in general, describes the origin of a force (Figure 3).

In the study of forces and force systems, the word *particle* will be used, and it should be considered as the location or point where the forces are acting. Here, the size and shape of the body under consideration will not affect the solution. For example, if we consider the anchor bracket shown in Figure 4(a), three forces—F_1, F_2, and F_3—are applied. The intersection of these three forces occurs at point O; therefore, for all practical purposes, we can represent the same system as three forces applied on particle O, as shown in Figure 4(b).

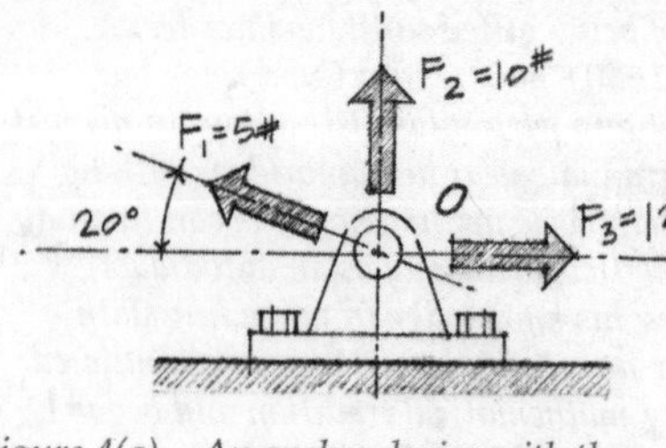

Figure 4(a) An anchor device with three applied forces.

Magnitude refers to the quantity of force, a numerical measure of the intensity. Basic units of force that will be used throughout this text are the *pound* (lb. or #) and the *kilo pound* (kip or k = 1,000#). In metric (SI) units, force is expressed as the *newton* (N) or *kilonewton* (kN) where 1 kN = 1,000 N.

The *direction* of a force is defined by its line of action and sense. The line of action represents an infinite straight line along which the force is acting.

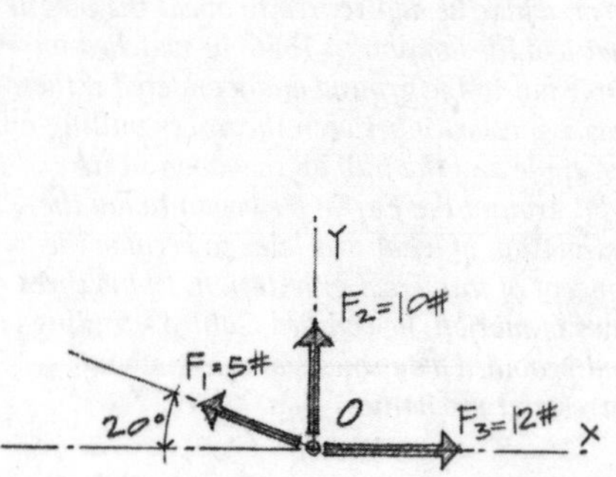

Figure 4(b) Force diagram of the anchor.

In Figure 5, the external effects on the box are essentially the same whether the person uses a short or long cable, provided the pull exerted is along the same line of action and of equal magnitude.

If a force is applied such that the line of action is neither vertical nor horizontal, some reference system must be established. Most commonly accepted is the angular symbol of θ (theta) or ϕ (phi) to denote the number of degrees the line of action of the force is in relation to the horizontal or vertical axis, respectively. Only one (θ or ϕ) needs to be indicated. An alternative to angular designations is a slope relationship.

The sense of the force is indicated by an arrowhead. For example, in Figure 6, the arrowhead gives the indication that a pulling force (tension) is being applied to the bracket at point *O*.

By reversing only the arrowhead (Figure 7), we would have a pushing force (compression) applied on the bracket with the same magnitude ($F = 10$ k), point of application (point *O*), and line of action ($\theta = 22.6°$ from the horizontal).

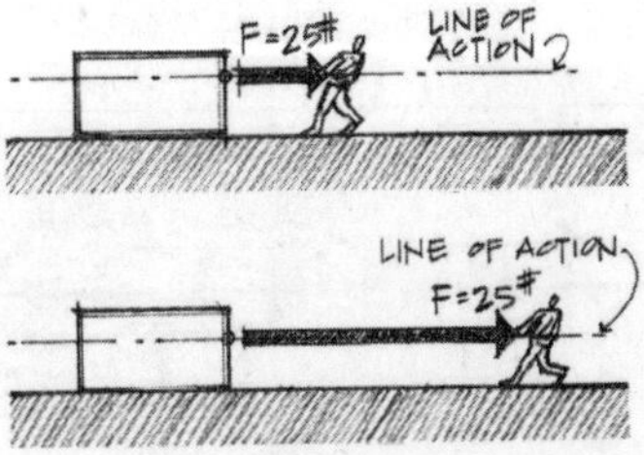

Figure 5   Horizontal force applied to a box.

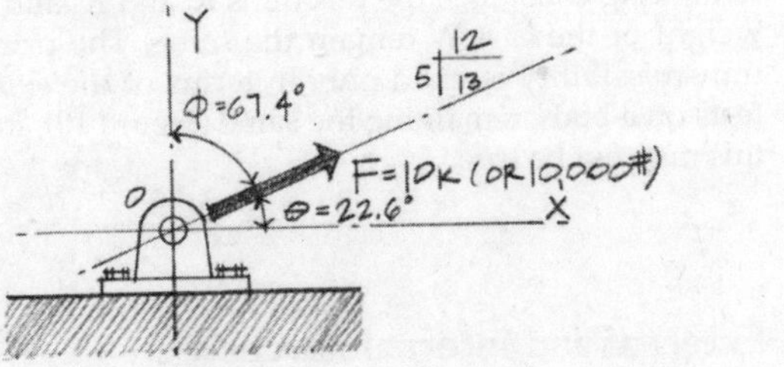

Figure 6   Three ways of indicating direction for an angular tension force.

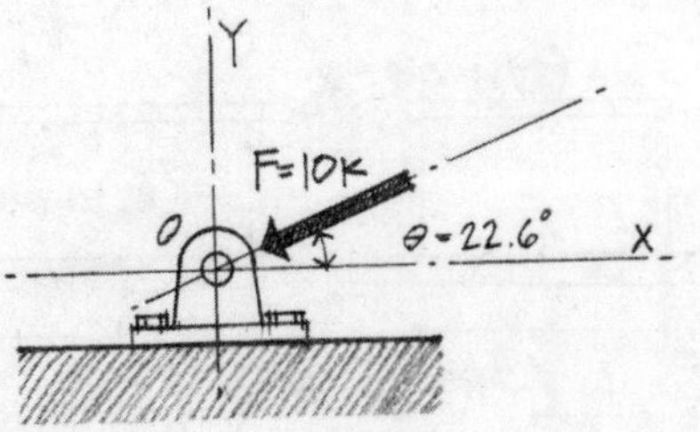

Figure 7   Force in compression.

Rigid Bodies

Practically speaking, any body under the action of forces undergoes some kind of deformation (change in shape). In statics, however, we deal with a body of matter (called a *continuum*) that, theoretically, undergoes no deformation. This we call a *rigid body*.

When a force of $F = 10\#$ is applied to a box, as shown in Figure 8, some degree of deformation will result. The deformed box is referred to as a *deformable body*, whereas in Figure 8(b) we see an undeformed box called the *rigid body*. Again, you must remember that the rigid body is a purely theoretical phenomenon but necessary in the study of statics.

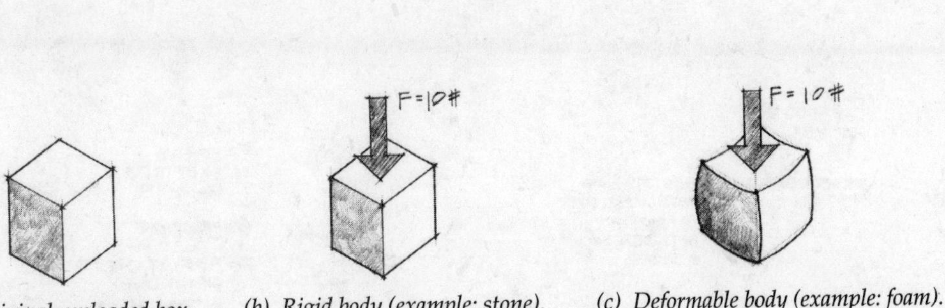

(a) Original, unloaded box.   *(b) Rigid body (example: stone).*   *(c) Deformable body (example: foam).*

Figure 8   Rigid body/deformable body.

Principle of Transmissibility

An important principle that applies to rigid bodies in particular is the *principle of transmissibility*. This principle states that the external effects on a body (cart) remain unchanged when a force F_1 acting at point A is replaced by a force F_2 of equal magnitude at point B, provided that both forces have the same sense and line of action (Figure 9).

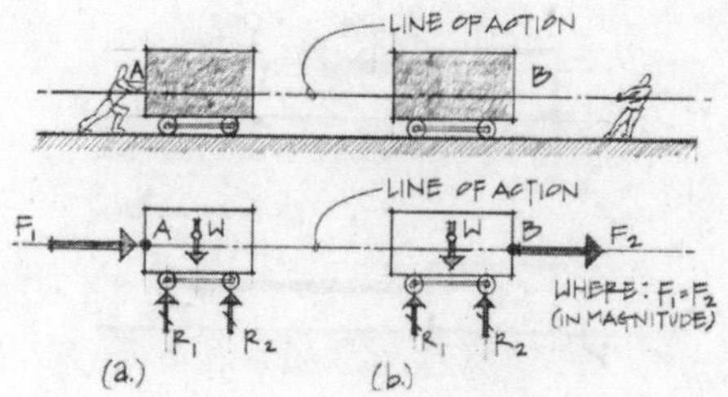

Figure 9 An example of the principle of transmissibility.

In Figure 9(a), the reactions R_1 and R_2 represent the reactions of the ground onto the cart, opposing the weight of the cart W. Although in Figure 9(b) the point of application for the force changes (magnitude, sense, and line of action remaining constant), the reactions R_1 and R_2 and also the weight of the cart W remain the same. The principle of transmissibility is valid only in terms of the external effects on a body remaining the same (Figure 10); internally, this may not be true.

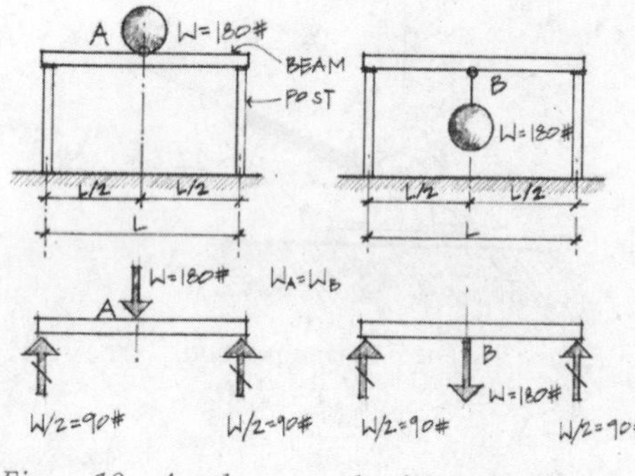

Figure 10 Another example of the principle of transmissibility.

External and Internal Forces

Let's consider an example of a nail being withdrawn from a wood floor (Figure 11).

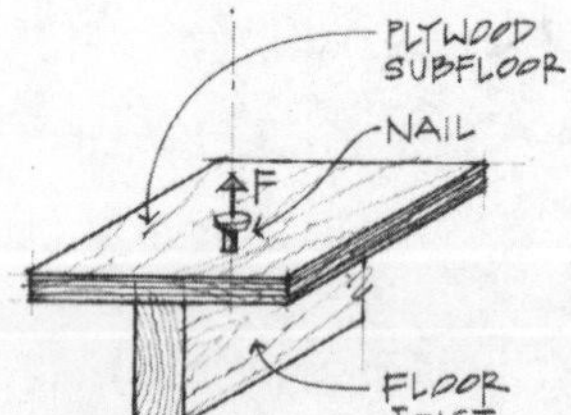

Figure 11 Withdrawal force on a nail.

If we remove the nail and examine the forces acting on it, we discover frictional forces that develop on the embedded surface of the nail to resist the withdrawal force F (Figure 12).

Treating the nail as the body under consideration, we can then say that forces F and S are external forces. They are being applied outside the boundaries of the nail. External forces represent the action of other bodies on the rigid body.

Let's consider just a portion of the nail and examine the forces acting on it. In Figure 13, the frictional force S plus the force R (the resistance generated by the nail internally) resist the applied force F. This internal force R is responsible for keeping the nail from pulling apart.

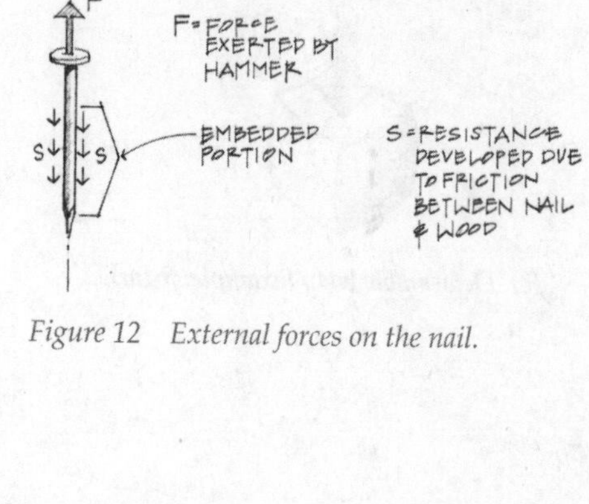

Figure 12 External forces on the nail.

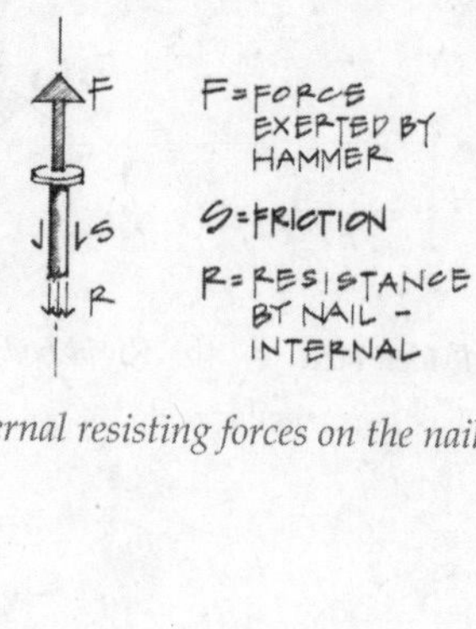

Figure 13 Internal resisting forces on the nail.

Examine next a column-to-footing arrangement with an applied force F, as illustrated in Figure 14. To appropriately distinguish which forces are external and which are internal, we must define the system we are considering. Several obvious possibilities exist here: Figure 15(a), column and footing taken together as a system; Figure 15(b), column by itself; and Figure 15(c), footing by itself.

In Figure 15(a), taking the column and footing as the system, the external forces are F (the applied force), W_{col}, W_{ftg}, and R_{soil}. Weights of bodies or members are considered as external forces, applied at the *center of gravity* of the member. Center of gravity (mass center) will be discussed in a later section.

The reaction or resistance the ground offers to counteract the applied forces and weights is R_{soil}. This reaction occurs on the base of the footing, outside the imaginary system's boundary; therefore, it is considered separately.

When a column is considered separately, as a system by itself, the external forces become F, W_{col}, and R_1. The forces F and W_{col} are the same as in Figure 15(b), but the force R_1 is a result of the resistance the footing offers to the column under the applied forces (F and W_{col}) shown.

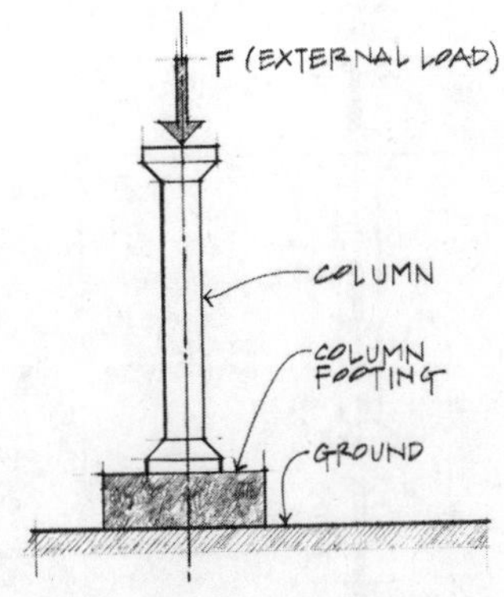

Figure 14 A column supporting an external load.

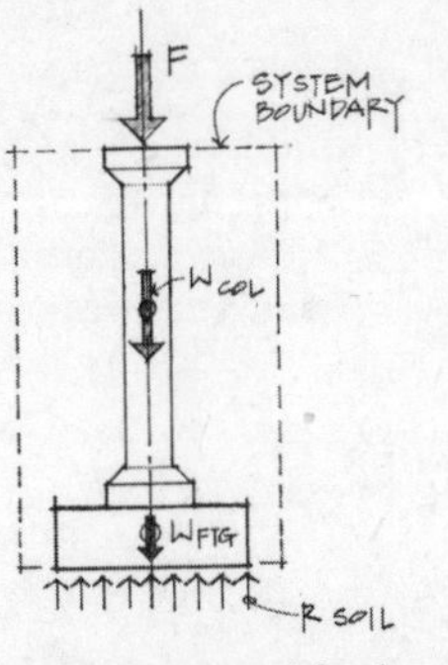

(a) Column and footing.

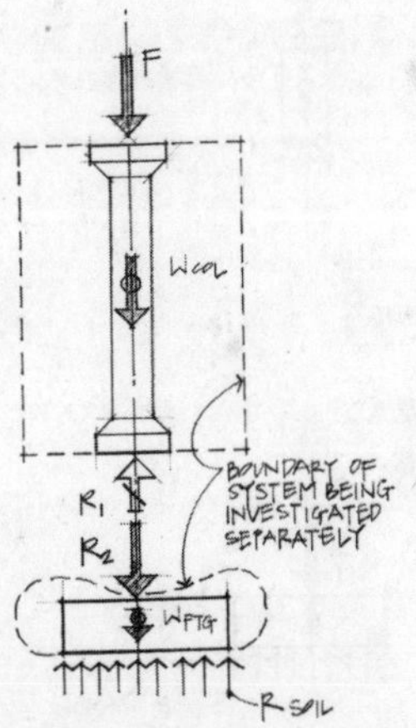

(b) Column.

(c) Footing.

Figure 15 Different system groupings.

The last case, Figure 15(c), considers the footing as a system by itself. External forces acting on the footing are R_2, W_{ftg}, and R_{soil}. The R_2 force represents the reaction the column produces on the footing, and W_{ftg} and R_{soil} are the same as in Figure 15(a).

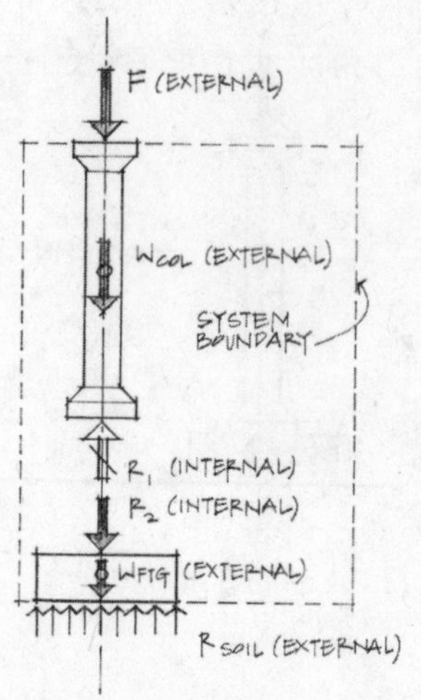

(a) Relationship of forces between the column and footing.

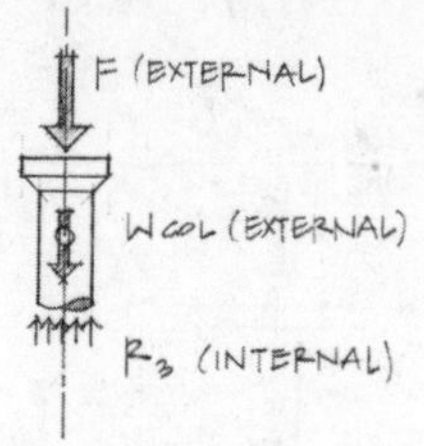

(b) Column.

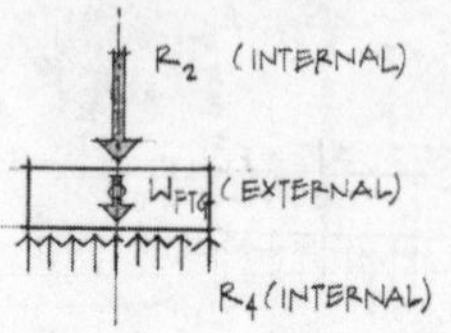

(c) Footing.

Figure 16 External and internal forces.

Now let's examine the internal forces that are present in each of the three cases examined above (Figure 16).

Examination of Figure 16(a) shows forces R_1 and R_2 occurring between the column and footing. The boundary of the system is still maintained around the column and footing, but by examining the interaction that takes place between members within a system, we infer internal forces. Force R_1 is the reaction of the footing on the column, while R_2 is the action of the column on the footing. From Newton's third law, we can then say that R_1 and R_2 are equal and opposite forces.

Internal forces occur between bodies within a system, as in Figure 16(a). Also, they may occur within the members themselves, holding together the particles forming the rigid body, as in Figure 16(b) and 16(c). Force R_3 represents the resistance offered by the building material (stone, concrete, or steel) to keep the column intact; this acts in a similar fashion for the footing.

Types of Force Systems

Force systems are often identified by the type or types of systems on which they act. These forces may be *collinear, coplanar,* or *space force systems*. When forces act along a straight line, they are called *collinear*; when they are randomly distributed in space, they are called *space forces*. Force systems that intersect at a common point are called *concurrent*, while parallel forces are called *parallel*. If the forces are neither concurrent nor parallel, they fall under the classification of *general force systems*. Concurrent force systems can act on a particle (point) or a rigid body, whereas parallel and general force systems can act only on a rigid body or a system of rigid bodies. (See Figure 17 for a diagrammatic representation of the various force system arrangements.)

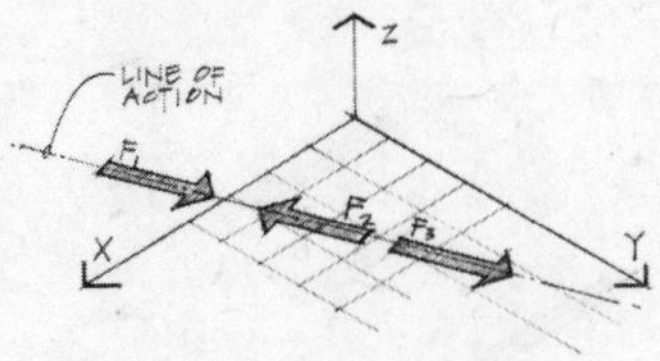

***Collinear**—All forces acting along the same straight line.*

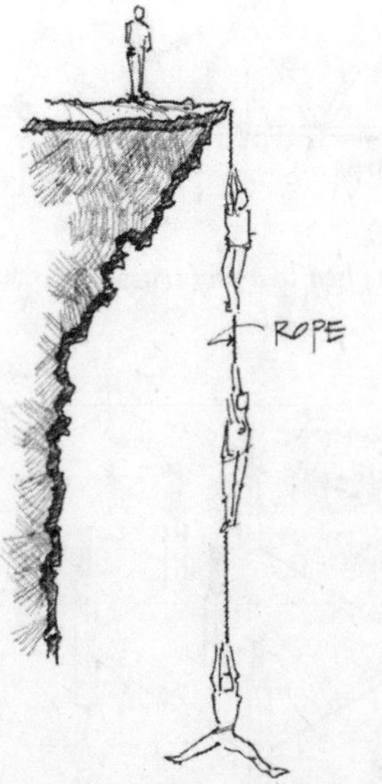

One intelligent hiker observing three other hikers dangling from a rope.

Figure 17(a) Particle or rigid body.

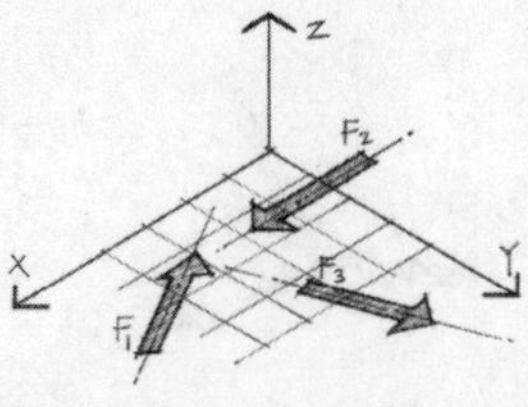

***Coplanar**—All forces acting in the same plane.*

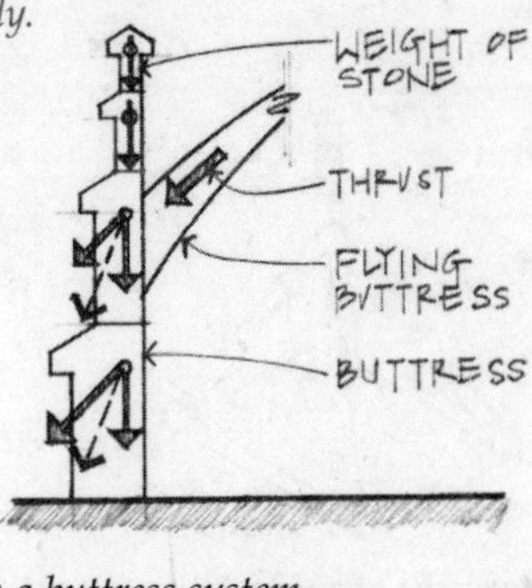

Forces in a buttress system.

Figure 17(b) Rigid bodies.

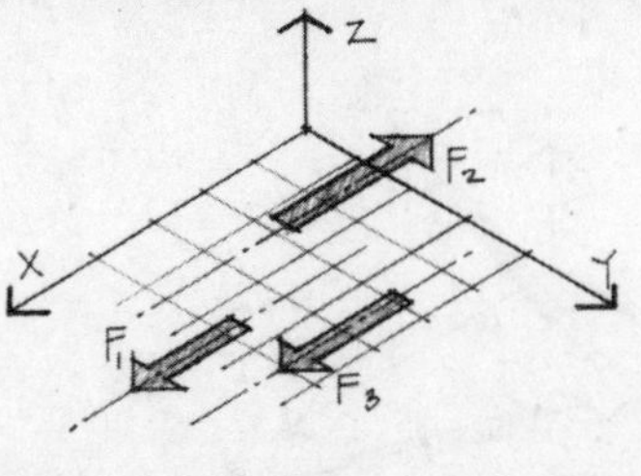

***Coplanar, parallel**—All forces are parallel and act in the same plane.*

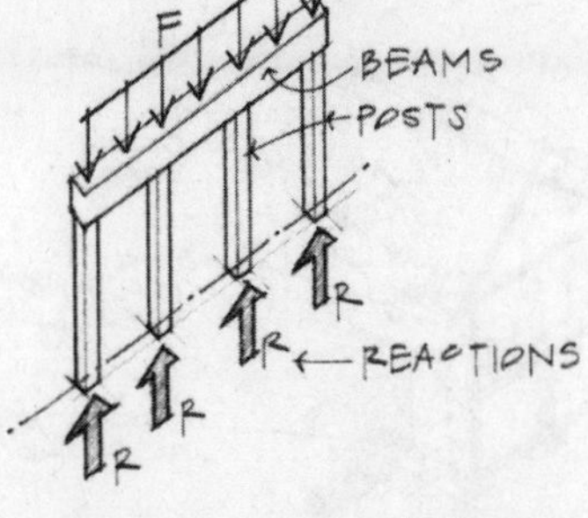

A beam supported by a series of columns.

Figure 17(c) Rigid bodies.

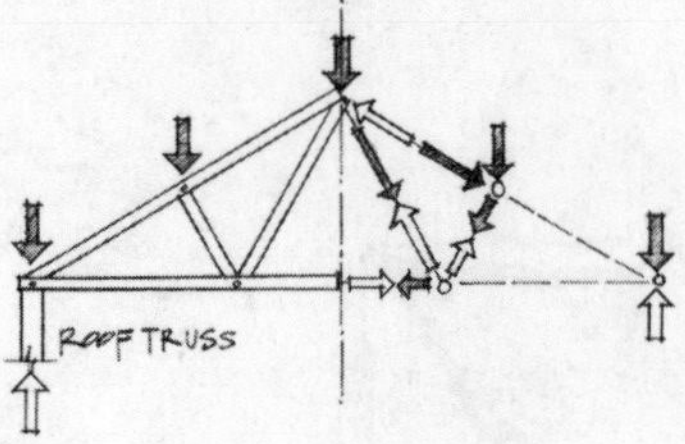

Loads applied to a roof truss.

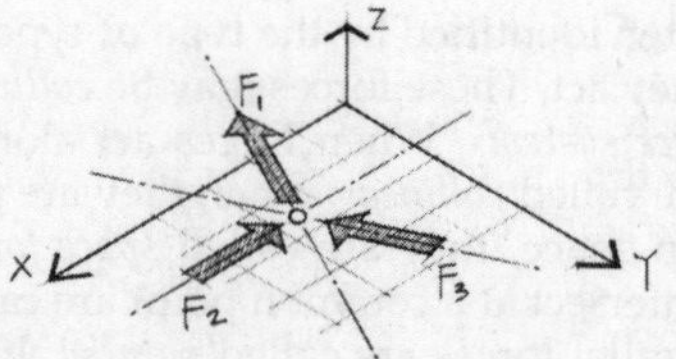

Coplanar, concurrent—*All forces intersect at a common point and lie in the same plane.*

Figure 17(d) *Particle or rigid body.*

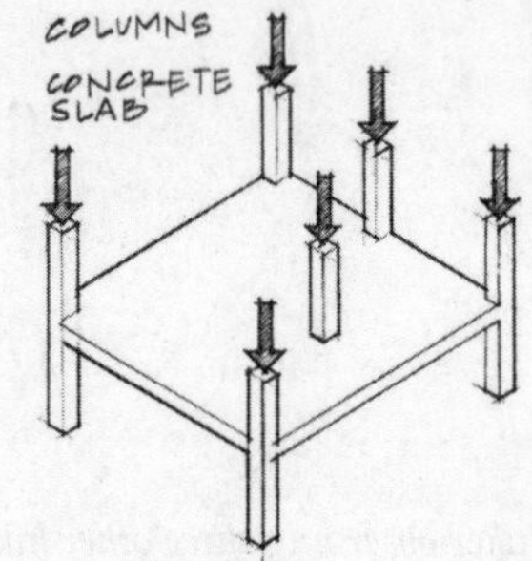

Column loads in a concrete building.

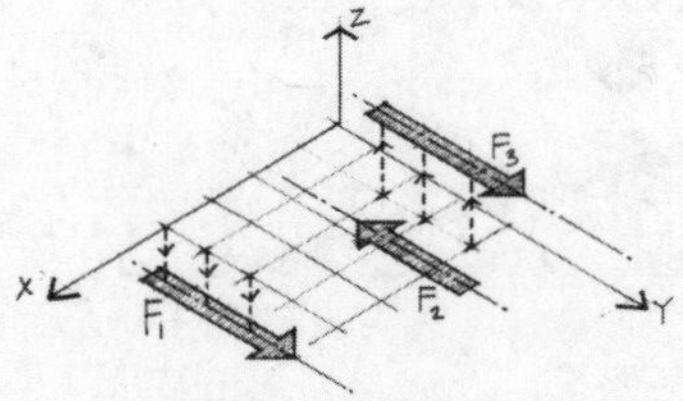

Noncoplanar, parallel—*All forces are parallel to each other, but not all lie in the same plane.*

Figure 17(e) *Rigid bodies.*

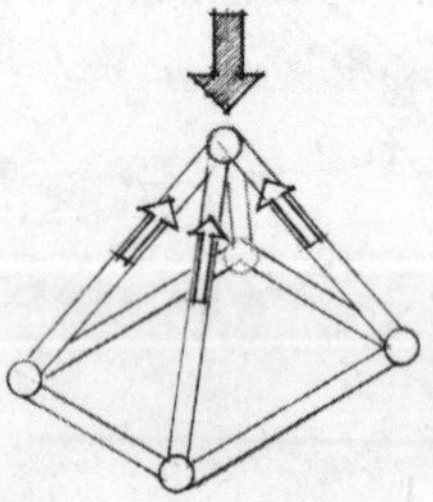

One component of a three-dimensional space frame.

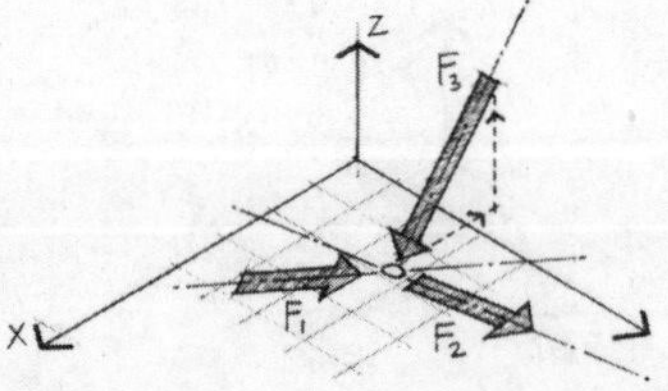

Noncoplanar, concurrent—*All forces intersect at a common point but do not all lie in the same plane.*

Figure 17(f) *Particle or rigid bodies.*

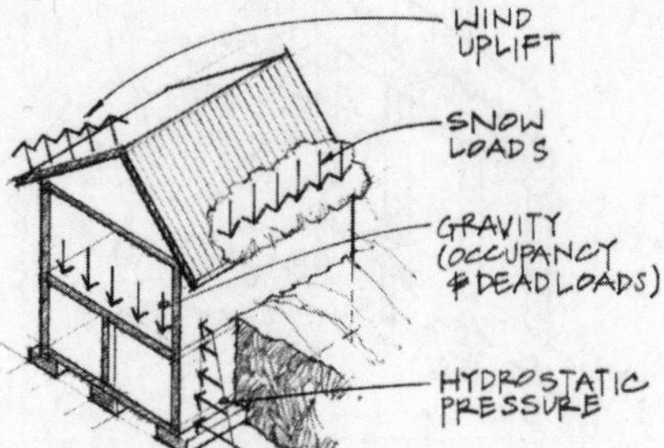

Array of forces acting simultaneously on a house.

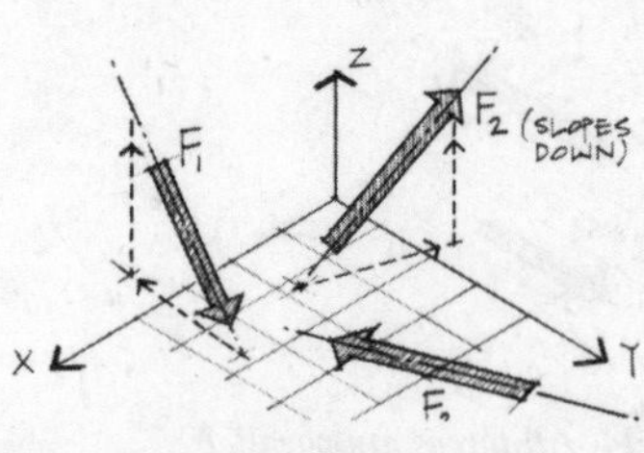

Noncoplanar, nonconcurrent—*All forces are skewed.*

Figure 17(g) *Rigid bodies.*

2 VECTOR ADDITION

Characteristics of Vectors

An important characteristic of vectors is that they must be added according to the parallelogram law. Although the idea of the parallelogram law was known and used in some form in the early 17th century, the proof of its validity was supplied many years later by Sir Isaac Newton and the French mathematician Pierre Varignon (1654–1722). In the case of scalar quantities, where only magnitudes are considered, the process of addition involves a simple arithmetical summation. Vectors, however, have magnitude and direction, thus requiring a special procedure for combining them.

Using the parallelogram law, we may add vectors graphically or by trigonometric relationships. For example, two forces W and F are acting on a particle (point), as shown in Figure 18; we are to obtain the vector sum (resultant). Because the two forces are not acting along the same line of action, a simple arithmetical solution is not possible.

The graphical method of the parallelogram law simply involves the construction, to scale, of a parallelogram using forces (vectors) W and F as the legs. Complete the parallelogram, and draw in the diagonal. The diagonal represents the vector addition of W and F. A convenient scale is used in drawing W and F, whereby the magnitude of R is scaled off using the same scale. To complete the representation, the angle θ must be designated from some reference axis—in this case, the horizontal axis (Figure 19).

An Italian mathematician and engineer, Giovanni Poleni (1685–1761), published a report in 1748 on St. Peter's dome using a method of illustration shown in Figure 20. Poleni's thesis of the absence of friction is demonstrated by the wedge-shaped voussoirs with spheres, which are arranged exactly in accordance with the line of thrust, thus supporting one another in an unstable equilibrium. In his report, Poleni refers to Newton and his theorem of the parallelogram of forces and deduces that the line of thrust resembles an inverted catenary.

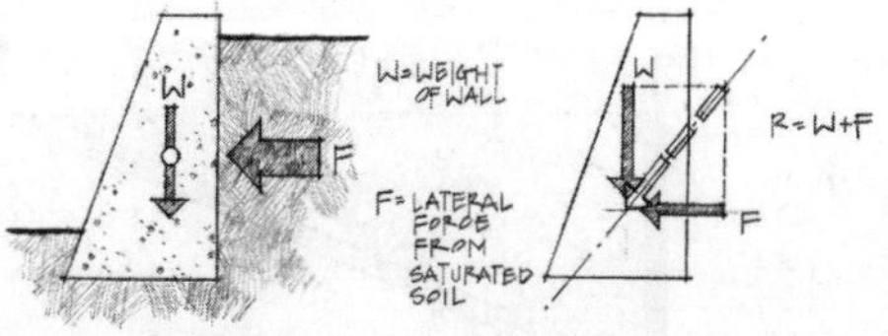

Figure 18 Cross-section through a gravity-retaining wall.

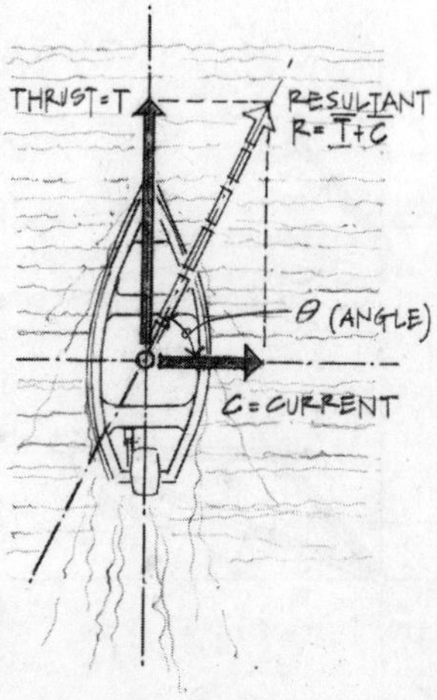

Figure 19 Another illustration of the parallelogram.

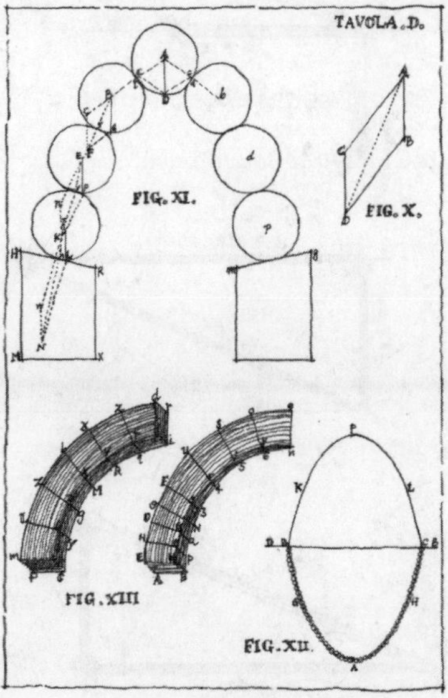

Figure 20 Poleni's use of the parallelogram law in describing the lines of force in an arch. From Giovanni Poleni, Memorie istoriche della Gran Cupola del Tempio Vaticano, *1748.*

Example Problems: Vector Addition

1 Two forces are acting on a bolt as shown. Determine graphically the resultant of the two forces using the parallelogram law of vector addition.

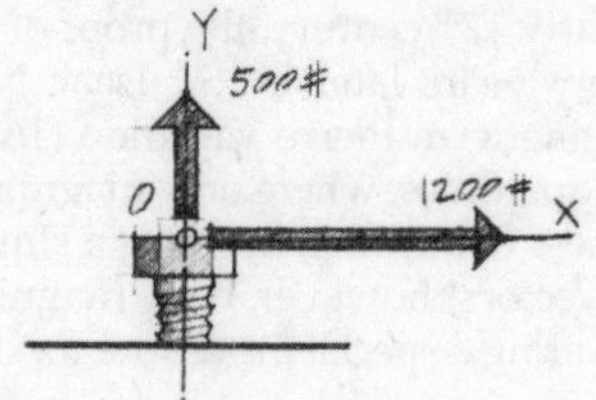

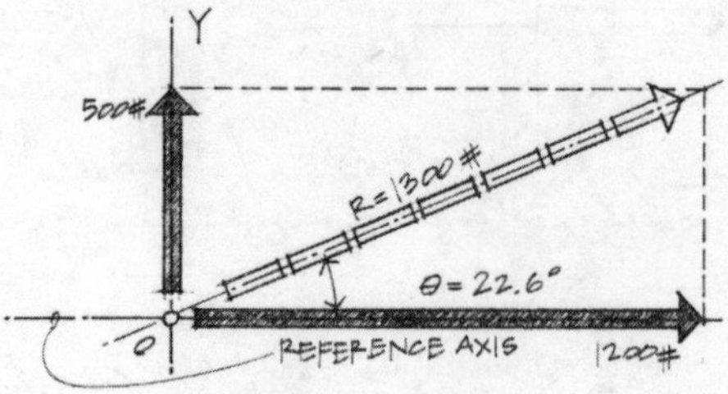

1. Draw the 500# and 1,200# forces to scale with their proper directions.
2. Complete the parallelogram.
3. Draw the diagonal, starting at the point of origin O.
4. Scale off the magnitude of R.
5. Scale off the angle θ from a reference axis.
6. The sense (arrowhead direction) in this example moves away from point O.

Another vector addition approach, which preceded the parallelogram law by 100 years or so, is the *triangle rule* or *tip-to-tail* method (developed through proofs by a 16th century Dutch engineer/mathematician, Simon Stevin).

To follow this method, construct only half of the parallelogram, with the net result being a triangle. The sum of two vectors A and B may be found by arranging them in a tip-to-tail sequence with the tip of A to the tail of B or vice versa.

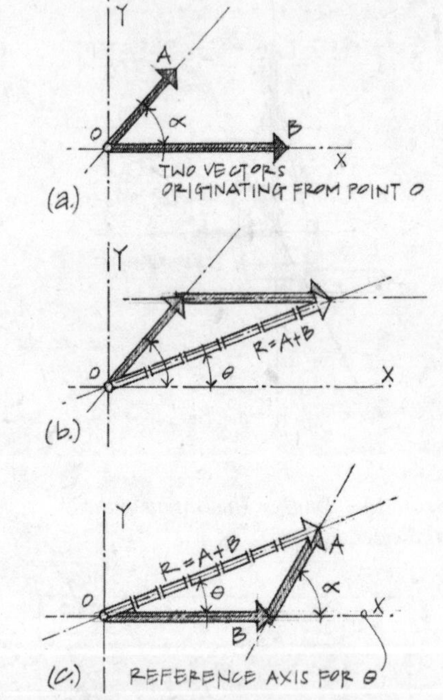

Figure 21 Tip-to-tail method.

In Figure 21(a), two vectors A and B are to be added by the tip-to-tail method. By drawing the vectors to scale and arranging it so that the tip of A is attached to the tail of B, as shown in Figure 21(b), the resultant R can be obtained by drawing a line beginning at the tail of the first vector, A, and ending at the tip of the last vector, B. The sequence of which vector is drawn first is not important. As shown in Figure 21(c), vector B is drawn first, with the tip of B touching the tail of A. The resultant R obtained is identical in both cases for magnitude and inclination θ. Again, the sense of the resultant moves from the origin point O to the tip of the last vector. Note that the triangle shown in Figure 21(b) is the upper half of a parallelogram, and the triangle shown in Figure 21(c) forms the lower half. Because the order in which the vectors are drawn is unimportant, where $A + B = B + A$, we can conclude that the vector addition is commutative.

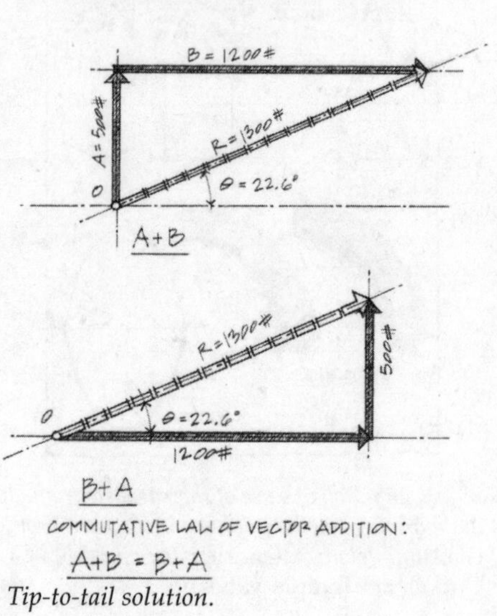

Tip-to-tail solution.

2 Solve the same problem shown in Example Problem 1, but use the tip-to-tail method.

Graphical Addition of Three or More Vectors

The sum of any number of vectors may be obtained by applying repeatedly the parallelogram law (or tip-to-tail method) to successive pairs of vectors until all of the given vectors are replaced by a single resultant vector.

Note: *The graphical method of vector addition requires all vectors to be coplanar.*

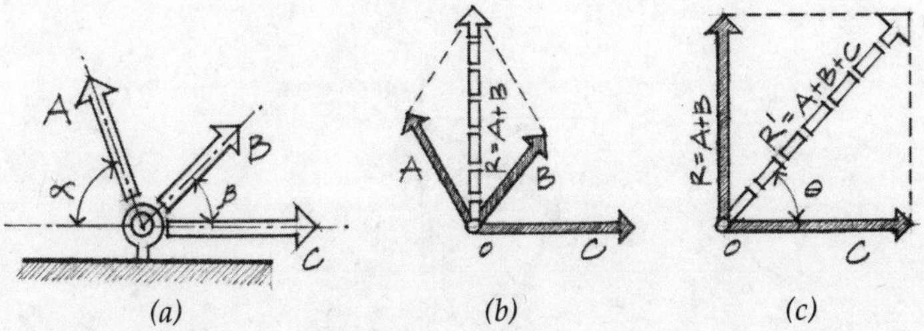

Figure 22 Parallelogram method.

Assume that three coplanar forces *A*, *B*, and *C* are acting at point *O*, as shown in Figure 22(a), and that the resultant of all three is desired. In Figure 22(b) and 22(c), the parallelogram law is applied successively until the final resultant force *R′* is obtained. The addition of vectors *A* and *B* yields the intermediate resultant *R*; *R* is then added vectorially to vector *C*, resulting in *R′*.

A simpler solution may be obtained by using the tip-to-tail method, as shown in Figure 23. Again, the vectors are drawn to scale but not necessarily in any particular sequence.

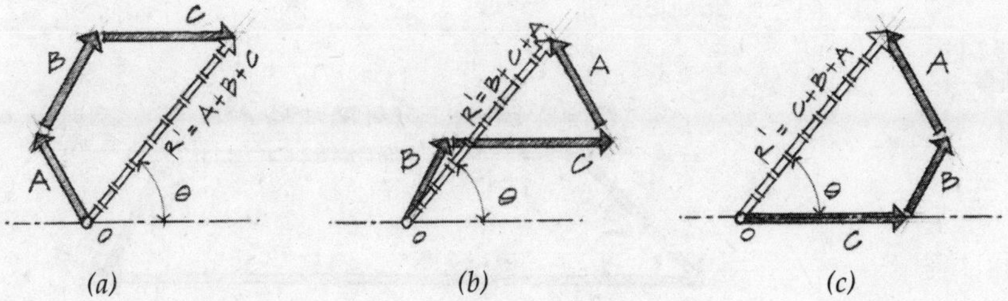

Figure 23 Illustration of the tip-to-tail method.

Example Problems: Graphical Addition of Three or More Vectors

3 Two cables suspended from an eyebolt carry 200# and 300# loads as shown. Both forces have lines of action that intersect at point O, making this a concurrent force system. Determine the resultant force the eyebolt must resist. Do a graphical solution using a scale of $1'' = 100\#$.

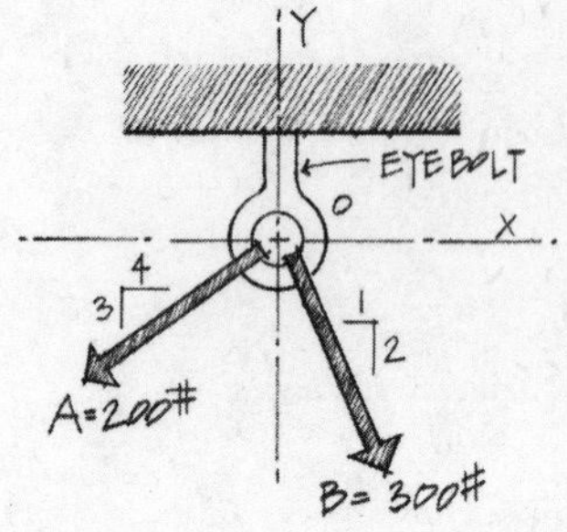

Solution:

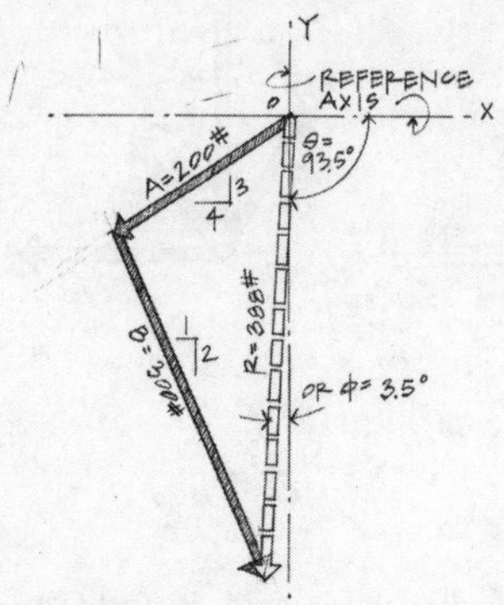

4 Three structural members A, B, and C of a steel truss are bolted to a gusset plate as shown. The lines of action (line through which the force passes) of all three members intersect at point O, making this a concurrent force system. Determine graphically (parallelogram law or tip-to-tail) the resultant of the three forces on the gusset plate. Use a scale of 1 mm = 400 N.

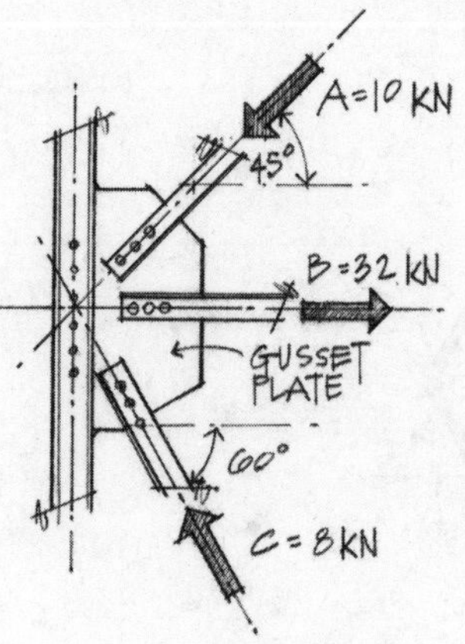

Note: *The resultant must be denoted by a magnitude and direction.*

Solution:

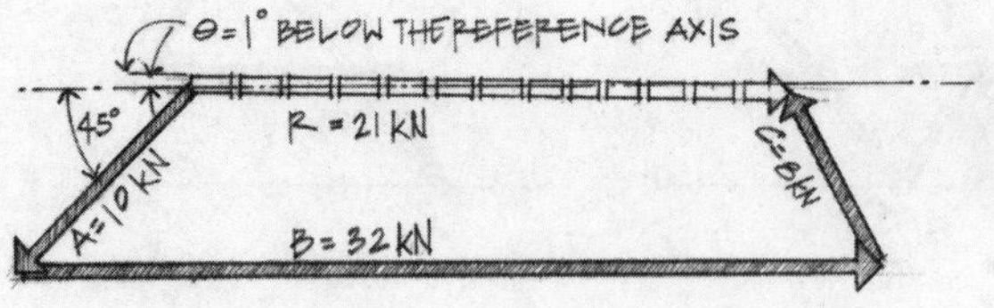

5 Two workers are pulling a large crate as shown. If the resultant force required to move the crate along its axis line is 120#, determine the tension each worker must exert. Solve graphically, using a scale of 1″ = 40#.

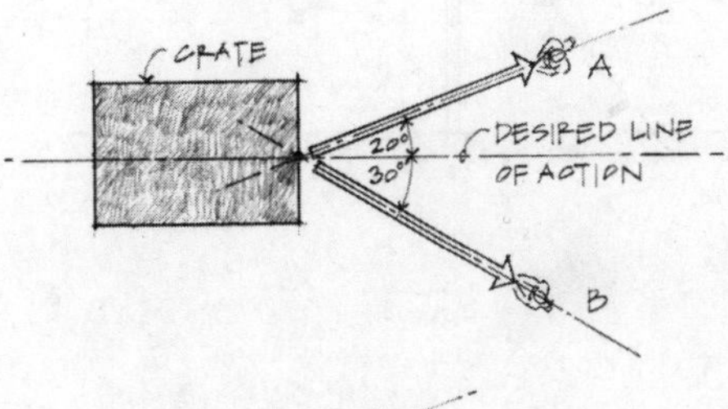

Solution:

Using the parallelogram law, begin by constructing the resultant force of 120# (horizontally to the right) to scale. The sides of the parallelogram have unknown magnitudes, but the directions are known. Close the parallelogram at the tip of the resultant (point *m*) by drawing line *A*′ parallel to *A* and extending it to intersect with *B*. The magnitude of *B* may now be determined. Similarly, line *B*′ may be constructed and the magnitude of force *A* determined. From scaling, *A* = 79#, *B* = 53#.

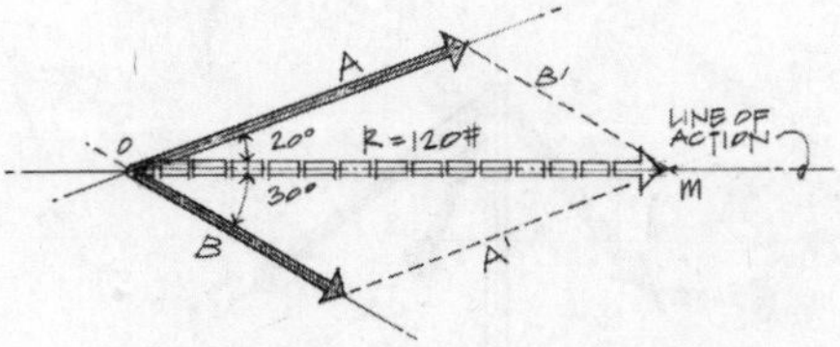

Problems

Construct graphical solutions using the parallelogram law or the tip-to-tail method.

1 Determine the resultant of the two forces shown (magnitude and direction) acting on the pin. Scale: 1″ = 100#.

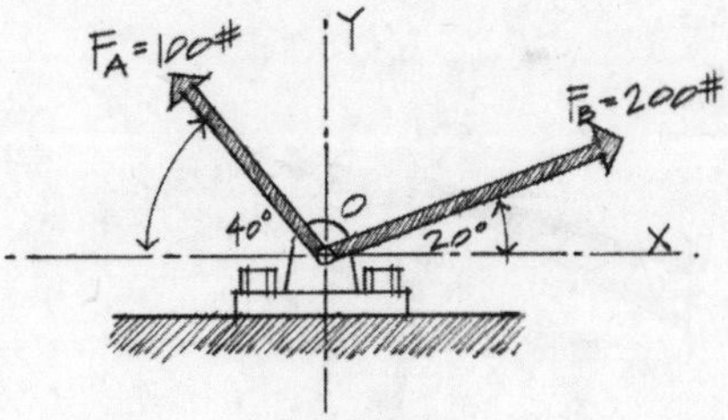

2 Three forces are acting on the eyebolt as shown. All forces intersect at a common point *O*. Determine the resultant magnitude and direction. Scale: 1 mm = 100 N.

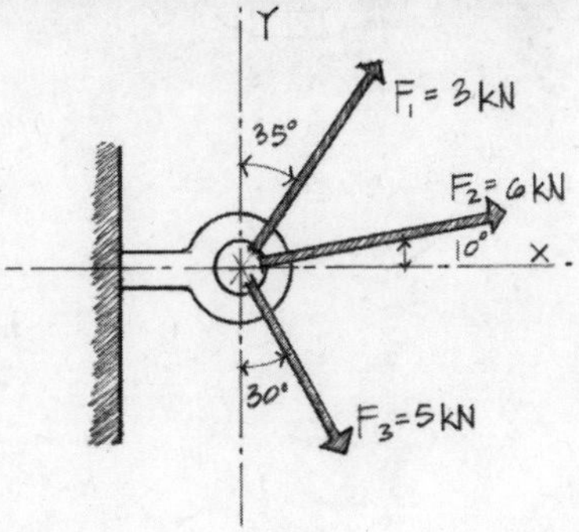

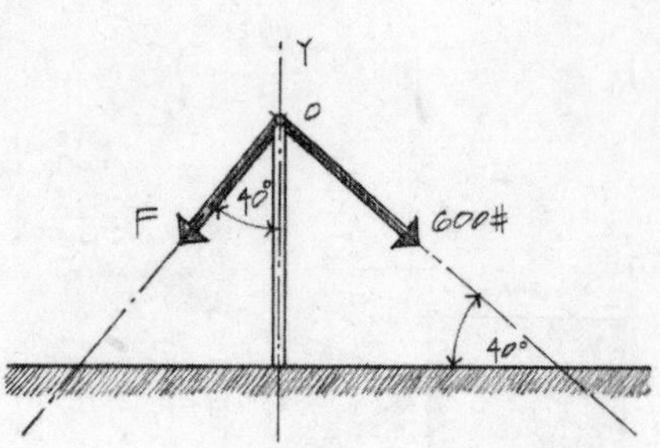

3 Determine the force F required to counteract the 600# tension so that the resultant force acts vertically down the pole. Scale: 1″ = 400#.

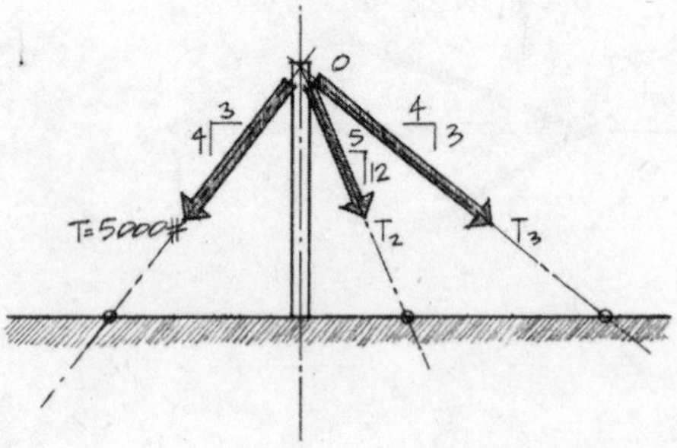

4 Three forces are concurrent at point O, and the tension in cable T_1 = 5,000# with the slope as shown. Determine the magnitudes necessary for T_2 and T_3 such that the resultant force of 10 k acts vertically down the axis of the pole. Scale: 1″ = 2,000#.

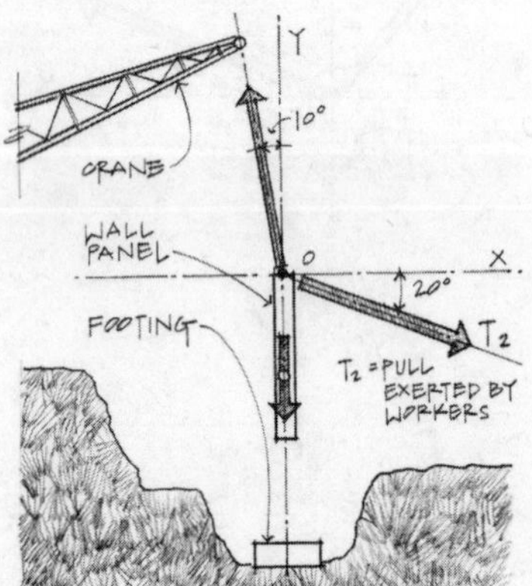

5 A precast concrete wall panel is being hoisted into place as shown. The wall weighs 18 kN with the weight passing through its center through point O. Determine the force T_2 necessary for the workers to guide the wall into place. Scale: 1 mm = 100 N.

3 FORCE SYSTEMS

Resolution of Forces into Rectangular Components

A reverse effect of vector addition is the resolution of a vector into two perpendicular components. Components of a vector (or force) are usually perpendicular to each other and are called *rectangular components*. The x and y axes of a rectangular coordinate system are most often assumed to be horizontal and vertical, respectively; however, they may be chosen in any two mutually perpendicular directions for convenience (Figure 24).

A force F with a direction θ from the horizontal x axis can be resolved into its rectangular components F_x and F_y as shown in Figure 24. Both F_x and F_y are trigonometric functions of F and θ, where

$$F_x = F\cos\theta; \quad F_y = F\sin\theta$$

In effect, the force components F_x and F_y form the legs of a parallelogram, with the diagonal representing the original force F. Therefore, by using the Pythagorean theorem for right triangles,

$$F = \sqrt{F_x^2 + F_y^2} \quad \text{and,}$$

$$\tan\theta = \frac{F_y}{F_x}, \quad \text{or,} \quad \theta = \tan^{-1}\left(\frac{F_y}{F_x}\right)$$

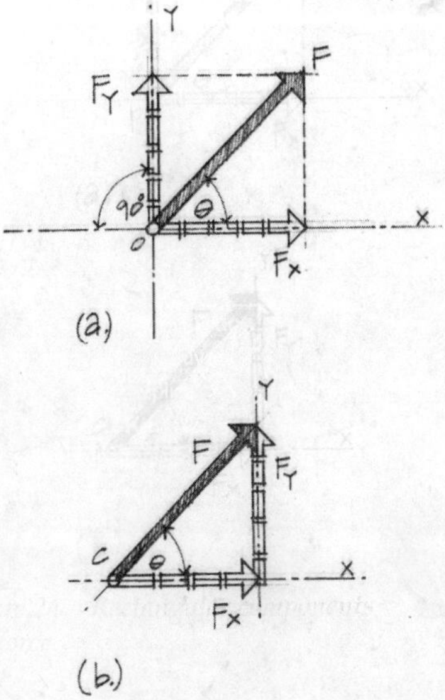

Figure 24 Rectangular components of a force.

Example Problems: Resolution of Forces into Rectangular Components

6 An anchor bracket is acted upon by a 1,000# force at an angle of 30° from the horizontal. Determine the horizontal and vertical components of the force.

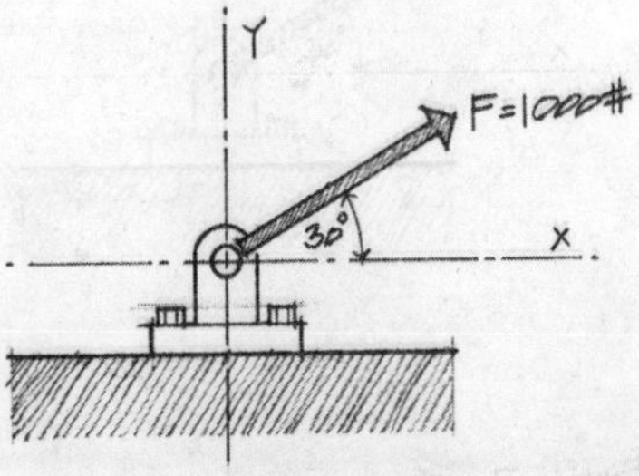

Solution:

$$\theta = 30°$$
$$F_x = F\cos\theta = F\cos 30°$$
$$F_x = 1{,}000\#(0.866) = 866\#$$
$$F_y = F\sin\theta = F\sin 30°$$
$$F_y = 1{,}000\#(0.50) = 500\#$$

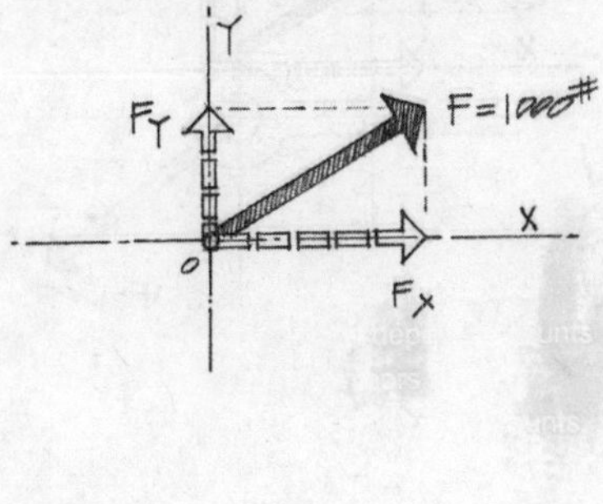

***Note:** Since the point of application of force F is at point O, the components F_x and F_y must also have their points of application at O.*

7 An eyebolt on an inclined ceiling surface supports a 100 N vertical force at point A. Resolve P into its x and y components, assuming the x axis to be parallel with the inclined surface.

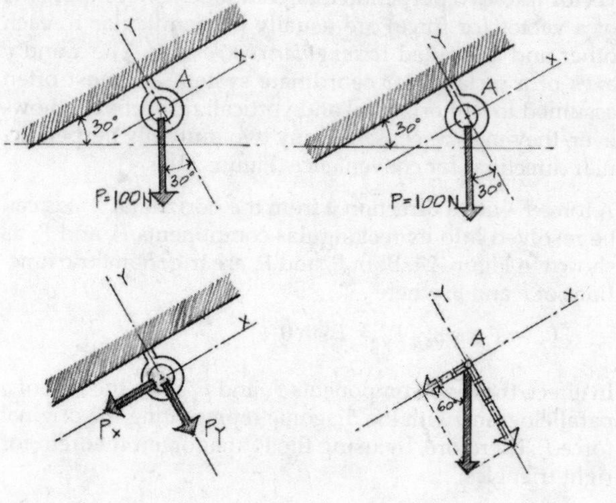

Solution:

$$P_x = P\cos 60° = P\sin 30°$$
$$P_x = 100\,\text{N}(0.5) = 50\,\text{N}$$

$$P_y = P\sin 60° = P\cos 30°$$
$$P_y = 100\,\text{N}(0.866) = 86.6\,\text{N}$$

Note: *Again, you must be careful in placing the component forces* P_x *and* P_y *so that their point of application is at* A *(a pulling-type force), using the same application point as the original force* P.

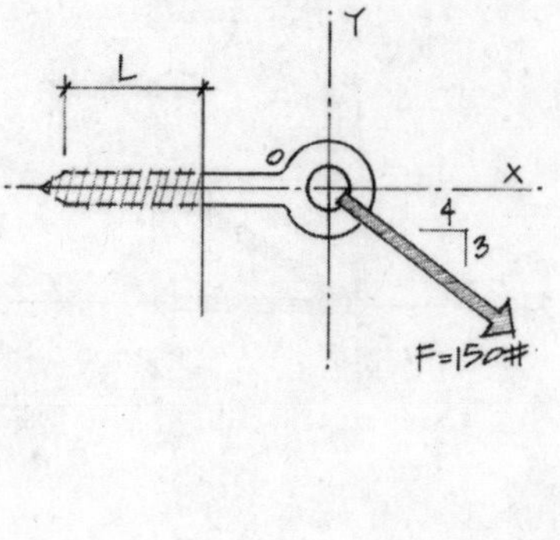

8 A clothesline with a maximum tension of 150# is anchored to a wall by means of an eye screw. If the eye screw is capable of carrying a horizontal pulling force (withdrawal force) of 40# per inch of penetration, how many inches L should the threads be embedded into the wall?

Solution:

For this problem, notice that the direction of the force F is given in terms of a slope relationship. The small-slope triangle has the same angle θ from the horizontal as the force F makes with the x axis. Therefore, we may conclude that both the small-slope triangle and the large triangle (as shown in the tip-to-tail diagram) are similar.

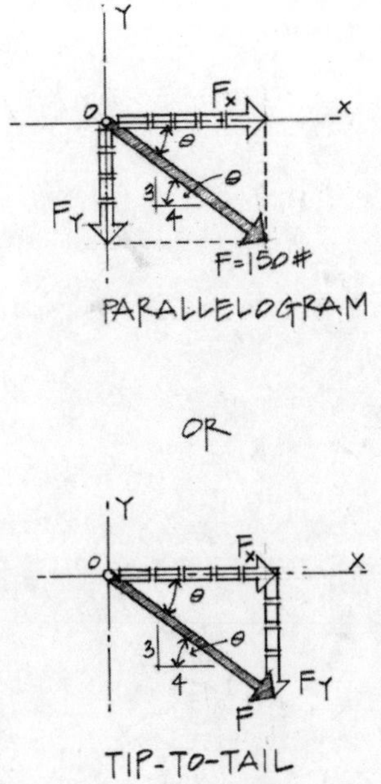

By similar triangles,

$$\frac{F_x}{4} = \frac{F_y}{3} = \frac{F}{5}$$

$\therefore$ solving for the component forces,

$$\cos\theta = \frac{4}{5} = \frac{F_x}{F}$$

$$\sin\theta = \frac{3}{5} = \frac{F_y}{F}$$

then,

$$\frac{F_x}{4} = \frac{F}{5}$$

$$F_x = \frac{4}{5}(F) = \frac{4}{5}(150\#) = 120\#$$

or

$$F_x = F\cos\theta, \text{ but } \cos\theta = \frac{4}{5} \text{ (per slope triangle)}$$

$$F_x = 150\#\left(\frac{4}{5}\right) = 120\# \Leftarrow \text{CHECKS}$$

Continuing with the similar triangle relationship,

$$\frac{F_y}{3} = \frac{F}{5}$$

$$F_y = \frac{3}{5}(F) = \frac{3}{5}(150\#) = 90\#$$

$$F_y = F\sin\theta = 150\#\left(\frac{3}{5}\right) = 90\# \Leftarrow \text{CHECKS}$$

If the eye screw is capable of resisting a 40 #/in. penetration in the horizontal direction, the length of embedment required may be calculated as

$$F_x = 120\# = (40\,\#\text{-}in.) \times (L)$$

$$L = \frac{120\#}{40\,\#\text{-in.}} = 3'' \text{ embedment}$$

A word of caution concerning the equations for the x and y force components: The components of a force depend on how the reference angle is measured, as shown in Figure 25.

In Figure 25(a), the components F_x and F_y may be stated as

$$F_x = F\cos\theta$$
$$F_y = F\sin\theta$$

where the direction of force F is defined by the angle θ measured from the horizontal x axis. In the case of Figure 25(b), the direction of F is given in terms of an angle ϕ measured from the y reference axis. This therefore changes the trigonometric notation, where

$$F_x = F\sin\phi$$
$$F_y = F\cos\phi$$

Note: *The reversal of sine and cosine depends on how the reference angle is measured.*

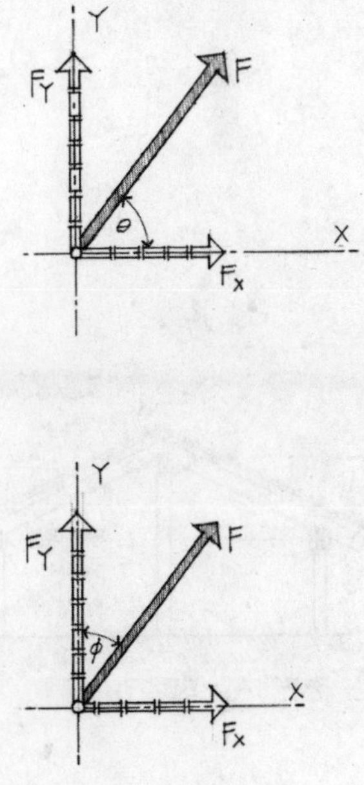

Figure 25 *Force and components.*

Problems

Resolution of forces into *x* and *y* components.

6 Determine the *x* and *y* components of the force, *F*, shown.

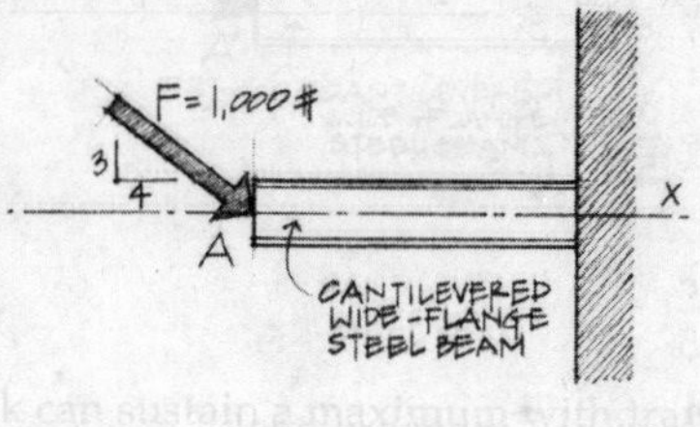

7 If a hook can sustain a maximum withdrawal force of 250 N in the vertical direction, determine the maximum tension *T* that can be exerted.

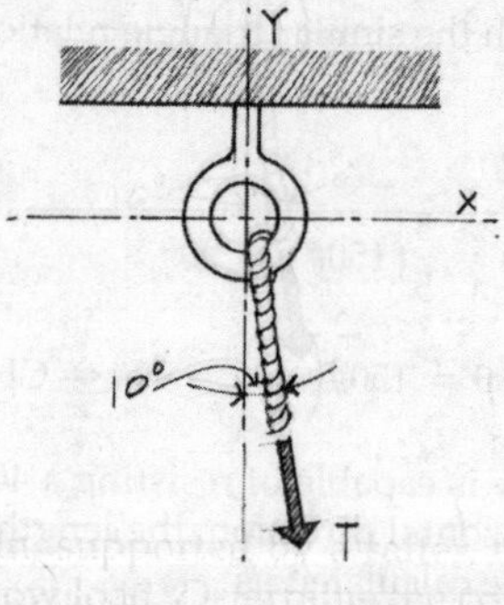

8 A roof purlin, supported by a rafter, must support a 300# vertical snow load. Determine the components of *P*, perpendicular and parallel to the axis of the rafter.

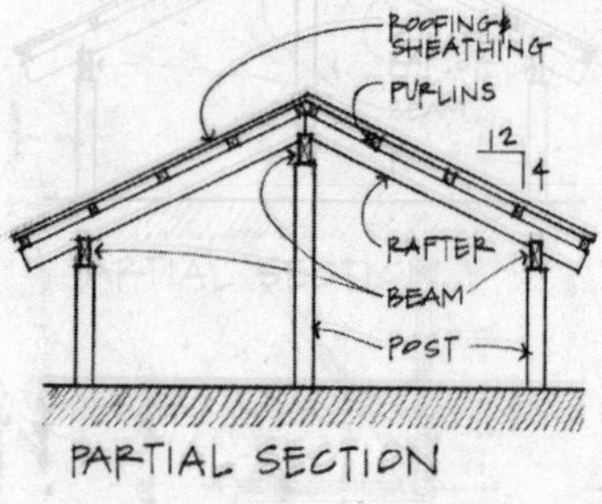

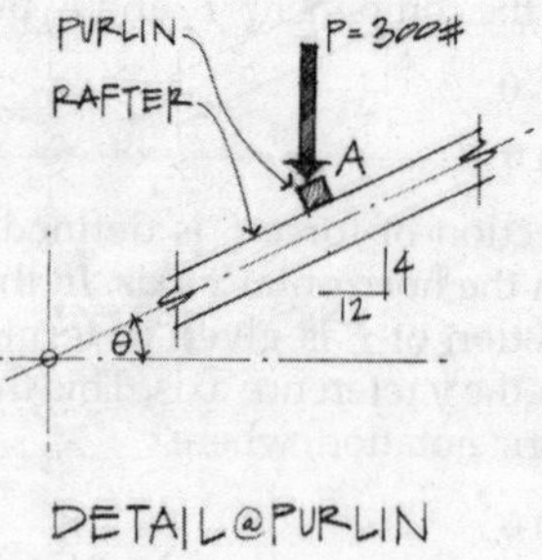

Vector Addition by the Component Method

As was shown in previous sections, vectors may be added graphically by using the parallelogram law or the modified tip-to-tail method.

Now, with the concept of resolution of vectors into two rectangular components, we are ready to begin the *analytical* approach to vector addition. The first step in the analytical approach involves resolving each force of a force system into its respective components. Then, the essential force components may be added algebraically (as opposed to a graphical vector addition) to yield a resultant force. For example, assume we have three forces *A*, *B*, and *C* acting on a particle at point *O* (Figure 26).

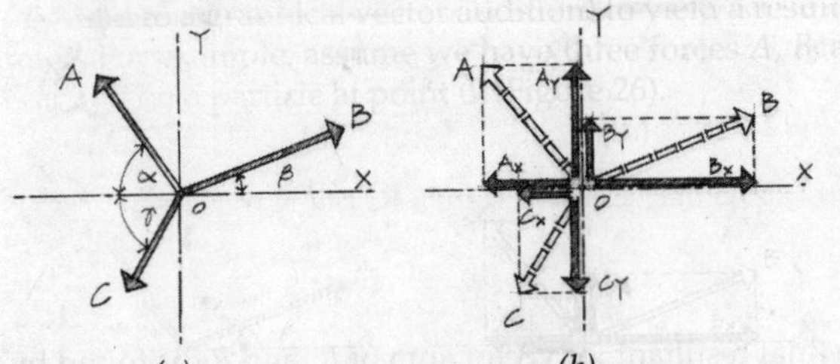

Figure 26 Analytical method of vector addition.

In Figure 26(b), each force is replaced by its respective x and y force components. All of the component forces acting on point O produce the same effect as the original forces A, B, and C.

The horizontal and vertical components may now be summed algebraically. It is important to note here that although A_x, B_x, and C_x are acting along the horizontal x axis, they are not all acting in the same direction. To keep the summation process systematic, it is essential to establish a sign convention (Figure 27).

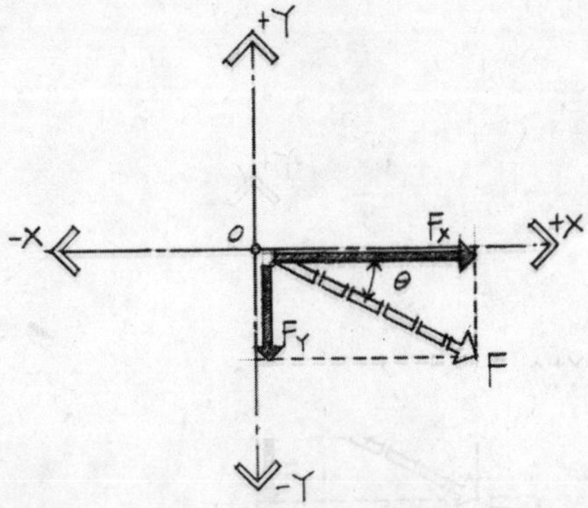

Figure 27 Sign convention for forces.

The most commonly used sign convention for a rectangular coordinate system defines any vector acting toward the right as denoting a positive x direction and any vector acting upward as denoting a positive y direction. Anything to the left or down denotes a negative direction.

In Figure 27, a force F is resolved into its x and y components. For this case, the F_x component is directed to the right, therefore denoting a positive x force component. The F_y component is pointed down, representing a negative y force.

Returning to the problem shown in Figure 26, horizontal components will be summed algebraically such that

$$R_x = -A_x + B_x - C_x$$

or

$$R_x = \Sigma F_x$$

where R denotes a resultant force.

Vertical components may be summed similarly, where

$$R_y = +A_y + B_y - C_y$$

or

$$R_y = \Sigma F_y$$

Thus, the three forces have been replaced by two resultant components, R_x and R_y (Figure 28).

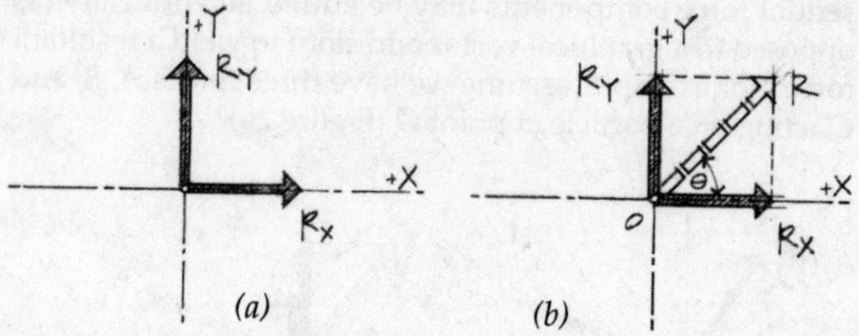

Figure 28 Final resultant R *from* R_x *and* R_y.

The final resultant, or vector sum of R_x and R_y, is found by the Pythagorean theorem, where

$$R = \sqrt{(R_x)^2 + (R_y)^2}$$

$$\tan\theta = \frac{R_y}{R_x} = \frac{\Sigma F_y}{\Sigma F_x};$$

$$\theta = \tan^{-1}\left(\frac{R_y}{R_x}\right)$$

Example Problems: Vector Addition by the Component Method

9 An anchor device is acted upon by two forces F_1 and F_2 as shown. Determine the resultant force analytically.

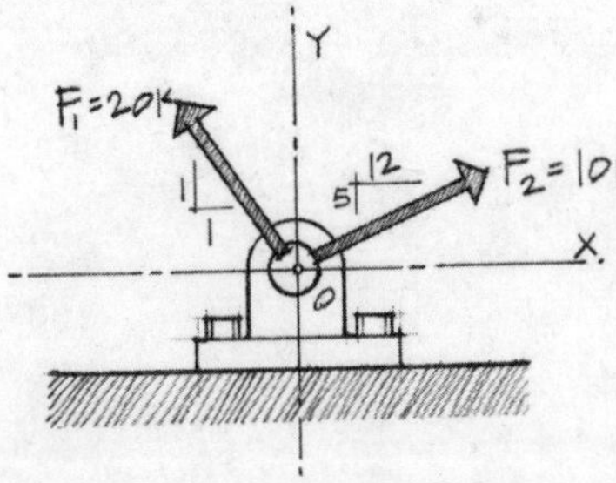

Solution:

Step 1: *Resolve each force into its x and y components.*

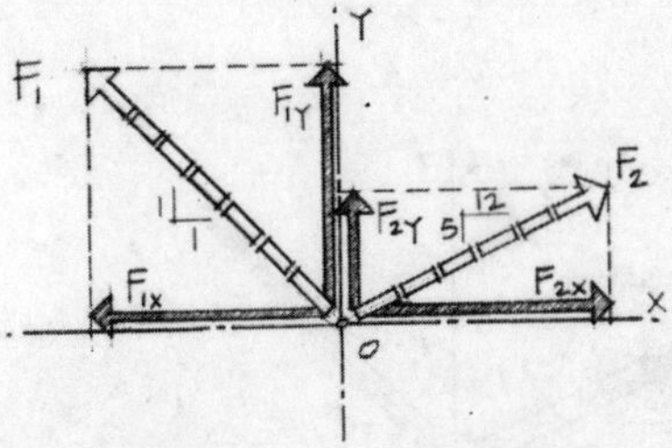

$$F_{1x} = -F_1 \cos \alpha$$
$$F_{1y} = +F_1 \sin \alpha$$
$$F_{2x} = +F_2 \cos \beta$$
$$F_{2y} = +F_2 \sin \beta$$

$$\cos \alpha = \frac{1}{\sqrt{2}} \qquad \sin \alpha = \frac{1}{\sqrt{2}}$$

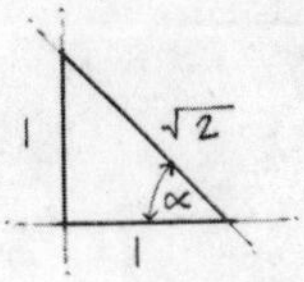

$$\cos \beta = \frac{12}{13} \qquad \sin \beta = \frac{5}{13}$$

$$F_{1x} = -F_1\left(\frac{1}{\sqrt{2}}\right) = -20\,\text{k}\left(\frac{1}{\sqrt{2}}\right) = -14.14\,\text{k}$$

$$F_{1y} = F_1\left(\frac{1}{\sqrt{2}}\right) = 20\,\text{k}\left(\frac{1}{\sqrt{2}}\right) = +14.14\,\text{k}$$

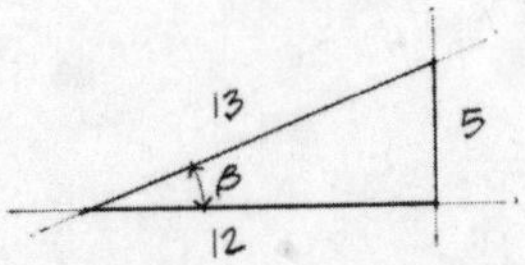

$$F_{2x} = F_2\left(\frac{12}{13}\right) = 10\,\text{k}\left(\frac{12}{13}\right) = +9.23\,\text{k}$$

$$F_{2y} = F_2\left(\frac{5}{13}\right) = 10\,\text{k}\left(\frac{5}{13}\right) = +3.85\,\text{k}$$

Step 2: *Resultant along the horizontal x axis.*

$$R_x = \Sigma F_x = -F_{1x} + F_{2x}$$
$$= -14.14\,\text{k} + 9.23\,\text{k} = -4.91\,\text{k}$$

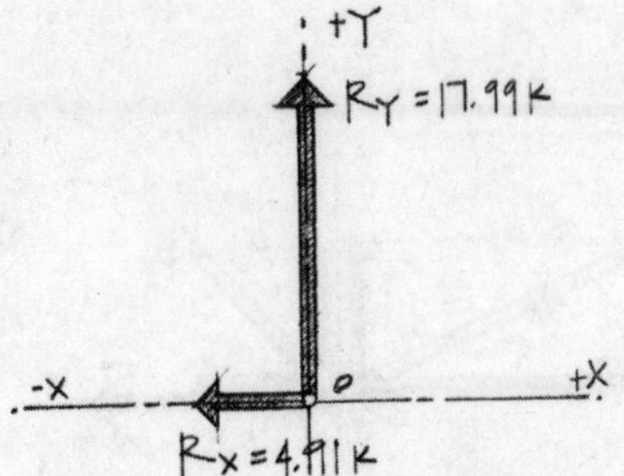

Step 3: *Resultant along the vertical y axis.*

$$R_y = \Sigma F_y = +F_{1y} + F_{2y}$$
$$= +14.14\,\text{k} + 3.85\,\text{k} = +17.99\,\text{k}$$

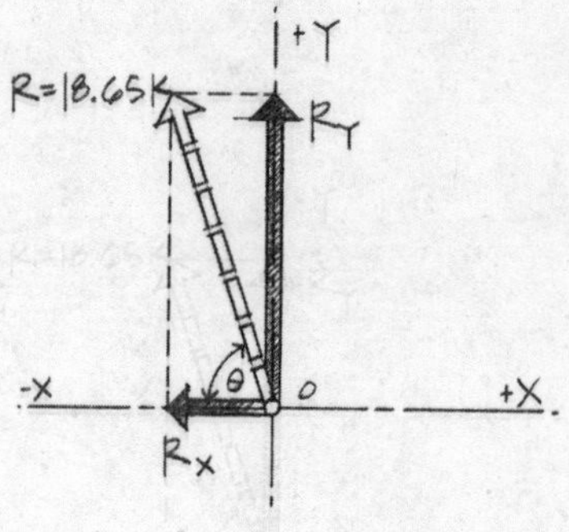

Step 4: *Resultant of* R_x *and* R_y.

$$R = \sqrt{R_x^2 + R_y^2} = \sqrt{(-4.91)^2 + (17.99)^2} = 18.65\text{ k}$$

$$\theta = \tan^{-1}\left(\frac{R_y}{R_x}\right) = \tan^{-1}\left(\frac{17.99}{4.91}\right) = \tan^{-1}3.66 = 74.7°$$

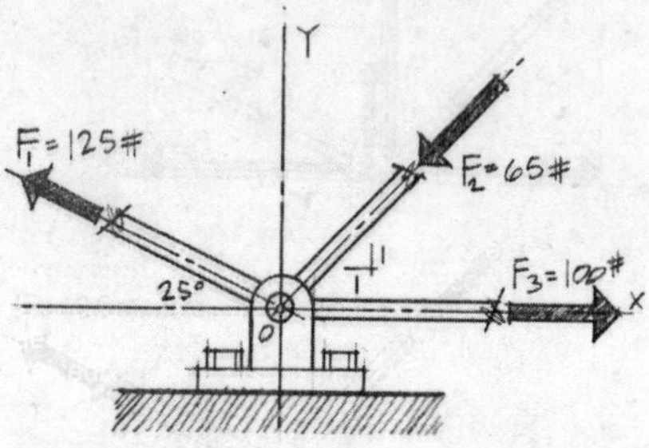

10 An anchoring device is subjected to the three forces as shown. Determine analytically the resultant force the anchor must resist.

Solution:

Resolve each force into its component parts.

$$-F_{1x} = F_1 \cos 25° = 125\#(0.906) = -113\#$$
$$+F_{1y} = F_1 \sin 25° = 125\#(0.423) = +53\#$$

$$-F_{2x} = F_2\left(\frac{1}{\sqrt{2}}\right) = 65\#\left(\frac{1}{\sqrt{2}}\right) = -46\#$$

$$-F_{2y} = F_2\left(\frac{1}{\sqrt{2}}\right) = 65\#\left(\frac{1}{\sqrt{2}}\right) = -46\#$$

$$+F_{3x} = F_3 = +100\#$$

or by applying the *principle of transmissibility*,

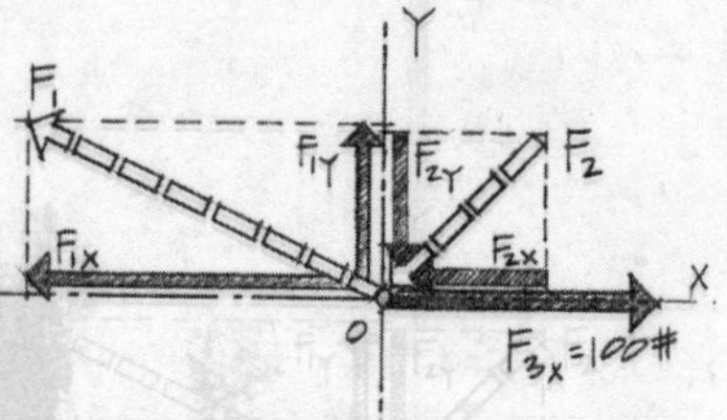

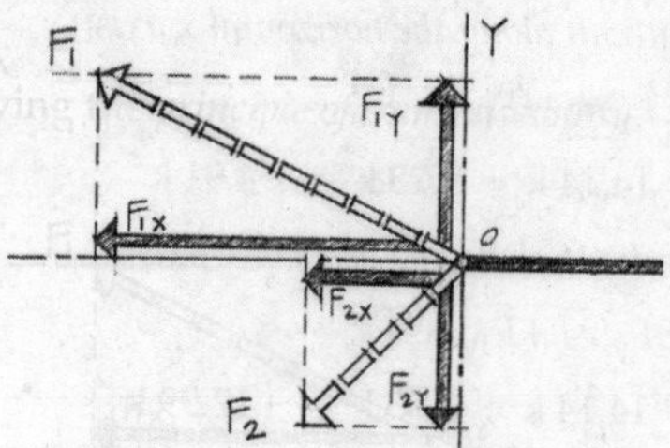

Force F_2 is moved along its line of action until it becomes a pulling, rather than a pushing, force. However, the external effects on the anchor device remain the same.

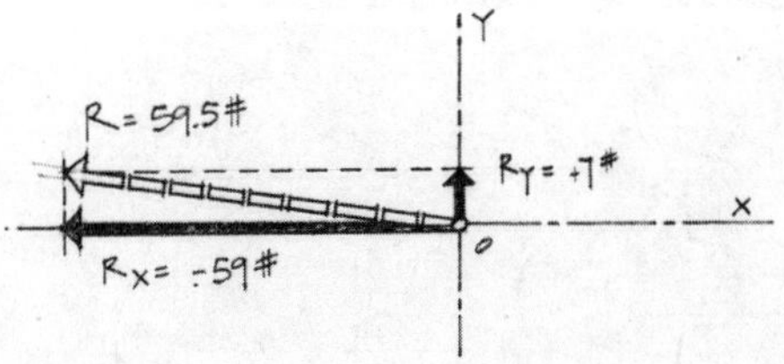

$$R_x = \Sigma F_x = -F_{1x} - F_{2x} + F_{3x}$$
$$R_x = -113\# - 46\# + 100\# = -59\# \leftarrow$$

$$R_y = \Sigma F_y = +F_{1y} - F_{2y}$$
$$R_y = +53\# - 46\# = +7\#\uparrow$$

$$R = \sqrt{(R_x)^2 + (R_y)^2} = \sqrt{(-59)^2 + (7)^2} = 59.5\#$$

$$\tan\theta = \frac{R_y}{R_x} = \frac{7}{59} = 0.119$$

$$\theta = \tan^{-1}(.119) = 6.8°$$

Graphical Check:

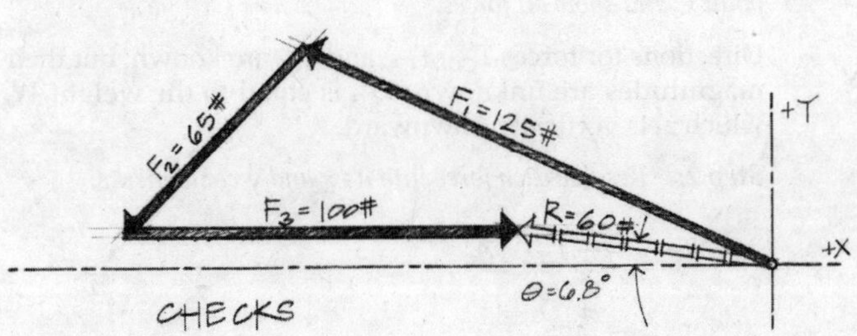

Scale: 1″ = 40#

11 A block of weight $W = 500$ N is supported by a cable CD, which in turn is suspended by cables AC and BC. Determine the required tension forces T_{CA} and T_{CB} so that the resultant force at point C equals zero.

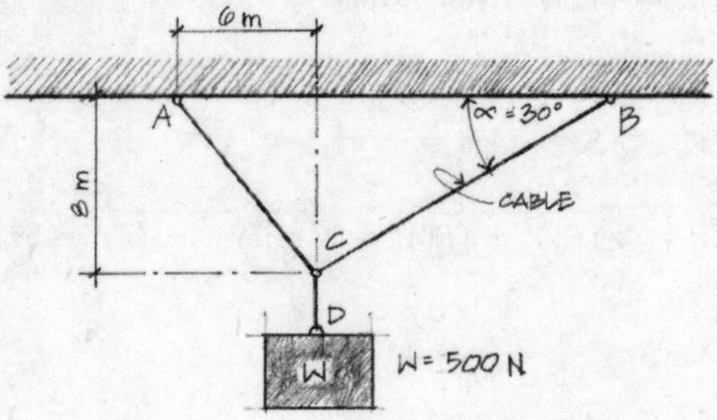

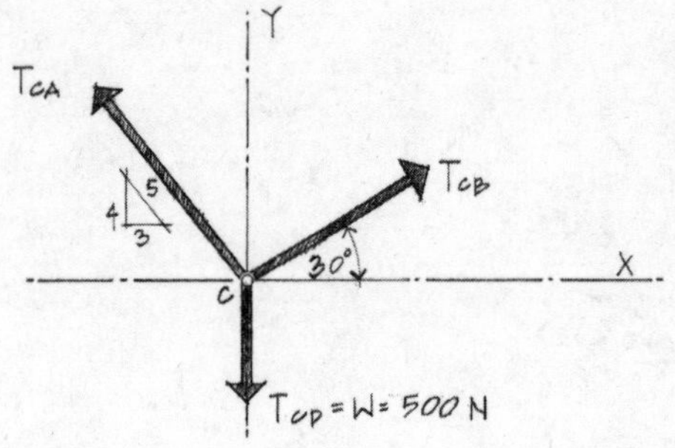

Solution:

Step 1: *Because all cables are concurrent at point C, isolate point C and show all forces.*

Directions for forces T_{CD}, T_{CA}, and T_{CB} are known, but their magnitudes are unknown. T_{CD} is equal to the weight W, which acts vertically downward.

Step 2: *Resolve each force into its x and y components.*

$$T_{CA_x} = \frac{3}{5} T_{CA}$$

$$T_{CA_y} = \frac{4}{5} T_{CA}$$

$$T_{CB_x} = T_{CB} \cos 30° = 0.866 T_{CB}$$
$$R_{CB_y} = T_{CB} \sin 30° = 0.5 T_{CB}$$

$$T_{CD} = W = 500 \text{ N}$$

Step 3: *Write the resultant component force equations.*

$$R_x = \Sigma F_x = T_{CA_x} + T_{CB_x} = 0$$

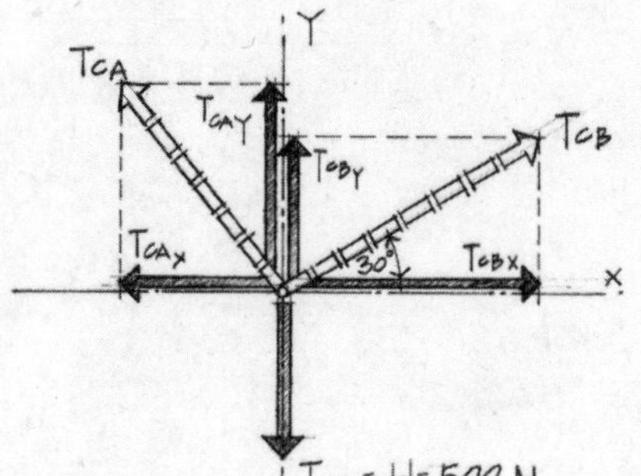

We set $R_x = 0$ to comply with the condition that no resultant force develops at point C; that is, all forces are balanced at this point.

$$\therefore R_x = -\frac{3}{5} T_{CA} + 0.866 T_{CB} = 0$$

$$\frac{3}{5} T_{CA} = 0.866 T_{CB} \tag{1}$$

then,

$$R_y = \Sigma F_y = +T_{CA_y} + T_{CB_y} - 500 \text{ N} = 0$$

$$\therefore R_y = \frac{4}{5} T_{CA} + .5 T_{CB} - 500 \text{ N} = 0$$

$$\frac{4}{5} T_{CA} + 0.5 T_{CB} = 500 \text{ N} \tag{2}$$

From writing the resultant equations T_{CA} and T_{CB}, we obtain two equations, (1) and (2), containing two unknowns. Solving the two equations simultaneously,

$$\frac{3}{5}T_{CA} = 0.866T_{CB} \qquad (1)$$

$$\frac{4}{5}T_{CA} + 0.5T_{CB} = 500\text{ N} \qquad (2)$$

From equation (1),

$$T_{CA} = \frac{5}{3}(0.866\,T_{CB}) = 1.44\,T_{CB}$$

Substituting into equation (2),

$$\frac{4}{5}(1.44T_{CB}) + 0.5T_{CB} = 500\text{ N}$$

$$\therefore\ 1.15T_{CB} + 0.5T_{CB} = 500\text{ N}$$

Solving for T_{CB},

$$1.65T_{CB} = 500\text{ N}$$

$$T_{CB} = \frac{500\text{ N}}{1.65} = 303\text{ N}$$

Substituting the value of T_{CB} back into equation (1) or (2),

$$T_{CA} = 436.4\text{ N}$$

Graphical Check:

Because T_{CD} has a known magnitude and direction, it will be used as the starting (or base) force.

Step 1: *Draw the force polygon using the tip-to-tail method.*

Step 2: *Draw force* T_{CD} *first, to scale.*

Step 3: *Draw the lines of action for* T_{CA} *and* T_{CB}*; the order does not matter.*

Forces T_{CA} and T_{CB} have known directions but unknown magnitudes; therefore, only their lines of action are drawn initially. We know that because $R = 0$, the tip of the last force must end at the tail (the origin) of the first force—in this case, T_{CD}.

Step 4: *The intersection of the two lines of action determines the limits for* T_{CB} *and* T_{CA}.

Step 5: *Scale off the magnitudes for* T_{CB} *and* T_{CA}.

Step 6:

$$T_{CA} = 436.4\text{ N}$$

CHECKS

$$T_{CB} = 303\text{ N}$$

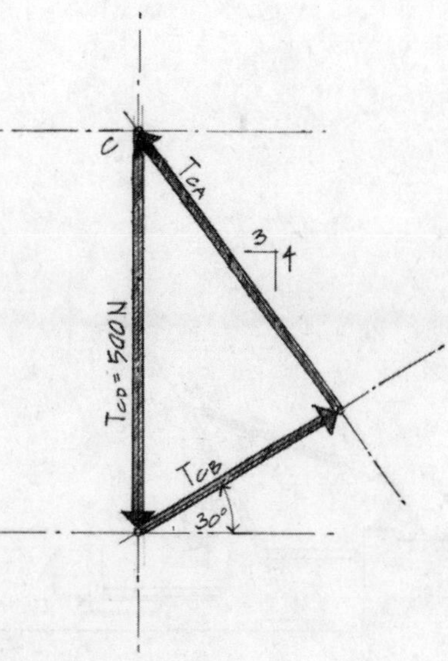

Scale: 1 mm = 5 N

Problems

Analytical solutions using force components. Check graphically.

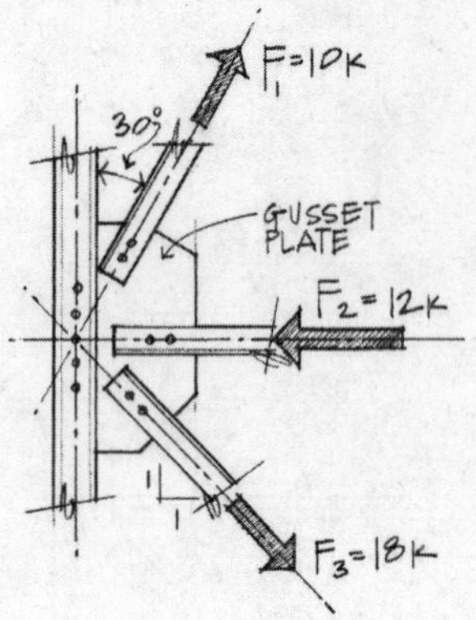

9 Three members of a truss frame into a steel gusset plate as shown. All forces are concurrent at point *O*. Determine the resultant of the three forces that must be carried by the gusset plate.

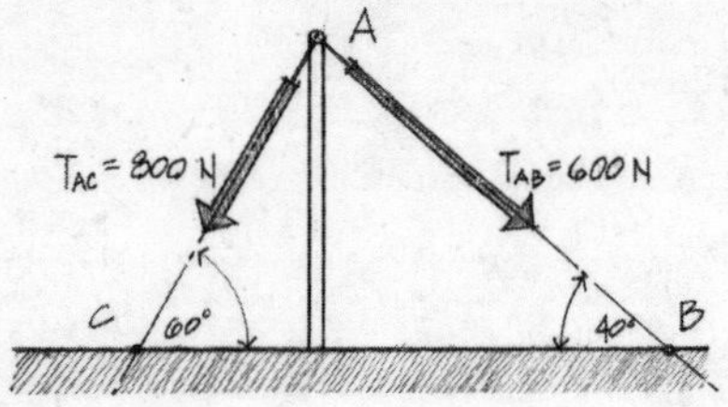

10 Two cables with known tensions as shown are attached to a pole at point *A*. Determine the resultant force to which the pole is subjected. Scale: 1 mm = 10 N.

***Note:** The pole and cables are coplanar.*

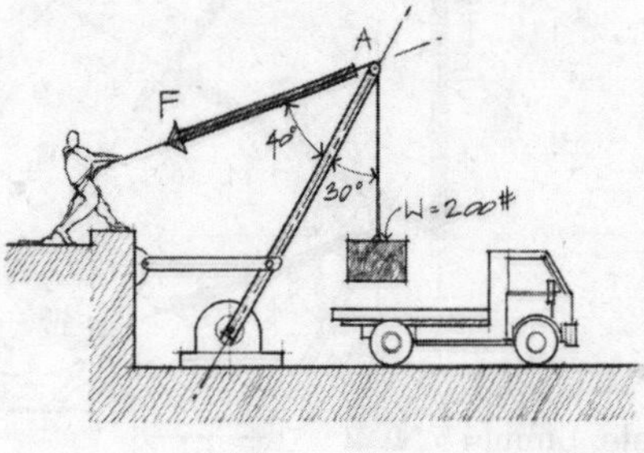

11 A laborer is hoisting a weight, *W* = 200#, by pulling on a rope as shown. Determine the force *F* required to hold the weight in the position shown if the resultant of *F* and *W* acts along the axis of the boom.

12 One end of a timber roof truss is supported on a brick wall but not securely fastened. The reaction of the brick wall can therefore be only vertical. Assuming that the maximum capacity of either the inclined or horizontal member is 7 kN, determine the maximum magnitudes of F_1 and F_2 so that their resultant is vertical through the brick wall.

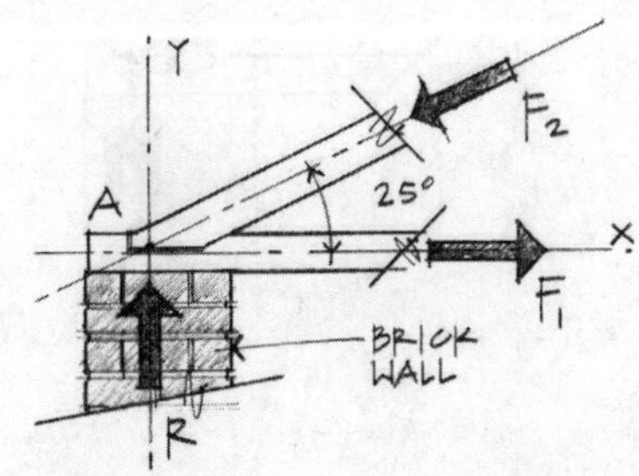

13 The resultant of three tensions in the guy wires anchored at the top of the tower is vertical. Find the unknown but equal tensions T in the two wires. All three wires and the tower are in the same vertical plane.

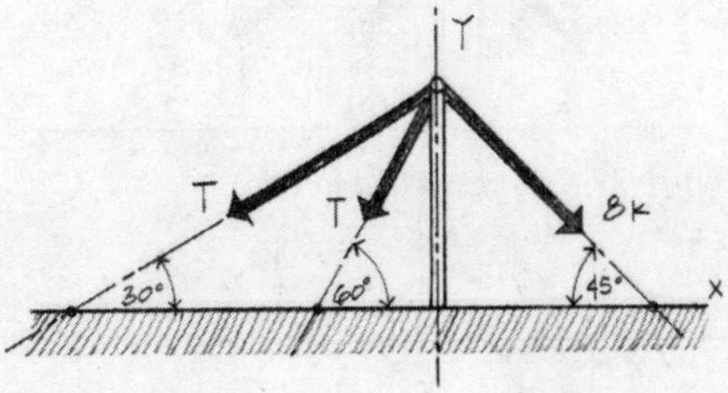

Moment of a Force

The tendency of a force to produce rotation of a body about some reference axis or point is called the *moment of a force* (see Figures 29a and 29b). Quantitatively, the moment M of a force F about a point A is defined as the product of the magnitude of the force F and perpendicular distance d from A to the line of action of F. In equation form,

$$M_A = F \times d$$

The subscript A denotes the point about which the moment is taken.

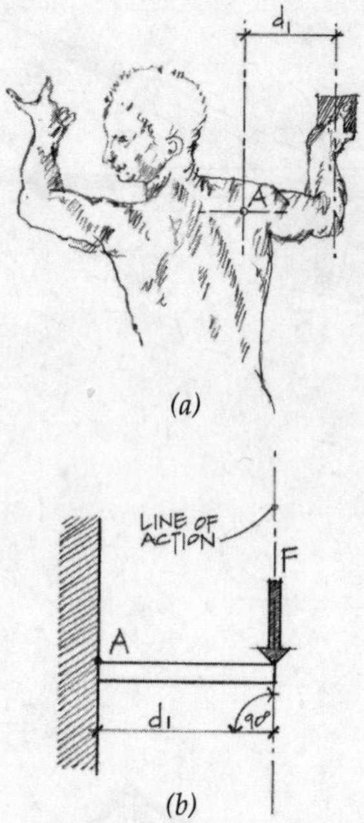

Figure 29 Moment of a force.

Assume, as shown in Figure 29(a), that a person is carrying a weight of magnitude F at a distance d_1 from an arbitrary point A on the person's shoulder. The point A has no significance except to establish some reference point about which the moments can be measured. In Figure 29(b) a schematic is shown with the force F applied on a beam at a distance d_1 from point A. This is an equivalent representation of the pictorial sketch in Figure 29(a), where the moment of point A is

$$M_A = F \times d_1$$

If the person now extends his arm so that the weight is at distance d_2 from point A, as shown in Figure 30(b), the amount of physical energy needed to carry the weight is increased. One reason for this is the increased moment about point A due to the increased distance d_2. The moment is now equal to that shown in Figure 30(a):

$$M_A = F \times d_2$$

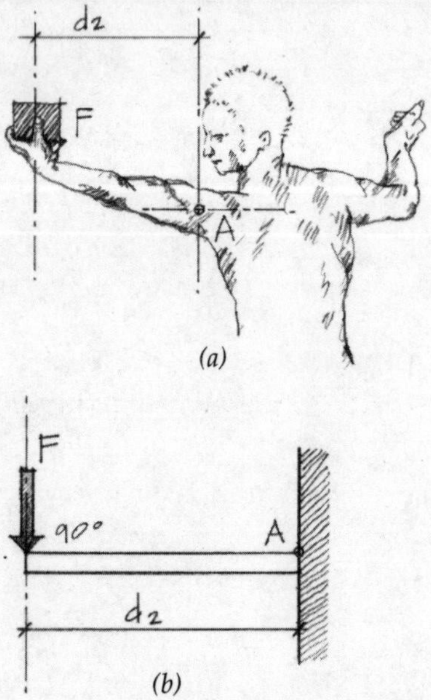

Figure 30 Moment of a force with an increased moment arm.

In measuring the distance *d* (often referred to as the *moment arm*) between the applied force and the reference point, it is important to note that the distance must be the perpendicular measurement to the line of action of the force (Figure 31).

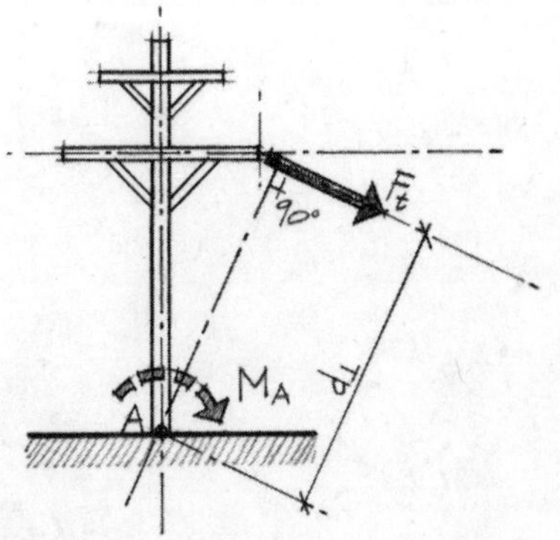

Figure 31 Perpendicular moment arm.

A moment of a force is a vector quantity. The force producing the rotation has a magnitude and direction; therefore, the moment produced has a magnitude and a direction. Units used to describe the magnitude of a moment are expressed as pound-inch (#-in., lb.-in.), pound-foot (#-ft.), kip-inch (k-in.), or kip-foot (k-ft.). The corresponding metric (SI) units are newton-meter (N-m) or kilonewton-meter (kN-m). Direction of a moment is indicated by the type of rotation developed, either clockwise rotation or counterclockwise rotation (Figure 32).

In discussing forces in a previous section, we established a sign convention where forces acting to the right or upward were considered to be positive and those directed to the left or downward were considered to be negative. Likewise, a sign convention should be established for moments. Because rotation is either clockwise or counterclockwise, we may arbitrarily assign a plus (+) to the counterclockwise rotation and a minus (−) to the clockwise rotation.

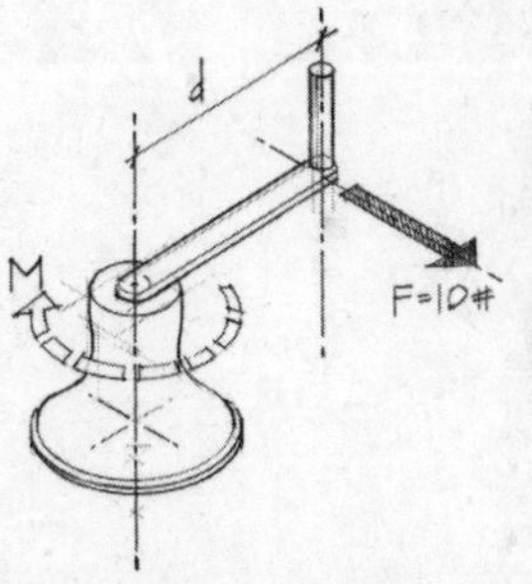

Figure 32 Sailboat winch-rotation about an axis.

It is perfectly permissible to reverse the sign convention if desired; however, use the same convention throughout an entire problem. A consistent sign convention reduces the chances of error.

Moments cause a body to have the tendency to rotate. If a system tries to resist this rotational tendency, bending or torsion results. For example, if we examine a cantilever beam with one end securely fixed to a support, as in Figure 33(a), the beam itself generates a resistance effect to rotation. In resisting the rotation, bending occurs, which results in a deflection Δ, as in Figure 33(b).

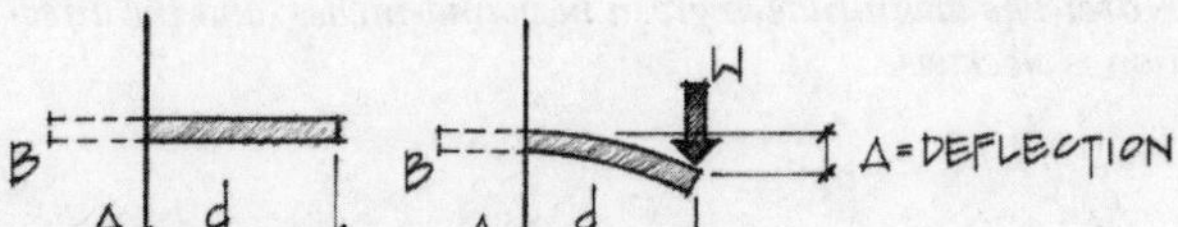

(a) Unloaded. *(b) Loaded.*

Figure 33 Moment on a cantilever beam.

Next, consider a situation where torsion (twisting) occurs because of the system trying to resist rotation about its longitudinal axis (Figure 34).

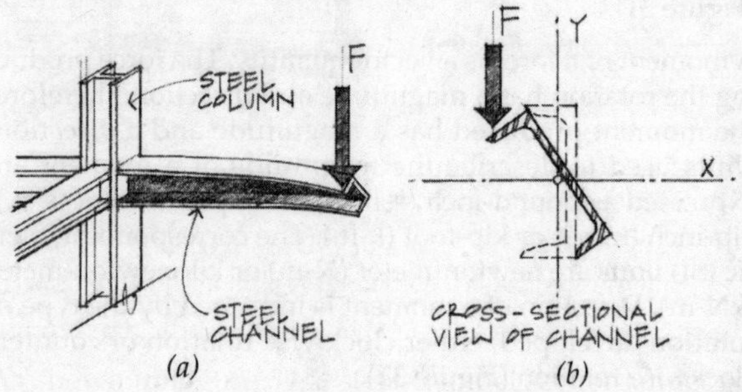

Figure 34 An example of torsion on a cantilever beam.

As shown in Figure 34, a steel channel section under eccentric loading is subjected to a rotational effect called *torsion*. Moments about a circular shaft or rod are usually referred to as *torque*.

If in Figure 34(a) the fixed support were replaced by a hinge or pin, no distortion of the beam would occur. Instead, simple rotation at the pin or hinge would result.

Example Problems: Moment of a Force

12 What is the moment of the force F about point A?

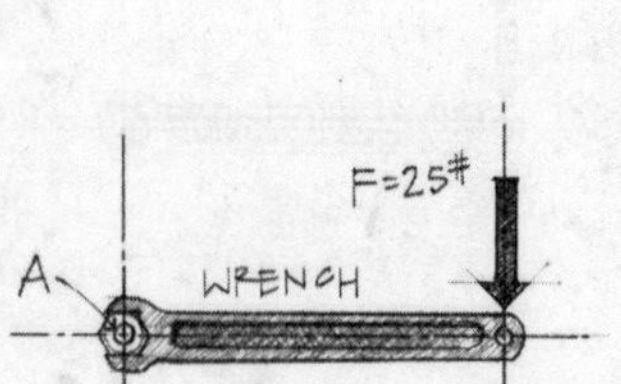

Solution:

The perpendicular distance between point A (on the head of the bolt) and the line of action of force F is 15 inches. Therefore,

$$M_A = (-F \times d) = (-25\# \times 15'') = -375\,\#\text{-in.}$$

Note: *The magnitude is given in pound-inches, and the direction is clockwise.*

13 What is M_A, with the wrench inclined at a 3 in 4 slope?

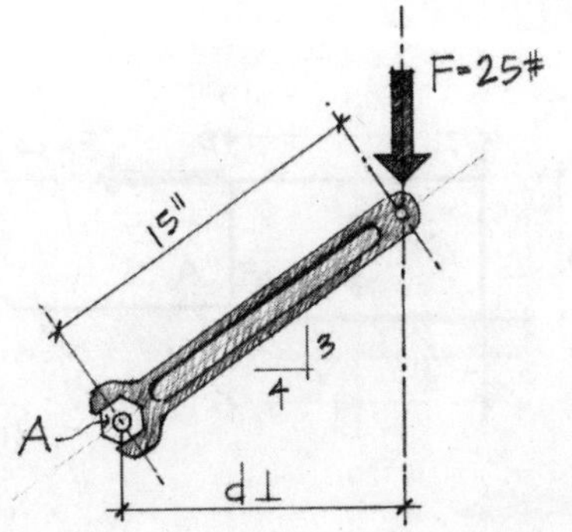

$$d\pm = \frac{4}{5}(15'') = 12''$$

$d\pm$ is the perpendicular distance from A to line of action of F.

$$M_A = (-F)(d) = -25\#(12'') = -300\,\#\text{-in.}$$

14 The equivalent forces due to water pressure and the self-weight of the dam are shown. Determine the resultant moment at the toe of the dam (point A). Is the dam able to resist the applied water pressure? The weight of the dam is 36 kN.

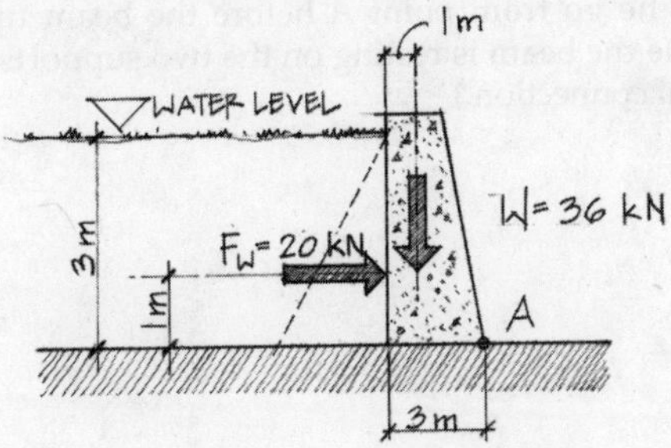

Solution:

The overturning effect due to the water is clockwise, while the weight of the dam has a counterclockwise rotational tendency about the "toe" at A. Therefore, the resultant moment about point A is

$M_{A_1} = M_A = -F_W(1\,\text{m}) = -20\,\text{kN}(1\,\text{m}) = -20\,\text{kN-m}$

(overturning)

$M_{A_2} = M_A = +W(2\,\text{m}) = +36\,\text{kN}(2\,\text{m}) = +72\,\text{kN-m}$

(stabilizing)

because $M_{A_2} > M_{A_1}$

The dam is stable, and, thus, will not overturn.

Problems

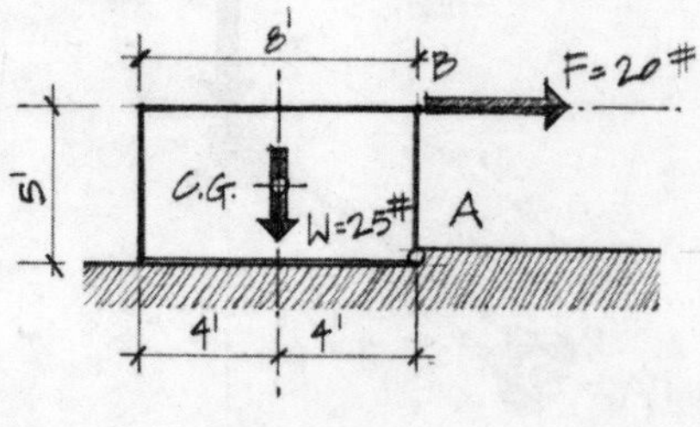

14 A box weighing 25 pounds (assumed concentrated at its center of gravity) is being pulled by a horizontal force F equal to 20 pounds. What is the moment about point A? Does the box tip over?

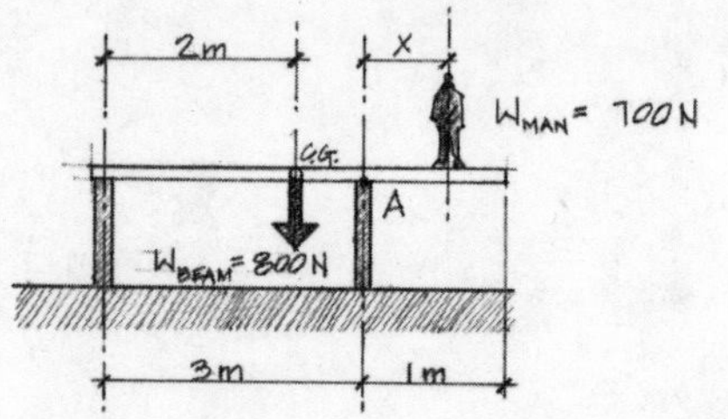

15 A large wood beam weighing 800 N is supported by two posts as shown. If an *unthinking man* weighing 700 N were to walk on the overhang portion of the beam, how far can he go from point A before the beam tips over? (Assume the beam is resting on the two supports with no physical connection.)

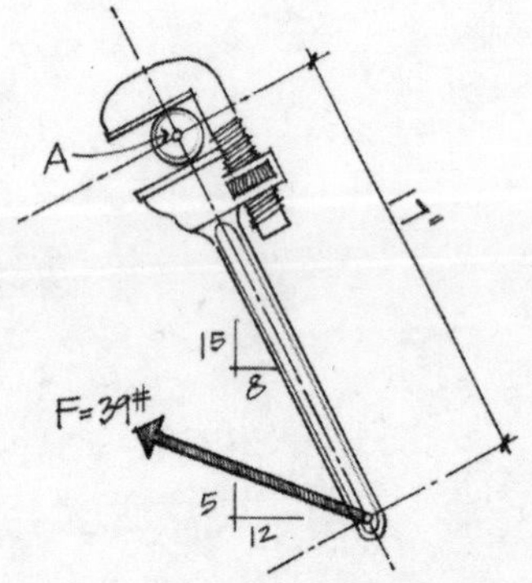

16 Calculate the moment through the center of the pipe due to the force exerted by the wrench.

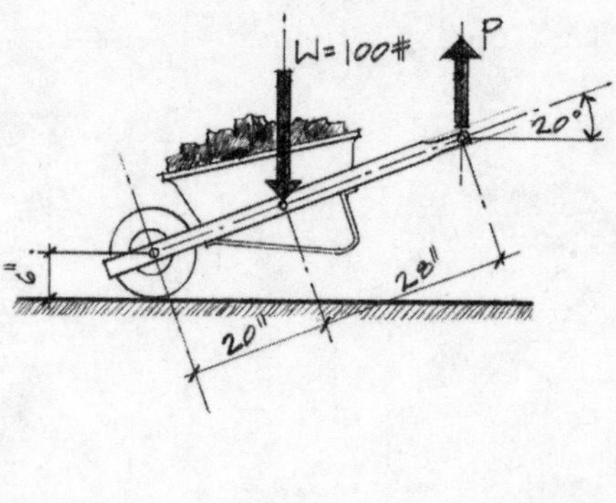

17 For the wheelbarrow shown, find the moment of the 100# weight about the center of the wheel. Also, determine the force P required to resist this moment.

18 A 200# stone is being lifted off the ground by a levering bar. Determine the push P required to keep the stone in the position shown.

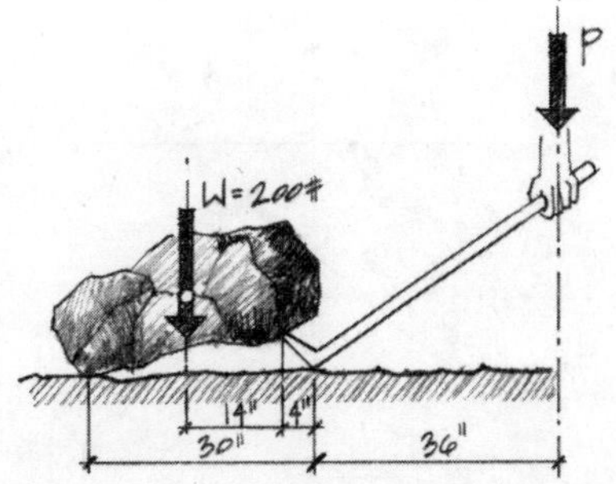

Varignon's Theorem

The French mathematician Pierre Varignon developed a very important theorem of statics. It states that the moment of a force about a point (axis) is equal to the algebraic sum of the moments of its components about the same point (axis). This may be best illustrated by an example (Figure 35).

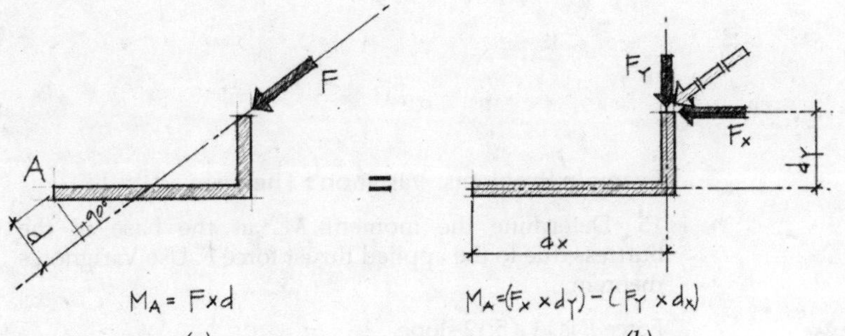

Figure 35 Moment of a force—Varignon's theorem.

If we examine an upturned cantilevered beam subjected to an inclined force F, as shown in Figure 35(a), the moment M_A is obtained by multiplying the applied force F by the perpendicular distance d (from A to the line of action of the force). Finding the distance d is often very involved; therefore, the use of Varignon's theorem becomes very convenient. The force F is resolved into its x and y components, as shown in Figure 35(b).

The force is broken down into a horizontal component and a vertical component, and the moment arm distances d_x and d_y of the respective components are obtained. The resulting moment M_A is obtained by algebraically summing the moments about point A generated by each of the two component forces. In both cases, the moments are identical in magnitude and in direction.

A proof of Varignon's theorem may be illustrated as in Figure 36:

$$F(d) = F_y(d \cos \theta) + F_x(d \sin \theta)$$

Substituting for F_x and F_y,

$$F(d) = F \cos \theta(d \cos \theta) + F \sin \theta(d \sin \theta)$$
$$F(d) = Fd \cos^2 \theta + Fd \sin^2 \theta = Fd(\cos^2 \theta + \sin^2 \theta)$$

But from the known trigonometric identity,

$$\sin^2 \theta + \cos^2 \theta = 1$$
$$F(d) = F(d) \qquad \therefore \text{CHECKS}$$

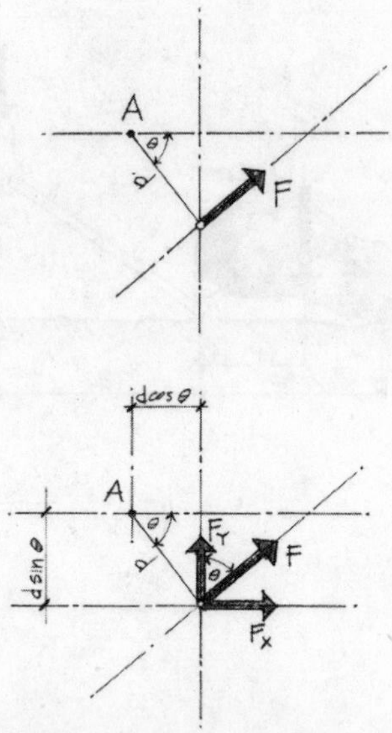

Figure 36 Varignon's theorem.

Example Problems: Varignon's Theorem

15 Determine the moment M_A at the base of the buttress due to the applied thrust force F. Use Varignon's theorem.

Force F is at a 5:12 slope.

Solution:

From Varignon's theorem, resolve F into F_x and F_y; then,

$$M_A = +5\,k(15') - 12\,k(24') = +75 \text{ k-ft.} - 288 \text{ k-ft.}$$
$$= -213 \text{ k-ft.}$$

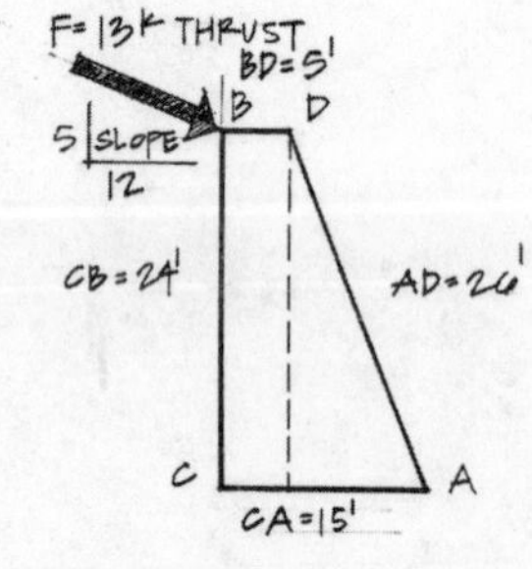

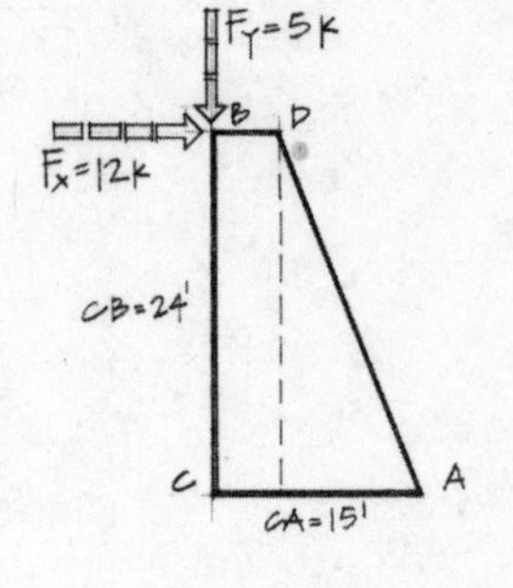

16 A 1.5 kN force from a piston acts on the end of a 300 mm lever. Determine the moment of the force about the axle through reference point O.

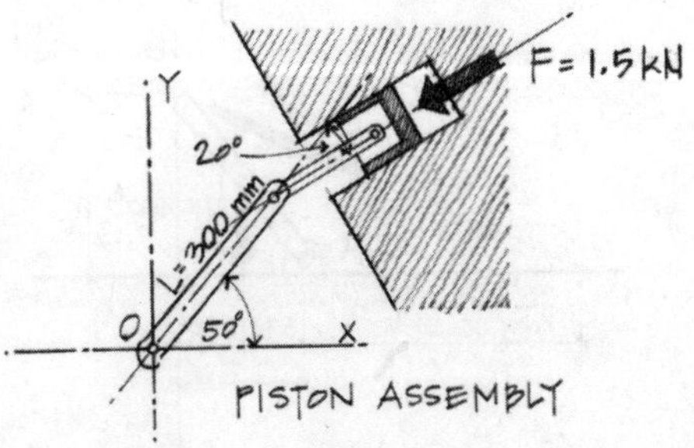

Solution:

In this case, finding the perpendicular distance d for the force F can be quite complicated; therefore, Varignon's theorem will be utilized.

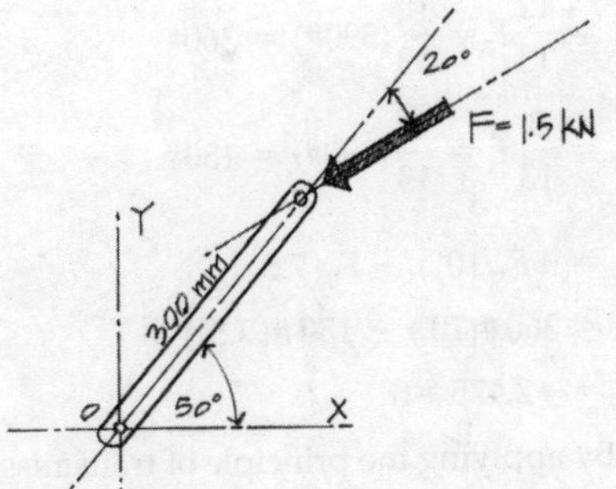

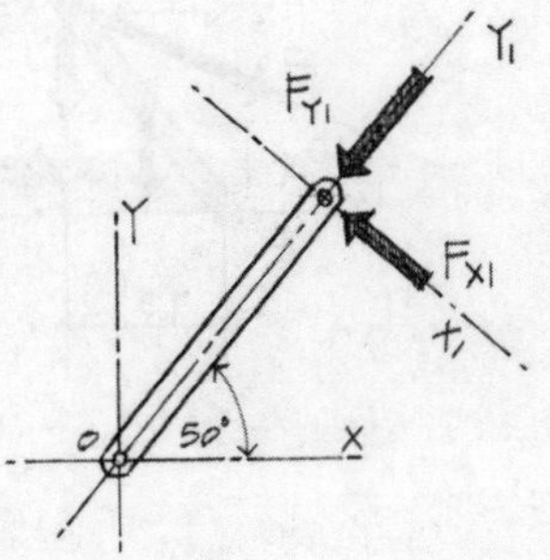

$$F_{y1} = F\cos 20^\circ$$
$$F_{y1} = 1.5\,\text{kN}(0.94) = 1.41\,\text{kN}$$

$$F_{x1} = F\sin 20^\circ$$
$$F_{x1} = 1.5\,\text{kN}\,(0.342) = 0.51\,\text{kN}$$

Note: *300 mm = 0.3 m.*

$$+M_o = +F_{x1}(0.3\,\text{m}) + F_{y1}(0)$$
$$M_o = +(+0.51\,\text{kN})(0.3\,\text{m}) + 0 = +0.153\,\text{kN-m}$$

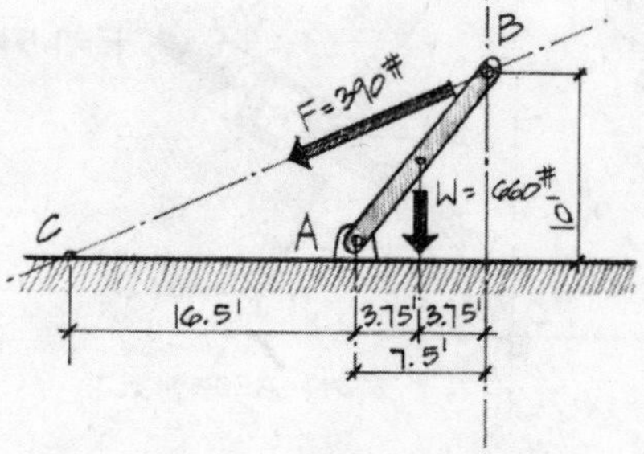

17 Determine the moment of the 390# force about A by:

a. Resolving the force into x and y components acting at B.
b. Resolving the force into x and y components acting at C.
c. Determining the moment due to the weight W about point A.

Solution:

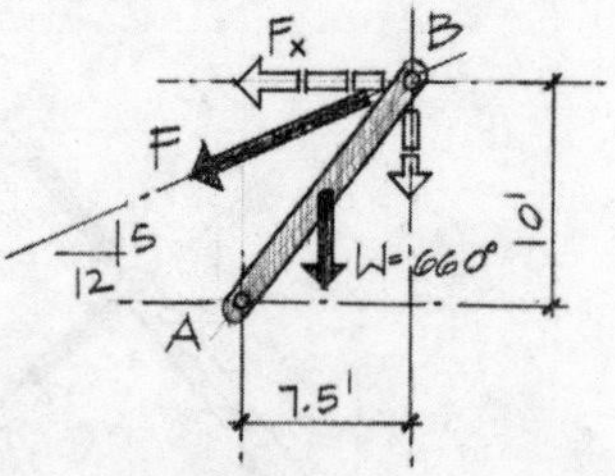

a. Isolate point B, and resolve $F = 390\#$ into its x and y components.

$$F_x = \frac{12}{13}F = \frac{12}{13}(390\#) = 360\#$$

$$F_y = \frac{5}{13}F = \frac{5}{13}(390\#) = 150\#$$

$$M_A = +F_x(10') - F_y(7.5')$$
$$M_A = 360\#(10') - 150\#(7.5')$$
$$M_A = +2{,}475\#\text{-ft.}$$

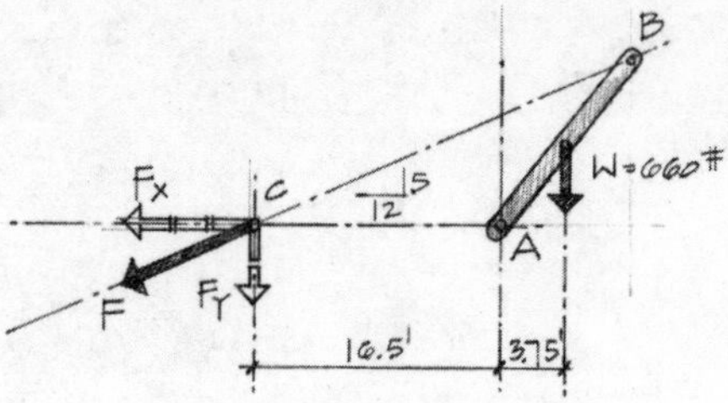

b. By applying the principle of transmissibility, we can move force F down to point C without really altering the external effects on the system.

$$F_x = \frac{12}{13}F = 360\#$$

$$F_y = \frac{5}{13}F = 150\#$$

$$M_A = F_x(0') + F_y(16.5')$$
$$M_A = 0 + 150\#(16.5') = 2{,}475\#\text{-ft.}$$

c. The weight $W = 660\#$ is assumed at the center of gravity of the boom. The moment due to W about A can be expressed as

$$M_A = -W(3.75') = -660\#(3.75') = -2{,}475\#\text{-ft.}$$

Note: *The moments from forces* F *and* W *are balanced and, thus, keep boom* AB *from rotating. This condition will be referred to later as moment equilibrium.*

Problems

19 The figure shows the forces exerted by wind on each floor level of a six-story steel frame building. Determine the resultant overturning moment at the base of the building at A.

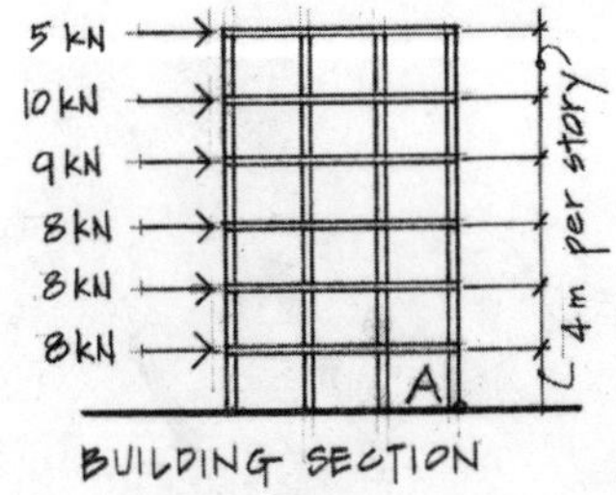

20 Determine the moment of the 1,300# force applied at truss joint D about points B and C. Use Varignon's theorem.

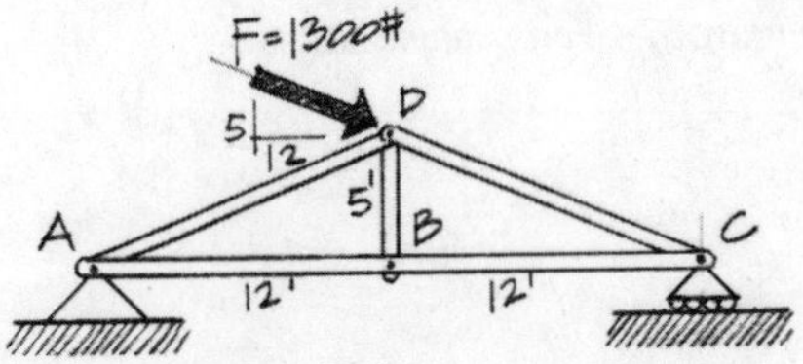

21 A rain gutter is subjected to a 30# force at C as shown. Determine the moment developed about A and B.

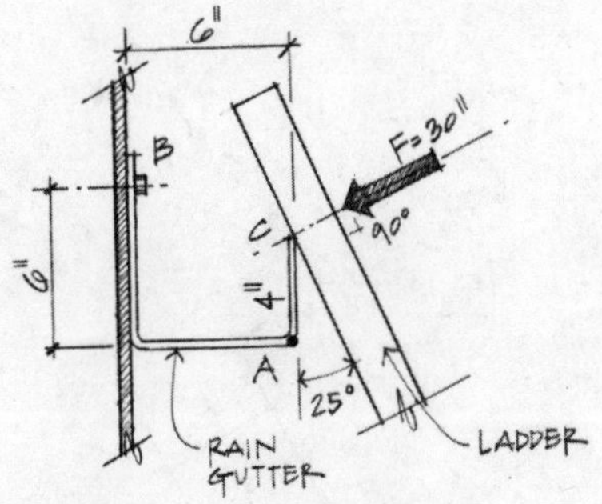

22 Compute the moment of the 1.5 kN force about point A.

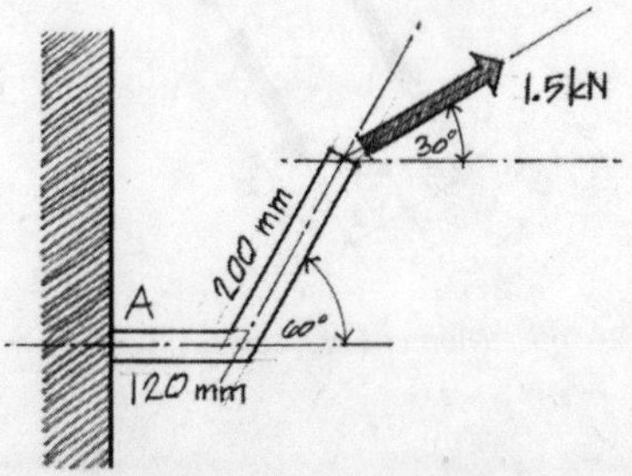

23 Determine the weight W that can be supported by the boom if the maximum force that the cable T can exert is 2,000#. Assume that no resultant rotation will occur at point C. (In other words, $M_C = 0$.)

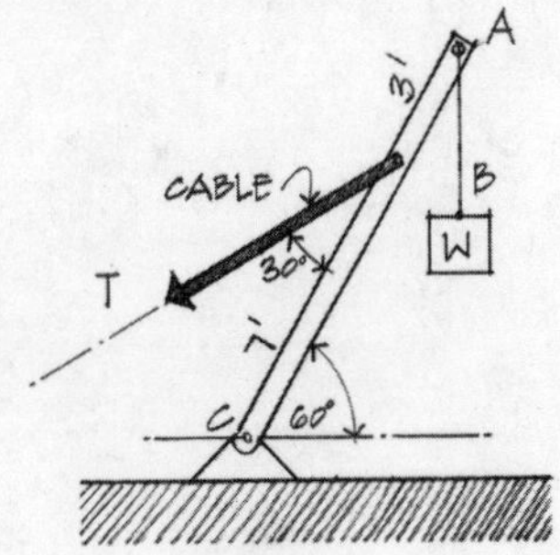

Couple and Moment of a Couple

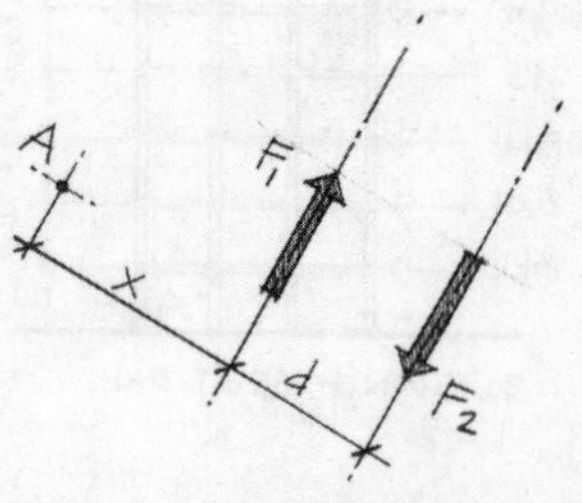

Figure 37 Force couple system.

A *couple* is defined as two forces having the same magnitude, parallel lines of action, but opposite sense (arrowhead direction). Couples have pure rotational effects on a body with no capacity to translate the body in the vertical or horizontal direction, because the sum of their horizontal and vertical components is zero.

Let's examine a rigid body in the x-y plane acted upon by two equal, opposite, and parallel forces F_1 and F_2 (Figure 37).

Assume a point A on the rigid body about which the moment will be calculated. Distance x represents the perpendicular measurement from reference point A to the applied force F, and d is the perpendicular distance between the lines of action of F_1 and F_2.

$$M_A = +F_1(x) - F_2(x + d)$$

where

$$F_1 = F_2$$

and because F_1 and F_2 form a couple system,

$$M_A = +Fx - Fx - Fd$$

$$\therefore M_A = -Fd$$

The final moment M is called the *moment of the couple.* Note that M is independent of the location of the reference point A. M will have the same magnitude and the same rotational sense regardless of the location of A (Figure 38).

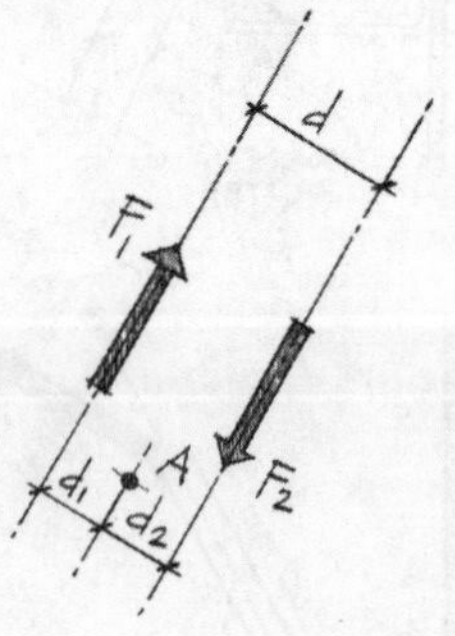

Figure 38 Moment of a couple about A.

$$M_A = -F(d_1) - F(d_2) = -F(d_1 + d_2)$$

but

$$d = d_1 + d_2$$

$$M_A = -Fd$$

It can be concluded, therefore, that the moment M of a couple is constant. Its magnitude is equal to the product $(F) \times (d)$ of either F (F_1 or F_2) and the perpendicular distance d between their lines of action. The sense of M (clockwise or counterclockwise) is determined by direct observation.

Example Problems: Couple and Moment of a Couple

18 A cantilevered beam is subjected to two equal and opposite forces. Determine the resultant moment M_A at the beam support.

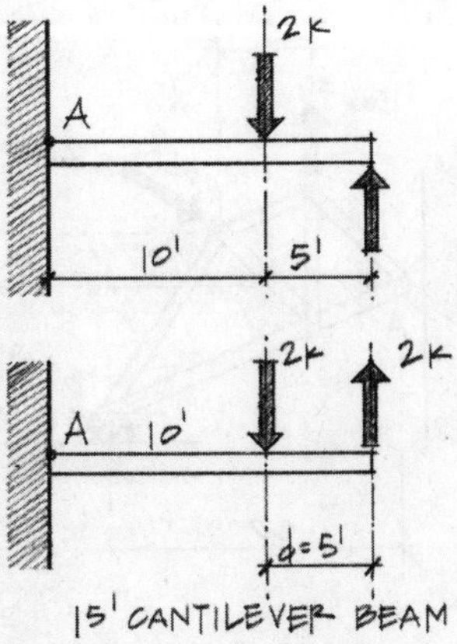

Solution:

By definition, $M_A = F(d)$

$$M_A = +2\,\text{k}(5') = +10\,\text{k-ft.}$$

Check:

$$M_A = -2\,\text{k}(10') + 2\,\text{k}(15')$$
$$M_A = -20\,\text{k-ft.} + 30\,\text{k-ft.} = +10\,\text{k-ft.}$$

Let's examine another case where the beam is extended another five feet.

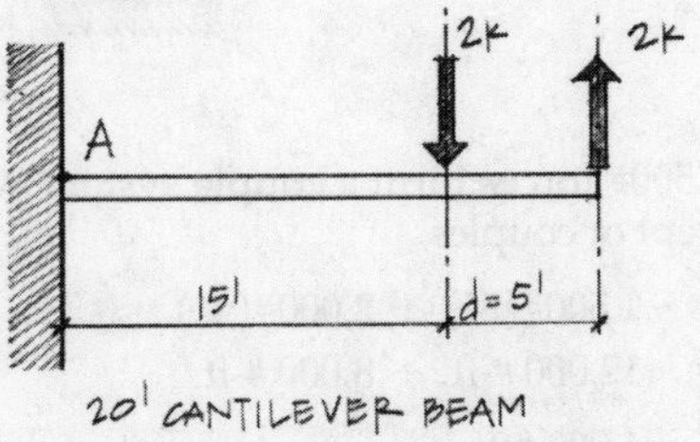

$$M_A = +2\,\text{k}(5') = +10\,\text{k-ft.}$$

Check:

$$M_A = -2\,\text{k}(15') + 2\,\text{k}(20')$$
$$M_A = -30\,\text{k-ft.} + 40\,\text{k-ft.} = +10\,\text{k-ft.}$$

We again notice that the moment of a couple is a constant for a given rigid body. The sense of the moment is obtained by direct observation (using your intuition and judgment).

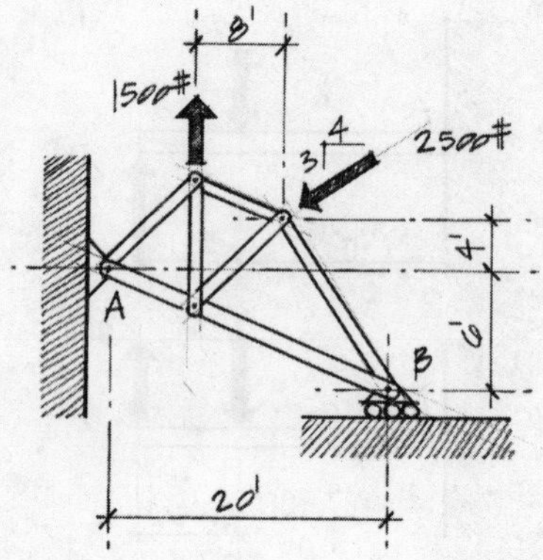

19 An inclined truss is subjected to two forces as shown. Determine the moments at *A* and *B* due to the two forces.

Solution:

By using Varignon's theorem, the 2,500# inclined force can be resolved into horizontal and vertical components.

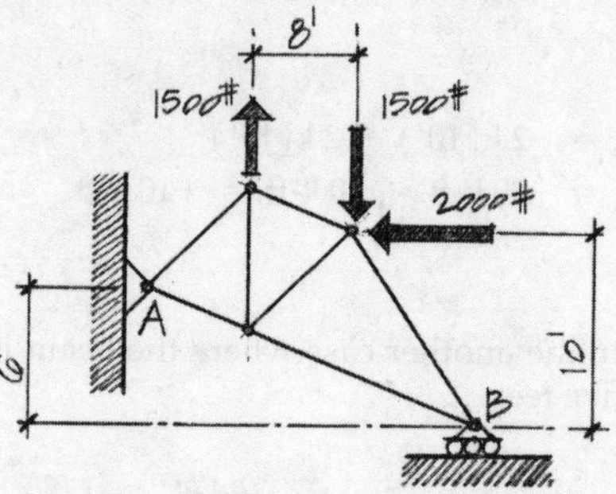

The two 1,500# forces form a couple system. Making use of the concept of couples,

$$M_A = -1{,}500\#(8') + 2{,}000\#(4')$$
$$= -12{,}000 \text{ \#-ft.} + 8{,}000 \text{ \#-ft.}$$
$$M_A = -4{,}000 \text{ \#-ft.}$$

$$M_B = -1{,}500\#(8') + 2{,}000\#(10')$$
$$M_B = -12{,}000 \text{ \#-ft.} + 20{,}000 \text{ \#-ft.} = +8{,}000 \text{ \#-ft.}$$

Resolution of a Force into a Force and Couple Acting at Another Point

In the analysis of some types of problems, it may be useful to change the location of an applied force to a more convenient point on the rigid body. In a previous section, we discussed the possibility of moving a force F along its line of action (principle of transmissibility) without changing the external effects on the body, as shown in Figure 39. However, we cannot move a force away from the original line of action without modifying the external effects on the rigid body, as shown in Figure 40.

$F_1 = F_2$ (same line of action)

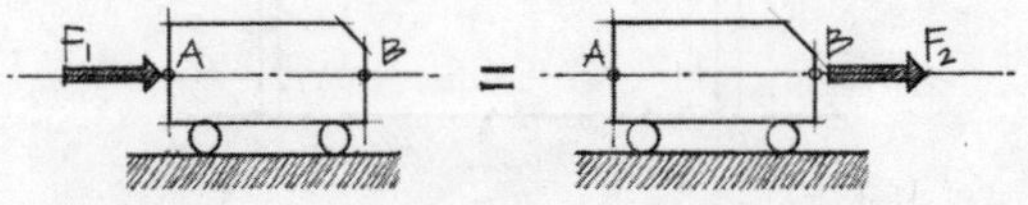

Figure 39 Force moved along its line of action.

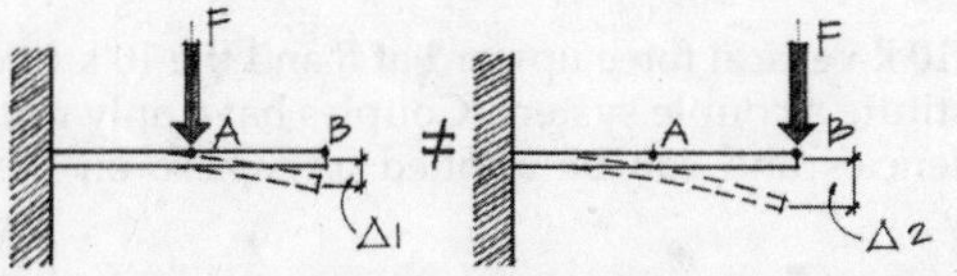

$$\Delta_1 < \Delta_2$$

Figure 40 Force moved to a new line of action.

Examination of Figure 40 shows that if the applied force F is changed from point A to point B on the cantilevered beam, differing deflections at the free end result. The deflection Δ_2 (F applied at point B) is considerably larger than Δ_1 (F applied at point A).

Let's apply a force F at point B as shown in Figure 41(a). The objective is to have F moved to point A without changing the effects on the rigid body. Two forces F and F' are applied at A in Figure 41(b) with a line of action parallel to that of the original force at B. The addition of the equal and opposite forces at A does not change the effect on the rigid body. We observe that the forces F at B and F' at A are equal and opposite forces with parallel lines of action, thus forming a couple system.

By definition, the moment due to the couple is equal to $(F)(d)$ and is a constant value anywhere on the rigid body. The couple M can then be placed at any convenient location with the remaining force F at A, as shown in Figure 41(c).

The preceding example may then be summarized as follows:

> *Any force* F *acting on a rigid body may be moved to any given point* A *(with a parallel line of action) provided that a couple* M *is added. The moment* M *of the couple is equal to* F *times the perpendicular distance between the original line of action and the new location* A.

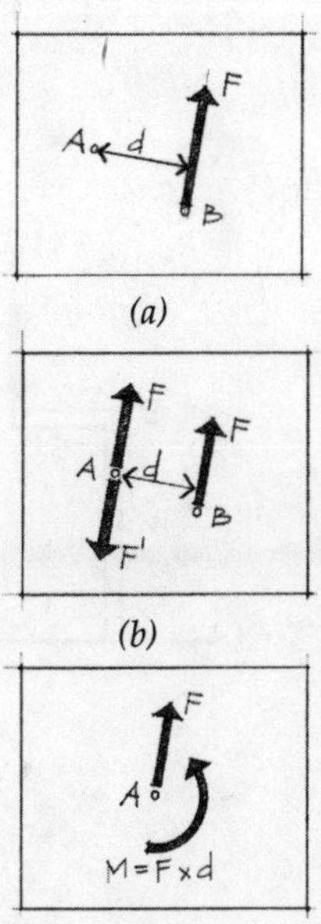

Figure 41 Moving a force to another parallel line of action.

Example Problems: Resolution of a Force into a Force and Couple Acting at Another Point

20 A bent concrete column is subjected to a downward force of 10 k. To design the column, it is necessary to have the compressive force applied through the axis of the column. Show the equivalent force system when the force is moved from A to B. Apply an equal and opposite pair of forces at B.

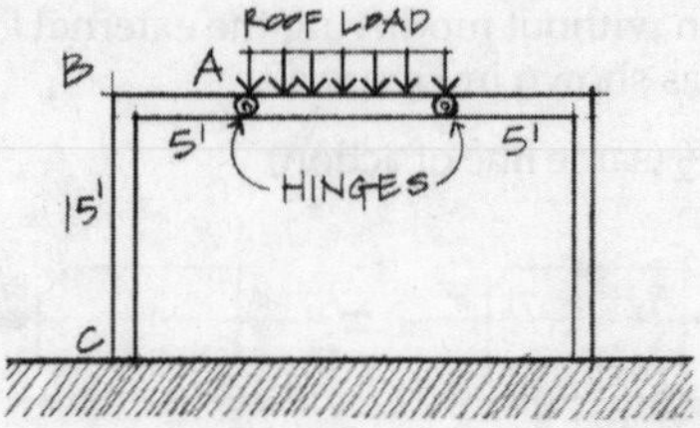

Solution:

The 10 k vertical force upward at B and the 10 k force at A constitute a couple system. Couples have only rotational tendencies and can be applied anywhere on the rigid body.

$$M_{\text{couple}} = -10\,\text{k}(5') = -50\,\text{k-ft.}$$

An equivalent representation with the 10 k force acting at B is accompanied by an applied moment of 50 k-ft. clockwise. The effect on the column is compression plus bending.

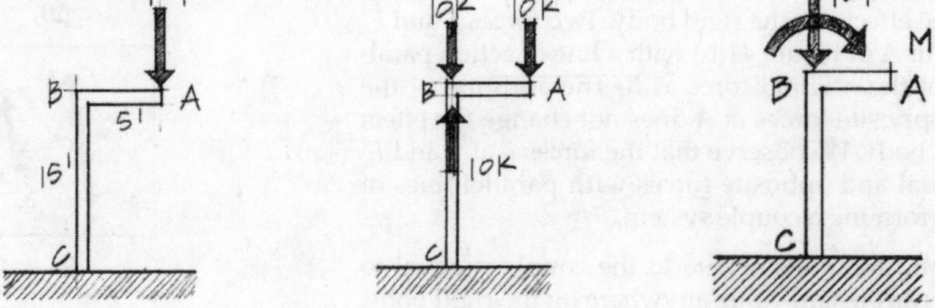

21 A major precast concrete column supports beam loads from the roof and second floor as shown. Beams are supported by seats projecting from the columns. Loads from the beams are assumed to be applied one foot from the column axis.

Determine the equivalent column load condition when all beam loads are shown acting through the column axis.

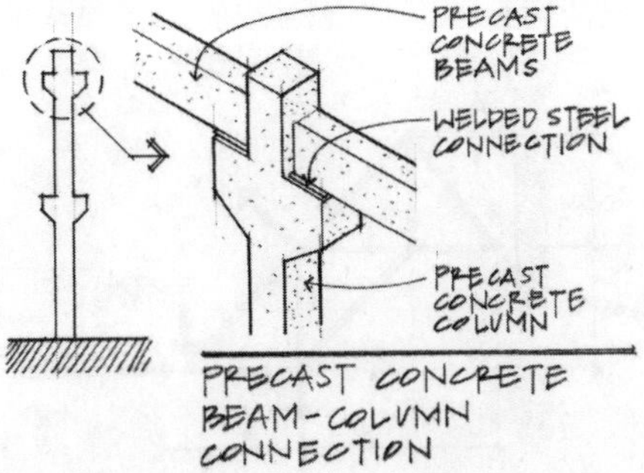

Solution:

The 12 k force produces a +12 k-ft. moment when moved to the column axis, while the 10 k force counters with a −10 k-ft. clockwise moment. The resultant moment equals +2 k-ft.

$$M_{roof} = +12\,\text{k-ft.} - 10\,\text{k-ft.} = +2\,\text{k-ft.}$$

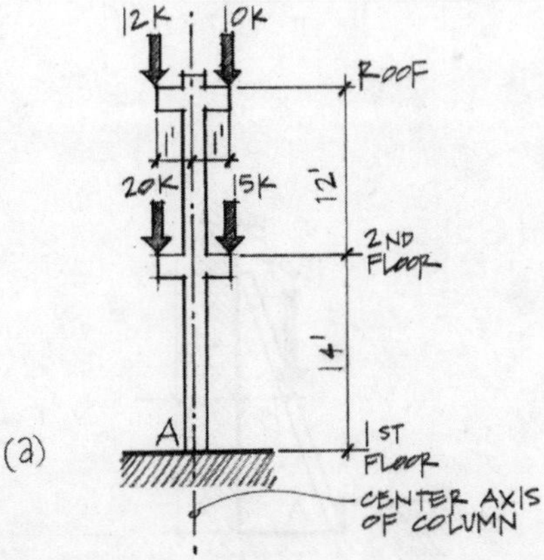

At the second-floor level,

$$M_2 = +20\,\text{k-ft.} - 15\,\text{k-ft.} = +5\,\text{k-ft.}$$

The resultant effect due to the column loads at the base A equals

$$F_{resultant} = +22\,\text{k} + 35\,\text{k} = +57\,\text{k (compression)}$$
$$M_{resultant} = +2\,\text{k-ft.} + 5\,\text{k-ft.} = +7\,\text{k-ft.}$$

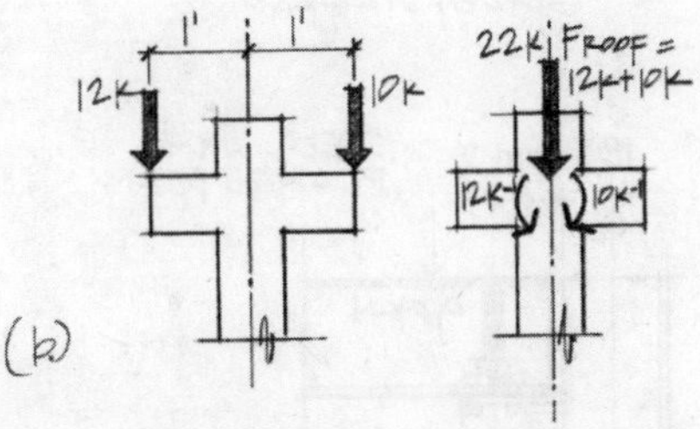

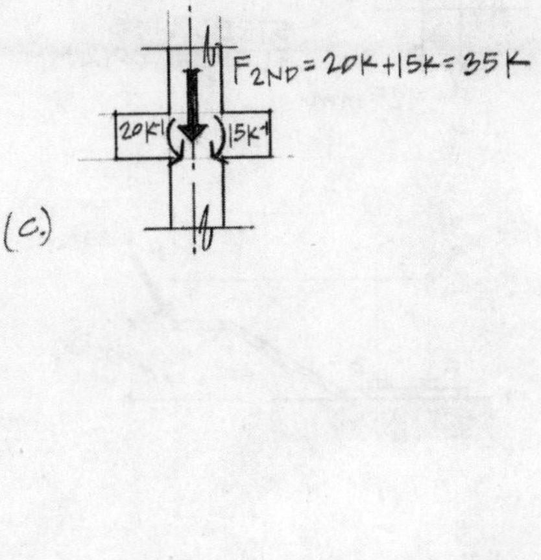

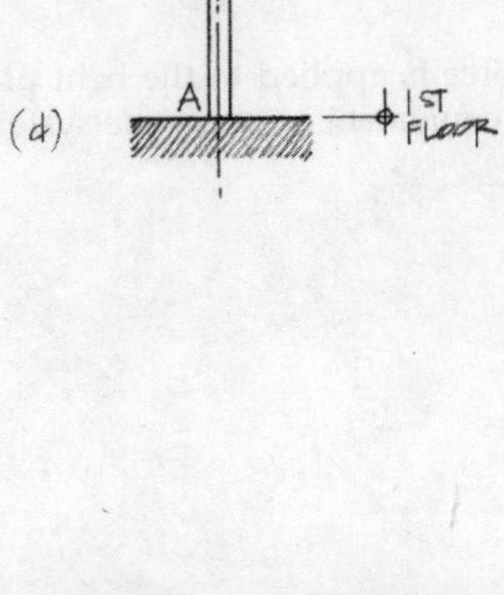

Problems

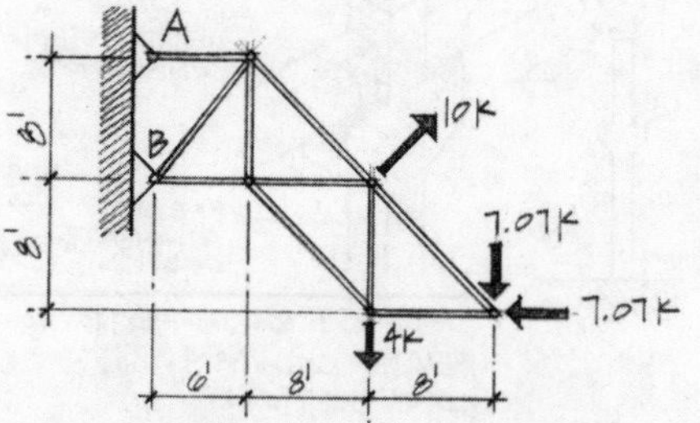

24 Determine the resultant moment at support points *A* and *B* due to the forces acting on the truss as shown.

Assume that the 10 k force is acting perpendicular to the truss slope.

25 A ladder supports a painter weighing 150# at mid-height. The ladder is supported at points *A* and *B*, developing reactions as shown in the free-body diagram (see Section 5). Assuming that reaction forces R_{Ax} and R_{Bx} develop magnitudes of 25# each and R_{Ay} = 150#, determine M_A, M_B, and M_C.

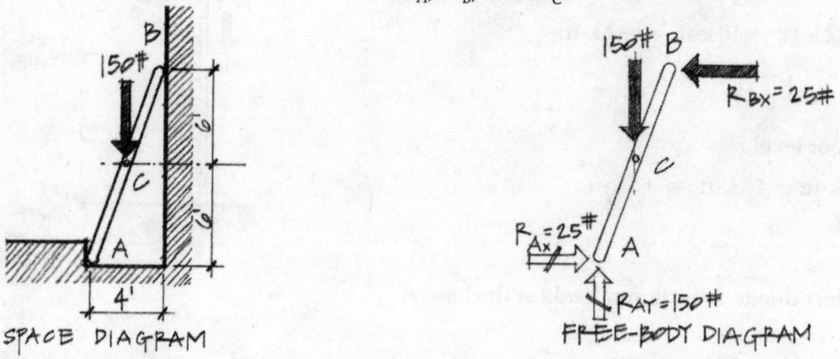

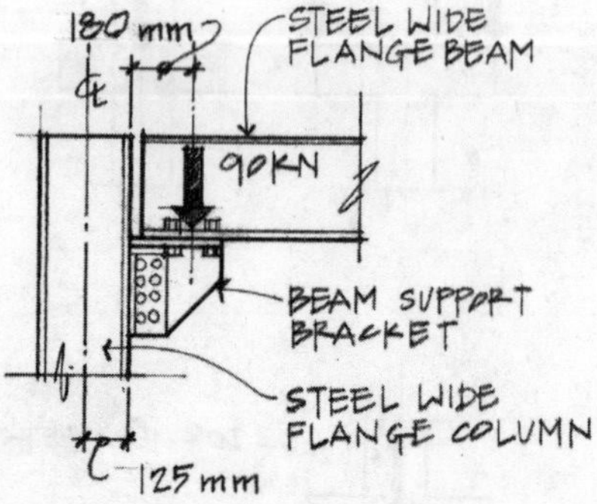

26 Replace the 90 kN beam load by an equivalent force-couple system through the column centerline.

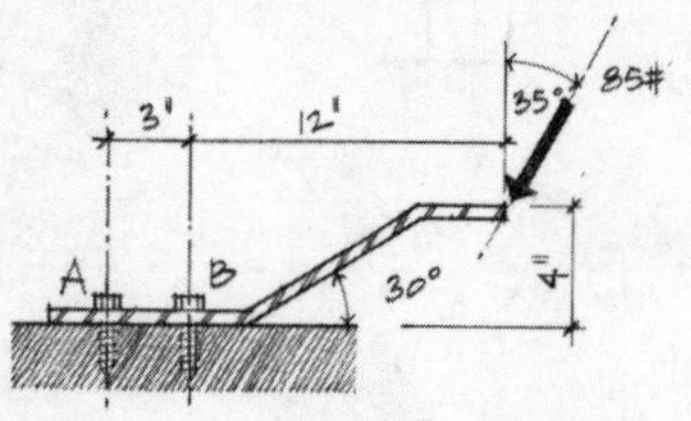

27 An 85# force is applied to the bent plate as shown. Determine an equivalent force-couple system (a) at *A* and (b) at *B*.

Resultant of Two Parallel Forces

Suppose we wish to represent the two forces A and B shown on the girder in Figure 42(a) with a single resultant force R, which produces an equivalent effect as the original forces. The equivalent resultant R must produce the same translational tendency as forces A and B as well as the same rotational effect, as shown in Figure 42(b).

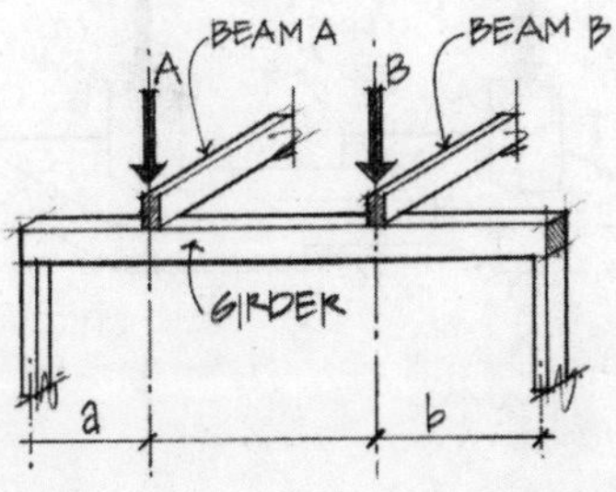

Figure 42(a) *Two parallel forces acting on a girder.*

Because forces by definition have magnitude, direction, sense, and a point of application, it is necessary to establish the exact location of the resultant R from some given reference point. Only a single location R will produce an equivalent effect as the girder with forces A and B.

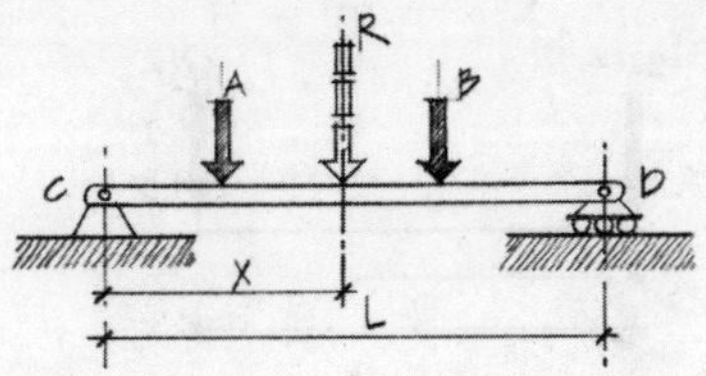

Figure 42(b) *Equivalent resultant force* R *for* A *and* B.

The magnitude of the resultant R of the parallel forces A and B equals the algebraic summation of A and B, where $R = A + B$.

Direction of the forces must be accounted for by using a convenient sign notation, such as positive for upward-acting forces and negative for downward-acting forces.

Location of the resultant R is obtained by the principle of moments.

Example Problem: Resultant of Two Parallel Forces

22 Determine the single resultant R (magnitude and location) that would produce an equivalent effect as the forces shown on the combined footing.

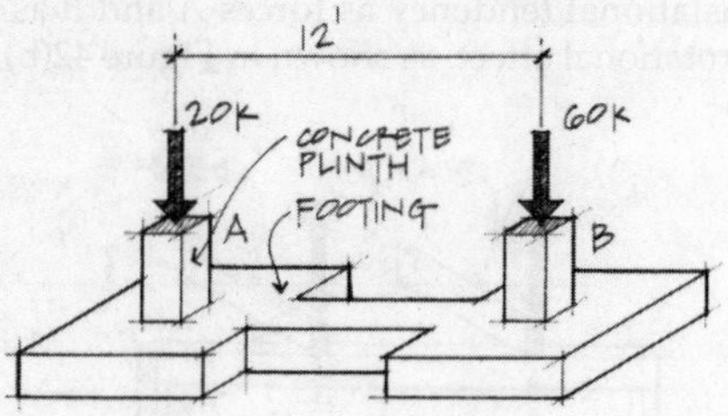

Solution:

Magnitude of resultant:

$$R = -20\,\text{k} - 60\,\text{k} = -80\,\text{k}$$

To find the location of R, pick a convenient reference point and calculate moments.

$$M_A = -60\,\text{k}(12') = -720\,\text{k-ft.}$$

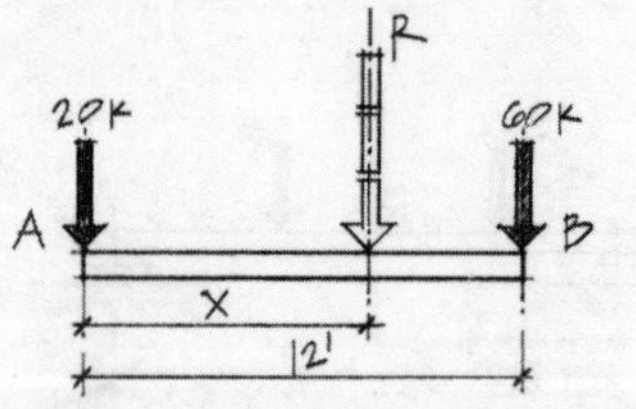

The moment about point A due to R must be equal to the M_A of the original force system to maintain equivalence.

$$\therefore M_A = -R(x)$$

$$-720\,\text{k-ft.} = -R(x),\ \text{but}\ R = 80\,\text{k}$$

$$\therefore x = \frac{-720\,\text{k-ft.}}{-80\,\text{k}} = 9'$$

R must be located nine feet to the right of point A.

4 EQUILIBRIUM EQUATIONS: TWO-DIMENSIONAL

Equilibrium

Equilibrium refers, essentially, to a state of rest or balance. Recall Newton's first law, which states:

> *Any body at* **rest** *will remain at rest and any body in motion will move uniformly in straight lines unless acted upon by a force.*

The concept of a body or particle at rest unless acted upon by some force indicates an initial state of static equilibrium, whereby the net effect of all forces on the body or particle is zero. Equilibrium or nonmotion is simply a special case of motion (Figures 44 and 45).

The mathematical requirement necessary to establish a condition of equilibrium can be stated as

$$R_x = \Sigma F_x = 0$$
$$R_y = \Sigma F_y = 0$$
$$M_i = \Sigma M = 0; \quad \text{where } i = \text{any point}$$

Various types of problems require the selection of only one, and others maybe all, of the equations of equilibrium. However, for any one particular type of problem, the minimum number of equations of equilibrium necessary to justify a state of balance is also the maximum number of equations of equilibrium permitted.

Because various force systems require differing types and numbers of equations of equilibrium, each will be discussed separately.

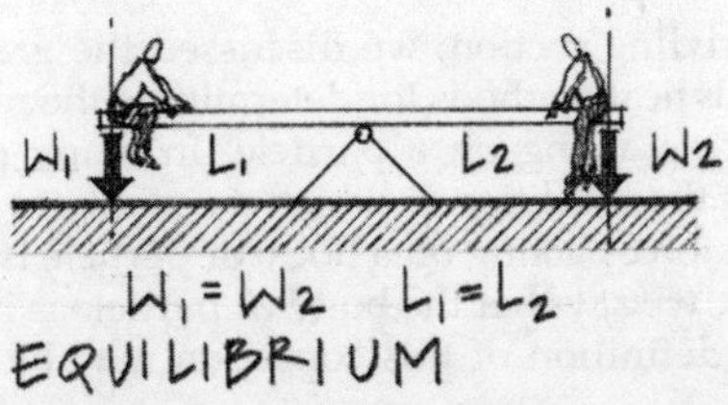

Figure 44 Example of equilibrium.

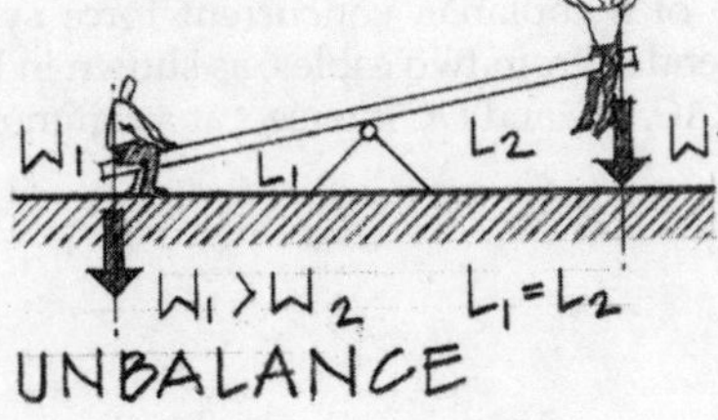

Figure 45 Example of nonequilibrium or unbalance.

Figure 43 Leonardo da Vinci (1452–1519).

Although most popularly known as the painter of The Last Supper, *the* Mona Lisa, *and his self-portrait, Leonardo was also an inventive engineer who conceived of devices and machines that were way ahead of his time. He was the first to solve the problem of defining force as a vector, he conceptualized the idea of force parallelograms, and he realized the need for determining the physical properties of building materials. He is reputed to have constructed the first elevator, for the Milan Cathedral. Leonardo's keen sense of observation and amazing insight led him to the notion of the principle of inertia and preceded Galileo (by a century) in understanding that falling bodies accelerate as they fall. As was the tradition, keen competition existed among the "artist-architect-engineers" of the day in their efforts to attach themselves to those who would most generously support them. Unfortunately, competition was so fierce that Leonardo felt it necessary to guard his ideas with great secrecy, writing much of his notebooks in code. Because of this, and because so many of Leonardo's achievements were visionary rather than actual, his influence on professional development has generally been considered to be minimal. It is unknown whether a channel existed through which some of his ideas may have served to inspire his successors, most notably Galileo Galilei. Leonardo figures prominently in this section's discussion of physical laws.*

Collinear Force System

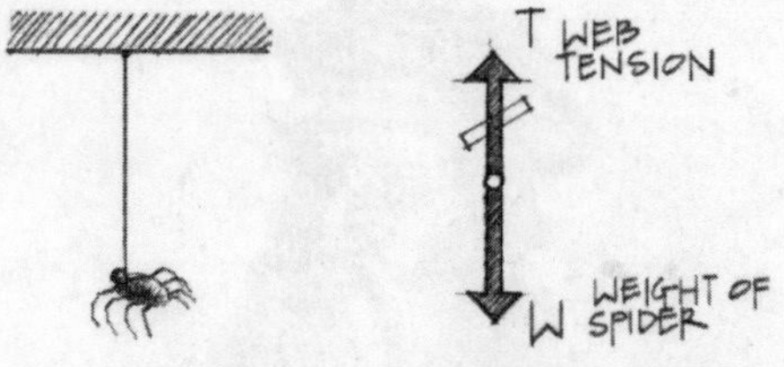

Figure 46 Tension force developed in the web to carry the weight of the spider.

A collinear force system involves the action of forces along the same line of action. There is no restriction on the direction or on the magnitude of each force as long as all forces act along the same line.

In Figure 46, a spider is shown suspended from its web. Assuming that the spider is currently in a stationary position, a state of equilibrium exists; therefore, the $\Sigma F_y = 0$. The tension developed in the web must be equal to the weight W of the spider for equilibrium.

Another example of a collinear force system is a tug-of-war in a deadlocked situation in which no movement is taking place, as shown in Figure 47(a). If we assume that the force exerted by each of the four participants is along the axis of the horizontal portion of the rope, as shown in Figure 47(b), then all forces are collinear. In equation form,

$$\Sigma F_x = 0$$

$$-F_1 - F_2 + F_3 + F_4 = 0$$

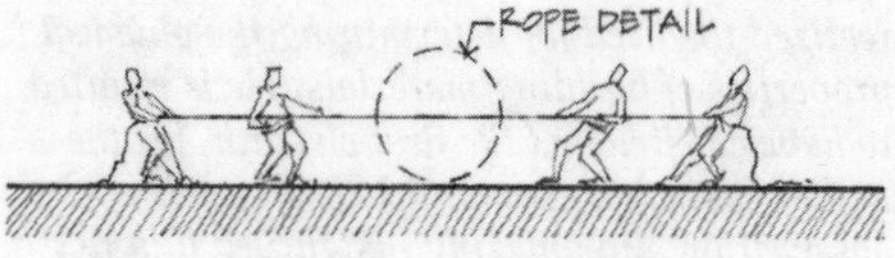

Figure 47(a) Tug-of-war (deadlocked).

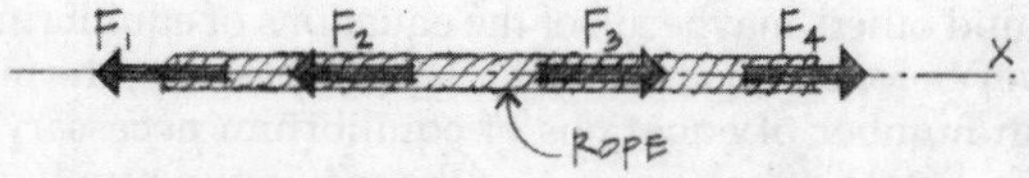

Figure 47(b) Detail of rope—collinear forces.

Concurrent Force System

Equilibrium of a particle

In the preceding section, we discussed the graphical as well as analytical methods for determining the resultant of several forces acting on a particle. In many problems, there exists the condition in which the resultant of several concurrent forces acting on a body or particle is zero. For these cases, we say that the body or particle is in equilibrium. The definition of this condition may be stated as follows:

When the resultant of all concurrent forces acting on a particle is zero, the particle is in a state of equilibrium.

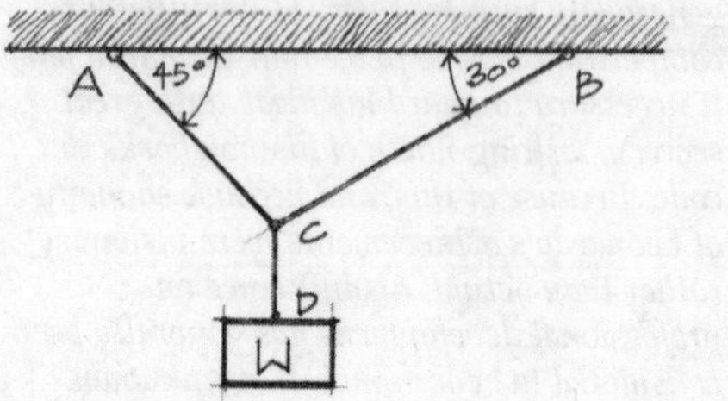

Figure 48 Concurrent force system at C.

An example of a coplanar, concurrent force system is a weight suspended from two cables, as shown in Figure 48. Cable forces AC, BC, and DC intersect at a common point C.

Using the concurrent point C as the origin, a force diagram (Figure 49) of the forces at point C is drawn.

We found in Section 2 that by resolving each force (for a series of concurrent forces) into the primary x and y components, we can algebraically determine the resultant Rx and Ry for the system. To justify a condition of equilibrium in a coplanar (two-dimensional), concurrent force system, two equations of equilibrium are required:

$$R_x = \Sigma F_x = 0$$
$$R_y = \Sigma F_y = 0$$

These two conditions must be satisfied before equilibrium is established. No translation in either the x or y direction is permitted.

Equilibrium of collinear and coplanar–concurrent force systems are discussed later, under the heading *Equilibrium of a Particle.*

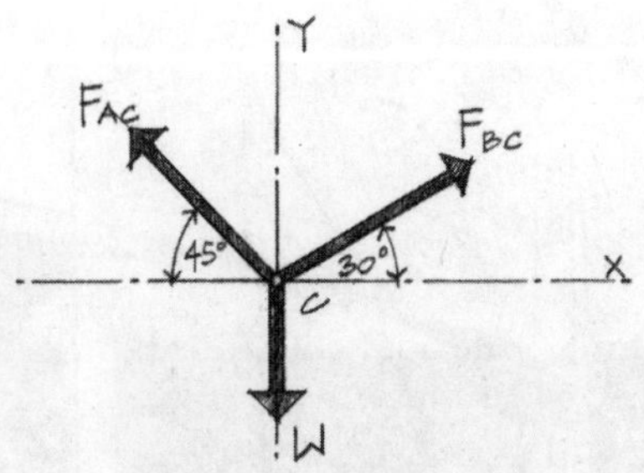

Figure 49 Force diagram of concurrent point C.

Nonconcurrent, Coplanar Force System

Equilibrium of a rigid body

We will now consider the equilibrium of a rigid body (a rigid body being assumed as a system consisting of an infinite number of particles, such as beams, trusses, columns, etc.) under a force system that consists of forces as well as couples.

In his notes, Leonardo da Vinci (1452–1519), as shown Figure 43, included not only sketches of innumerable machines and mechanical devices but also many illustrated theoretical relationships to derive or explain physical laws. He dealt with the center of gravity, the principle of the inclined plane, and the essence of force. One part of da Vinci's studies included the concept of static equilibrium, as shown in Figure 50.

A rigid body is said to be in equilibrium when the external forces acting on it form a system of forces equivalent to zero. Failure to provide equilibrium for a system may result in disastrous consequences, as shown in Figure 51. Mathematically, it may be stated as

$$\Sigma F_x = 0$$
$$\Sigma F_y = 0$$
$$\Sigma M_i = 0 \quad \text{where } i = \text{any point on the rigid body}$$

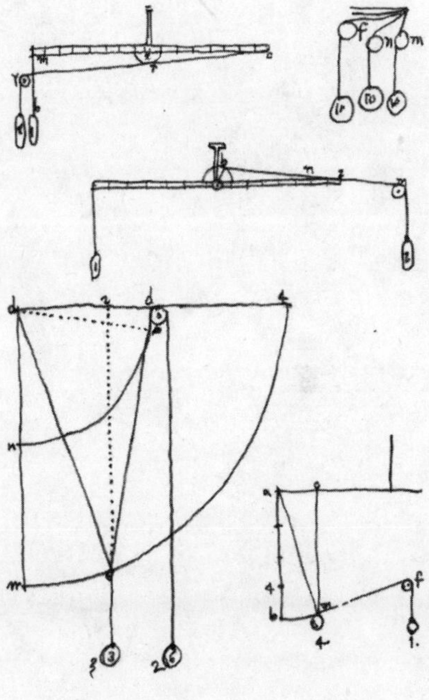

Figure 50 Studies of static equilibrium by Leonardo da Vinci.

Figure 51 An example of nonequilibrium—Tacoma Narrows bridge before collapse.

Courtesy of the University of Washington Libraries, Special Collections, UW21413.

These equations are necessary and sufficient to justify a state of equilibrium. Because only three equations may be written for the coplanar system, no more than three unknowns can be solved.

Alternate sets of equilibrium equations may be written for a rigid body; however, it is required that there always be three equations of equilibrium. One force equation with two moment equations or three moment equations represent alternate sets that are valid.

$$\Sigma F_x = 0; \quad \Sigma M_i = 0; \quad \Sigma M_j = 0$$

or

$$\Sigma F_y = 0; \quad \Sigma M_i = 0; \quad \Sigma M_j = 0$$

or

$$\Sigma M_i = 0; \quad \Sigma M_j = 0; \quad \Sigma M_k = 0$$

Free-Body Diagrams

An essential step in solving equilibrium problems involves the drawing of *free-body diagrams.*

The free-body diagram, or FBD, is the essential key to modern mechanics. Everything in mechanics is reduced to forces in an FBD. This method of simplification is very efficient in reducing apparently complex mechanisms into concise force systems.

What, then, is an FBD? An FBD is a simplified representation of a particle or rigid body that is isolated from its surroundings and on which all applied forces and reactions are shown. All forces acting on a particle or rigid body must be considered when constructing the free-body, and equally important, any force not directly applied on the body must be excluded. A clear decision must be made regarding the choice of the free-body to be used.

Forces that are normally considered to be acting on a rigid body are as follows:

- Externally applied forces.
- Weight of the rigid body.
- Reaction forces or constraints.
- Externally applied moments.
- Moment reactions or constraints.
- Forces developed within a sectioned member.

Free-Body Diagrams of Particles

The *FBD of a particle* is relatively simple, because it only shows concurrent forces emanating from a point. Figure 52(a) and 52(b) give examples of such FBDs.

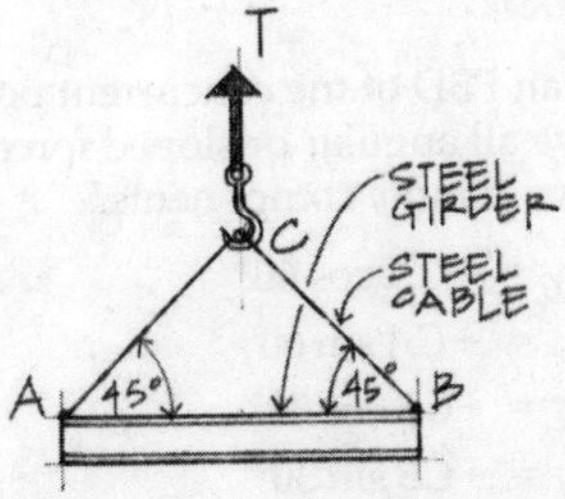

Figure 52(a)   Beam being hoisted by a crane cable.

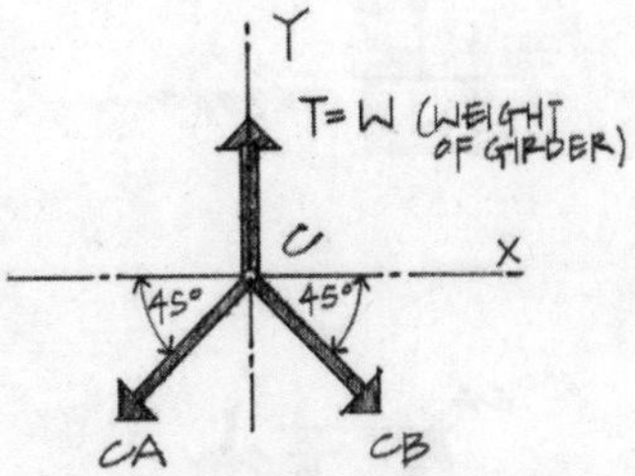

FBD of concurrent point C.

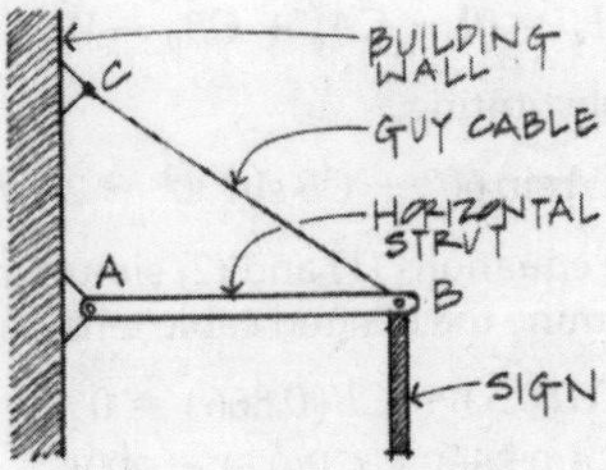

Figure 52(b)   Sign suspended from a strut and cable.

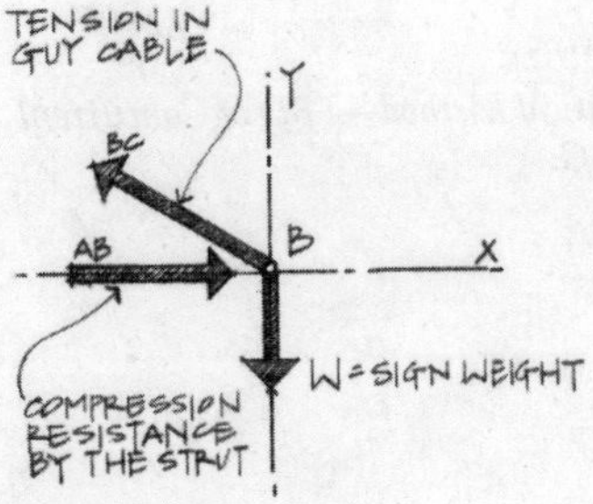

FBD of concurrent point B.

Example Problems: Equilibrium of a Particle

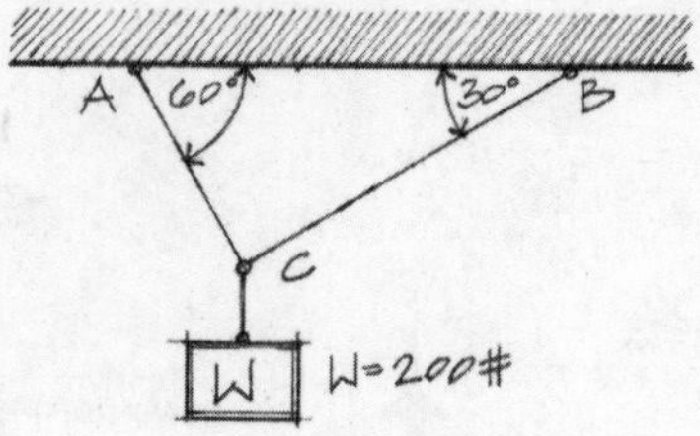

23 Two cables are used to support a weight $W = 200\#$ suspended at C. Using both an analytical as well as a graphical method, determine the tension developed in cables *CA* and *CB*.

Analytical Solution:

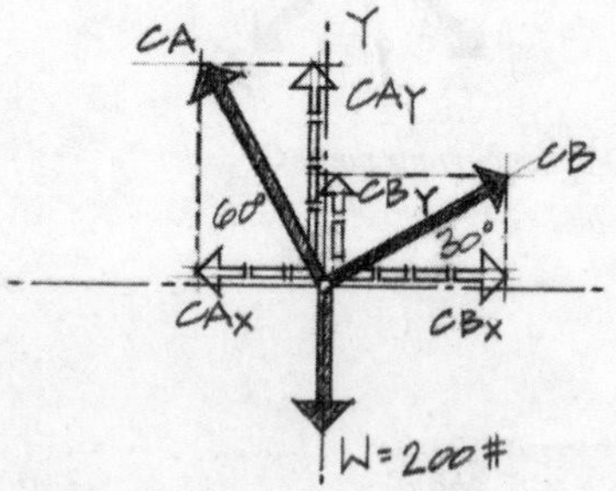

Analytical Method—FBD of Concurrent Point C.

a. Draw an FBD of the concurrent point C.
b. Resolve all angular or sloped forces into their respective x and y components.

$$CA_x = -CA\cos 60^\circ$$
$$CA_y = +CA\sin 60^\circ$$
$$CB_x = +CB\cos 30^\circ$$
$$CB_y = +CB\sin 30^\circ$$

c. For the particle at C to be in equilibrium,

$$\Sigma F_x = 0 \text{ and } \Sigma F_y = 0$$
$$[\Sigma F_x = 0] - CA_x + CB_x = 0$$

or by substituting,

$$-CA\cos 60^\circ + CB\cos 30^\circ = 0 \qquad (1)$$

$$[\Sigma F_y = 0] + CA_y + CB_y - W = 0$$

by substituting,

$$+CA\sin 60^\circ + CB\sin 30^\circ - 200\# = 0 \qquad (2)$$

d. Solve equations (1) and (2) simultaneously to determine the desired cable tensions.

$$-CA(0.5) + CB(0.866) = 0 \qquad (1)$$
$$+CA(0.866) + CB(0.5) = 200\# \qquad (2)$$

Rewriting equation (1),

$$CA = \frac{+(0.866)CB}{0.5} = 1.73\,CB \qquad (1)$$

Substituting into equation (2),

$$1.73\,(0.866)CB + 0.5CB = 200\#$$
$$2CB = +200\#;$$
$$\therefore\ CB = +100\#$$
$$CA = 1.73(100\#) = +173\#$$

Perhaps a more convenient method of accounting for force components before writing the equations of equilibrium is to construct a table.

Force	F_x	F_y
CA	$-CA\cos 60° = -0.5CA$	$+CA\sin 60° = +0.866CA$
CB	$+CB\cos 30° = +0.866CB$	$+CB\sin 60° = +0.5CB$
$W = 200\#$	0	$-200\#$

The two equations of equilibrium are then written by summing vertically all of the forces listed under the F_x column, and similarly for the F_y column.

Graphical Solution (Scale: 1″ = 200#):

In the graphical solution, either the tip-to-tail or the parallelogram method may be employed.

Tip-to-Tail Method:

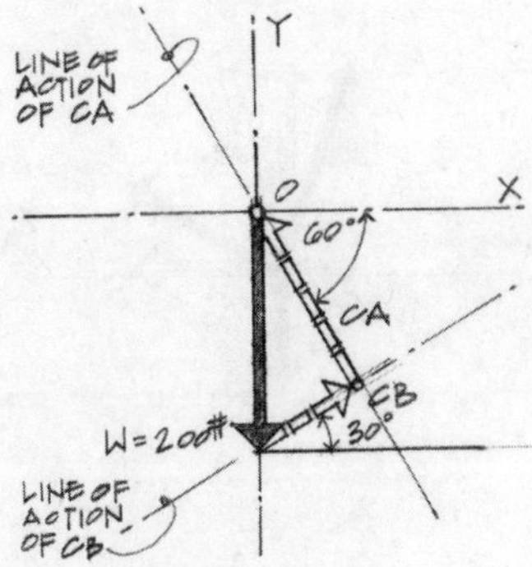

a. Begin the solution by establishing a reference origin point O on the x-y coordinate axis.
b. Draw the weight $W = 200\#$ to scale in the given downward direction.
c. To the tip of the first force W, place the tail of the second force CB. Draw CB at a 30° inclination from the horizontal.
d. Because the magnitude of CB is still unknown, we are unable to terminate the force. Only the line of action of the force is known.
e. Equilibrium is established in the graphical solution when the tip of the last force closes on the tail of the first force W. Therefore, the tip of force CA must close at the origin point O. Construct the line of action of force CA at an angle of 60° from the horizontal. The intersection of lines CA and CB defines the limits of each force. The magnitudes of CB and CA can now be scaled off.

Parallelogram Method:

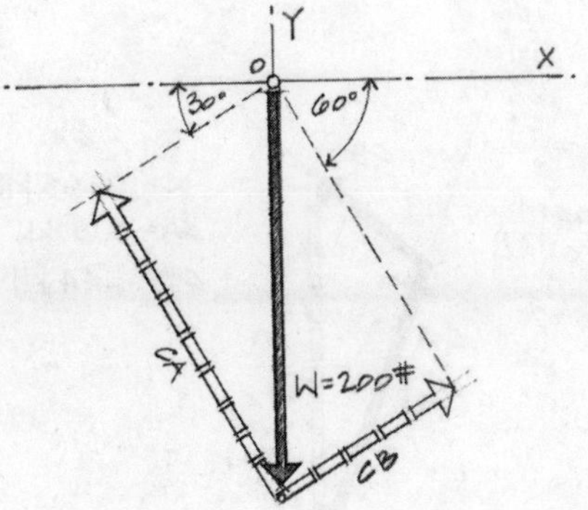

a. Draw the known force W to scale, originating at reference point O.
b. Construct a parallelogram using the weight W to represent the resultant force or diagonal of the parallelogram. The lines of action of each cable, CB and CA, are drawn from both the tip and the tail of force W. Where the lines of CB and CA intersect (the corners of the parallelogram), the limit of each force is established.

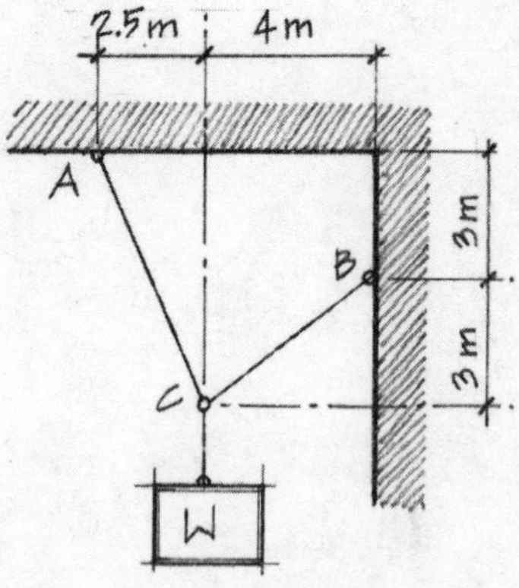

24 Two cables are tied together at C and loaded as shown. Assuming that the maximum permissible tension in CA and CB is 3 kN (the safe capacity of the cable), determine the maximum W that can be safely supported.

Force	F_x	F_y
CA	$-\frac{5}{13}CA$	$+\frac{12}{13}CA$
CB	$+\frac{4}{5}CB$	$+\frac{3}{5}CB$
W	0	$-W$

$$[\Sigma F_x = 0] \; -\frac{5}{13}CA + \frac{4}{5}CB = 0 \qquad (1)$$

$$CA = \frac{13}{5} \times \frac{4}{5}CB = \frac{52}{25}CB$$

$$\therefore CA = 2.08\,CB$$

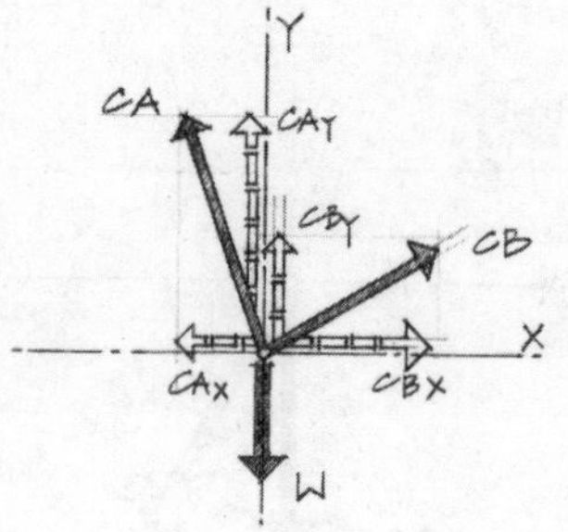

This relationship is crucial, because it tells us that for the given arrangement of cables, CA will carry more than twice the load in CB for equilibrium to exist. Because the maximum cable tension is restricted to 3 kN, this value should be assigned to the larger of the two cable tensions.

$$\therefore CA = 3\,\text{kN}$$

$$CB = \frac{CA}{2.08} = \frac{3\,\text{kN}}{2.08} = 1.44\,\text{kN}$$

***Note:** If the 3 kN value were assigned to* CB, *then* CA *would be 6.24 kN, which obviously exceeds the allowable cable capacity.*

This problem is completed by writing the second equation of equilibrium.

$$[\Sigma F_y = 0] + \frac{12}{13}CA + \frac{3}{5}CB - W = 0 \qquad (2)$$

Substituting the values for CA and CB into equation (2),

$$+\frac{12}{13}(3\,\text{kN}) + \frac{3}{5}(1.44\,\text{kN}) = W$$

$$W = 2.77\,\text{kN} + 0.86\,\text{kN} = 3.63\,\text{kN}$$

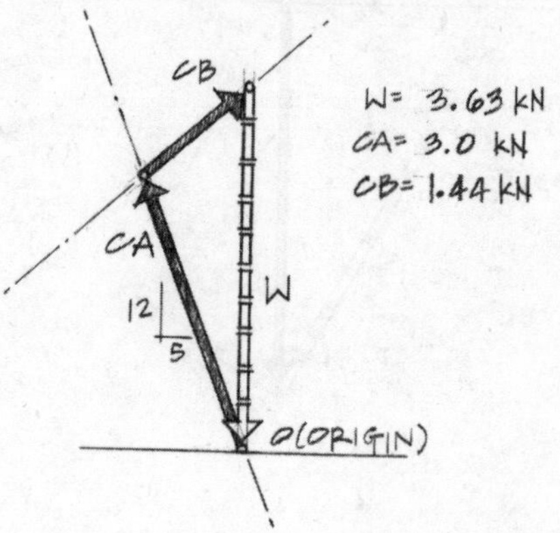

Graphical Solution (Scale: 1 mm = 50 N):

Using the tip-to-tail method, a force triangle is constructed such that W, CA, and CB form a closed triangle. The tip of the last force must end on the tail of the first force for

$$R_x = \Sigma F_x = 0 \quad \text{and} \quad R_y = \Sigma F_y = 0$$

Weight W is known to be a vertical force that closes at the origin O. The only thing known about CB and CA is their lines of action. Visually, however, it is apparent that CA must be the 3 kN tension force so that CB does not exceed the allowable tension. If CB were drawn as 3 kN, CA would end up being much larger.

25 The tension in the cable CB must be of a specific magnitude necessary to provide equilibrium at the concurrent point of C. If the force in the boom AC is 4,000# and Q is 800#, determine the load P (vertical) that can be supported. In addition, find the tension developed in cable CB. Solve this problem analytically as well as graphically using a scale of 1″ = 800#.

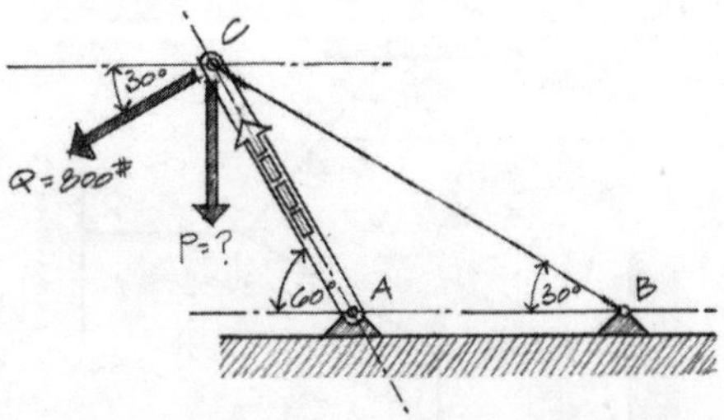

Analytical Solution:

Force	F_x	F_y
Q	$-Q\cos 30° = -800\#(0.866) = -693\#$	$-Q\sin 30° = -800\#(0.5) = -400\#$
AC	$-AC\cos 60° = -4{,}000\#(0.5) = -2{,}000\#$	$+AC\sin 60° = +4{,}000\#(0.866) = +3{,}464\#$
P	0	$-P$
CB	$+CB\cos 30° = +0.866\,CB$	$-CB\sin 30° = -0.5\,CB$

$$\underbrace{R_x = \Sigma F_x = 0 \quad R_y = \Sigma F_y = 0}_{\text{For equilibrium to exist}}$$

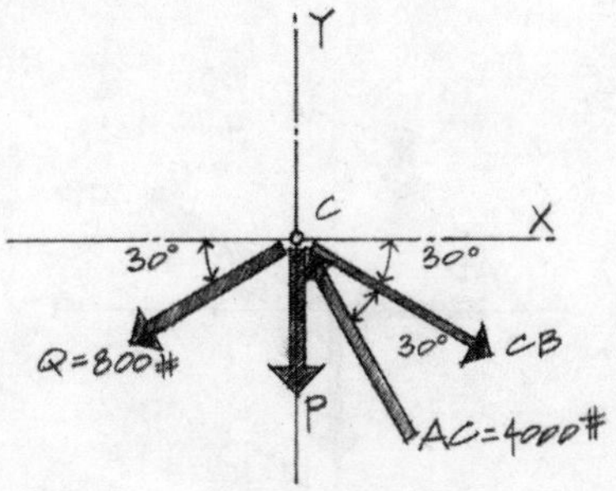

$$\therefore R_x = [\Sigma F_x = 0] - 693\# - 2{,}000\# + 0.866CB = 0$$

$$CB = \frac{+693\# + 2{,}000\#}{0.866} = 3{,}110\#$$

$$R_y = [\Sigma F_y = 0] - 400\# + 3{,}464\# - P - 0.5(3{,}110\#) = 0$$

$$P = 3{,}464\# - 400\# - 0.5(3{,}110\#); \quad P = 1{,}509\#$$

Graphical Solution:

Begin the graphical solution by drawing the known force AC = 4,000# (a 5″ line at 60° from the horizontal axis). Then, to the tip of AC, draw force Q (1″ long and 30° from the horizontal). Force P has a known direction (vertical) but an unknown magnitude. Construct a vertical line from the tip of Q to represent the line of action of force P. For equilibrium to be established, the last force CB must close at the origin point C. Draw CB with a 30° inclination passing through C. The intersection of the lines P and CB defines the limits of the forces. Magnitudes of P and CB are obtained by scaling the respective force lines.

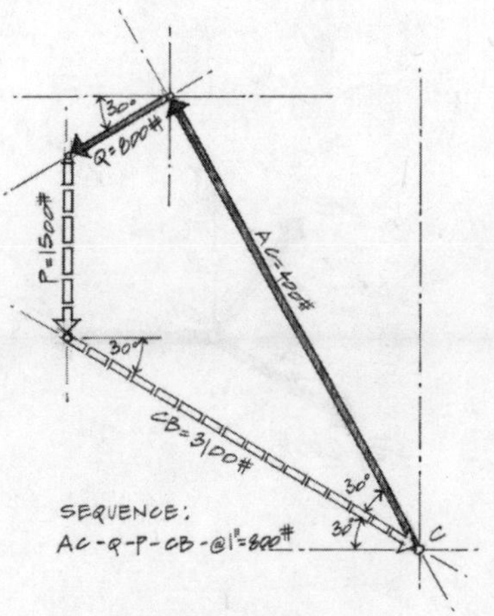

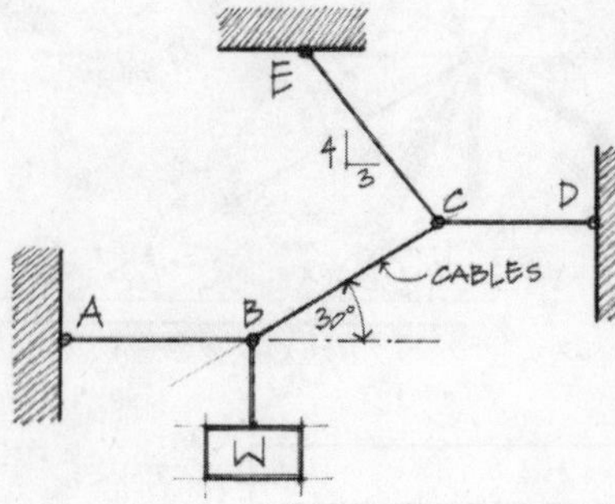

26 Determine the tensile forces in the cables *BA*, *BC*, *CD*, and *CE* assuming $W = 100\#$.

Analytical Solution:

Because this problem involves solving four unknown cable forces, a single FBD of the entire system would be inappropriate, because only two equations of equilibrium can be written. This problem is best solved by isolating the two concurrent points *B* and *C* and writing two distinct sets of equilibrium equations to solve for the four unknowns.

Note: *The FBD of particle* B *shows that only two unknowns,* AB *and* CB, *are present.*

In the FBD of *B*, the directions of cable forces *BA* and *BC* have been *purposely* reversed to illustrate how forces assumed in the wrong direction are handled.

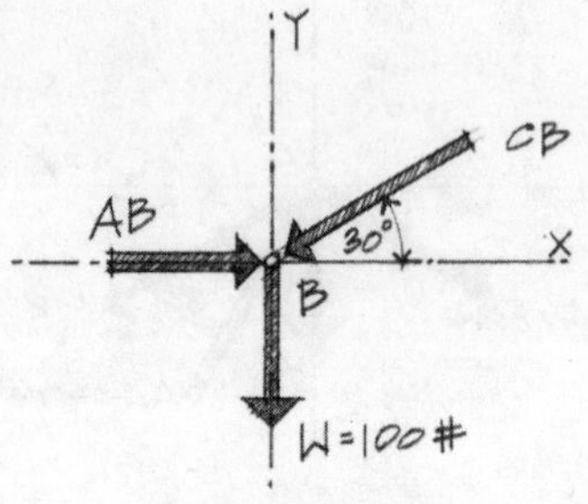

Force	F_x	F_y
AB	$+AB$	0
CB	$-CB\cos 30°$	$-CB\sin 30°$
W	0	$-100\#$

$$[\Sigma F_x - 0] + AB - CB\cos 30° = 0 \quad (1)$$

$$AB = +0.866(CB)$$

$$[\Sigma F_y = 0] - CB\sin 30° - 100\# = 0 \quad (2)$$

$$+0.5CB = -100\#$$

$$\therefore CB = -200\#$$

The negative sign indicates that the assumed direction for *CB* is incorrect; *CB* is actually a tension force. The magnitude of 200# is correct even though the direction was assumed incorrectly. Substituting the value of *CB* (including the negative sign) into equation (1),

$$AB = +0.866(-200\#)$$

$$AB = -173.2\#$$

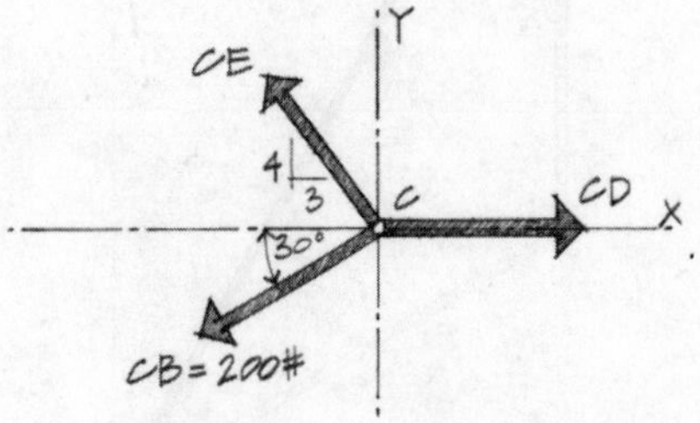

AB was also assumed initially as a compressive force, but the negative sign in the result indicates that it should be tensile.

Note: *In the FBD above, the direction of force* CB *(tension) has been changed to reflect its correct direction.*

Force	F_x	F_y
CB	$-(200\#)\cos 30° = -173.2\#$	$-(200\#)\sin 30° = -100\#$
CD	$+CD$	0
CE	$-\frac{3}{5}CE$	$+\frac{4}{5}CE$

$$[\Sigma F_y = 0] - 100\# + \frac{4}{5}CE = 0$$

$$CE = \frac{5}{4}(+100\#) = +125\#$$

$$[\Sigma F_x = 0] - 173.2\# + CD - \frac{3}{5}CE = 0$$

$$CD = +173.2\# + \frac{3}{5}(+125\#)$$

$$CD = +248\#$$

Problems

For problems 28 through 33, draw FBDs.

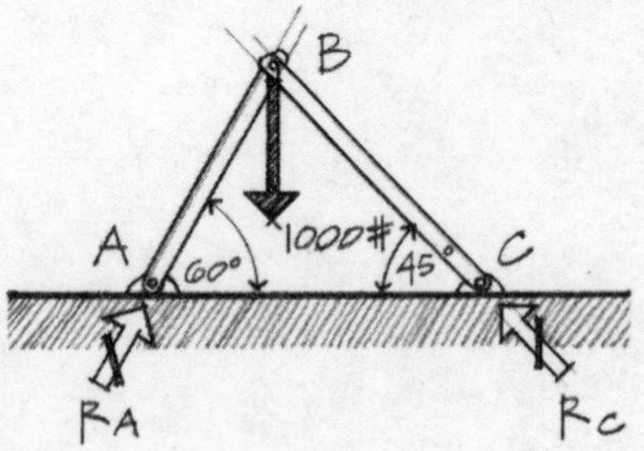

28 The small derrick shown on the right consists of two posts, AB and BC, supporting a weight W = 1,000#. Find the reactions R_A and R_C.

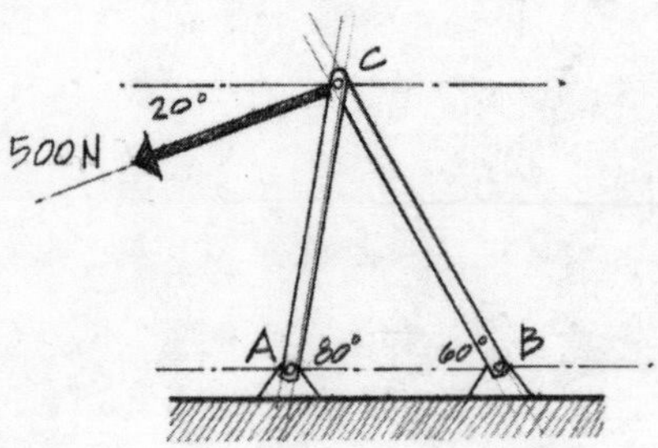

29 Two members AC and BC are pinned together at C to provide a frame for resisting a 500 N force as shown. Determine the forces developed in the two members by isolating joint C.

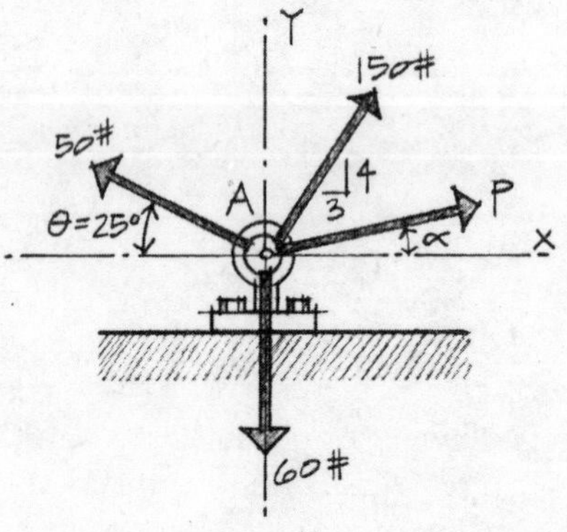

30 An eyebolt at A is in equilibrium under the action of the four forces shown. Determine the magnitude and direction of P.

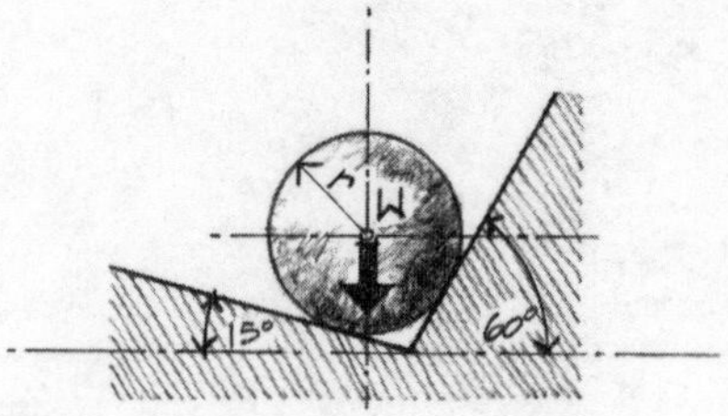

31 A sphere weighing 2.5 kN has a radius r = 0.15 m. Assuming the two supporting surfaces are smooth, what forces does the sphere exert on the inclined surfaces?

Note: *Reactions on round objects act perpendicular to the supporting surface and pass through the center of the object.*

32 A worker is positioning a concrete bucket, weighing 2,000#, by pulling on a rope attached to the crane's cable at *A*. The angle of the cable is 5° off vertical when the worker pulls with a force of *P* at a 20° angle from the horizontal. Determine the force *P* and the cable tension *AB*.

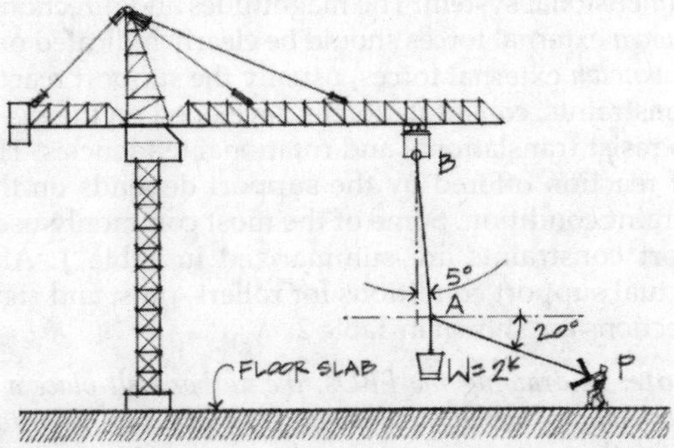

33 A weight *W* = 200# is supported by a cable system as shown. Determine all cable forces and the force in the vertical boom *BC*.

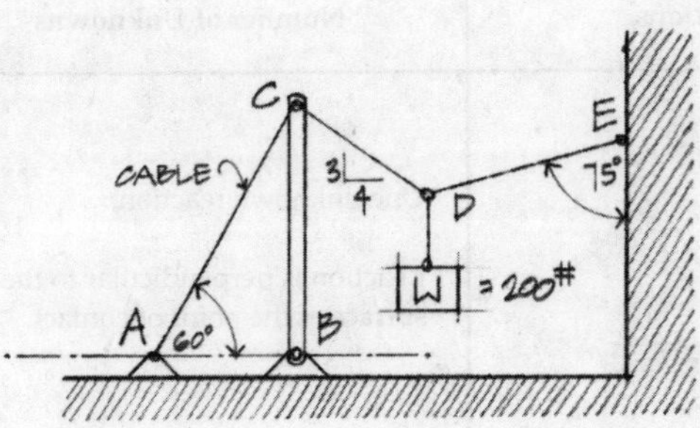

5 FREE-BODY DIAGRAMS OF RIGID BODIES

Free-body diagrams of rigid bodies include a system of forces that no longer have a single point of concurrency. Forces are nonconcurrent but remain coplanar in a two-dimensional system. The magnitudes and directions of the *known* external forces should be clearly indicated on FBDs. *Unknown* external forces, usually the support reactions or constraints, constitute forces developed on the rigid body to resist translational and rotational tendencies. The type of reaction offered by the support depends on the constraint condition. Some of the most commonly used support constraints are summarized in Table 1. Also, the actual support conditions for rollers, pins, and rigid connections are shown in Table 2.

Note: *In drawing the FBDs, the author will place a "hash" mark on force arrows that denote reactions. This helps to distinguish the reaction forces from other applied forces and loads.*

Table 1(a)   Support conditions for coplanar structures.

Idealized Symbol	**Reactions**	**Number of Unknowns**
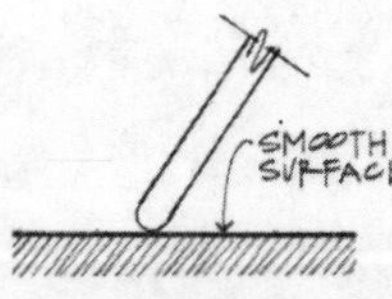	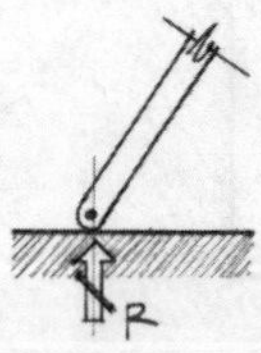	One unknown reaction. Reaction is perpendicular to the surface at the point of contact.
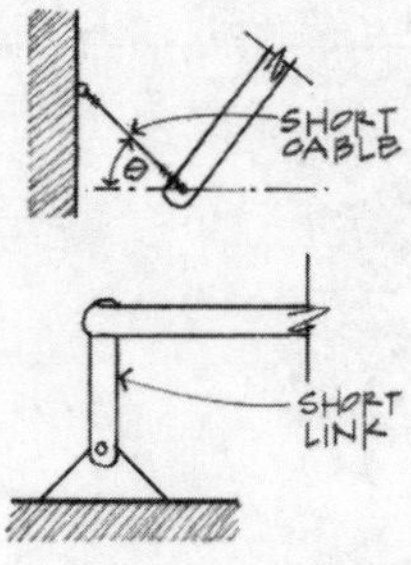	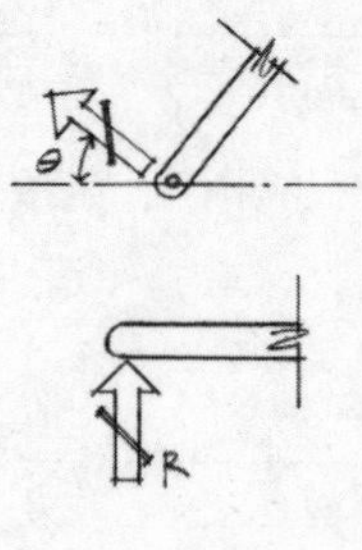	One unknown reaction. The reaction force acts in the direction of the cable or link.

Table 1(b) Supports and connections for coplanar structures.

Idealized Symbol	Reactions	Number of Unknowns
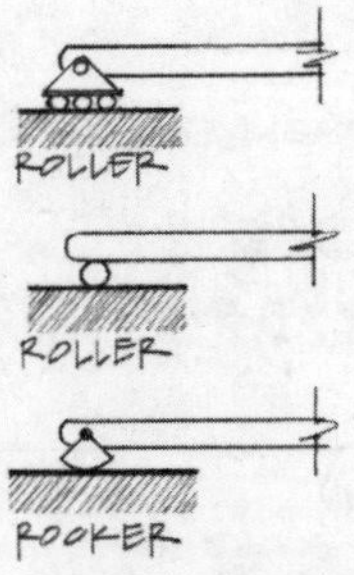	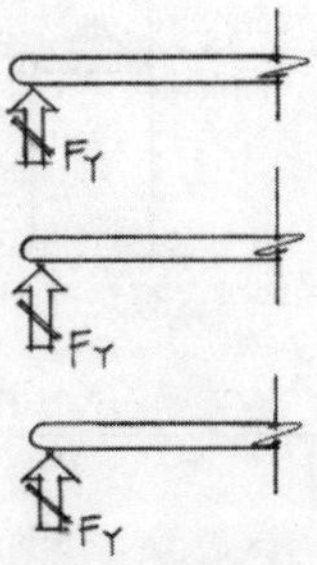	One unknown reaction. Reaction is perpendicular to the supporting surface.
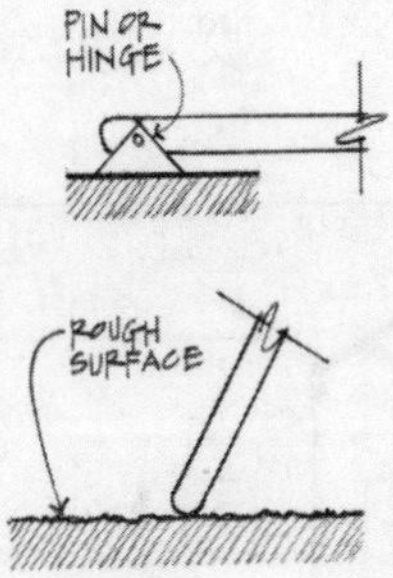	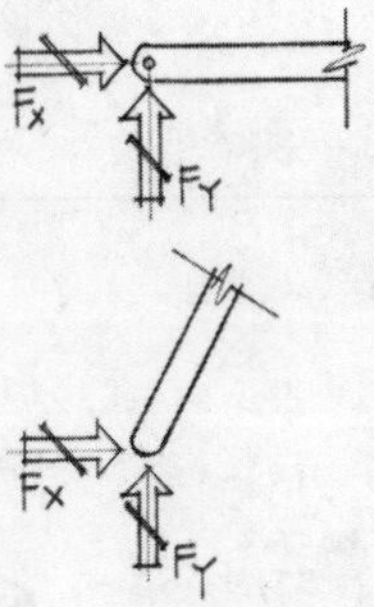	Two unknown reactions. Unknown reactions. F_x and F_y.
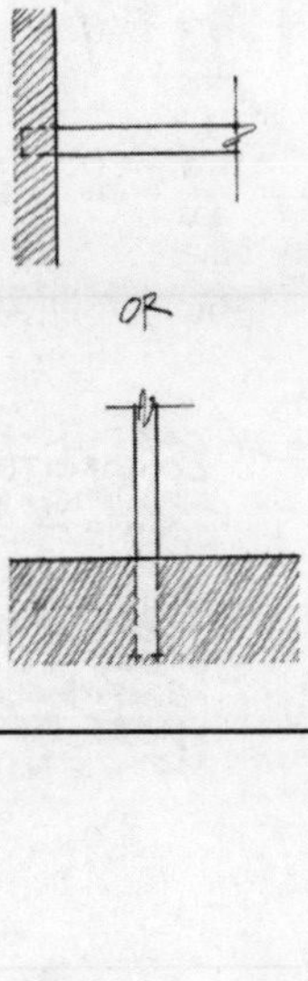	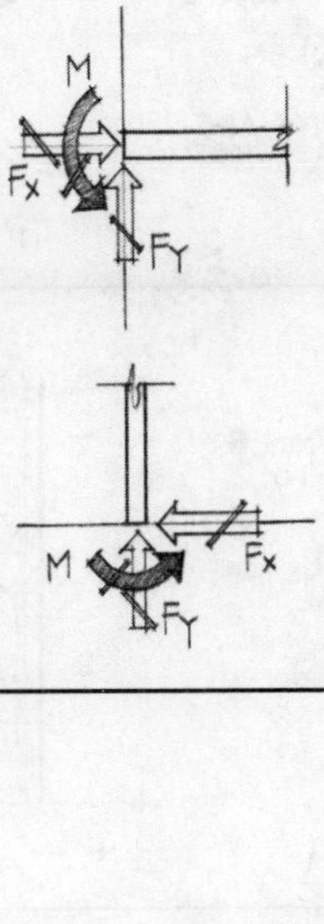	Three unknown reactions. Unknown reactions. Forces F_x, F_y, and resisting moment M.

Table 2 Connection and support examples.

Roller	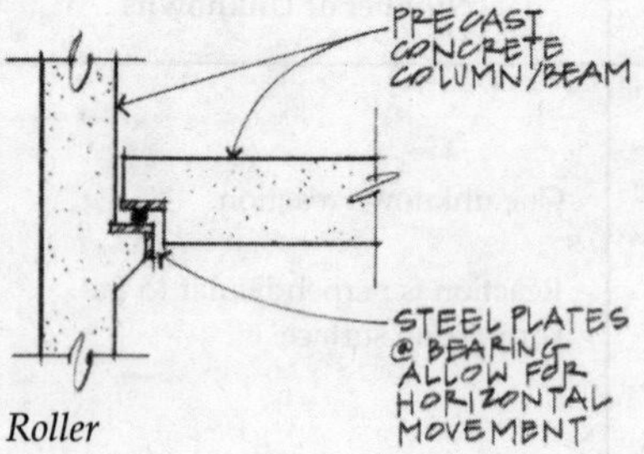	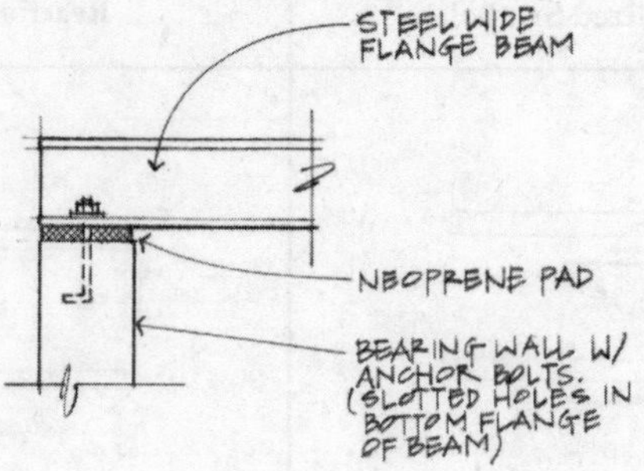
Rocker	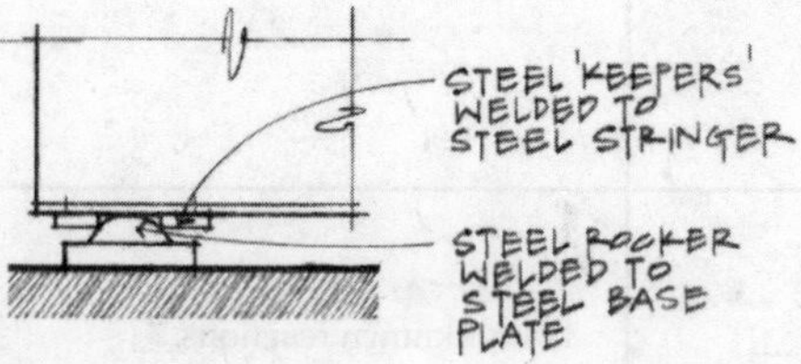	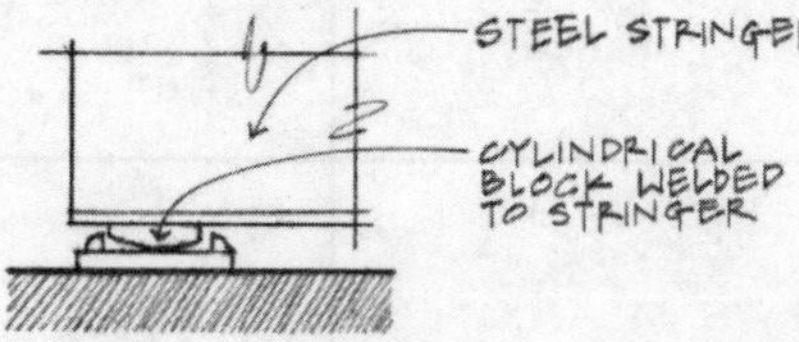
Pin	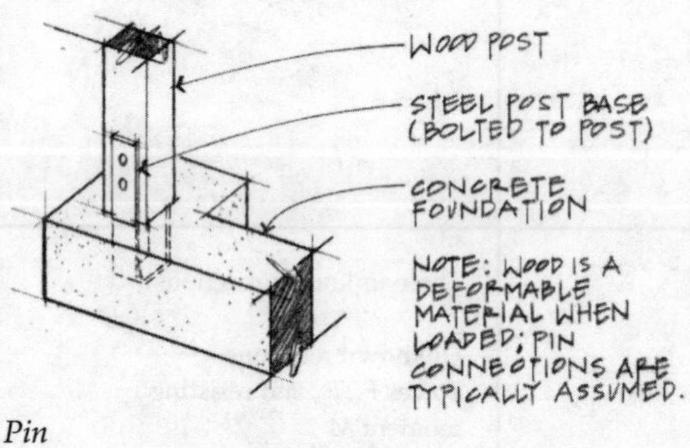	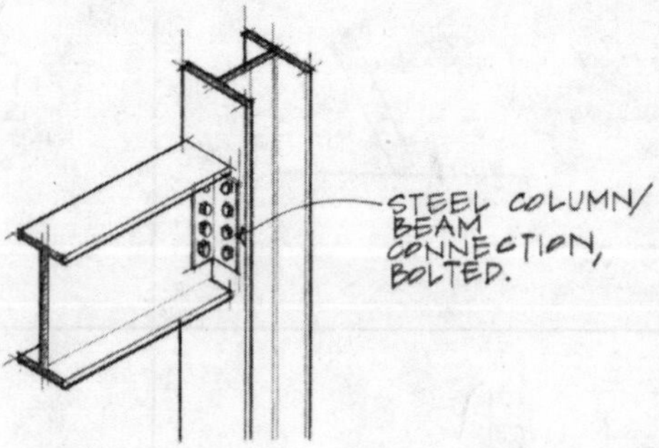
Fixed	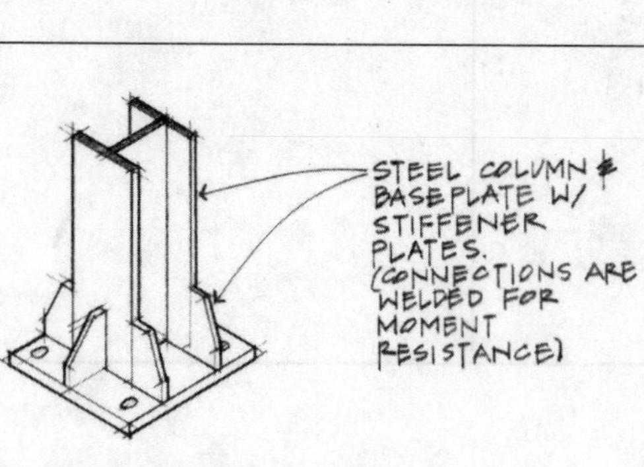	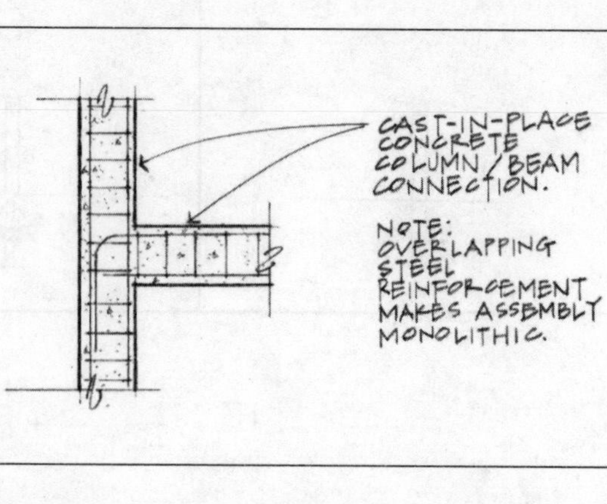

Most problems dealt with in this text will be assumed weightless unless otherwise specified. Whenever the rigid body weight is significant in a problem, one can easily include it in the calculations by adding another force passing through the centroid (center of gravity) of the rigid body.

When the sense of the reacting force or moment is not apparent, arbitrarily assign a direction to it. If your assumption happens to be incorrect, the calculated answer(s) in the equilibrium equations will result in a negative value. The magnitude of the numerical answer is still correct; only the assumed *direction* of the force or moment is wrong.

If the negative answer is to be used in further computations, substitute it into equations with the negative value. It is recommended that no changes in vector direction be attempted until all computations are completed.

Free-body diagrams should include slopes and critical dimensions, because these may be necessary in computing moments of forces. Figures 53 through 55 show examples of such FBDs.

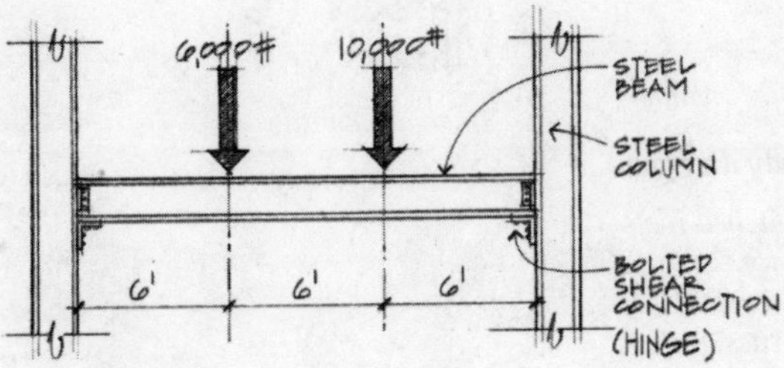

(a) Pictorial diagram.

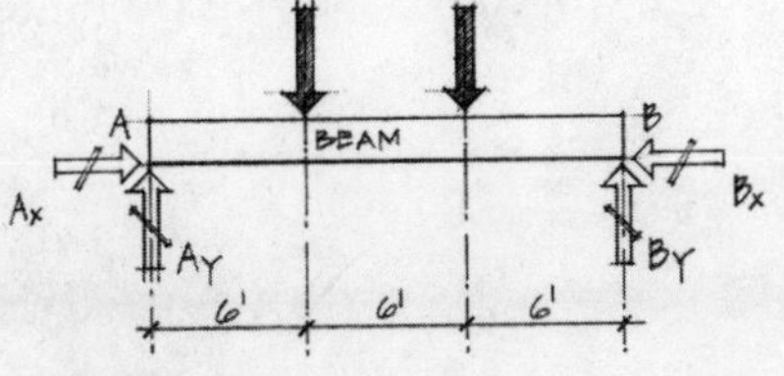

(b) Free-body diagram of the beam.

Figure 53 Simple beam with two concentrated loads.

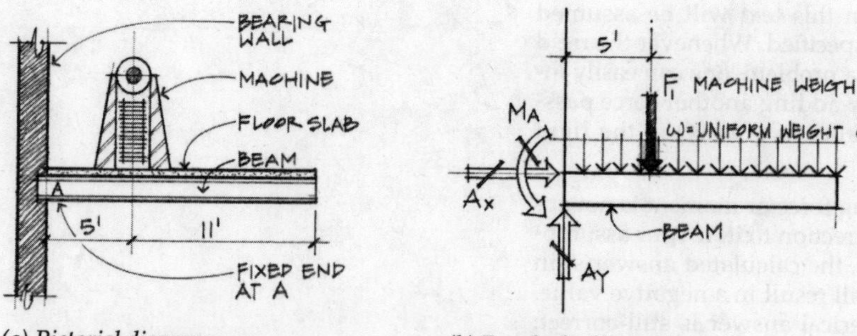

(a) Pictorial diagram. *(b) Free-body diagram.*

Figure 54 Cantilever beam with a concentrated and uniform load.

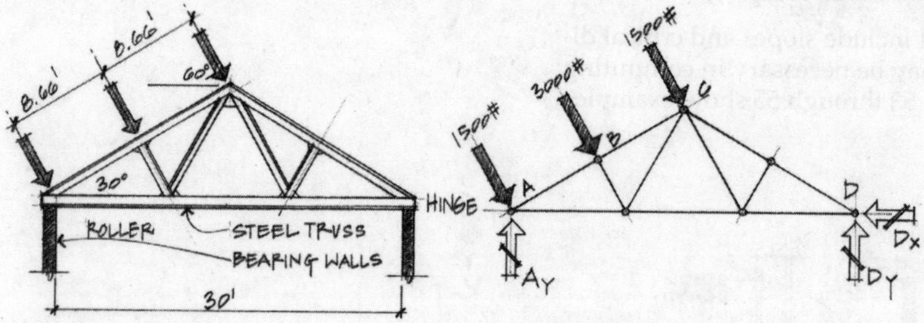

(a) Pictorial diagram. *(b) Free-body diagram.*

Figure 55 Wind load on a pitched roof. Wind loads on pitched roofs are generally applied perpendicular to the windward surface. Another analysis would examine the uplift forces on the leeward slope. Purlins that run perpendicular to the plane of the truss are generally located at the truss joints to minimize bending in the top chord member.

Example Problems: Equilibrium of Rigid Bodies

27 A beam loaded with a 500# force has one end pin supported and the other resting on a smooth surface. Determine the support reactions at A and B.

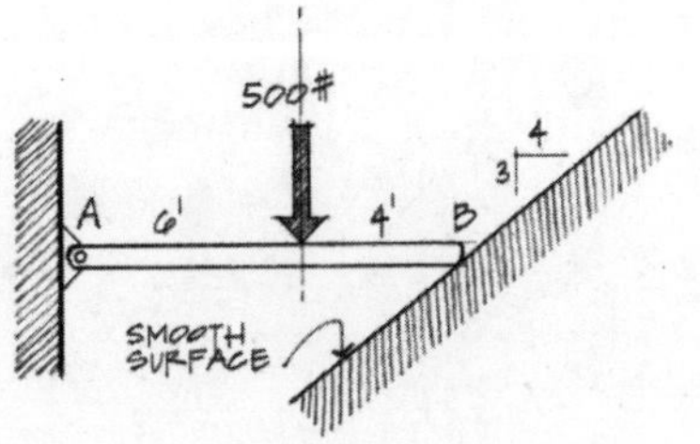

Solution:

The first step in solving any of these equilibrium problems is the construction of an FBD. Directions of A_x, A_y, and B are arbitrarily assumed.

a. The pin support at A develops two reaction constraints: A_x and A_y. Both forces are independent of each other and constitute two separate unknowns.
b. Reaction B from the smooth surface develops perpendicular to the incline of the surface.
c. Because the force equations of equilibrium ($\Sigma F_x = 0$ and $\Sigma F_y = 0$) are in the x and y reference coordinate system, forces that are inclined should be resolved into x and y components.

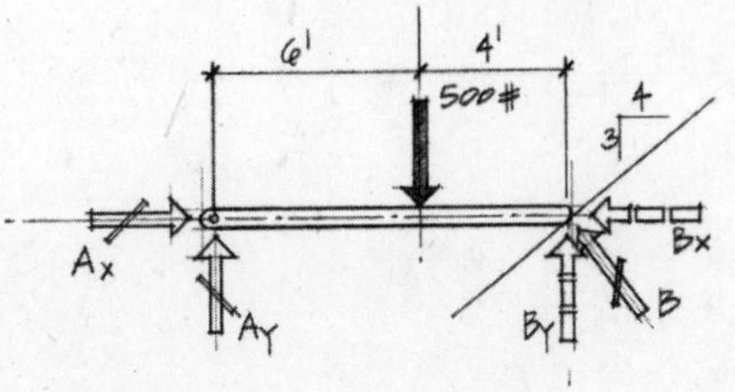

$$B_x = \frac{3}{5}B \quad \text{and} \quad B_y = \frac{4}{5}B$$

***Note:** The slope of reaction force B (4:3) is the reverse of the surface slope (3:4).*

B_x and B_y are components of the reaction force B and are not independent of each other as A_x and A_y were. By writing B_x and B_y as functions of B, the FBD still involves only three unknowns, which correspond to the three equations of equilibrium necessary for a rigid body.

$$[\Sigma F_x = 0] + A_x - B_x = 0 \quad (1)$$

But since $B_x = \frac{3}{5}B$,

$$A_x - \frac{3}{5}B = 0$$

then, $A_x = \dfrac{+3B}{5}$

$$[\Sigma F_y = 0] + A_y - 500\# + B_y = 0 \quad (2)$$

$$A_y = 500\# - \frac{4}{5}B$$

$$[\Sigma M_A = 0] = 500\#(6') + B_y(10') = 0 \quad (3)$$

***Note:** The moment equation can be written about any point. Normally, the point chosen is where at least one of the unknowns is concurrent. Thus, the intersecting unknown can be excluded in the moment equation, because it has no moment arm.*

Solving equation (3),

$$(10')B_y = +(500\#)(6')$$

$$(10')\left(\frac{4}{5}\right)B = +3{,}000\#\text{-ft.}$$

$$B = +375\#$$

The positive sign for the solution of B indicates that the assumed sense for B in the FBD was correct.

Substituting into equations (1) and (2),

$$A_x = +\frac{3}{5}(+375\#) = +255\#$$

$$A_y = 500\# - \frac{4}{5}(+375\#) = +200\#$$

The assumed directions for A_x and A_y were correct.

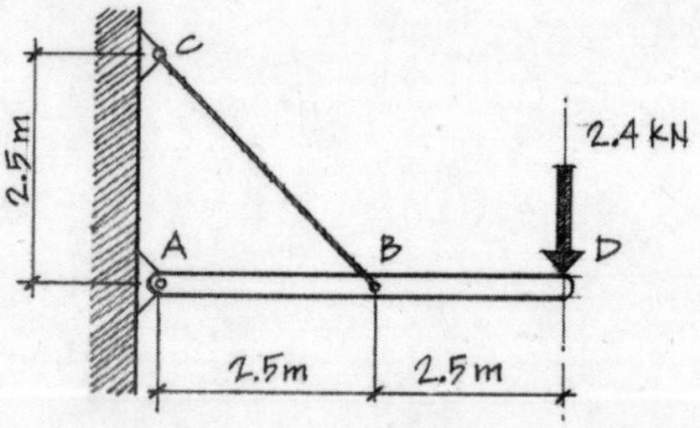

28 Draw an FBD of member ABD. Solve for support reactions at A and the tension in cable BC.

Solution:

The directions for A_x, A_y, and BC are all assumed. Verification will come through the equilibrium equations.

$$[\Sigma M_A = 0] + 0.707BC(2.5\text{ m}) - 2.4\text{ kN}(5\text{ m}) = 0 \quad (1)$$

$$BC = \frac{2.4\text{ kN}(5\text{ m})}{0.707(2.5\text{ m})} = 6.79\text{ kN}$$

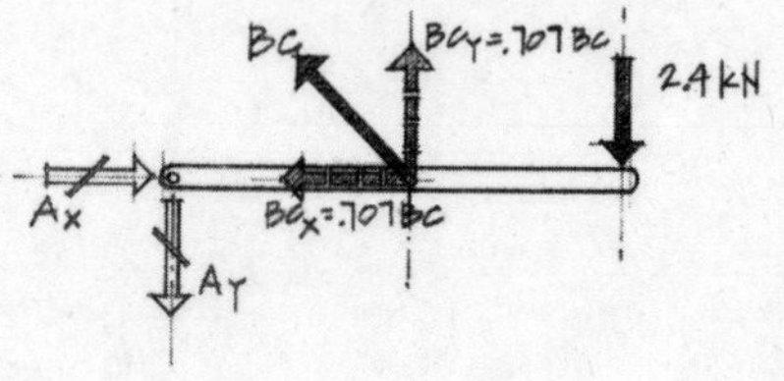

$$\therefore BC_x = 0.707(6.79\text{ kN}) = 4.8\text{ kN}$$

$$\therefore BC_y = 0.707(6.79\text{ kN}) = 4.8\text{ kN}$$

$$[\Sigma F_x = 0] + A_x - 4.8\text{ kN} = 0 \quad (2)$$

$$A_x = +4.8\text{ kN}$$

$$[\Sigma F_y = 0] - A_y + 4.8\text{ kN} - 2.4\text{ kN} = 0 \quad (3)$$

$$A_y = +2.4\text{ kN}$$

29 Determine the support reactions for the truss at joints *A* and *D*.

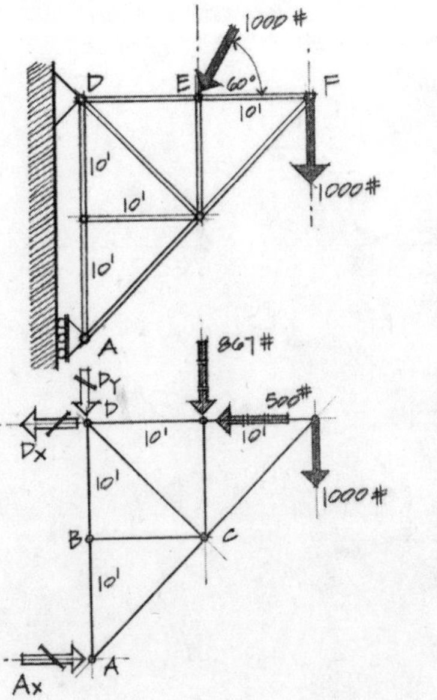

Solution:

$$[\Sigma M_D = 0] + A_x(20') - 867\#(10') - 1{,}000\#\ (20') = 0 \quad (1)$$

$A_x = +1{,}434\#$; Assumed direction correct

$$[\Sigma F_x = 0] - D_x - 500\# + A_x = 0 \quad (2)$$

$D_x = 1{,}434\# - 500\# = +934\#$; Assumed direction OK

$$[\Sigma F_y = 0] - D_y - 867\# - 1{,}000\# = 0 \quad (3)$$

$D_y = -1{,}867\#$; Assumed direction incorrect

30 Determine the resisting moment M_{RA} at the base of the utility pole assuming forces $T_1 = 200\#$ and $T_2 = 300\#$ are as shown. What are the horizontal reactions A_x and A_y at the base? (Show FBD.)

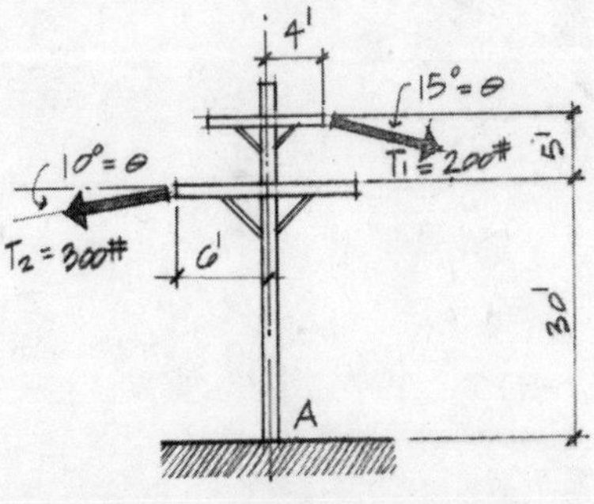

Solution:

$$T_{1x} = T_1 \cos 15° = 200\#(0.966) = 193\#$$

$$T_{1y} = T_1 \sin 15° = 200\#(0.259) = 51.8\#$$

$$T_{2x} = T_2 \cos 10° = 300\#(0.985) = 295.4\#$$

$$T_{2y} = T_2 \sin 10° = 300\#(0.174) = 52\#$$

$$[\Sigma M_A = 0] - M_{RA} + 295.4\#(30') - 193\#(35') \quad (1)$$

$$+ 52\#(6') - 51.8\#(4') = 0$$

solving for M_{RA}: $M_{RA} = +2{,}212$ #-ft.

$$[\Sigma F_x = 0] - 295.4\# + 193\# + A_x = 0 \quad (2)$$

$$\therefore A_x = +102.4\#$$

$$[\Sigma F_y = 0] - 52\# - 51.8\# + A_y = 0 \quad (3)$$

$$\therefore A_y = +103.8\#$$

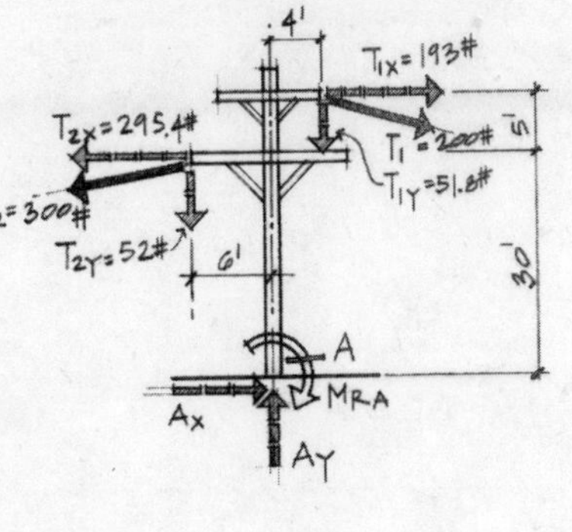

31 A compound beam supports two vertical loads as shown. Determine the support reactions developed at *A*, *B*, and *E*, and also the internal constraint forces at C and *D*.

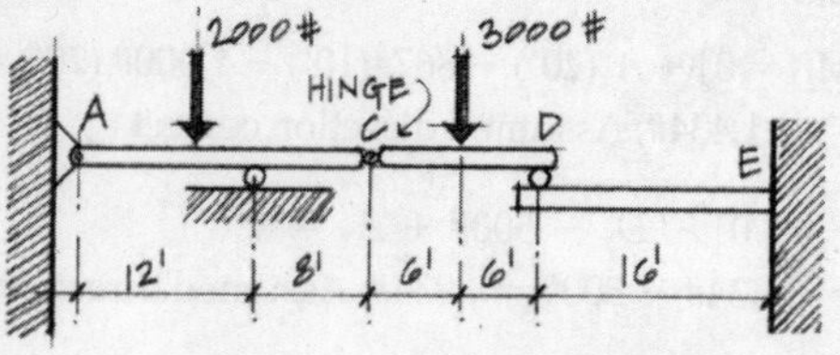

Solution:

The FBD of the entire beam system shows a total of six constraint reactions developed. Because only three equations of equilibrium are available for a given FBD, all support reactions cannot be determined.

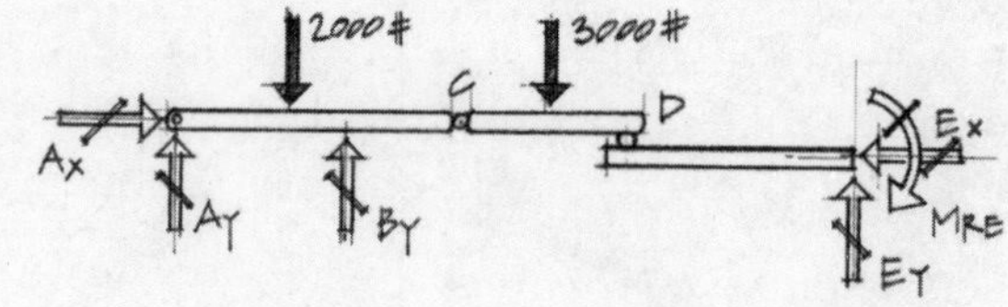

In cases such as these, where the system is composed of several distinct elements, the method of solution should involve drawing FBDs of the individual elements.

Note: *Internal constraint forces at* C *and* D *are shown equal and opposite on each of the connected elements.*

Select the elemental FBD with the fewest number of unknown forces, and solve the equations of equilibrium.

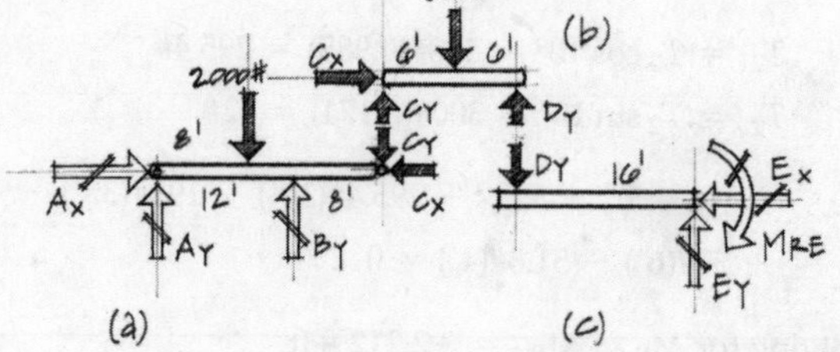

FBD (b):

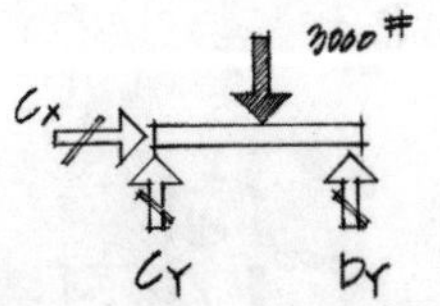

(b)

$[\Sigma F_x = 0] C_x = 0$

$[\Sigma M_C = 0] - 3{,}000\#(6') + D_y(12') = 0$

$D_y = +1{,}500\#$

$[\Sigma F_y = 0] + C_y - 3{,}000\# + D_y = 0$

$C_y = +3{,}000\# - 1{,}500\#$

$C_y = +1{,}500\#$

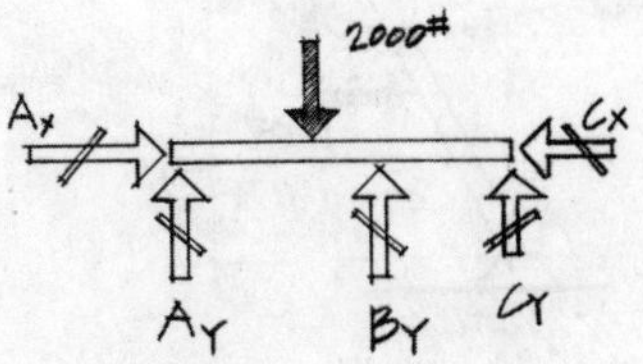

(a)

C_x, C_y, and D_y are now known forces for FBDs (a) and (c).

FBD (a):

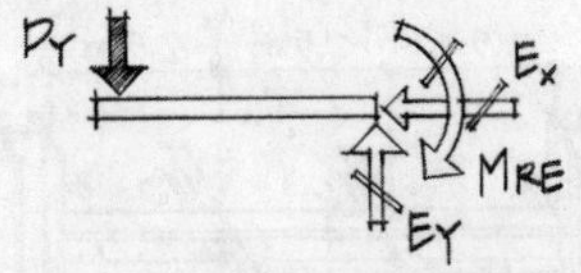

(c)

$[\Sigma F_x = 0] + A_x - C_x = 0$

but $C_x = 0$;

$\therefore A_x = 0$

$[\Sigma M_A = 0] - 2{,}000\#(8') + B_y(12') - C_y(20') = 0$

$$B_y = \frac{+2{,}000\#(8') + 1{,}500\#(20')}{12'} = +3{,}830\text{ \#-ft.}$$

$[\Sigma F_y = 0] + A_y - 2{,}000\# + B_y - C_y = 0$

$A_y = +2{,}000\# - 3{,}830\# + 1{,}500\# = -330\#$

Note: *The negative result for* A_y *indicates that the initial assumption about its direction is wrong.*

FBD (c):

$[\Sigma F_x = 0] E_x = 0$

$[\Sigma F_y = 0] - D_y + E_y = 0$

$E_y = +1{,}500\#$

$[\Sigma M_E = 0] + D_y(16') - M_{R_E} = 0$

$M_{R_E} = +(1{,}500\#)(16') = +24{,}000\text{ \#-ft.}$

Problems

34 A pole *AB* leans against a smooth, frictionless wall at *B*. Calculate the vertical and horizontal components of the reactions of *A* and *B*.

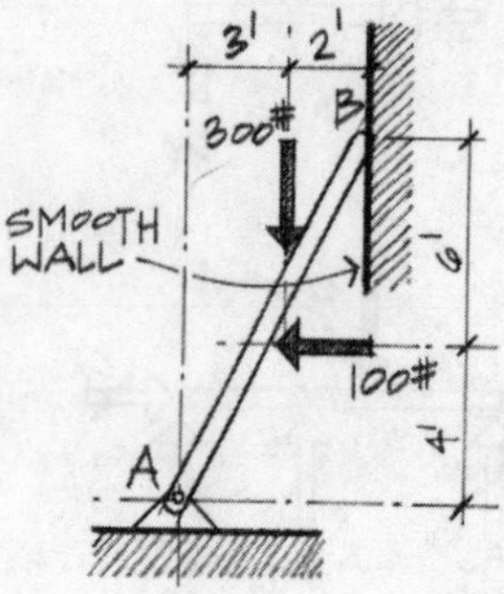

35 The girder shown is supported by columns at *A* and *B*. Two smaller beams push downward on the girder with a force of 40 kN at *C*, and two other beams push downward with a force of 50 kN at *D*. Find the reactions at *A* and *B*.

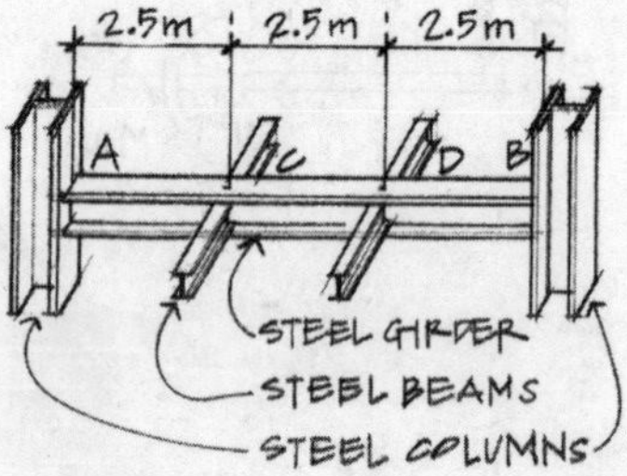

36 A bridge over a river is loaded at three panel points. Determine the support reactions at *A* and *B*.

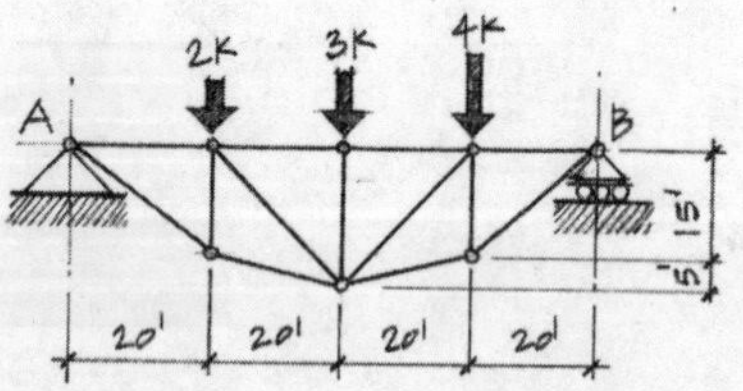

37 Wind forces on the windward roof slope are applied normally to the upper truss chord. Determine the wall reactions developed at *A* and *D*.

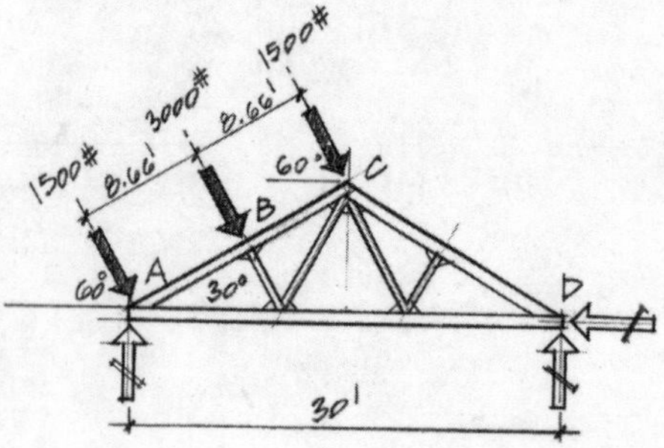

38 An inclined king-post truss supports a vertical and horizontal force at C. Determine the support reactions developed at A and B.

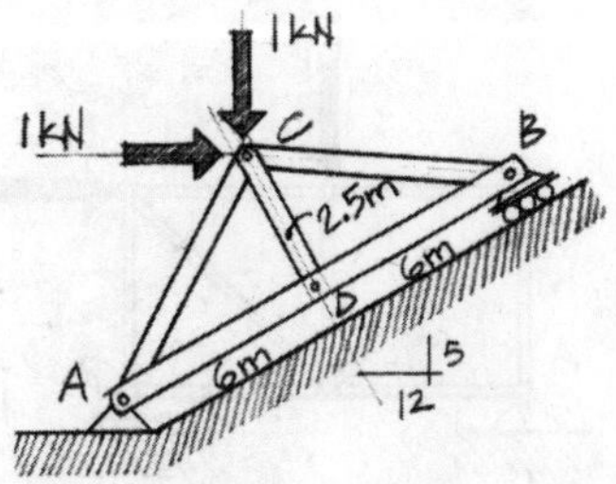

39 A three-span overhang beam system is used to support the roof loads for an industrial building. Draw appropriate FBDs, and determine the support reactions at A, B, E, and F as well as the pin (hinge) forces at C and D.

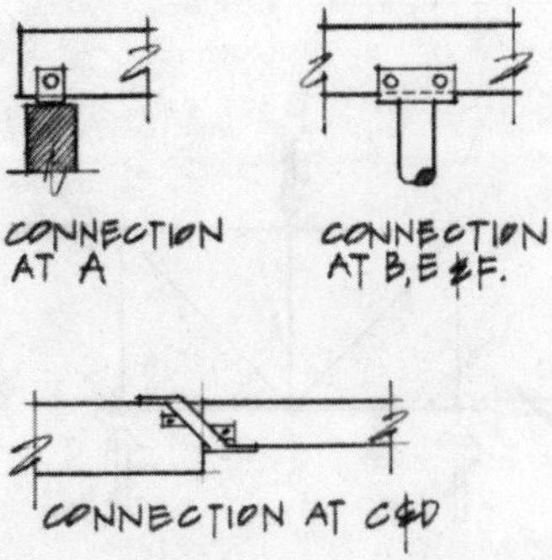

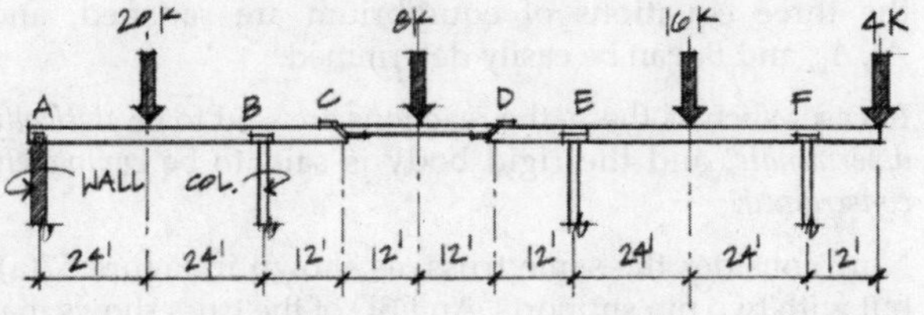

40 Determine the reactions developed at support points A, B, C, and D.

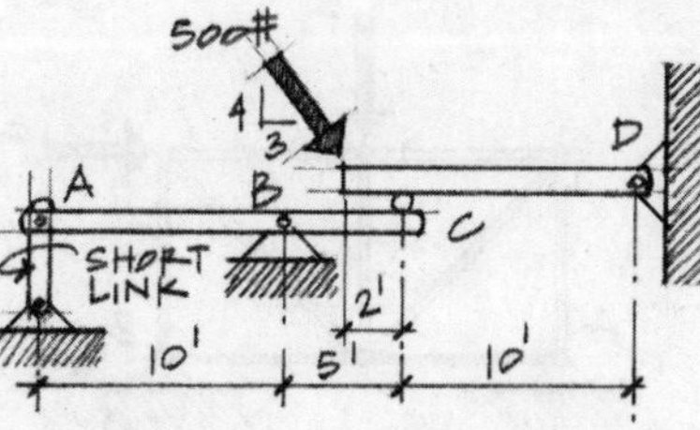

41 Solve for the support reactions at A, B, and C.

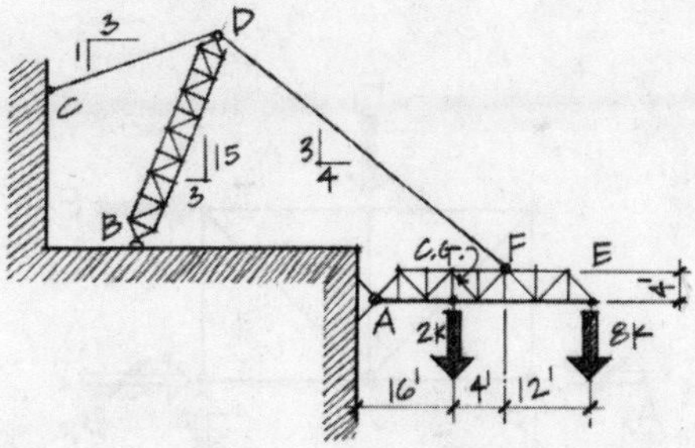

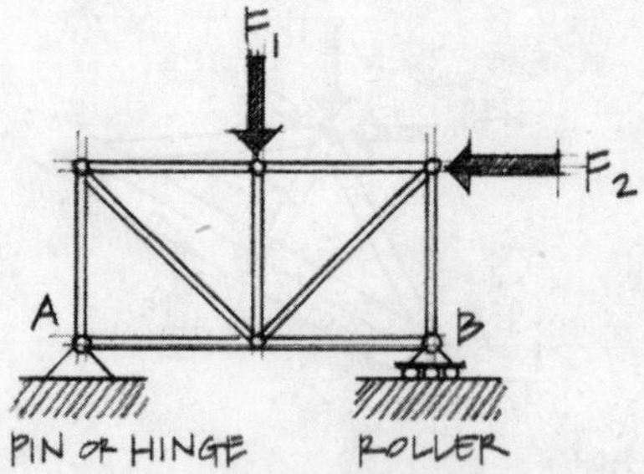

Figure 56(a) Truss with hinge and roller support.

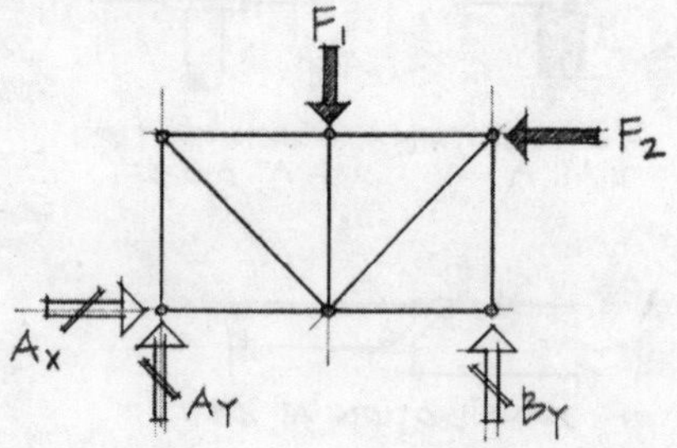

Figure 56(b) FBD—Determinate and constrained.

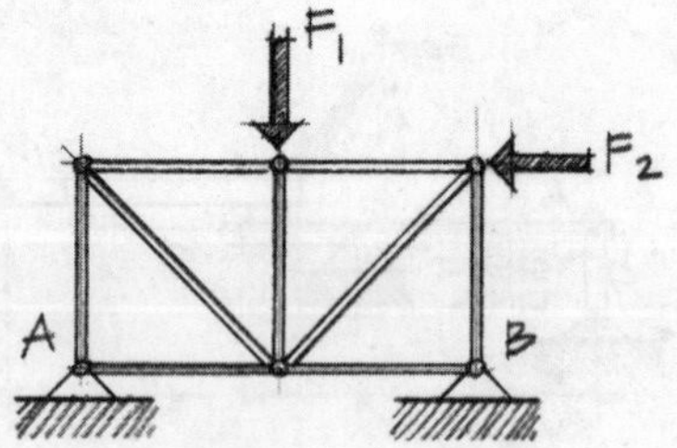

Figure 57(a) Truss with two hinged supports.

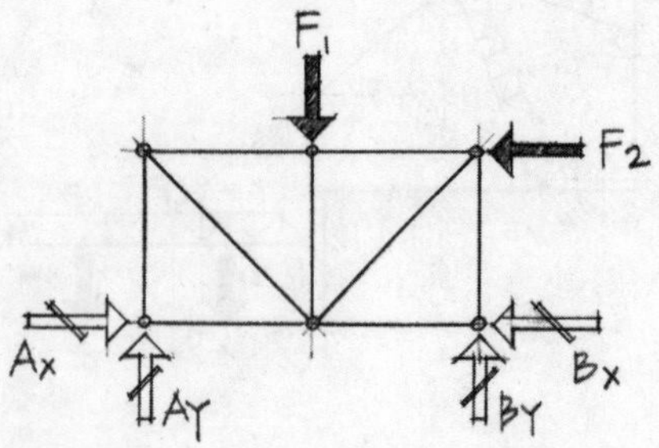

Figure 57(b) FBD—Statically indeterminate externally.

6 STATICAL INDETERMINACY AND IMPROPER CONSTRAINTS

In the analysis of a beam, truss, or framework, the first step usually involves the drawing of an FBD. From the FBD, we can determine (a) whether the necessary and available equations of equilibrium are sufficient to satisfy the given load conditions and (b) the unknown support forces.

As an example, let's examine a truss, as shown in Figure 56(a), with two applied loads, F_1 and F_2. A hinge (pin) support is provided at A and a roller support at B.

An FBD of this truss shows that two support forces are developed at A and only a vertical reaction exists at B, as shown in Figure 56(b). The three support forces are sufficient to resist translation in both the x and y directions as well as rotational tendencies about any point. Therefore, the three equations of equilibrium are satisfied, and A_x, A_y, and B_y can be easily determined.

In cases such as these, the reactions are said to be *statically determinate*, and the rigid body is said to be *completely constrained.*

Now consider the same truss, as shown in Figure 57(a), but with two pin supports. An FBD of the truss shows that a total of four support reactions are present: A_x, A_y, B_x, and B_y.

These support constraints adequately resist translational (x and y) as well as rotational tendencies to satisfy the primary conditions of equilibrium, Figure 57(b).

Three equations of equilibrium
Four unknown support reactions

When the number of unknowns exceeds the number of equations of equilibrium, the rigid body is said to be *statically indeterminate* externally. The degree of indeterminacy is equal to the difference between the number of unknowns and the number of equations of equilibrium. As with the case shown in Figure 57(b), the truss constraints are indeterminate to the first degree.

Two supports are provided for the truss in Figure 58(a); both are rollers. The FBD reveals that only two vertical support reactions develop. Both A_y and B_y have the capability for resisting the vertical force F_1, but no horizontal reaction is provided to resist horizontal translation caused by force F_2.

Three equations of equilibrium
Two unknown support reactions

The minimum number of equilibrium conditions that must be satisfied is three, but because only two support constraints exist, this truss is *unstable* (or *partially constrained*).

A generalization that seems apparent from the three previous examples is that the number of support unknowns must be equal to the number of equations of equilibrium for a rigid body to be completely constrained and statically determinate. Note, however, that while this generalization is necessary, it is not sufficient. Consider, for example, the truss shown in Figure 59(a) and 59(b), which is supported by three rollers at *A*, *B*, and *C*.

Three equations of equilibrium
Three unknown support reactions

Although the number of unknowns is equal to the number of equations of equilibrium, no support capability exists that can restrain horizontal translation. These constraints are improperly arranged, and this condition is referred to as *improperly constrained*.

A rearrangement of the three rollers shown in Figure 60(a) and 60(b) could easily make the truss stable as well as statically determinate.

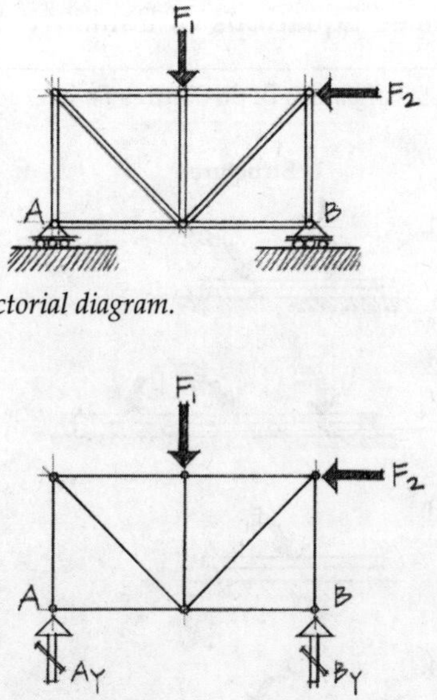

(a) Pictorial diagram.

(b) Free-body diagram.

Figure 58 Two rollers—partially constrained/unstable.

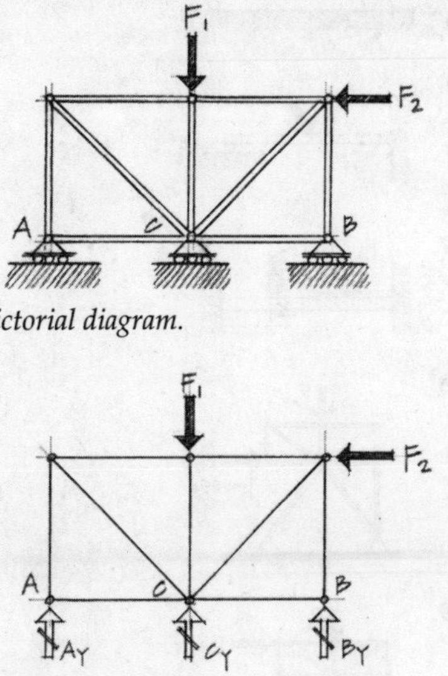

(a) Pictorial diagram.

(b) Free-body diagram.

Figure 59 Two rollers—partially constrained/unstable.

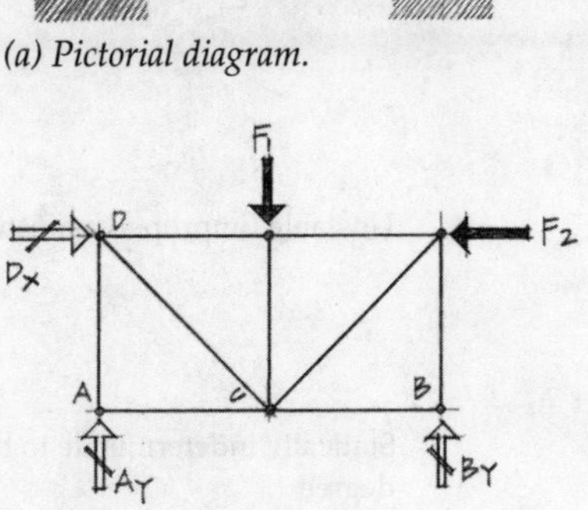

(a) Pictorial diagram.

(b) Free-body diagram.

Figure 60 Three supports—stable and determinate.

Three Equations of Equilibrium and Three Unknown Support Reactions

Classification of Structures Based on Constraints

Structure	Number of Unknowns	Number of Equations	Statical Condition
1. 	3	3	Statically determinate (called a *simple beam*)
2. 	5	3	Statically indeterminate to the second degree (called a *continuous beam*)
3. 	2	3	Unstable
4. 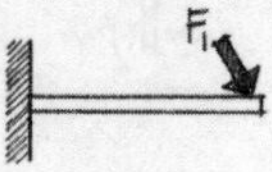	3	3	Statically determinate (called a *cantilever*)
5. 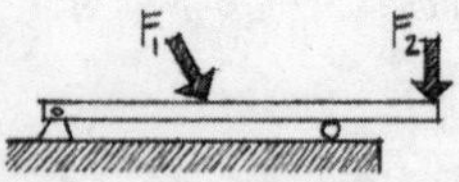	3	3	Statically determinate (called an *overhang beam*)
6. 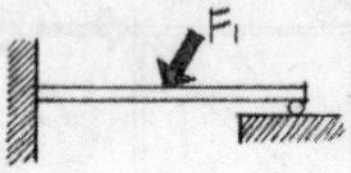	4	3	Statically indeterminate to the first degree (called a *propped beam*)
7. 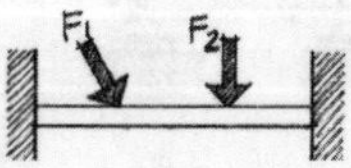	6	3	Statically indeterminate to the third degree (called a *fixed-ended beam*)
8. 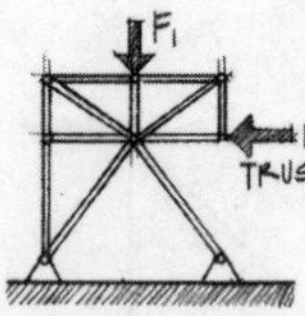	3	3	Statically determinate
9. 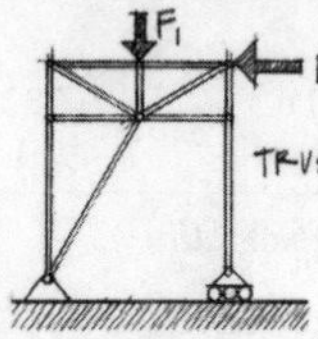	3	3	Unstable (improperly constrained)
10. 	6	3	Statically indeterminate to the third degree

Supplementary Problems

Vector Addition: Section 2

42 Determine the resultant of the two forces acting at point O. Scale: 1/2″ = 100#.

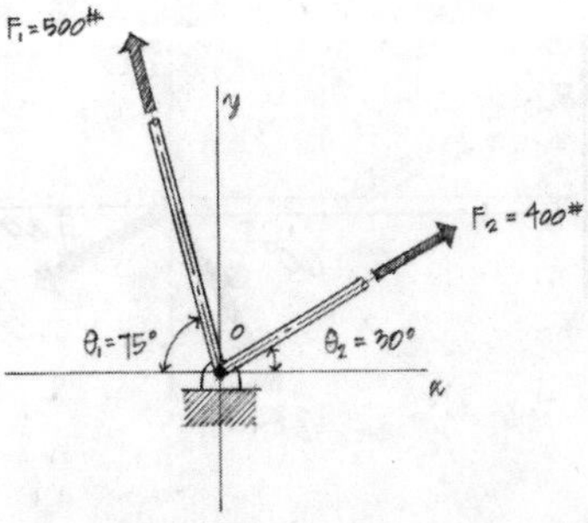

43 Determine the resultant of the three forces shown acting on the anchor device. Use the tip-to-tail graphical method in your solution. Follow a sequence of *A-B-C*. Scale: 50 mm = 1 kN or 1 mm = 20 N.

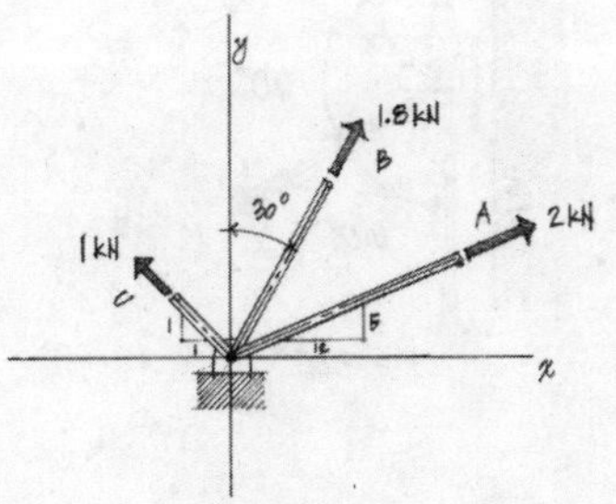

44 A pile resists the tension developed by three stay cables for a major tent (membrane) structure. Assuming no bending is desired in the pile (no resultant horizontal component), what is the magnitude of the force *S* if the angle $\theta_S = 30°$?

If the pile resists with a capacity of 500# per square foot of embedded surface, what is the required penetration *h* for the pile? Scale: 1″ = 8 k.

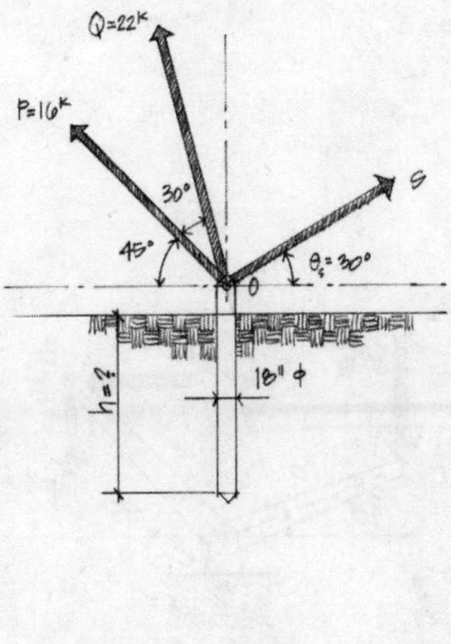

Force Systems: Section 3

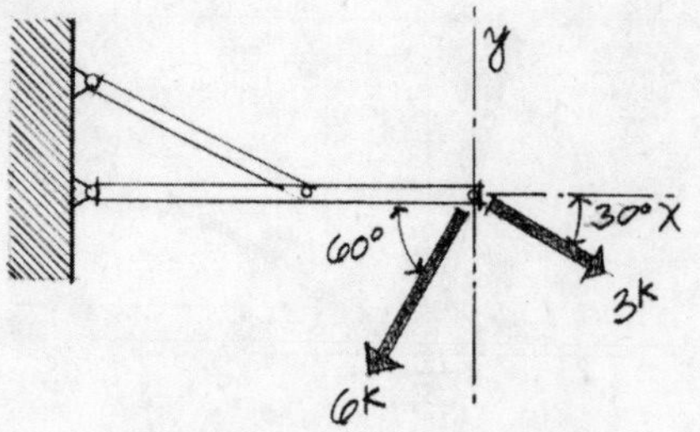

45 Solve for the resultant force at *A* using the analytical method.

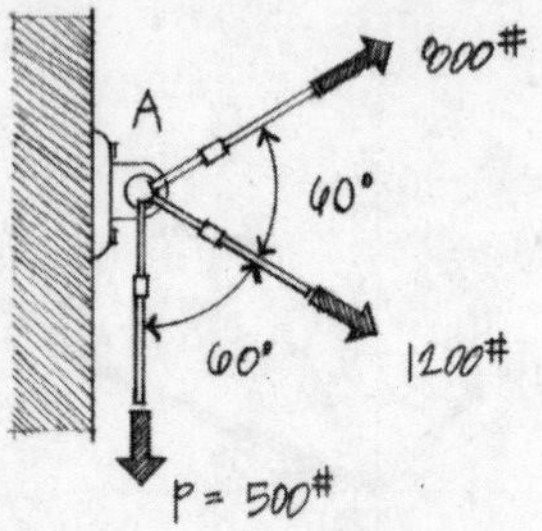

46 Knowing that the magnitude of the force *P* is 500#, determine the resultant of the three forces applied at *A*.

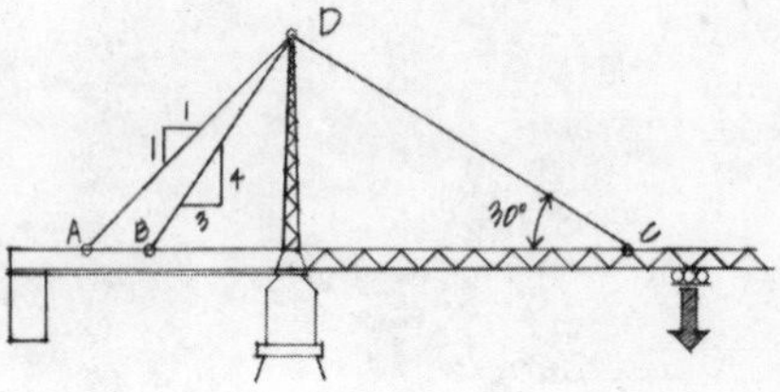

47 Determine the resultant at point *D* (which is supported by the crane's mast) if *AD* = 90 kN, *BD* = 45 kN, and *CD* = 110 kN.

Moment of a Force: Section 3

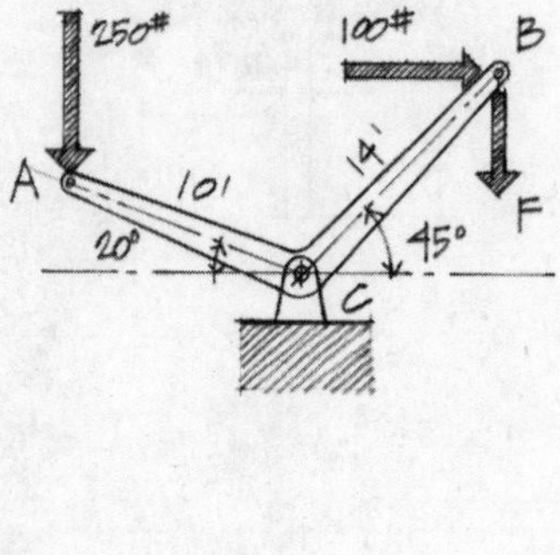

48 Determine the force *F* required at *B* such that the resultant moment at *C* is zero. Show all necessary calculations.

49 A crooked cantilever beam is loaded as shown. Determine the resultant moment at A.

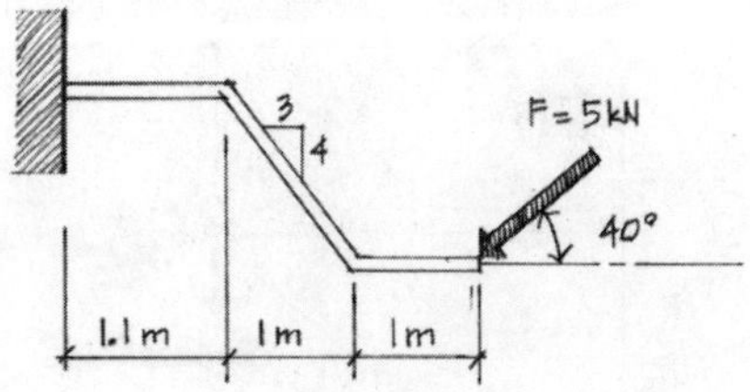

50 Determine the resultant moment M_A at the base of the utility pole assuming forces T_1 and T_2 as shown.

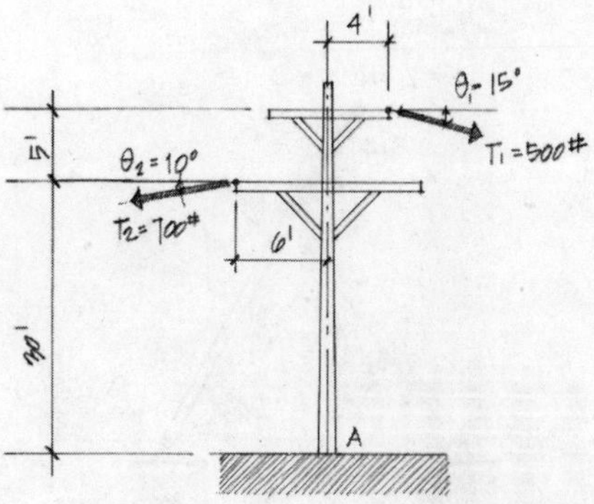

Resultant of Parallel Forces: Section 3

51 Find the single resultant force that would duplicate the effect of the four parallel forces shown. Use the reference origin given in the diagram.

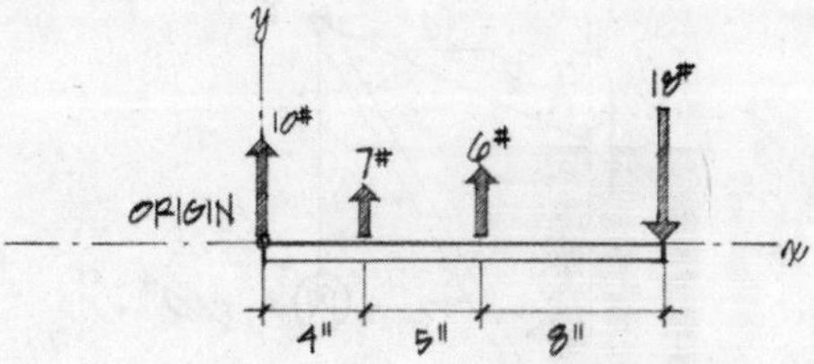

52 A three-meter-long horizontal wood beam weighs 30 N per meter of length and supports two concentrated vertical loads as shown. Determine the single resultant force that would duplicate the effect of these three parallel forces. Use the reference origin shown.

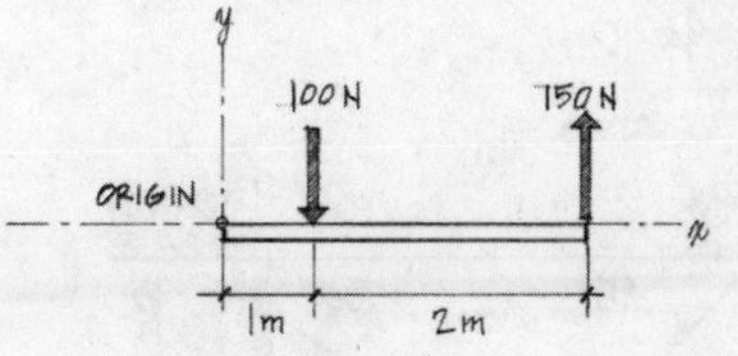

53 A 16-foot-long horizontal wood member weighs 20 lb./ft. and supports three concentrated loads. Determine the magnitudes of components A and B that would be equivalent in effect as the four parallel forces acting on the system.

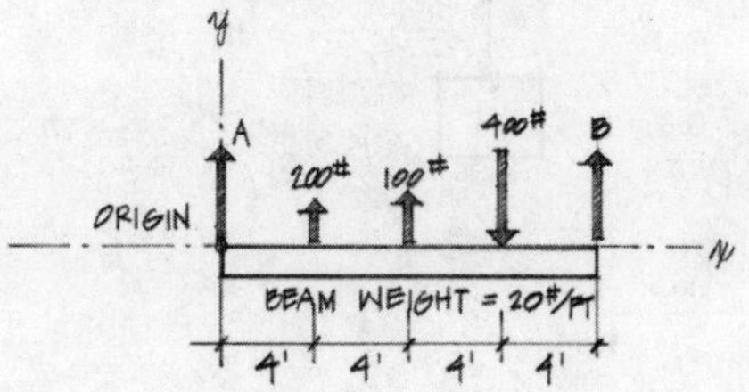

Equilibrium of a Particle: Section 4

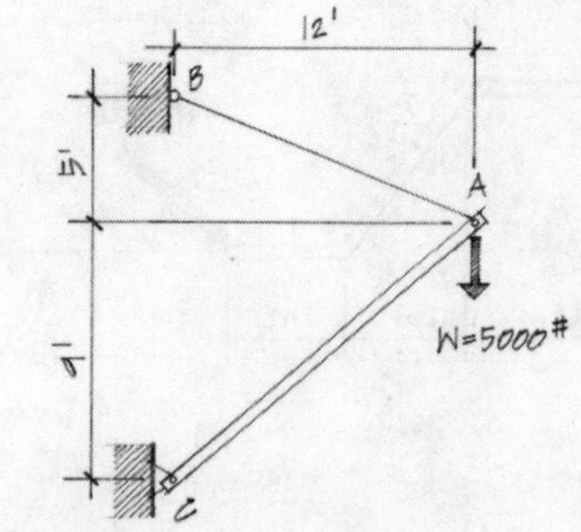

54 Determine the tension in cable *AB* and the force developed in strut *AC*.

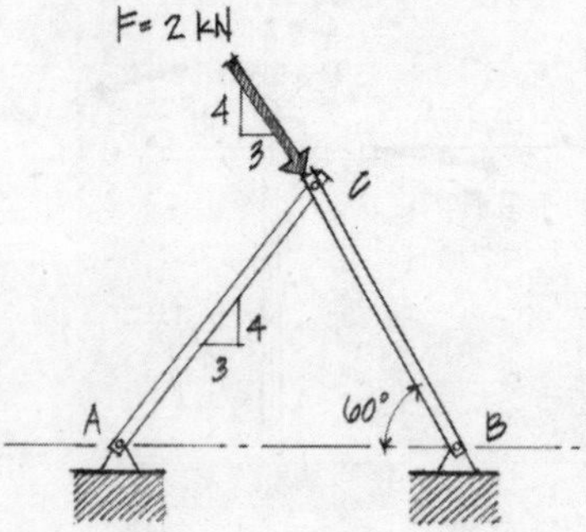

55 Determine the force developed in members *AC* and *BC* due to an applied force $F = 2$ kN at concurrent joint *C*. In your final answer, indicate whether the members are in tension or compression. Solve this problem analytically and graphically. Scale: 1 mm = 20 N.

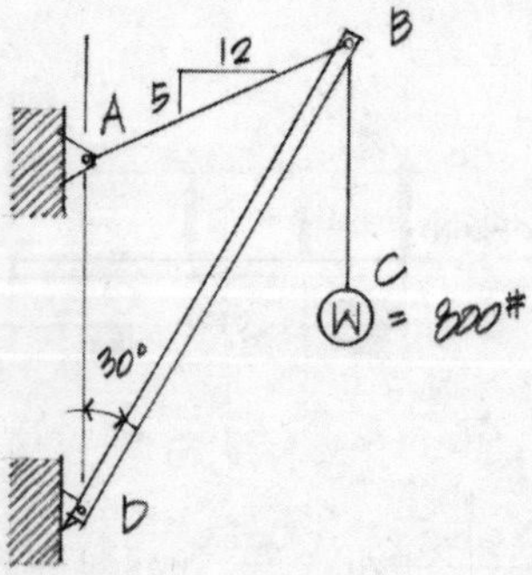

56 Cables *BA* and *BC* are connected to boom *DB* at concurrent point *B*. Determine the forces in cable *BA* and boom *DB* using the analytical method. Assume a condition of equilibrium exists at *B*.

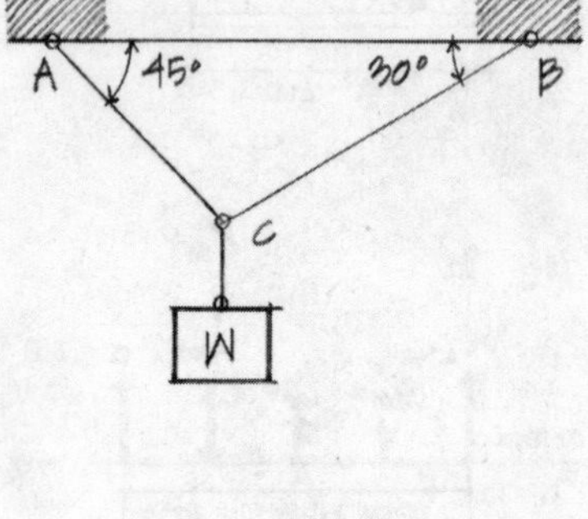

57 Determine the tensions in *CA* and *CB* and the maximum weight *W* if the maximum cable capacity for *AC* and *CB* is 1.8 kN.

58 Determine the weight W required to produce a tensile force of 1,560# in cable AB. Also, determine the forces in BC, BE, and CD.

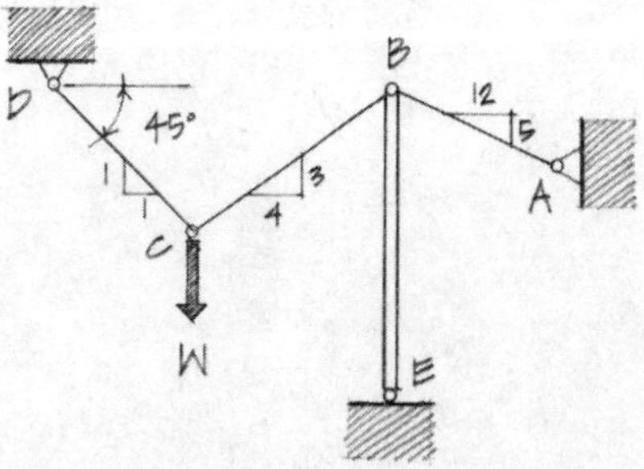

Equilibrium of Rigid Bodies: Section 5

59 Determine the support reactions at A and B.

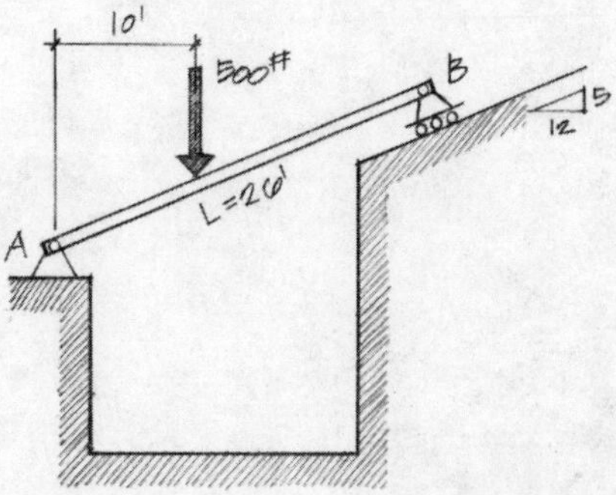

60 Construct the appropriate FBDs, and solve for the support reactions at A and C.

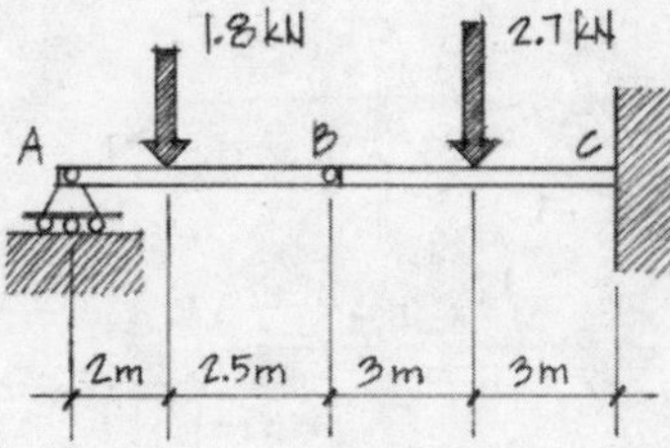

61 A bridge spans across a river carrying the loads shown. Determine the support reactions at A and B.

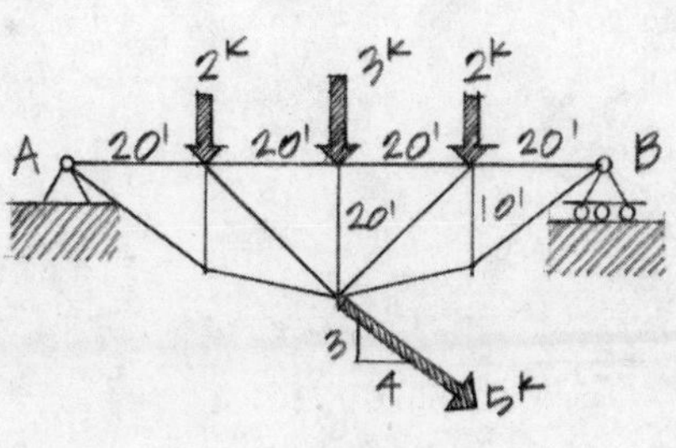

62 Calculate the beam reactions at supports A, C, and D. Draw all appropriate FBDs.

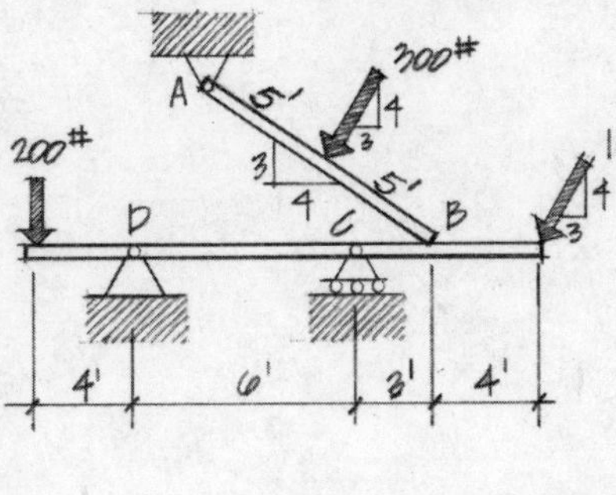

Summary

- Force is defined as a push or a pull on a body and tends to change the body's state of rest or motion. Also, a force is a vector, characterized by its magnitude, direction, sense, and point of application.
- The principle of transmissibility, as it applies to rigid bodies, states that a force may be moved anywhere along its line of action without changing the external effects on the body.
- Two forces (vectors) add according to the parallelogram law, in which the components form the sides of the parallelogram and the resultant is represented by the diagonal.
- A reverse of vector addition is the resolution of a force into two perpendicular components, generally the x and y axes. Force F, having an inclination θ with respect to the horizontal x axis, is resolved into x and y components expressed as $F_x = F \cos\theta$ and $F_y = F \sin\theta$.

  The force F represents the diagonal of a rectangle, and F_x and F_y are the respective sides. From the Pythagorean theorem for right triangles,

  $$F = \sqrt{F_x^2 + F_y^2} \quad \text{and} \quad \tan\theta = \frac{F_y}{F_x} \quad \text{or} \quad \theta = \tan^{-1}\left(\frac{F_y}{F_x}\right)$$

- A resultant of a series of concurrent forces is expressed as

  $$R = \sqrt{R_x^2 + R_y^2} \quad \text{and} \quad R_x = \Sigma F_x \quad \text{and} \quad R_y = \Sigma F_y$$

- The direction of the resultant force is determined by using the trigonometric function:

  $$\theta = \tan^{-1}\left(\frac{R_y}{R_x}\right)$$

- Algebraic summation of forces in the x and y directions assumes a sign convention in which horizontal forces directed to the right are considered to be positive (negative if directed to the left) and vertical forces acting upward are considered to be positive (negative if acting downward).
- Moment is expressed as a force times the perpendicular distance to a reference point: $M = F \times d_{\perp}$.

  Direction is determined by the tendency of a force to produce clockwise or counterclockwise rotation about the reference.

- Varignon's theorem states that the moment of a force about a point is equal to the algebraic sum of the moments of its components about the same point.

- A moment couple is the product of two forces having the same magnitude, parallel lines of action, but opposite sense. Couples produce pure rotation with no translation.
- The resultant of two parallel forces must produce an equivalent effect (translational and rotational) as the original forces.
- Equilibrium of a coplanar-concurrent force system (equilibrium of a particle) requires the application of two equations:

$$R_x = \Sigma F_x = 0 \quad \text{and} \quad R_y = \Sigma F_y = 0$$

- Coplanar forces acting on a rigid body must satisfy three conditions for equilibrium:

$$\Sigma F_x = 0, \quad \Sigma F_y = 0; \quad \Sigma M_i = 0$$

- An essential step in solving equilibrium problems involves the construction of FBDs.

Answers to Selected Problems

1 R = 173 lb.; θ = 50° from the horiz.; ϕ = 40° from the vertical

3 F_2 = 720 lb.

5 T_2 = 3.6 kN

6 F_x = 800 lb.; F_y = 600 lb.

8 P_x = 94.9 lb.; P_y = 285 lb.

10 R = 1,079 N; θ = 86.8° from the horizontal reference axis

12 F_1 = 6.34 kN; F_2 = 7 kN

13 T = 4.14 kips; R = –11.3 k

14 M_A = 0. The box is just on the verge of tipping over.

16 M_A = –420 lb.-in. (clockwise)

18 P = 10.3 lb.

19 M_A = –656 kN-m (clockwise)

21 M_A = 108.8 lb.-in. (counterclockwise); M_B = –130.6 lb.-in. (clockwise)

23 W = 1,400 lb.

25 $M_A = M_B = M_C = 0$

27 M_A = –850 lb.-in.; M_B = –640 lb.-in.

28 A = 732 lb.; C = 518 lb.

29 AC = 768 N (compression); BC = 672 N (tension)

31 A = 2.24 kN; B = 0.67 kN

33 CD = 245.6 lb. (T); DE = 203.4 lb. (T); AC = 392.9 lb. (T); BC = 487.7 lb. (C)

35 A = 43.33 kN; B = 46.67 kN

37 A_y = 3,463 lb.; D_x = 3,000 lb.; D_y = 1,733 lb.

38 A_x = .705 kN; A_y = .293 kN; B_x = .295 kN; B_y = .707 kN

40 A_y = 240 lb. (↓); B_x = 0; B_y = 720 lb. (↑); C_y = 480 lb.; D_x = 300 lb. (←); D_y = 80 lb. (↓)

41 FD = 18.9 k; A_x = 15.2 k; A_y = 1.3 k (↓); BD = 17.2 k; DC = 17.5 k

42 R = 720 lb.; θ_R = 72.5°

44 S = 20.5 k; R = 42.5 k; h = 78′

46 R = 1,867 lb.; θ = 22°

48 F = 137.4 lb.

50 M_A = 3,990 lb.-ft. (counterclockwise)

52 R = 40 N (↓) at an imaginary location where x = 5.4 m to the left of the origin

54 $AC = 5.36$ k (C); $AB = 4.64$ k (T)

56 $BA = 658.2$ lb.; $DB = 1{,}215.2$ lb.

58 $BC = 1{,}800$ lb.; $BE = 1{,}680$ lb.;
$CD = 2{,}037$ lb.; $W = 2{,}520$ lb.

60 $A_y = 1$ kN; $B_x = 0$; $B_y = 0.8$ kN;
$C_x = 0$; $C_y = 3.5$ kN; $M_C = 12.9$ kN-m

62 $A_x = 180$ lb. ($\rightarrow$); $A_y = 52.5$ lb. ($\uparrow$);
$B_y = 187.5$ lb.; $C_y = 322$ lb. ($\uparrow$);
$D_x = 60$ lb. ($\rightarrow$); $D_y = 145.5$ lb. ($\uparrow$)

Analysis of Selected Determinate Structural Systems

Analysis of Selected Determinate Structural Systems

Figure 1 Hinged connection of a support end—Ravenna Bridge, Seattle. Hinged supports feature prominently in the structural systems discussed in this chapter. The symbol for a hinged connection is shown in Table 2.1(b). Photo by Chris Brown.

1 EQUILIBRIUM OF A PARTICLE

Simple Cables

Cables are a highly efficient structural system with a variety of applications such as:

- Suspension bridges.
- Roof structures.
- Transmission lines.
- Guy wires, etc.

Cables or suspension structures constitute one of the oldest forms of structural systems, as attested to by the ancient vine-and-bamboo bridges of Asia. As a structural system, a cable system is logical and objectifies the laws of statics in visual terms. A layperson can look at it and understand how it works.

Figure 2 Cable-stayed pedestrian bridge. Photo by author.

It is a simple engineering reality that one of the most economical ways to span a large distance is the cable. This in turn derives from the unique physical fact that a steel cable in tension, pound for pound, is several times stronger than steel in any other form. In the cable-stayed pedestrian bridge shown in Figure 2, the great strength factor of steel in tension is put to work to reduce enormously the dead load of the structure while providing ample strength to support the design live load. Cables are relatively light, and unlike beams, arches, or trusses, they have virtually no rigidity or stiffness.

The most common material used for building cable structures (suspension bridges, roof structures, transmission lines, etc.) is high-strength steel.

Cables are assumed to be flexible elements because of their relatively small cross-sectional dimension in relation to their length. The bending capacity in cables therefore is usually assumed to be negligible. Cables can carry load only in tension, and they must be kept in tension at all times if they are to remain stable. The stability of a tensile structure must be achieved through a combination of shape (geometry) and prestress.

Beams and arches subject to changing loads develop bending moments, but a cable responds by changing its shape or configuration (Figure 3).

Figure 3 Cable shapes respond to specific load conditions.

The Principal Elements

Every practical suspension system must include all of the following principal elements in one form or another.

Vertical supports or towers

These provide the essential reactions that keep the cable system above the ground. Each system requires some kind of supporting towers. These may be simple vertical or sloping piers or masts, diagonal struts, or a wall. Ideally, the axes of the supports should bisect the angle between the cables that pass over them (Figure 4).

Figure 4 Cable-supported roof—Bartle Hall, Kansas City, Missouri. Photo by Matt Bissen.

Main cables

These are the primary tensile elements, carrying the roof (or sometimes floors) with a minimum of material. Steel used in cable structures has breaking stresses that exceed 200,000 psi (pounds per square inch).

Anchorages

Although the main cables carry their loads in pure tension, they are usually not vertical, whereas the gravity forces are. This resolution is accomplished because some part of the structure provides a horizontal force resistance; this is called the *anchorage*. In the case of a suspension bridge, the main cables are carried over gently curved saddles on top of the towers and on down into massive concrete abutments or into bedrock, as shown in Figure 5(a).

In the cable-stayed bridge system shown in Figure 5(b), the vertical cable on one side of the vertical tower is balanced by an equivalent cable on the other side. Horizontal thrust is resolved in the longitudinal bridge-deck framework.

(a) *Suspension bridge.*

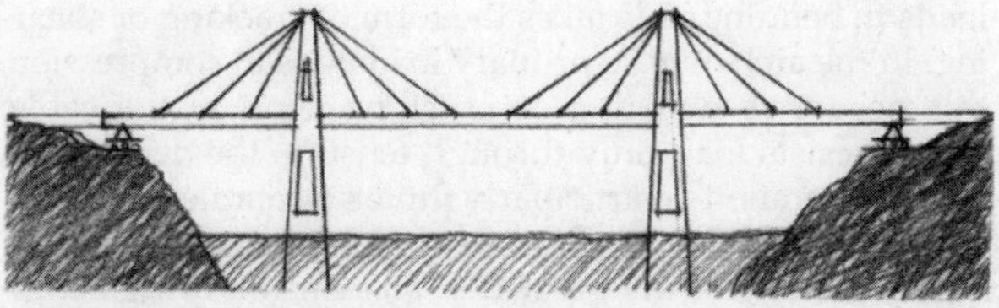

(b) *Cable-stayed bridge.*

Figure 5 Cable-supported bridges.

For buildings, the resolution of horizontal thrust is usually very cumbersome, involving tremendous mass. It is usually best to use some part of the building itself as the anchorage: a floor that can act as a brace from one side to the other or, more simply, a compression ring if the building forms a smooth, closed curve in plan. Circular plans are well suited to, and commonly used for, suspension roofs (Figure 6).

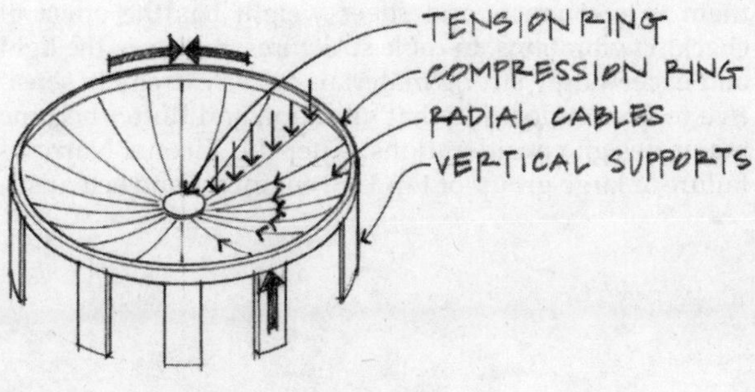

Figure 6 Suspended roof system.

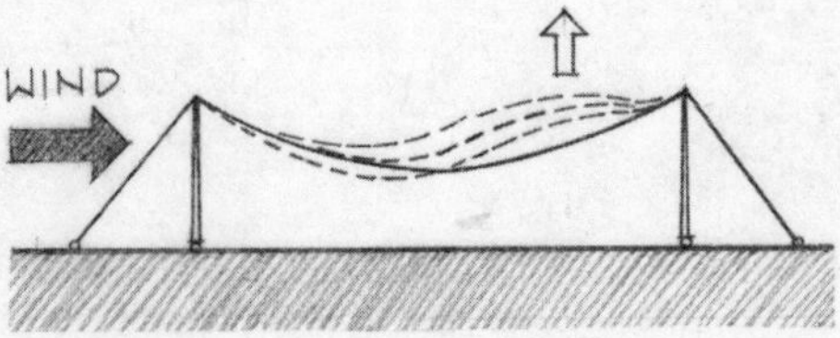

Figure 7 Cable flutter in a lightweight roof.

Figure 8 "Galloping Gertie," Tacoma Narrows Bridge. Courtesy of the University of Washington Libraries, Special Collections, UW 21422.

Stabilizers

Stabilizers are the fourth element required to prevent cables from undergoing extreme shape changes under varying load conditions. Lightweight roof systems, such as cables or membranes, are susceptible to pronounced undulation or fluttering when acted upon by wind forces (Figure 7).

Every form of a building, like every physical law, has its limitations or breaking points. In the beam, which resists loads in bending, this takes the form of cracking or shearing. In the arch, whose primary loading is in compression, this occurs as buckling or crushing. And in the cable, which resists load only through tension, the destructive force is vibration—particularly flutter, a complex phenomenon that belies the lightness of its name. David B. Steinman, one of the great U.S. suspension bridge engineers, isolated and identified this phenomenon of flutter in 1938.

All materials of whatever nature have a natural molecular vibration or frequency range. If an outside force acting upon a material comes within that frequency range, causing the material to vibrate internally, or flutter, a vibrational state may be reached where the outer and inner forces are in tune (called *resonance*), and the material undergoes destruction. Even without reaching resonance, the uneven loading of outside forces, such as wind, may cause a material to vibrate visibly up and down, building up rhythmically to destruction. It was these allied forces, plus design flaws, that reduced the Tacoma Narrows Bridge to rubble (Figure 8).

In heavy, earthbound, compressive structures, the natural frequencies are so low that few external forces can bring them to resonance, and sheer weight has the effect of checking vibrations. In cable structures, however, the light and exceedingly strong materials are so extremely sensitive to uneven loading that vibration and flutter become major design considerations. After the Tacoma Narrows failure, a large group of top U.S. engineers and scientists, particularly in the aerodynamics field, thoroughly investigated and reported on the phenomenon. David Steinman worked independently for 17 years, devising an integral system of damping that subtly outwits the phenomenon without a sacrifice in weight or economy.

With buildings, the problem and its solution are related to the roof surface. What is to be used to span across the cables? If it is some type of membrane, such as a tent structure, acting only in tension, then the problem of dynamic instability begins immediately and may be solved by pretensioning. If, however, the surface is to be wood planking, metal decking, or a thin concrete slab, it is then rigid and can resist *normal* (perpendicular) forces through bending. The problem of flutter and movement is minimized for the surface but remains a concern for the main cables (Figure 9).

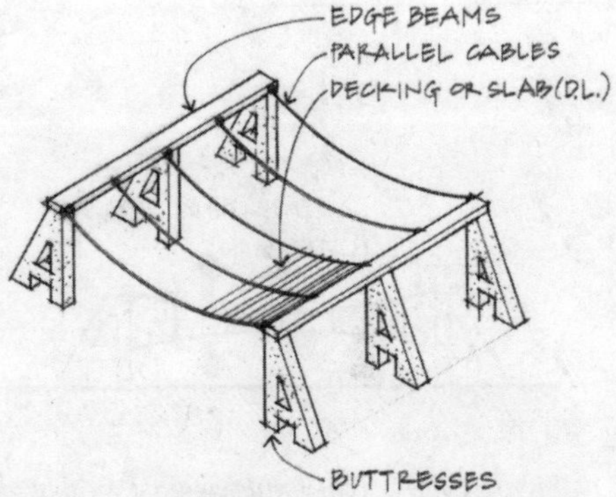

Figure 9 Stabilizing the roof structure.

The stabilizing factors for the primary cables can be dead weight, a rigid surface that includes the main cables, a set of secondary pretensioned cables with reverse curvature from the main cables, or restraining cables (Figure 10).

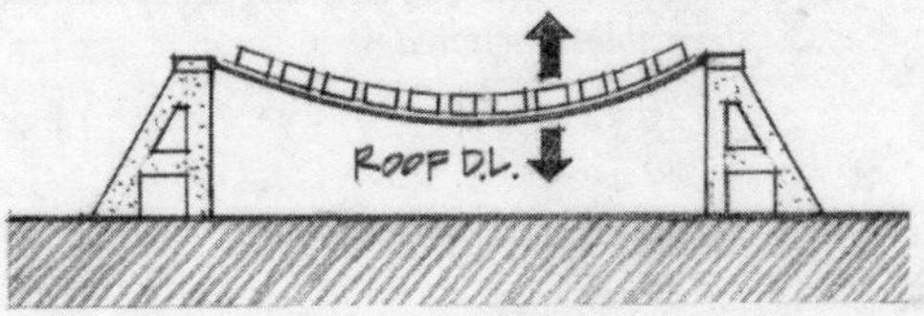

Figure 10(a) Increase of dead weight.

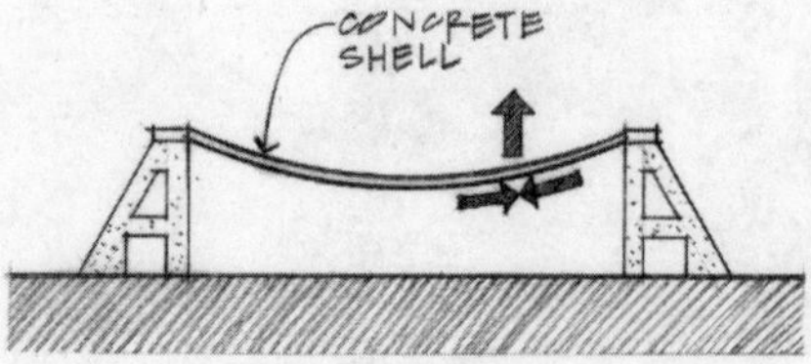

Figure 10(b) Stiffening through construction as an inverted arch (or shell).

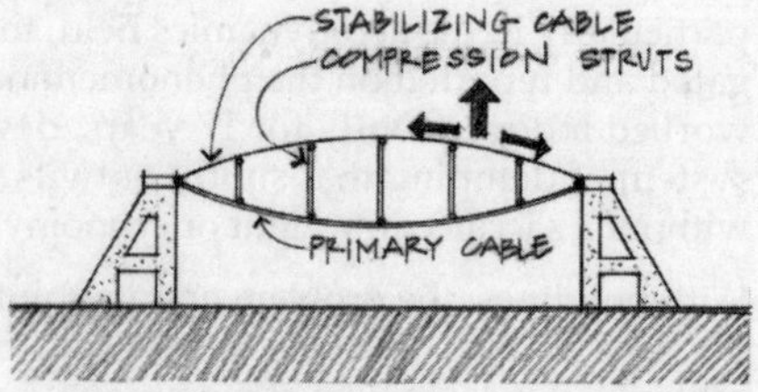

Figure 10(c) Spreading against a cable with opposite curvature.

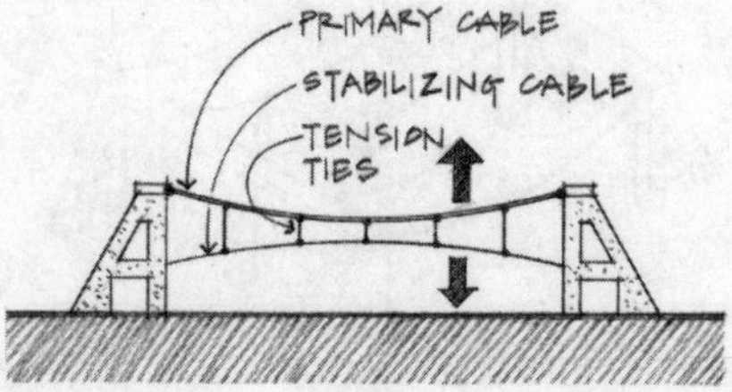

Figure 10(d) Tensioning against a cable with opposite curvature.

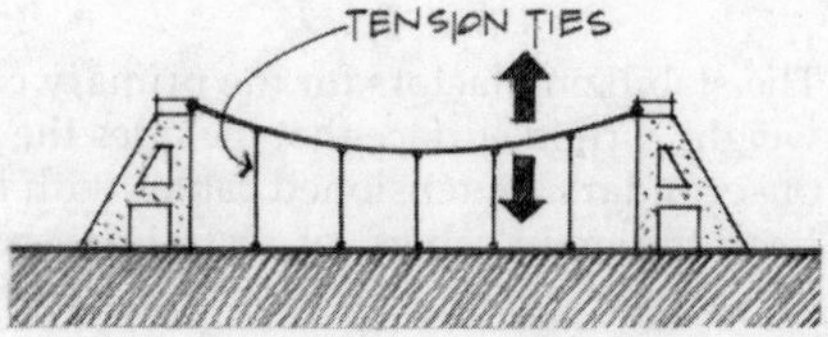

Figure 10(e) Fastening with transverse cables anchored.

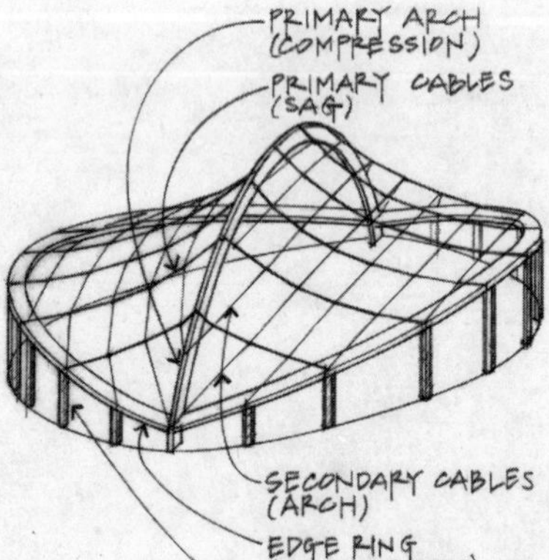

Figure 10(f) Cable net structure.

Cable Geometry and Characteristics

One of the advantages of tension structures is the simplicity with which one can visualize the shape of the tension elements under load. A perfectly flexible cable or string will take on a different shape for every variation in loading; this is referred to as the *funicular* or *string polygon.*

Under the action of a single concentrated load, a cable forms two straight lines meeting at the point of application of the load; when two concentrated loads act on the cable, it forms three straight lines (polygon form); and so on. If the loads are uniformly distributed horizontally across the entire span (suspension bridge), the cable assumes the shape of a parabola. If the loads are distributed uniformly along the length of the cable rather than horizontally, such as a suspended chain loaded by its own weight, then the cable assumes the natural (funicular) shape called a *catenary,* a curve very similar to a parabola (Figure 11).

Changes in shape due to asymmetrical loading, such as snow, over only portions of the roof are essentially the same as those due to moving loads. In both cases, the greater the live load/dead load ratio, the greater the movement.

Some of the basic characteristics of a cable system are inherent in its geometry (Figure 12).

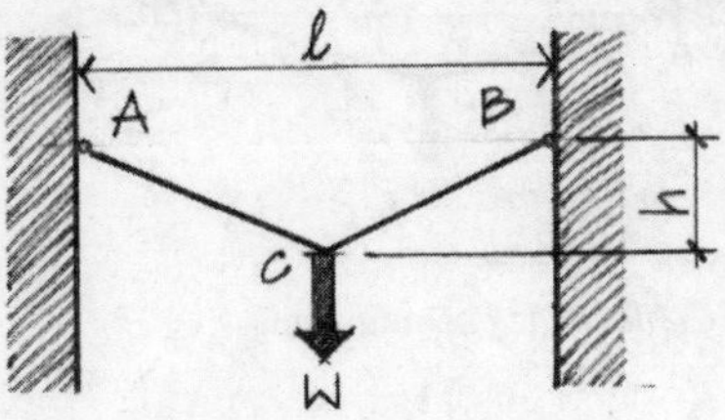

Figure 12 Cable characteristics.

ℓ = cable span
$L = AC + CB$ = cable length
h = sag
$r = h/\ell$ = sag-to-span ratio

The values of r usually are small—in most cases, on the order of $\frac{1}{10}$ to $\frac{1}{15}$. Cable length L for a single concentrated load can be determined easily by using the Pythagorean theorem. Sag h and cable span ℓ are usually given or known.

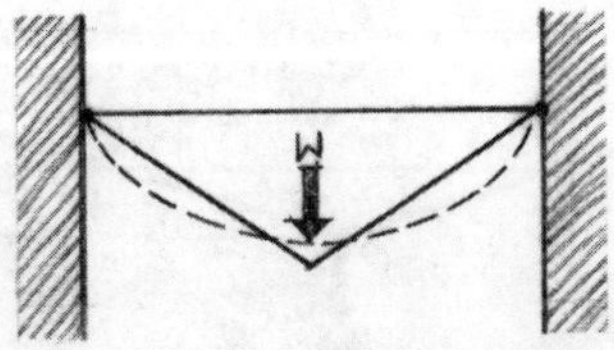

(a) Simple concentrated load—triangle.

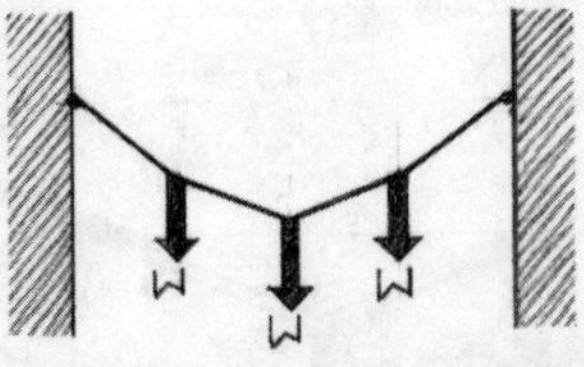

(b) Several concentrated loads—polygon.

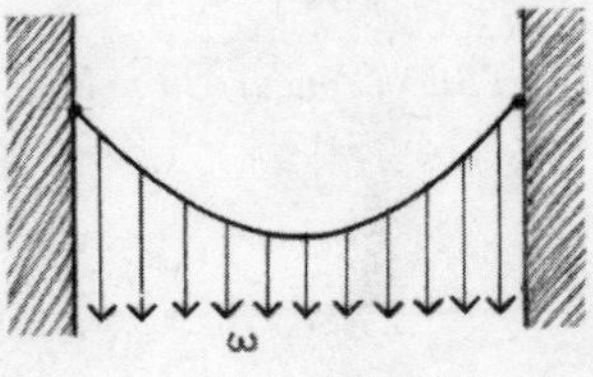

(c) Uniform loads (horizontally)—parabola.

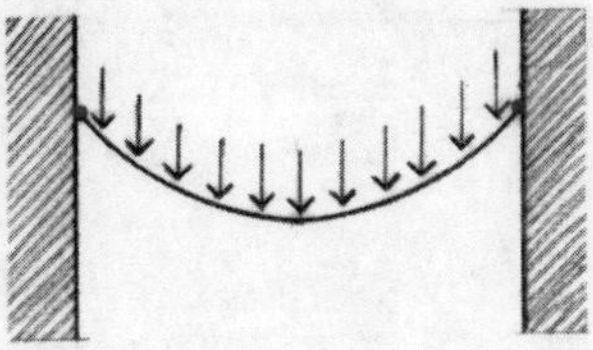

(d) Uniform loads (along the cable length)—catenary.

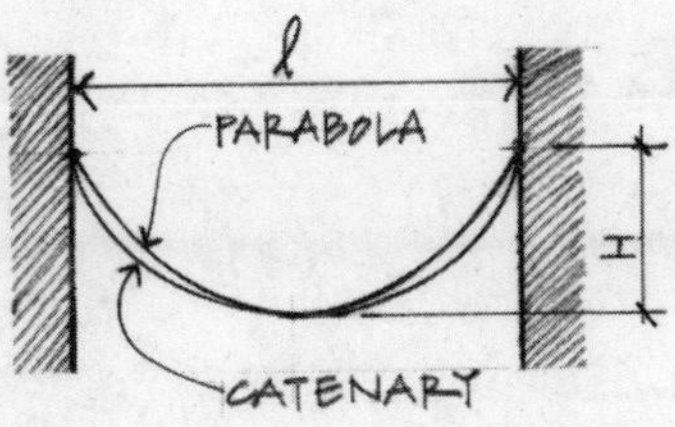

(e) Comparison of a parabolic and a catenary curve.

Figure 11 Geometric funicular forms.

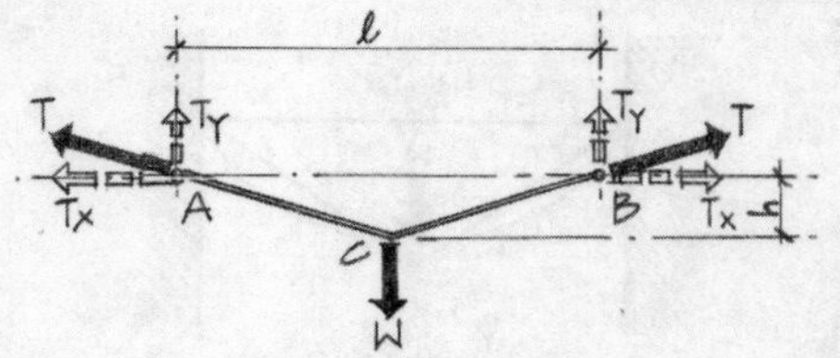

Figure 13 FBD of a cable with a single concentrated load.

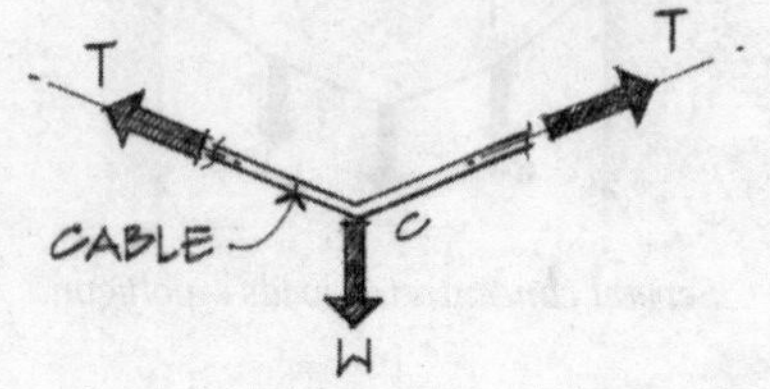

Figure 14 FBD of concurrent point C.

Cables with a Single Concentrated Load

When a cable is subjected to a single concentrated load at midspan, the cable assumes a symmetrical triangular shape. Each half of the cable transmits an equal tensile force to the support.

In Figure 13, assume that $\ell = 24'$ and $h = 3'$ and that these are known values.

The cable length L can be found by:

$$L = AC + CB = \ell\sqrt{1 + 4r^2} = \sqrt{\ell^2 + 4h^2}$$

derived from the Pythagorean theorem.

For this particular geometry and load condition, the force throughout the cable is the same. The tensile force developed in the cable passes through the axis, or line of action, of the cable. Cables, therefore, perform similarly to rigid two-force members.

Isolating the concurrent point C, we can draw the FBD shown in Figure 14.

The sag in a cable is important, because without it, loads cannot be transmitted to the support (Figure 15).

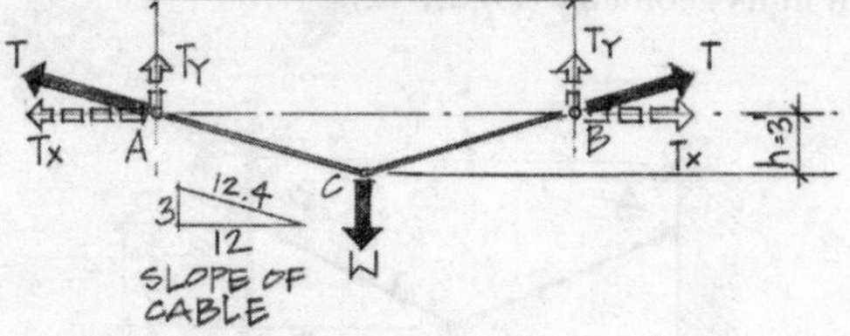

Figure 15 Cable loaded at midspan.

$$T_y = \frac{3}{12.4}T \quad T_x = \frac{12}{12.4}T$$

$$r = \frac{h}{\ell} = \frac{3'}{24'} = \frac{1}{8}$$

$$L = \ell\sqrt{1 + 4r^2} = 24\sqrt{1 + 4\left(\frac{1}{8}\right)^2} = 24.8'$$

Because the T_y component at each support is equal,

$$\left[\Sigma F_y = 0\right] 2T_y - W = 0; \; T_y = \frac{W}{2}$$

By virtue of the slope,

$$T_x = \frac{12}{3}T_y = \frac{12}{3}\left(\frac{W}{2}\right) = 2W$$

The horizontal component T_x developed at the support is known as the *thrust*.

Example Problems: Cables

1 In this example (Figure 16), we assume that as the sag increases (r increases), the tension in the cable decreases. Minimizing the sag in a cable causes large tensile forces to develop.

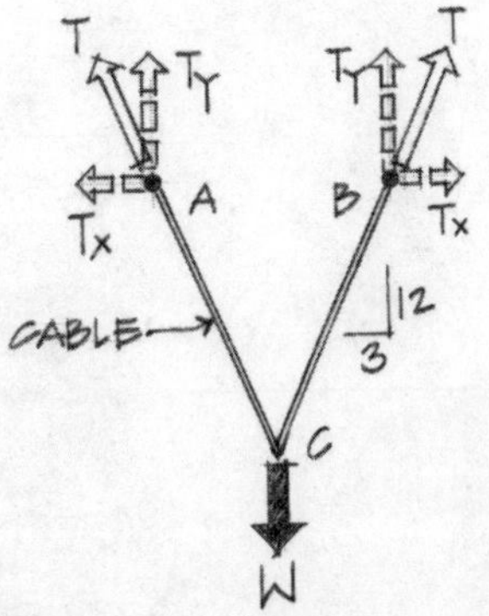

Figure 16 FBD of a large-sag cable with a load at midspan.

Solution:

(Extremely large sag) $h = 12', L = 6'$

$$T_x = \frac{3}{12.4}T;\ T_y\frac{12}{12.4}T$$

$$[\Sigma F_y = 0]\,2T_y - W = 0;\ T_y = \frac{W}{2}$$

$$T_x = \frac{3}{12}T_y = \frac{3}{12}\left(\frac{W}{2}\right) = \frac{W}{8}$$

$$r = \frac{h}{\ell} = \frac{12}{6} = 2$$

2 Is it possible to have a cable support a load and have zero sag (Figure 17)?

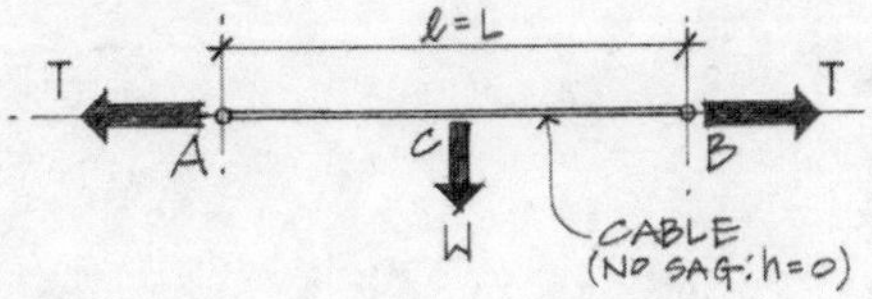

Figure 17 Cable with no sag.

Solution:

This cable system cannot support W, because no T_y components exist for $[\Sigma F_y = 0]$. The tension developed is completely horizontal, where

$$T_x = T, T_y = 0$$

It is impossible to design a cable with zero sag, or to quote Lord Kelvin:

There is no force, however great,
Can stretch a cord, however fine,
Into a horizontal line
That shall be absolutely straight.

3 Determine the tension developed in the cable, the support reactions, and the cable length L (Figure 18).

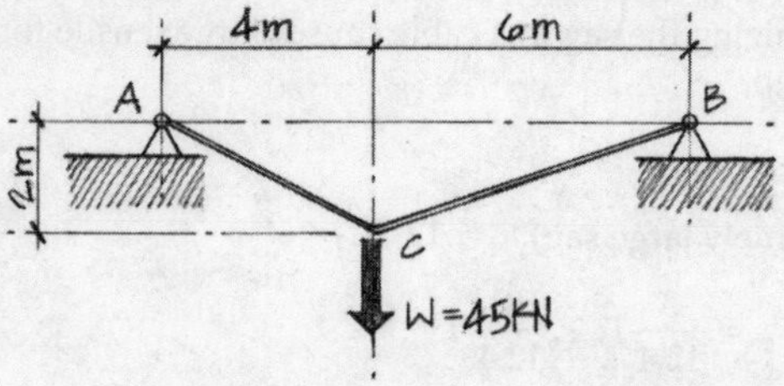

Figure 18(a) *Cable with a single concentrated load.*

Solution:

$$\ell = 10\,\text{m}$$

$$h = 2\,\text{m}$$

$$r = \frac{h}{\ell} = \frac{2}{10} = \frac{1}{5}$$

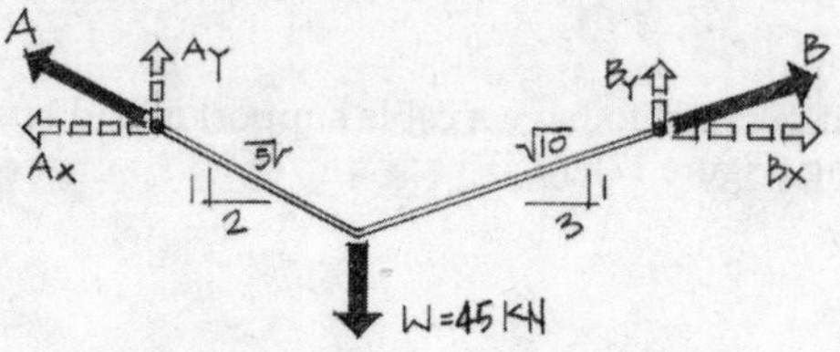

Figure 18(b) *FBD of the cable.*

$$A_x = \frac{2}{\sqrt{5}}A \qquad B_x = \frac{3B}{\sqrt{10}}$$

$$A_y = \frac{A}{\sqrt{5}} \qquad B_y = \frac{B}{\sqrt{10}}$$

$$\left[\Sigma M_A = 0\right] + \frac{B}{\sqrt{10}}(10\,\text{m}) - 45\,\text{kN}(4\,\text{m}) = 0$$
$$B = 18\sqrt{10}\,\text{kN} = 56.9\,\text{kN}$$

$$B_x = \frac{3}{\sqrt{10}}(18\sqrt{10}\,\text{kN}) = 54\,\text{kN}$$

$$B_y = \frac{18\sqrt{10}\,\text{kN}}{\sqrt{10}} = 18\,\text{kN}$$

$$[\Sigma F_y = 0] A_y - 45\,\text{kN} + 18\,\text{kN} = 0$$
$$A_y = 27\,\text{kN}$$

Note that $A_y \neq B_y$ due to asymmetrical loading:

$$A_x = 2A_y = 54\,\text{kN}$$

$$A = \frac{\sqrt{5}}{2}A_x = \frac{\sqrt{5}}{2}(54\,\text{kN}) = 27\sqrt{5}\,\text{kN}$$
$$= 60.4\,\text{kN} \Leftarrow \text{Critical Tension}$$

Note: *$A_x = B_x$; the horizontal component of the tension force is the same at any point of the cable, because $\Sigma F_x = 0$.*

The support forces and cable forces are of the same magnitude but opposite sense.

The cable length is determined as

$$L = \sqrt{(2\,\text{m})^2 + (4\,\text{m})^2} + \sqrt{(2\,\text{m})^2 + (6\,\text{m})^2}$$

$$L = \sqrt{20\,\text{m}^2} + \sqrt{40\,\text{m}^2} = 10.79\,\text{m}$$

4 Determine the support reactions, cable tensions, and elevations of points B and D with respect to the supports (Figure 19). The cable weight is assumed to be negligible.

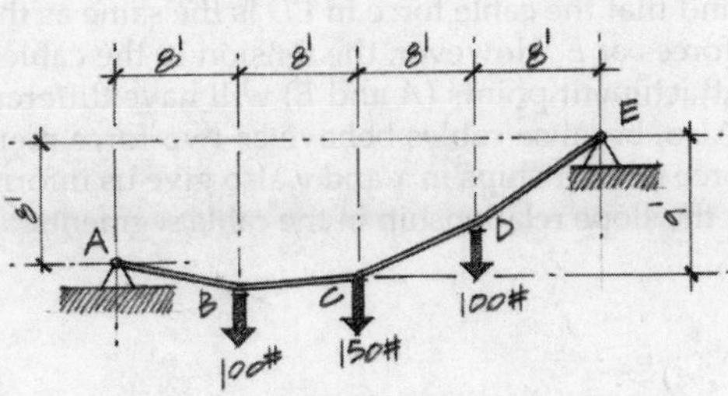

Figure 19 Cable with multiple concentrated loads.

Solution:

$$\left[\Sigma M_E = 0\right] - A_y(32') - A_x(8') + 100\#(24') \quad (1)$$
$$+ 150\#(16') + 100\#(8') = 0$$
$$= 32A_y + 8A_x = 5{,}600\#\text{-ft.}$$

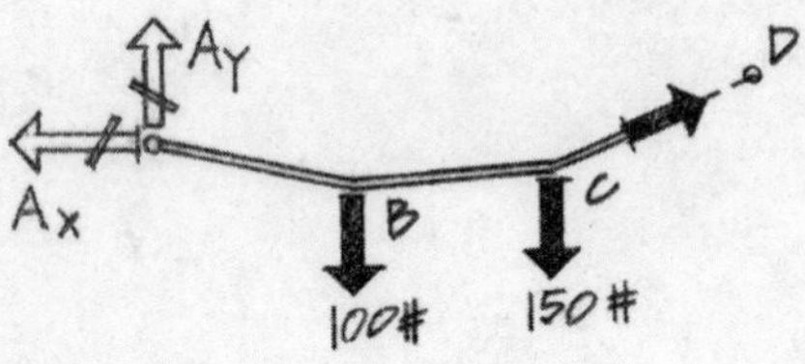

FBD (b) Portion of the cable.

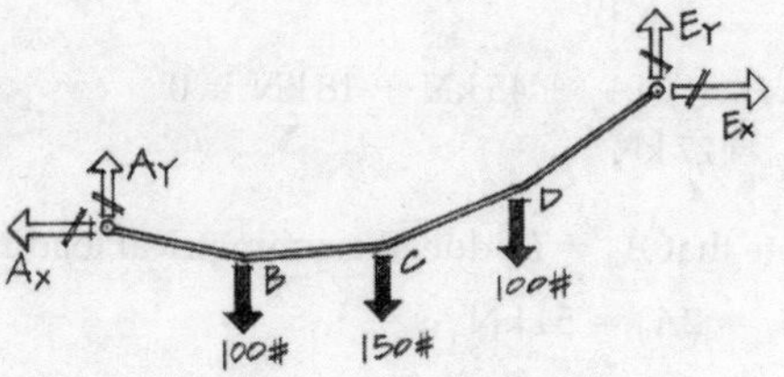

FBD (a) Entire cable.

$$\left[\Sigma M_C = 0\right] + A_x(1') - A_y(16') + 100\#(8') = 0 \quad (2)$$
$$16A_y - A_x = 800\#\text{-ft.}$$

Solving equations (1) and (2) simultaneously,

$A_x = 400\#, A_y = 75\#; T_{AB} = 407\#$

$$\left[\Sigma F_y = 0\right] + 75 - 100\# - 150\# - 100\# + E_y = 0 \quad (3)$$
$$E_y = +275\#$$

$$\left[\Sigma F_x = 0\right] - 400\# + E_x = 0 \quad (4)$$
$$E_x = 400\#$$

Knowing the support reactions at *A* and *E*, we can assume that the force in cable *AB* is the same as the support forces at *A* and that the cable force in *ED* is the same as the support forces at *E*. However, the tension in the cable at the two attachment points (*A* and *E*) will have different values. Also, because cables behave as two-force members, the force relationships in *x* and *y* also give us information about the slope relationship in the cable segments.

For example,

$$\frac{y}{8'} = \frac{A_y}{A_x}$$

$$y = \frac{75\#}{400\#}(8') = 1.5'$$

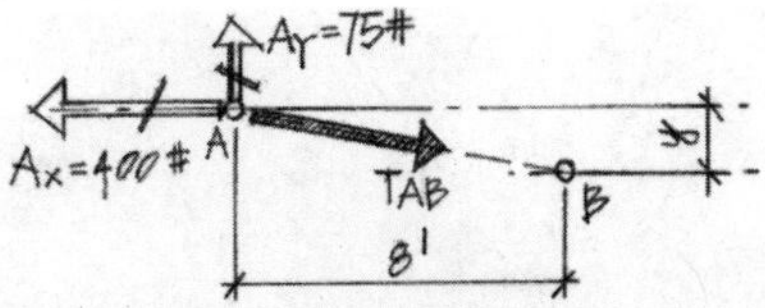

$$\frac{y}{8'} = \frac{E_y}{E_x}; \; y = \frac{275\#}{400\#}(8') = 5.5'$$

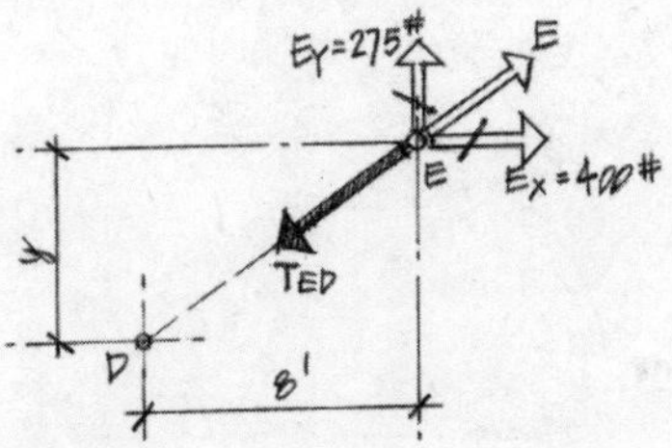

Now that the elevations of points B, C, and D are known, tension forces in BC and CD can be determined.

$$T_{BC_y} = \frac{.5}{8.02} T_{BC}; \; T_{BC_x} = \frac{8}{8.02} T_{BC}$$

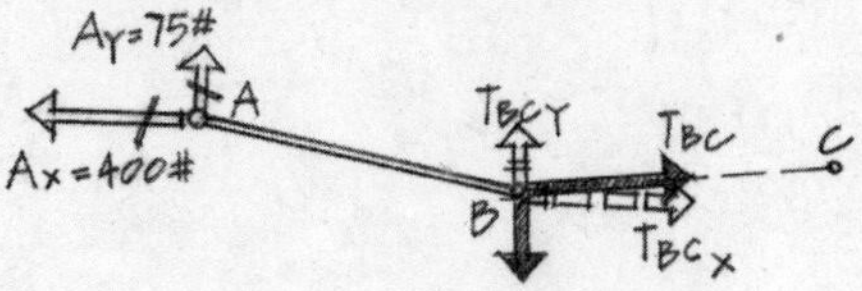

$$\left[\Sigma F_x = 0\right] - 400\# + \frac{8}{8.02} T_{BC} = 0; \; T_{BC} = 401\#$$

$$T_{BC_x} = \frac{8}{8.02}(401\#) = 400\#$$

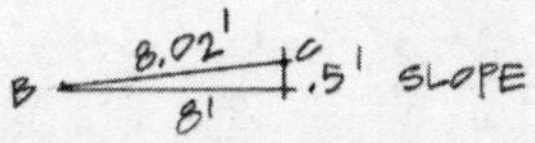

$$T_{BC_y} = \frac{.5}{8.02}(401\#) = 25\#$$

$$T_{DC_x} = \frac{8}{8.73} T_{DC}; \; T_{DC_y} = \frac{3.5}{8.75} T_{DC}$$

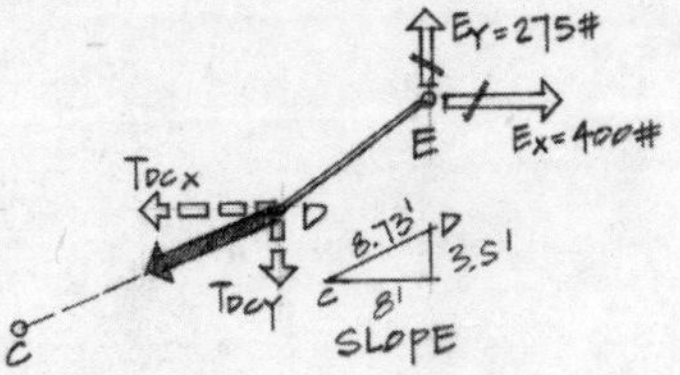

$$\left[\Sigma F_x = 0\right] - T_{DC_x} + 400\# = 0;$$

$$T_{DC_x} = 400\#$$

$$T_{DC_y} = \frac{3.5}{8}(400\#) = 175\#$$

$$T_{DC} \frac{8.73}{8}(400\#) = 436.5\#$$

Summary:

$T_{AB} = 407\#$
$T_{BC} = 401\#$
$T_{DC} = 436.5\#$
$T_{DE} = 485.4\#$
Note: $T_{AB} \neq T_{DE}$

Problems

1 Three equal loads are suspended from the cable as shown. If $h_B = h_D = 4'$, determine the support components at E and the sag at point C.

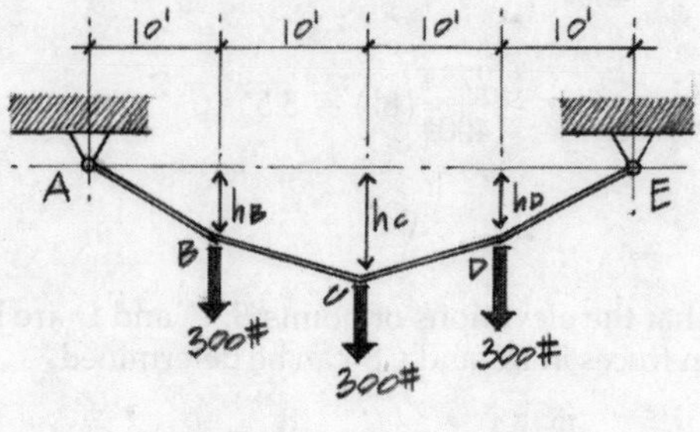

2 Using the diagram in Problem 1, determine the sag at point C if the maximum tension in the cable is 1,200#.

3 Determine the cable tension between each force, and determine the required length of the cable, for the system shown.

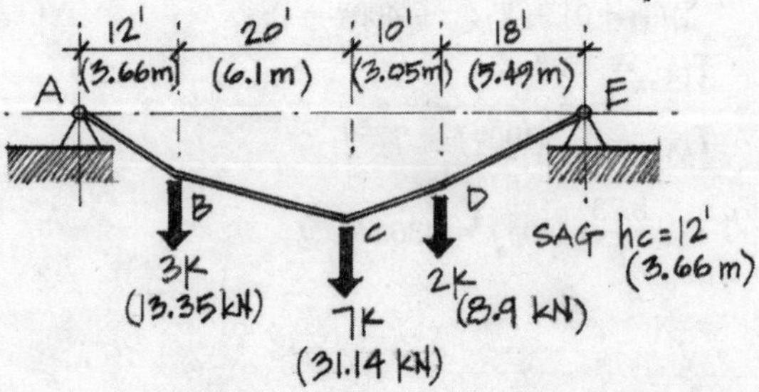

4 If the cable in Problem 3 had a maximum tensile capacity of 20 k, determine the minimum sag permitted at C.

2 EQUILIBRIUM OF RIGID BODIES

Simple Beams with Distributed Loads

Distributed loads, as the term implies, act on a relatively large area—too large to be considered as a point load without introducing an appreciable error. Examples of distributed loads include:

- Furniture, appliances, people, etc.
- Wind pressure on a building.
- Fluid pressure on a retaining wall.
- Snow load on a roof.

Point or *concentrated loads* have a specific point of application, whereas *distributed loads* are scattered over large surfaces. Most common load conditions on building structures begin as distributed loads. (See Figures 20 to 24.)

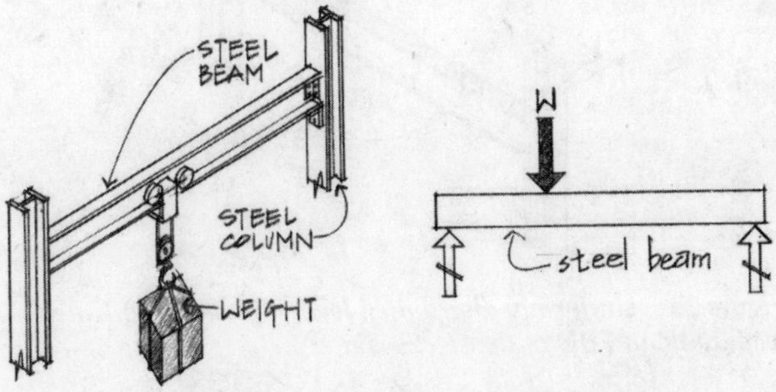

Figure 20 Single concentrated load, with an FBD of the steel beam.

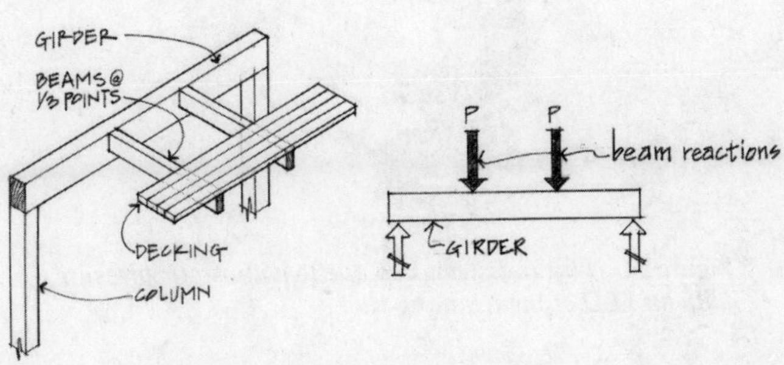

Figure 21 Multiple concentrated loads, with an FBD of the wood girder.

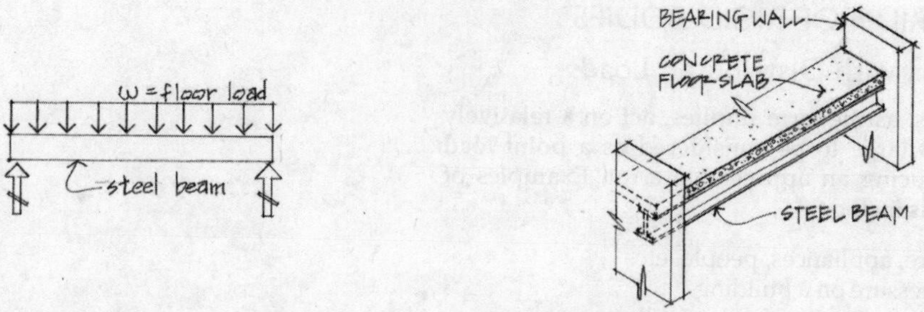

Figure 22 Uniformly distributed load with an FBD of the steel beam.

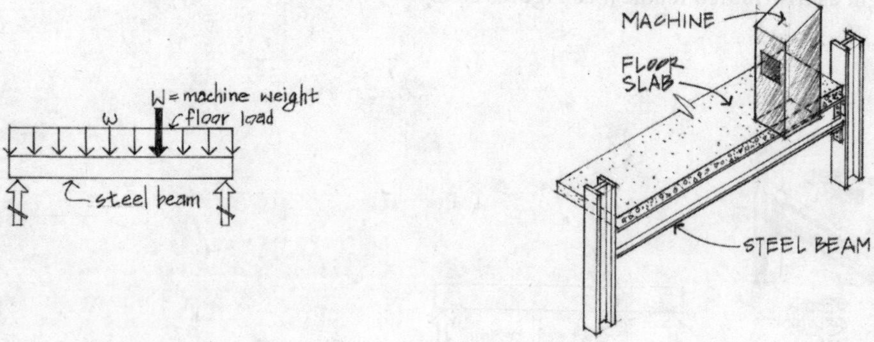

Figure 23 Uniformly distributed load, with a concentrated load, with an FBD of the steel beam.

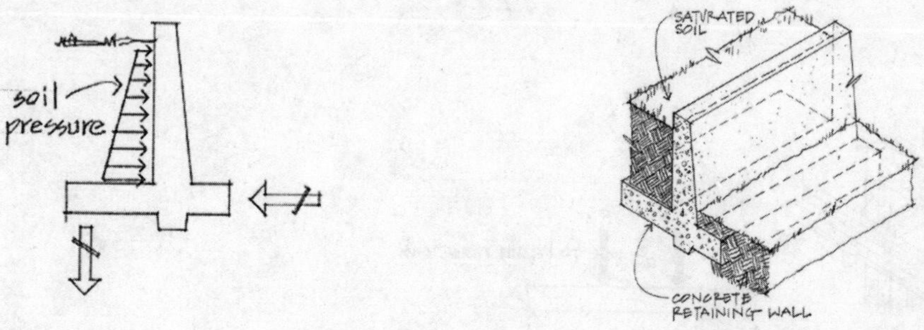

Figure 24 Linear distribution due to hydrostatic pressure, with an FBD of the retaining wall.

Support reactions for beams and other rigid bodies are calculated in the same manner employed for concentrated loads. The equations of equilibrium,

$$\Sigma F_x = 0; \Sigma F_y = 0; \text{and } \Sigma M = 0$$

are still valid and necessary.

To compute the beam reactions, a distributed load is replaced by an equivalent concentrated load, which acts through the center of gravity of the distribution, or what is referred to as the *centroid* of the load area. The magnitude of the equivalent concentrated load is equal to the area under the load curve.

It should be noted, however, that the concentrated load is equivalent to the distributed load only as far as external forces are concerned. The internal stress condition, primarily bending, and the deformation of the beam are very much affected by a change of a uniform load to a concentrated load.

Distributed loads (Figure 25) may be thought of as a series of small concentrated loads F_i. For this reason, the magnitude of the distribution is equal to the summation of the load series.

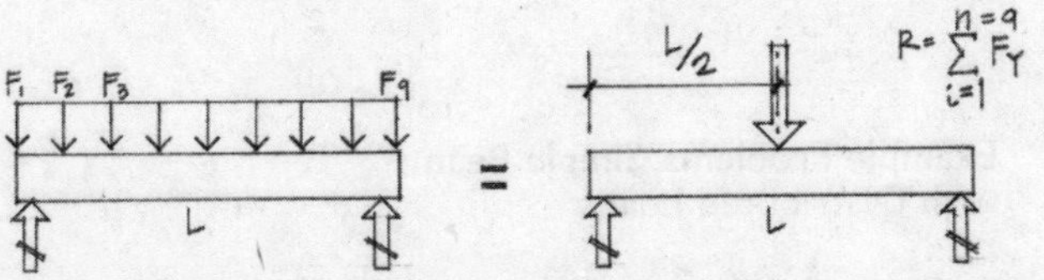

Figure 25 Equivalent load systems.

The location of the equivalent concentrated load is based on the centroid of the load area. By geometric construction, the centroids of two primary shapes are shown in Figures 26 and 27.

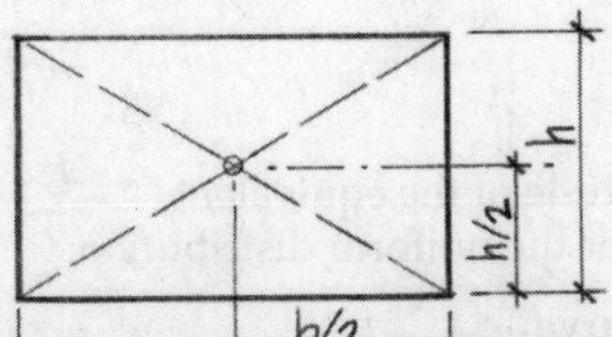

Figure 26 Centroid of a rectangle (Area = b × h).

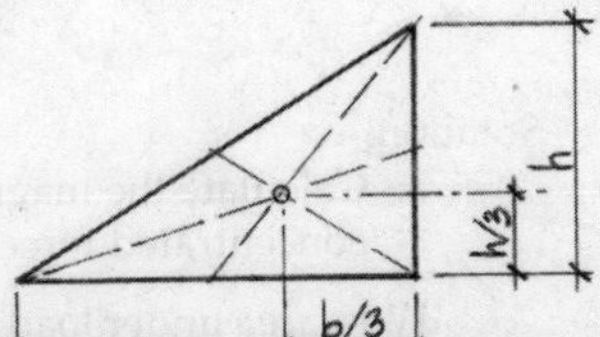

Figure 27 Centroid of a triangle (Area = 1/2 × b × h).

Trapezoidal shapes may be thought of as two triangles, or as a rectangle with a triangle. These two combinations are illustrated in Figure 28.

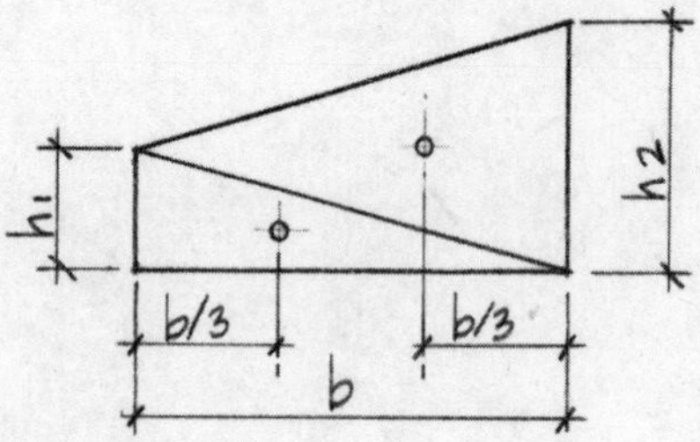

Figure 28(a) *Area* = $(1/2 \times b \times h_1) + (1/2 \times b \times h_2)$.

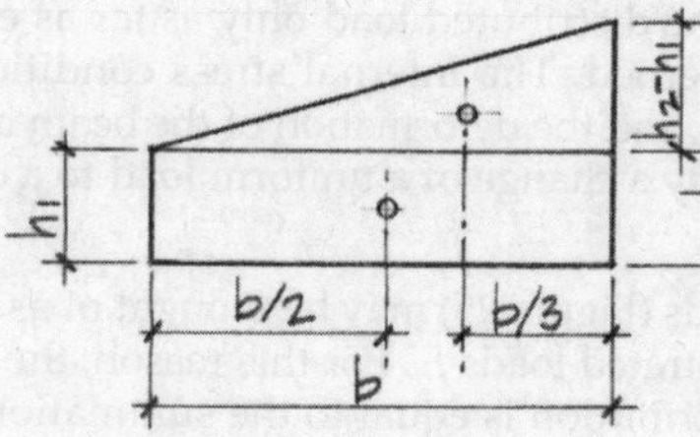

Figure 28(b) *Area* = $(b \times h_1) + (1/2 \times b \times (h_2 - h_1))$.

Example Problems: Simple Beams with Distributed Loads

5 Determine the support reactions at *A* and *B*.

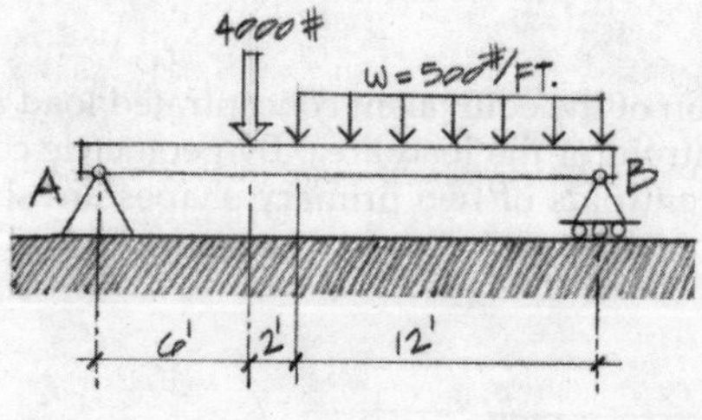

Solution:

a. Calculate the magnitude of the equivalent concentrated force for the uniform distribution.

W = area under load curve

$W = (\omega)12' = (500\,\#/\text{ft.})12'$

$W = 6{,}000\#$

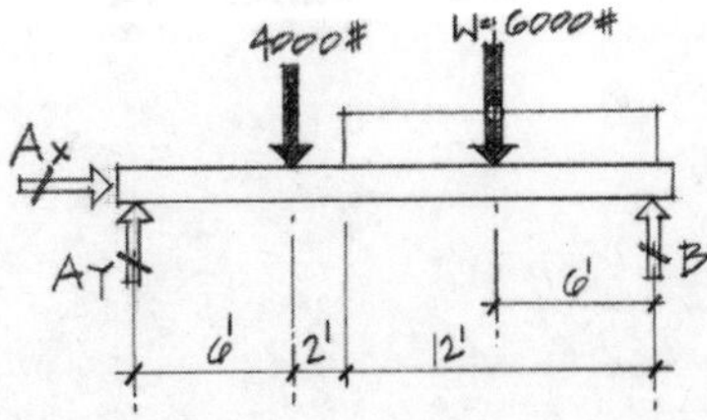

b. The equivalent concentrated force must be placed at the centroid of the load area. Because the load area is rectangular in this case, the centroid is located at half of the distance of the distribution.

c. Three equations of equilibrium can now be written, and the support reactions A_x, A_y, and B_y can be determined.

$$\left[\Sigma F_x = 0\right] A_x = 0$$

$$\left[\Sigma M_A = 0\right] - 4{,}000\#(6') - 6{,}000\#(14') + B_y(20') = 0$$
$$B_y = +5{,}400\#$$

$$\left[\Sigma F_y = 0\right] + A_y - 4{,}000\# - 6{,}000\# + B_y = 0$$
$$A_y = +4{,}600\#$$

6 Solve for the support reactions at A and B.

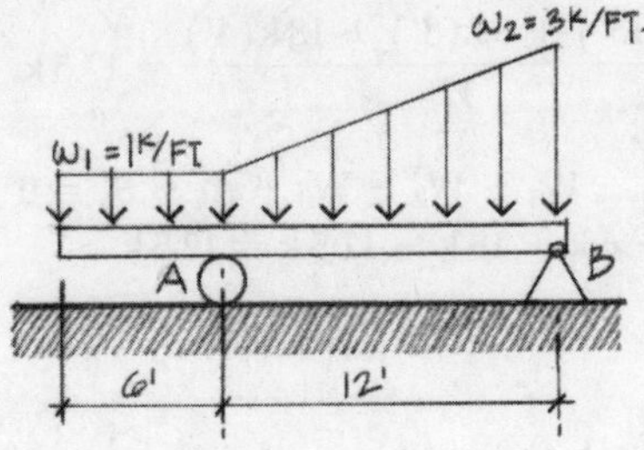

Solution:

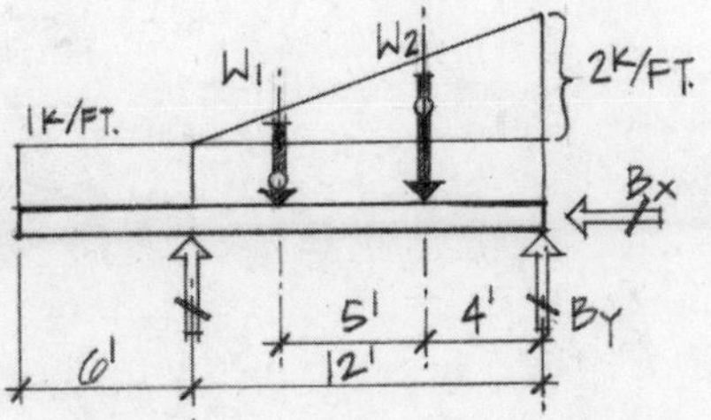

A trapezoidal distribution may be handled as a rectangle plus a triangle, or as two triangles. This problem will be solved in two ways to illustrate this concept.

Alternate 1:

$$W_1 = 1\,\text{k/ft.}(18') = 18\,\text{k}$$
$$W_2 = 1/2(12')(2\,\text{k/ft.}) = 12\,\text{k}$$

$$[\Sigma F_x = 0]B_x = 0$$

$$[\Sigma M_B = 0] + W_2(4') + W_1(9') - A_y(12') = 0$$

$$A_y = \frac{12\,\text{k}(4') + 18\,\text{k}(9')}{12'}$$

$$A_y = +17.5\,\text{k}$$

$$[\Sigma F_y = 0] + A_y - 18\,\text{k} - 12\,\text{k} + B_y = 0$$
$$B_y = +18\,\text{k} + 12\,\text{k} - 17.5\,\text{k} = 12.5\,\text{k}$$

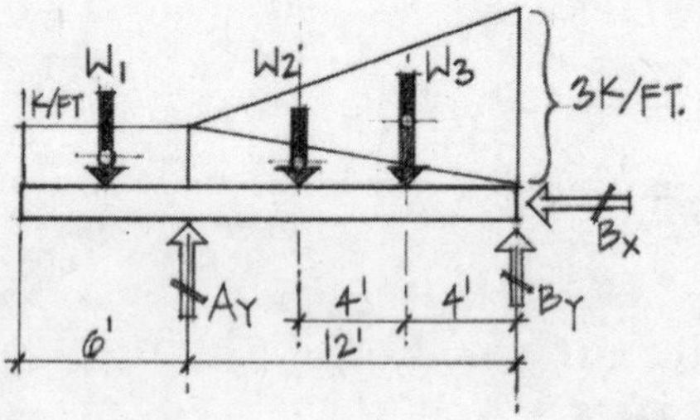

Alternate 2:

$$W_1 = 6'(1\,\text{k/ft.}) = 6\,\text{k}$$
$$W_2 = 1/2(12')(1\,\text{k/ft.}) = 6\,\text{k}$$
$$W_3 = 1/2(12')(3\,\text{k/ft.}) = 18\,\text{k}$$

$$[\Sigma F_x = 0]B_x = 0$$

$$[\Sigma M_B = 0] + W_1(15') + W_2(8') + W_3(4') - A_y(12') = 0$$

$$A_y = \frac{6\,\text{k}(15') + 6\,\text{k}(8') + 18\,\text{k}(4')}{12'} = 17.5\,\text{k}$$

$$[\Sigma F_y = 0] - W_1 - W_2 - W_3 + A_y + B_y = 0$$
$$B_y = 6\,\text{k} + 6\,\text{k} + 18\,\text{k} - 17.5\,\text{k} = 12.5\,\text{k}$$

Problems

For the problems below, draw FBDs, and determine the support reactions.

5 The beam supports a roof that weighs 300 pounds per foot and supports a concentrated load of 1,200 pounds at the overhanging end. Determine the support reactions at *A* and *B*.

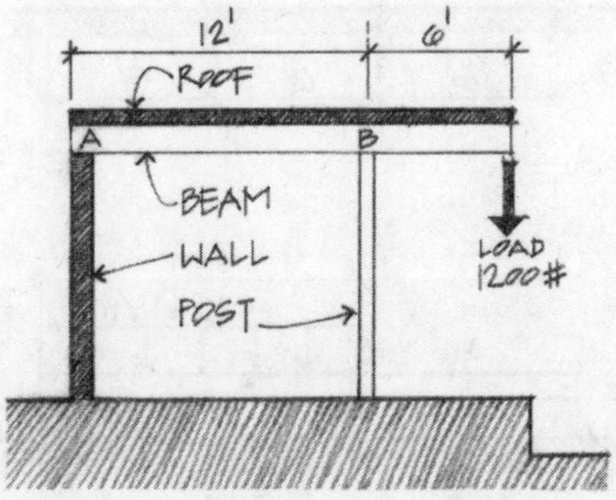

6 The carpenter on the scaffold weighs 800 N. The plank *AB* weighs 145 N/m. Determine the reactions at *A* and *B*.

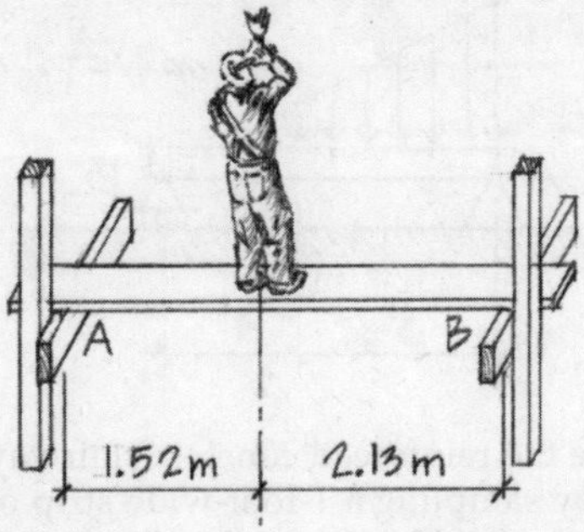

7 A timber beam is used to support two concentrated loads and a distributed load over its cantilevered end. Solve for the post reactions at *A* and *B*.

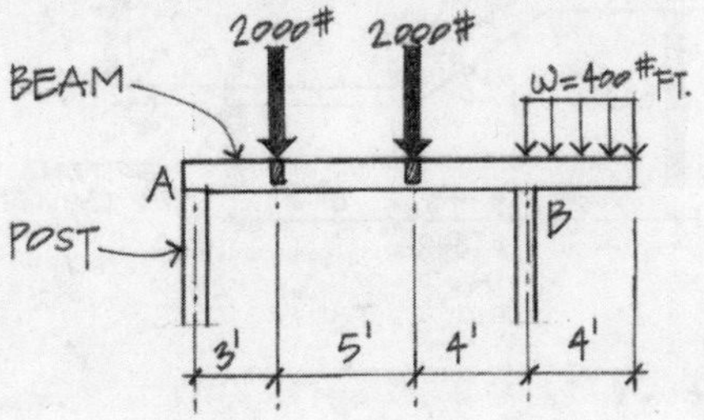

For Problems 8 through 10, solve for the support reactions at *A* and *B*.

8

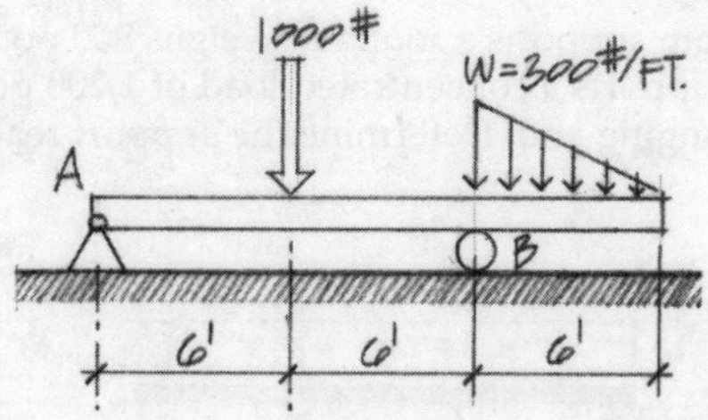

9

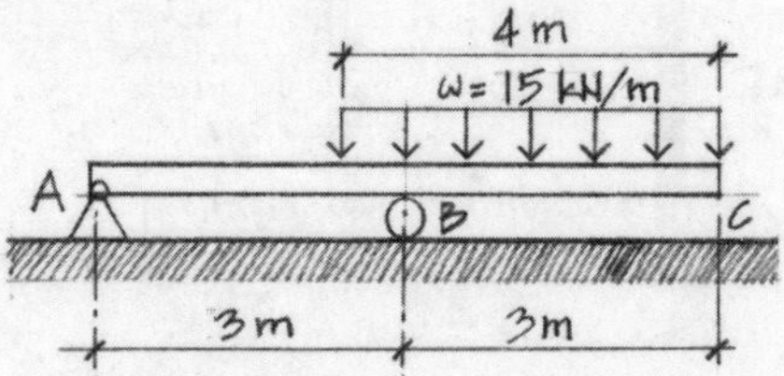

10

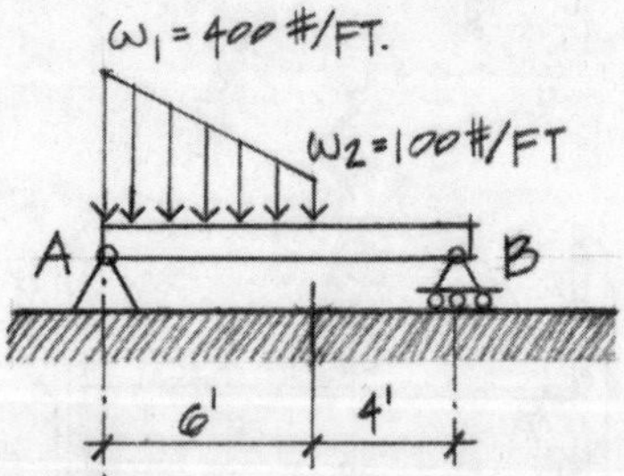

11 Analyze the reinforced concrete stairway and landing shown by sampling a 1-foot-wide strip of the structure. Concrete (dead load) weighs 150 pounds per cubic foot, and the live load (occupancy) is equal to about 100 psf.

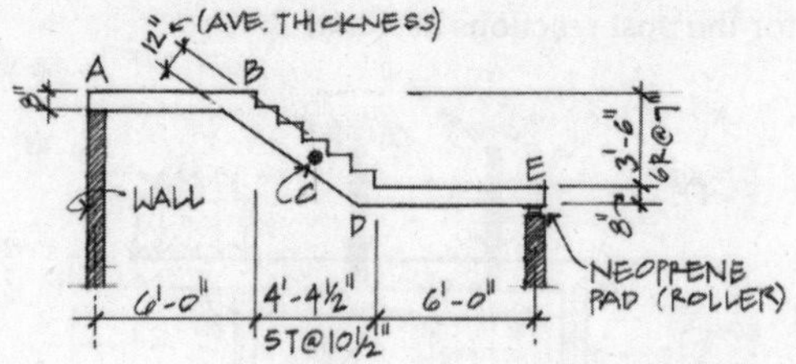

3 PLANE TRUSSES

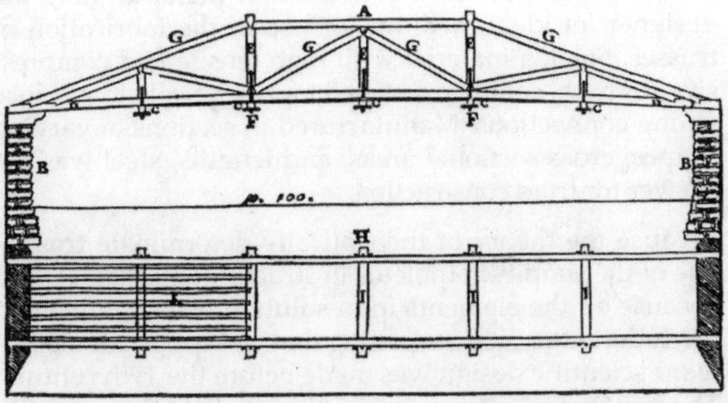

Figure 29 Illustration of a truss bridge by Palladio (bottom of Plate IV, Book III, The Four Books of Architecture*).*

Development of the Truss

The history of the development of the truss is a legacy of fits and starts. The earliest evidence of truss technology appears in Roman structures. This early evidence of the existence of the truss is seen in Vitruvius's writings on Roman buildings. In these writings, Vitruvius clearly points out the presence of modern truss technology and leaves us with little doubt that the Roman builders understood the ideas embodied in the distribution of forces as carried by a triangular arrangement of members.

This concept of triangular bracing in truss frameworks before the Roman example is still a topic of debate for architectural historians, largely because no physical evidence of earlier trussed wooden roof structures appears to have survived. Historical research into Asian building traditions has also been unable to confirm any earlier evidence of truss technology.

After a period of disuse, Palladio, during the Renaissance, revived the use of truss frameworks and built several timber bridges exceeding 100 feet in span (Figure 29). Since Palladio, records indicate a continued tradition of truss construction for bridges and many other types of structures.

The first trusses used wood as their main structural material. However, with the advent of large-scale iron smelting and the increased span requirements of ever-larger bridges, the inclusion of other materials was inevitable. Iron and then steel emerged as the dominant truss materials and greatly contributed to the popularity of the technology by allowing greater and greater spanning possibilities.

Figure 30 The Firth of Forth Bridge in Scotland, by Benjamin Baker, represents an innovative understanding of truss behavior. Photographer unknown.

To this day, buildings and highways are dotted with trusses fabricated from structural steel. The introduction of structural steel as a construction material gave the designer an ideal medium for use in the fabrication of trusses. Steel, a material with high tensile and compressive strength, could be fastened together easily to produce strong connections. Manufactured in sections of varying shapes, cross-sectional areas, and lengths, steel was the answer for truss construction.

Because the theory of the statically determinate truss is one of the simplest problems in structural mechanics, and because all the elements for a solution were available in the 16th century, it is surprising that no serious attempt toward scientific design was made before the 19th century. The impetus was provided by the needs of the railways, whose construction commenced in 1821. The entire problem of analysis and design was solved between 1830 and 1860 (Figure 30). Since that time, truss construction has been applied to other structures, such as long-span roofs, in addition to bridges (Figure 31).

Figure 31 Trussed arches (haunches) used in the construction of the blimp hangars during World War II. NAS Tillamook, Oregon (1942). Photograph courtesy of Tillamook County Pioneer Museum.

Definition of a Truss

A *truss* represents a structural system that distributes loads to supports through a linear arrangement of various-sized members in patterns of planar triangles. The triangular subdivision of the planar system, Figure 32(b), produces geometric units that are nondeformable (stable).

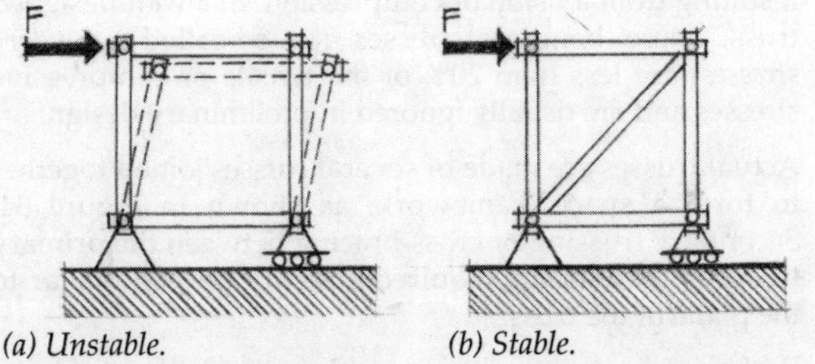

(a) *Unstable.* (b) *Stable.*

Figure 32 A frame and a truss.

An *ideal* pin-connected truss is defined as a stable framework consisting of elements connected only at their ends; thus, no member is continuous through a joint. No element is restrained from rotation about any axis perpendicular to the plane of the framework and passing through the ends of the elements.

The early trusses were joined at their ends by pins, resulting—except for some friction—in an ideal truss. Hence, under loads applied only at the joints, the members assume either tensile (elongation) or compressive (shortening) forces. In reality, however, it is impractical to join truss members by pins. The current method of joining members is by bolting, welding, or a combination of the two (Figure 33).

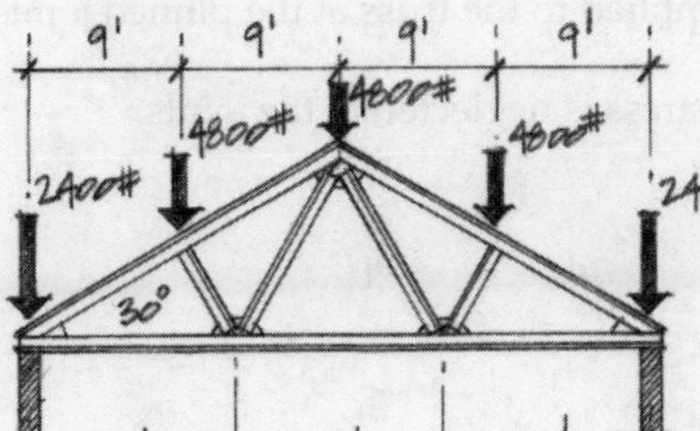

Figure 33(a) Actual truss.

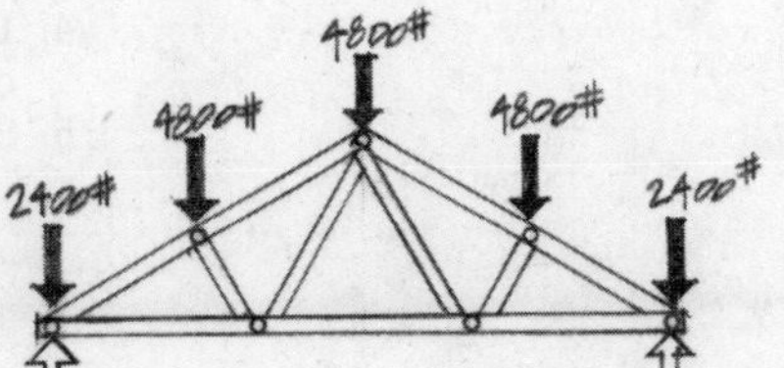

Figure 33(b) Idealized truss with pin joints.

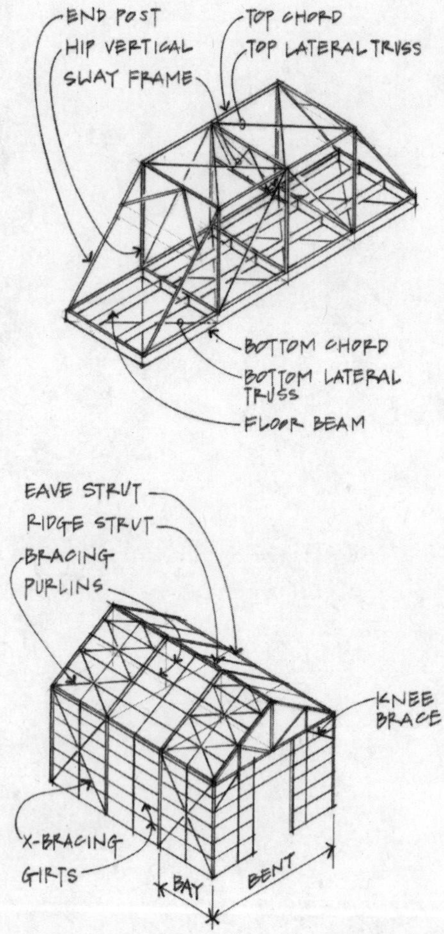

Figure 34 Typical use of trusses in bridges and buildings.

Because a single bolt or a spot weld is usually not sufficient to carry the load in a truss member, groups of such fasteners are needed. Whenever more than one individual fastener is used at a joint, the joint becomes a somewhat rigid connection, with the ability to develop some moment resistance. Hence, the members of a real truss, besides elongating or shortening, also tend to bend. Bending stresses, however, are often small in comparison to those resulting from tension or compression. In a well-designed truss, these bending stresses (or so-called *secondary stresses*) are less than 20% of the tensile or compressive stresses and are usually ignored in preliminary design.

Actual trusses are made of several trusses joined together to form a space framework, as shown in Figure 34. Secondary trussing or cross-bracing between the primary trusses provides the required stability perpendicular to the plane of the truss.

Each truss is designed to carry those loads that act in its plane and, thus, may be treated as a two-dimensional structure. In general, the members of a truss are slender and can support little bending due to lateral loads. All loads, therefore, should be applied to the various joints and not directly on the members themselves.

The weights of the members of the truss are also assumed to be applied to the joints; half of the weight of each member is applied to each of the two joints the member connects. In most preliminary truss analyses, member weights are neglected, because they are small in comparison to the applied loads.

In summary, a preliminary truss analysis assumes the following:

1. Members are linear.
2. Members are pin-connected at the ends (joints).
3. The weight of truss members is usually neglected.
4. Loads are applied to the truss at the pinned joints only.
5. Secondary stress is neglected at the joints.

Thus, each member of the truss may be treated as a two-force member, and the entire truss may be considered as a group of two-force members joined by pins. Two-force members are assumed to have their loads applied only at the end pin or hinge; the resultant force in the member *must* be along the axis of the member. An individual member may be subjected to either tensile or compressive forces.

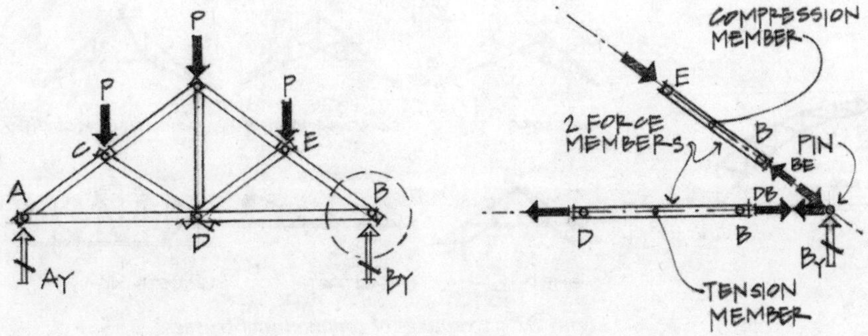

(a) FBD of the truss. *(b) FBD of joint* B.

Figure 35 FBDs of a truss and a joint.

When isolated as an FBD, a two-force member is in equilibrium under the action of two forces—one at each end. These end forces, therefore, must be equal, opposite, and collinear, as shown in Figure 35(b). Their common line of action must pass through the centers of the two pins and be coincident with the axis of the member. When a two-force member is cut, the force within it is known to act along its axis.

Figure 36 gives examples of bridge trusses. Common roof trusses are shown in Figure 37.

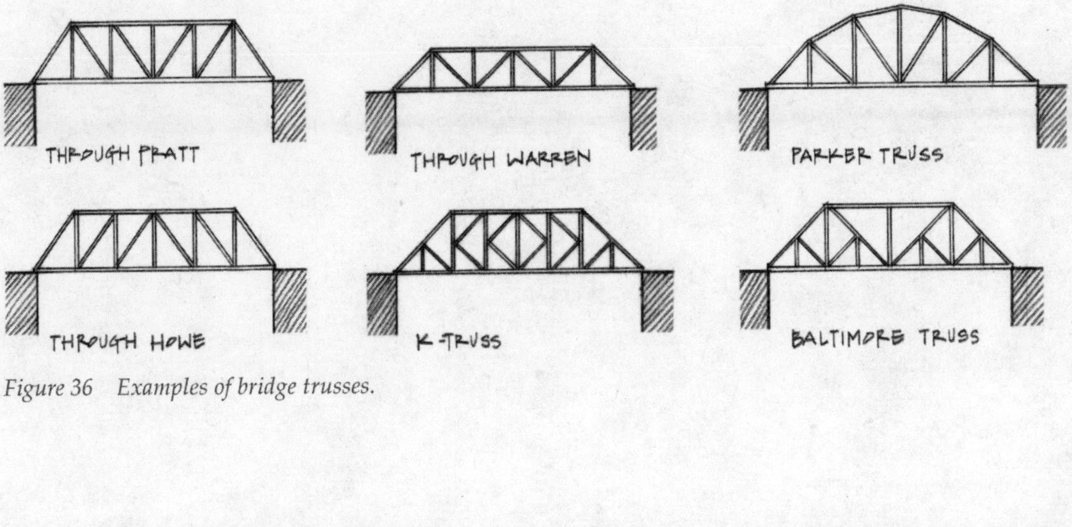

Figure 36 Examples of bridge trusses.

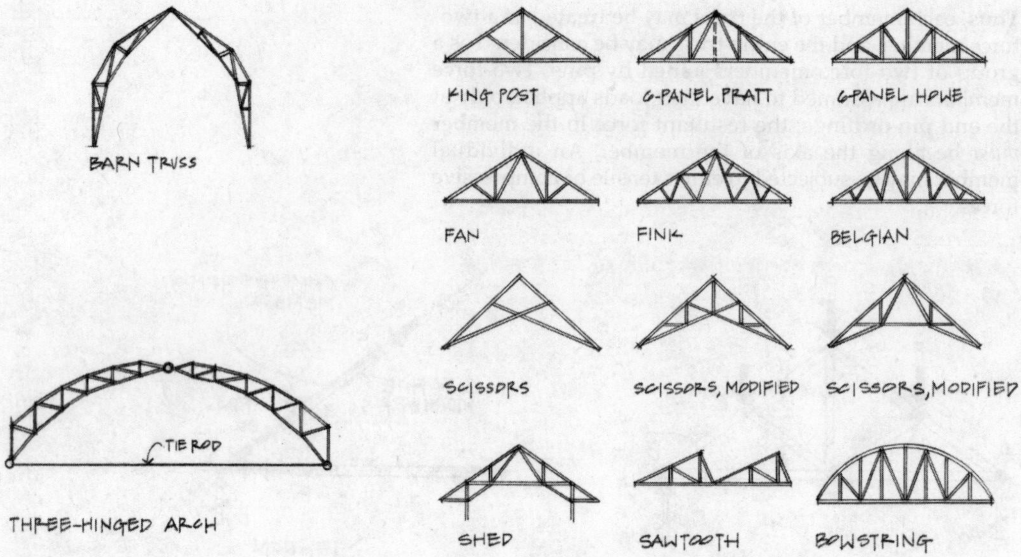

Figure 37 Examples of common roof trusses.

Stability and Determinacy of Trusses

An initial first step in the analysis of a truss is the calculation of its external determinacy or indeterminacy. If there are more reaction components than applicable equations of equilibrium, the truss is statically indeterminate with regard to reactions—or, as usually stated, the truss is *statically indeterminate* externally. If there are fewer possible reaction components than applicable equations of equilibrium, the structure is unstable and undergoes excessive displacement under certain load applications. (Figure 38).

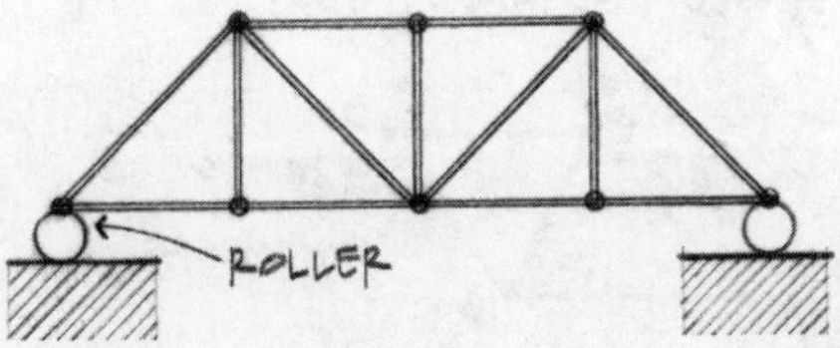

(a) Unstable (horizontally).

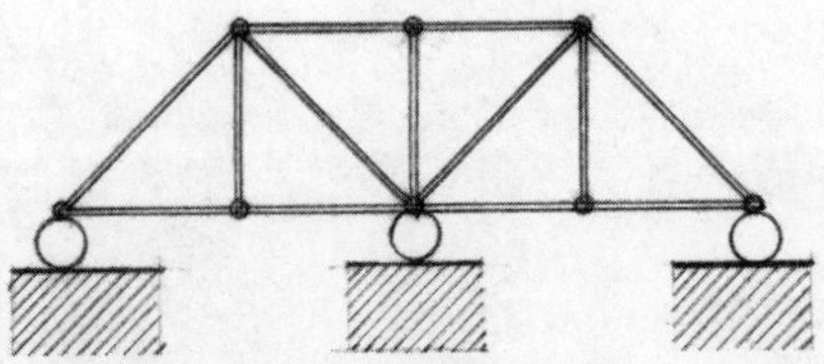

(b) Unstable (horizontally).

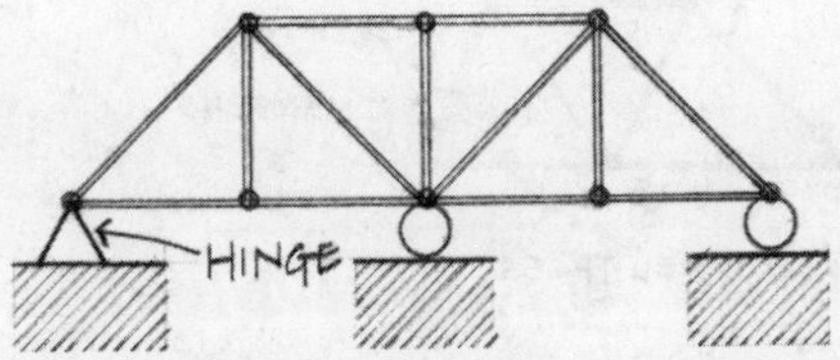

(c) Indeterminate (vertically).

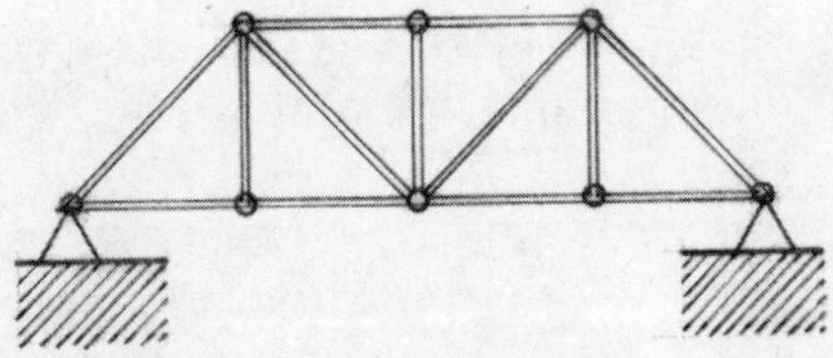

(d) Indeterminate (horizontally).

Figure 38 *Examples of external instability and indeterminacy.*

A truss can also be determinate, indeterminate, or unstable internally with respect to the system of bar arrangement. A truss can be statically determinate internally and statically indeterminate externally, and the reverse of this can also be true.

For the bars to form a stable configuration that can resist loads applied at the joints, the bars must form triangular figures.

The simplest stable, statically determinate truss consists of three joints and three members, as shown in Figure 39(a). A larger truss can be created by adding to the simple truss. This requires the addition of one joint and two members, as shown in Figure 39(b).

If the process of assembling larger and larger trusses continues, as shown in Figure 39(c), a definite relationship between the number of joints and the number of members is observed. Every time two new members are added, the number of joints is increased by one.

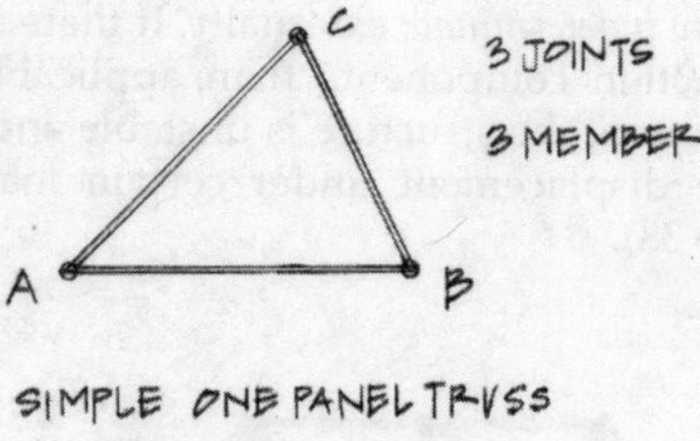

(a)

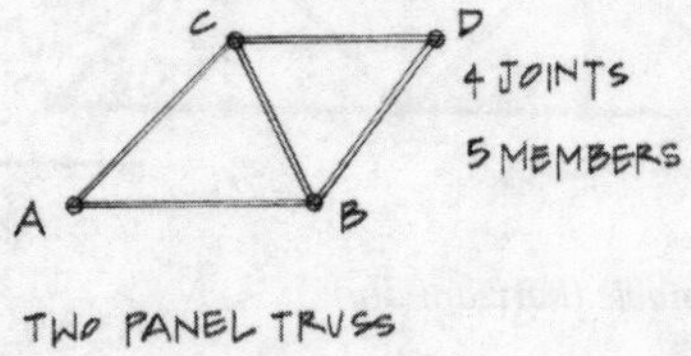

(b)

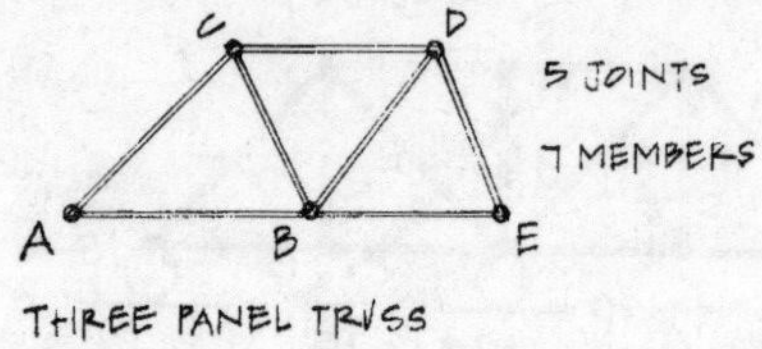

(c)

Figure 39 Truss development.

The number of bars as a function of the number of joints for any trussed structure consisting of an assemblage of bars forming triangles can be expressed as

$$b = 2n - 3$$

where b equals the number of members (bars) and n equals the number of joints.

This equation is useful in determining the internal determinacy and stability of a truss; however, it is not sufficient by itself. Visual inspection and an intuitive sense must also be utilized in assessing the stability of the truss.

Figure 40 shows examples of internal stability, instability, and determinacy. Note that the truss shown in Figure 40(d) is unstable. Here, the equation alone is insufficient in establishing stability. The square panel in the center makes this truss unstable.

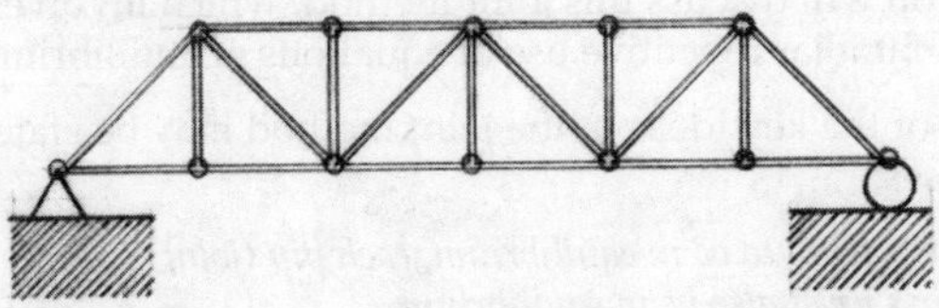

b = 21   n = 12 2(n) – 3 = 2(12) – 3 = 21

(a) Determinate.

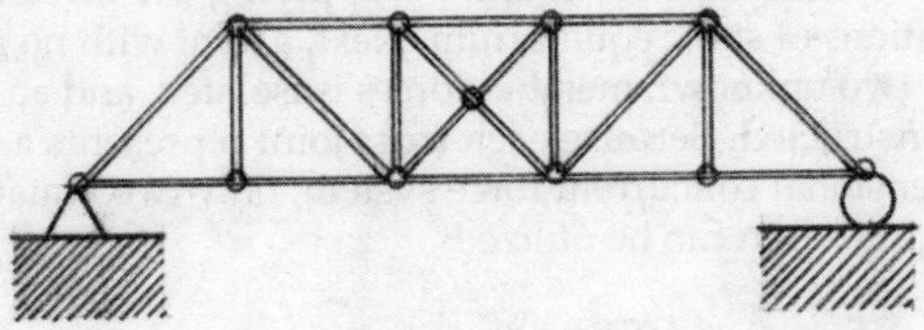

b = 18   n = 10 b = 18 > 2(10) – 3 = 17
(Too many members)

(b) Indeterminate.

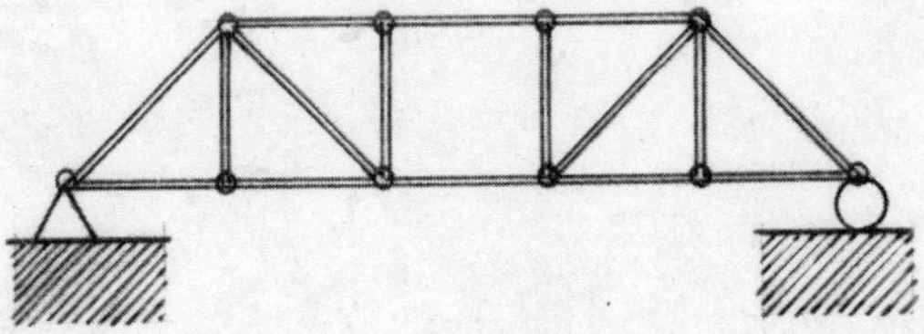

b = 16   n = 10 b = 16 < 2(10) – 3 = 17
(Too few members—square panel is unstable)

(c) Unstable.

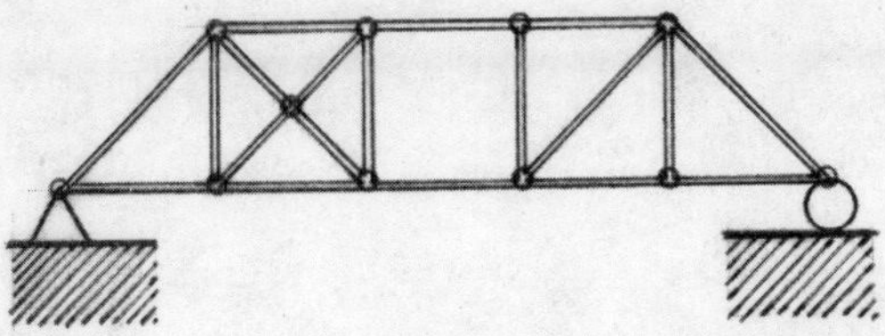

b = 17   n = 10 b = 17 = 2(10) – 3 = 17

(d) Unstable.

Figure 40 Examples of internal stability and determinacy.

Force Analysis by the Method of Joints

The first historical record of a truss analysis was done in 1847 by Squire Whipple, an American bridge builder. In 1850, D. J. Jourawski, a Russian railway engineer, developed the method referred to as the *resolution of joints*. This section will discuss this joint method, which involves the now-familiar repetitive use of equations of equilibrium.

One of the key ideas in the joint method may be stated as follows:

> *For a truss to be in equilibrium, each pin (joint) of the truss must also be in equilibrium.*

The first step in the determination of the member forces in a truss is to determine all the external forces acting on the structure. After the applied forces are determined, the support reactions are found by applying the three basic equations of static equilibrium. Next, a joint with no more than two unknown member forces is isolated, and an FBD is constructed. Because each truss joint represents a two-dimensional concurrent force system, only two equations of equilibrium can be utilized:

$$\Sigma F_x = 0 \text{ and } \Sigma F_y = 0$$

These two equilibrium equations permit only two unknowns to be solved. Progression then goes from joint to joint, always selecting the next joint that has no more than two unknown bar forces.

Example Problems: Force Analysis by the Method of Joints

7 Solve for the support reactions at A and C, and then determine all member forces (Figure 41).

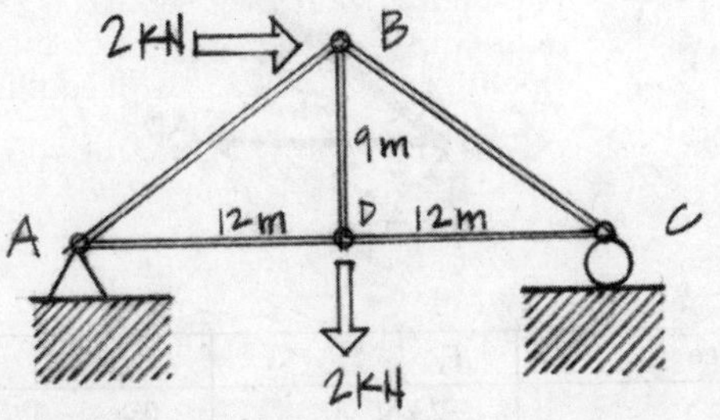

Figure 41 Method of joints.

Solution:

Step 1: *Construct the FBD of the entire truss.*

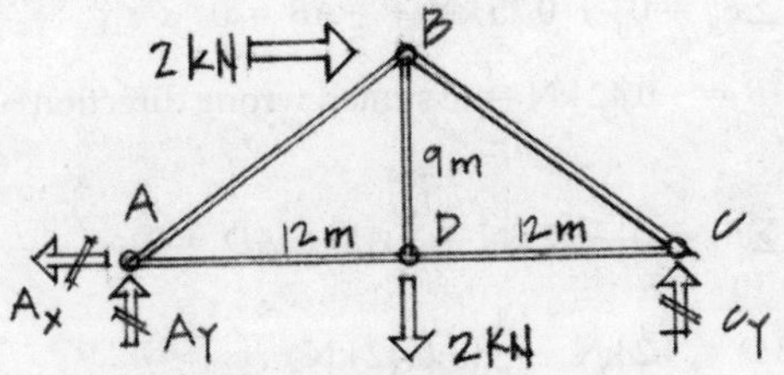

Step 2: *Solve for external support reactions.*

$[\Sigma F_x = 0]\ -A_x + 2\,\text{kN} = 0$
$A_x = 2\,\text{kN}$

$[\Sigma M_A = 0]\ -2\,\text{kN}(9\,\text{m}) - 2\,\text{kN}(12\,\text{m})$
$+ C_y(24\,\text{m}) = 0$
$C_y = +1.75\,\text{kN}$

$[\Sigma F_y = 0]\ +A_y - 2\,\text{kN} + C_y = 0$
$A_y = 0.25\,\text{kN}$

Step 3: *Isolate a joint with no more than two unknown member forces.*

AD and AB are assumed as tension forces. The equations of equilibrium will verify the assumed directions.

Step 4: *Write and solve the equations of equilibrium.*

Assume both members are in tension.

Joint A

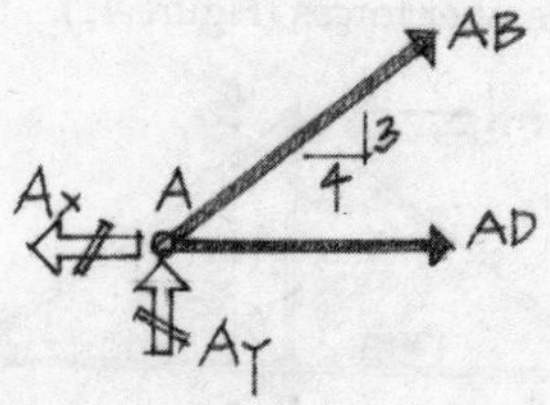

Force	F_x	F_y
A_x	–2 kN	0
A_y	0	+.25 kN
AB	$+\frac{4}{5}AB$	$+\frac{3}{5}AB$
AD	$+AD$	0

$$\left[\Sigma F_y = 0\right] + 0.25\text{ kN} + \frac{3}{5}AB = 0$$

$$AB = -0.42\text{ kN} \Leftarrow \text{assumed wrong direction}$$

$$\left[\Sigma F_x = 0\right] - 2\text{ kN} + \frac{4}{5}AB + AD = 0$$

$$AD = +2\text{ kN} - \frac{4}{5}(-0.42\text{ kN})$$

$$AD = +2\text{ kN} + 0.33\text{ kN} = +2.33\text{ kN}$$

Note: *The FBD of joint A represents the forces applied to the theoretical pin at joint A. These forces are acting equal and opposite on the corresponding members, as shown in Figure 42.*

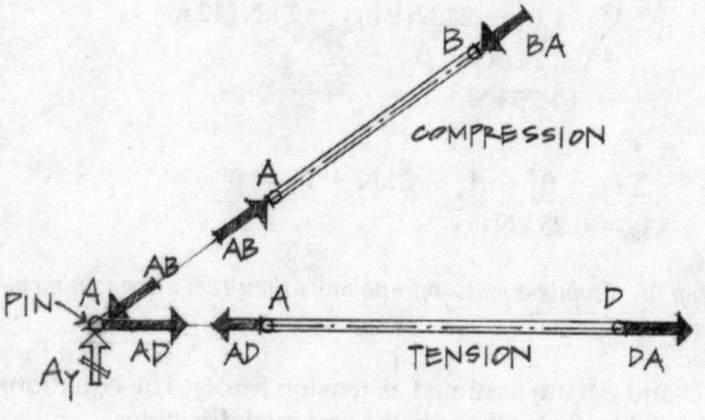

Figure 42 FBD of members and pin.

Forces directed away from a pin (joint) are tension forces on the pin; conversely, forces pushing toward a pin are compression forces. These pin forces should be shown in the opposite direction on the members. An assumption must be made about the direction of each member force on the joint. Intuition about the way the force is applied is perfectly acceptable, because the equations of equilibrium will verify the initial assumption in the end. A positive result for the equation indicates a correct assumption; conversely, a negative answer means that the initial assumption should be reversed. Many engineers prefer to assume in all cases that the forces from all unknown members are in tension. The resultant sign from the solution of the equations of equilibrium will conform to the usual sign convention for trusses—that is, plus (+) for tension and minus (−) for compression.

Step 5: *Proceed to another joint with no more than two unknown forces.*

Joint D

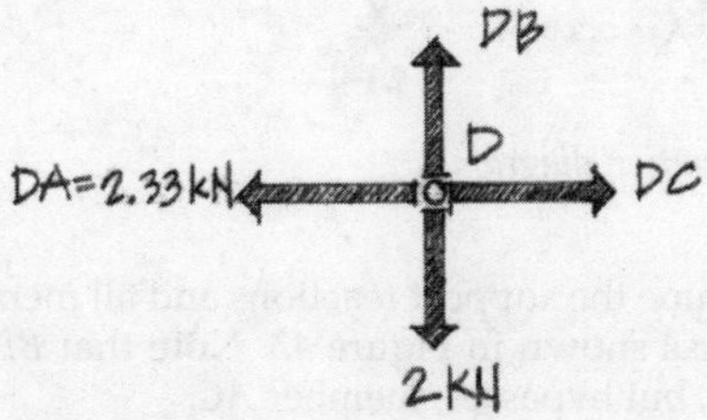

$$\left[\Sigma F_x = 0\right] - 2.33\text{ kN} + DC = 0$$
$$DC = +2.33\text{ kN}$$

$$\left[\Sigma F_y = 0\right] + DB - 2\text{ kN} = 0$$
$$DB = +2\text{ kN}$$

Joint B

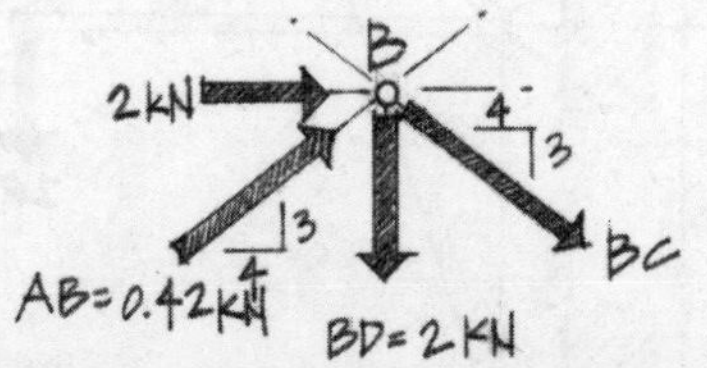

Known forces should be shown in the correct direction.

Force	F_x	F_y
2 kN	+2 kN	0
BD	0	−2 kN
AB	$+\frac{4}{5}(.42\text{ kN}) = +.33\text{ kN}$	$+\frac{3}{5}(0.42\text{ kN}) = +.25\text{ kN}$
BC	$+\frac{4}{5}BC$	$-\frac{3}{5}BC$

$$\left[\Sigma F_x = 0\right] + 2\text{ kN} + 0.33\text{ kN} + \frac{4}{5}BC = 0$$

$$BC = -2.92\text{ kN} \Leftarrow \text{wrong direction assumed}$$

$$\left[\Sigma F_y = 0\right] - 2\text{ kN} + 0.25\text{ kN} - \frac{3}{5}(-2.92\text{ kN}) = 0$$

$$-2\text{ kN} + .25\text{ kN} + 1.75\text{ kN} = 0 \Leftarrow \text{CHECKS}$$

A summary diagram, called a *force summation diagram*, should be drawn as a last step.

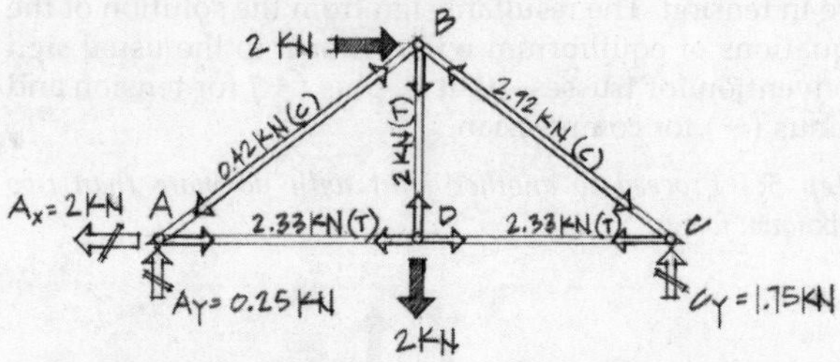

Force summation diagram.

8 Determine the support reactions and all member forces for the truss shown in Figure 43. Note that *BD* does not connect to, but bypasses, member *AC*.

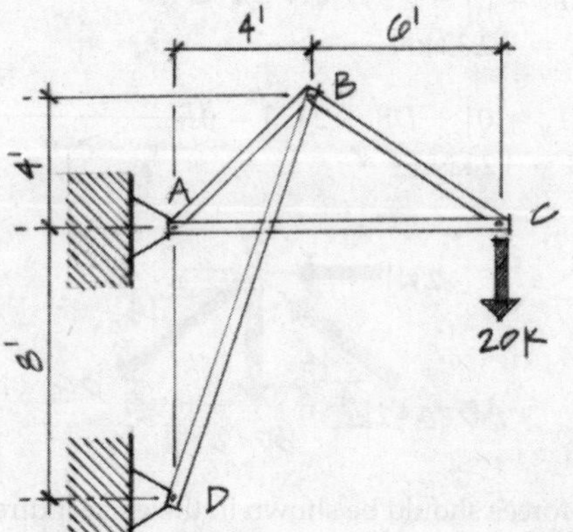

Figure 43 Truss.

Note: *A hinge at both* A *and* D *enables the wall to function as a force member* AD*, thus making this a stable configuration. If a roller were used at* D*, the framework would be unstable, resulting in collapse.*

Solution:

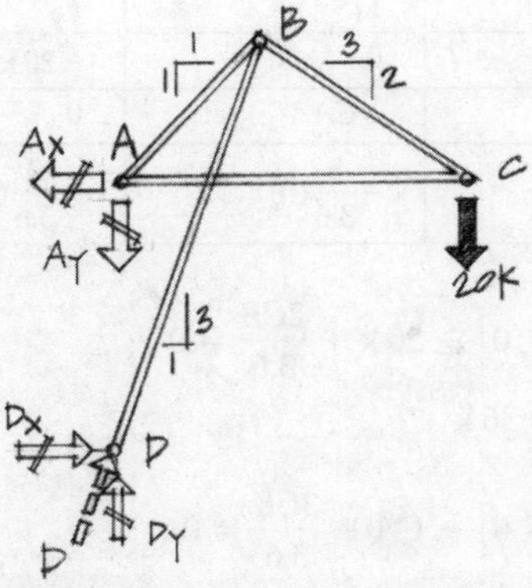

FBD of entire truss.

All truss members are assumed to be two-force members when loads are applied at the joints only. Member forces are therefore assumed to pass through the axis of the member.

Because only member BD is attached to the hinge support at D, we can assume that support reactions D_x and D_y must be related by virtue of the slope of BD, where

$$D_x = \frac{D}{\sqrt{10}} \text{ and } D_y = \frac{3D}{\sqrt{10}}$$

Support reactions A_x and A_y, however, have no distinguishable slope relationship, because A_x and A_y must serve as a support for two members, AB and AC. When only one two-force member frames into a support, we can establish a slope relationship with respect to the member.

Therefore,

$$[\Sigma M_A = 0] - 20(10') + D_x(8') = 0$$
$$D_x = +25\text{ k}$$
$$D = D_x\sqrt{10} = +25\text{ k}(\sqrt{10}), \text{and}$$
$$D_y = \frac{3D}{\sqrt{10}} = \frac{3(25\sqrt{10})}{\sqrt{10}} = +75\text{ k}$$
$$[\Sigma F_x = 0] - A_x + D_x = 0$$
$$A_x = +25\text{ k}$$
$$[\Sigma F_y = 0] - A_y + D_y - 20\text{ k} = 0$$
$$A_y = +75\text{ k} - 20\text{ k} = +55\text{ k}$$

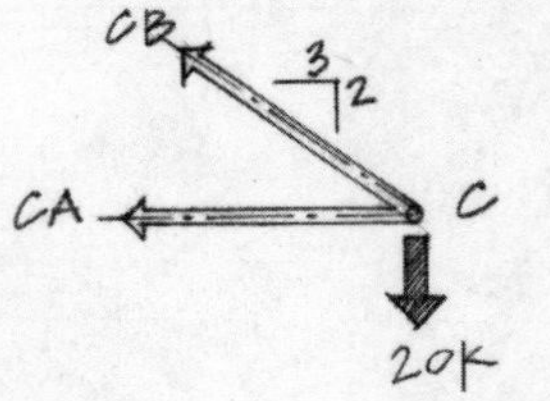

Isolate Joint C

Force	F_x	F_y
20 k	0	−20 k
CA	$-CA$	0
CB	$-\frac{3}{3.6}CB$	$+\frac{2}{3.6}CB$

$$\left[\Sigma F_y = 0\right] - 20\,\text{k} + \frac{2CB}{3.6} = 0$$

$$CB = +36\,\text{k}$$

$$\left[\Sigma F_x = 0\right] - CA - \frac{3CB}{3.6} = 0$$

$$CA = -\frac{3(+36\,\text{k})}{3.6} = -30\,\text{k}$$

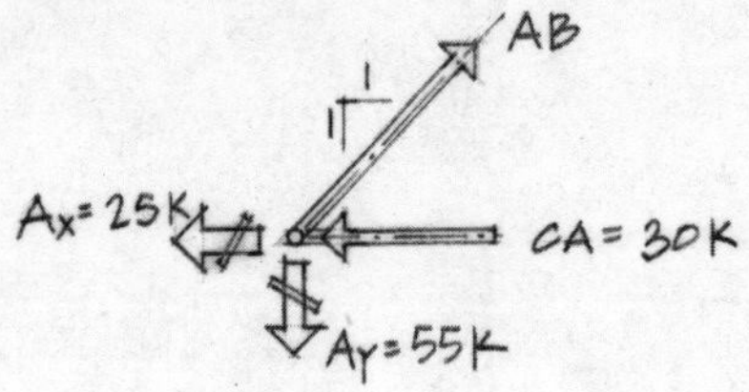

Joint A

Force	F_x	F_y
A_x	−25 k	0
A_y	0	−55 k
CA	−30 k	0
AB	$+\frac{AB}{\sqrt{2}}$	$+\frac{AB}{\sqrt{2}}$

Only one equation of equilibrium is necessary to determine force AB, but the second equation may be written as a check.

$$\left[\Sigma F_y = 0\right] - 55\,\text{k} + \frac{AB}{\sqrt{2}} = 0$$

$$AB = +\left(55\sqrt{2}\right)\text{k}$$

$$\left[\Sigma F_x = 0\right] - 25\,\text{k} - 30\,\text{k} + \frac{\left(55\sqrt{2}\right)\text{k}}{\sqrt{2}} = 0$$

$$0 = 0 \Leftarrow \text{CHECK}$$

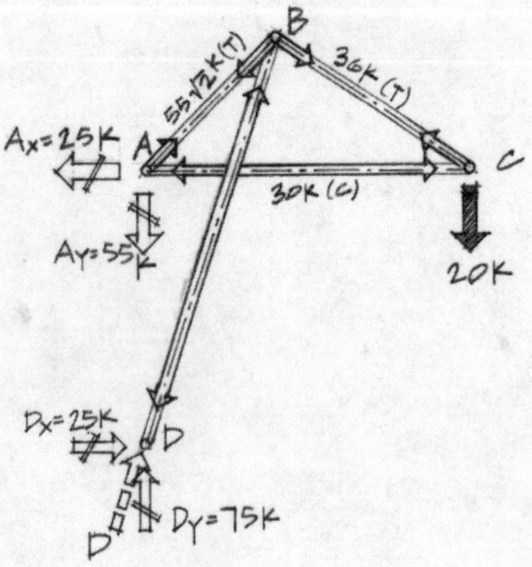

Force summation diagram.

9 This example will illustrate a "shortcut" version of the method of joints. The principle of equilibrium is still adhered to; however, separate FBDs will not be drawn for each successive joint. Instead, the original FBD drawn for the determination of support equations will be used exclusively. The steps outlined in the earlier examples are still valid and, thus, will be employed in this "quick" method (Figure 44).

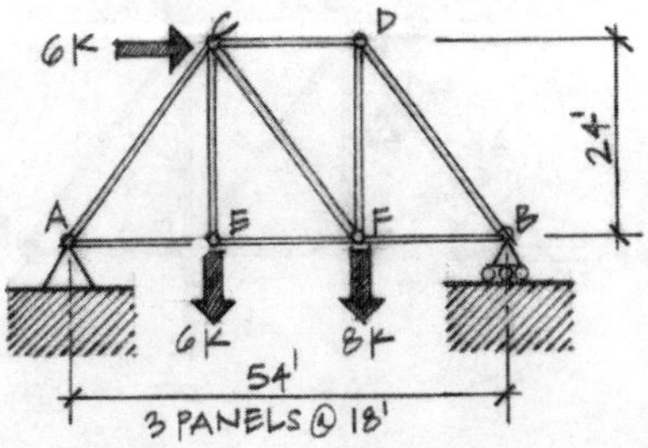

Figure 44 Quick method of joints.

Step 1: *Draw an FBD of the entire truss.*

Step 2: *Solve for the support reactions at A and B.*

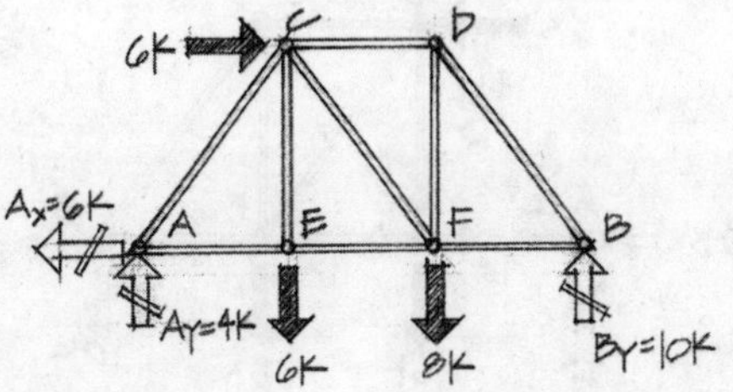

FBD (a)

Step 3: *Isolate a joint with no more than two unknowns.*

In this method, it is unnecessary to draw an FBD of the joint. Instead, use the FBD from steps 1 and 2, and record your solutions directly on the truss. It is usually easier to find the horizontal and vertical components in all the members first and then determine the actual resultant member forces at the very end.

It is common in truss analysis to use slope relationships instead of angle measurements. In this illustration, diagonal members have vertical: horizontal slopes of 4:3 (3:4:5 triangle). Because all truss members are assumed to be two-force members, the vertical and horizontal force components are related by the slope relationship 4:3.

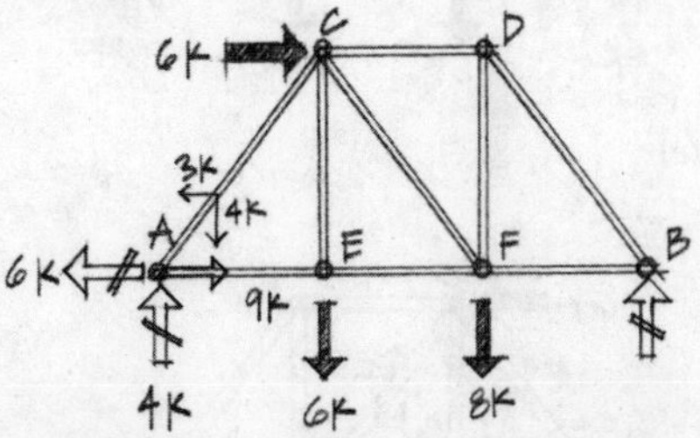

FBD (b)

Step 4: *Equations of equilibrium for the isolated joint will be done mentally, without writing them out. Occasionally, however, some complex geometries will require equations to be written out and solved simultaneously.*

Let's begin at joint *A* (joint *B* is also a possible starting point). Members *AC* (horizontal and vertical components) and *AE* (horizontal component only) are unknown. Because member *AC* has a vertical component, solve $\Sigma F_y = 0$. This results in a vertical component of 4 k (to balance $A_y = 4\text{ k}$). Therefore, with $AC_y = 4\text{ k}$, and because AC_x and AC_y are related by virtue of their slope relationship,

$$AC_x = \frac{3}{4} AC_y = 3\text{ k} \leftarrow$$

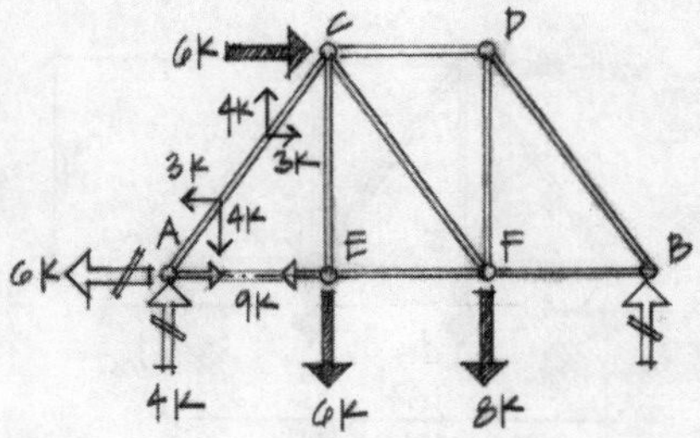

FBD (c)

Next, solve the horizontal equilibrium condition. Reaction $A_x = 6\,\text{k}$ is directed to the left; therefore, *AE* must be a force of 9 k going to the right. Joint *A* is now in equilibrium. Record the results (in component form) at the opposite end of each member.

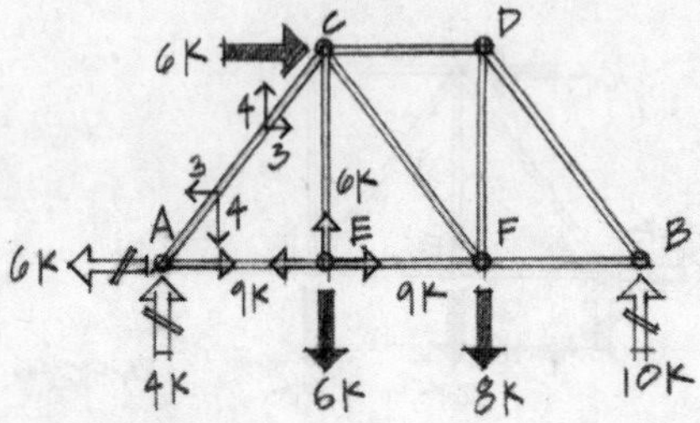

FBD (d)

Step 5: *Proceed to the next joint with no more than two unknowns. Let's solve joint* E.

The two unknowns *EF* (horizontal) and *EC* (vertical) are readily solved, because each represents a singular unknown *x* and *y*, respectively. In the horizontal direction, *EF* must resist with 9 k to the left. Member force *EC* = 6 k upward to counter the 6 k applied load.

Record member forces *EF* and *EC* at joints *F* and *C*, respectively.

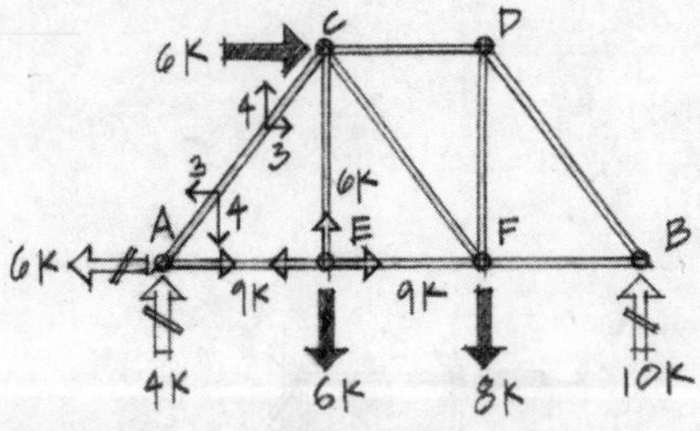

FBD (e)

Continue to another joint with no more than two unknowns. Try joint *C*. Members *CD* (horizontal) and *CF* (horizontal and vertical) are unknown. Solve the vertical condition of equilibrium first. $CA_y = 4\,\text{k}$ is upward and $CE = 6\,\text{k}$ is downward, leaving an unbalance of 2 k in the down direction. Therefore, CF_y must resist with a force of 2 k upward. Through the slope relationship,

$$CF_x = \frac{3}{4}CF_y = 1.5\,\text{k}$$

In the horizontal direction, *CD* must develop a resistance of 7.5 k to the left.

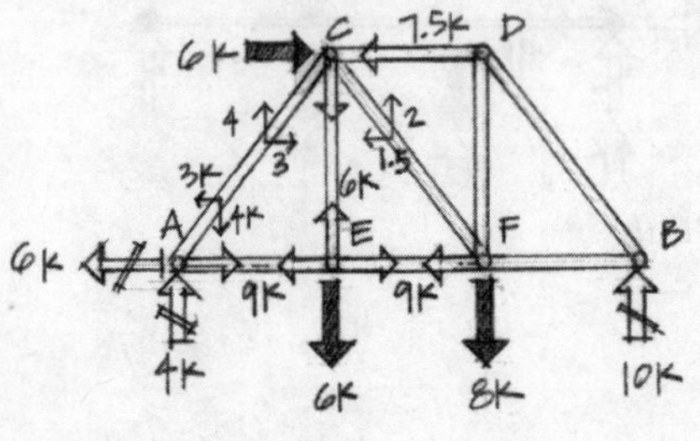

FBD (f)

Step 6: *Repeat Step 5 until all member forces are determined. The final results are shown in the force summation diagram. At this point, resultant member forces may be computed by using the known slope relationship for each member.*

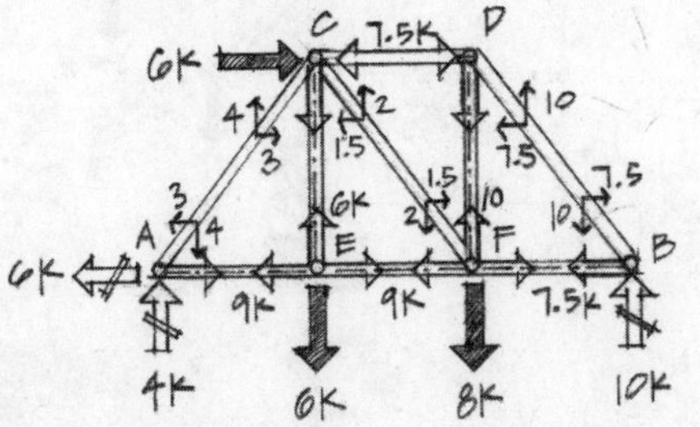

FBD (g)

Force summation diagram.

Problems

Using the method of joints, determine the force in each member of the truss shown. Summarize the results on a force summation diagram, and indicate whether each member is in tension or compression. You may want to try the "quick" method for Problems 14 through 17.

12

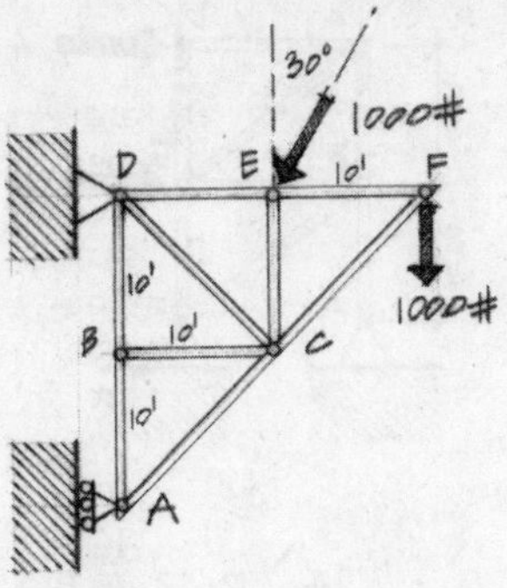

13

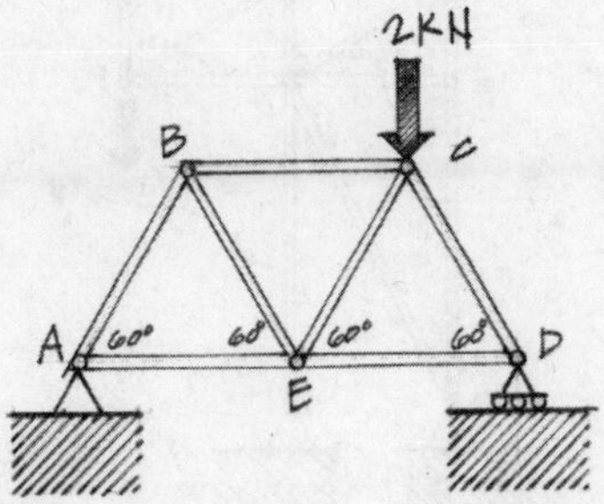

14

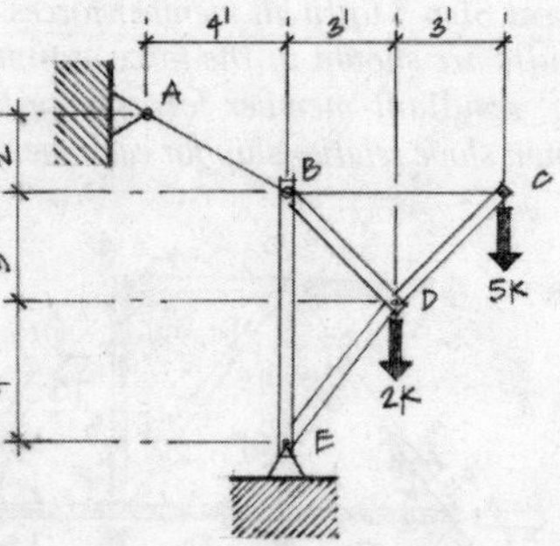
4'
3'
3'
A
2'
B
C
3'
5K
D
2K
4'
E

15

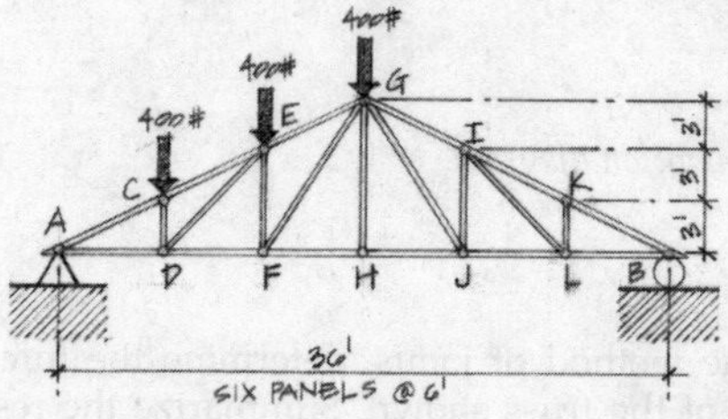
400#
400#
400#
G
E
C
I
K
3'
3'
3'
A
D
F
H
J
L
B
36'
SIX PANELS @ 6'

16

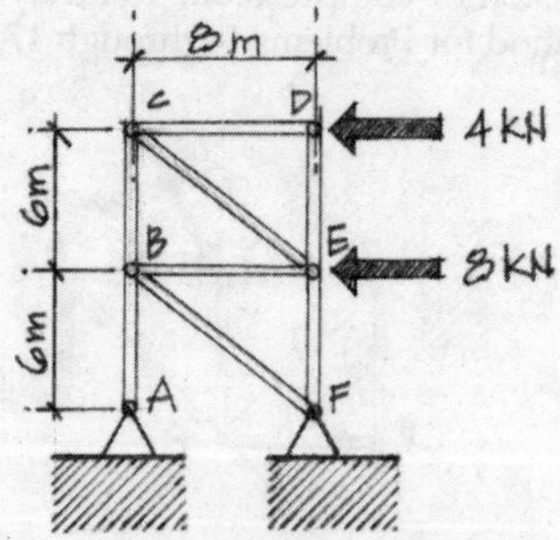
8m
C
D
4KN
6m
B
E
8KN
6m
A
F

17

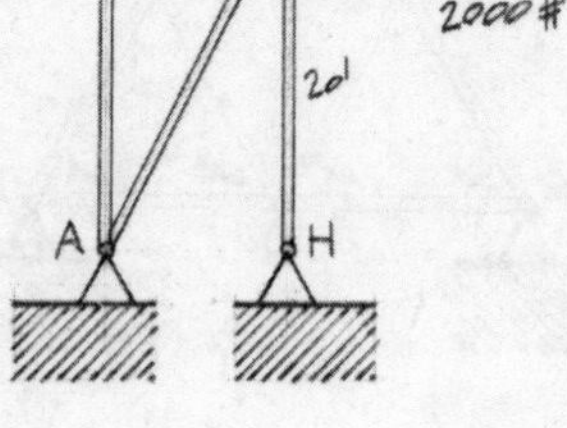
C
10'
D
10'
E
30°
30°
B
G
F
2000#
20'
A
H

Method of Sections

In 1862, the German engineer, August Ritter, devised another analytical approach to truss analysis, the *method of sections*. Ritter cut the truss along an imaginary line and replaced the internal forces with equivalent external forces. By making specific cuts and taking moments about convenient points on the truss section (cut) FBD, the magnitude and direction of the desired member forces were obtained.

The method of sections is particularly useful when the analysis requires the solution of forces in a few specific members. This method avoids the laborious task of a joint-by-joint analysis for the entire truss. In some instances, the geometry of the truss may necessitate use of the method of sections in conjunction with the method of joints.

Example problems will be used to illustrate the procedure for solving specific member forces by the method of sections.

Example Problems: Method of Sections

10 Solve for member forces *BC* and *BE*, as shown in Figure 45.

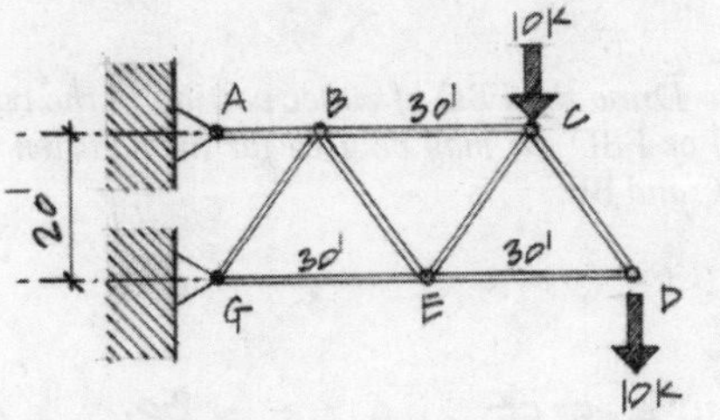

Figure 45 Space diagram of the truss.

Solution:

Step 1: *Draw an FBD of the entire truss. Solve for the support reactions. This may not be necessary in some cases, depending on which sectioned FBD is used.*

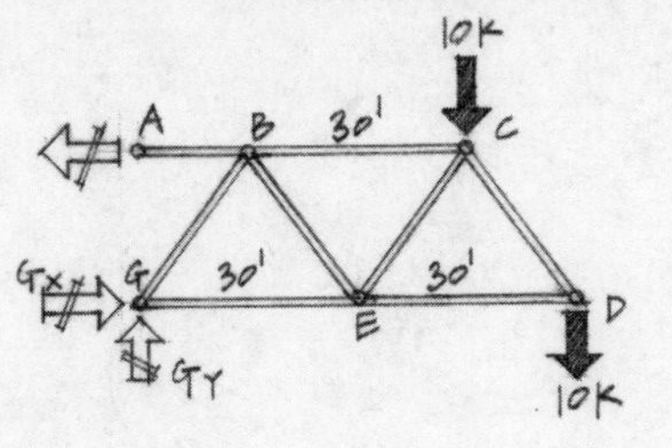

FBD (a) Entire truss.

$$\left[\Sigma M_G = 0\right] - 10\,\text{k}(45') - 10\,\text{k}(60') + A_x(20') = 0$$
$$A_x = +52.5\,\text{k}$$

$$\left[\Sigma F_y = 0\right] + G_y - 10\,\text{k} - 10\,\text{k} = 0$$
$$G_y = +20\,\text{k}$$

$$\left[\Sigma F_x = 0\right] - A_x + G_x = 0$$
$$G_x = +52.5\,\text{k}$$

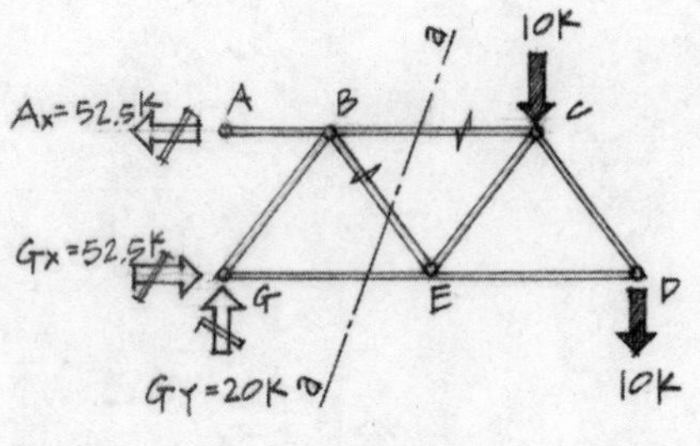

FBD (b) Section cut through truss. Squiggle lines indicate the desired member forces.

Step 2: *Pass an imaginary line through the truss (the section cut). The section line a-a must not cut across more than three unknown members, one of which is the desired member. This line divides the truss into two completely separate parts but does not intersect more than three members. Either of the two portions of the truss obtained may then be used as an FBD.*

Note: *The internal forces in the members cut by the section line are shown as external dotted lines to indicate the line of action of these member forces.*

Step 3: *Draw the FBD of either portion of the truss. Either FBD (c) or FBD (d) may be used for the solution of member forces BC and BE.*

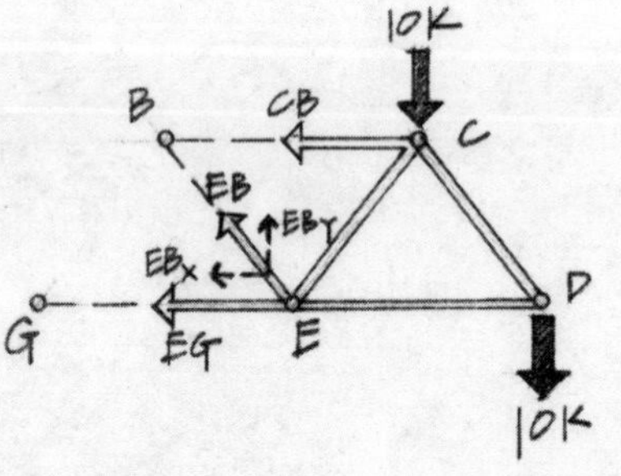

FBD (d) Right portion of the truss.

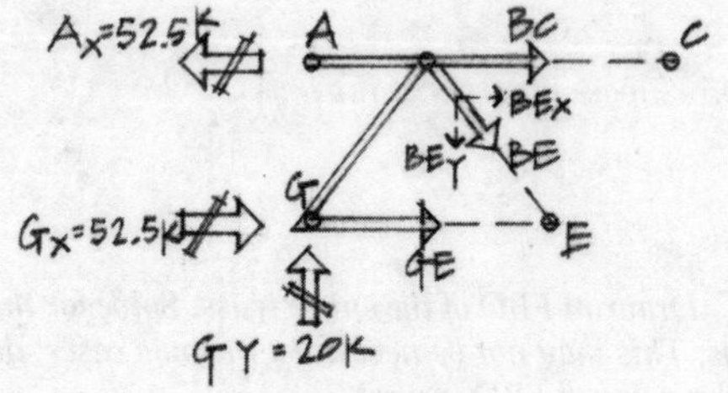

FBD (c) Left portion of the truss.

In FBD (c), joints C and E are imaginary, and joints A, B, and G are real. The method of sections operates on the idea of external force equilibrium. Uncut members AB and BG have internal forces only and do not affect the external force equilibrium. Note that if FBD (c) is chosen for the solving of member forces BC and BE, the support reactions are essential and must be solved first. Cut members BC, BE, and GE are *assumed* to act in tension (T), as opposed to compression (C).

Solving for BC,

$$\left[\Sigma M_E = 0\right] + A_x(20') - G_y(30') - BC(20') = 0'$$
$$(BC)(20') = (52.5\,\text{k})(20') - (20\,\text{k})(30')$$
$$BC = +22.5\,\text{k (T)}$$

Moments are taken about imaginary joint E because the other two unknown forces, BE and GE, intersect at E; therefore, they need not be considered in the equation of equilibrium. The solution of BC is completely independent of BE and GE.

Solving for BE,

$$\left[\Sigma F_y = 0\right] + G_y - BE_y = 0$$
$$\therefore BE_y = +20\,\text{k;}$$

but

$$BE_y = \frac{4}{5}BE,$$

then

$$BE = \frac{5}{4}BE_y = \frac{5}{4}(20\,\text{k}) = +25\,\text{k(T)}$$

An equation involving the summation of forces in the vertical direction was chosen, because the other two cut members, BC and GE, are horizontal; therefore, they are excluded from the equation of equilibrium. Again, BE was solved independent of the other two members.

If member force GE is desired, an independent equation of equilibrium can be written as follows:

$$\left[\Sigma M_B = 0\right] + G_x(20') - G_y(15') + GE(20') = 0$$
$$GE = -37.5\,\text{k (C)}$$

Equations of equilibrium based on FBD (d) would yield results identical to those with FBD (c). In this case, support reactions are unnecessary, because none appears in FBD (d). Members *CB*, *EB*, and *EG* are the cut members; therefore, they are shown as forces. Joints *B* and *G* are imaginary, because they were removed by the section cut.

Solving for *CB*,

$$\left[\Sigma M_E = 0\right] + CB(20') - 10\,\text{k}(15') - 10\,\text{k}(30') = 0$$

$$CB = +22.5\,\text{k}(\text{T})$$

Solving for *EB*,

$$\left[\Sigma F_y = 0\right] - 10\,\text{k} - 10\,\text{k} + EB_y = 0$$

$$EB_y = +20\,\text{k}$$

$$EB = \frac{5}{4}EB_y = \frac{5}{4}(20\,\text{k}) = +25\,\text{k}\ (\text{T})$$

Solving for *EG*,

$$\left[\Sigma M_B = 0\right] - EG(20') - 10\,\text{k}(30') - 10\,\text{k}(45') = 0$$

$$EG = -37.5\,\text{k}\ (\text{C})$$

11 Determine the force in members *BC*, *BG*, and *HG*, as shown in Figure 46.

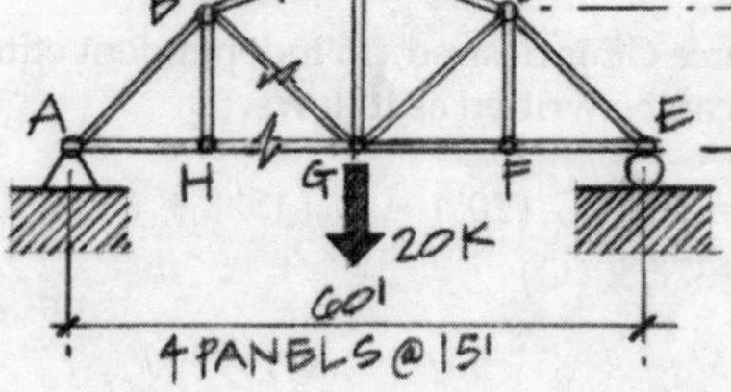

Figure 46 Bowstring or crescent truss.

Solution:

Solve for the support reactions, and then pass section *a-a* through the truss.

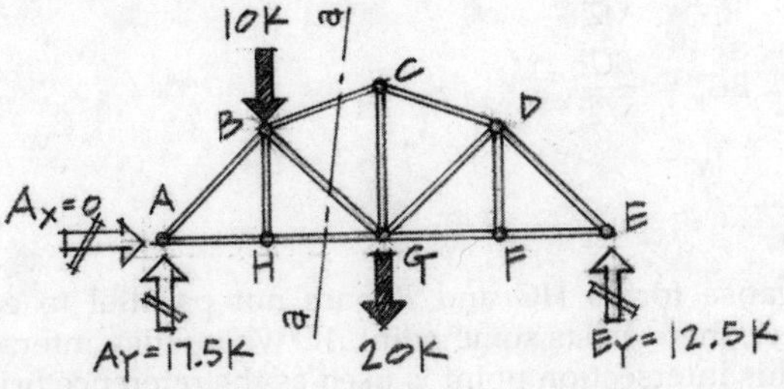

FBD (a) Entire truss.

Solving for *HG*,

$$\left[\Sigma M_B = 0\right] + HG(15') - 17.5\,\text{k}(15') = 0$$
$$HG = +17.5\,\text{k (T)}$$

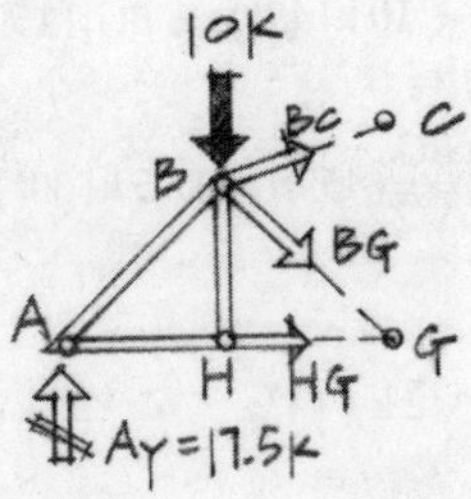

FBD (b)

Next, solve for *BC*,

$$BC_x = \frac{3BC}{\sqrt{10}};\quad BC_y = \frac{BC}{\sqrt{10}}$$
$$\left[\Sigma M_G = 0\right] - A_y(30') + 10\,\text{k}(15') - BC_x(15') - BC_y(15') = 0$$

FBD (c)

substituting:

$$\frac{3BC}{\sqrt{10}}(15') + \frac{BC}{\sqrt{10}}(15') = -17.5\,\text{k}(30') + 10\,\text{k}(15')$$
$$BC = -6.25\sqrt{10}\,\text{k (C)}$$

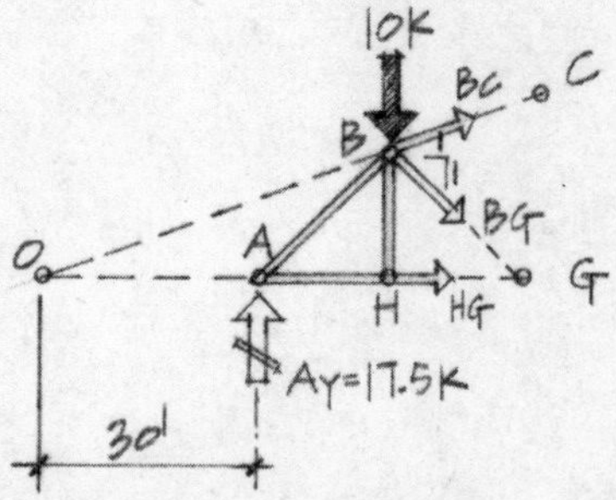

The solution for member force *BG* can be solved independent of the already known member forces *HG* and *BC* by modifying FBD (b).

$$BG_x = \frac{BG}{\sqrt{2}}$$

$$BG_y = \frac{BG}{\sqrt{2}}$$

Because forces *HG* and *BC* are not parallel to each other, there exists some point *AO* where they intersect. If this intersection point is used as the reference origin for summing moments, *HG* and *BC* would not appear in the equation of equilibrium, and *BG* could be solved independently.

The horizontal length *AO* is determined by using the slope of force *BC* as a reference. By utilizing a similar triangle relationship, *AO* is determined to be 30′. Therefore,

$$[\Sigma M_o = 0] - 10\,\text{k}(45') - BG_x(15') - BG_y(45') + A_y(30') = 0$$

$$\frac{BG}{\sqrt{2}}(15') + \frac{BG}{\sqrt{2}}(45') = 17.5\,\text{k}(30') - 10\,\text{k}(45')$$

$$BG = +1.25\sqrt{2}\,\text{k (T)}$$

Problems

18 Solve for *AC*, *BC*, and *BD* using only one section cut. Use the right portion for the FBD.

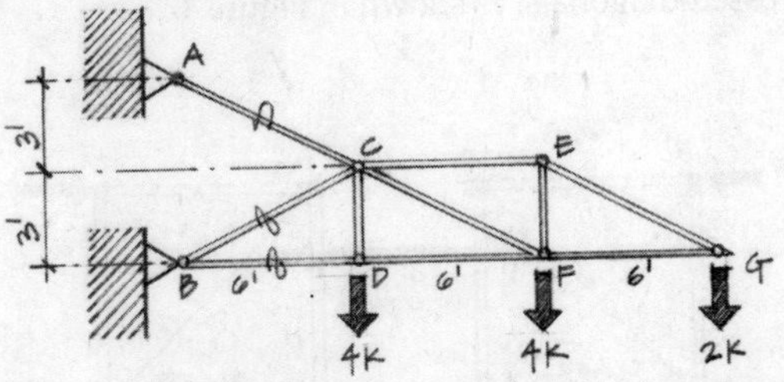

19 Solve for *BC*, *CH*, and *FH*.

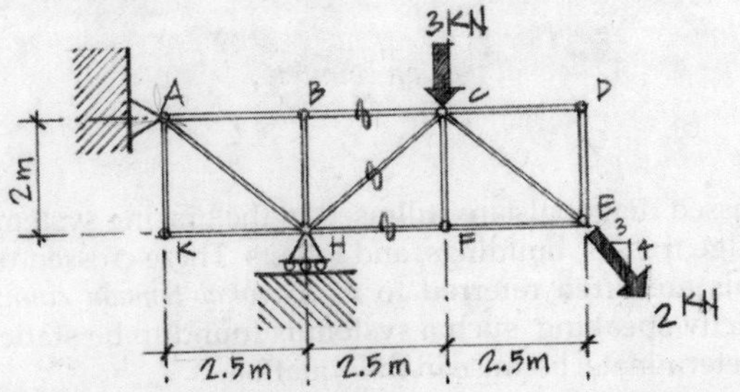

20 Solve for *BE*, *CE*, and *FJ*.

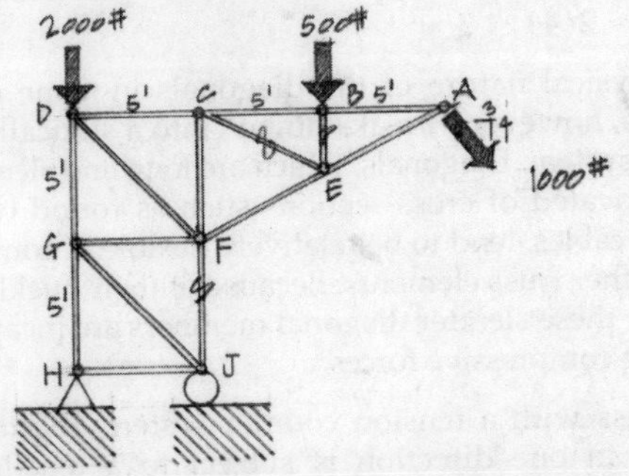

21 Solve for *AB*, *BH*, and *HG*. Use only one section cut.

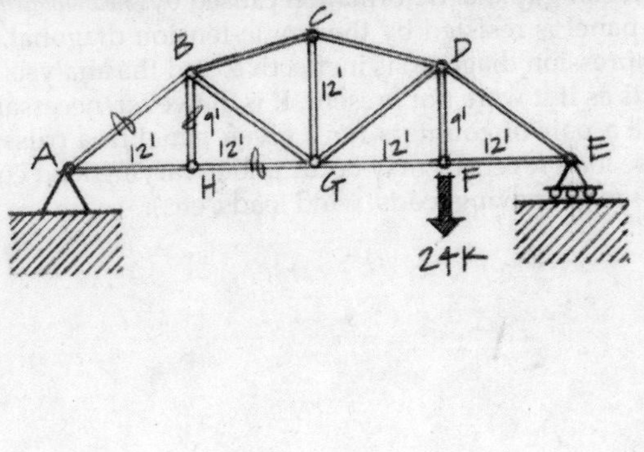

Diagonal Tension Counters

An arrangement of web members within a panel, which was commonly used in the early truss bridges, consisted of crossed diagonals, as shown in Figure 47.

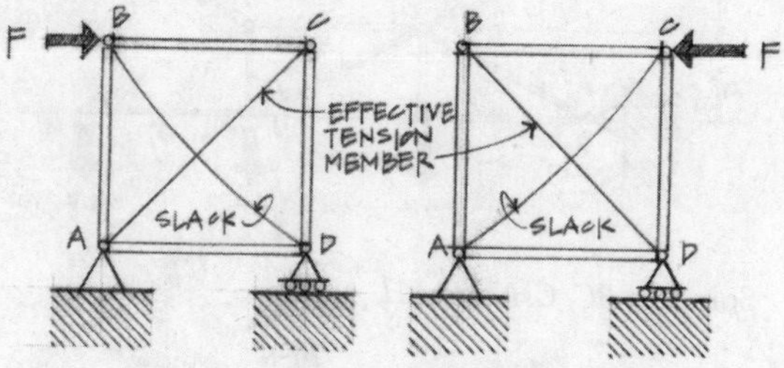

Figure 47 Diagonal tension counters.

Crossed diagonals are still used in the bracing systems of bridge trusses, buildings, and towers. These crossed diagonals are often referred to as *diagonal tension counters*. Strictly speaking, such a system is found to be statically indeterminate, because in the equation,

$$b = 2n - 3;$$
$$b = 6, n = 4$$
$$6 > 2(4) - 3$$

The physical nature of the diagonals in some of these systems, however, "breaks down" into a statically determinate system. Diagonals, which are long and slender and are fabricated of cross-sections such as round bars, flat bars, or cables, tend to be relatively flexible in comparison to the other truss elements. Because of their buckling tendencies, these slender diagonal members are incapable of resisting compressive forces.

In a truss with a tension counter system, the diagonal sloping in one direction is subject to a tensile force, whereas the other sloping member would be subject to a compressive force. If the compressive member buckles, the racking (panel deformation caused by *shear loading*) in the panel is resisted by the single-tension diagonal. The compression diagonal is ineffective, and the analysis proceeds as if it were not present. It is, however, necessary to have a pair of counters for a given panel in a truss, because load reversals may occur under varying load conditions (e.g., moving loads, wind loads, etc.).

Determining the effective tension counter can be accomplished readily using a *modified* method of sections approach. The modification involves cutting through four truss members, including both counters, rather than the usual three-member cut required in applying the method of sections, as indicated in the previous section.

Example Problem: Diagonal Tension Counters

12 For the truss shown in Figure 48, determine the effective tension counter and the resulting load developed in it.

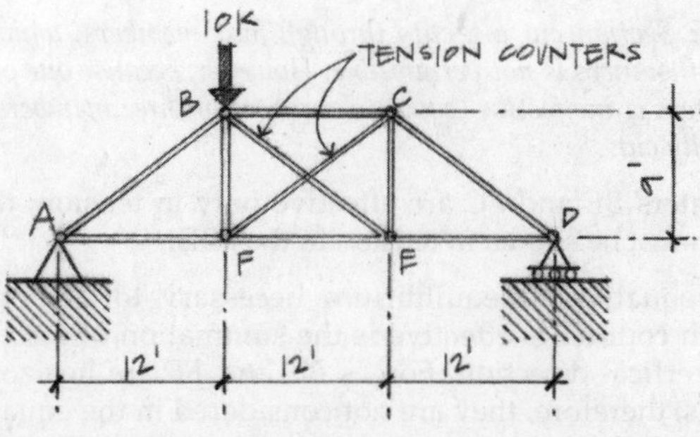

Figure 48 Truss with diagonal tension counters.

Solution:

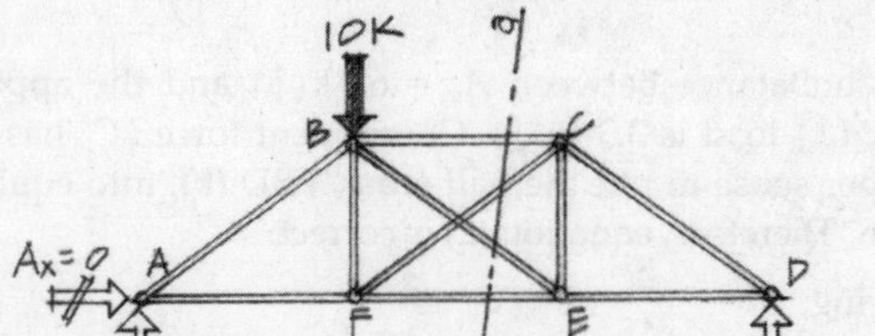

FBD (a) Section a-a cutting through four members.

Step 1: *Draw an FBD of the entire truss.*

Step 2: *Solve for the support reactions at A and D.*

Step 3: *Pass a section through the truss, cutting the counters and members BC and FE.*

Step 4: *Isolate one portion of the cut truss.*

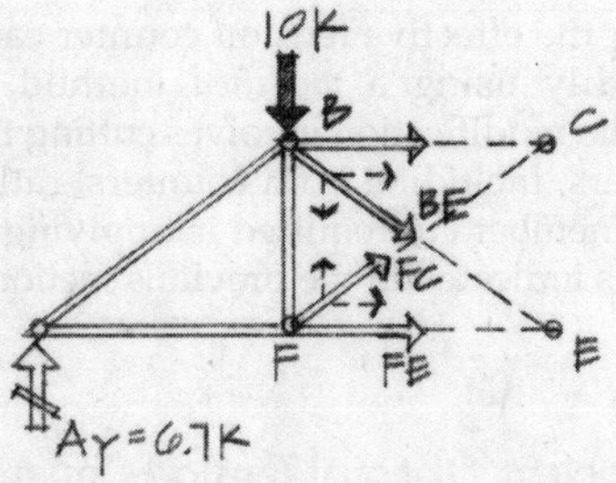

FBD (b).

Note: *Section cut* a-a *cuts through four members, which in most instances is not permissible. However, because one of the counters is ineffective (equal to zero), only three members are actually cut.*

Counters *BE* and *FC* are effective only in tension; thus, they must be shown in tension in the FBD.

The equation of equilibrium necessary to determine which counter is effective is the summation of forces in the vertical direction. Forces *BC* and *FE* are horizontal forces; therefore, they are not considered in the equation of equilibrium.

$$\left[\Sigma F_y = 0\right] + A_y - 10\,\text{k} - BE_y = 0 \tag{1}$$

or

$$+A_y - 10\,\text{k} + FC_y = 0 \tag{2}$$

The unbalance between $A_y = 6.7\,\text{k}(\uparrow)$ and the applied 10 k ($\downarrow$) load is 3.3 k ($\downarrow$). Component force FC_y has the proper sense to put the half-truss, FBD (b), into equilibrium. Therefore, equation (2) is correct.

Solving:

$$FC_y = 3.3\,\text{k}$$

but

$$FC = \frac{5}{3} FC_y = +5.55\,\text{k (T)}$$

Counter *BE* is ineffective and assumed to be zero.

Problems

Determine the effective tension counters and their respective magnitudes.

22

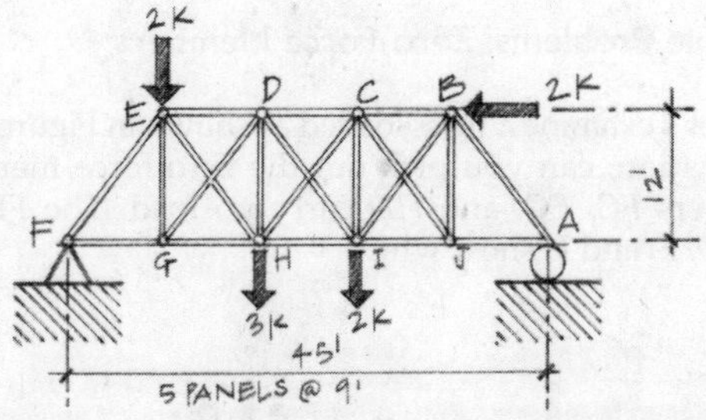

23

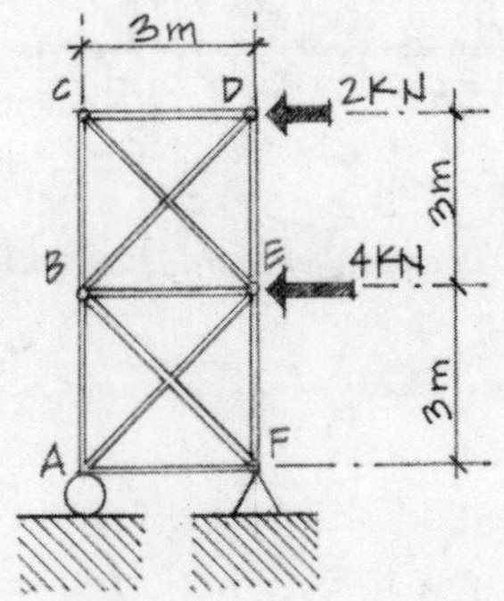

24

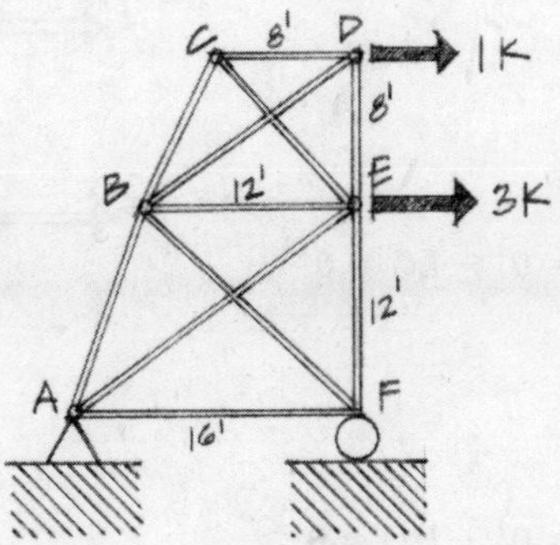

Zero-Force Members

Many trusses that appear complicated can be simplified considerably by recognizing members that carry no load. These members are often referred to as *zero-force members.*

Example Problems: Zero-Force Members

13 Let's examine a truss loaded as shown in Figure 49. By observation, can you pick out the zero-force members? Members *FC, EG,* and *HD* carry no load. The FBDs of joints *F, E,* and *H* show why.

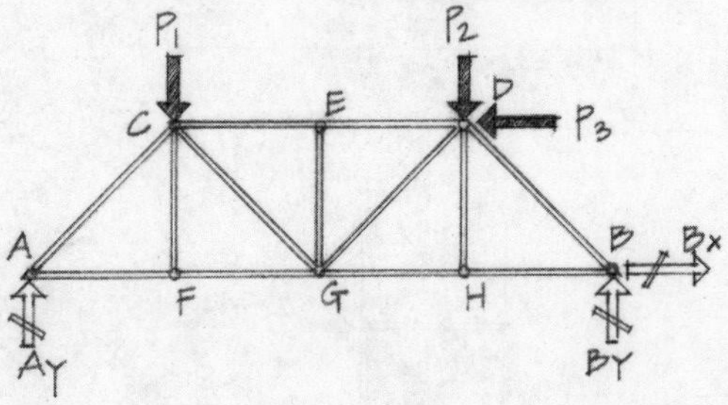

Figure 49 FBD of a parallel chord truss with zero-force members.

Solution:

Joint *F*

$$\left[\Sigma F_y = 0\right] +FC = 0$$

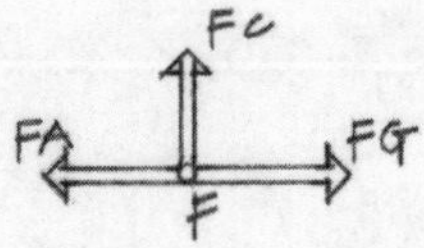

Joint *E*

$$\left[\Sigma F_y = 0\right] - EG = 0$$

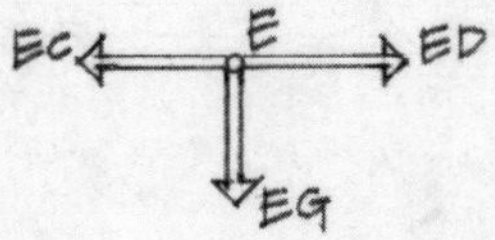

Joint *H*

$$\left[\Sigma F_y = 0\right] + HD = 0$$

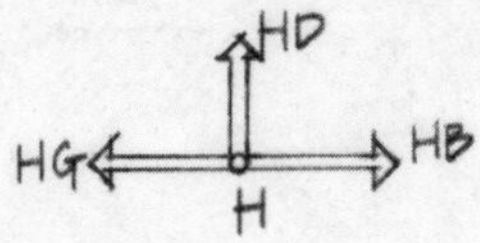

14 Visual inspection of the truss shown in Figure 50 indicates that members *BL*, *KC*, *IE*, and *FH* are zero-force members (refer to the previous problem).

FBDs of joints *K* and *I*, similar to the previous problem, would show that *KC* and *IE* are zero, because $\Sigma F_y = 0$.

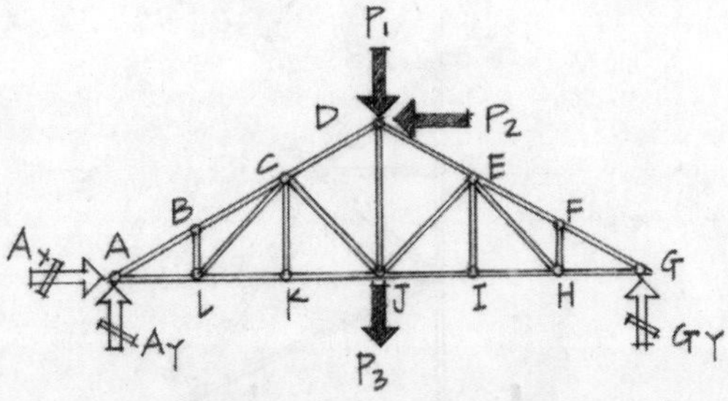

Figure 50 FBD of a roof truss with zero-force members.

Construct an *x-y* axis system in which the *x* axis is along member lines *BA* and *BC*. Member force *BL* is the only one that has a *y* component.

Solution:

$$\left[\Sigma F_y = 0\right] - BL_y = 0$$
$$\therefore BL = 0$$

The same condition is also true at joint *F*. A general rule that can be applied in determining zero-force members by inspection may be stated as follows:

> *At an unloaded joint where three members frame together, if two members are in a straight line, the third is a zero-force member.*

Therefore, under further inspection, *LC*, *CJ*, *JE*, and *EH* are also found to be zero.

Remember, zero-force members are not useless members. Even if they carry no load under a given loading condition, they may carry loads if the loading condition changes. Also, these members are needed to support the weight of the truss and maintain the desired shape.

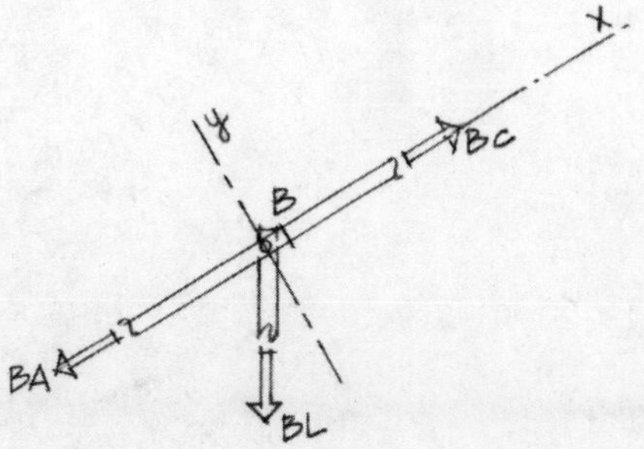

Joint B (similar for joint F).

Problems

Identify the zero-force members in the trusses below.

25

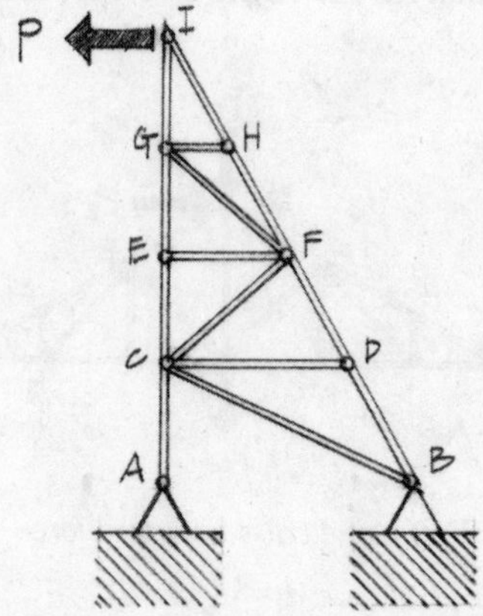

26

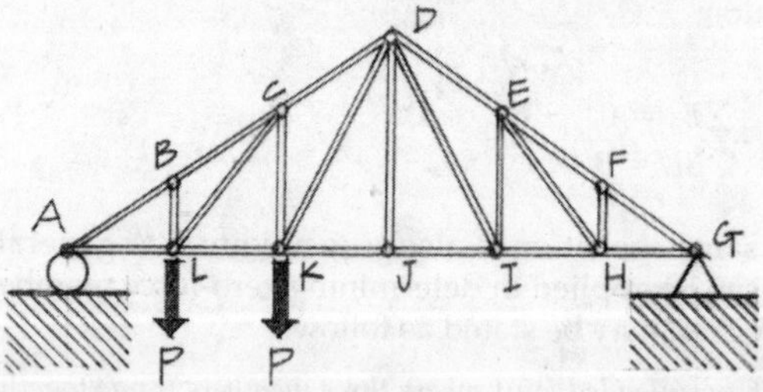

27

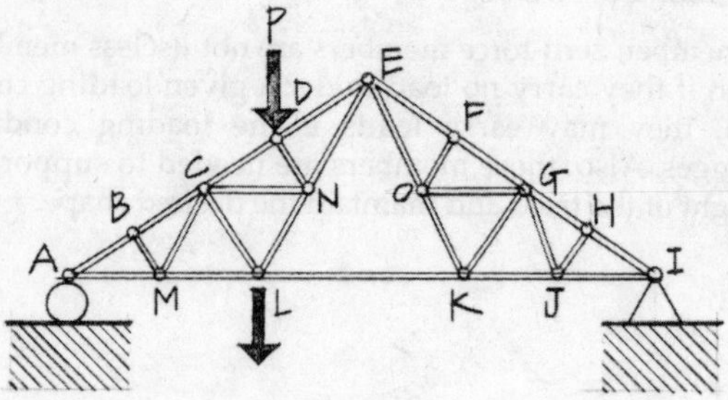

4 PINNED FRAMES (MULTIFORCE MEMBERS)

Figure 51 Heavy timber-framed barn. This is an example of a pinned wood frame. Photographer unknown.

Multiforce Members

In Section 3, trusses were discussed as structures consisting entirely of pin joints and of straight two-force members where the resultant force developed was directed along the member's axis. Now we will examine structures that contain members that are *multiforce* members—that is, a member acted upon by three or more forces (Figure 51 and Figure 52). These forces are generally not directed along the member's axis; thus, the resultant member force direction is unknown. Bending of the member is typically the outcome.

Pinned frames are structures containing multiforce members that are usually designed to support an array of load conditions. Some pinned frames may also include two-force members.

Forces applied to a truss or pinned frame must pass through the structural framework and, eventually, work their way to the supports. In pinned frames, forces act first on the members, and then members load the internal pins and joints. Pins redirect the loads to other members and, eventually, to the supports. Examine the FBDs of both the truss and frame shown in Figures 53 and 54, respectively, and compare the load transfers that result in the members and pins.

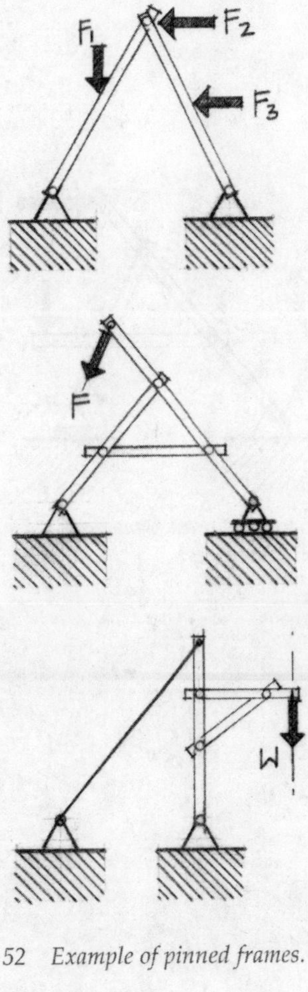

Figure 52 Example of pinned frames.

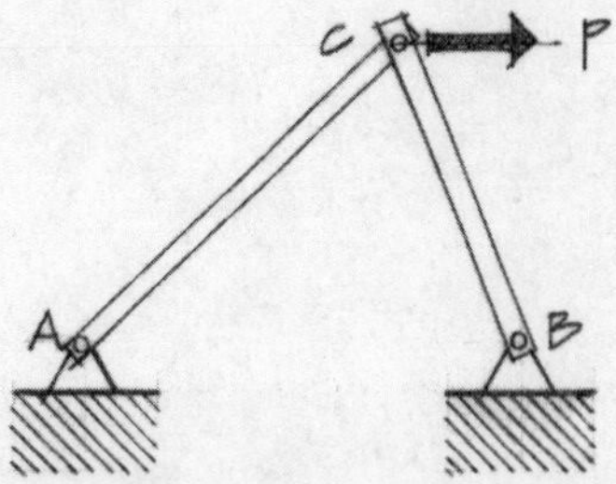

Figure 53(a) Members AC and BC are two-force.

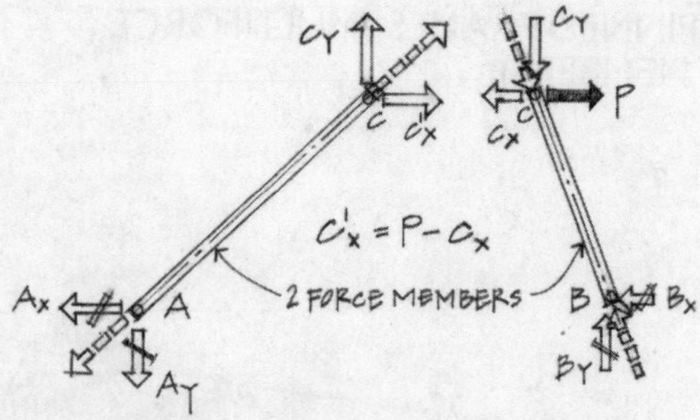

Figure 53(b) FBD of each two-force member.

***Note:** In the FBD of member BC, shown in Figure 53(b), C_x together with P will result in an x component compatible to C_y and produce a resultant C that passes through the axis of the member.*

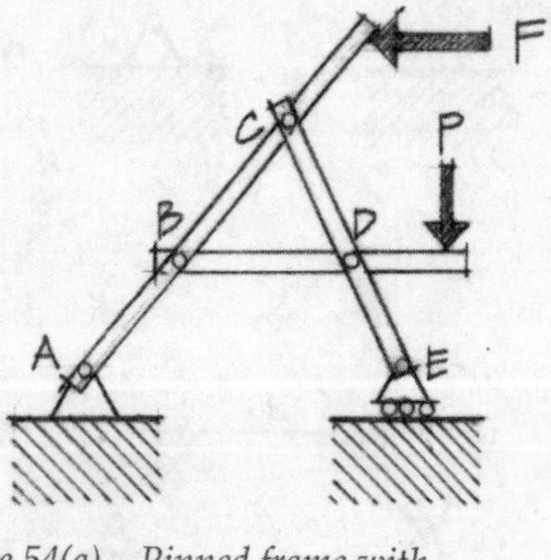

Figure 54(a) Pinned frame with multiforce members.

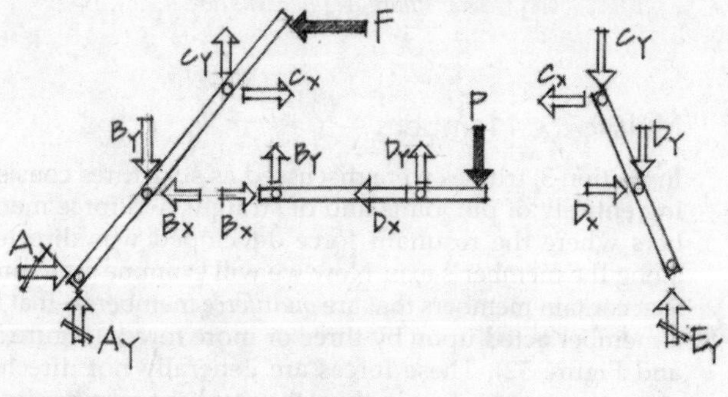

Figure 54(b) FBD of each multiforce member.

Resultants of the component forces at pin joints do not pass through the axis of the respective member. The lines of action of the pin forces are unknown.

Rigid and Nonrigid Pinned Frames in Relation to Their Support

Some pinned frames cease to be rigid and stable when detached from their supports. These types of frames are usually referred to as *nonrigid*, or collapsible (Figure 55). Other frames remain entirely *rigid* (retain their geometry) even if the supports are removed (Figure 56).

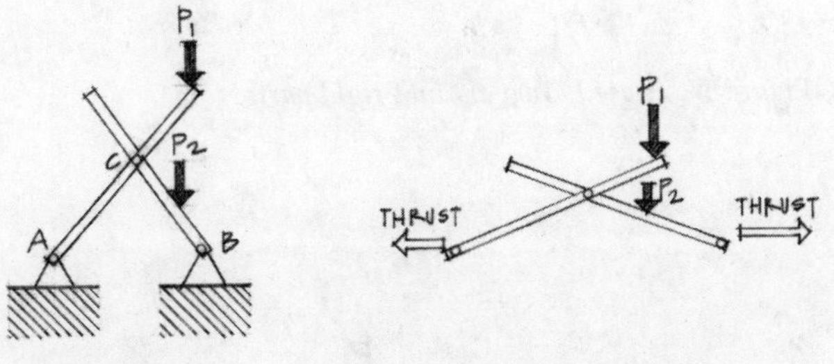

(a) With supports. *(b) Supports removed.*

Figure 55 Case I: Nonrigid without supports.

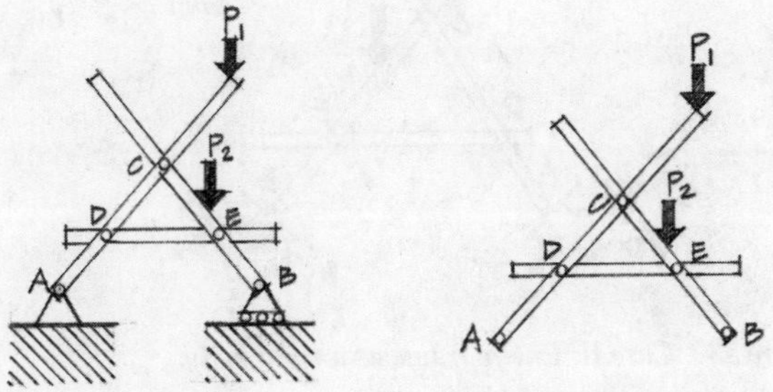

(a) With supports. *(b) Supports removed.*

Figure 56 Case II: Rigid without supports.

In Case I (nonrigid), the pinned frame cannot justly be considered as a rigid body, because the frame collapses under loading when either or both of the two pin supports are removed. Members *AC* and *BC* should be treated as two separate, distinct rigid parts (Figure 57).

On the other hand, the frame in Case II (rigid) maintains its geometry with the pin and roller supports removed. Stability is maintained because the introduction of member *DE* forms a triangular, trusslike configuration. The entire pinned frame is easily transportable and can be considered as a rigid body (Figure 58).

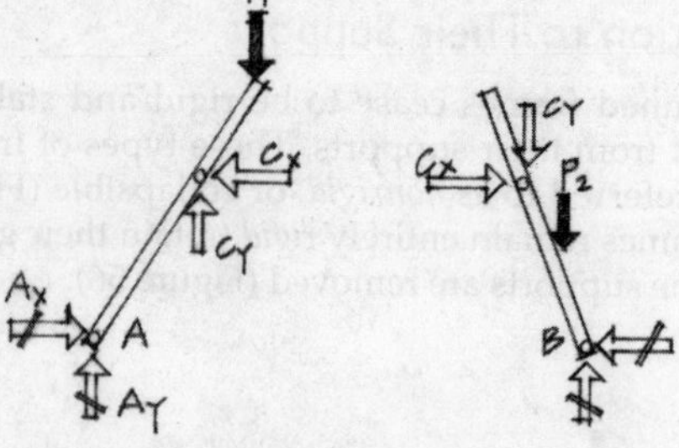

Figure 57 Case I: Two distinct rigid parts.

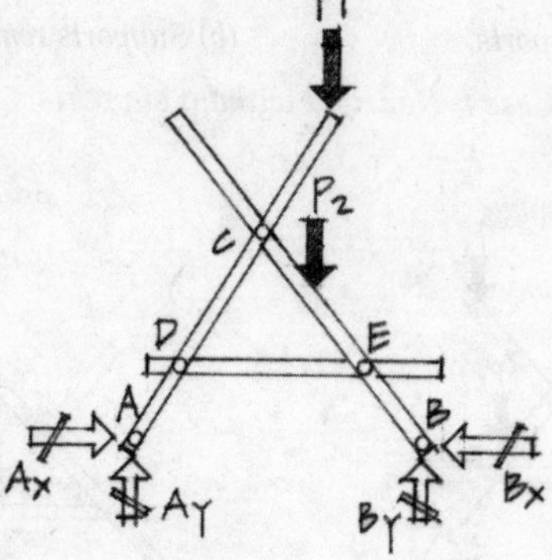

Figure 58 Case II: Entire frame as a rigid body.

***Note:** Although a structure may be considered as nonrigid without its supports, an FBD of the entire nonrigid frame can be drawn for equilibrium calculations.*

Procedure for Analysis of a Pinned Frame

1. Draw an FBD of the entire frame.
2. Solve for the external reactions.
   a. If the frame is statically determinate externally (three equations of equilibrium, three unknown reactions), all reactions can be solved (Figure 59).

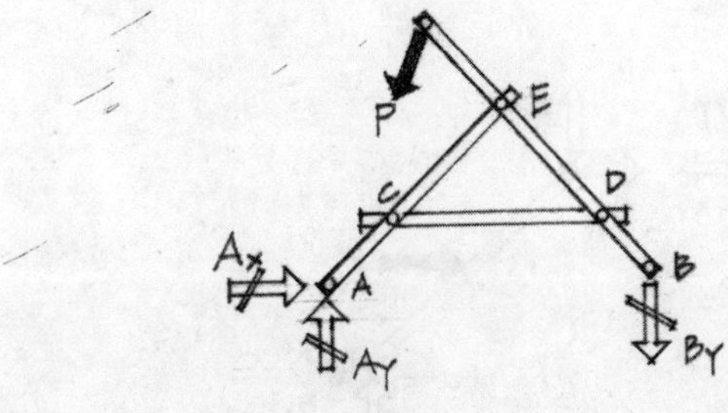

Figure 59 Pinned frame.

- Three unknowns: A_x, A_y, and B_y
- Three equations of equilibrium

Note: *Direction for the external reactions or pin reactions may be assumed. A wrong assumption will yield the correct magnitude but have a negative sign.*

   b. If the frame is statically indeterminate externally, reactions must be solved through other means (Figure 60).

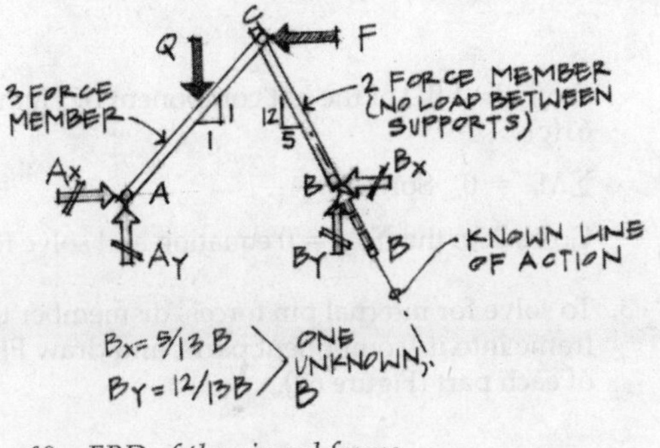

Figure 60 FBD of the pinned frame.

- By recognizing two-force members.
- By writing another equation of equilibrium for the extra unknown. This is accomplished by separating the frame into its rigid parts and drawing FBDs of each part [Figure 61(c)].

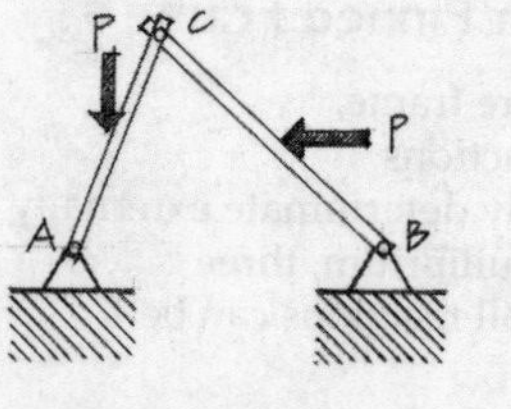

(a) *Pictorial diagram.*

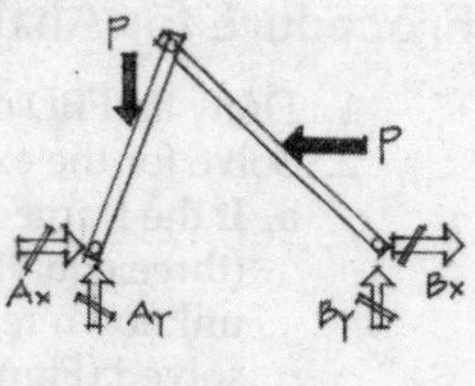

(b) *FBD—entire frame.*

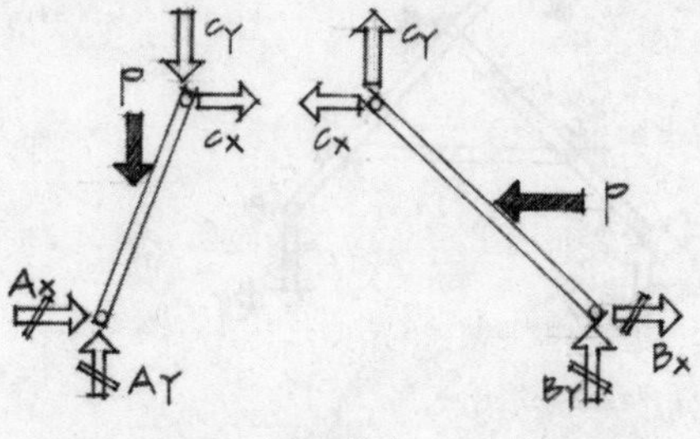

(c) *FBD of the components.*

Figure 61 FBD of the frame and components.

For example, from the FBD of the entire frame shown in Figure 61(b),

$\Sigma M_B = 0$ Equation includes A_y. Solve for A_y.

$\Sigma M_A = 0$ Solve for B_y.

$\Sigma F_x = 0$ Equation in terms of A_x and B_x.

From the FBD of the left component of Figure 61(c),

$\Sigma M_C = 0$ Solve for A_x.

Go back to the $\Sigma F_x = 0$ equation and solve for B_x.

3. To solve for internal pin forces, dismember the frame into its component parts, and draw FBDs of each part (Figure 62).

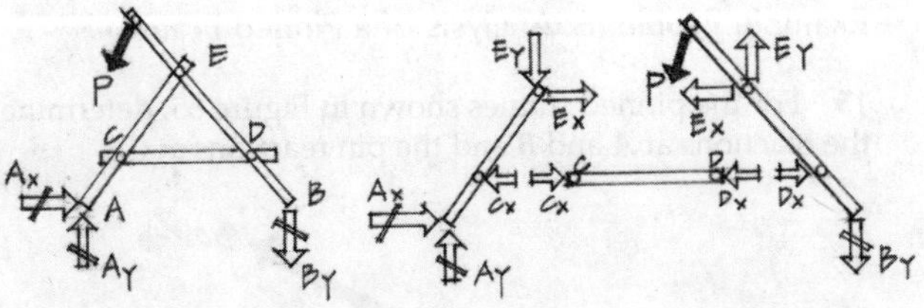

Figure 62 FBD of (a) entire frame and (b) components.

***Note:** Equal and opposite forces at pins (Newton's third law).*

4. Calculate the internal pin forces by writing equilibrium equations for the component parts.
5. The FBDs of the component parts do not include an FBD of the pin itself. Pins in frames are considered as integral with one of the members. When the pins connect three or more members, or when a pin connects a support to two or more members, it becomes very important to assign the pin to a particular member. For example, see Figure 63.

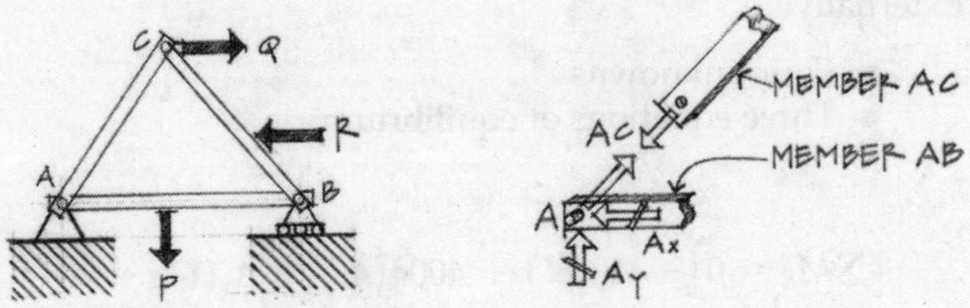

Figure 63 Pin assigned to member AB.

6. When loads are applied at a joint, the load may be arbitrarily assigned to either member. Note, however, that the applied load must appear only once. Or, a load can be assigned to the pin, and the pin may or may not be assigned to a member. Then, a solution for the pin could be done as a separate FBD (Figure 64).

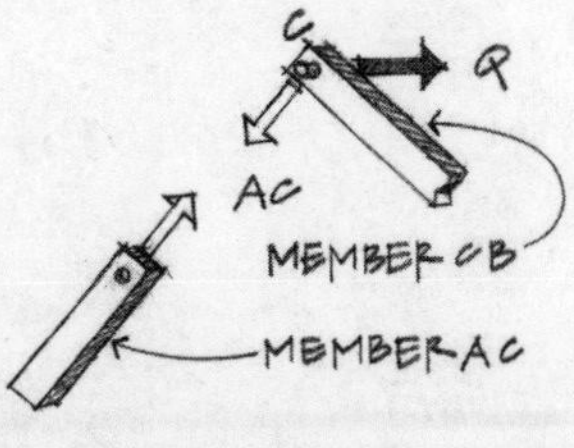

Figure 64 FBD of joint C.

Example Problems: Analysis of a Pinned Frame

15 For the pinned frames shown in Figure 65, determine the reactions at *A* and *B* and the pin reactions at C.

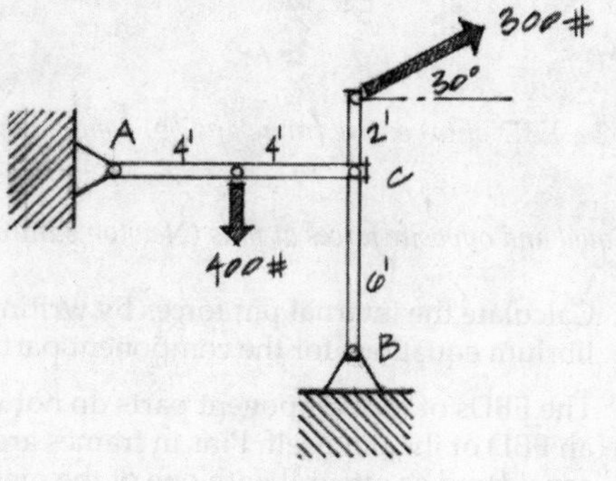

Figure 65(a) Pinned frames.

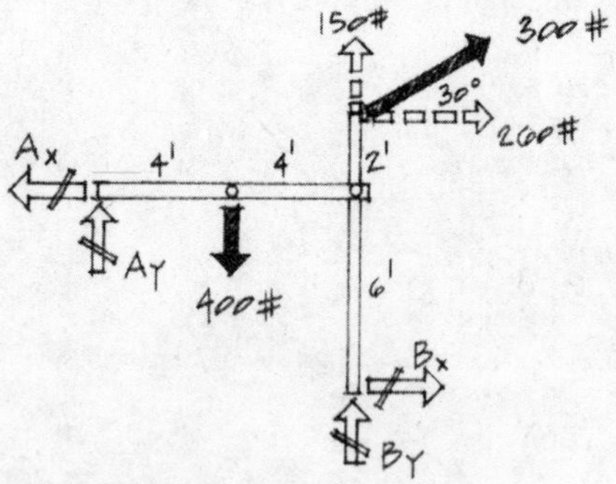

Figure 65(b) FBD of entire pinned frame.

Solution:

Step 1: *Draw an FBD of the entire frame. Solve for as many external reactions as possible.*

Externally:

- Four unknowns
- Three equations of equilibrium

$$\left[\Sigma M_B = 0\right] - A_y(8') + 400\#(4') + A_x(6') - 260\#(8') = 0$$

$$\left[\Sigma F_x = 0\right] - A_x + 260\# + B_x = 0$$

$$\left[\Sigma F_y = 0\right] + A_y - 400\# + 150\# + B_y = 0$$

Because no support reactions can be solved using the FBD of the entire frame, go on to step 2.

Step 2: *Break the frame up into its component parts.*

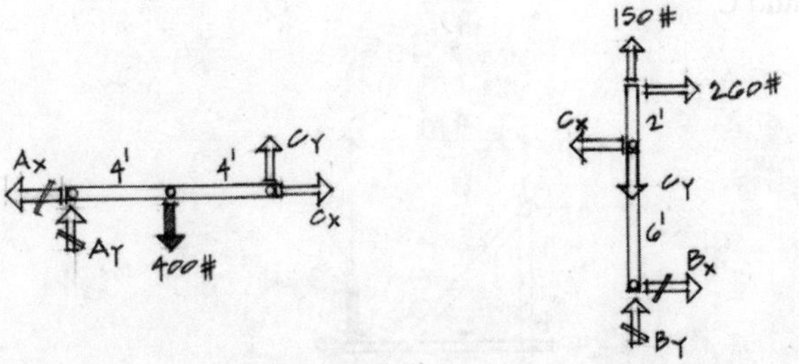

FBD (a) *FBD (b)*

FBDs of component parts.

From FBD (a),

$$[\Sigma M_c = 0] - A_y(8') + 400\#(4') = 0$$
$$A_y = +200\# \text{ Assumption OK}$$

Going back to the $[\Sigma M_B = 0]$ equation for the entire frame,

$$A_x = \frac{200\#(8') + 260\#(8') - 400\#(4')}{6'} = +346.7\#$$

$$B_x = A_x - 260\# = 347\# - 260\# = +87\#$$
$$B_y = 400\# - A_y - 150\# = 400\# - 200\# - 150\#$$
$$= +50\#$$

From FBD (a),

$$[\Sigma F_x = 0] - A_x + C_x = 0$$
$$C_x = +347\#$$

$$[\Sigma F_y = 0] + A_y - 400\# + C_y = 0$$
$$C_y = +200\#$$

or from FBD (b),

$$[\Sigma F_x = 0] - C_y + 260\# + B_x = 0$$
$$C_x = 260\# + 87\# = +347\# \Leftarrow \text{CHECKS}$$

$$[\Sigma F_y = 0] + 150\# - C_y + B_y = 0$$
$$C_y = 150\# + 50\# = +200\# \Leftarrow \text{CHECKS}$$

16 For the pinned frame shown in Figure 66, determine the support reactions at E and F and the pin reactions at A, B, and C.

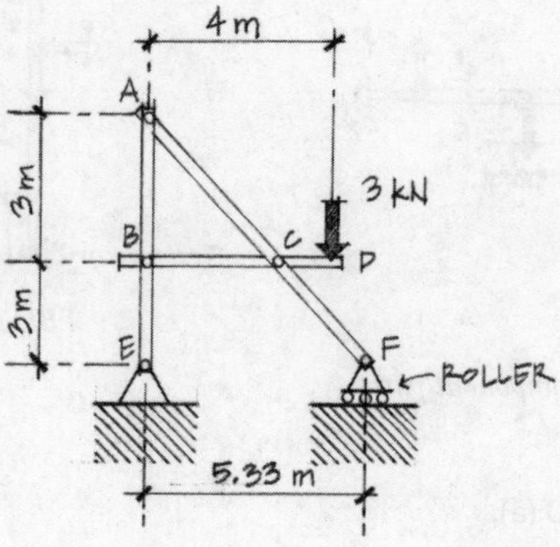

Figure 66 Pinned frame.

Solution:

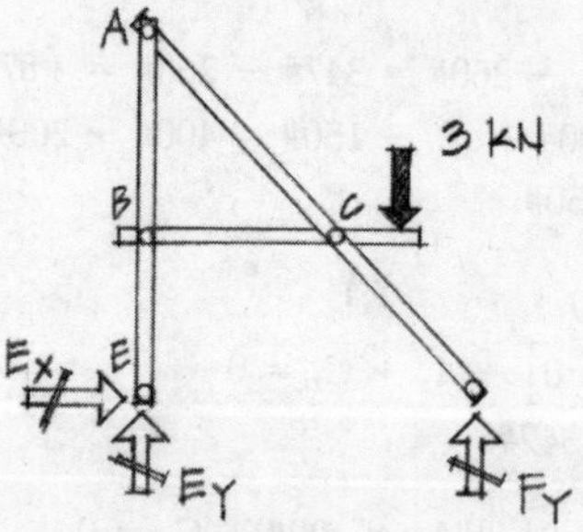

FBD of entire frame.

Statically determinate externally:

- Three unknowns
- Three equations of equilibrium

$$\left[\Sigma M_E = 0\right] + F_y(5.33\,\text{m}) - 3\,\text{kN}(4\,\text{m}) = 0$$
$$F_y = 2.25\,\text{kN}$$

$$\left[\Sigma F_y = 0\right] + E_y - 3\,\text{kN} + 2.25\,\text{kN} = 0$$
$$E_y = +0.75\,\text{kN}$$

$$\left[\Sigma F_x = 0\right] E_x = 0$$

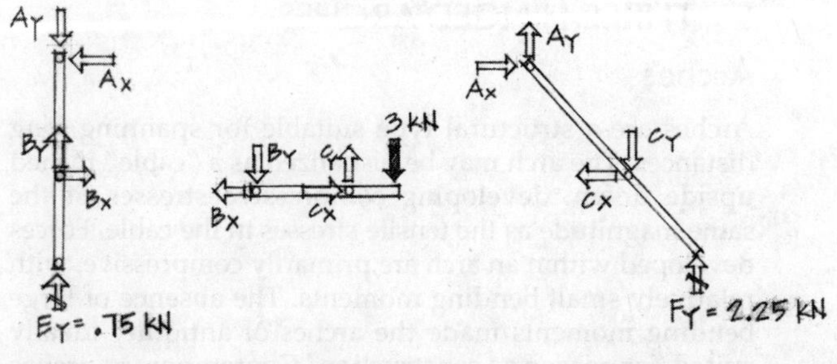

FBD (a) *FBD (b)* *FBD (c)*

Component FBDs.

From FBD (b),

$$\left[\Sigma M_C = 0\right] + B_y(2.67\,\text{m}) - 3\,\text{kN}(1.33\,\text{m}) = 0$$
$$B_y = +1.5\,\text{kN}$$

$$\left[\Sigma F_y = 0\right] - B_y + C_y - 3\,\text{kN} = 0$$
$$C_y = 3\,\text{kN} + 1.5\,\text{kN} = +4.5\,\text{kN}$$

From FBD (a),

$$\left[\Sigma M_B = 0\right] A_x = 0$$

$$\left[\Sigma F_x = 0\right] B_x = 0$$

$$\left[\Sigma F_y = 0\right] - A_y + B_y + E_y = 0$$
$$A_y = +1.5\,\text{kN} + 0.75\,\text{kN} = +2.25\,\text{kN}$$

From FBD (c),

$$\left[\Sigma F_x = 0\right] + A_x - C_x = 0,$$

but

$$A_x = 0,$$

therefore

$$C_x = 0$$

Check:

$$\left[\Sigma F_y = 0\right] + 2.25\,\text{kN} - 4.5\,\text{kN} + 2.25\,\text{kN} = 0$$

5 THREE-HINGED ARCHES

Arches

Arches are a structural type suitable for spanning long distances. The arch may be visualized as a "cable" turned upside down, developing compressive stresses of the same magnitude as the tensile stresses in the cable. Forces developed within an arch are primarily compressive, with relatively small bending moments. The absence of large bending moments made the arches of antiquity ideally suited for masonry construction. Contemporary arches may be constructed as three-hinged, two-hinged, or hingeless (fixed) (Figure 67).

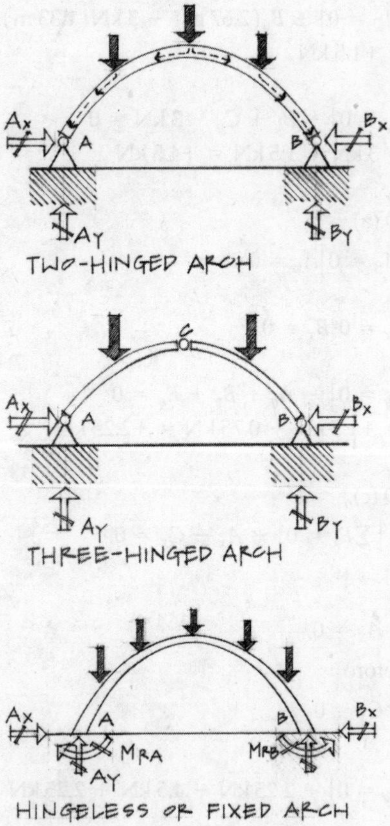

Figure 67 Contemporary arch types.

An arch is a structural unit supported by vertical as well as horizontal reactions, as shown in Figure 67. The horizontal reactions must be capable of resisting thrust forces, or the arch tends to flatten out under load. Arches incapable of resisting horizontal thrust degrade into a type of curved beam, as shown in Figure 68.

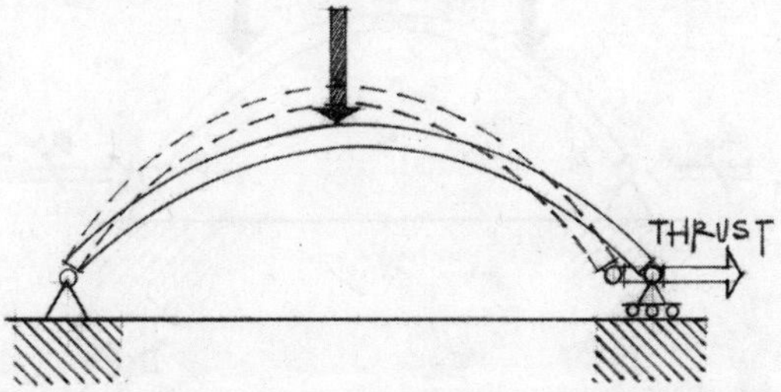

Figure 68 Curved beam.

Curved beams tend to have large bending moments, similar to straight beams, and possess none of the characteristics of a true arch. Regardless of the shape taken by an arch, the system should provide an unbroken compressive path through the arch to minimize its bending. The efficiency of an arch is determined by the geometry of its curved form relative to the load intended to be supported (funicular shape). Some of the more efficient geometric forms for specific loading conditions are shown in Figure 69.

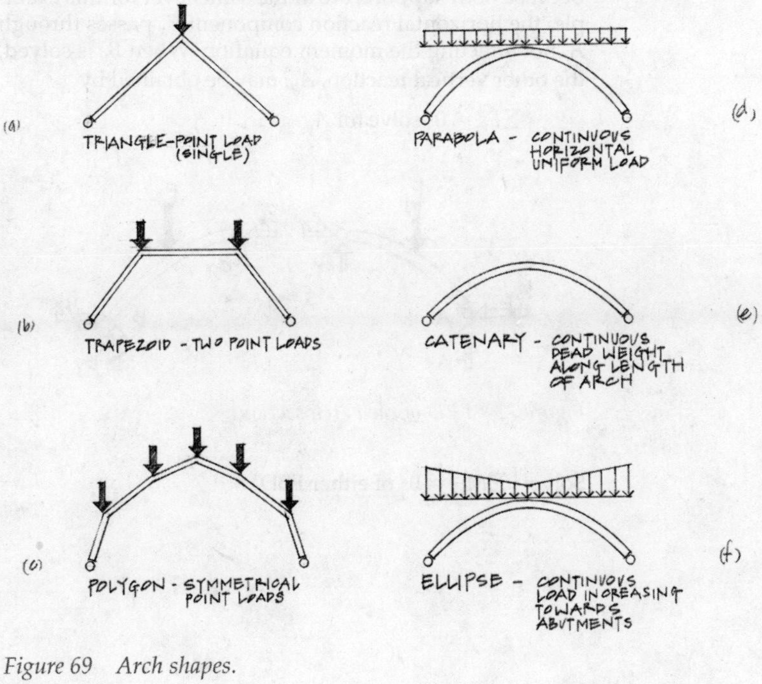

Figure 69 Arch shapes.

Three-hinged arches (Figure 70) are statically determinate systems and will be the only contemporary arch type studied in the subsequent examples.

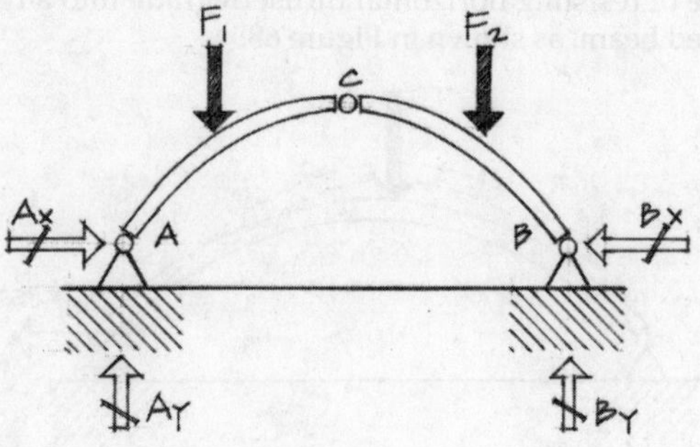

Figure 70 Three-hinged arch.

Examination of the three-hinged arch shown in Figure 70 reveals two reaction components at each support, with a total of four unknowns. Three equations of equilibrium from statics, plus an additional equation of equilibrium of zero moment at the internal (crown) hinge, make this into a statically determinate system. The arch in Figure 70 is solved by taking moments at one support end to obtain the vertical reaction component at the second support. For example,

$$\left[\Sigma M_A = 0\right] \text{ solve directly for } B_y$$

Because both supports are at the same level for this example, the horizontal reaction component B_x passes through A, not affecting the moment equation. When B_y is solved, the other vertical reaction, A_y, may be obtained by

$$\left[\Sigma F_y = 0\right] \text{ solve for } A_y$$

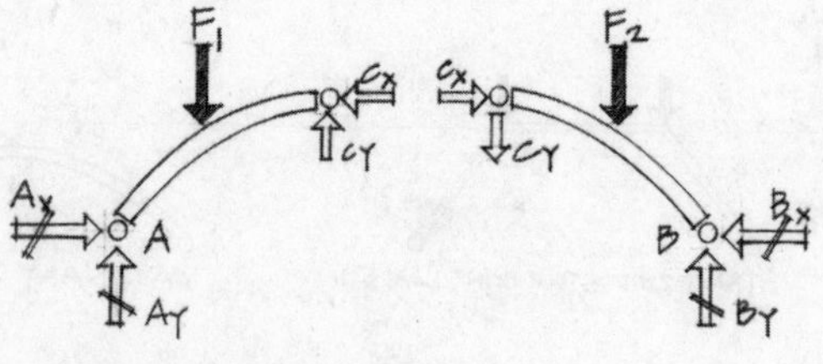

Figure 71 FBD of each arch section.

Solve: $\left[\Sigma M_C = 0\right]$ of either FBD

The horizontal reaction components are obtained by taking moments at the crown hinge C, as shown in Figure 71. The only unknown appearing in either equation is the horizontal reaction component at A or B. The other horizontal component is found by writing

$[\Sigma F_x = 0]$ solve for remaining horizontal reaction

The three-hinged arch has been used for both buildings and bridges (sometimes in the form of a trussed arch, as shown in Figure 72). Three-hinged arches can undergo settlements of supports without inducing large bending moments in the structure. This is the primary advantage of the three-hinged arch over the other statically *indeterminate* systems.

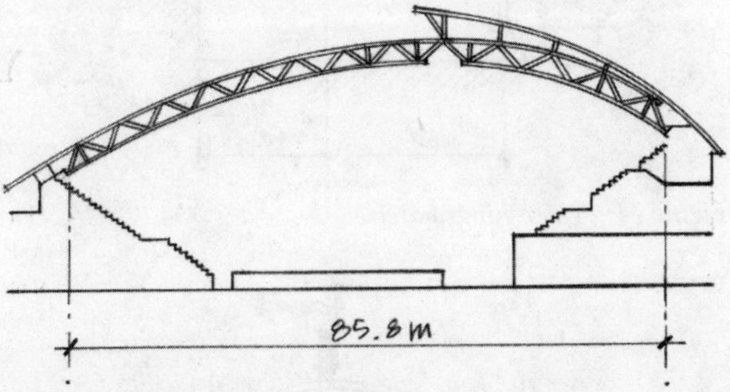

Figure 72 Three-hinged timber arch, Lillehammer, Norway, Olympic Hockey Arena.

Arches require foundations capable of resisting large thrusts at the supports. In arches for buildings, it is possible to carry the thrust by tying the supports together with steel rods, cable, steel sections, buttresses, foundation abutments, or specially designed floors. Good rock foundations provide ideal supports for resisting horizontal thrust (Figure 73).

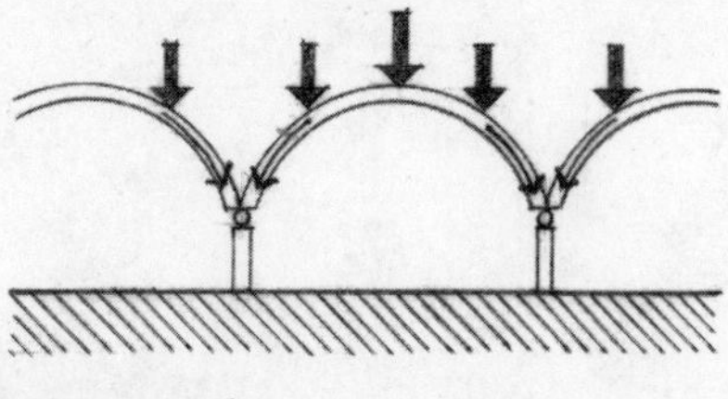

Continuous arches.

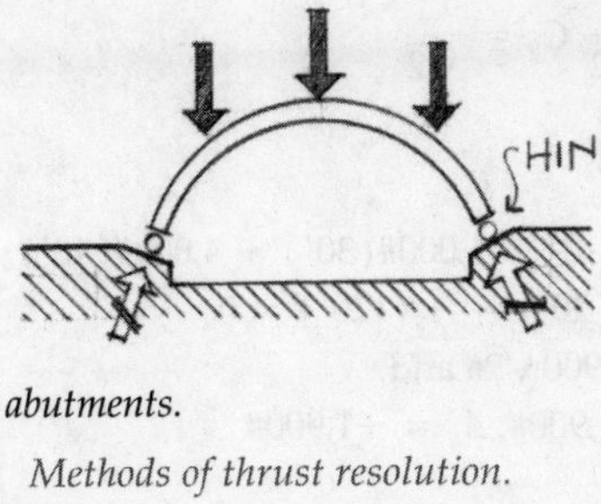

Arch with abutments.

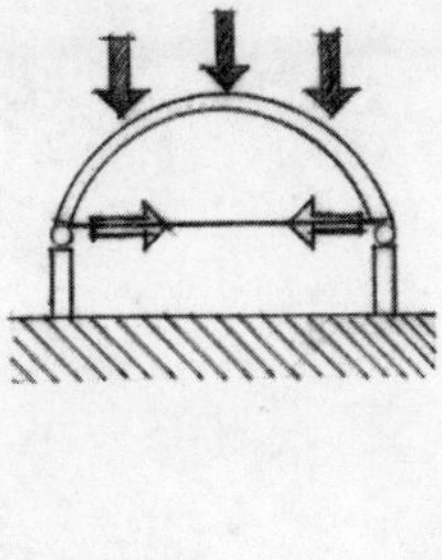

Tied arch.

Figure 73 Methods of thrust resolution.

Example Problems: Three-Hinged Arch

17 Determine the support reactions at A and B and the internal pin forces at C. This example utilizes a three-hinged arch with supports at different elevations, as shown in Figure 74.

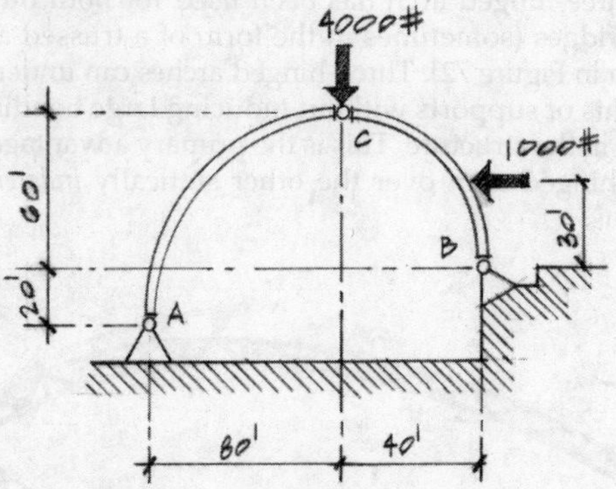

Figure 74 Three-hinged arch.

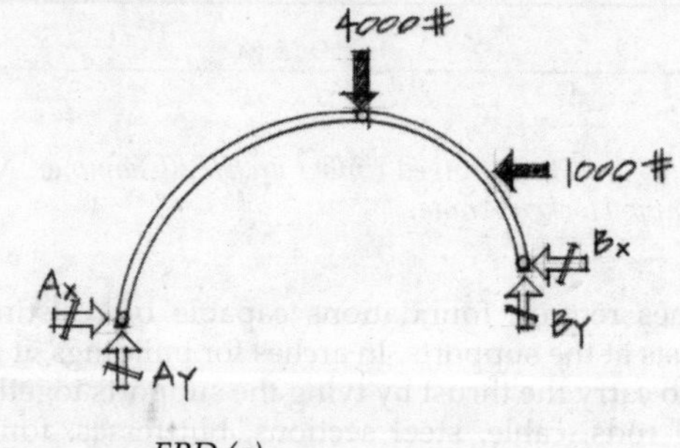

FBD (a)

Solution:

$$A_x = \frac{A}{\sqrt{2}}, A_y = \frac{A}{\sqrt{2}}$$

$$C_x = \frac{C}{\sqrt{2}}, C_y = \frac{C}{\sqrt{2}}$$

From FBD (a),

$$\left[\Sigma M_B = 0\right] + 1{,}000\#(30') + 4{,}000\#(40') + A_x(20') - A_y(120') = 0$$

$$A = +1{,}900\sqrt{2}\# \text{ and}$$

$$A_x = +1{,}900\#, A_y = +1{,}900\#$$

***Note:** A_x and A_y result in a 1 : 1 relationship identical to that of the imaginary slope along the line connecting A and C.*

From FBD (b),

$$\left[\Sigma F_x = 0\right] + A_x - C_x = 0$$
$$C_x = +1{,}900\#$$

$$\left[\Sigma F_y = 0\right] + A_y - C_y = 0$$
$$C_y = +1{,}900\#$$

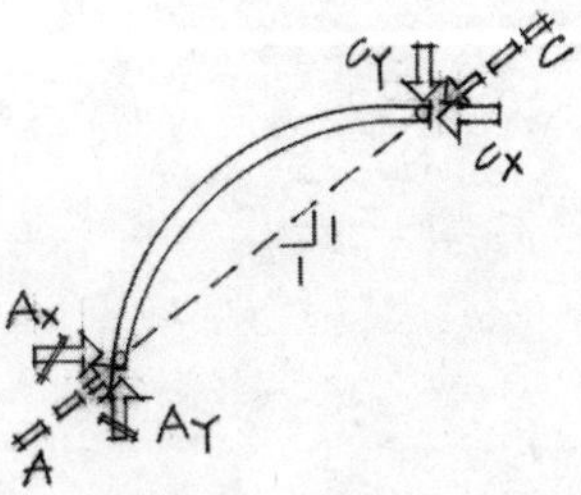

FBD (b)

From FBD (c),

$$\left[\Sigma F_x = 0\right] + C_x - 1{,}000\# - B_x = 0$$
$$B_x = +1{,}900\# - 1{,}000\# = +900\#$$

$$\left[\Sigma F_y = 0\right] - 4{,}000\# + C_y + B_y = 0$$
$$B_y = +4{,}000\# - 1{,}900\# = +2{,}100\#$$

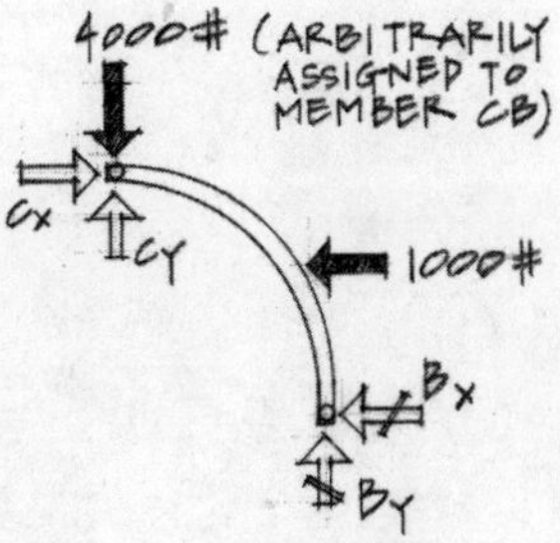

FBD (c)

Check:

Using FBD (a) again,

$$\left[\Sigma F_x = 0\right] + A_x - 1{,}000\# - B_x = 0$$
$$+1{,}900\# - 1{,}000\# - 900\# = 0 \Leftarrow \text{CHECKS}$$

18 A steel gabled frame (assembled as a three-hinged arch) is subjected to wind forces as shown in Figure 75. Determine the support reactions at *A* and *B* and the internal pin forces at *C*.

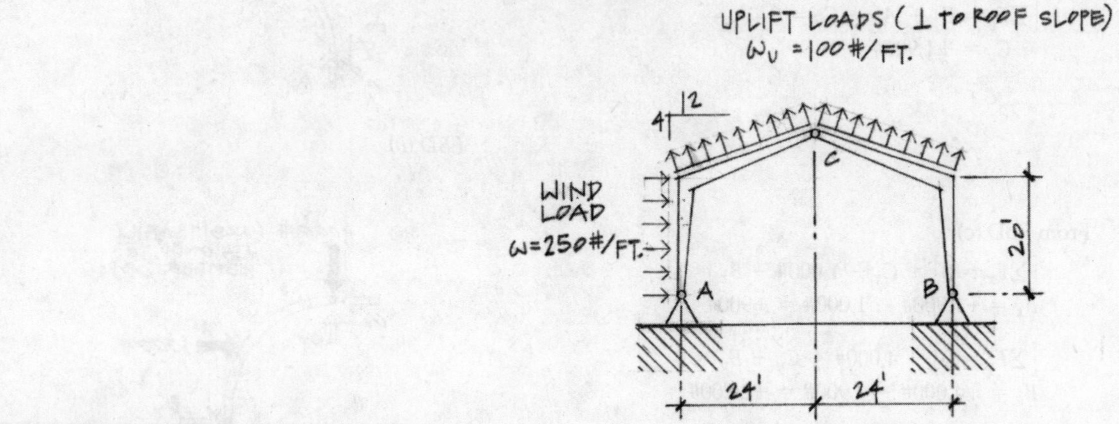

Figure 75 *Three-hinged gabled frame.*

Solution:

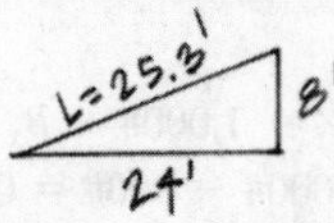

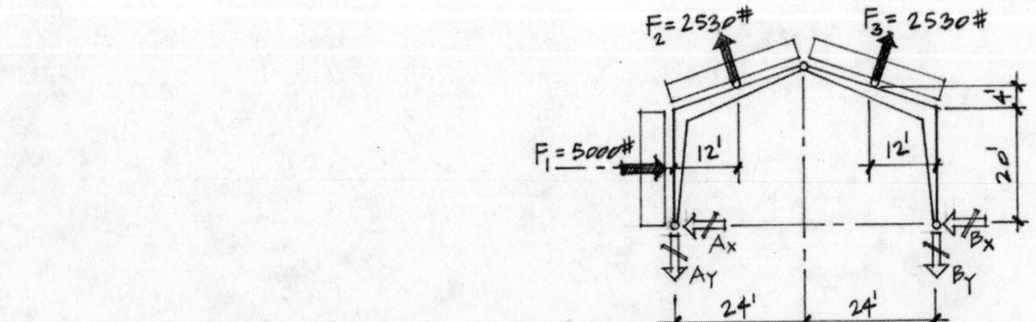

FBD of frame (a).

Determine the equivalent wind forces F_1, F_2, and F_3.

$$F_1 = 250\,\#/\text{ft.}(20') = 5{,}000\#$$
$$F_2 = 100\,\#/\text{ft.}(25.3') = 2{,}530\#$$
$$F_3 = 100\,\#/\text{ft.}(25.3') = 2{,}530\#$$

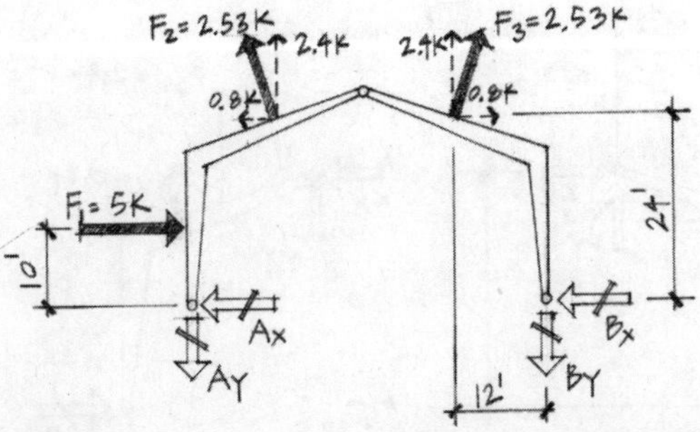

FBD of frame (b)

Resolve forces F_2 and F_3 into x and y component forces:

$$F_{2_x} = F_{3_x} = \frac{8}{25.3}(2.53\,\text{k}) = 0.8\,\text{k}$$

$$F_{2_y} = F_{3_y} - \frac{24}{25.3}(2.53\,\text{k}) = 2.4\,\text{k}$$

Solve for the vertical support reactions A_y and B_y.

$$\left[\Sigma M_A = 0\right] - F_1(10') + F_{2_x}(24') + F_{2_y}(12') - F_{3_x}(24') + F_{3_y}(36') - B_y(48') = 0$$

$$-5\,\text{k}(10') + .8\,\text{k}(24') + 2.4\,\text{k}(12') - .8\,\text{k}(24') + 2.4\,\text{k}(36') - B_y(48') = 0$$

$$\therefore B_y = +1.36\,\text{k}(\downarrow)$$

$$\left[\Sigma F_y = 0\right] - A_y + 2.4\,\text{k} + 2.4\,\text{k} - 1.36\,\text{k} = 0$$

$$\therefore A_y = 3.44\,\text{k}(\downarrow)$$

Separate the frame at the crown joint C, and draw an FBD of the left *or* right half.

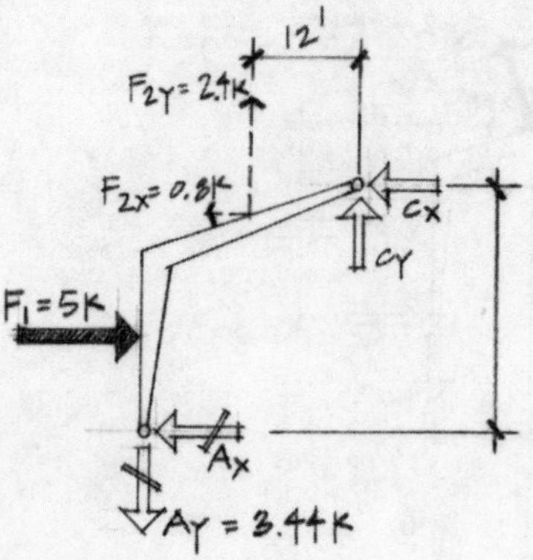

FBD (c)

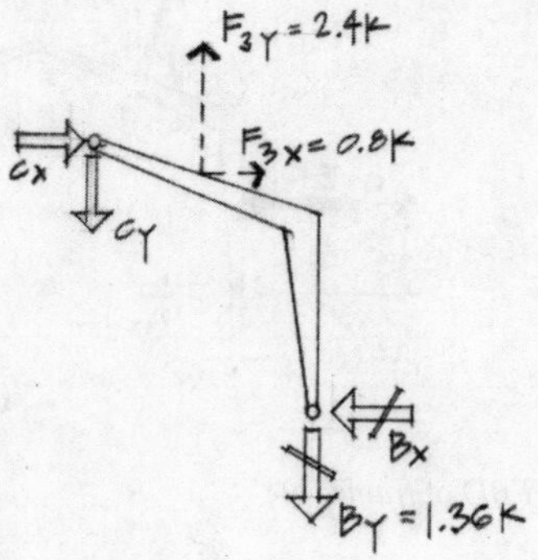

FBD (d)

Using FBD (c),

$$\left[\Sigma M_C = 0\right] - 2.4\,\text{k}(12') - 0.8\,\text{k}(4') + 5\,\text{k}(18') + 3.44\,\text{k}(24') - A_x(28') = 0$$

$$28A_x = 140.56$$
$$\therefore A_x = 5.02\,\text{k}(\leftarrow)$$

For the internal pin forces at C,

$$\left[\Sigma F_x = 0\right] + 5\,\text{k} - 5.02\,\text{k} - 0.8\,\text{k} + C_x = 0$$
$$\therefore C_x = +0.82\,\text{k}$$

$$\left[\Sigma F_y = 0\right] - 3.44\,\text{k} + 2.4\,\text{k} + C_y = 0$$
$$\therefore C_y = +1.04\,\text{k}$$

Going back to FBD (b) of the entire frame, solve for B_x:

$$\left[\Sigma F_x = 0\right] + 5\,\text{k} - 5.02\,\text{k} - 0.8\,\text{k} + 0.8\,\text{k} - B_x = 0$$
$$\therefore B_x = -0.02\,\text{k}$$

The negative sign in the result for B_x indicates that the original direction assumed in the FBD was incorrect.

$$\therefore B_x = 0.02\,\text{k}(\rightarrow)$$

Problems

Determine all support and pin forces for the multiforce member diagrams listed below.

28

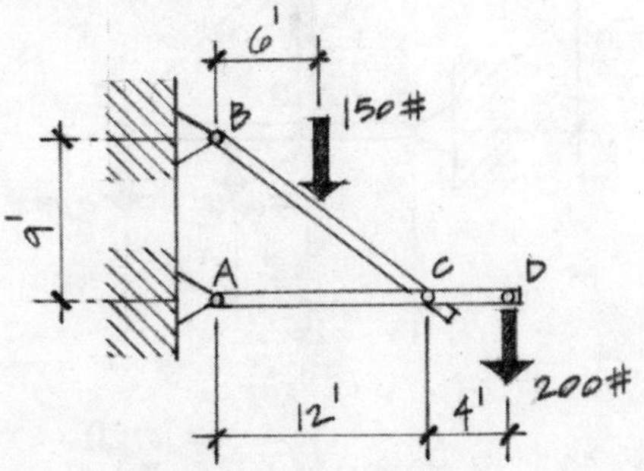

29

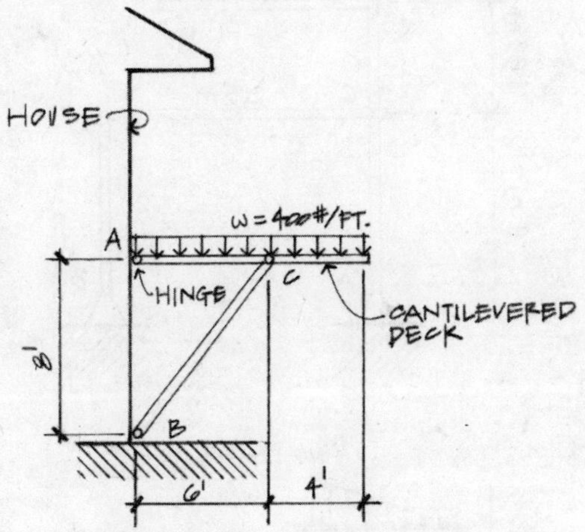

30

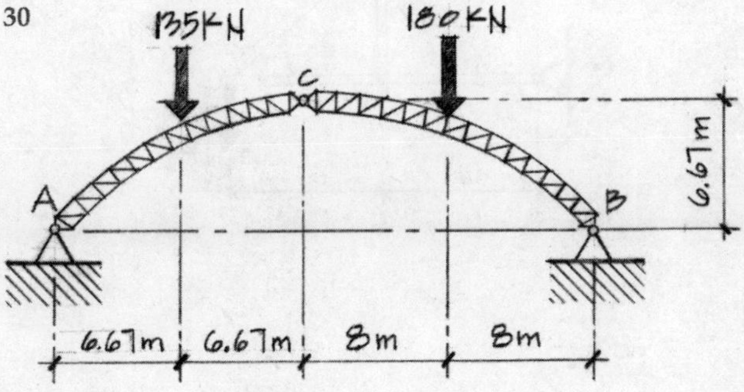

31

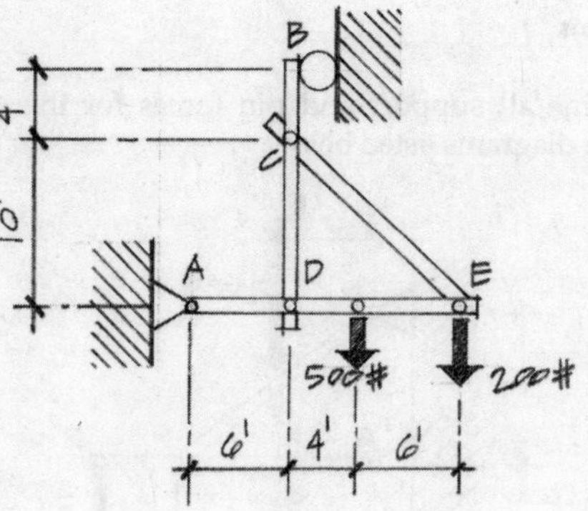

32

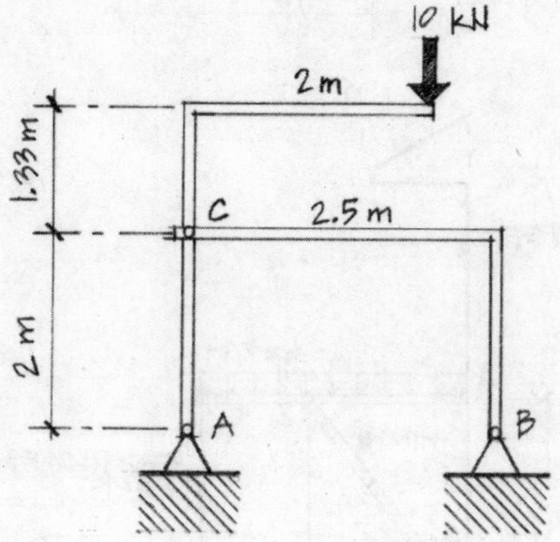

33

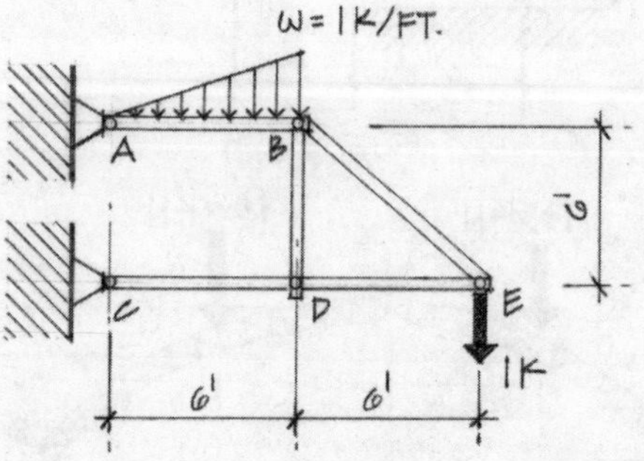

6 RETAINING WALLS

As the name implies, *retaining walls* are used to hold back (retain) solid or other granular material to maintain a difference in ground elevation. A *dam* is a retaining wall used to resist the lateral pressure of water or other fluids.

There are three general types of retaining walls: (a) the gravity wall (Figure 76), (b) the reinforced concrete cantilever retaining wall (Figure 77), and (c) the reinforced concrete cantilever retaining wall with counterforts (Figure 78).

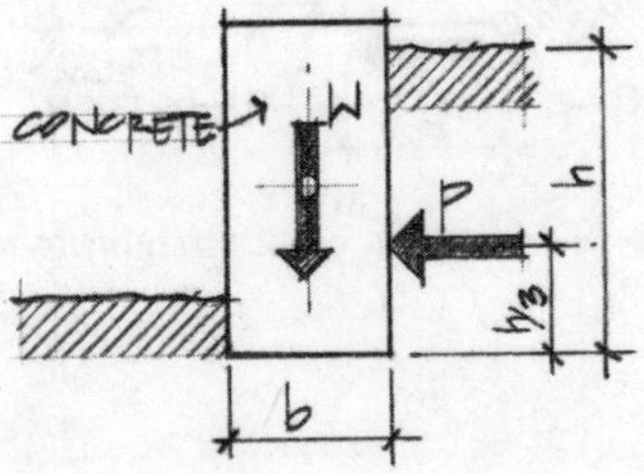

Figure 76 Gravity retaining wall.

Gravity retaining walls are generally built of plain concrete or masonry. Height h is generally less than four feet (1.3 m). A gravity wall depends on its mass to give it stability against the horizontal forces from the soil. Sliding resistance (friction) is developed between the concrete and soil at the base. Some major dams are constructed as gravity wall systems, but understandably, the base dimensions are immense.

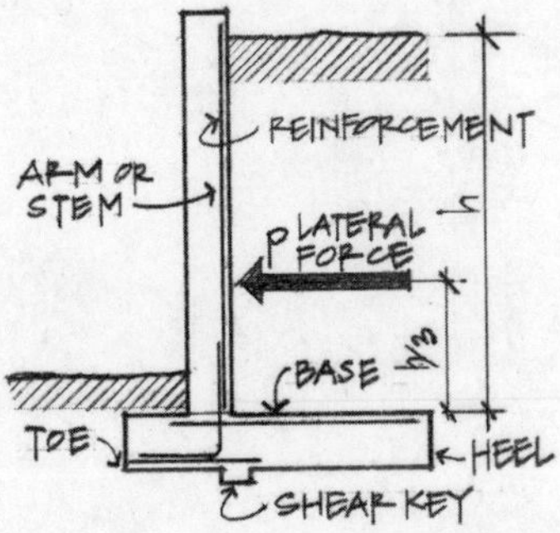

Figure 77 Reinforced cantilever retaining wall.

Reinforced concrete cantilever retaining walls are the most frequently used type of retaining wall, with an effectiveness up to a height (h) of about 20 to 25 feet (6 to 7.6 m). Stability of this wall type is achieved by the weight of the structure and the weight of the soil on the heel of the slab base. Sometimes a shear key is included at the bottom of the slab base to increase the wall's resistance to sliding. Retaining walls should have their foundations well below the frost line, and adequate drainage (weep) holes near the bottom of the wall should be provided to permit the water accumulation behind the wall to escape.

As the height of a retaining wall increases, the bending moment in the cantilever wall increases, requiring more thickness. The addition of counterforts (vertical triangular-shaped cross-walls) provides the additional depth at the base to absorb the large bending stresses. Counterfort walls behave like one-way slabs that span horizontally between the counterforts. Counterforts are called *buttresses* when this same configuration is used for the retained earth that is on the flat side of the wall.

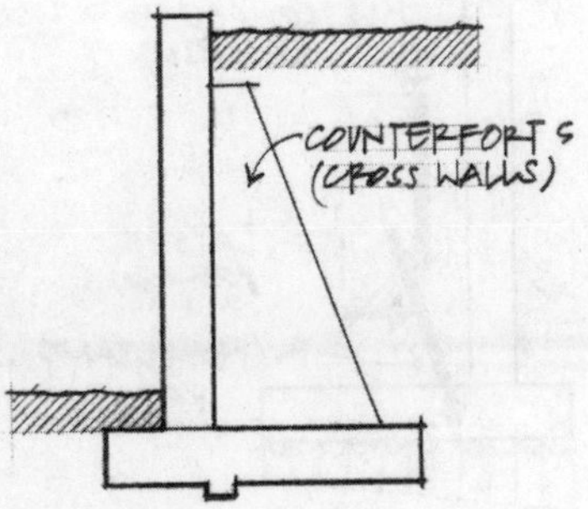

Figure 78 Counterfort wall.

Saturated loose sand or gravel, granular soil, or mud cause pressures against retaining walls in a manner similar to true fluids (liquids) by exerting a horizontal pressure. In true liquids, like water, the horizontal pressure and the vertical pressure are the same at a given depth. However, in soil, the horizontal pressure is less than the vertical pressure, with the ratio dependent on the physical

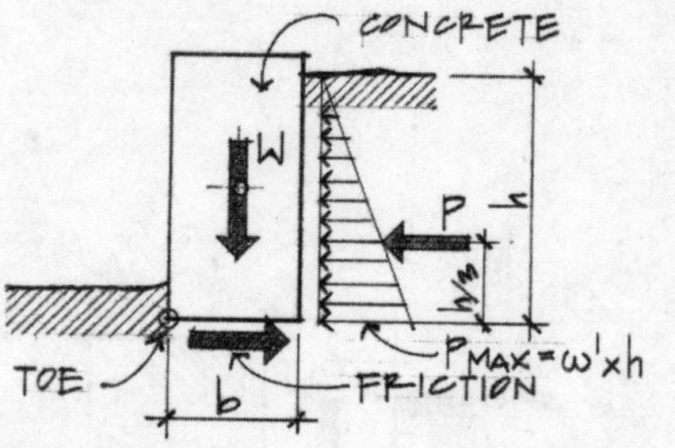

Figure 79 FBD of a gravity retaining wall.

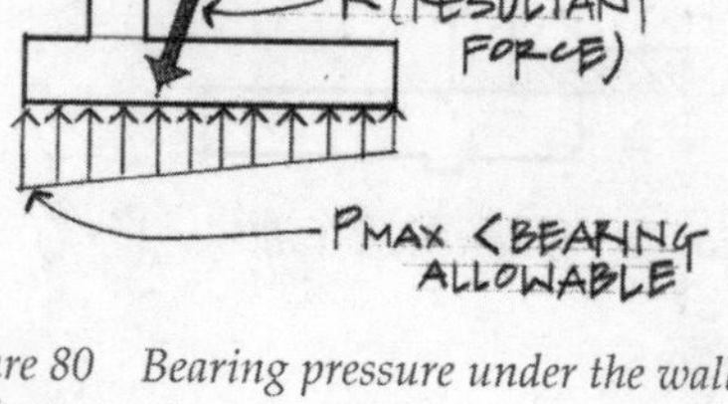

Figure 80 Bearing pressure under the wall footing.

properties of the soil. Soil pressure, as with liquids, increases proportionately with its depth below grade (Figure 79).

Lateral pressure increases linearly from zero at the top to a maximum at the bottom of the footing.

$$p = \omega' \times h$$

where

p = the magnitude of the earth pressure in psf or (kN/m^2)

ω' = the "equivalent" fluid weight (density) of the soil in pounds per cubic feet. Values range from a minimum of 30 pcf (for well-graded, clean gravel-sand mixes) to 60 pcf (for clayey sands). SI values are 4.7 to 9.4 kN/m^3.

h = soil depth in feet (m).

Therefore,

$$P = \frac{1}{2} \times (p_{max} \times h) \times 1 \text{ ft. or } 1 \text{ m}$$

where P = the lateral force (pounds, kips, N, or kN) based on the area of the pressure distribution acting on a 1-foot-wide (1-m-wide) strip of wall.

p_{max} = the maximum pressure at depth h (psf or kN/m^2)

Equivalent fluid pressure against a retaining wall may create conditions of instability. Retaining walls are susceptible to three failure modes: (a) sliding—when the friction at the footing base is insufficient to resist sliding; (b) overturning about the toe—when the lateral force produces an overturning moment greater than the stabilizing moment from the wall's weight, slab base weight, and the soil mass above the heel; and (c) excessive bearing pressure at the toe—when the combination of the vertical downward force and the compression at the toe caused by the horizontal force exceeds the allowable bearing pressure of the soil.

The pressure distribution under the base (Figure 80) depends upon the location and magnitude of the resultant (vertical and horizontal forces) force as it passes through the footing base.

Analysis of a cantilever retaining wall requires that the equilibrium summation of moments about the toe is stable; that is, the weight of the wall plus the backfill on the heel exceeds the overturning moment of the active soil pressure by a factor of at least 1.5 (a safety factor imposed by building codes). Once a stable configuration is achieved, the soil pressure distribution on the footing must be calculated to ensure that the bearing pressures are within allowable limits for the soil on site.

Building codes require that a safety factor of 1.5 also be provided to prevent sliding failure. In addition to general instability issues, individual components of a retaining wall (wall thickness, base size, base thickness, and reinforcement steel quantity and location) must be designed to resist the bending moments and shear forces induced by the soil pressure.

Many of the factors concerned with sliding go beyond the scope of statics; therefore, problems in this section will be limited to investigating a wall's resistance to overturning and bearing pressure beneath the toe.

Example Problems: Overturning Stability

19 A small gravity retaining wall (Figure 81) is used to accommodate a $4\frac{1}{2}$ foot drop in elevation. Determine the wall's factor of safety against overturning.

$\gamma_{concrete} = 150\frac{\#}{ft.^3}$ and the equivalent fluid density

$\omega' = 40\frac{\#}{ft.^3}$

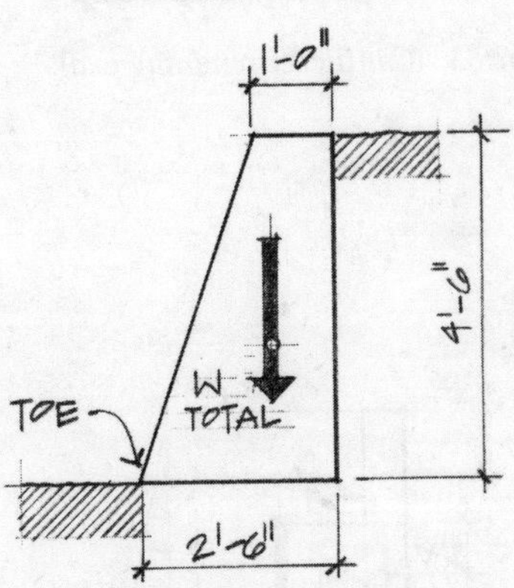

Figure 81 Small gravity dam.

Solution:

Analyze the retaining wall by assuming a 1 foot tributary length of the wall as a representation of the entire wall (Figure 82).

$$W_1 = \frac{1}{2}(1.5\,\text{ft.})(4.5\,\text{ft.})(1\,\text{ft.})\left(150\frac{\#}{\text{ft.}^3}\right) = 506\#$$

$$W_2 = (1\,\text{ft.})(4.5\,\text{ft.})(1\,\text{ft.})\left(150\frac{\#}{\text{ft.}^3}\right) = 675\#$$

$$P_{max} = \omega' \times h = \left(40\frac{\#}{\text{ft.}^3}\right) \times (4.5\,\text{ft.}) = 180\frac{\#}{\text{ft.}^2}$$

$$P_3 = \frac{1}{2}(p_{max}) \times (h) \times (1\,\text{ft.}) = \frac{1}{2}\left(180\frac{\#}{\text{ft.}^2}\right)(4.5\,\text{ft.})(1\,\text{ft.})$$

$$= 405\#$$

The overturning moment M_{OTM} about the toe at A is

$$M_{OTM} = P_3 \times 1.5\,\text{ft.} = (405\#) \times (1.5\,\text{ft.}) = 608\#\text{-ft.}$$

The *stabilizing* moment or *righting* moment, M_{RM} is equal to

$$M_{RM} = W_1 \times (1\,\text{ft.}) + W_2 \times (2\,\text{ft.})$$
$$M_{RM} = (506\#)(1\,\text{ft.}) + (675\#)(2\,\text{ft.}) = 1{,}856\#\text{-ft.}$$

The factor of safety against overturning at A is

$$SF = \frac{M_{RM}}{M_{OTM}} = \frac{(1{,}856\#\text{-ft.})}{(608\#\text{-ft.})} = 3.05 > 1.5$$

∴ The wall is stable against overturning.

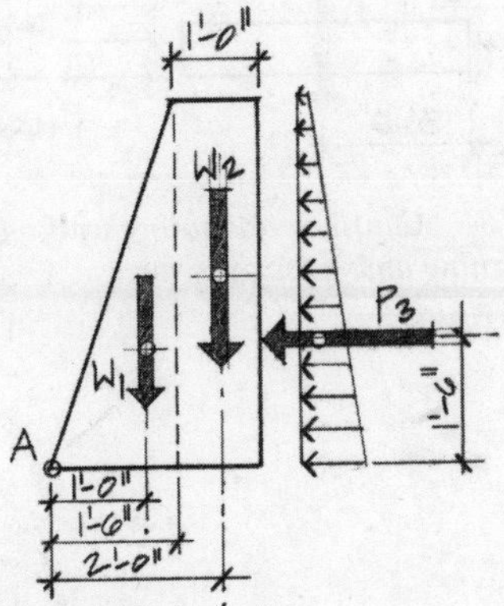

Figure 82 Overturning and stabilizing forces acting on the dam.

Force $P_3 = 405\#$ represents the horizontal sliding force that must be resisted at the base of the footing through frictional resistance.

20 Determine the overturning stability of the reinforced cantilever retaining wall shown in Figure 83. What is the sliding force that needs to be resisted at the base of the footing?

$$\gamma_{conc.} = 150 \text{ pcf}; \quad \gamma_{soil} = 110 \text{ pcf}$$
$$\omega' = 35 \text{ pcf (equivalent fluid density)}$$

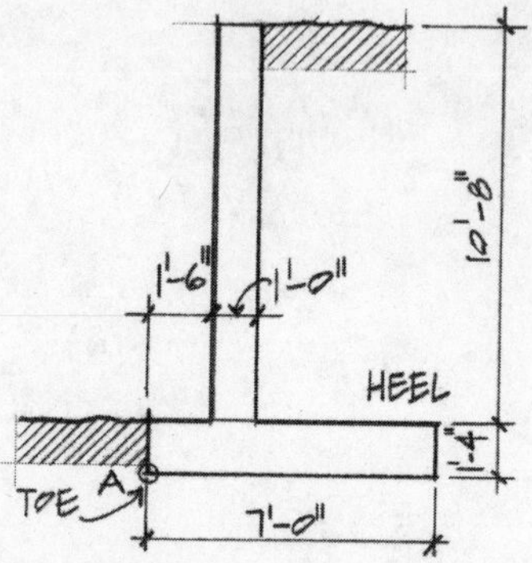

Figure 83 Cantilever retaining wall.

Solution:

Assume a 1-foot-wide strip of wall as representative of the entire wall (Figure 84).

$$\underset{(wall)}{W_1} = (1 \text{ ft.})(10.67 \text{ ft.})(1 \text{ ft.})\left(150\frac{\#}{\text{ft.}^3}\right) = 1{,}600\#$$

$$\underset{(base)}{W_2} = (1.33 \text{ ft.})(7 \text{ ft.})(1 \text{ ft.})\left(150\frac{\#}{\text{ft.}^3}\right) = 1{,}397\#$$

$$\underset{(soil)}{W_3} = (4.5 \text{ ft.})(10.67 \text{ ft.})(1 \text{ ft.})\left(110\frac{\#}{\text{ft.}^3}\right) = 5{,}282\#$$

Evaluating the moments about the toe at A,

$$p_{max} = \omega' \times h = \left(35\frac{\#}{\text{ft.}^3}\right) \times (12 \text{ ft.}) = 420\frac{\#}{\text{ft.}^2}$$

$$P_4 = \left(\frac{1}{2}\right) \times (p_{max}) \times h = \left(\frac{1}{2}\right) \times \left(420\frac{\#}{\text{ft.}^2}\right) \times (12 \text{ ft.})$$
$$= 2{,}520\#$$

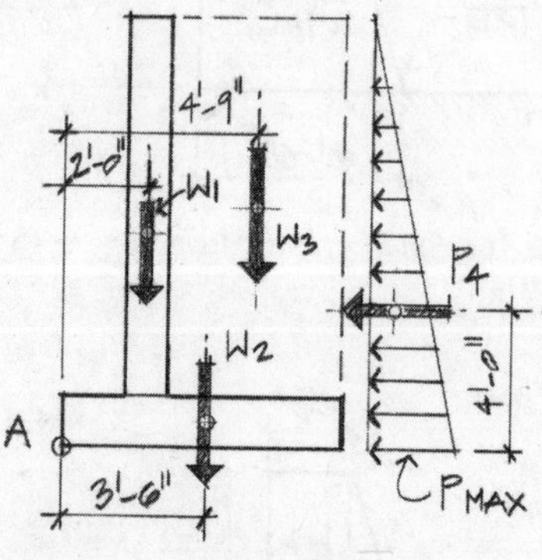

Figure 84 Cantilever retaining wall with overturning and stabilizing forces.

$$M_{OTM} = P_4 \times (4 \text{ ft.}) = (2{,}520\#) \times (4 \text{ ft.}) = 10{,}080\#\text{-ft.}$$

The righting moment, or the stabilizing moment, about A is equal to

$$M_{RM} = W_1(2 \text{ ft.}) + W_2(3.5 \text{ ft.}) + W_3(4.75 \text{ ft.})$$
$$= (1{,}600\#)(2 \text{ ft.}) + (1{,}397\#)(3.5 \text{ ft.}) + (5{,}282\#)(4.75 \text{ ft.})$$

$$M_{RM} = 33{,}180\#\text{-ft.}$$

The safety factor against overturning is computed as

$$SF = \frac{M_{RM}}{M_{OTM}} = \frac{33{,}180\#\text{-ft.}}{10{,}080\#\text{-ft.}} = 3.29 > 1.5$$

The retaining wall is stable against overturning about the toe.

Frictional resistance developed between the bottom of the footing and the soil must be a factor of 1.5 (safety factor) the horizontal fluid force $P_4 = 2{,}520\#$, or $3{,}780\#$.

Retaining wall design, in its proportioning and element sizing, must ensure that the bearing pressure under the footing (at the toe) remains below the allowable limit for the soil involved. The pressure distribution varies, depending on the location and magnitude of the resultant (vector sum of the horizontal and vertical forces) as it passes through the base of the footing (Figures 85 through 87). Not all resultant forces are located beneath the wall section. However, it is generally more economical if the resultant is located within the middle third of the base (Figure 85), because then the bearing pressures will be in compression throughout the base. If the resultant is located right on the edge of the middle third, where $x = \frac{a}{3}$, the pressure distribution results in a triangle, as shown in Figure 86. When the resultant force is located outside the middle third, where $x < \frac{a}{3}$, the pressure would indicate tension at or near the heel. Tension cannot develop between soil and a concrete footing that rests on it. Therefore, the pressure distribution shown in Figure 87 results, with the implication that a slight lifting off the soil occurs at the heel. Historical examples exist of some cathedrals built during the Middle Ages that suffered catastrophic failure when the resultant forces passing through the stone walls and footings fell outside of the middle third of the base. It is generally good practice to proportion the retaining wall to have the resultant fall within the middle third. This practice helps to reduce the magnitude of the maximum pressure, and it will minimize the variation between the maximum and minimum pressures.

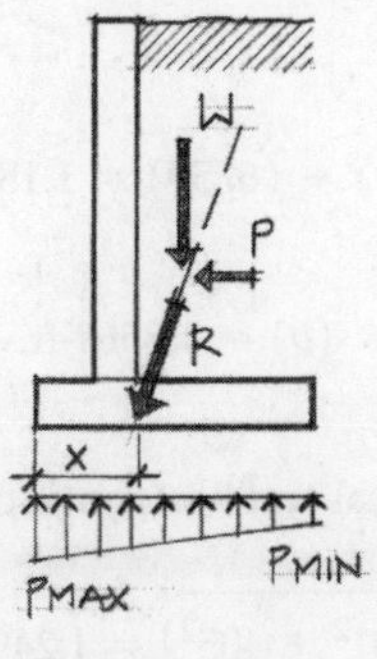

Figure 85 Trapezoidal pressure distribution.

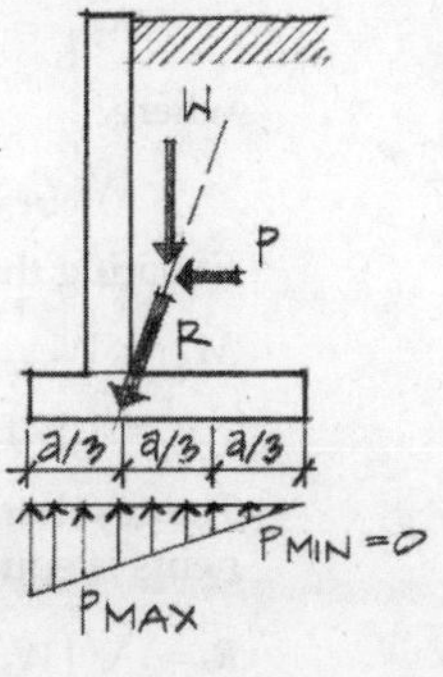

Figure 86 Resultant at the third point—a triangular pressure distribution.

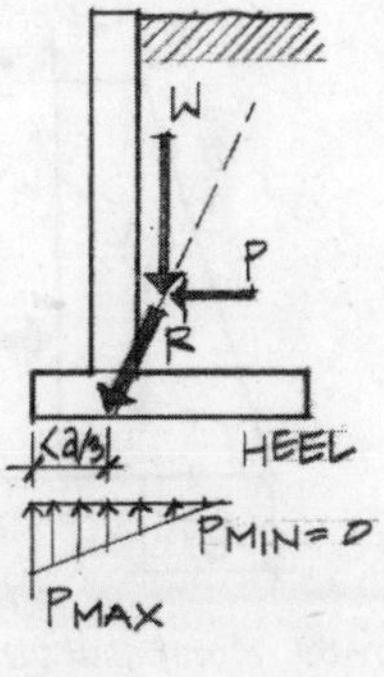

Figure 87 Tension possible at the heel.

Force diagram in Figure 85:

$$P_{max} = \frac{W}{a_2}(4a - 6x) \qquad P_{min} = \frac{W}{a^2}(6x - 2a)$$

Force diagram in Figure 86:

$$P_{max} = \frac{2W}{a} \qquad P_{min} = 0$$

Force diagram in Figure 87:

$$P_{max} \frac{2W}{3x} \qquad P_{min} = 0$$

If a wall were to be constructed on highly compressible soil, such as some types of clay, a pressure distribution as found in Figures 86 and 87 would result. The larger settlement of the toe, as compared to the heel, would result in a tilting of the wall. Foundations constructed on compressible soils should have resultants falling at or near the center of the footing. Resultants can fall outside the middle third if the foundation is constructed on very incompressible soil, such as well-compacted gravel or rock.

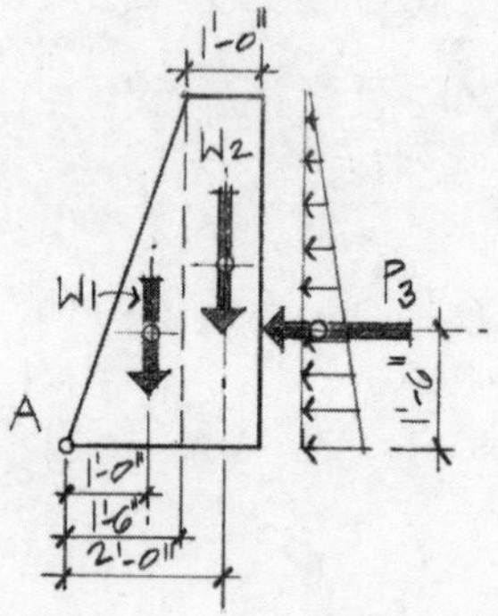

Figure 88 Forces on the retaining wall.

21 The bearing pressure will be checked for the gravity retaining wall found in Example Problem 19. Assume that the allowable bearing pressure is 2,000 psf.

Wall weights and the horizontal fluid force P_3 are as shown in Figure 88. The location of the resultant vertical force W_{total} is obtained by writing a moment equation in which

$$M_A = W_1 \times (1\text{ ft.}) + W_2 \times (2\text{ ft.})$$

$$M_A = (506\#)(1\text{ ft.}) + (675\#)(2\text{ ft.}) = 1{,}856\#\text{-ft.}$$

From Figure 89, a moment equation due to the wall weight can also be written as

$$M_A = (W_{total}) \times (b)$$

where

$$W_{total} = W_1 + W_2 = (506\#) + (675\#) = 1{,}181\#$$

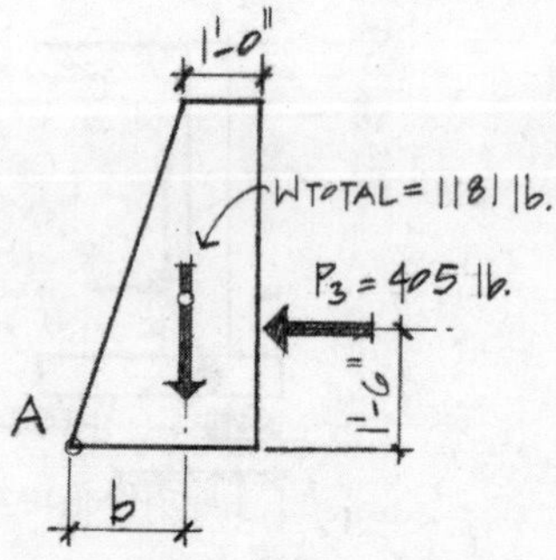

Figure 89 Total wall weight at its centroid.

Equating the two equations,

$$M_A = W_{total} \times (b) = (1{,}181\#) \times (b) = 1{,}856\#\text{-ft.}$$

$$\therefore b = 1.57\text{ ft.}$$

The resultant force R of the vertical and horizontal components is equal to:

$$R = \sqrt{(W_{total}^2 + P_3^2)} = \sqrt{(1{,}181^2 + 405^2)} = 1{,}249\#$$

Locating the point where the resultant intersects the base of the footing utilizes Varignon's theorem, in which the moment caused by the vertical and horizontal forces about the toe at A is the same as the moment resulting from R_y (which is equal to W_{total}) times the distance x from point A (Figure 90).

$$x = \frac{M_{RM} - M_{OTM}}{W_{total}}$$

Values for the overturning moment (M_{OTM}) and the righting moment (M_{RM}) are obtained from work done in Example Problem 19.

$$x = \frac{(1{,}856\#\text{-ft.}) - (608\#\text{-ft.})}{(1{,}181\#)} = 1.06 \text{ ft.}$$

The dimension $x = 1.06$ ft. falls within the middle third of the base dimension.

$$\frac{a}{3} \le x = 1.06 \text{ ft.} \le \frac{2a}{3}$$

Because the resultant is within the middle third of the base dimension, the equations for the maximum and minimum bearing pressures are

$$p_{max} = \frac{W}{a^2}(4a - 6x) = \frac{(1{,}181\#)}{(2.5^2)}(4 \times 2.5 \text{ ft.} - 6 \times 1.06 \text{ ft.})$$

$$p_{max} = \left(189\frac{\#}{\text{ft.}^2}\right)(10 - 6.36) = 688\frac{\#}{\text{ft.}^2}$$

$$p_{min} = \frac{W}{a^2}(6x - 2a) = \left(\frac{1181\#}{2.5^2}\right)(6 \times 1.06 - 2 \times 2.5)$$

$$= 257\frac{\#}{\text{ft.}^2}$$

The maximum bearing pressure is well within the allowable bearing stress limit of 2,000 psf.

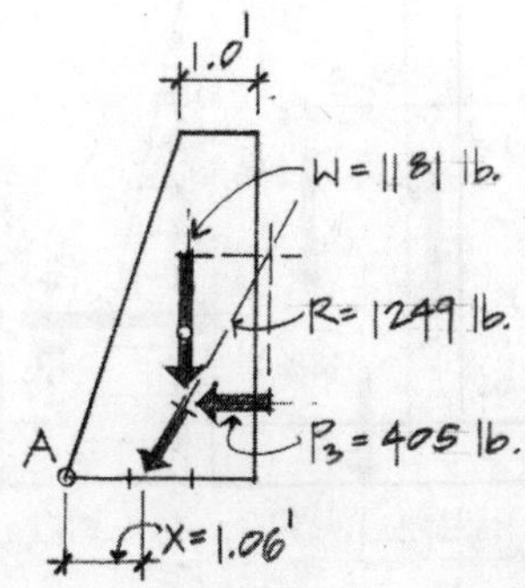

Figure 90 Resultant within the middle third.

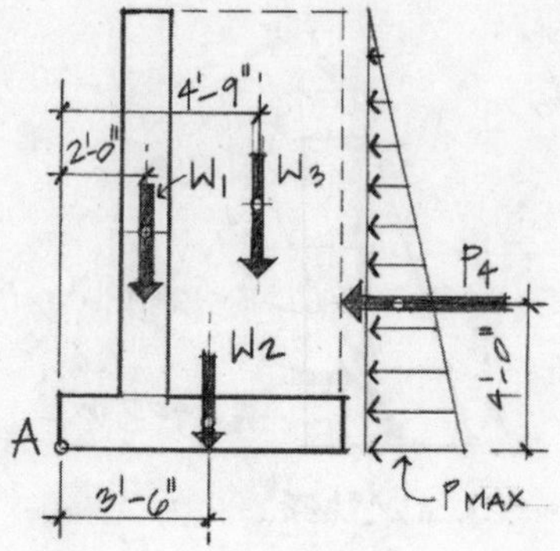

Figure 91 Retaining wall forces.

22 Perform a check of the bearing pressure beneath the wall footing in Example Problem 20. Assume an allowable bearing pressure 3,000 psf.

Solution:

The total downward force W_{total} and its location can be found as follows (Figure 91):

$$W_{total} = W_1 + W_2 + W_3$$
$$W_{total} = (1{,}600\#) + (1{,}400\#) + (5{,}280\#) = 8{,}280\#$$
$$M_A = (W_1 \times 2\text{ ft.}) + (W_2 \times 3.5\text{ ft.}) + (W_3 \times 4.75\text{ ft.})$$
$$M_A = (1{,}600\# \times 2\text{ ft.}) + (1{,}400\# \times 3.5\text{ ft.}) + (5{,}280\,\# \times 4.75\text{ ft.}) = 33{,}180\,\#\text{-ft.}$$

Also, $M_A = W_{total} \times b$.

Equating both equations,

$$M_A = (8{,}280\#) \times (b) = 33{,}180\,\#\text{-ft.}$$
$$\therefore b = 4.0\text{ ft.}$$

The resultant force R is computed as

$$R = \sqrt{(W_{total}^2 + P_4^2)} = \sqrt{(8{,}280^2) + (2{,}520^2)} = 8{,}655\#$$

Using the moment values obtained in the solution of Example Problem 20, the distance x from the toe at A can be solved.

$$x = \frac{M_{RM} - M_{OTM}}{W_{total}} = \frac{(33{,}180\#\text{-ft.}) - (10{,}080\#\text{-ft.})}{8{,}280\#}$$
$$= 2.8\text{ ft.}$$

$$\frac{a}{3} = 2.33\text{ ft.} < x = 2.8\text{ ft.} < \frac{2a}{3} = 6.67\text{ ft.}$$

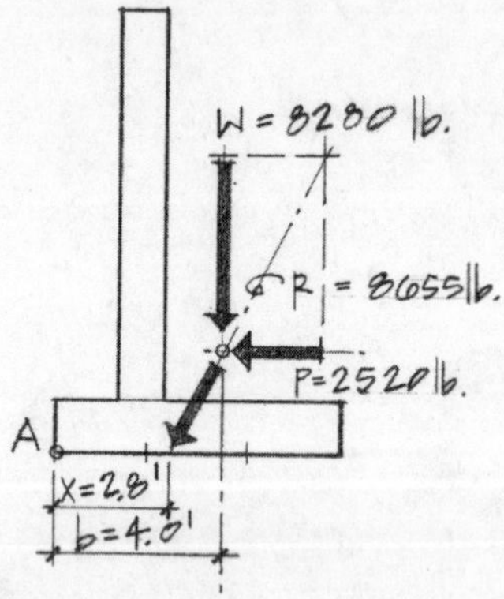

Figure 92 Resultant force passing through the base.

The resultant is within the middle third of the base, as shown in Figure 92; therefore, the entire bearing pressure will be in compression. A trapezoidal distribution results, in which

$$p_{max} = \frac{W}{a^2}(4a - 6x) = \left(\frac{8{,}280}{7^2}\right)(4 \times 7\text{ ft.} - 6 \times 2.8\text{ ft.})$$
$$= 1{,}893\text{ psf}$$
$$p_{max} = 1893\text{ psf} < 3000\text{ psf}; \therefore \text{OK.}$$

$$p_{min} = \frac{W}{a^2}(6x - 2a)$$

$$= \left(\frac{8{,}280}{7^2}\right)(6 \times 2.8 - 2 \times 7) = 473 \text{ psf}$$

23 Eight-inch nominal concrete masonry (CMU) blocks are used to retain soil as shown in Figure 93. Determine the wall's stability against overturning, then check the bearing pressure under the footing base at the toe (*A*). Assume that the allowable bearing pressure for the soil is limited to 2,500 psf.

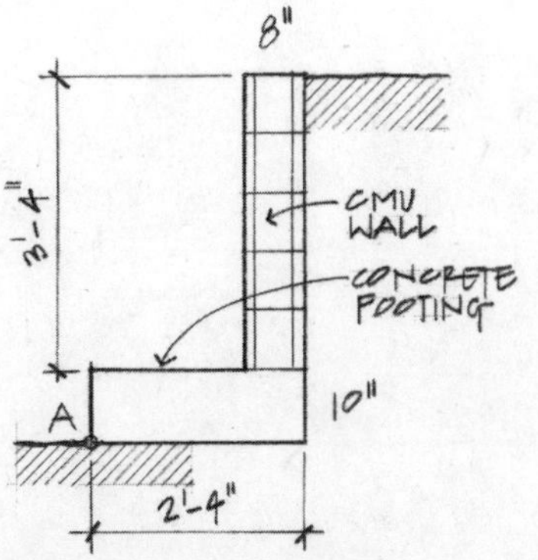

Figure 93 Reinforced CMU retaining wall.

Assume: $\gamma_{CMU} = 125\text{\#-ft.}^3$;

$\gamma_{conc} = 150\frac{\#}{ft^3}$; equivalent design fluid pressure

$\omega' = 40\frac{\#}{ft^3}$

Solution:

Assume a 1-foot-wide width of wall as representative of the entire wall (Figure 94).

$$W_1 = W_{CMU} = (1\text{ ft.})(3.33\text{ ft.})\left(\frac{8}{12}\text{ft.}\right)\left(125\frac{\#}{ft^3}\right) = 279\#$$

$$W_2 = W_{ftg} = (1\text{ ft.})\left(\frac{10}{12}\text{ft.}\right)(2.33\text{ ft.})\left(150\frac{\#}{ft^3}\right) = 291\#$$

$$W_{total} = W_1 + W_2 = 279\# + 291\# = 570\#$$

The horizontal force on the wall due to the fluid pressure is equal to

$$p_{max} = \left(40\frac{\#}{ft^3}\right)(4.17\text{ ft.}) = 167 \text{ psf}$$

$$P = \frac{1}{2}(p_{max})(h)(1\text{ ft.}) = \frac{1}{2}(167\text{\#-ft.}^2)(4.17\text{ ft.})(1\text{ ft.})$$

$$= 348\#$$

The location of the resultant weight W_{total} is determined by summing moments about the toe at *A*.

$M_A = W_1 \times (2\text{ ft.}) + W_2 \times (1.17\text{ ft.})$

$M_A = (279\#)(2\text{ ft.}) + (291\#)(1.17\text{ ft.}) = 899\text{\#-ft.}$

$M_A = W_{total} \times (b) = (570\#) \times (b) = 899\text{\#-ft.}$

$\therefore b = 1.58\text{ ft.} \cong 1.6\text{ ft.}$

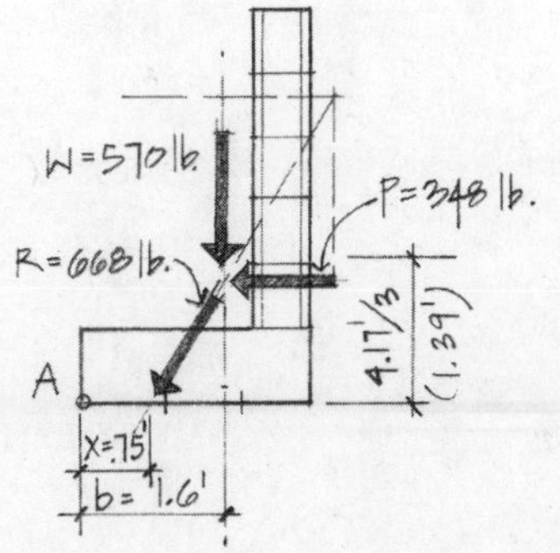

Figure 94 Resultant force outside the middle third.

The resultant force on the retaining wall is

$$R = \sqrt{(570^2 + 348^2)} = 668\#$$

The overturning moment caused by the horizontal force about the toe at *A* is

$$M_{OTM} = (348\#) \times \left(\frac{4.17\text{ ft.}}{3}\right) = 484\text{\#-ft.}$$

The righting or stabilizing moment due to the total weight of the retaining wall is calculated as

$$M_{RM} = W_{total} \times b = (570\#) \times (1.6\,\text{ft.}) = 912\#\text{-ft.}$$

Checking the safety factor against overturning:

$$SF = \frac{M_{RM}}{M_{OTM}} = \frac{912\#\text{-ft.}}{484\#\text{-ft.}} = 1.9 > 1.5 \quad \therefore \text{OK}$$

Resultant force R intersects the footing base at

$$x = \frac{M_{RM} - M_{OTM}}{W_{total}} = \frac{(912 - 484)\#\text{-ft.}}{570\#} = 0.75\,\text{ft.}$$

$$\frac{a}{3} = 0.78\,\text{ft.} > x = 0.75\,\text{ft.}$$

$\therefore$ The resultant falls outside the middle third section of the footing base.

$$p_{max} = \frac{2W}{3x} = \frac{3(570)}{3(0.75)} = 507\,\text{psf} < 2{,}500\,\text{psf}$$

$\therefore$ OK

Supplementary Problems

Distributed Loads: Section 2

Determine the support reactions for the problems below. Draw all appropriate FBDs.

34

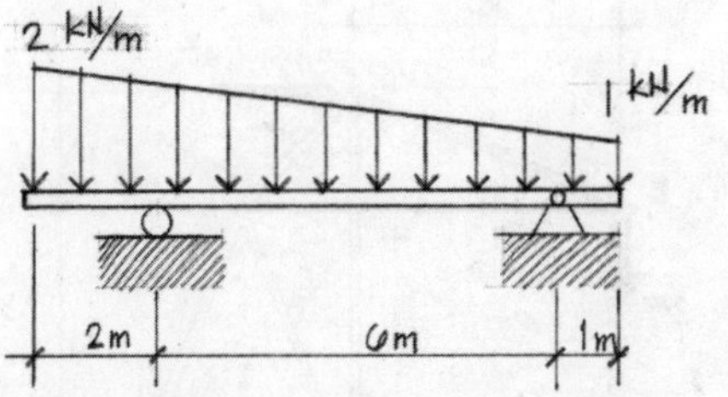

35

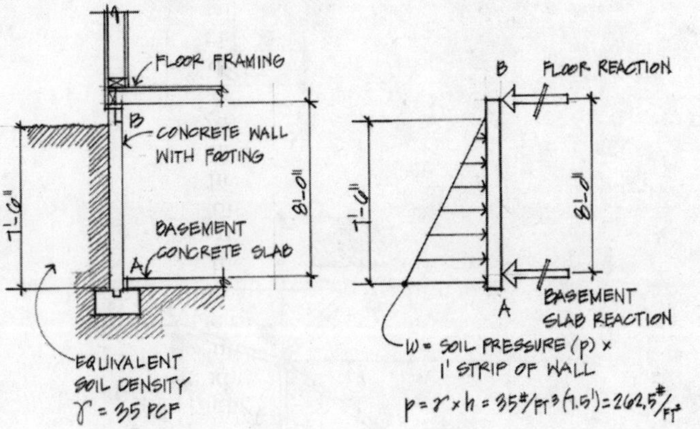

36

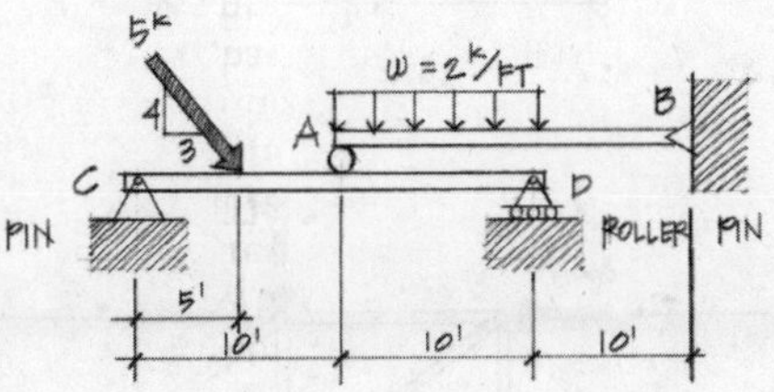

37

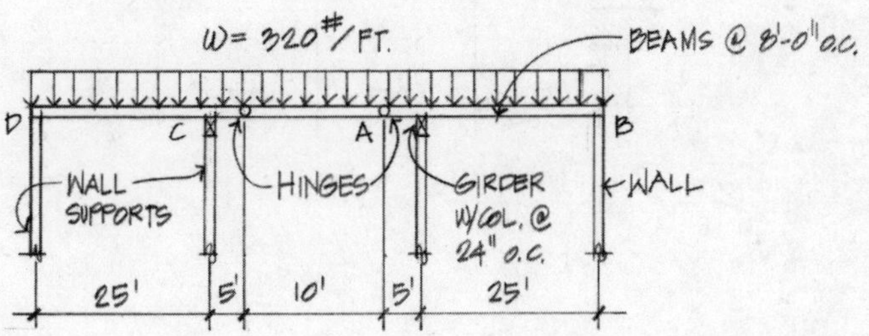

Trusses—Method of Joints: Section 3

Using the method of joints, determine the force in each member. Summarize your results in a force summation diagram.

38

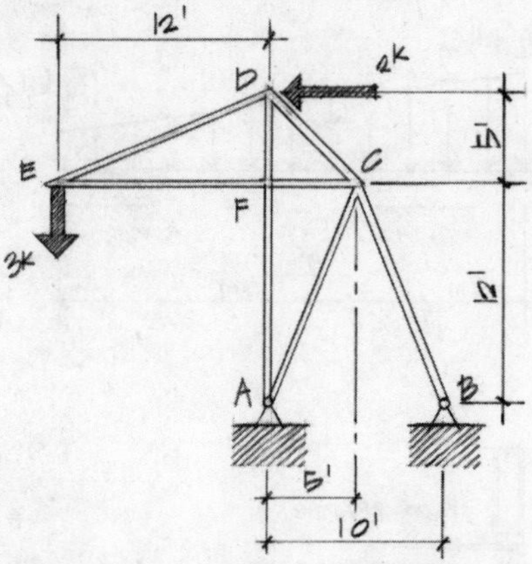

39

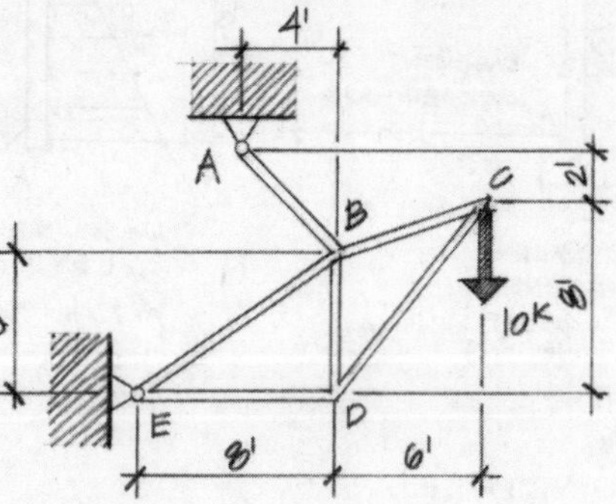

40

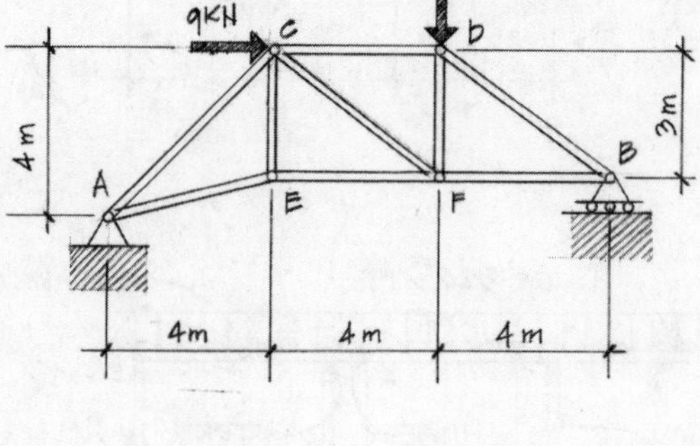

41

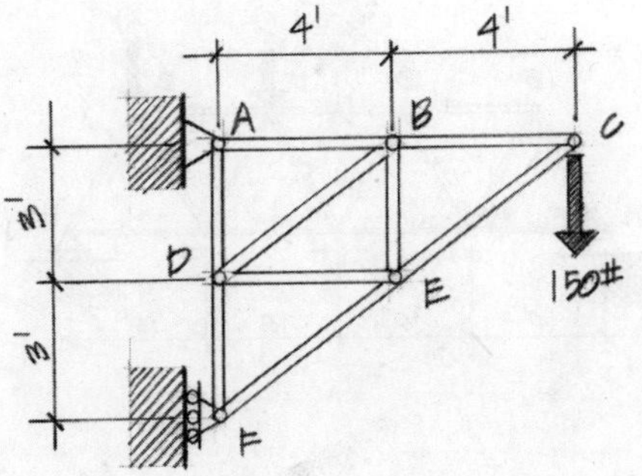

42

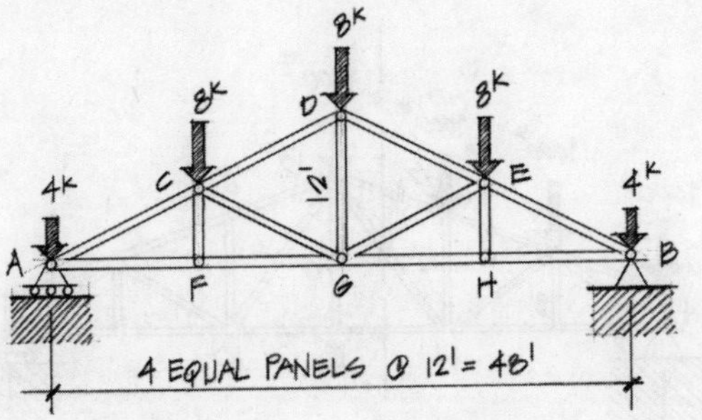

Trusses—Method of Sections: Section 3

43 Solve for *FG*, *DG*, and *AB*.

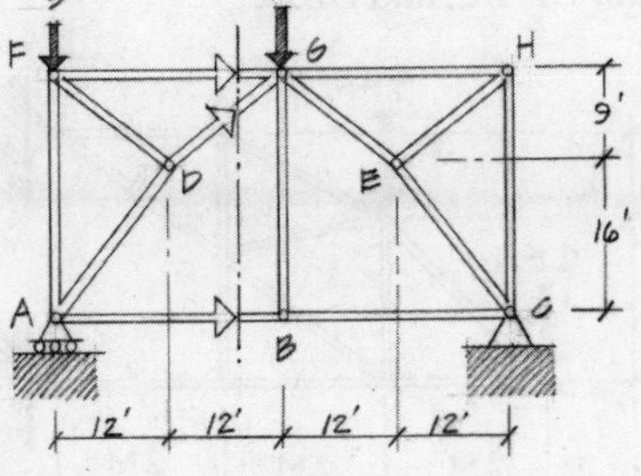

44 Solve for *CD, HD,* and *HG.*

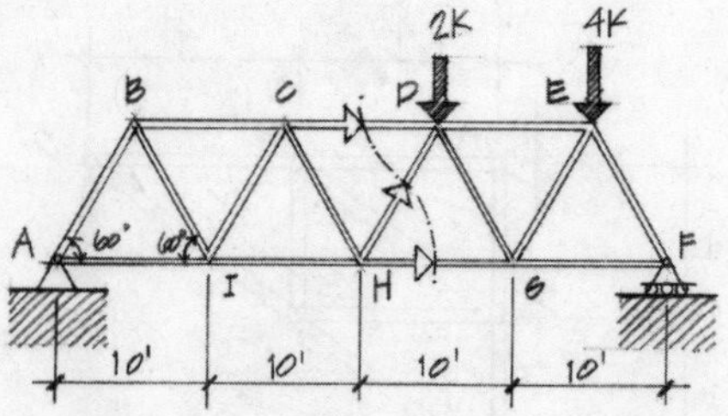

45 Solve for *GB, HB, BE,* and *HE.*

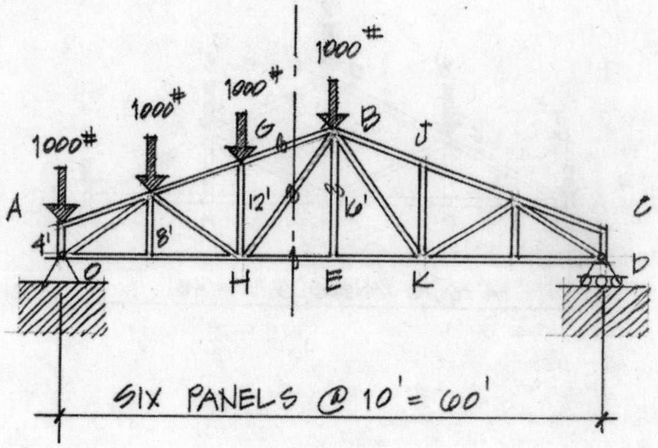

46 Solve for *AB, BC,* and *DE.*

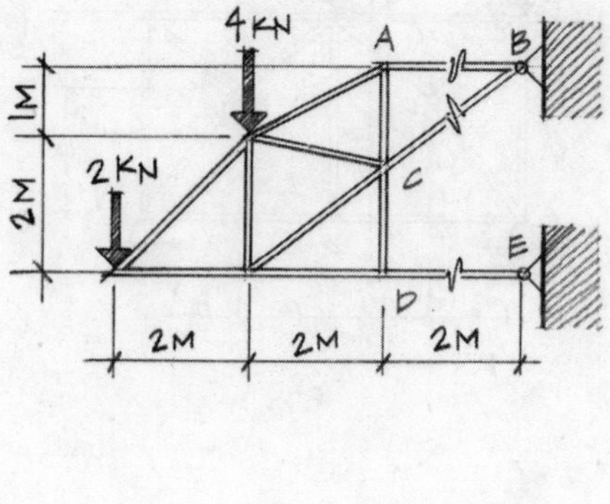

Trusses—Diagonal Tension Counters: Section 3

Determine the effective tension counters using the method of sections.

47

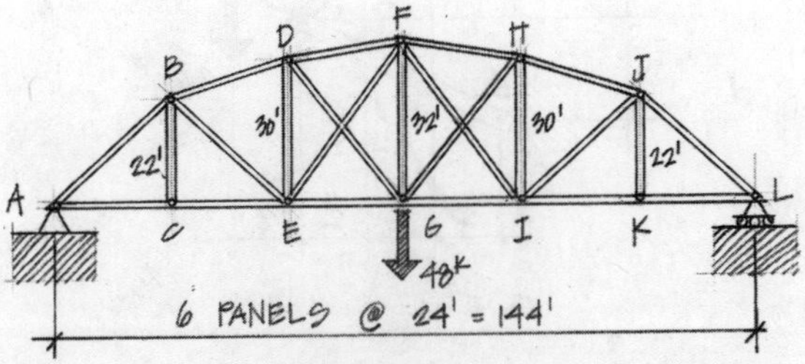

48

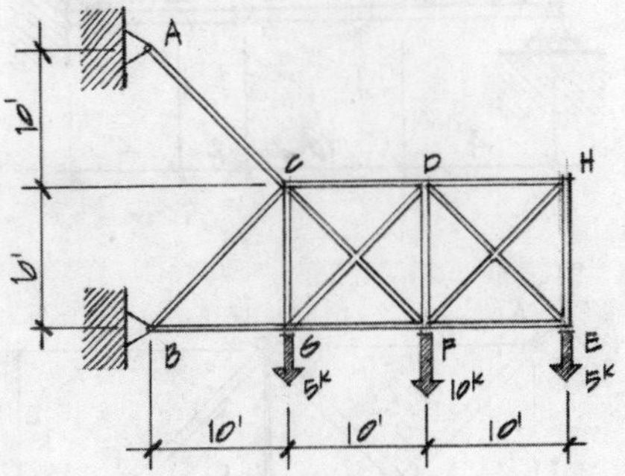

Method of Members: Sections 4 and 5

Determine the support reactions and all internal pin forces.

49

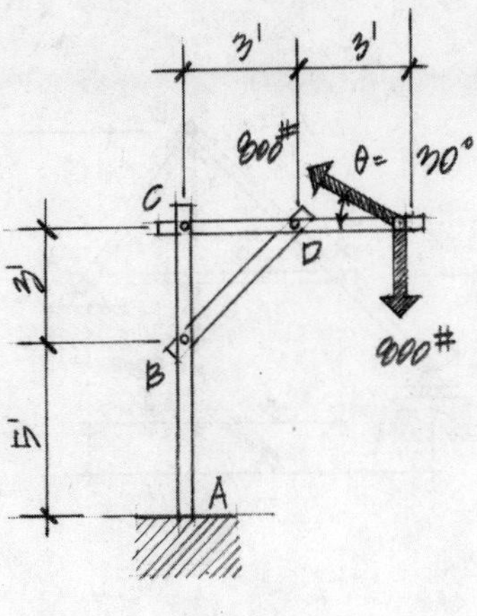

50

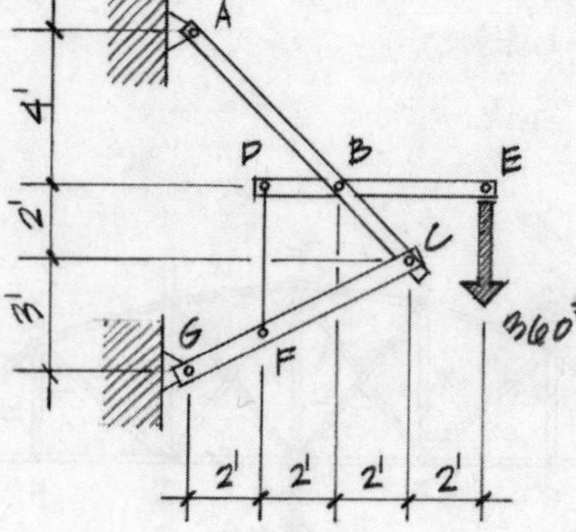
A
D
B
E
C
G
F
360#
4'
2'
3'
2'
2'
2'
2'

51

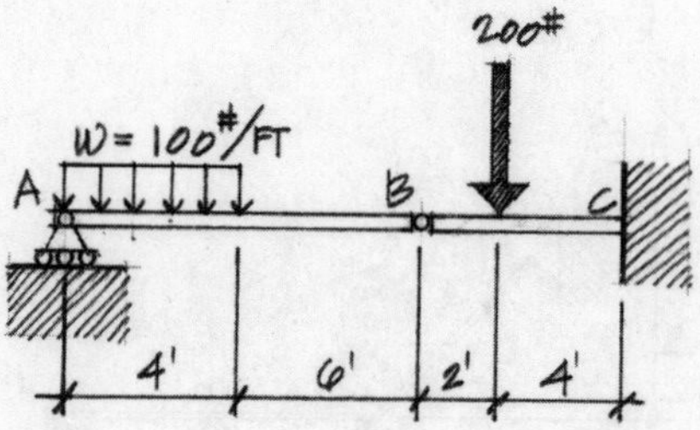
200#
W = 100#/FT
A
B
C
4'
6'
2'
4'

52

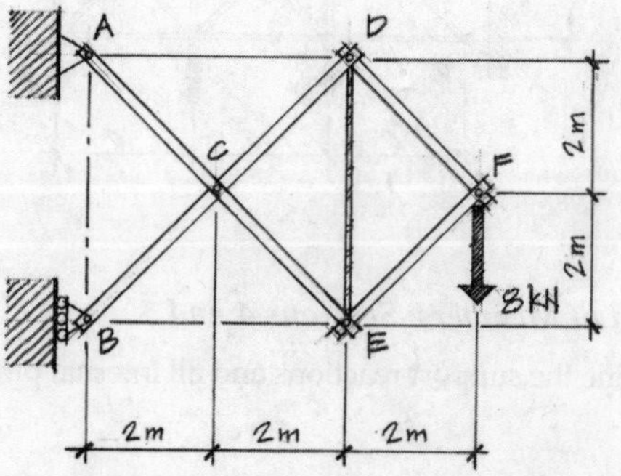
A
D
C
F
B
E
8KN
2m
2m
2m
2m
2m

53

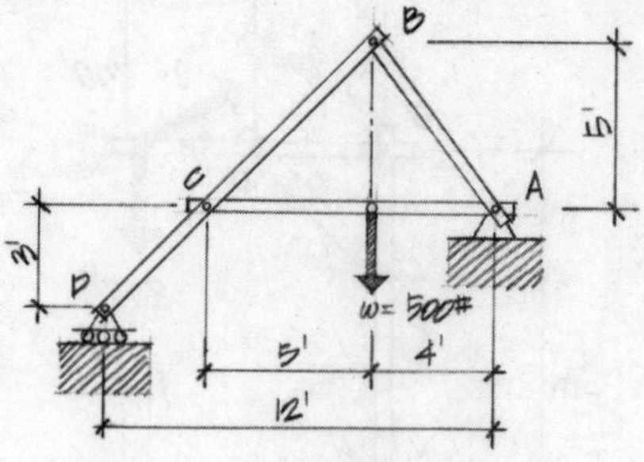
B
C
A
D
5'
3'
w= 500#
5'
4'
12'

54

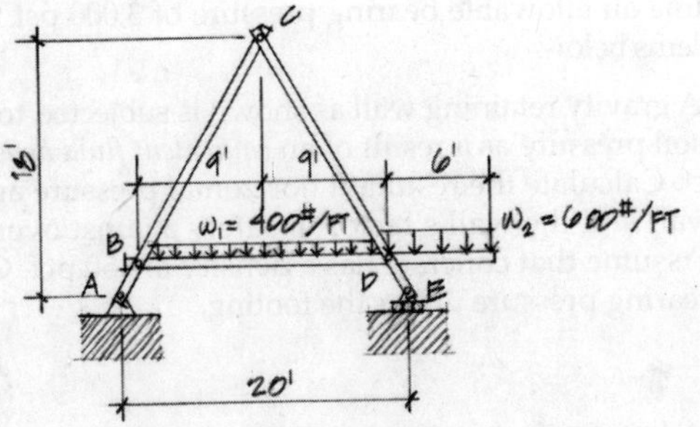
C
10'
9'
9'
6'
$w_1 = 400^{\#}/FT$
$w_2 = 600^{\#}/FT$
B
A
D
E
20'

55

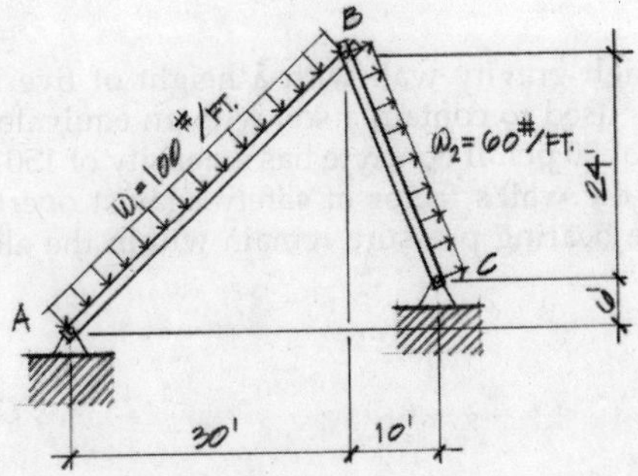
B
$w = 100^{\#}/FT.$
$w_2 = 60^{\#}/FT.$
24'
3'
A
C
30'
10'

56

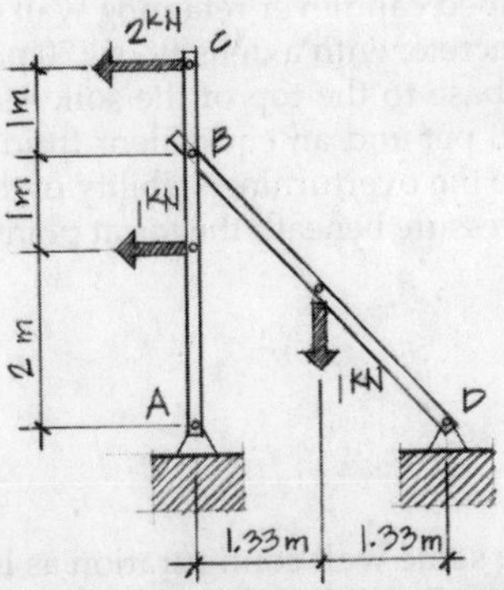
2KN
C
1m
B
1m
1KN
2 m
A
1KN
D
1.33m
1.33m

57

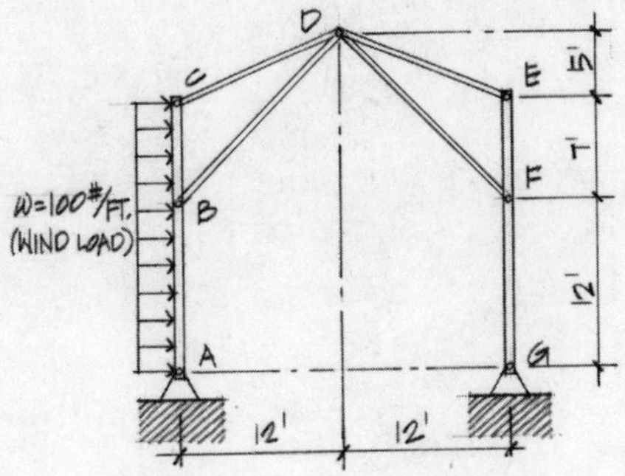
D
C
E
5'
7'
F
$w=100^{\#}/FT.$
(WIND LOAD)
B
12'
A
G
12'
12'

Retaining Walls: Section 6

Assume an allowable bearing pressure of 3,000 psf for all problems below.

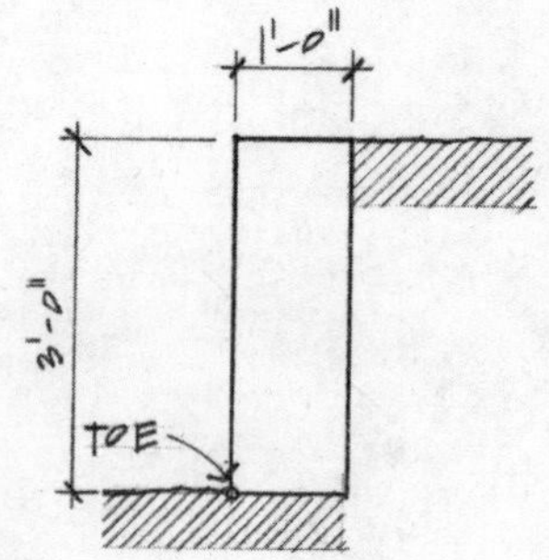

58 A gravity retaining wall as shown is subjected to a lateral soil pressure as a result of an *equivalent fluid density* of 35 pcf. Calculate the resultant horizontal pressure against the wall and the wall's factor of safety against overturning. Assume that concrete has a density of 150 pcf. Check the bearing pressure under the footing.

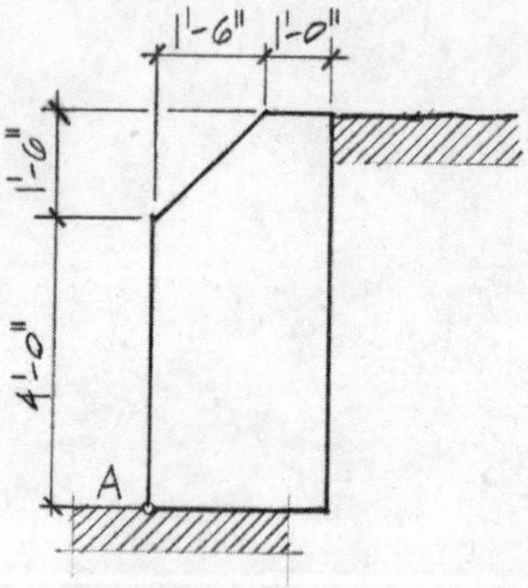

59 A high gravity wall with a height of five feet, six inches is used to contain a soil with an equivalent fluid density of 30 pcf. If concrete has a density of 150 pcf, determine the wall's factor of safety against overturning. Does the bearing pressure remain within the allowable limit?

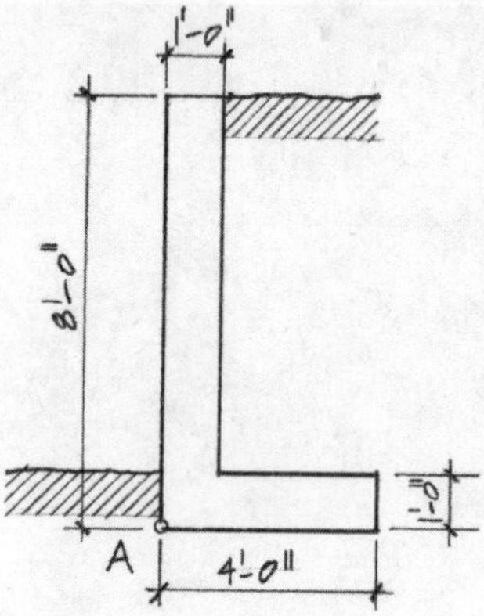

60 An L-shaped cantilever retaining wall constructed of reinforced concrete, with a density of 150 pcf, is eight feet tall from the base to the top of the soil. Assuming a soil density of 120 pcf and an equivalent fluid density of 40 pcf, determine the overturning stability of the wall. Check the bearing pressure beneath the toe at point *A*.

61 Using the same wall configuration as in Problem 60, determine the wall stability if the wall stem is projected to the opposite side with no soil above it. Check the bearing pressure.

62 Determine the overturning stability of the cantilever retaining wall shown. The equivalent fluid density is 5.5 kN/m3, soil density is 18 kN/m3, and the concrete weighs 23.5 kN/m3. Does the bearing pressure beneath the toe remain within the allowable bearing pressure limit?

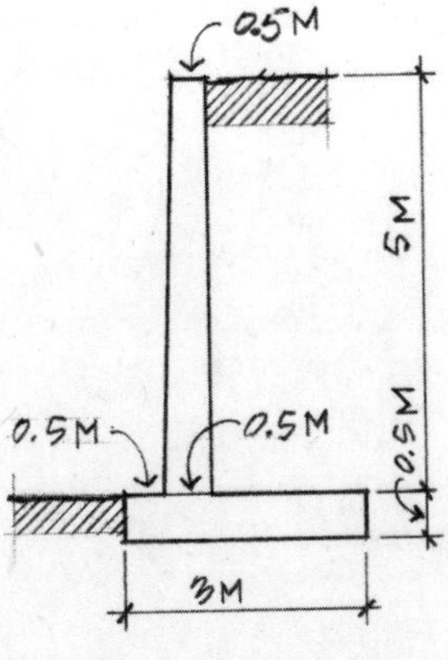

63 Check on the overturning stability of the wall shown if the equivalent fluid pressure is 40 pcf and the soil density equals 115 pcf. Use a concrete density of 150 pcf. Evaluate the bearing pressure developed at the base of the footing.

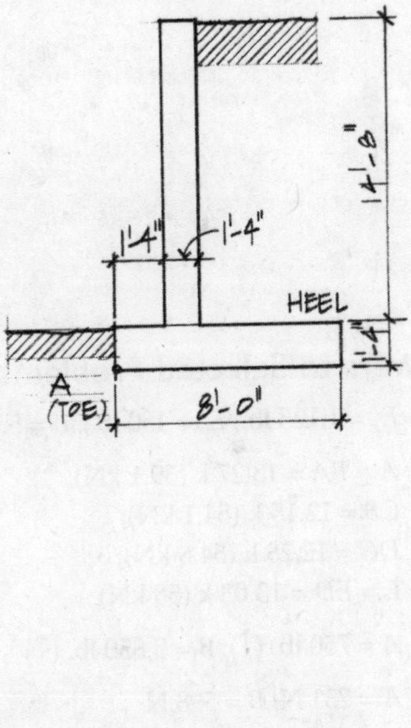

Summary

- To solve for the support reactions of rigid bodies (beams, trusses, and frames) with distributed loads, an equivalent concentrated load(s) is substituted through the centroid (center) of the load area. The magnitude of the equivalent concentrated load is equal to the area under the distributed load curve.
- Planar trusses consist of an arrangement of linear elements joined by frictionless pins, forming a pattern of triangles. The truss is viewed as a rigid body with individual members subjected to tension or compression forces when external loads are applied at the truss joints. Members are considered as two-force members.
- Force analysis of planar trusses can be carried out using the method of joints or the method of sections. Both methods require the use of FBDs and the equations of equilibrium.
- Pinned frames contain members that are multiforce members—that is, a member acted upon by three or more forces, generally resulting in the member experiencing bending moment(s). Multiple FBDs with several sets of equilibrium equations are required to determine the support reactions and internal pin forces of the frame.
- Three hinged arches are analyzed in a manner similar to pinned frames.

Answers to Selected Problems

1 $E_x = 1{,}125$ lb.; $E_y = 450$ lb.; $h_c = 5.33'$

3 $A = BA = 13.27$ k (59.1 kN);
$CB = 12.15$ k (54.1 kN);
$DC = 12.28$ k (54.6 kN);
$E = ED = 13.03$ k (58 kN)

5 $A = 750$ lb. (↑); $B = 5{,}850$ lb. (↑)

6 $A = 731$ N; $B = 598$ N

8 $A_x = 0$; $A_y = 350$ lb.; $B_y = 1{,}550$ lb.

10 $A_x = 0$; $A_y = 1{,}140$ lb.; $B_y = 360$ lb.

11 $A = 1{,}900$ lb.; $E = 1{,}900$ lb.

13 $AB = .577$ kN (C); $BC = .577$ kN (C);
$CD = 1.732$ kN (C); $BE = .577$ kN (T);
$EC = .577$ kN (C); $AE = .289$ kN (T);
$ED = .866$ kN (T)

14 $AB = 5.75$ k (T); $BC = 5$ k (T);
$BE = 2.42$ k (T); $BD = .21$ k (T);
$CD = 7.07$ k (C); $DE = 8.56$ k (C)

16 $AB = 12$ kN (C); $BC = 3$ kN (C);
$CD = 4$ kN (C); $DE = 0$; $EF = 3$ kN (T);
$CE = 5$ kN (T); $BE = 12$ kN (C);
$BF = 15$ kN (T)

18 $AC = 20.1$ k (T); $BC = 2.24$ k (C);
$BD = 16$ k (C)

20 $BE = 500$ lb. (C); $CE = 250\sqrt{5}$ lb. (T);
$FJ = 4{,}000$ lb. (C)

22 $EH = 3.41$ k (T); $HC = .34$ k (T);
$BI = 2.84$ k (T)

24 $DB = 1.2$ k (T); $EA = 4.7$ k (T)

25 *GH*, *GF*, *EF*, *FC*, *CD*, and *CB*

27 *BM*, *MC*, *FO*, *OG*, *GK*, *GJ*, and *JH*, *EO*, *OK*

28 $A_x = 455$ lb. (→); $A_y = 67$ lb. (↓);
$B_x = 455$ lb. (←); $B_y = 417$ lb. (↑);
$C_x = 455$ lb.; $C_y = 267$ lb.

30 $A_x = 171.6$ kN; $A_y = 153.4$ kN;
$B_x = 171.6$ kN; $B_y = 161.6$ kN;
$C_x = 171.6$ kN; $C_y = 18.4$ kN

32 $A_x = 10$ kN (→); $A_y = 2$ kN (↑);
$B_x = 10$ kN (←); $B_y = 8$ kN (↑);
$C_x = 10$ kN; $C_y = 8$ kN

33 $A_x = 4$ k (←); $A_y = 1$ k (↑);
$C_x = 4$ k (→); $C_y = 3$ k (↑);
$BD = 6$ k; $E_x = 4$ k; $E_y = 4$ k;
$B_x = 4$ k; $B_y = 4$ k

35 $A_x = 676$ lb.; $B_x = 308$ lb.

36 $A_y = 15$ k; $B_x = 0$; $B_y = 5$ k;
$C_x = 3$ k; $C_y = 10.5$ k; $D_y = 8.5$ k

37 $A = 9{,}600$ lb.; $B = 3{,}200$ lb.

39 $A_x = A_y = 10$ k; $E_x = 10$ k; $E_y = 0$;
$AB = 10\sqrt{2}$ k; $BC = 10.54$ k; $BE = 0$;
$CD = 16.67$ k; $BD = 13.33$ k; $ED = 10$ k

41 $A_x = 200$ lb.; $A_y = 150$ lb.; $F_x = 200$ lb.;
$AB = 200$ lb. (T); $BC = 200$ lb. (T);
$AD = 150$ lb. (T); $DF = 150$ lb. (T);
$FE = 250$ lb. (C); $EC = 250$ lb. (C);
$BD = BE = DE = 0$

43 $A_y = 10$ k (↑); $C_x = 0$; $C_y = 5$ k (↑);
$DG = 8.33$ k (C); $AB = 4.8$ k (T);
$FG = 1.87$ k (T)

45 $BG = 2{,}700$ lb. (C); $HE = 1{,}875$ lb. (T);
$HB = 1{,}179$ lb. (T)

47 $DG = HG = 25$ k (T); $DF = 54.2$ k (C);
$EG = 38.4$ k (T)

49 $A_x = 693$ lb. (→); $A_y = 400$ lb. (↑);
$M_A = 3{,}144$ lb.-ft (clockwise);
$C_x = 107$ lb.; $C_y = 400$ lb.; $B_x = B_y = 800$ lb.;
$D_x = D_y = 800$ lb.

51 $A_y = 320$ lb.; $B_x = 0$; $B_y = 80$ lb.
$C_x = 0$; $C_y = 280$ lb.; $M_C = 1{,}280$ lb.-ft.

53 $A_x = 0$; $A_y = 333.3$ lb.; $D_y = 166.7$ lb.;
$C_x = 44.4$ lb.; $C_y = 222.2$ lb.; $AB_x = 44.4$ lb.;
$AB_y = 55.5$ lb.

55 $A_x = 2{,}714$ lb. (←); $A_y = 286$ lb. (↑);
$C_x = 1{,}726$ lb. (←); $C_y = 2{,}114$ lb. (↑);
$B_x = 286$ lb.; $B_y = 2{,}714$ lb.

56 $A_x = .33$ kN (←); $A_y = 4.26$ kN (↑);
$D_x = 3.33$ kN (→); $D_y = 3.26$ kN (↓);
$B_x = 3.33$ kN; $B_y = 4.26$ kN

58 P = 157.5 lb., S. F. = 1.43 < 1.50, $p_{max} = 2{,}000$ psf

60 $M_{OTM} = 3{,}420$ lb.-ft., $M_{RM} = 8{,}025$ lb.-ft., S.F. = 2.35 > 1.50, $p_{max} = 2{,}530$ psf

62 P = 83.2 kN, $M_{OTM} = 152$ kN-m, $M_{RM} = 457$ kN-m, S.F. = 3.0 > 1.5, $p_{max} = 164.4$ kN/m^2

Load Tracing

Figure 1 Load tracing can be visualized in the exposed light-frame construction of an apartment complex through the roof trusses, stud walls (bearing and partition), floor joists, and foundation. Photo courtesy of the Southern Forest Products Association.

1 LOAD TRACING

Early in the structural design phase of a project, an initial assumption is made by the designer about the path across which forces must travel as they move throughout the structure to the foundation (ground). Loads (forces) travel along *load paths,* and the analysis method is often referred to as *load tracing* (Figure 1).

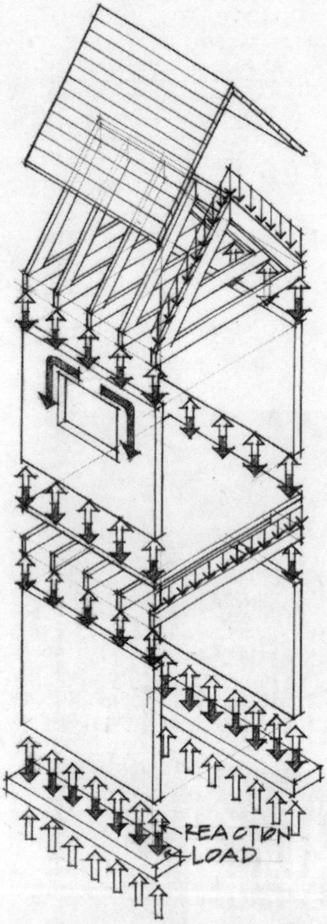

Figure 2 Load paths through a simple building.

Engineers often view structures as interdependent mechanisms by which loads are distributed to their individual members, such as roof sheathing, floor slabs, rafters, joists (a regular, relatively closely spaced series of secondary beams), beams, and columns (Figure 2). The structural designer makes judgments regarding the amount of load assigned to each member and the manner in which loads travel throughout the structure (load path).

Load tracing involves the systematic process of determining loads and support reactions of individual structural members as they in turn affect the loading of other structural elements (Figure 3). Simple determinate structures can be thoroughly analyzed using FBDs in conjunction with the basic equations of equilibrium studied previously.

Usually, the process begins with the very uppermost member or level, tracing loads downward, layer by layer, until the last affected member under investigation is solved. In other words, start from the uppermost roof element, and work your way down through the structure until you reach the foundation.

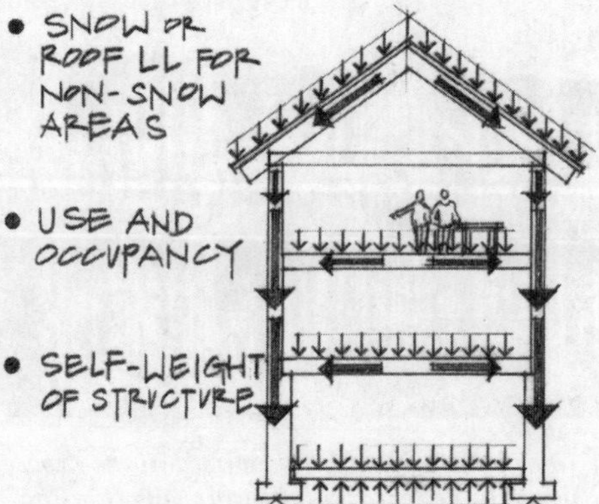

Figure 3 Loads and load paths.

Load Paths

In general, the shorter the load path to its foundation and the fewer elements involved in doing so, the greater the economy and efficiency of the structure. The most efficient load paths also involve the unique and inherent strengths of the structural materials used—tension in steel, compression in concrete, and so on. Bending, however, is a relatively inefficient way to resist loads, and as a result, beams become relatively large as loads and spans increase.

Sketches of structural members in the form of FBDs are used extensively to clarify the force conditions of individual elements as well as other interconnected members. Simple determinate structures can be thoroughly analyzed using FBDs in conjunction with the basic equations of equilibrium studied previously. As long as each element is determinate, the equations of equilibrium are sufficient to determine all supporting reactions. Load tracing requires an initial assessment of the general structural framework to determine where the analysis should begin (Figure 4).

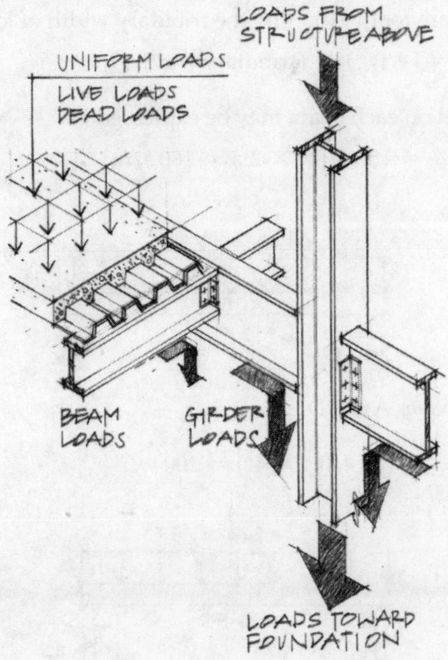

Figure 4 Decking-beam-girder-column load path.

Each time the load path is redirected, a support condition is created, and the loads and reactions at each transfer must be analyzed (using FBDs) and solved (using equations) (Figure 5).

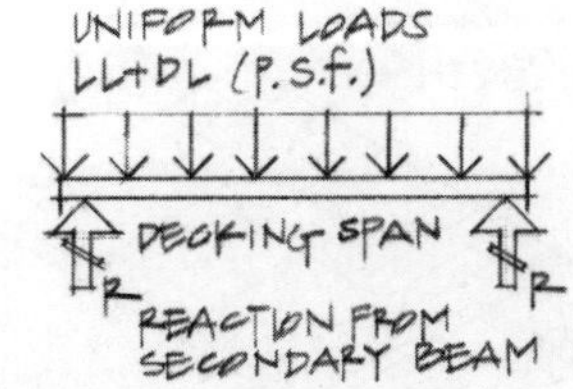

Figure 5(a) FBD of the decking.

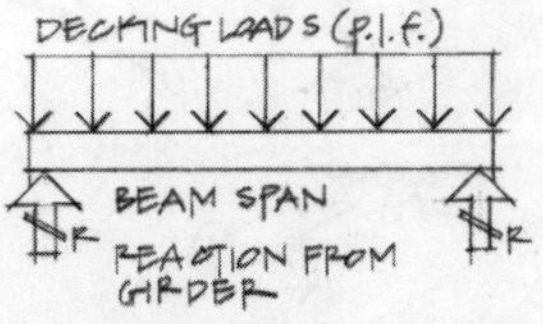

Figure 5(b) FBD of the beam.

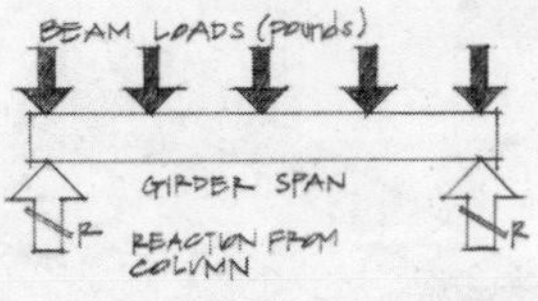

Figure 5(c) FBD of the girder.

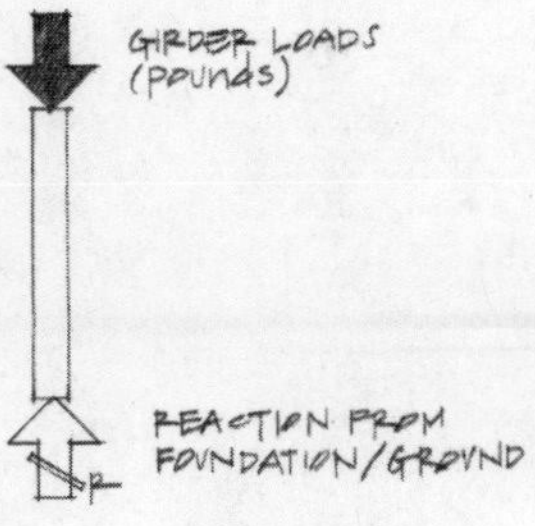

Figure 5(d) FBD of the column.

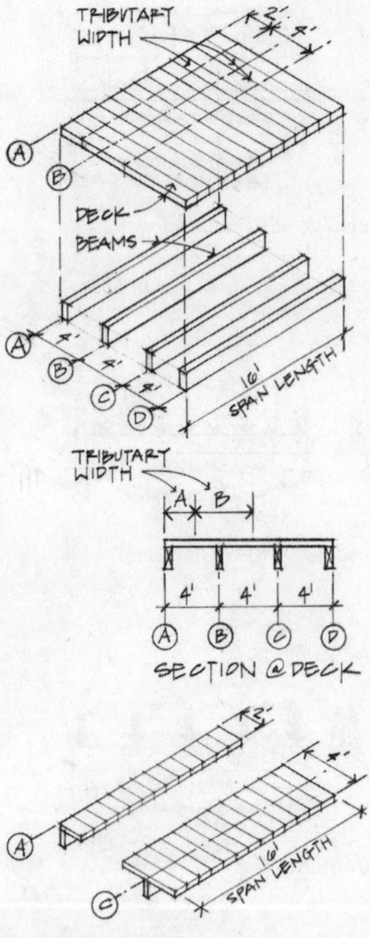

Figure 6 *Wood floor system with decking and beams.*

Tributary Area

Loads uniformly distributed over an area of roof or floor are assigned to individual members (rafters, joists, beams, girders) based on the concept of *distributive area, tributary area*, or *contributory area*. This concept typically considers the area that a member must support as being halfway between the adjacent similar members.

A section of a wood floor framing system (Figure 6) will be used to illustrate this concept. Assume that the general load over the entire deck area is a uniform 50 #/ft.^{2}.

- The tributary width contributing to the load on beam B is $\frac{1}{2}$ the distance (plank span) between A and B plus $\frac{1}{2}$ the distance between B and C.
- The tributary width of load on beam $B = 2 + 2 = 4'$. The same is true for beam C.
- Similarly, the tributary width for edge beams A and $D = 2'$.

Beam loads resulting from a uniformly applied load condition are determined by multiplying the load in pounds per square foot (#/ft.^{2}) by the tributary width of load:

$$\omega = (\#/\text{ft.}^2) \times (\text{tributary width})$$

The load on each beam may be expressed as

$$\omega_{A,D} = (50\,\#/\text{ft.}^2 \times 2') = 100\,\#/\text{ft.}$$

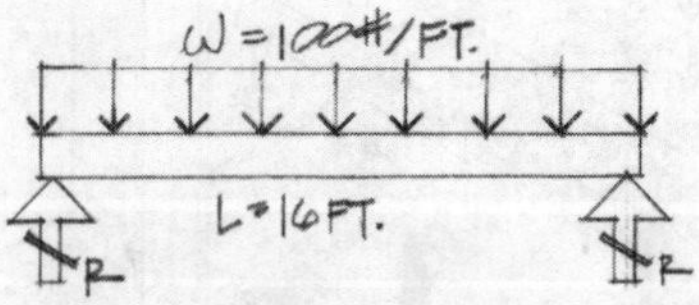

FBD of beams A *and* D.

$$\omega_{B,C} = (50\,\#/\text{ft.}^2 \times 4') = 200\,\#/\text{ft.}$$

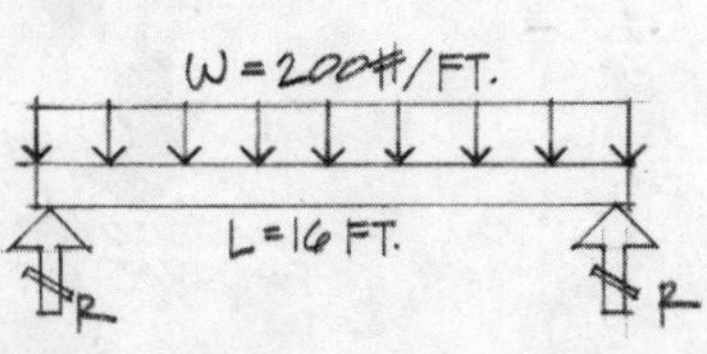

FBD of beams B *and* C.

Load tracing involves the systematic process of determining loads and support reactions of individual structural members as they in turn affect the loading of other structural elements.

Framing Design Criteria: Direction of Span

Architectural character

The structural framing, if exposed, can contribute significantly to the architectural expression of buildings.

Short joists loading relatively long beams yield shallow joists and deep beams. The individual structural bays are more clearly expressed in Figure 7.

Structural efficiency and economy

Considerations should include the materials selected for the structural system, the span capability, and the availability of material and skilled labor. Standard sections and repetitive spacing of uniform members are generally more economical.

Mechanical and electrical system requirements

The location and direction of mechanical systems should be coordinated with the intended structural system. Layering the structural system provides space for ducts and pipes to cross structural members, eliminating the need to cut openings in the beams. Flush or butt framing saves space in situations where floor-to-floor dimensions are limited by height restrictions.

Openings for stairs and vertical penetrations

Most framing systems accommodate openings, but generally, it is more economical to make openings parallel to the dominant spanning direction. Additional headers and connections create point loads on members that are typically designed for light, uniform loads, thus increasing their size.

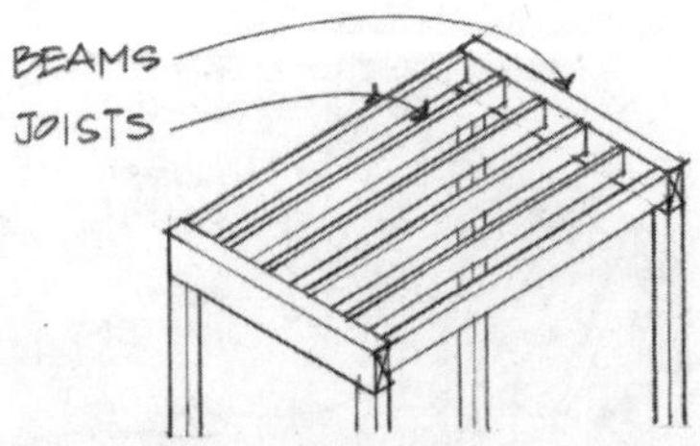

(a) Long, lightly loaded joists bearing on shorter beams create a more uniform structural depth. Space can be conserved if the joists and beams are flush framed.

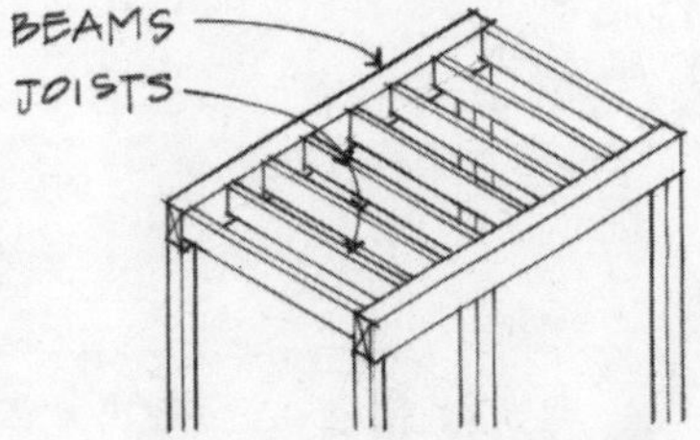

(b) Short joists loading relatively long beams yield shallow joists and deep beams. The individual structural bays are more clearly expressed.

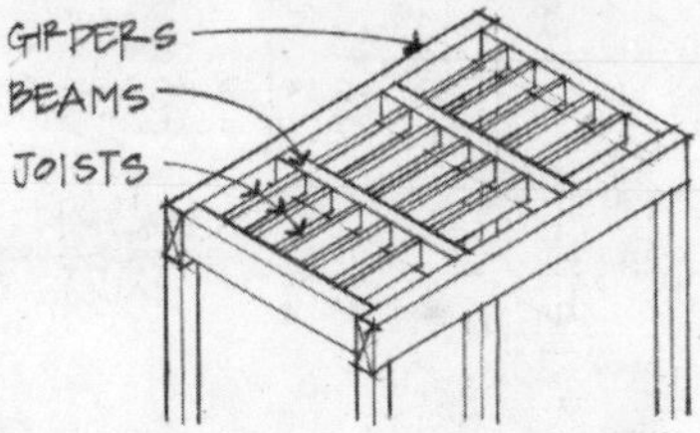

(c) Loads can be reduced on selected beams by introducing intermediate beams.

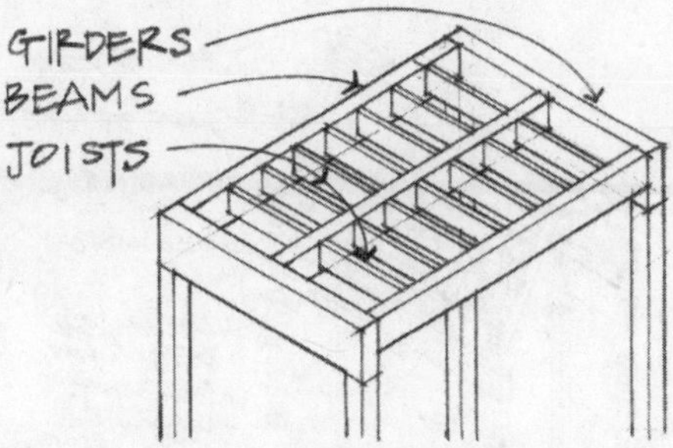

(d) The span capability of the decking material controls the spacing of the joists, whereas beam spacing is controlled by the allowable joist span.

(e) Three-level framing system. Photo by author.

Figure 7 Various framing options.

Load Paths: Pitched Roof Systems

Single-level framing

Rafters and ceiling joists combine to form a simple truss spanning from wall to wall. In addition to the truss action (rafters pick up compression forces, and ceiling joists develop tension to resist the horizontal thrust), rafters experience bending due to the uniform load along their length, as shown in Figures 8(a) and 8(b).

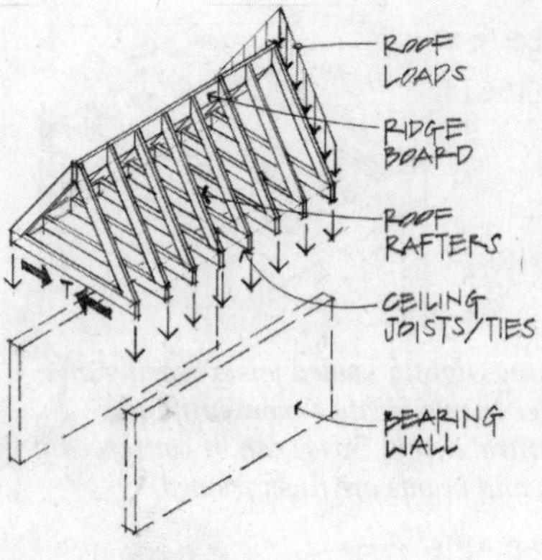

(a)

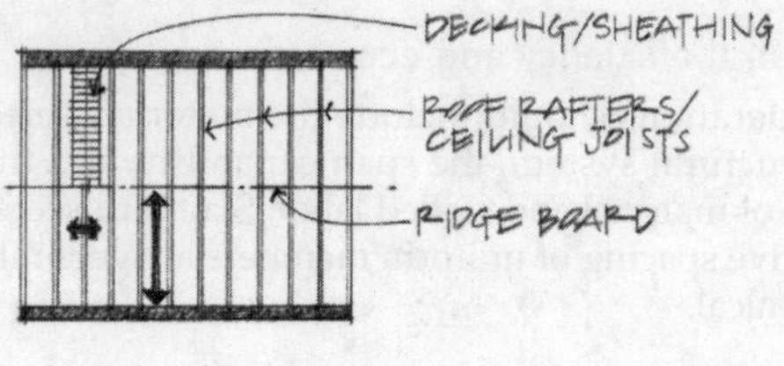

(b)

Double-level framing

Roof joists or beams are supported by a ridge beam at one end and a bearing wall or header beam at the other. No ceiling ties are used, because this arrangement does not develop a horizontal thrust (as in the previous example). Notice that each level of structural framing spans in a direction perpendicular to the next layer, as shown in Figures 8(c) and 8(d).

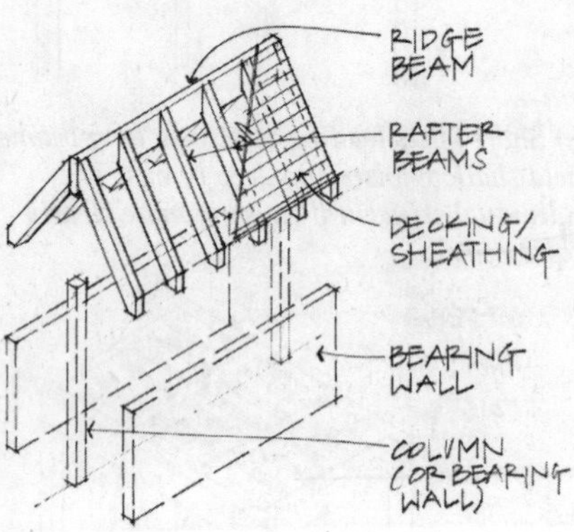

(c)

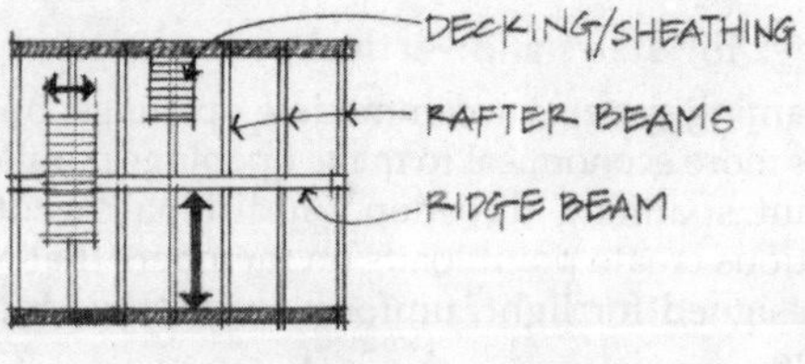

(d)

Three-level framing

The load path sequence in this arrangement starts with the loads transferred from the sheathing (decking) onto the purlins, which distribute concentrated loads onto the roof beams, which in turn transmit load to the ridge beam at one end and a bearing wall or wall beam at the other. Columns or wall framing support the ridge beam at either end, as shown in Figures 8(e) and 8(f).

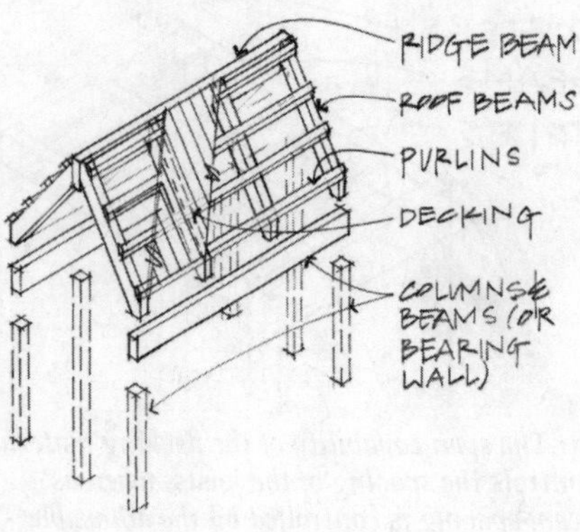

(e)

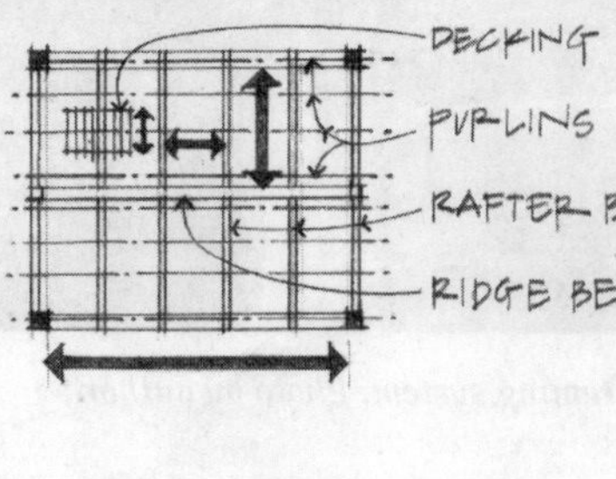

(f)

Figure 8 Framing for pitched roofs.

Construction: Pitched Roof Systems

Single-level framing

A common roof system for residential structures is a rafter/ceiling joist arrangement. Loads onto the roof are initially supported by the sheathing (plywood or other structural panels or skip sheathing, usually 1″ × 4″ boards spaced some distance apart), which in turn loads the rafters (Figure 9).

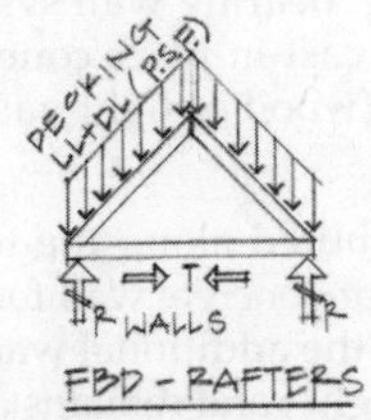

(a) FBD—rafters.

(b) Typical light-frame structure. Photo courtesy of the Southern Forest Products Association.

Figure 9 Single-level framing.

Double-level framing

Another common roof framing arrangement involves roof joists or beams that are supported by a ridge beam at one end and a bearing wall or header beam at the other. The ridge beam must be supported at each end by a column or bearing wall (Figure 10).

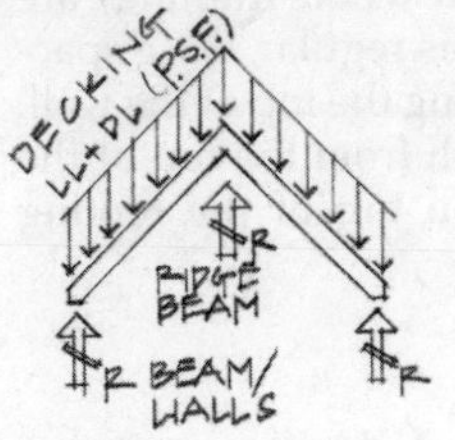

(a) FBD—rafters.

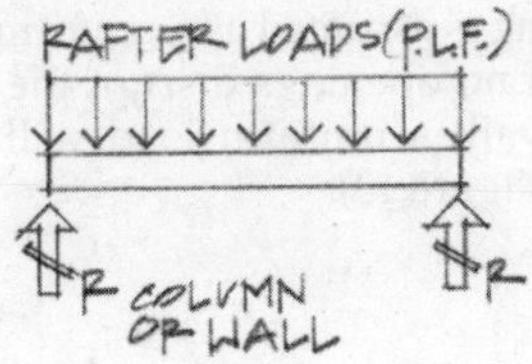

(b) FBD—ridge beam.

(c) Post-and-beam construction. Photo by author.

Figure 10 Double-level framing.

Three-level framing

A method used to achieve a heavier beam appearance is spacing the roof beams (rather than the rafters) farther apart, typically 4 to 12 feet o.c. Perpendicular to the roof beams are purlins, spaced from one foot, six inches to four feet o.c., supporting sheathing, decking, or a metal roof. In both the two- and three-level framing systems, the ceiling plane can follow the roof slope (Figure 11).

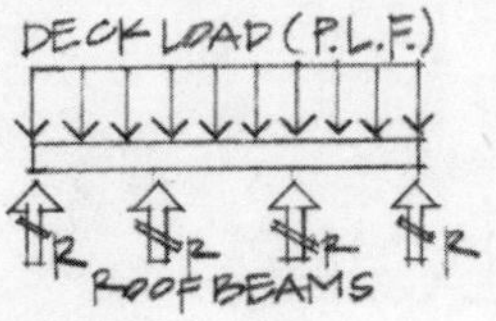

(a) FBD—purlins.

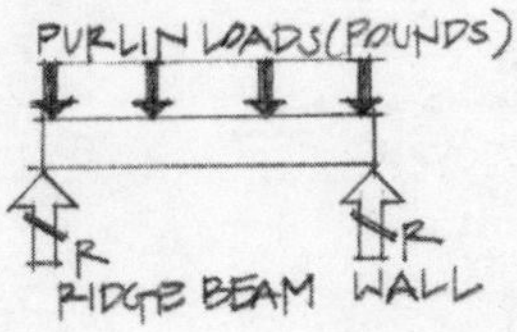

(b) FBD—roof beams.

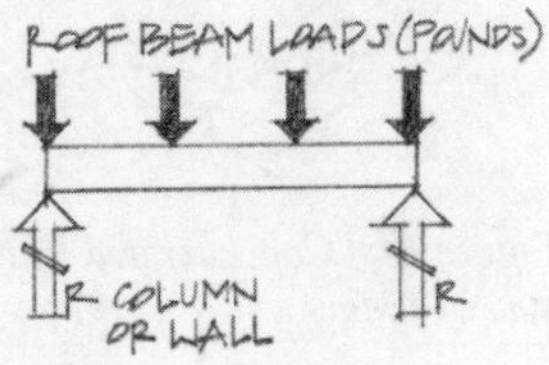

(c) FBD—ridge beam.

Figure 11 Three-level framing.

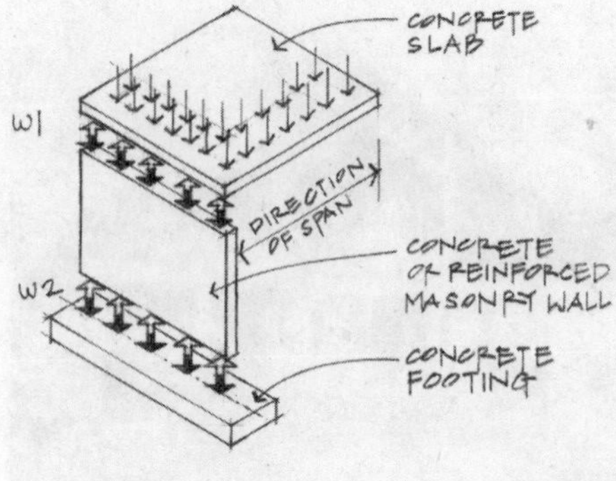

Figure 12 *Uniform wall load from a slab.*

Load Paths: Wall Systems

A bearing wall is a vertical support system that transmits compressive forces through the wall plane and to the foundation. Uniform compressive forces along the length of the wall result in a relatively uniform distribution of force. Concentrated loads or disruptions in the structural continuity of the wall, such as large window or door openings, will result in a nonuniform distribution of compressive forces on the footing. Bearing wall systems can be constructed with masonry, cast-in-place concrete, site-cast tilt-up concrete, or studs (wood or light-gauge metal framing).

Uniform slab loads are distributed along the top of the bearing wall as ω. A masonry or concrete wall footing will be required to support ω plus the additional wall weight. The load $\omega_2 = (\omega_1 + \text{wall weight})$ and remains a uniform load (Figure 12).

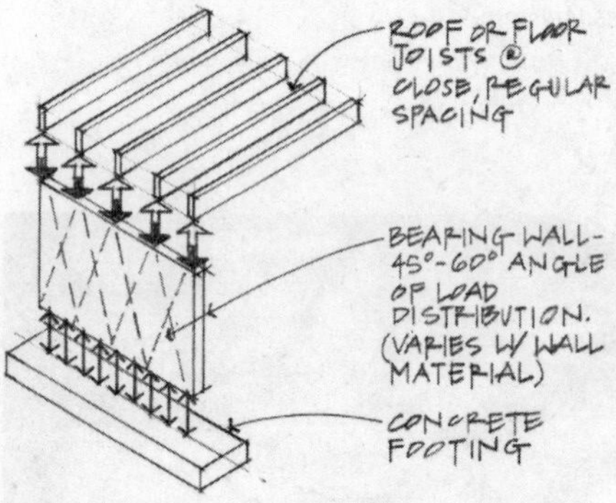

Figure 13 *Uniform wall load from rafters and joists.*

Uniform distribution

Roof or floor joists (in typical light-wood framing) are spaced 16 or 24 inches on center. This regular, close spacing is assumed as a uniform load along the top of the wall. If no openings disrupt the load path from the top of the wall, a uniform load will result on top of the footing (Figure 13).

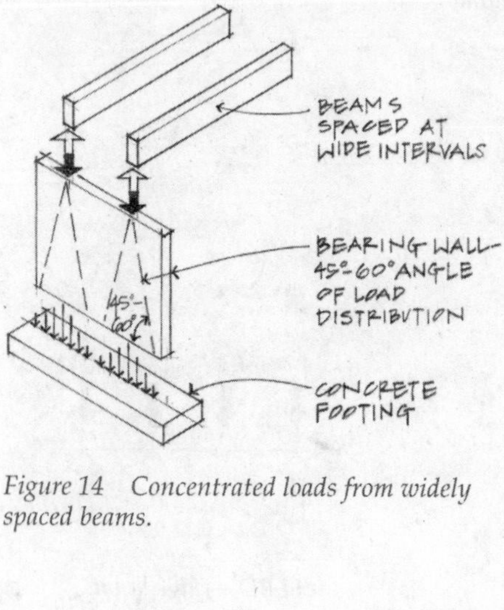

Figure 14 *Concentrated loads from widely spaced beams.*

Nonuniform distribution

Concentrated loads develop at the top of a wall when beams are spaced at wide intervals. Depending on the wall material, the concentrated load distributes along an angle of 45° to 60° as it moves down the wall. The resulting footing load will be nonuniform, with the largest forces directly under the applied load (Figure 14).

"Arching action" over opening

Openings in walls also redirect the loads to either side of the opening. The natural stiffness of a concrete wall under compression produces an "arching action" that contributes to the lateral distribution of the loads (Figure 15).

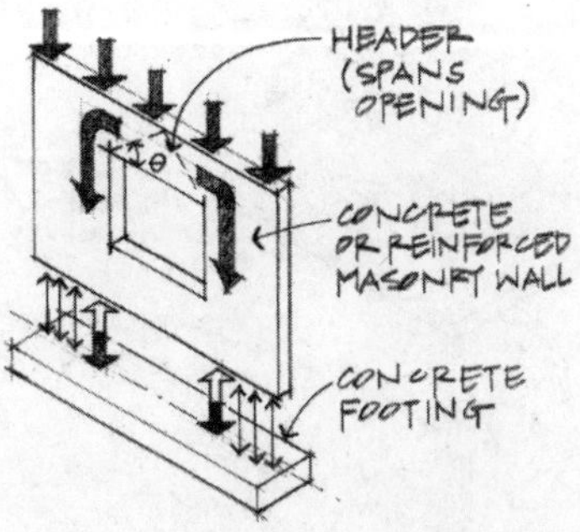

Figure 15 Arching over wall openings.

Opening in a stud wall

Stud walls (wood and metal) are generally idealized as monolithic walls (except for openings) when loaded uniformly from above. Openings require the use of headers (beams) that redirect the loads to either side. Concentrated loads from the header reactions must be supported by a buildup of studs resembling a column (Figure 16).

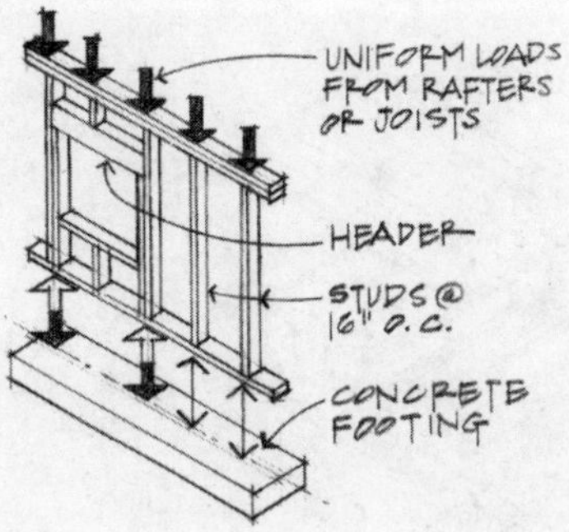

Figure 16 Stud wall with a window opening.

Concentrated loads—pilasters

In special cases where the concentrated loads are very large, walls may need to be reinforced with pilasters directly under the beam. Pilasters are essentially columns and carry the large concentrated loads directly to the footing. The walls between the pilasters are now considered as nonbearing walls except for carrying their own weight (Figure 17).

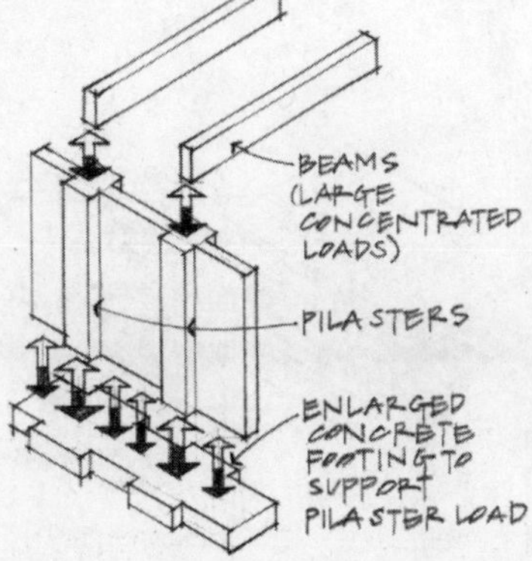

Figure 17 Pilasters supporting concentrated beam loads.

Load Paths: Roof and Floor Systems

One-level framing

Although it is not a common framing system, relatively long-spanning decking materials may transmit roof or floor loads directly to bearing walls (Figure 18).

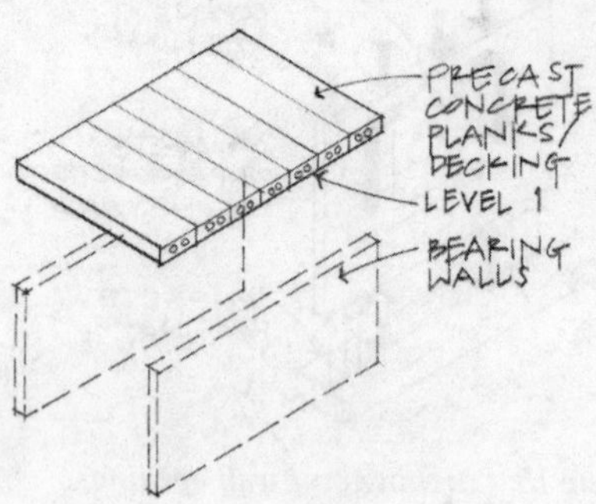

Figure 18 One-level framing (roof and floor).

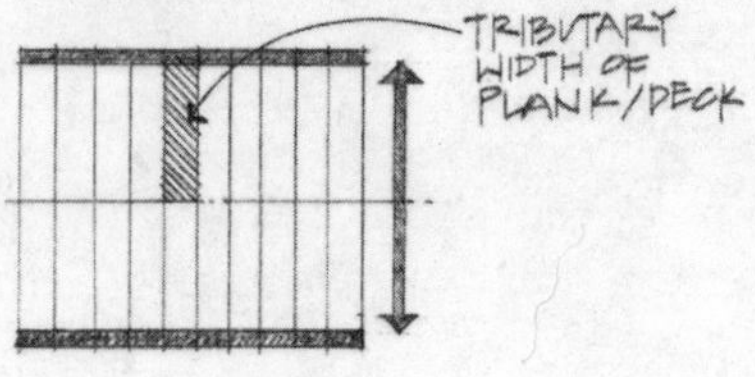

Framing plan.

Two-level framing

This is a very common floor system that uses joists to support a deck. The decking is laid perpendicular to the joist framing. Span distances between bearing walls and beams affect the size and spacing of the joists (Figure 19).

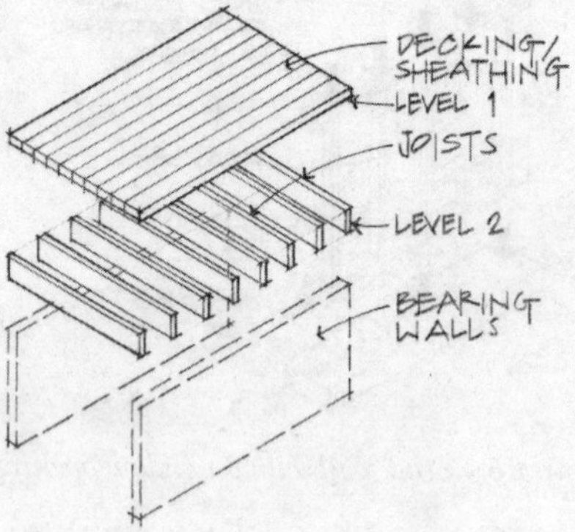

Figure 19 Two-level framing.

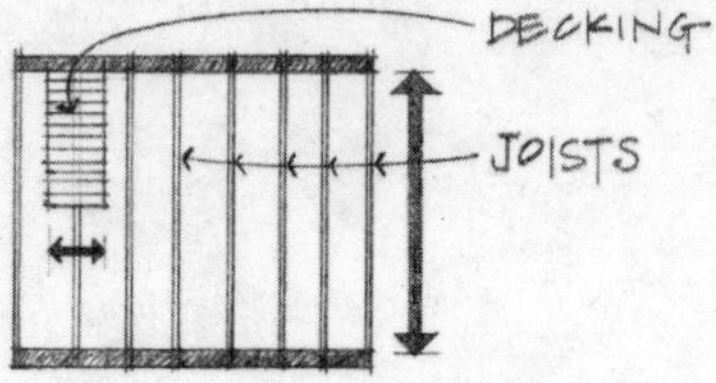

Framing plan.

Three-level framing

When bearing walls are replaced by beams (girders or trusses) spanning between columns, the framing involves three levels. Joist loads are supported by major beams, which transmit their reactions to girders, trusses, or columns. Each level of framing is arranged perpendicular to the level directly above it (Figure 20).

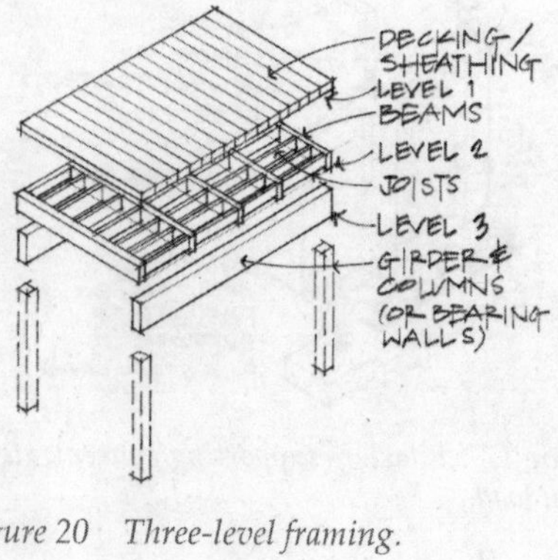

Figure 20 Three-level framing.

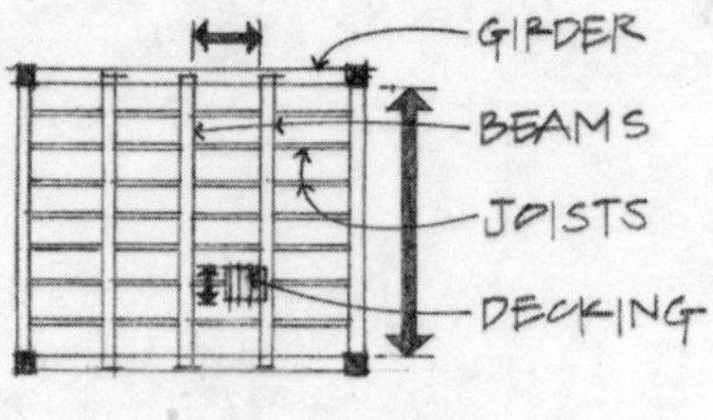

Framing plan.

Load Paths: Roof and Floor Systems

One-level framing

Precast hollow-core concrete planks or heavy-timber-plank decking can be used to span between closely spaced bearing walls or beams. Spacing of the supports (the distance between bearing walls) is based on the span capability of the concrete planks or timber decking (Figure 21).

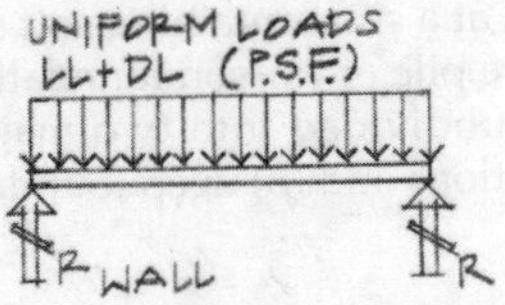

FBD—plank.

Figure 21 One-level framing.

Two-level framing

Efficient structural sections in wood and steel joists allow relatively long spans between bearing walls. Lighter deck materials, such as plywood panels, can be used to span between the closely spaced joists (Figure 22).

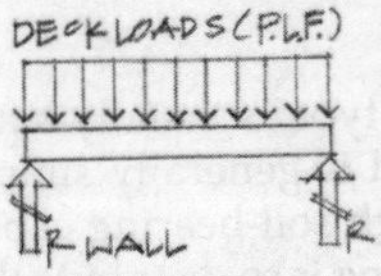

(a) FBD—decking.

(b) FBD—joists.

Figure 22 Two-level framing.

(c) Light-framed joist-beam assembly. Photo by Chris Brown.

Three-level framing

Buildings requiring large open floor areas, free of bearing walls and with a minimum number of columns, typically rely on the long span capability of joists supported by trusses or girders. The spacing of the primary structure and the layering of the secondary structural members establish regular bays that subdivide the space (Figure 23).

(a) FBD—decking.

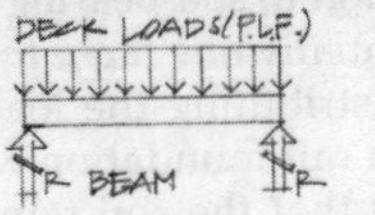

(b) FBD—joists.

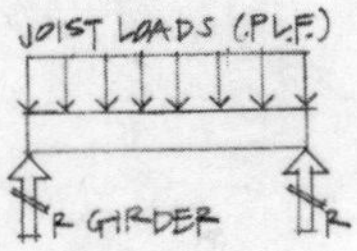

(c) FBD—beams.

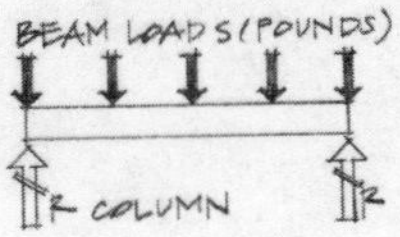

(d) FBD—girder.

(e) Joist-beam truss; three level-framing. Photo by Chris Brown.

Figure 23 Three-level framing.

Load Paths: Foundation Systems

The foundation system for a particular structure or building depends on the size of the building, the use of the structure, the subsurface conditions at the site, and the cost of the foundation system to be used.

A large building with heavy loads can often be supported on relatively inexpensive shallow footings if the subsurface soils are dense and stable. However, the same building constructed at a site containing soft soils or expansive clay may require pile or caisson foundations. Foundations are generally subdivided into two major categories: (a) shallow foundations and (b) deep foundations.

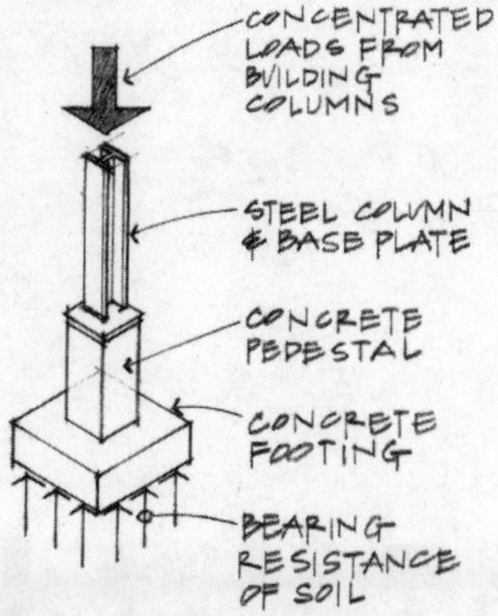

Figure 24 Spread footing.

Shallow foundations

Shallow foundations essentially obtain their support on soil or rock just below the bottom of the structure in direct bearing. Vertical loads are transmitted from walls or columns to a footing that distributes the load over an area large enough that the allowable load-carrying capacity of the soil is not exceeded and/or settlement is minimized. Shallow foundations are of three basic types: (a) spread footings—individual column footing, (b) continuous strip footings—supporting a bearing wall, and (c) mat foundations—covering the entire plan area of the building.

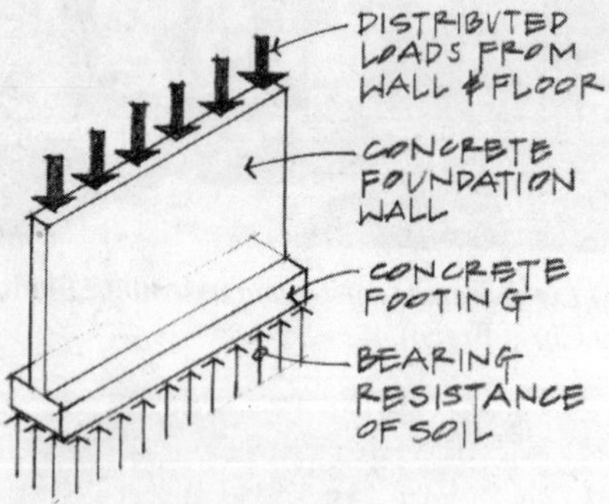

Figure 25 Wall footing.

Spread footing. This footing type is usually square or sometimes circular in plan and is generally simple and economical for moderate to high soil-bearing capacities. The purpose of this type of footing is to distribute the load over a large area of soil. Pedestal and footing are reinforced with steel (Figure 24).

Wall footing. Wall footings are one of the most common footing types and support relatively uniform bearing wall loads through a continuous foundation wall. The wall footing width remains constant throughout its length if no large concentrated loads occur (Figure 25).

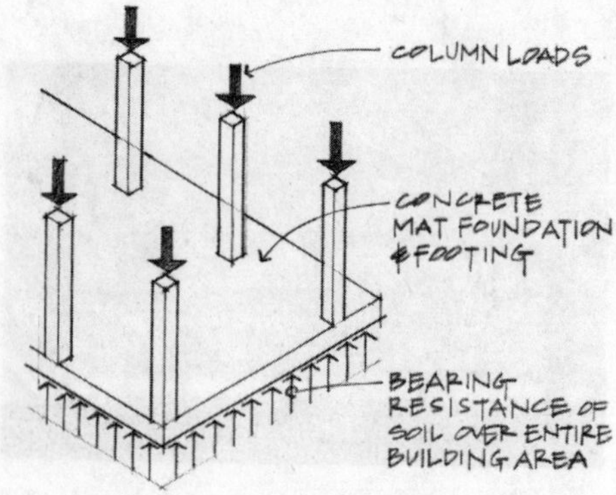

Figure 26 Mat or raft foundation.

Mat or raft foundations. Mat foundations are used when soil bearing is relatively low or the loads are heavy in relation to soil-bearing capacities. This foundation type is essentially one large footing under the entire building, thus distributing the load over the entire mat. A mat is called a raft foundation when it is placed deep enough in the soil that the soil removed during excavation equals most or all of the building's weight (Figure 26).

Deep foundations

The function of a deep foundation is to carry building loads beneath a layer of unsatisfactory soil to a satisfactory bearing stratum. Deep foundations are generally piles, piers, or caissons installed in a variety of ways. Normally, there is no difference between a drilled caisson and a drilled pier, and most often, only a modest difference in diameter exists between them. Piles, the most common deep-foundation system, are driven into the earth using pile-driving hammers powered by drop hammers, compressed air, or diesel engines. Building loads are distributed to the soil in contact with the surface area of the pile through skin friction (friction piles), in direct bearing (bearing piles) at the bottom of the pile on a sound stratum of earth or rock, or a combination of skin friction and direct bearing.

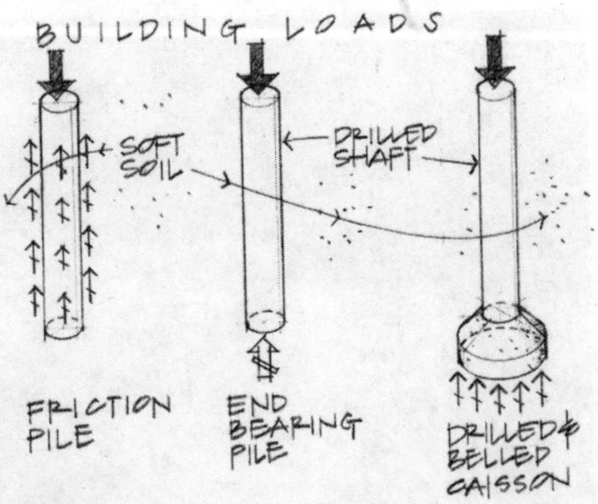

Figure 27 Pile foundations.

Pile foundations. Timber piles are normally used as friction piles, whereas concrete and steel piles are generally used as bearing piles. When bearing piles must be driven to great depths to reach suitable bearing, a combination of steel and concrete is used. Hollow steel shells are driven into the ground to a predetermined bearing point, and then the casings are filled with concrete (Figure 27).

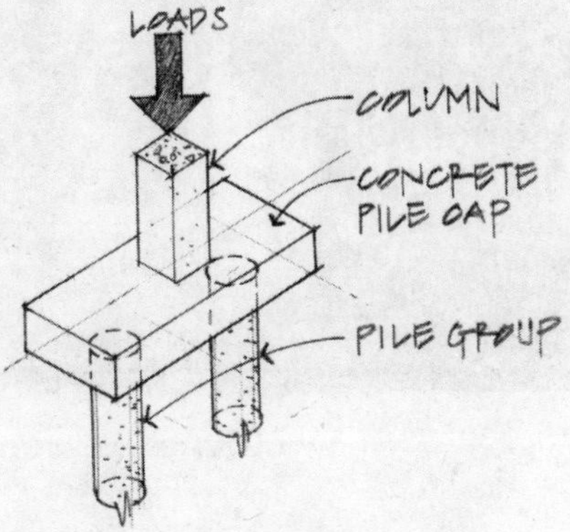

Figure 28 Pile cap on one pile group.

Pile caps. Individual building columns are generally supported by a group (cluster) of piles. A thick reinforced cap is poured on top of the pile group and distributes the column load to all the piles in the cluster (Figure 28).

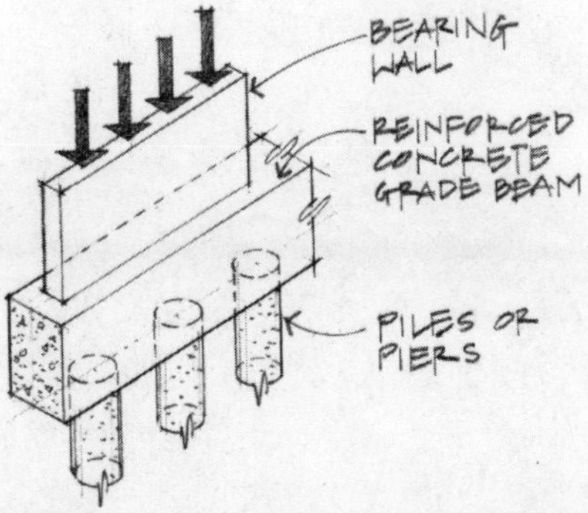

Figure 29 Grade beam supporting a bearing wall.

Grade beams. Piles or piers supporting bearing walls are generally spaced at regular intervals and connected with a continuous reinforced concrete grade beam. The grade beam is intended to transfer the loads from the building wall to the piles (Figure 29).

Figure 30 Light-frame construction—a drugstore in Quincy, Washington. Photo by Phil Lust.

Example Problems: Load Tracing

The example problems that follow will illustrate the load-tracing methodology as it applies to a variety of structural frameworks and arrangements. Note that most of the examples illustrated are wood-frame structures, such as those shown in Figures 1 and 30. Wood framing is the one structural material type that generally results in a determinate framing system, whereas steel and, particularly, cast-in-place concrete are often designed to capitalize on the advantages of indeterminacy through the use of rigid connections and/or continuity.

1 In the single-bay, post-and-beam deck illustrated, planks typically are available in nominal widths of four or six inches, but for the purposes of analysis, it is permissible to assume a unit width equal to one foot. Determine the plank, beam, and column reactions.

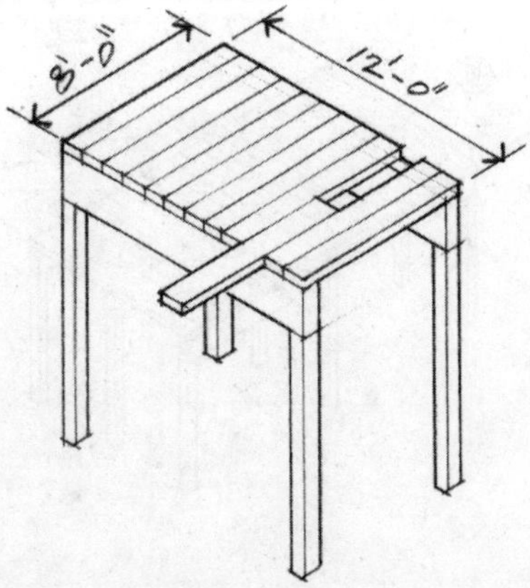

Solution:

Load on the deck (live load, or LL)	=	60 psf
Deck weight (dead load, or DL)	=	8 psf
Total load (LL + DL)	=	68 psf

PLANK REACTION Looking at the deck in elevation, the load ω is determined by multiplying the pounds per square foot load by the tributary width of the plank. Therefore:

$$\omega = 68\,\#/\text{ft.}^2(1') = 68\,\#/\text{ft.}$$

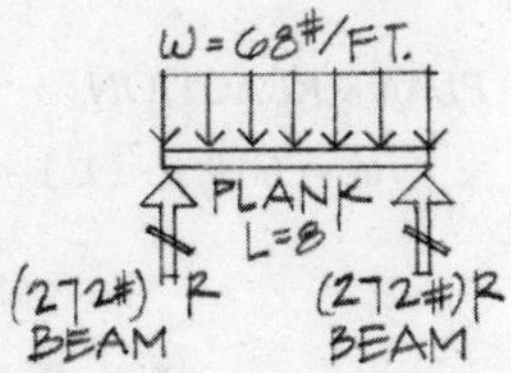

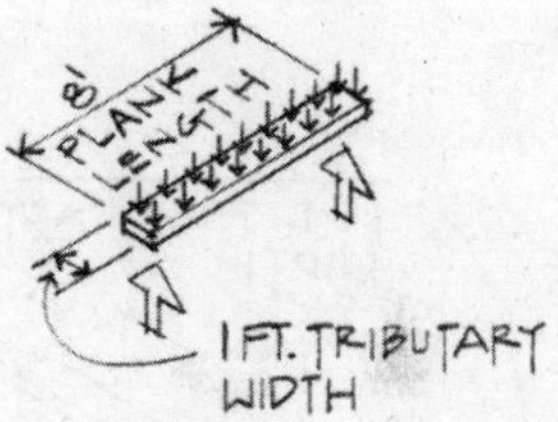

BEAM REACTION The planks load the beams with a load of 68# per foot of the plank span. Half of the plank load is transferred to each beam. The beams are loaded by the planks with a load of 272# per foot of the beam span.

$$R = \frac{\omega L}{2} = \frac{68\,\#/\text{ft.}^2(8')}{2} = 272\,\# \quad \text{(Beam reaction)}$$

In addition, the beam has a self-weight equivalent to 10 #/ft.

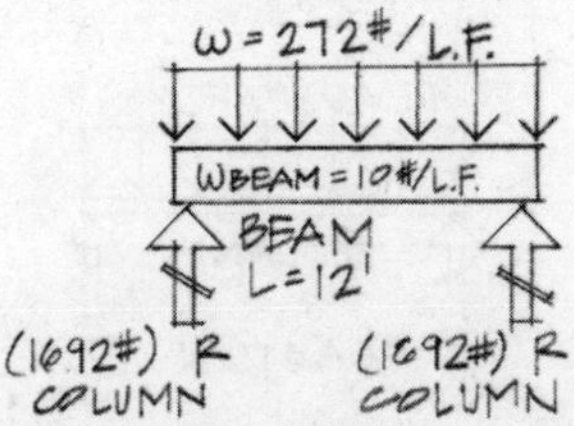

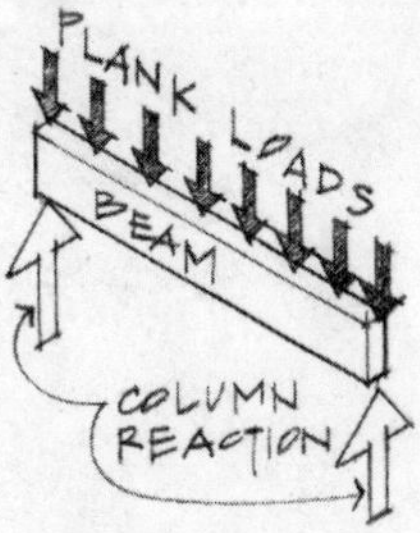

COLUMN REACTION Half of each beam load is transferred to the column at each corner of the deck. The columns are loaded by the beams with loads of 1,692# at each column. Assume each column has a self-weight of 100#.

$$R = \frac{\omega L}{2} = \frac{(272 + 10)\,\#/\text{ft.}(12')}{2}$$
$$= 1{,}692\,\# \quad \text{(Column reaction)}$$

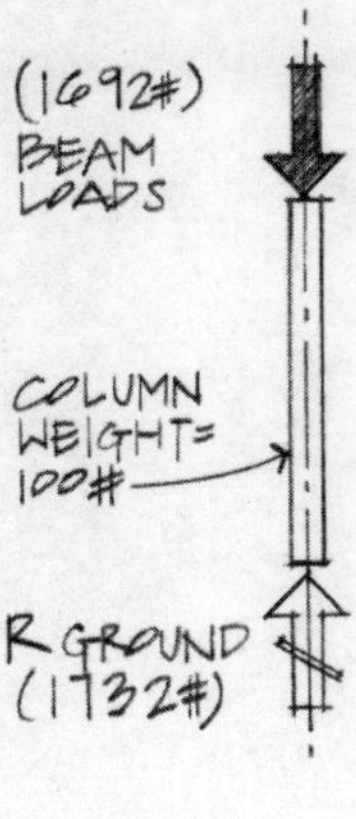

GROUND REACTION The load at each column is resisted by an equivalent ground reaction of 1,792#.

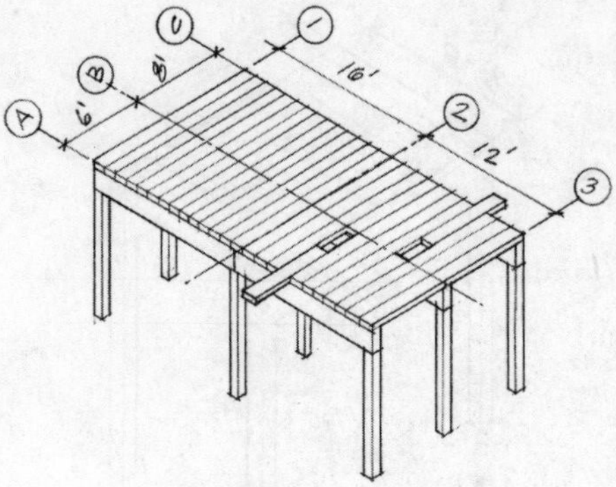

2 This problem represents an expansion of Example Problem 1, where the decking has an additional six feet to span and the beams are extended another bay. Loads on the structural system remain the same.

Determine the loads developed in each column support. Assume that columns are located at grids *1-A*, *2-A*, *3-A*, *1-B*, *2-B*, *3-B*, *1-C*, *2-C*, and *3-C*.

Solution:

Deck DL	=	8 psf
Deck LL	=	60 psf
Total load	=	68 psf
Beam self-weight	=	10 #/ft.
Column self-weight	=	100#

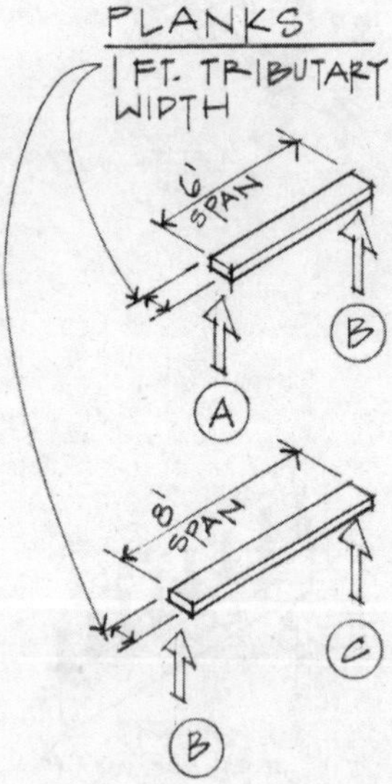

PLANK REACTION

$$\omega = 68\ \#/\text{ft.}^2(1') = 68\ \#/\text{ft.}$$

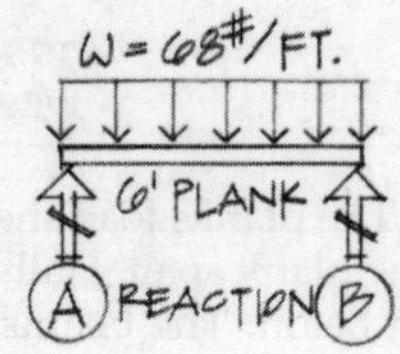

BEAM REACTION First, analyze the planks that span six feet between grid lines *A* and *B*.

$$R = \frac{\omega L}{2} = \frac{68\ \#/\text{ft.}^2(6')}{2} = 204\# \quad \text{(Beam reaction)}$$

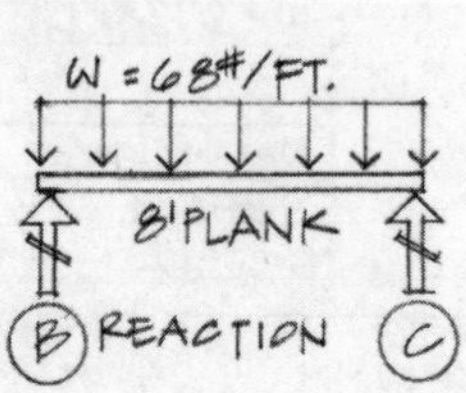

Next, analyze the plank loads and beam support for the eight foot span between grids *B* and *C*.

$$R = \frac{\omega L}{2} = \frac{68\ \#/\text{ft.}^2(8')}{2} = 272\# \quad \text{(Beam reaction)}$$

COLUMN REACTION All of the beam cases below represent uniformly loaded conditions with simply supported ends, which result in reactions that are $R = \omega L/2$. The resulting reactions of the beams represent the loads present in each column.

First, analyze the beams along grid line *A*:

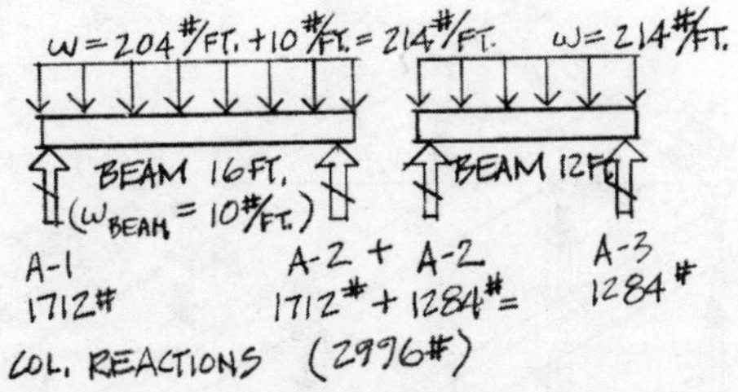

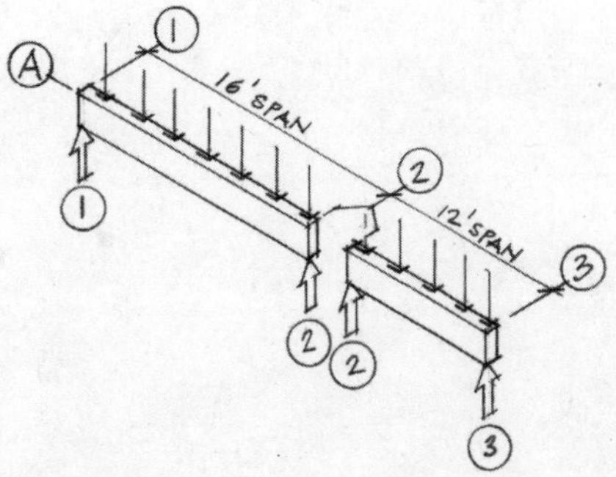

Next, analyze the beams along grid line *B*:

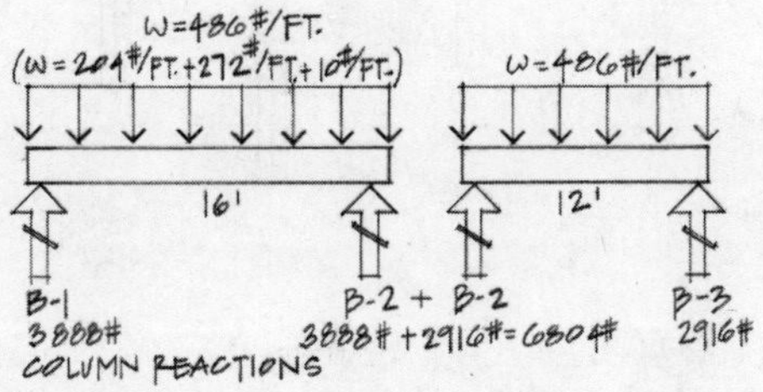

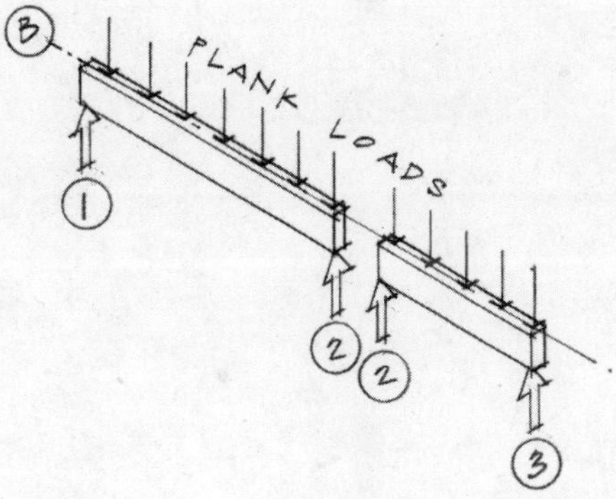

Then, analyze the beams along grid line C:

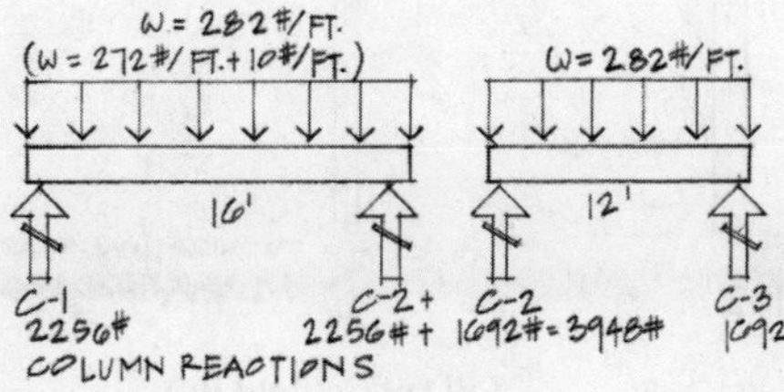

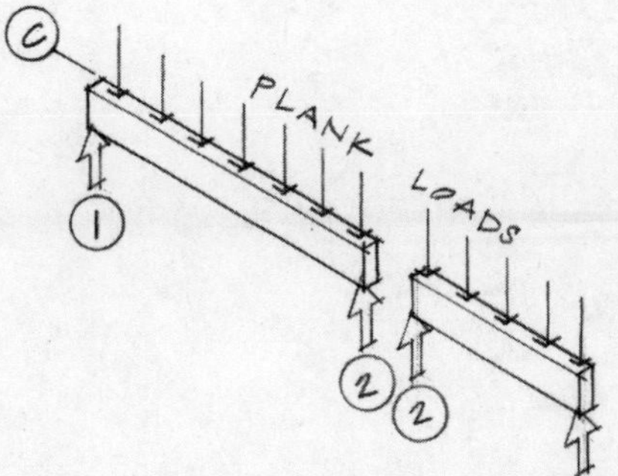

COLUMN LOADS AND REACTIONS The perimeter columns along grid lines *1* and *3* receive half of the load of each beam. The interior columns along grid line *2* receive loads from two beams, which are added together to calculate the column loads.

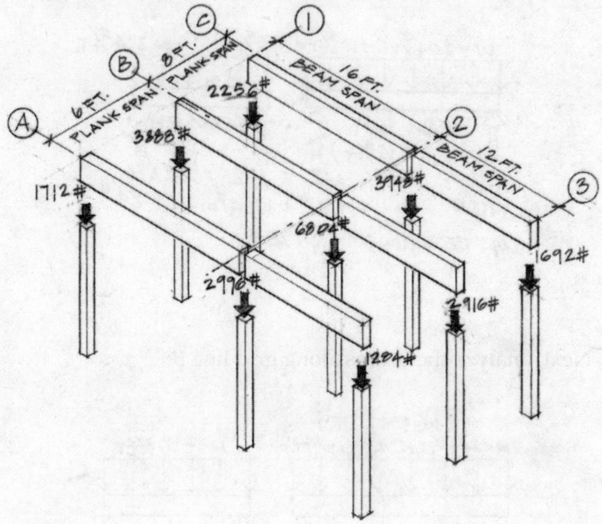

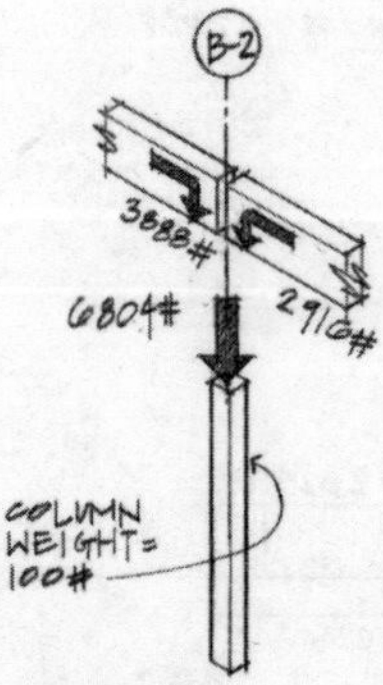

Column B-2

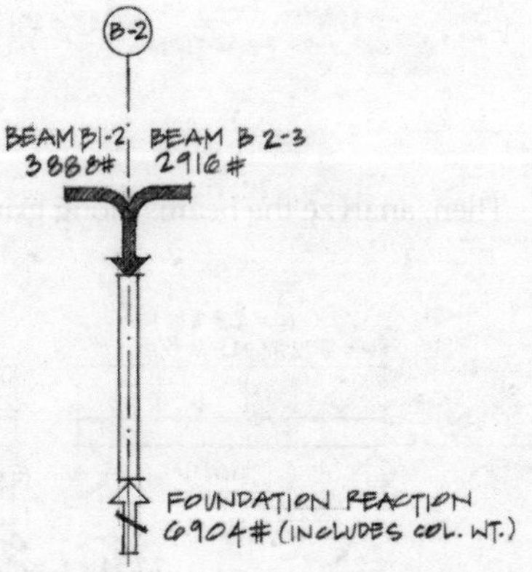

FBD of Column B-2

Example Problem 2—Alternate Method

Another technique may be employed in determining the beam reactions without going through an analysis of the planks. This may be accomplished by evaluating the tributary widths of load for each beam and directly calculating the ω for each beam. For example, in the following figure, the tributary width of load assigned to the beams along grid line *A* is three feet. Therefore:

$$\omega = 68\,\#/\text{ft.}^2(3') + 10\,\#/\text{ft.} = 214\,\#/\text{ft.}$$

This ω value corresponds to the result obtained in the previous method.

And along grid line *C*, with tributary width = 4′,

$$\omega = 68\,\#/\text{ft.}^2(4') + 10\,\#/\text{ft.} = 282\,\#/\text{ft.} \Rightarrow \text{CHECKS}$$

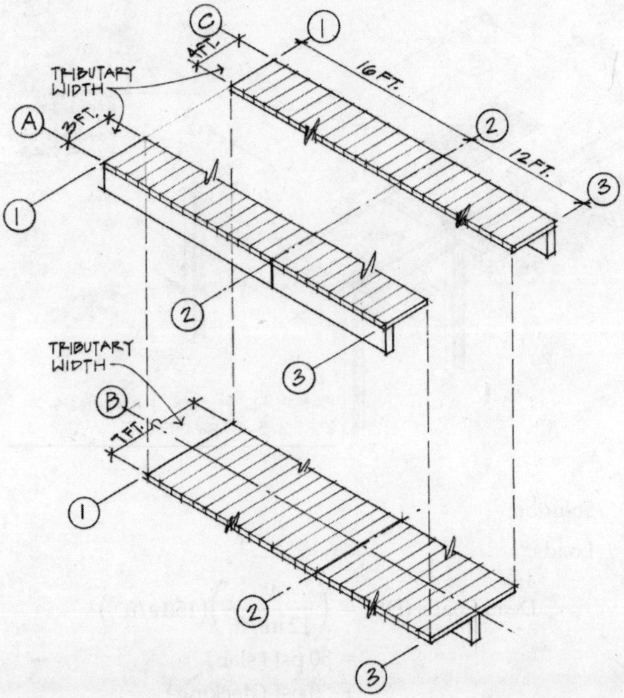

Similarly, for beams along gridline *B*:

$$\text{Tributary width} = 3' + 4' = 7'$$

$$\therefore \omega = 68\,\#/\text{ft.}^2(7') + 10\,\#/\text{ft.} = 486\,\#/\text{ft.} \Rightarrow \text{CHECKS}$$

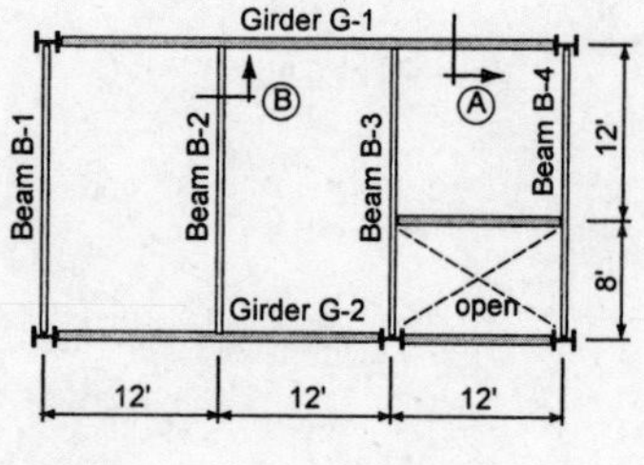

Partial floor framing plan

3 A steel-framed floor for an office building was designed to support a load condition as follows:

Loads:

Live Load	=	50 psf
Dead Loads:		
Concrete	=	150 #/ft.^{3}
Steel decking	=	5 psf
Mechanical equipment	=	10 psf
Suspended ceiling	=	5 psf
Steel beams	=	25 #/ft.
Steel girders	=	35 #/ft.

Using appropriate FBDs, determine the reaction forces for beams *B-1*, *B-2*, and *B-3* and for girder *G-1*.

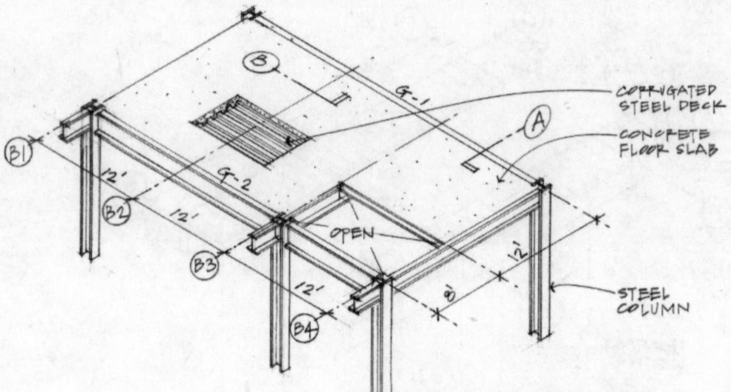

PARTIAL FLOOR FRAMING - OFFICE STRUCTURE

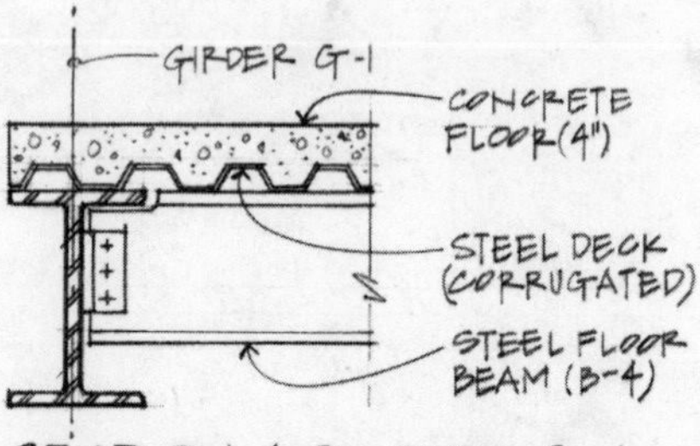

SECTION A @ GIRDER G-1

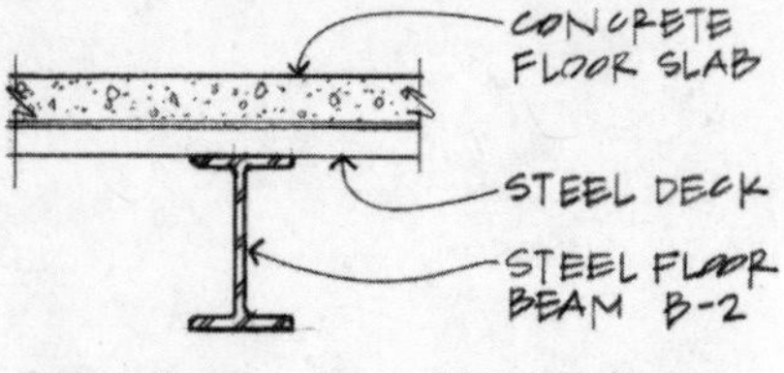

SECTION B @ BEAM B-2

Solution:

Loads:

$$\text{Dead Loads (DL)} = \left(\frac{4''}{12\text{ in./ft.}}\right)(150\,\#/\text{ft.}^3)$$

$$= 50\text{ psf (slab)}$$
$$+\ 5\text{ psf (decking)}$$
$$+\ 10\text{ psf (mechanical eq.)}$$
$$+\ 5\text{ psf (ceiling)}$$

$$\text{Total DL} = 70\text{ psf}$$

$$\text{DL} + \text{LL} = 70\text{ psf} + 50\text{ psf} = 120\text{ psf}$$

Beam *B-1*: (Tributary width of load is 6′)

$$\omega_1 = 120\,\#/\text{ft.}^2(6') + 25\,\#/\text{ft.} = 745\,\#/\text{ft.}$$

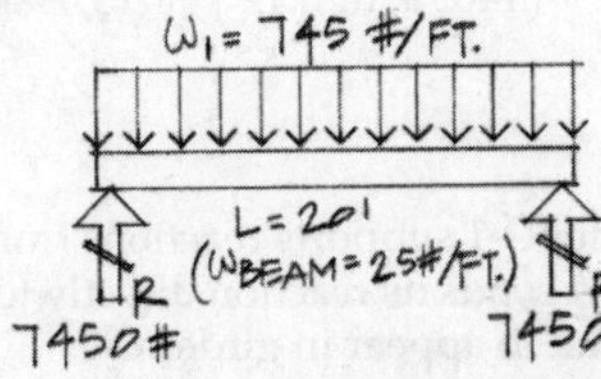

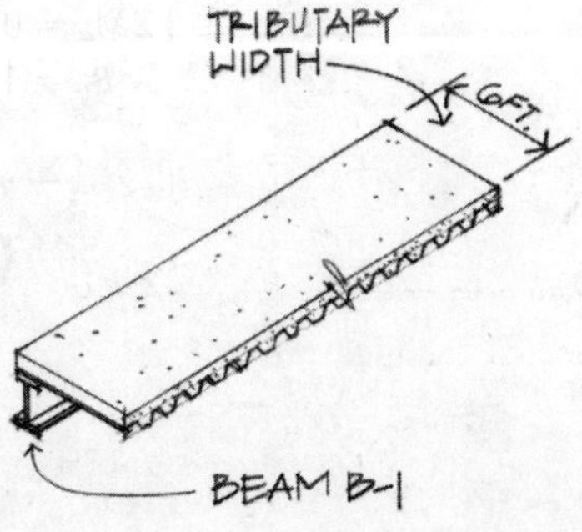

Beam *B-2*: (Tributary width of load is 6′ + 6′ = 12′)

$$\omega_2 = 120\,\#/\text{ft.}^2(12') + 25\,\#/\text{ft.} = 1{,}465\,\#/\text{ft.}$$

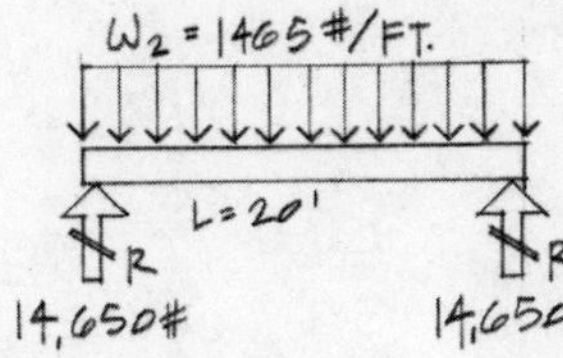

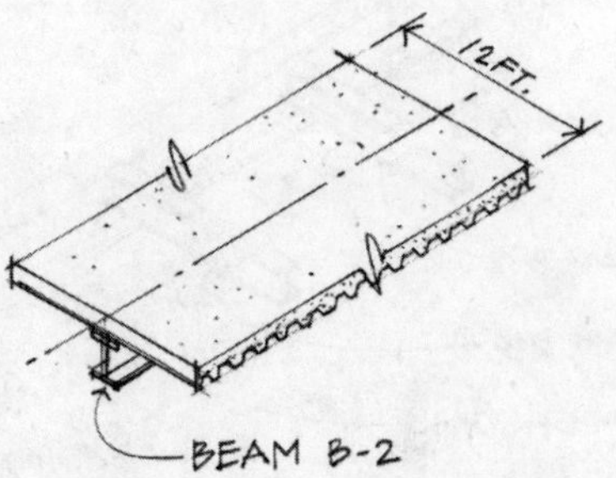

Beam *B-3*: This beam has two different load conditions due to the changing tributary width created by the opening.

For 12 feet of span,

$$\omega_3 = 120\,\#/\text{ft.}^2(12') + 25\,\#/\text{ft.} = 1{,}465\,\#/\text{ft.}$$

For six feet of span,

$$\omega_4 = 120\,\#/\text{ft.}^2(6') + 25\,\#/\text{ft.} = 745\,\#/\text{ft.}$$

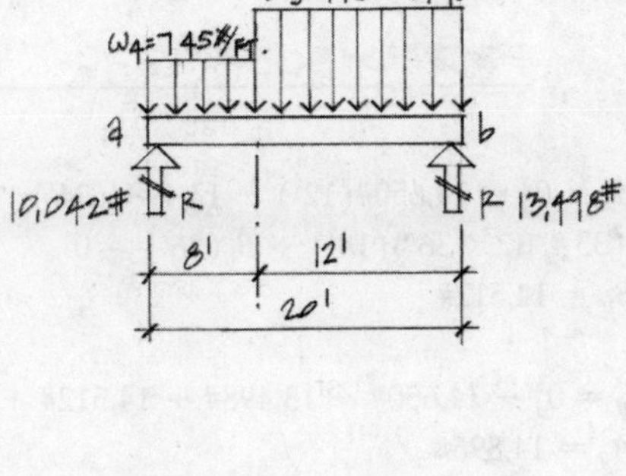

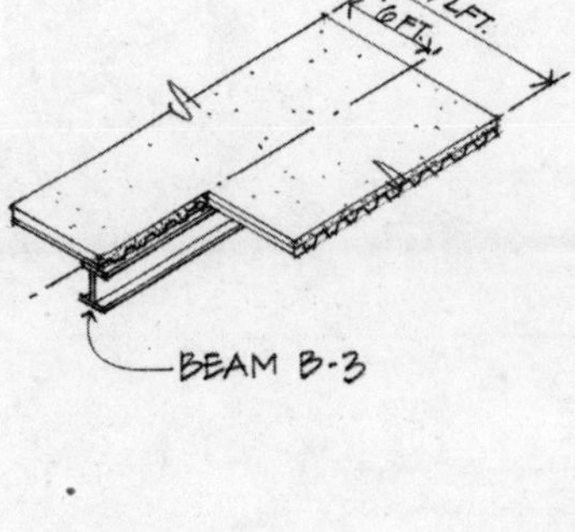

$$[\Sigma M_a = 0] - (745\,\#/\text{ft.})(8')(4') - (1{,}465\,\#/\text{ft.})(12')(14') + B_y(20') = 0$$
$$\therefore B_y = 13{,}498\#$$

$$[\Sigma F_y = 0] - (745\,\#/\text{ft.})(8') - (1465\,\#/\text{ft.})(12') + 13{,}498\# + A_y = 0$$
$$\therefore A_y = 10{,}042\#$$

Girder *G-1*: Girder *G-1* supports reactions from beams *B-2* and *B-3*. Beam *B-1* sends its reaction directly to the column and causes no load to appear in girder *G-1*.

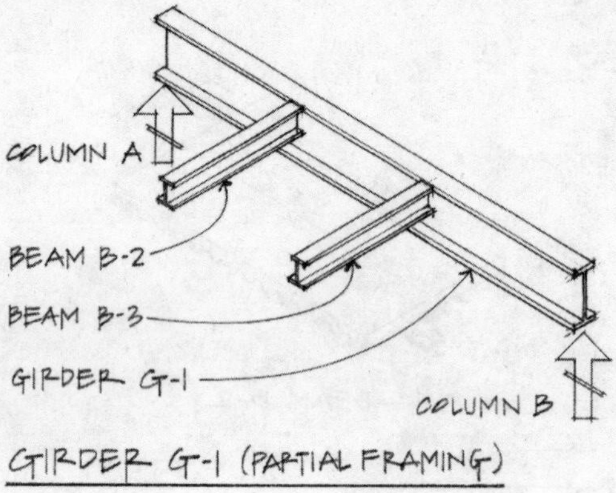

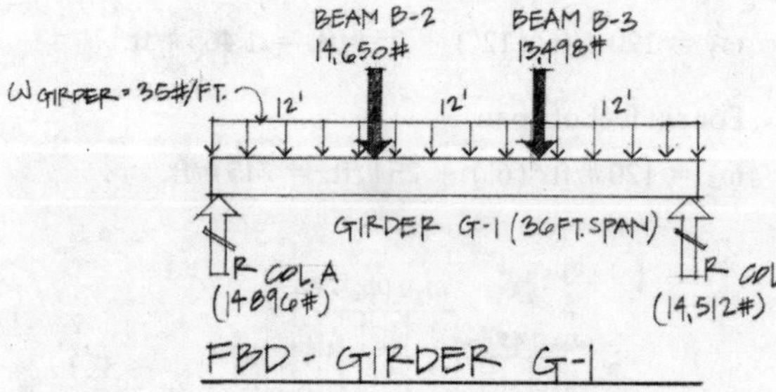

$$[\Sigma M_a = 0] - 14{,}650\#(12') - 13{,}498\#(24')$$
$$-(35\,\#/\text{ft.} \times 36')(18') + B_y(36') = 0$$
$$\therefore B_y = 14{,}512\#$$

$$[\Sigma F_y = 0] - 14{,}650\# - 13{,}498\# + 14{,}512\# + A_y = 0$$
$$\therefore A_y = 14{,}896\#$$

4 In this example, the load trace will involve the framing for a small deck addition to a residence. Once post reactions have been determined, a preliminary footing size will be designed assuming the soil capacity of 3,000 psf is known from a geotechnical investigation.

Loads:

Live Load = 60 $\#/\text{ft.}^2$

Dead Loads:

Decking = 5 $\#/\text{ft.}^2$

Beams = 5 #/ft.

Girder = 10 #/ft.

$\gamma_{concrete}$ = 150 $\#/\text{ft.}^3$ (density)

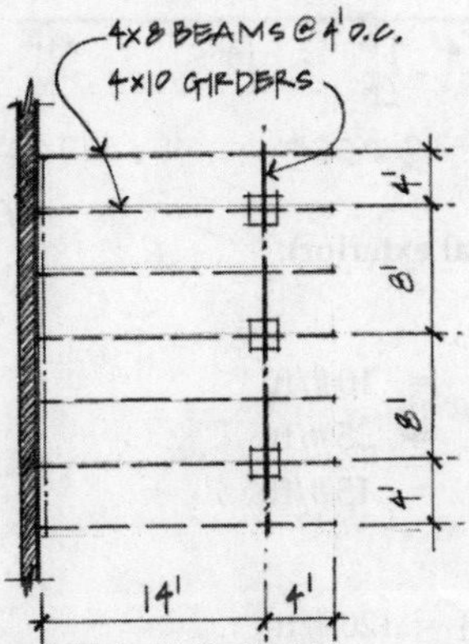

FRAMING PLAN

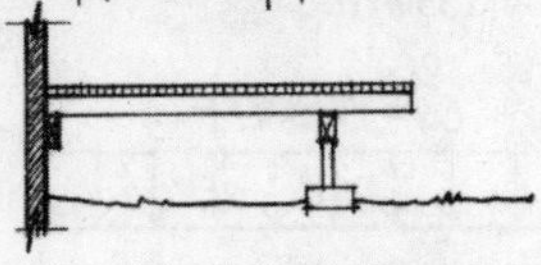

SIDE ELEVATION

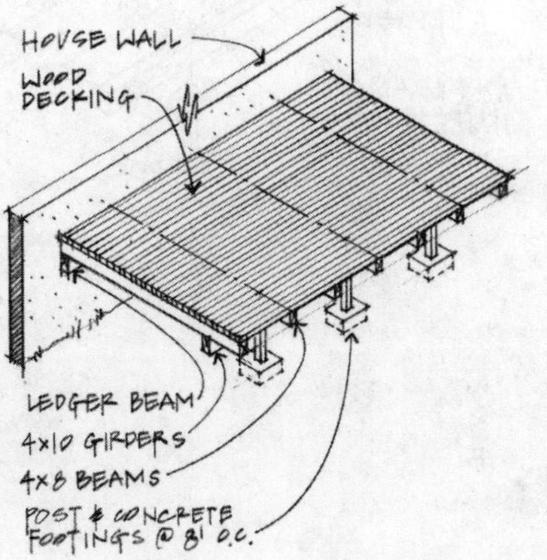

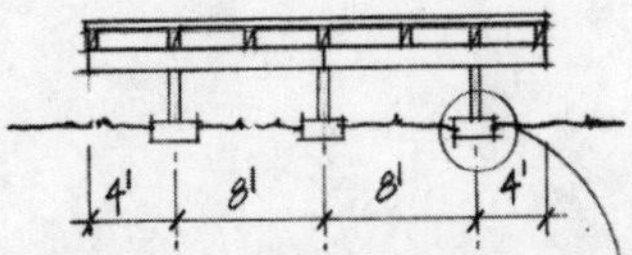

FRONT ELEVATION

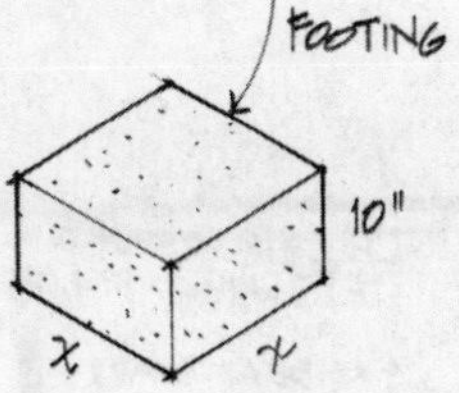

For this load-trace problem, we will investigate the following:

1. Draw an FBD of the typical beam with its load condition shown.
2. Draw an FBD of the girder with its load conditions shown.
3. Determine the load in each post.
4. Determine the size x of the critical pier footing (account for the weight of the concrete).

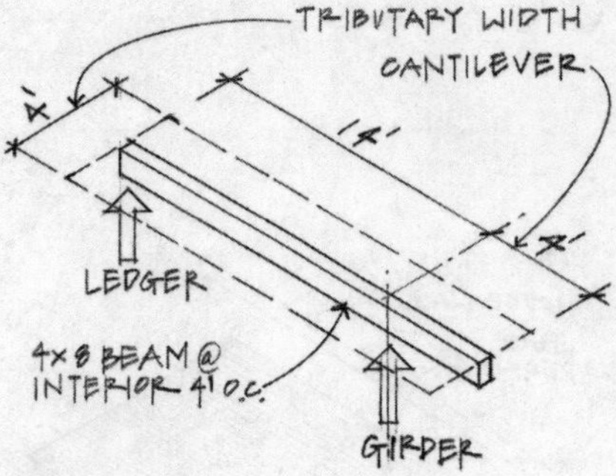

Solution:

1. Beam (typical interior):

Dead Load:

$$5\text{ psf }(4') = 20\ \#/\text{ft.}$$
$$\text{Beam wt.} = 5\ \#/\text{ft.}$$
$$\omega_{DL} = 25\ \#/\text{ft.}$$

Live Load:

$$60\text{ psf }(4') = 240\ \#/\text{ft.}$$
$$\omega_{DL+LL} = 265\ \#/\text{ft.}$$

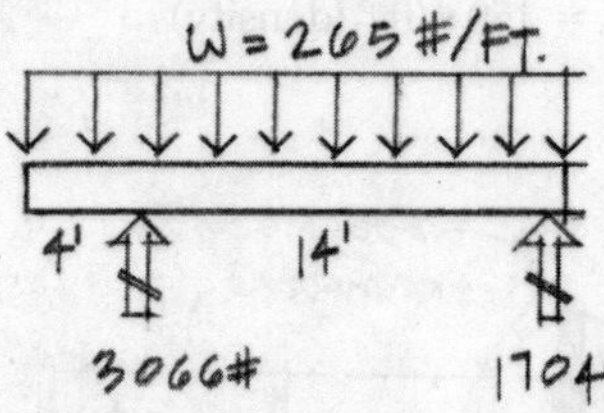

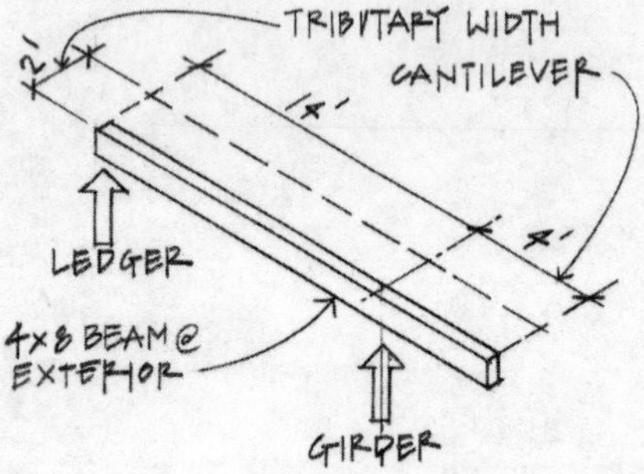

2. Beam (typical exterior):

Dead Load:

$$5\text{ psf }(2') = 10\ \#/\text{ft.}$$
$$\text{Beam wt.} = 5\ \#/\text{ft.}$$
$$\omega_{DL} = 15\ \#/\text{ft.}$$

Live Load:

$$60\text{ psf }(2') = 120\ \#/\text{ft.}$$
$$\omega_{DL+LL} = 135\ \#/\text{ft.}$$

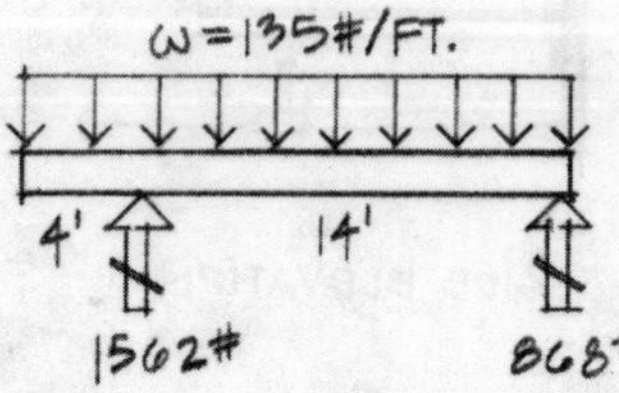

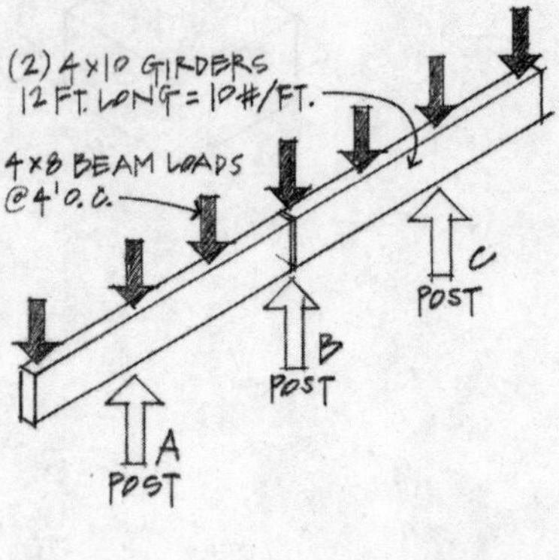

3/4. Girder and post:

$$[\Sigma M_B = 0] - 3{,}066\#(4') - 3{,}066\#(8') - 1{,}562\#(12')$$
$$-(10\ \#/\text{ft.})(12')(6') + A_y(8') = 0$$
$$\therefore A_y = 7{,}032\#$$

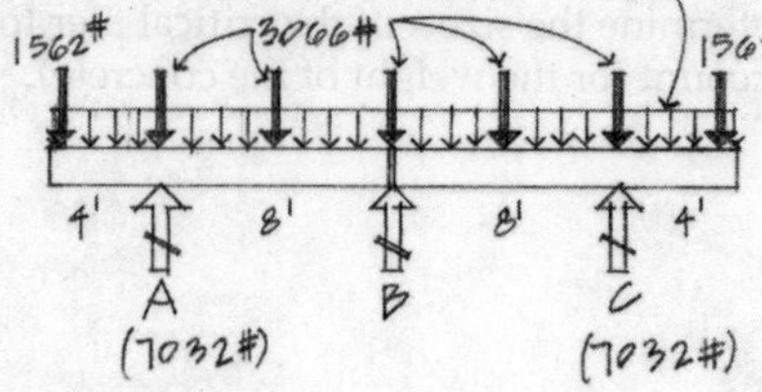

$$[\Sigma F_y = 0] - \frac{3{,}066\#}{2} - 3{,}066\# - 3{,}066\# - 1{,}562\#$$
$$-(10\,\#/\text{ft.})(12') + B_y(\text{right side}) + 7{,}032\# = 0$$
$$\therefore B_{yR} = 2{,}315\#$$

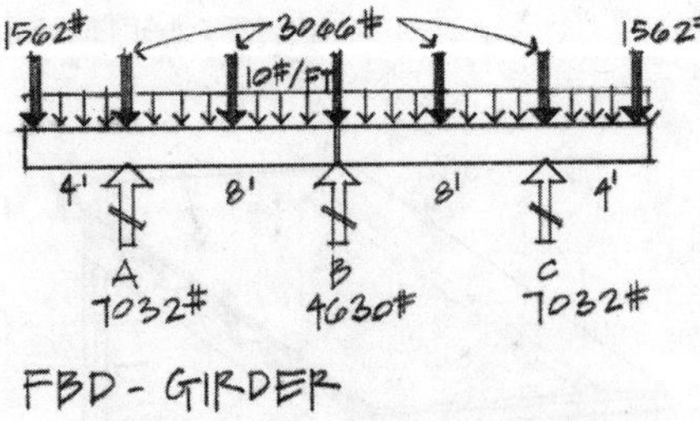

The total reaction at post B is the sum of the reactions:

$$B_{yR} + B_{yL} = 4{,}630\#$$

5. Critical footing:

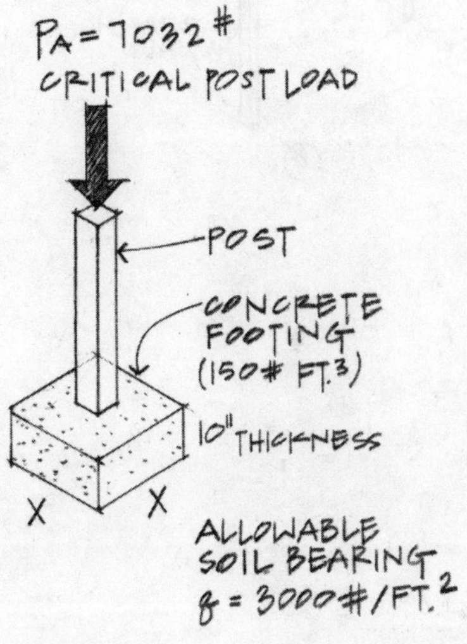

The soil is capable of resisting a total bearing pressure of 3,000 #/ft.^{2}

$$\text{Note: pressure} = \frac{\text{load}}{\text{area}};\ q = \frac{P}{A}$$

By setting $q = 3{,}000\,\#/\text{ft.}^2$ (allowable capacity of the soil), we need to deduct the weight of the footing itself to determine the footing's capacity to resist applied load from above. Therefore,

$$q_{\text{net}} = q - \text{footing weight (as pressure measured in psf)}$$

Footing weight can be solved by converting the density of concrete ($\gamma_{\text{concrete}} = 150\,\#/\text{ft.}^3$) into equivalent pounds per square foot units by multiplying:

$$\text{footing wt. (psf)} = (\gamma_{\text{concrete}})(\text{thickness of concrete in feet})$$

$$\therefore \text{footing wt.} = (150\,\#/\text{ft.}^3)(10''/12\,\text{in./ft.})$$
$$= 125\,\#/\text{ft.}^2$$

The remaining soil capacity to resist point loads is expressed as

$$q_{\text{net}} = 3{,}000\,\#/\text{ft.}^2 - 125\,\#/\text{ft.}^2 = 2{,}875\,\#/\text{ft.}^2$$

$$\text{Because pressure} = \frac{\text{load}}{\text{area}}$$

$$q_{\text{net}} = \frac{P}{A} = \frac{P}{x^2}$$

$$\therefore x^2 = \frac{P}{q_{\text{net}}} = \frac{7{,}032\#}{2{,}875\,\#/\text{ft.}^2} = 2.45\,\text{ft.}^2$$

$$\therefore x = 1.57' = 1'7''\ \text{square footing (theoretical size)}$$

Practical size may be $x = 2'0''$

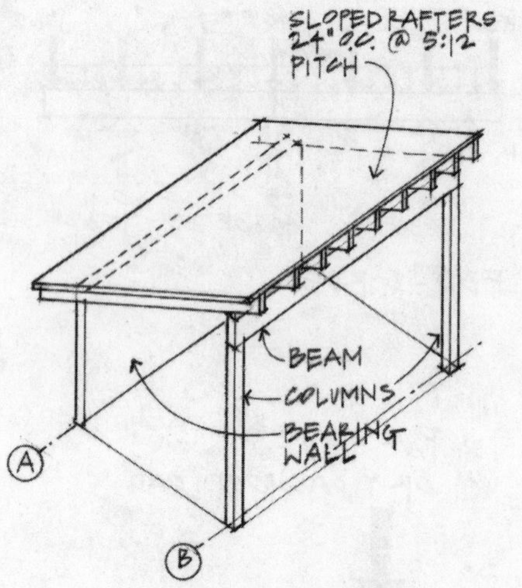

5 Calculate the load trace for a sloped roof structure.

Roofing	= 5 psf	Along rafter
Roof Sheathing	= 3 psf	
Rafters	= 4 #/ft.	

Snow load (SL): 40 psf on horizontal projection of rafter*

Beam: 16 #/ft.

**Snow loads are normally given as a load on the horizontal projection of a roof.*

Solution:

1. Rafter analysis:

Roofing: 5 psf

Sheathing: 3 psf

(8 psf) (24″/12 in./ft.) = 16 #/ft.

Rafter: + 4 #/ft.

20 #/ft.

(Along rafter length)

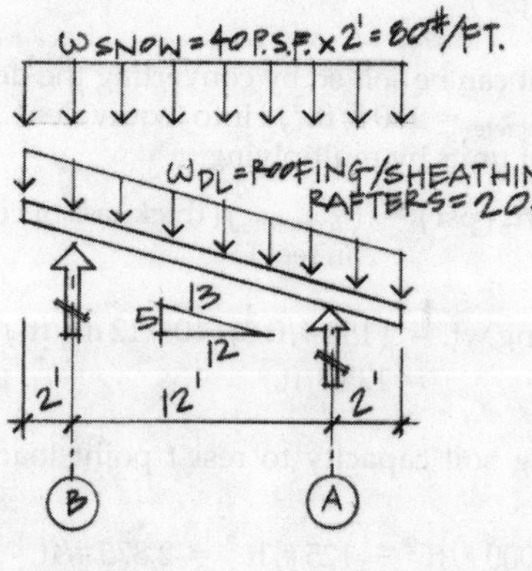

Adjust to horizontal projection: $\frac{13}{12}(20\,\#/\text{ft.}) = 21.7\,\#/\text{ft.}$

$$SL = 40\,\#/\text{ft.}^2 \times \frac{24''}{12\text{ in./ft.}} = 80\,\#/\text{ft.}$$

$$\omega = 21.7\,\#/\text{ft.} + 80\,\#/\text{ft.} = 101.7\,\#/\text{ft.}$$

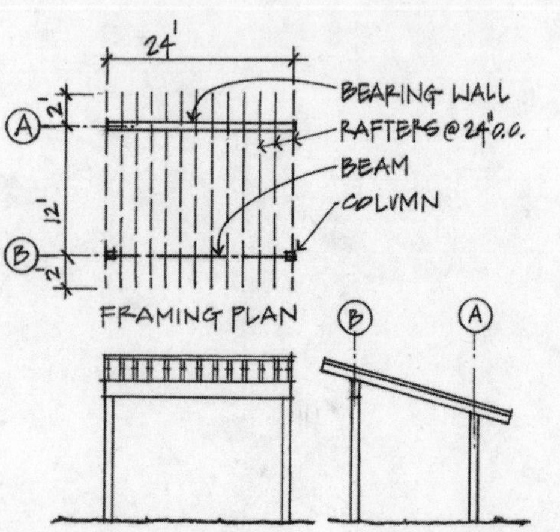

***Note:** Rafter horizontally projected for ease of computation.*

Using FBD sketches and computations, determine the load condition on (a) beam, (b) column, and (c) wall (typical stud).

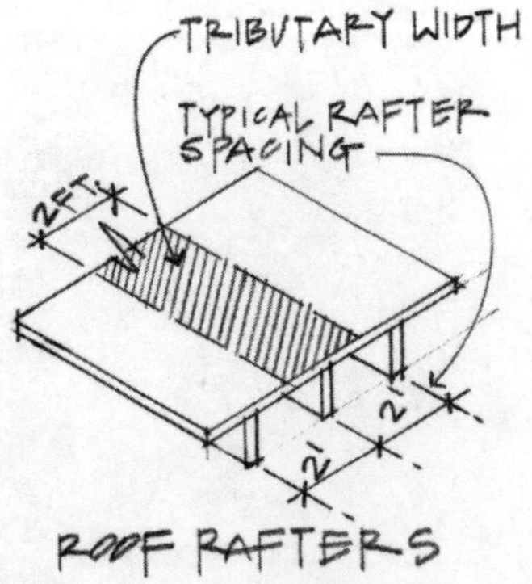

1. Beam analysis:

The reaction from a typical roof joist on top of the beam and stud wall is 813.6#. However, because the roof joists occur every two feet, the equivalent load ω is equal to

$$\omega = \frac{813.6\#}{2'} = 406.8\,\#/\text{ft.} + 16\,\#/\text{ft.}\,(\text{beam weight})$$
$$= 422.8\,\#/\text{ft.}$$

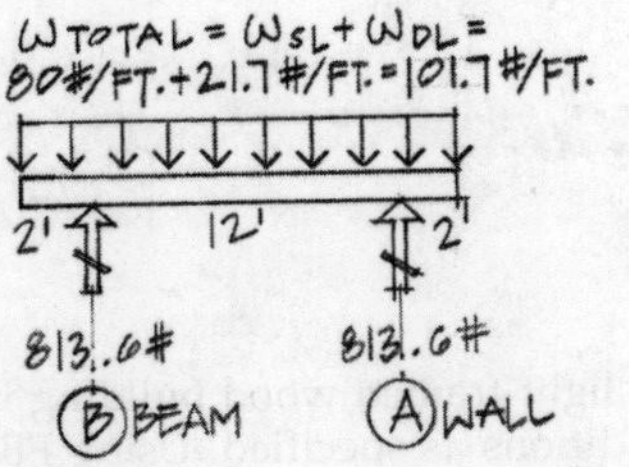

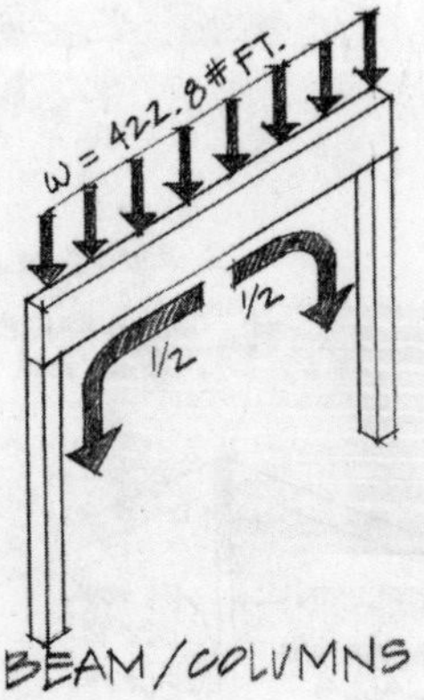

2. Column analysis:

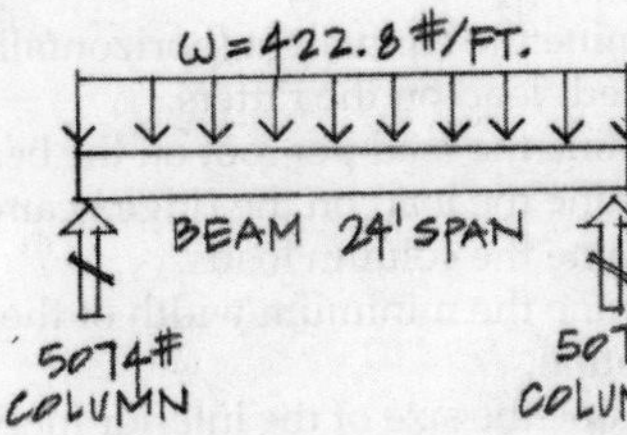

The column load is computed as

$$P = \frac{\omega L}{2} = \frac{422.8\,\#/\text{ft.}\,(24')}{2} = 5{,}074\#$$

Note: *This equation simply divides the total load on the rafter in half, because the rafter is symmetrically loaded.*

3. Stud wall:

Tributary wall length per stud is

$$16'' = \frac{16''}{12\,\text{in./ft.}} = 1.33'$$

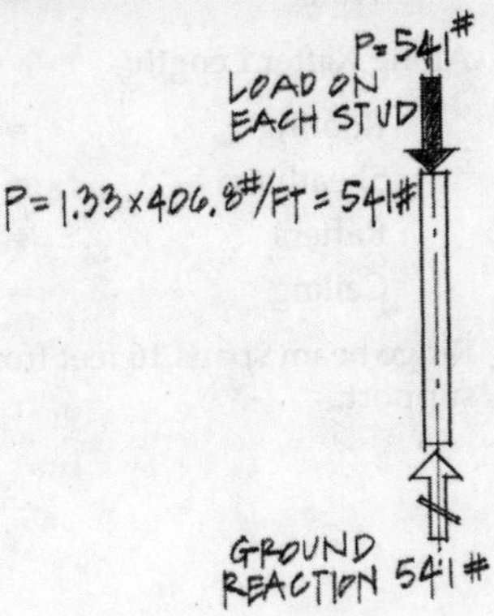

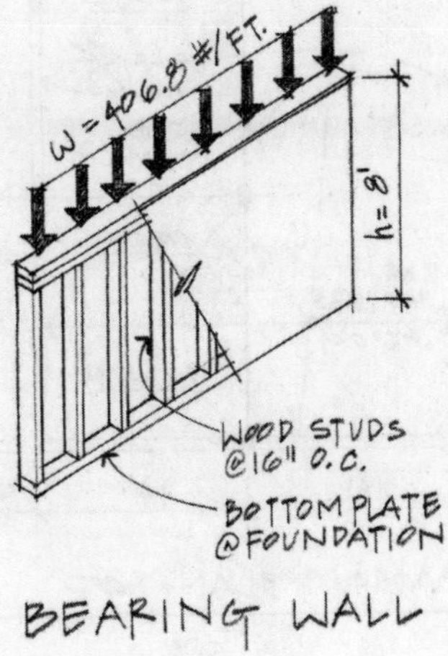

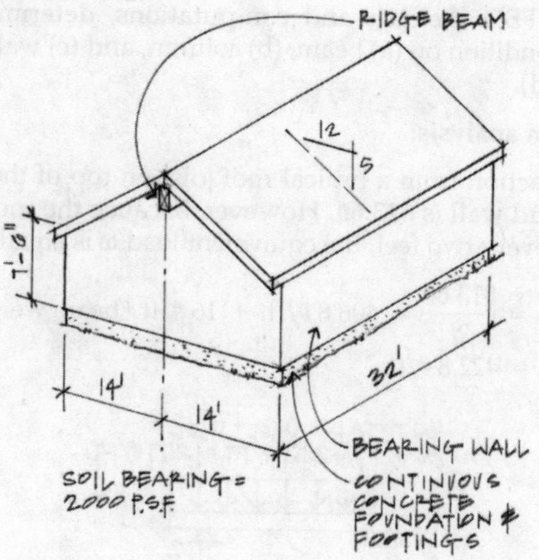

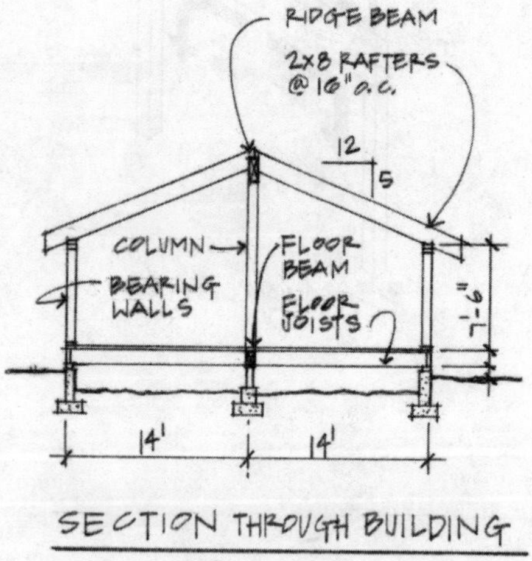

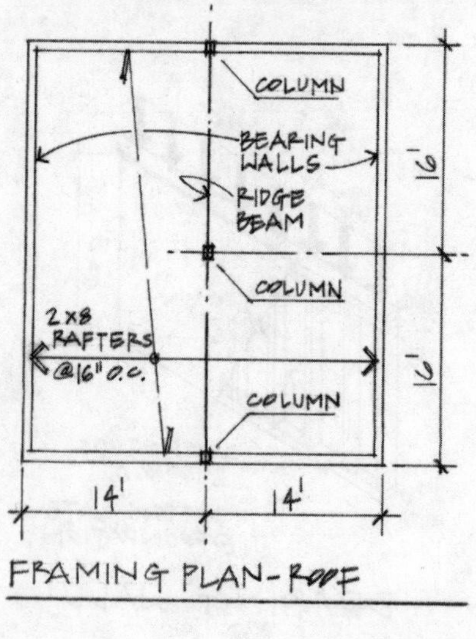

6 A simple light-framed wood building is subjected to the load conditions as specified. Using FBDs and equations of equilibrium, trace the loads through the building for the following elements:

1. Determine the equivalent (horizontally projected) load on the rafters.
2. Determine the load per foot on the bearing wall.
3. Determine the load on the ridge beam.
4. Determine the column loads.
5. Determine the minimum width of the continuous foundation.
6. Determine the size of the interior footings.

Load Conditions:

Soil Bearing Pressure	=	2,000 psf
Flooring	=	2 psf
Subfloor	=	5 psf
Joists	=	4 psf
LL (occupancy)	=	40 psf
SL	=	25 psf
Walls	=	7 psf

Along Rafter Length:

Roofing	=	5 psf
Sheathing	=	3 psf
Rafters	=	2 psf
Ceiling	=	2 psf

Ridge beam spans 16 feet from column support to column support.

Solution:

1. Rafters:

SL = 25 psf: rafters spaced 16″ on center.

$$\omega_{SL} = (25\,\#/\text{ft.}^2)\left(\frac{16}{12}\right)' = 33.3\,\#/\text{ft.}$$

(Horizontal projection)

Roof DL = 12 psf

$$\omega_{DL} = (12\,\#/\text{ft.}^2)\left(\frac{16}{12}\right)' = 16\,\#/\text{ft.}$$

(Along rafter length)

$$\omega'_{DL} = \left(\frac{13}{12}\right)(16\,\#/\text{ft.}) = 17.3\,\#/\text{ft.}$$

(Equivalent load horizontally projected)

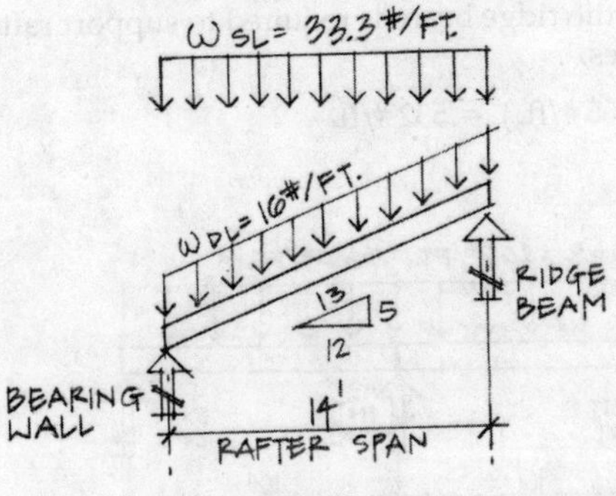

$$\omega_{total} = \omega_{SL} + \omega'_{DL}$$

$$\omega_{total} = 33.3\,\#/\text{ft.} + 17.3\,\#/\text{ft.} = 50.6\,\#/\text{ft.}$$

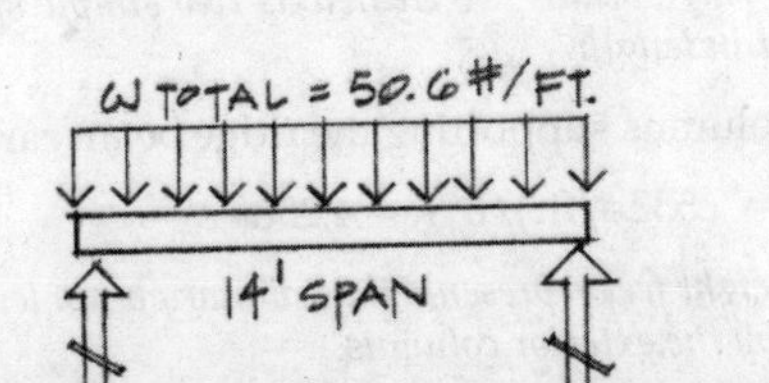

The reaction at each rafter support may be determined using equilibrium equations. When uniform loads on a simply supported member are present, a simple formula may be used where

$$R = \frac{\omega L}{2} = \frac{(50.6\,\#/\text{ft.})(14')}{2} = 354\#$$

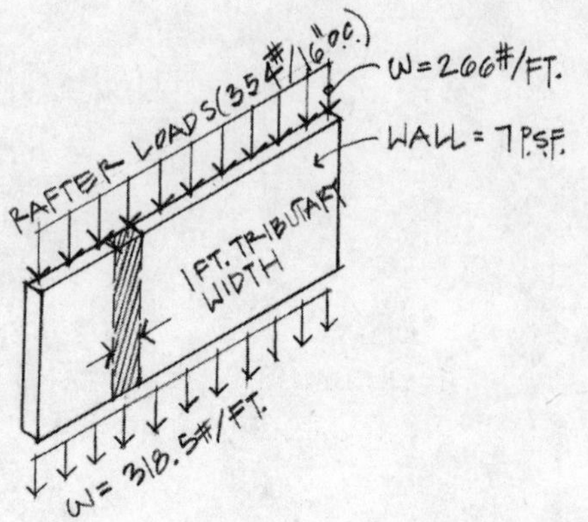

2. Bearing wall:

The reaction of the rafter onto the bearing wall is 354# every 16 inches. A conversion should be done to express the load at the top of the wall in pounds per lineal foot.

$$\omega = (354\#/16'')\left(\frac{12}{16}\right)' = 266\#/\text{ft.}$$

A strip of wall 1 foot wide and seven feet, six inches tall weighs

$$\omega_{\text{wall}} = 7\#/\text{ft.}^2(7.5') = 52.5\#/\text{ft.}$$

$$\omega = 266\#/\text{ft.} + 52.5\#/\text{ft.} = 318.5\#/\text{ft.}$$

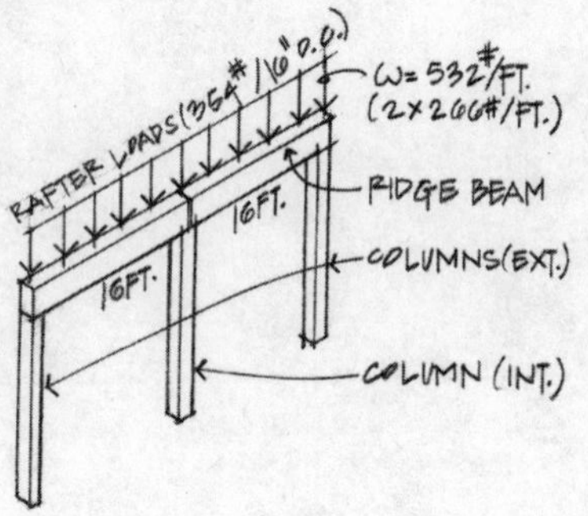

3. Ridge beam:

Rafter reactions are equal to 354# per 16 inches, or 266 #/ft. Because the ridge beam is required to support rafters from both sides,

$$\omega = 2(266\#/\text{ft.}) = 532\#/\text{ft.}$$

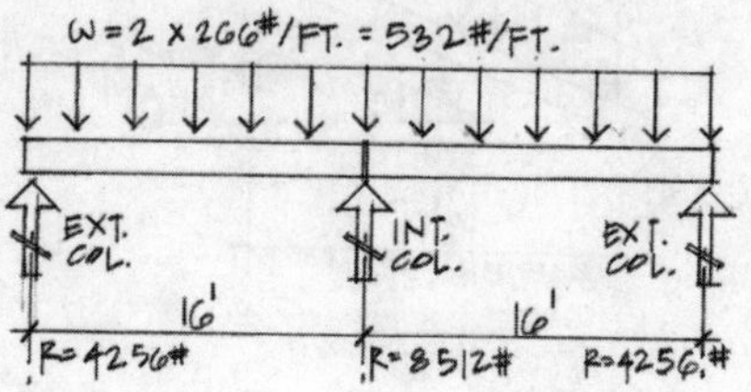

Note: *The ridge beams are treated as two simple span beams, each 16 feet in length.*

Exterior columns supporting the ridge beam carry

$$P_{\text{ext}} = (532\#/\text{ft.})(8') = 4{,}256\#$$

Note: *The eight feet represents the tributary beam length that is supported by the exterior columns.*

Interior columns support a tributary beam length of 16 feet; therefore,

$$P_{\text{int}} = (532\#/\text{ft.})(16') = 8{,}512\#$$

4. Floor joists:

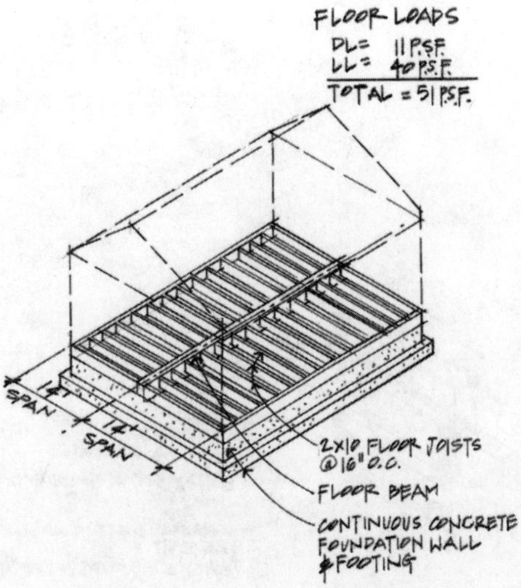

Joists are spaced 16 inches on center, which also represents the tributary width of load assigned to each joist.

Loads: DL + LL = 11 psf + 40 psf = 51 psf
(Floor Joist Loads and Reactions)

$$\omega_{D+L} = 51\,\#/\text{ft.}^2\left(\frac{16}{12}\right)' = 68\,\#/\text{ft.}$$

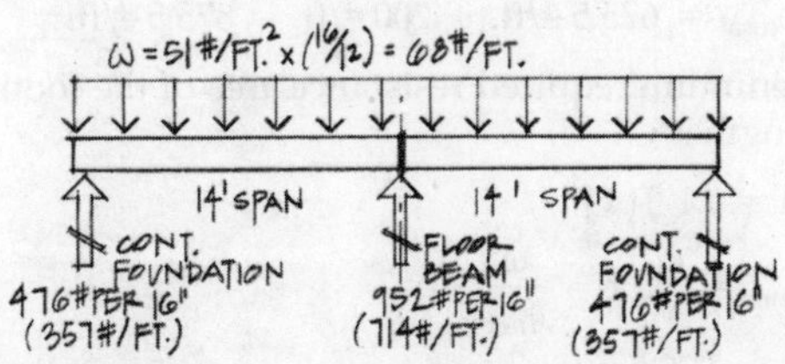

Foundation reactions may be obtained by

$$\text{Foundation} = (68\,\#/\text{ft.})(7'\ \{\text{tributary length}\}) = 476\,\#/16''$$

The central floor beam supports a floor joist reaction equal to

$$\text{Beam} = (68\,\#/\text{ft.})(14'\ \{\text{tributary length}\}) = 952\,\#/16''$$

Conversion of the floor joist reactions into load per foot results in

$$\text{Foundation: } \omega = (476\,\#/16\text{ in.})\left(\frac{12}{16}\right)' = 357\#$$

$$\text{Beam: } \omega = (952\,\#/16\text{ in.})\left(\frac{12}{16}\right)' = 714\#$$

5. Continuous foundation:

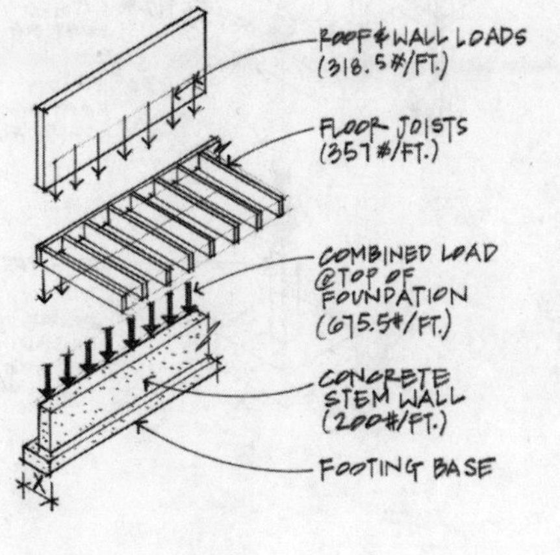

The stem wall measures eight inches thick and two feet tall. The footing base is eight inches thick and x wide.

Loads from the roof, wall, and floor are combined as a total load on top of the foundation stem:

$$\omega_{total} = 318.5\,\#/\text{ft.} + 357\,\#/\text{ft.} = 675.5\,\#/\text{ft.}$$

The foundation wall stem adds additional load on the footing equal to

$$\text{Stem weight} = \left(\frac{8}{12}\right)'(2')(150\,\#/\text{ft.}^3) = 200\,\#/\text{ft.}$$

Because the footing width x is unknown, the weight of the footing base must be computed in terms of pounds per square foot.

$$\text{Footing weight} = \left(\frac{8}{12}\right)'(150\,\#/\text{ft.}^3) = 100\,\#/\text{ft.}^2$$

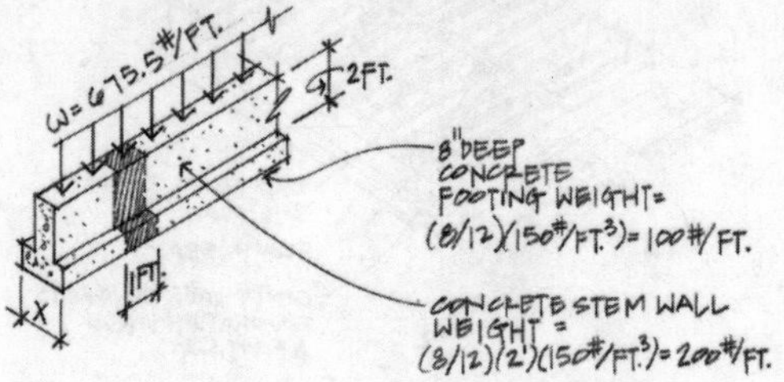

In determining the footing width, examine a unit length (1′) of foundation as a representation of the entire length.

$$q = \text{allowable soil bearing pressure} = 2{,}000 \text{ psf}$$

$$q_{\text{net}} = q - \text{footing weight} = 2{,}000 \text{ psf} - 100 \text{ psf} = 1{,}900 \text{ psf}$$

This value of q_{net} represents the resistance of the soil available to safely support the loads of roof, walls, floor, and foundation stem.

$$\omega_{\text{total}} = 675.5\,\#/\text{ft.} + 200\,\#/\text{ft.} = 875.5\,\#/\text{ft.}$$

The minimum required resistance area of the footing per unit length is

$$A = (1')(x)$$

$$q_{\text{net}} = \frac{\omega}{x};\ x = \frac{\omega}{q_{\text{net}}}$$

$$x = \frac{875.5\,\#/\text{ft.}}{1{,}900\,\#/\text{ft.}^2} = 0.46' \approx 6''$$

Note that a footing base of six inches would be less than the thickness of the stem wall. A minimum footing width for a one-story, light-framed assembly should be 12 inches. If a 12 inch base width is provided, the actual pressure on the soil will be

$$\text{Actual pressure} = \frac{\omega}{x = 1'} = \frac{875.5\,\#/\text{ft.}}{1'} = 875.5\,\#/\text{ft.}^2 < q_{\text{net}}$$

$\therefore$ OK.

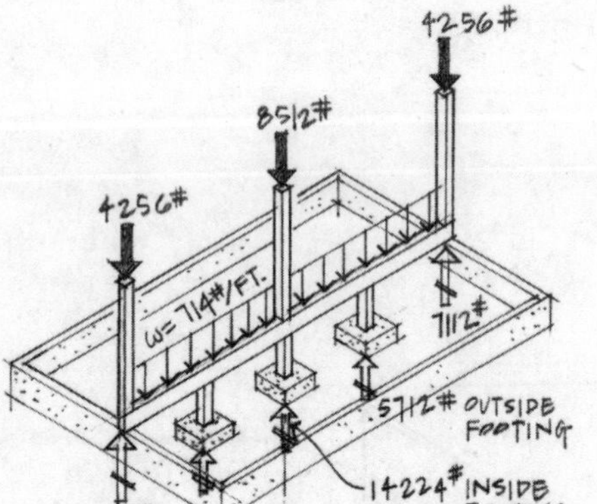

6. Interior spread footings:

A determination of individual post loads is necessary before footing sizes can be computed.

Assume the spread footings have a thickness of eight inches and $q = 2{,}000$ psf:

$$\omega_{\text{footing}} = \left(\frac{8}{12}\right)'(150\,\#/\text{ft.}^3) = 100\,\#/\text{ft.}^2$$

$$q_{\text{net}} = q - \text{footing wt.} = 2{,}000 \text{ psf} - 100 \text{ psf} = 1{,}900 \text{ psf}$$

Critical center column:

$$A = x^2 = \frac{P}{q_{\text{net}}} = \frac{14{,}224\#}{1{,}900\,\#/\text{ft.}^2} = 7.5 \text{ ft.}^2$$

$$\therefore x = 2.74' \approx 2'9'' \text{ square}$$

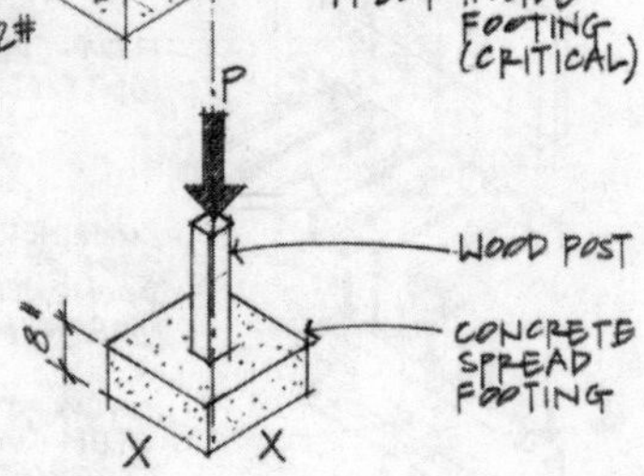

Other footing:

$$x^2 = \frac{5{,}712\#}{1{,}900\,\#/\text{ft.}^2} = 3.00 \text{ ft.}^2$$

$$\therefore x = 1.73' \approx 1'9'' \text{ square}$$

Problems

In each of the load-tracing problems below, construct a series of FBDs and show the propagation of loads through the various structural elements.

1 Determine the column loads assuming:

DL (decking, flooring, etc.)	=	10 psf
LL (occupancy)	=	40 psf
Total		50 psf

Beam *B-2* spans between girder *G-3* and column *B-2* and beam *B-3* spans between girder *G-3* and column *C-2*.

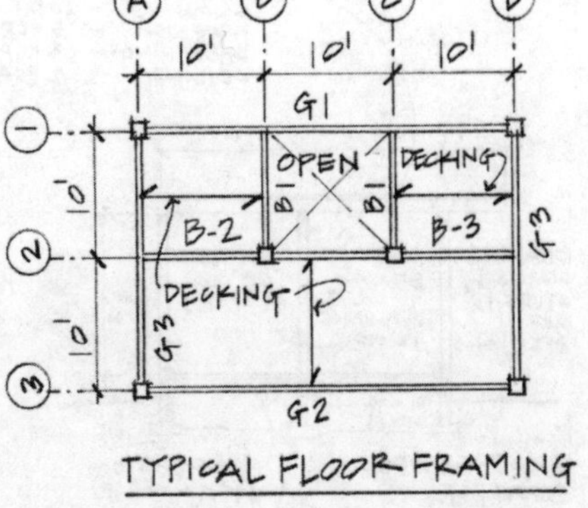

2 Loads:

Roof:	DL = 10 psf	
	LL = 25 psf	(snow horizontally projected)
Ceiling:	DL = 5 psf	
	LL = 10 psf	
Bearing walls:	DL = 10 psf	(2nd and 3rd floors)
Floors:	DL = 20 psf	(2nd and 3rd floors)
	LL = 40 psf	(2nd and 3rd floors)

1. Determine the equivalent (horizontally projected) load on the rafters spaced at two feet, zero inches 2′0″ on center.
2. Determine the load per foot on the bearing walls.
3. Determine the loading and beam reactions for each of the steel wide-flange beams.

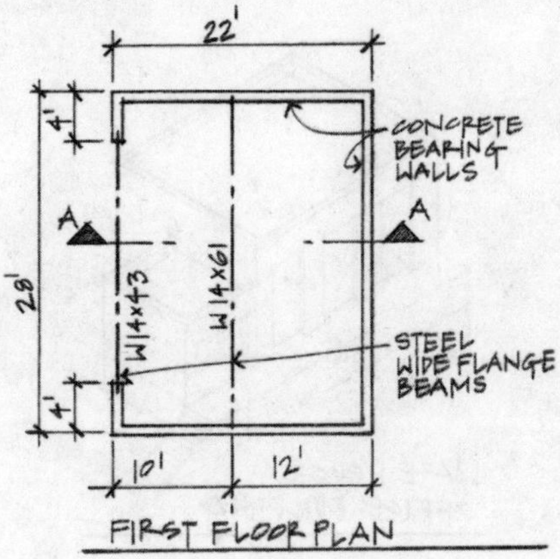

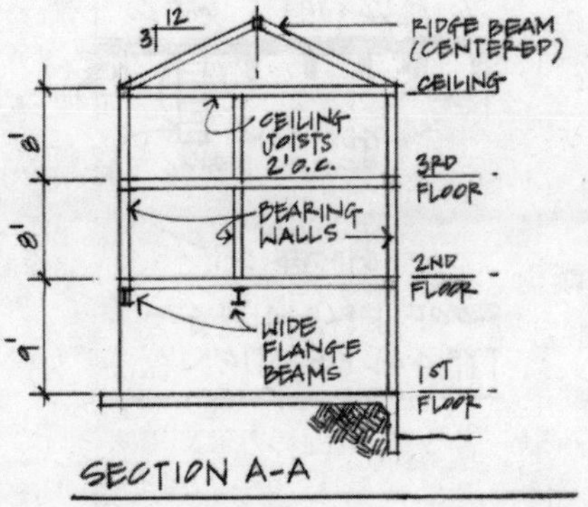

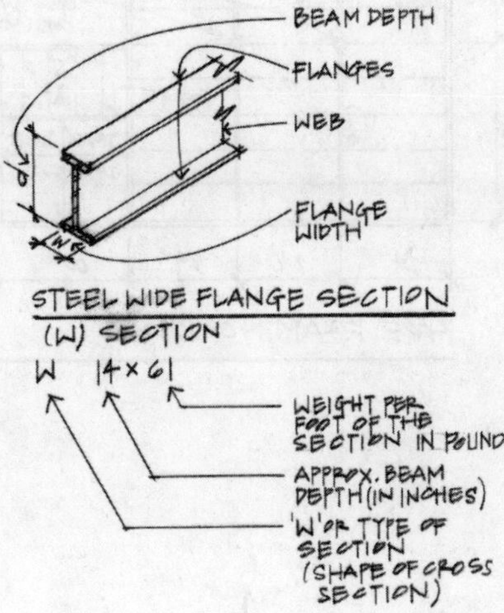

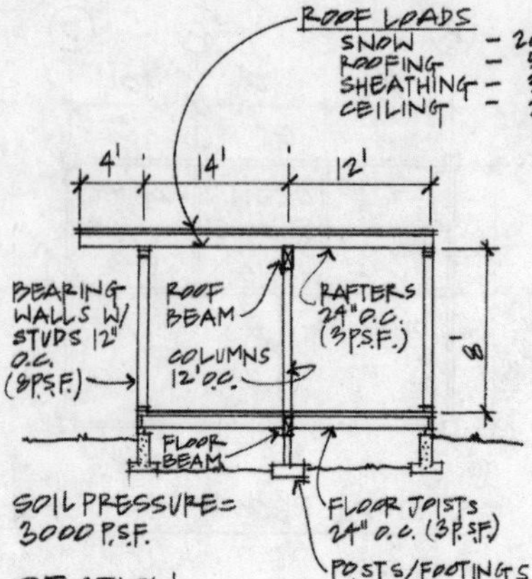

SECTION

3 Trace the loads through the following elements in this structure. Occupancy live load is 40 psf, with a floor dead load of 5 psf.

1. Rafters.
2. Stud walls.
3. Roof beam.
4. Columns (interior and exterior).
5. Floor joist.
6. Floor beam.
7. Load on top of continuous footings.
8. Critical interior footing load.

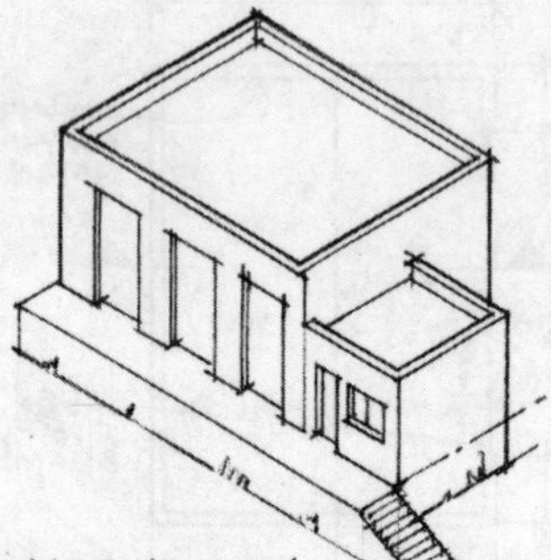
WAREHOUSE/ OFFICE BUILDING

4 Draw FBDs and show load conditions for *B-1*, *G-1*, interior column, *B-2*, and *G-2*.

Loads:

SL	= 25 psf
Roofing and joists (deck)	= 10 psf
Truss joist	= 3 psf
Insul., mech., elec.	= 5 psf
Beams *B-1* and *B-2*	= 15 #/ft.
Girders *G-1* and *G-2*	= 50 #/ft.

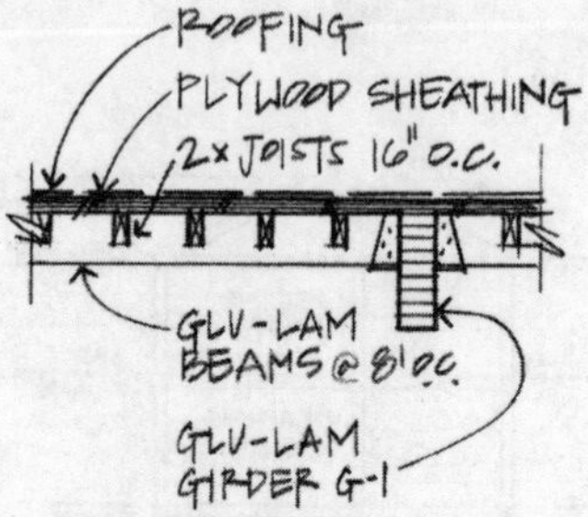

ROOF FRAMING – TYPICAL SECTION

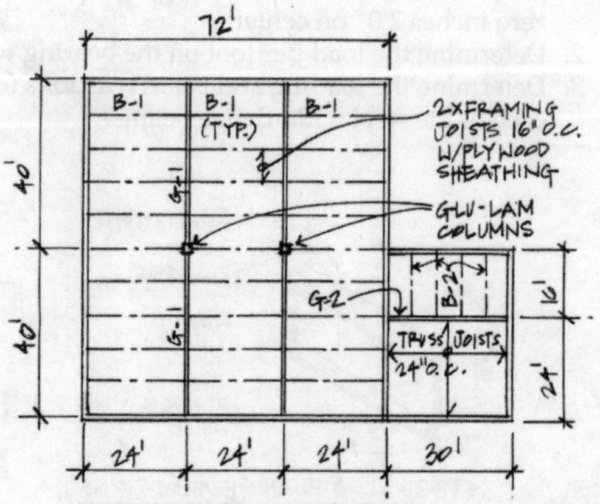

ROOF FRAMING PLAN

5 Roof Loads:

SL	= 20 psf
Shakes	= 5 psf
Plywood	= 2 psf
Insulation	= 5 psf
Joists	= 4 #/ft.
Ridge beam	= 40 #/ft.

1. Sketch the load and its magnitude acting on the 34-foot-long ridge beam.
2. What is the force in columns *A* and *B*, which support the ridge beam?

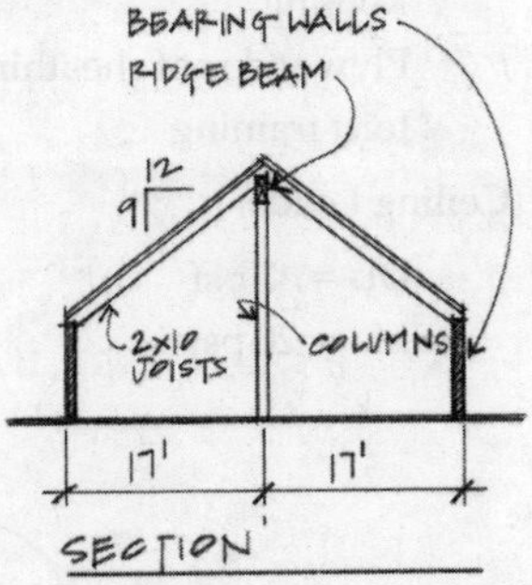

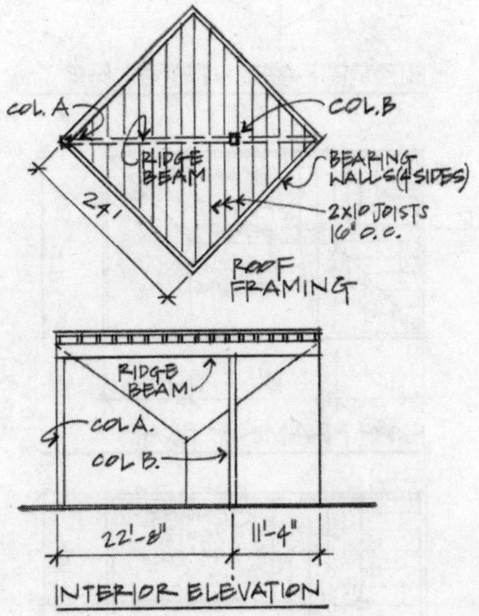

6 Show graphically (FBDs for each element) the load trace (load condition) for:

1. Rafter(s).
2. Roof beam.
3. Exterior stud wall(s).
4. Interior columns.
5. Floor joist(s).
6. Floor beam.
7. Floor post.
8. Exterior foundation width(s) (adequacy?).
9. Size of critical pier footing.

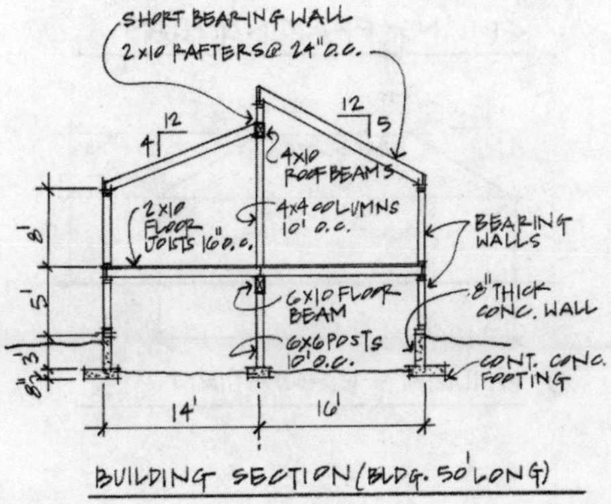

Load Conditions:

SL (horiz. proj.)	= 30 psf
Finish floor/subfloor	= 5 psf
Joists	= 3 psf
Insulation	= 2 psf
Occupancy (LL)	= 40 psf
Bearing walls	= 10 psf
$\gamma_{concrete}$ (*density of concrete*)	= 150 #/ft.^{3}

Along Rafter Length:

Roofing	= 8 psf
Sheathing	= 2 psf
Rafters	= 3 psf
Ceiling	= 3 psf
Insulation	= 2 psf
Soil bearing pressure	= 2,000 psf

7 For the illustrated hipped roof, evaluate the load conditions on:

1. Typical jack rafter.
2. Hip rafter.
3. Ceiling joist.
4. Beams *B-1*, *B-2*, and *B-3*.
5. Interior column.

Roof Live Loads:

SL = 25 psf

Roof Dead Loads:

Roofing	= 6 psf
Plywood roof sheathing	= 1.5 psf
Joist framing	= 4 #/ft.

Ceiling Loads:

DL = 7 psf

LL = 20 psf

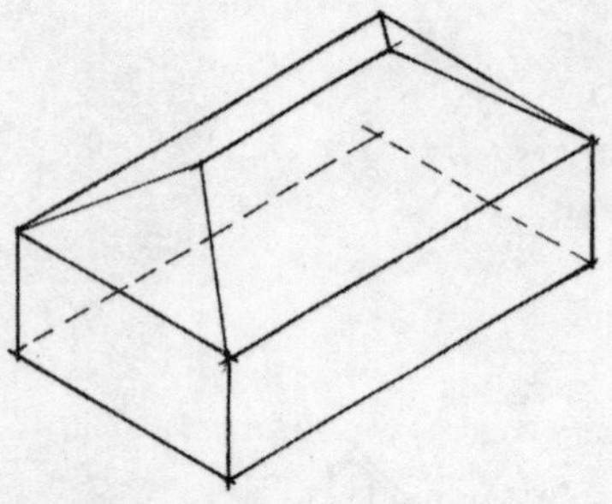

HIPPED ROOF STRUCTURE

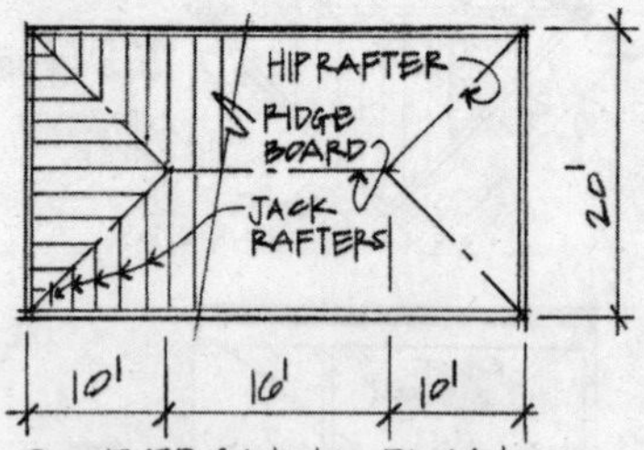

ROOF FRAMING PLAN

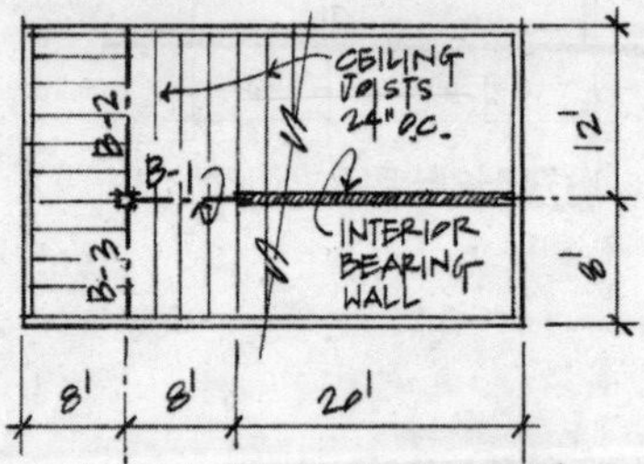

CEILING FRAMING PLAN

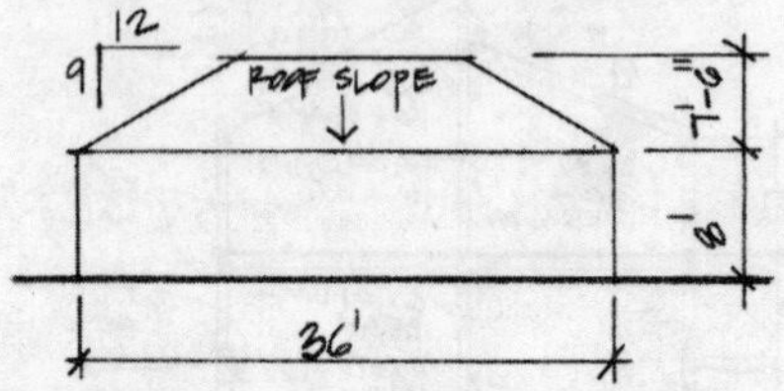

BUILDING ELEVATION

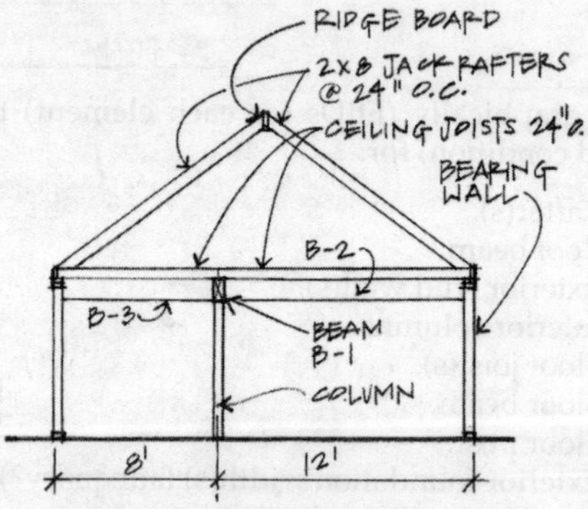

BUILDING SECTION

2 LATERAL STABILITY LOAD TRACING

The structure, be it large or small, must be stable and lasting, must satisfy the needs for which it was built, and must achieve the maximum result with minimum means.

These conditions: stability, durability, function, and maximum results with minimum means—or in current terms, economic efficiency—can be found to an extent in all construction from the mud hut to the most magnificent building. They can be summed up in the phrase "building correctly," which seems to me more suitable than the more specific: "good technical construction." It is easy to see that each of these characteristics, which at first seem only technical and objective, has a subjective—and I would add psychological—component which relates it to the aesthetic and expressive appearance of the completed work.

Stable resistance to loads and external forces can be achieved either by means of structures that the beholder can immediately or easily perceive or by means of technical artifices and unseen structures. It is evident that each approach causes a different psychological reaction which influences the expression of a building. No one could feel a sense of tranquil aesthetic enjoyment in a space whose walls or whose roof gave the visual sensation of being on the verge of collapse, even if in reality, because of unseen structural elements, they were perfectly safe. Similarly, an apparent instability might, under certain circumstances, create a feeling of particular aesthetic—though anti-architectural—expression.

Thus one can see that even the most technical and basic quality of construction, that of stability, can, through the different building methods employed to assure it, contribute greatly to the achievement of a determined and desired architectural expression.

—Pier Luigi Nervi, *Aesthetics and Technology in Building*, Harvard University Press, Cambridge, Mass., 1966. Pages 2 and 3.

Section 1 on load tracing followed the path of loads through a structural framework to the foundation. Dead and live loads on the structure were gravity-induced and assumed to be acting in a vertical, downward direction. Each joist, beam, girder, column, and the like could be

Figure 31 Examples of lateral instability. The top photo is of an old carport with knee braces added a bit too late. The other two photographs are of wooden structures damaged in the Kobe, Japan, earthquake of 1995. Photos by authors.

analyzed using appropriate FBDs along with equations of equilibrium (in the case of statically determinate systems). Although the conditions of equilibrium need to be satisfied for each element or member in the structural framework, it is not a sufficient condition to ensure the geometric stability of the whole structure (see Figure 31).

Stability can be problematic for a single structural element, such as an overloaded beam (Figure 32[a]) or a buckled column (Figure 32[b]), but sometimes an entire structural assembly may become unstable under certain load conditions. *Geometric stability* refers to a configurational property that preserves the geometry of a structure through its elements being strategically arranged and interacting together to resist loads.

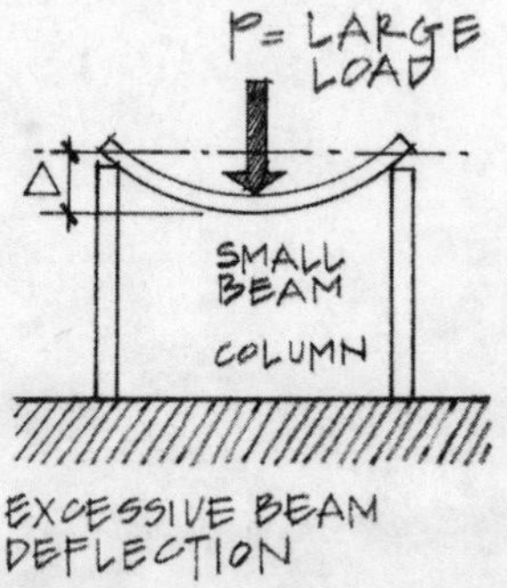

Figure 32(a) Excessive beam deflection.

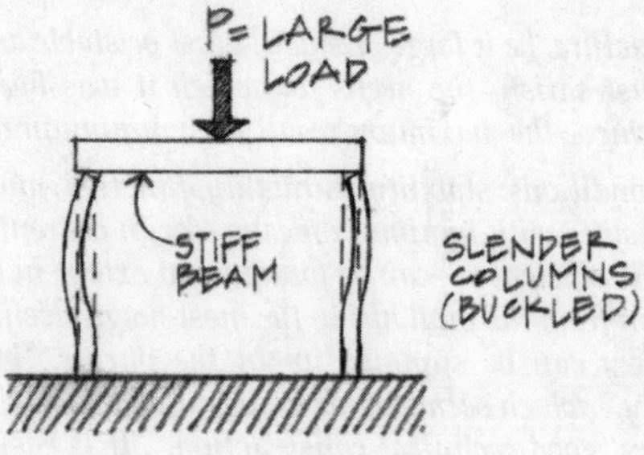

Figure 32(b) Column buckling.

All building structures require a certain set(s) of elements, referred to as a *bracing system* (Figure 33), which provides the requisite stability for the entire structural geometry. Decisions about the type and location of the bracing system to be used directly affect the organizational plan of the building and, ultimately, its final appearance.

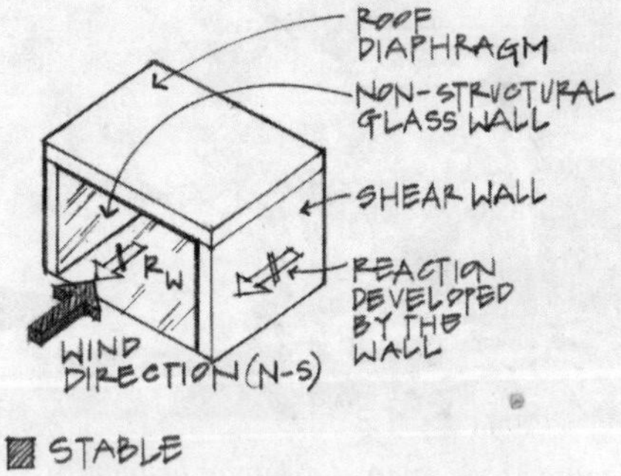

Figure 33 Wind acting parallel to the shearwalls.

A primary concern in the design of any structure is to provide sufficient stability to resist collapse and also prevent excessive lateral deformation (*racking*; see Figure 34), which may result in the cracking of brittle surfaces and glass. Every building should be adequately stiffened against horizontal forces coming from two perpendicular directions.

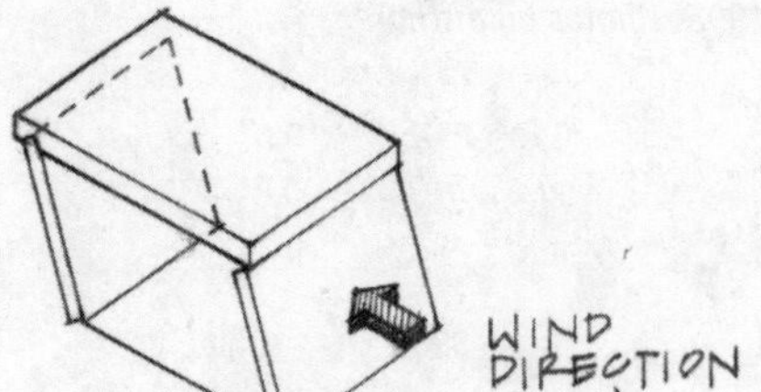

Figure 34 Wind acting perpendicular to the shearwalls.

Wind and seismic forces on buildings are assumed to act horizontally (laterally) and must be resisted in combination with gravity loads. For example, when wind forces push laterally on the side of a one-story, wood-framed building, these horizontal forces are transmitted by the sheathing or cladding to vertical framing elements (wall studs), which in turn transmit the loads to the roof and floor. The horizontal planes (roof and floor) must be supported against lateral movement. Forces absorbed by the floor plane are sent directly into the supporting foundation system, whereas the roof plane (referred to as the *roof diaphragm*) must be supported by the walls aligned parallel to the wind direction. In typical light-wood-framed structures, these lateral force-resisting walls are called *shearwalls*. The use of vertical wall framing and horizontal diaphragms is the most common system in wood-frame buildings, because the roof sheathing can be designed economically to function as both a vertical load-carrying and lateral load-carrying element.

Roof and floor diaphragms must be capable of transmitting the applied lateral forces to the shearwalls through their planar strength; alternately, bracing must be provided in the horizontal plane. Loads transferred from the roof diaphragm to the wall plane are then channeled to the foundation.

Let's return to the earlier diagram of the simple roof structure shown in Figure 35(a), which is supported by the two parallel (N-S) walls and which has two nonstructural walls (glass) on the other two parallel planes. A tributary slice (Figure 35[b]) through the framework reveals a rectilinear arrangement that is simplified, for analysis purposes, as a beam supported by two posts.

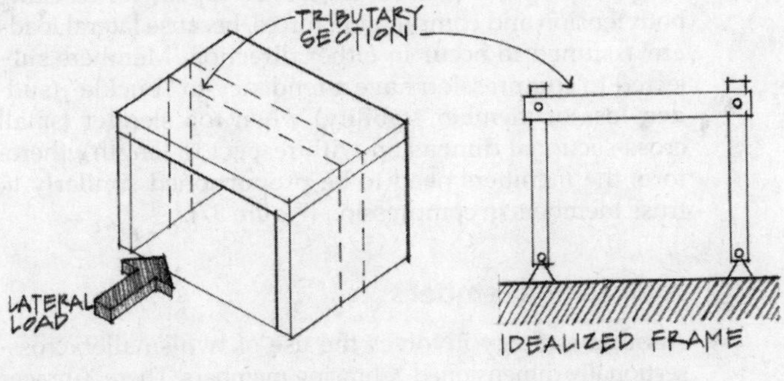

(a) Arrangement of lateral elements. *(b) Idealized frame.*

Figure 35 Structure with two parallel shearwalls.

If we assume the construction to be of wood, the beam and post connections are appropriately assumed as simple pins, and the base supports function as hinges. This simple rectilinear geometry with four hinges (Figure 36) is

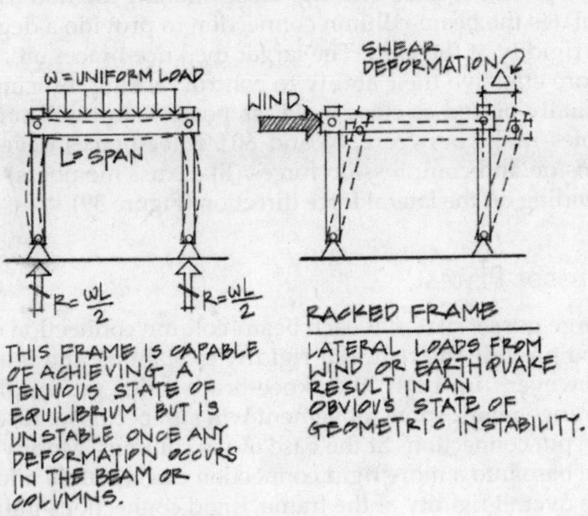

Figure 36 Simple frame with four hinges.

inherently unstable and requires the addition of other structural elements to prevent lateral collapse from horizontally applied loads or uneven vertical loading.

There are several ways of achieving stability and counteracting the racking of the frame under vertical and/or horizontal loading. Note that each solution has obvious architectural implications, and selection of the bracing system must be made for reasons beyond simply being the most "efficient structurally."

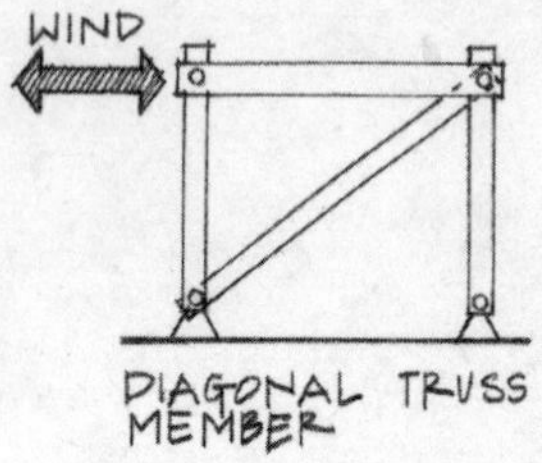

Figure 37 *Diagonal truss member.*

Diagonal Truss Member

A simple way of providing lateral stability is to introduce a simple diagonal member connecting two diagonally opposite corners. In effect, a vertical truss is created, and stability is achieved through triangulation. If a single diagonal member is used, it must be capable of resisting both tension and compression forces, because lateral loads are assumed to occur in either direction. Members subjected to compression have a tendency to "buckle" (sudden loss of member stability) when too slender (small cross-sectional dimension with respect to length); therefore, the members need to be proportioned similarly to truss members in compression (Figure 37).

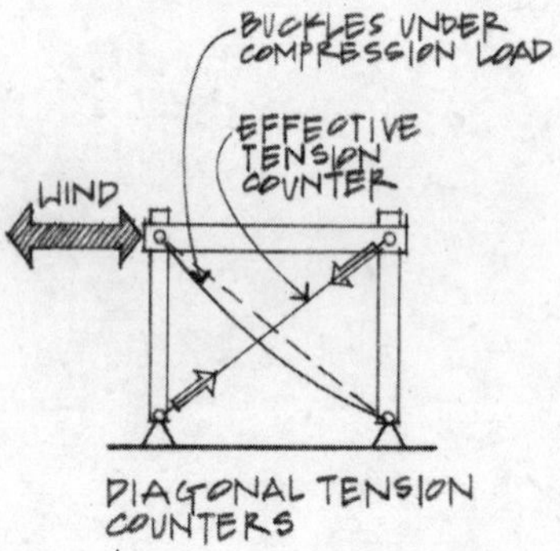

Figure 38 *Diagonal tension counters.*

X-Bracing Members

Another strategy involves the use of two smaller, cross-sectionally dimensioned X-bracing members. These X-braces are also known as *diagonal tension counters* (discussed in Section 3.3), where only one counter is effective in resisting a directional lateral load (Figure 38).

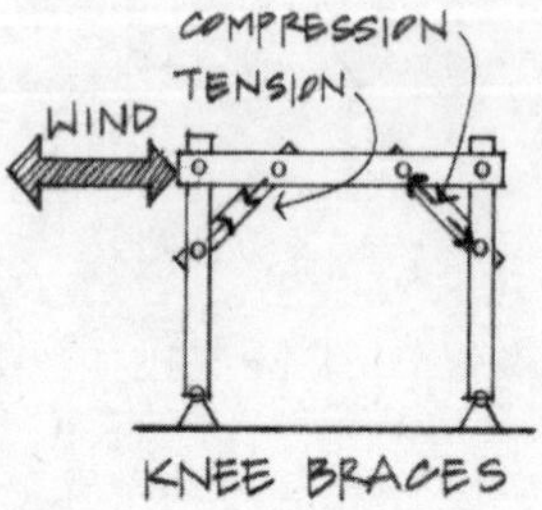

Figure 39 *Knee-bracing.*

Knee-Bracing

A commonly used arrangement in carports and elevated wood decks is knee-bracing. This stiffening method triangulates the beam-column connection to provide a degree of rigidity at the joint. The larger the knee-braces are, the more effective their ability to control racking. Bracing is usually placed as close to 45° as possible but will sometimes range between 30° and 60°. Knee-braces develop tension and compression forces (like truss members) depending on the lateral force direction (Figure 39).

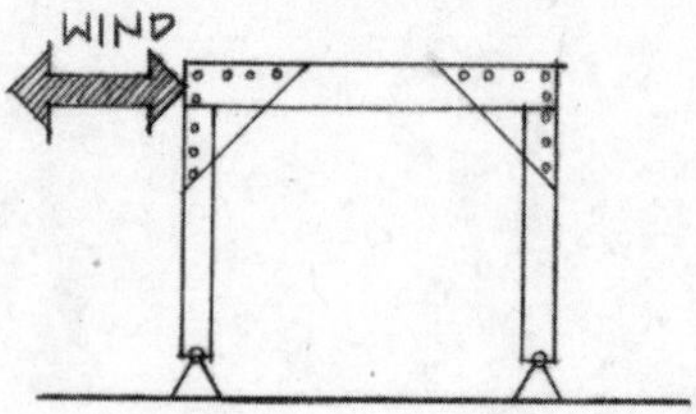

Figure 40 *Rigid joint connection.*

Gusset Plates

Large gusset plates at each beam-column connection can also provide the required rigidity to stabilize the frame. However, in both the knee-brace and gusset-plate arrangements, some movement will still occur because of the pin connections at the base of the columns. Modifying the base into a more rigid connection can certainly add to the overall rigidity of the frame. Rigid connections induce bending moments in the beams and columns (Figure 40).

Rigid Base Condition

Columns placed at some depth into the ground and set in concrete can provide a rigid base condition. Resistance to lateral loads comes through the columns acting as large vertical cantilevers and the horizontal beam transferring loads between the columns (Figure 41).

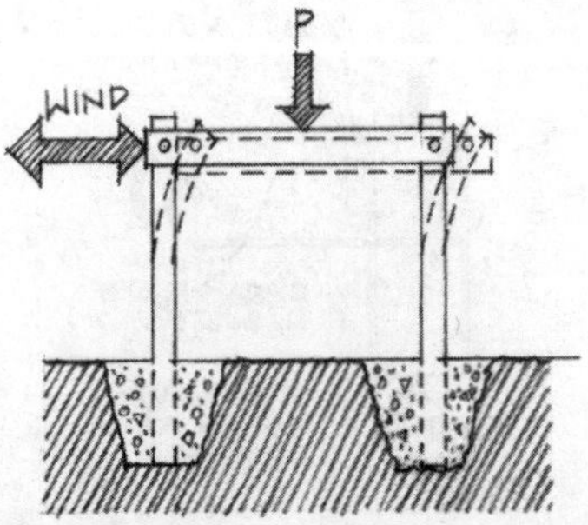

Figure 41 Pole structure—columns with rigid bases.

Combination Knee-Brace and Rigid Column Base

When knee-braces are used in conjunction with rigid column bases, all connections of the frame are now rigid, and lateral loads are resisted through the bending resistance offered by the beam and columns. The lateral displacements would be less than in the three previous examples (Figure 42).

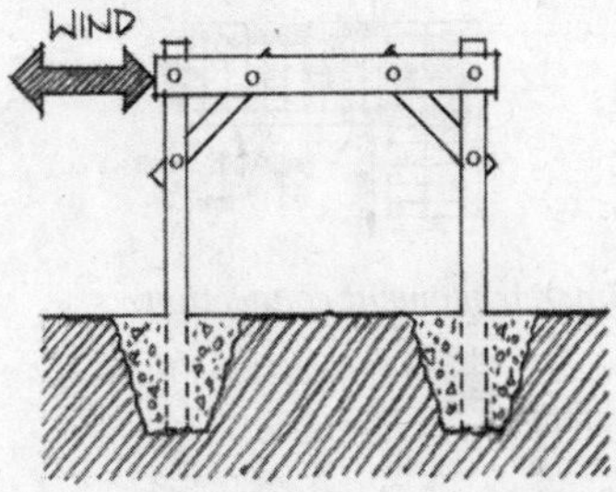

Figure 42 Rigid base and knee-bracing.

Rigid Beam/Column Joints

Moment-resisting frames consist of floor or roof members in plane with, and connected to, column members with rigid or semirigid joints. The strength and stiffness of a frame is proportional to the beam and column sizes and is inversely proportional to the column's unsupported height and spacing. A moment-resisting frame may be internally located within the building, or it may be in the plane of the exterior walls. Moment frames require considerably larger beams and columns, especially at the lower levels of tall structures.

All elements in a moment frame are actually beam-columns subjected to combined stresses (bending and tension or compression). Structural steel beams and columns may be connected together to develop moment frame action by means of welding, high-strength bolting, or a combination of the two (Figures 43 and 44).

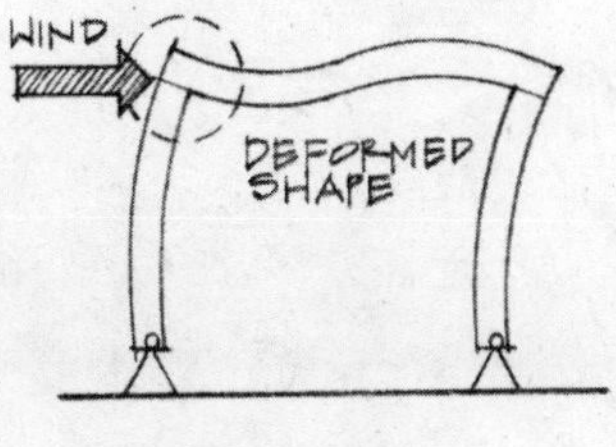

Figure 43 Steel or concrete frame (rigid joints).

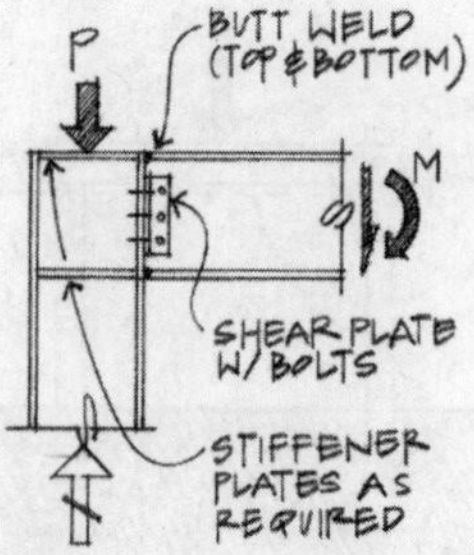

(a) Steel moment-resisting joint.

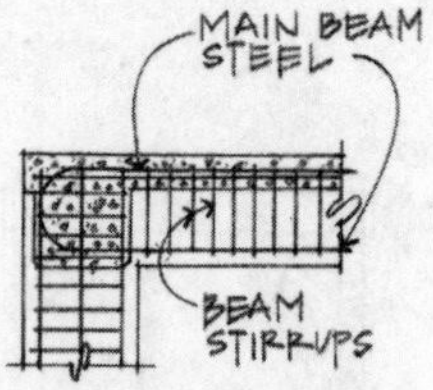

(b) Concrete moment connection.

Figure 44 Rigid connections in steel and concrete.

Cast-in-place concrete, or precast concrete with cast-in-place joints, provides the rigid or semirigid monolithic joints required. Frames may consist of beams and columns, flat slabs and columns, and slabs with bearing walls. The inherent continuity that occurs in the monolithic casting of concrete provides a naturally occurring moment-resistant connection and, thus, enables members to have cantilevers with very simple detailing of the reinforcing steel.

Joint connections become quite complex and labor intensive for a three-dimensional rigid frame in two directions. This translates into higher cost, so alternative lateral resistance systems, such as braced frames or shear walls in one of the directions, are preferred.

If we examine the idea of a beam on two columns and imagine a roof truss spanning between two columns, again the issue of lateral stability must be resolved. Although trusses are stable configurations as a result of triangulation, a truss supported on two pin-connected columns is unstable (Figure 45).

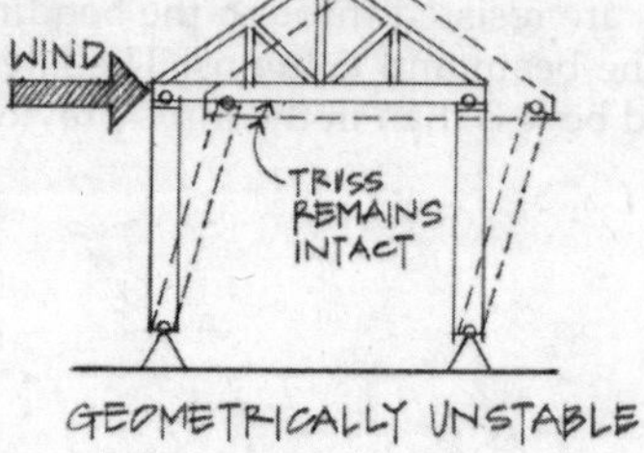

Figure 45 Geometrically unstable truss roof structure.

Because knee-braces help to develop rigidity at the corner connections for the beam and columns, a similar arrangement can be provided with the truss to develop resistance to racking. Knee-braces attach to continuous columns, thereby developing lateral resistance through the columns' bending capacity (Figure 46).

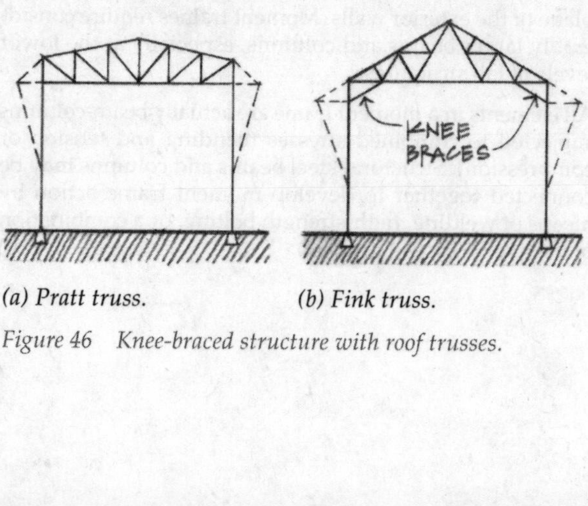

(a) Pratt truss. *(b) Fink truss.*

Figure 46 Knee-braced structure with roof trusses.

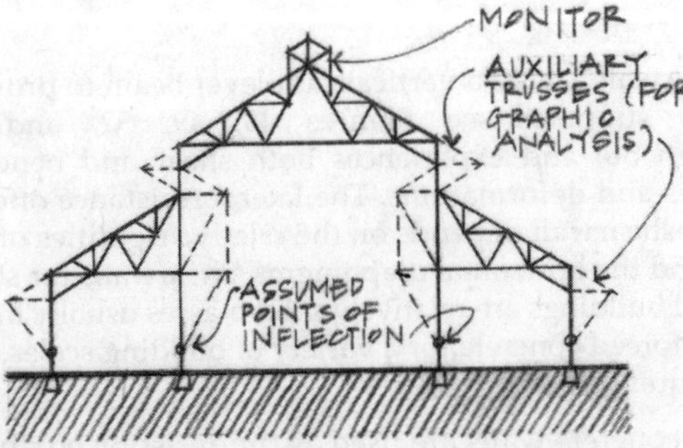

Figure 47 Modified Fink truss with side sheds and monitor.

The continuous column from the ground through the entire depth of the truss provides a very stiff bend (rigid connection) to resist lateral loads (Figure 47). Columns must be designed to resist the potentially large bending moments that develop.

Many residential and small to midscale commercial buildings depend on the walls (bearing and nonbearing) of the structure to develop the necessary resistance to lateral forces (Figure 48). This type of lateral restraint, referred to earlier as a *shearwall*, depends on the vertical cantilever capacity of the wall. The span of the cantilever is equal to the height of the wall.

Figure 48 Exploded view of a light-framed wood building showing the various lateral resisting components.

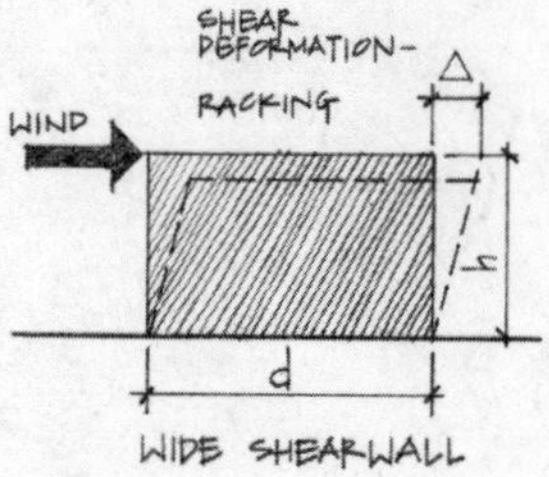

(a) Wide shearwall.

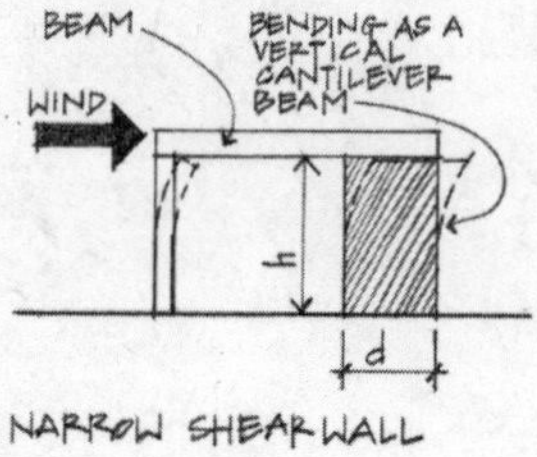

(b) Narrow shearwall.

Figure 49 Shearwall proportions.

Shearwalls

A shearwall acts as a vertical cantilever beam to provide lateral support (see Figures 48, 49, 52, and 54 through 56) and experiences both shear and bending stresses and deformations. The lateral resistance offered by the shearwall depends on the relative rigidities of the wall and the horizontal diaphragms. Shearwalls for steel-framed buildings are relatively solid masses usually made of reinforced concrete for a variety of building scales and configurations.

When concrete walls are used as fire-resisting compartment walls, stair and elevator cores, and vertical service shafts, it is reasonable to utilize them for stiffening the building against lateral loads. A common structural strategy is to use a braced or rigid frame in combination with concrete walls. The beams of the steel frame must be connected to the concrete cores or shearwalls to transmit the vertical and horizontal forces to them. Careful detailing of the framing elements to the shearwall is essential.

In Figure 49, the width of the shearwall d is relatively large compared with the height h; therefore, *shear deformation* replaces bending as the significant issue. Commonly used materials for shearwalls are concrete, concrete blocks, bricks, and wood sheathing products, such as plywood, oriented strand board (OSB), and wafer boards.

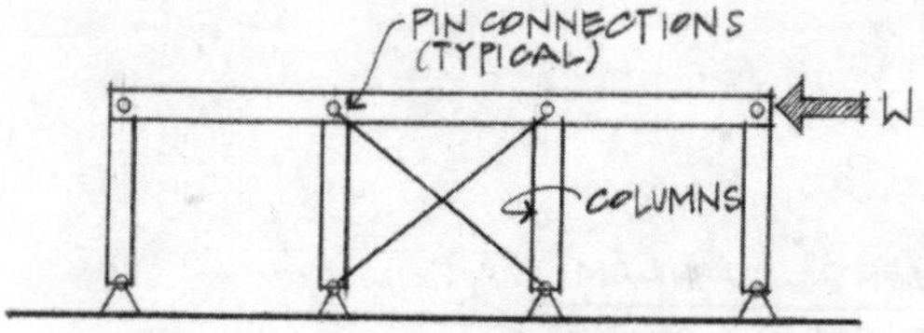

(a) Diagonal tension counters.

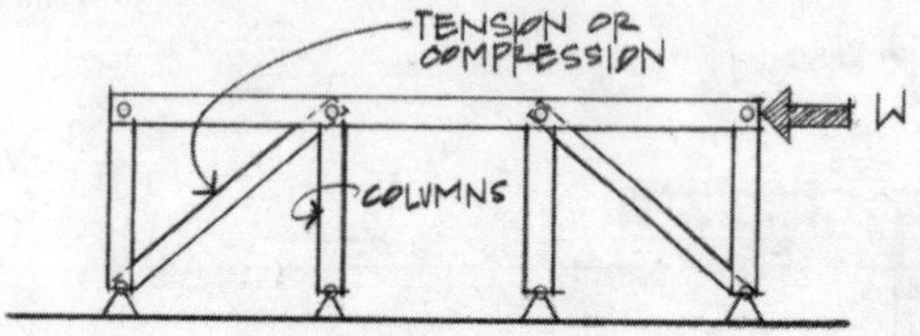

(b) Diagonal truss brace.

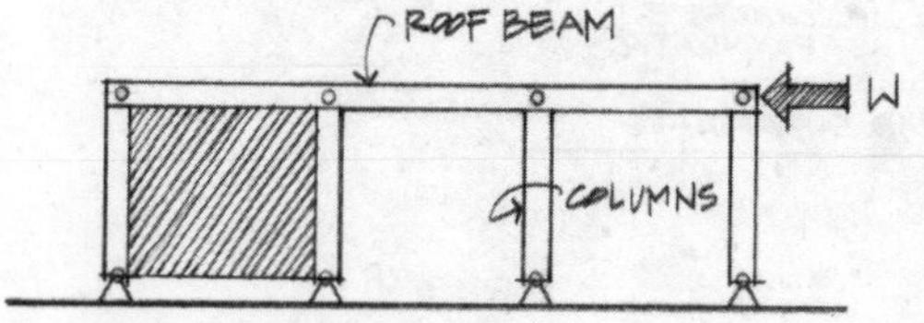

(c) Shearwall.

Figure 50 Bracing systems in multiple-bay structures.

Multiple Bays

Thus far, the discussion of frame stability from lateral loads has been limited to single-bay (panel) frames; however, most buildings contain multiple bays in the horizontal and vertical directions. The principles that apply to single-bay frames also hold true for multiple-frame structures.

Remember, single diagonals must be capable of tension or compression. The length of diagonals can become critical when subjected to compression due to buckling. Bracing diagonals should be kept as short as possible.

In the examples shown in Figure 50, it is quite possible that only one panel needs to be braced for the entire frame to be stabilized. It is rarely necessary for every panel to be braced to achieve stability.

Multistory, Multibay Structures

Multistory, multibay structures also use the same bracing principles. However, as the structures become much taller (height greater than three times the least building dimension), only certain types of bracing systems and materials of construction remain practical from a structural and/or economic standpoint. Knee-braces, although appropriate for smaller, one- or two-story structures, are not nearly as effective for larger structures. The horizontal force component of the knee-brace onto the column produces significant bending moments, which require larger column sizes. Larger diagonal braces that go across an entire panel from opposite diagonal points are much more effective structurally.

Diagonals, X-bracing, and K-trussing on multistory frames essentially form vertical cantilever trusses that transmit lateral loads to the foundation (Figure 51). These bracing techniques are generally limited to the exterior wall planes of the building to permit more flexibility for the interior spaces. Reinforced concrete (or masonry) and braced steel framing used for stairwells and elevators are often utilized as part of the lateral force strategy.

Combinations of bracing, shearwall, and/or rigid frames are used in many buildings (Figure 52). Larger, multistory buildings contain utility/service cores, which include elevators, stairs, ducts, and plumbing chases, that are strategically placed to meet functional and structural criteria. Because these cores are generally solid to meet fireproofing requirements, they can function as excellent lateral resisting elements, either in isolation or as part of a larger overall strategy.

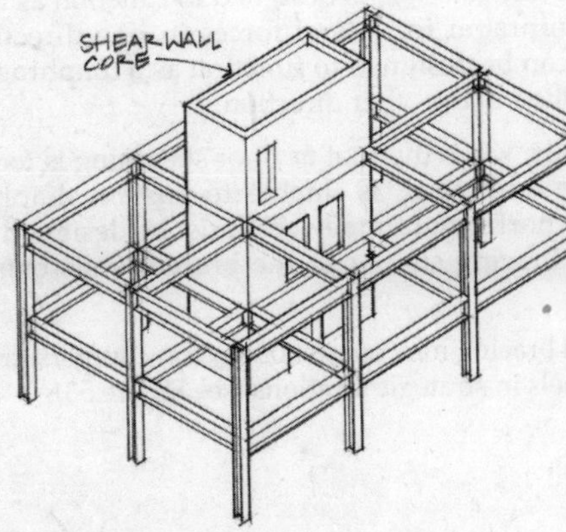

Figure 52 Combination of lateral resisting systems—steel frame with a central shearwall core.

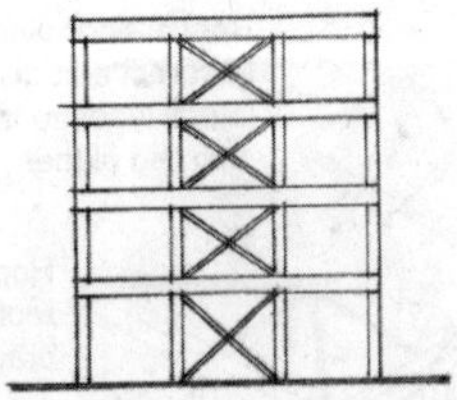

(a) X-bracing.

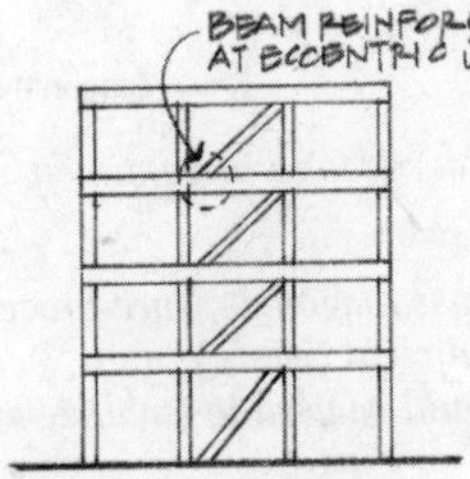

(b) Eccentric braced frame.

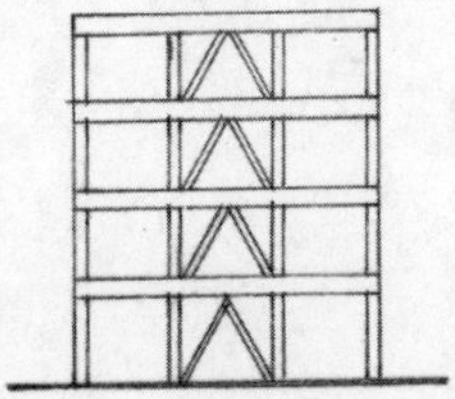

(c) K-trussing.

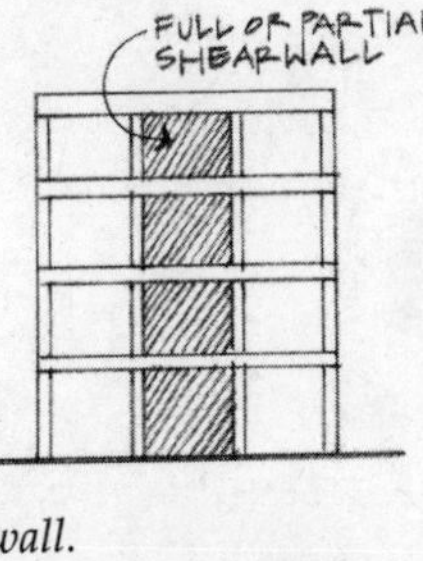

(d) Shearwall.

(e) Rigid frame.

Figure 51 Types of multistory bracing systems.

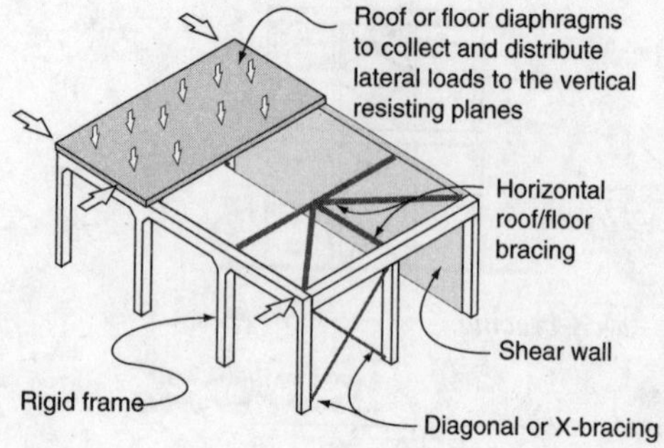

Figure 53 Bracing for a three-dimensional framework.

(X-bracing, truss diagonals, knee-braces, shearwalls, and rigid beam-column connections could be used to stabilize any of these planes.)

Three-Dimensional Frames

Figure 53 reminds us that buildings are, indeed, three-dimensional frameworks and not planar, two-dimensional frames. All of the frame examples illustrated previously assume that to understand the whole, only a representative portion of an entire structure needs to be examined. Each planar frame represents just one of several (or many) frames that constitute the structure. It is important to note, however, that a fundamental requirement of geometric stability for a three-dimensional structure is its ability to resist loads from three orthogonal directions.

A three-dimensional frame can be stabilized by use of bracing elements or shearwalls in a limited number of panels in the vertical and horizontal planes. In multistory structures, these bracing systems must be provided at each and every story level.

The transverse exterior walls of a building transmit the wind forces to the roof and floors, which in turn direct them to the utility/service cores, shearwalls, or braced frames. In most cases, the roof and floor systems form horizontal diaphragms, which can perform this function.

In wood-framed buildings or buildings with wood roof and floor systems, the roof or floor sheathing is designed and connected to the supporting framing members to function as a horizontal diaphragm capable of transferring lateral load to the shearwalls. In buildings with concrete roof and floor slabs, the slabs are also designed to function as diaphragms.

It is unlikely that the horizontal system used in one direction of loading will be different from the horizontal system used in the other direction. If the wood sheathing or reinforced concrete slab is designed to function as a horizontal diaphragm for lateral forces in one direction, it probably can be designed to function as a diaphragm for forces applied in the other direction.

Occasionally, when the roof or floor sheathing is too light or flexible and, thus, is unable to sustain diaphragm forces, the horizontal framework must be designed to incorporate bracing similar to the braced walls or shearwalls.

Horizontal bracing may consist of tension counters, trusses, or stiff panels in strategic locations (see Figure 53).

Bracing Configurations

Once the roof plane (or floors) has been configured to function as a diaphragm, a minimum requirement for stabilizing the roof is three braced (or shear) walls that are neither all parallel nor concurrent at a common point. The arrangement of the walls in relationship to one another is crucial in resisting loads from multiple directions (Figure 54). More than three braced (shear) walls are usually provided, thus increasing the structural stiffness of the framework in resisting lateral displacements (shear deformation).

Braced (shear) walls should be located strategically throughout a structure to minimize the potential of torsional displacements and moments. A common solution is to have two shearwalls parallel to one another (a reasonable distance apart) and a third wall (or perhaps more) perpendicular to the other two.

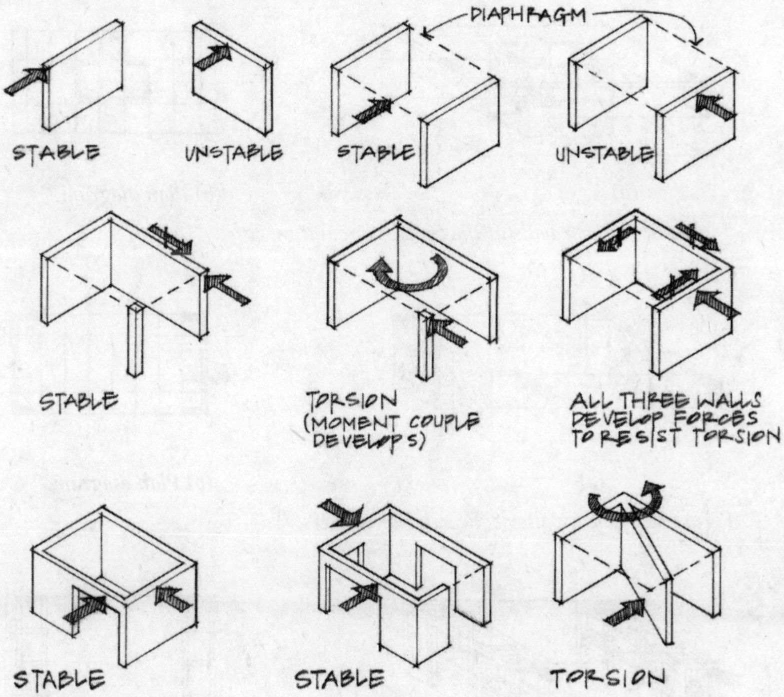

Figure 54 Various shearwall arrangements—some stable, others unstable.

Multistory Structures

In multistory structures, lateral loads (from wind or earthquake forces) are distributed to each of the floor (diaphragm) levels. At any given floor level, there must be a requisite number of braced (shear) walls to transfer the cumulative lateral forces from the diaphragms above. Each story level is similar to the simple structures examined previously, in which the diaphragm load was transferred from the upper level (roof) to the lower level (ground).

Multistory structures are generally braced with a minimum of four braced planes per story, with each wall being positioned to minimize torsional moments and displacement (Figures 55 through 57). Although it is often desirable to position the braced walls in the same position at each floor level, it is not always necessary. The transfer of shear through any one level may be examined as an isolated problem.

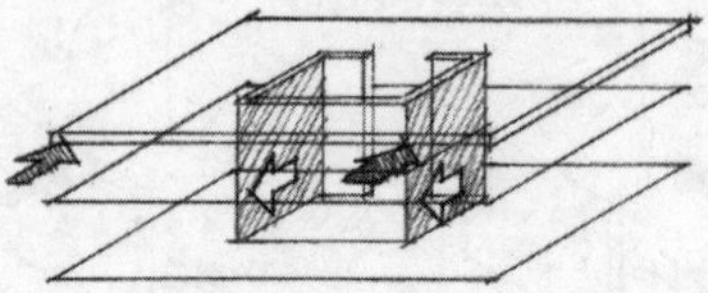

(a)

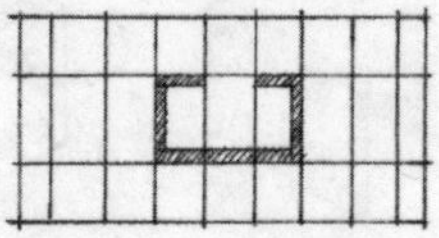

(b) Plan diagram.

Figure 55 Shearwalls at the central circulation core.

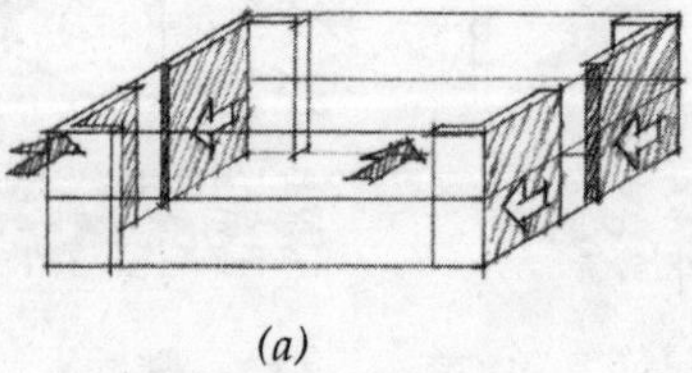

(a)

(b) Plan diagram.

Figure 56 Shearwalls at the exterior corners.

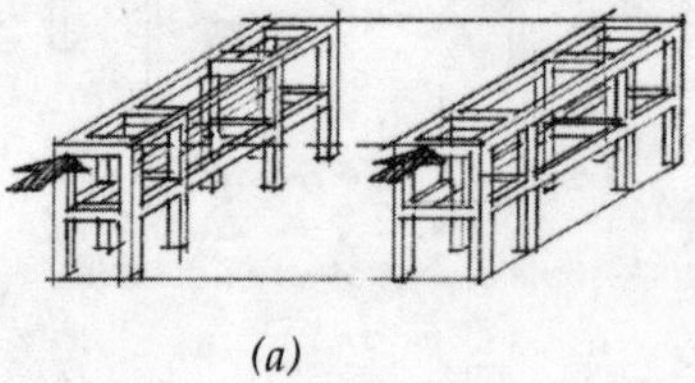

(a)

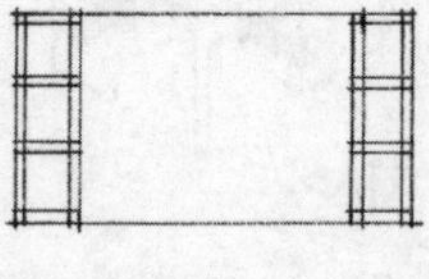

(b) Plan diagram.

Figure 57 Rigid frames at end bays (can also comprise the entire skeleton).

Example Problems: Lateral Stability/ Diaphragms and Shearwalls

7 An industrial building with a plan dimension of 30 feet × 30 feet and a height of 10 feet is subjected to a wind load of 20 psf. Two braced exterior walls parallel to the wind direction are used to resist the horizontal diaphragm force in the roof. Assuming diagonal tension counters in two of the three bays, determine the magnitude of force developed in each diagonal.

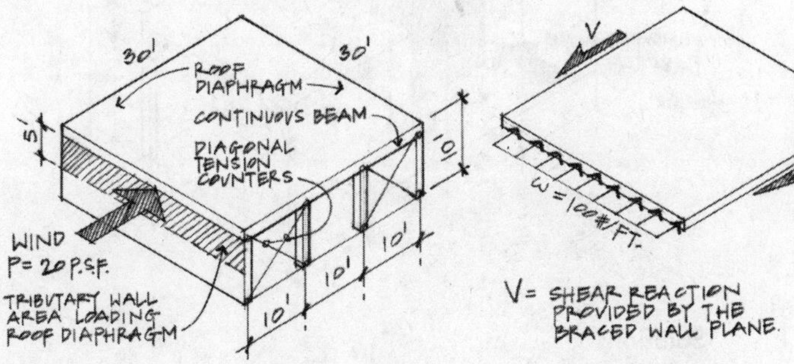

Solution:

Diagonal tension counters are always in pairs, because one counter will buckle as a result of compression loading. The method of sections was used in determining the effective counter.

$$\omega = 20\text{ psf} \times 5' = 100\,\#/\text{ft.}$$

$$V = \frac{\omega L}{2} = \frac{(100\,\#/\text{ft.})(30\text{ ft.})}{2} = 1{,}500\#$$

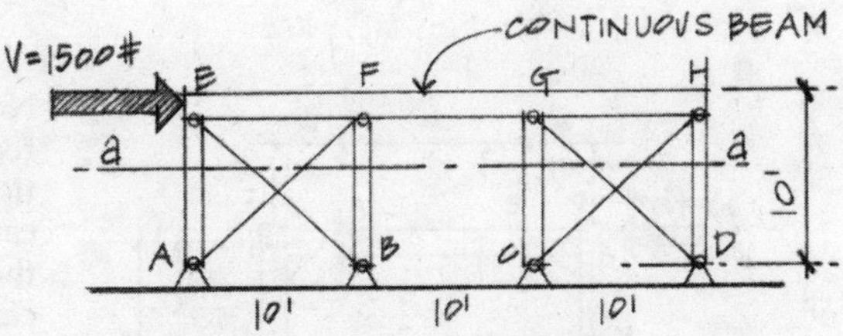

ELEVATION OF ONE BRACED WALL

In this case, counters *AF* and *CH* are effective in tension, whereas members *BE* and *DG* are assumed as zero-force members.

Utilizing the method of sections, draw an FBD of the frame above section cut *a-a*.

$$AF_x = AF_y = \frac{AF}{\sqrt{2}}$$

$$CH_x = CH_y = \frac{CH}{\sqrt{2}}$$

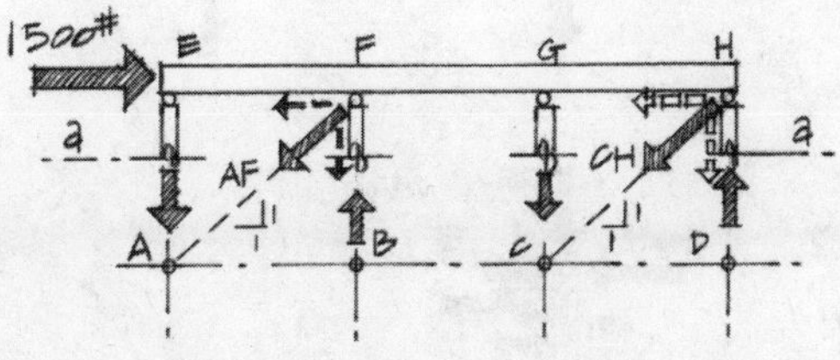

Only the *x* components of members *AF* and *CH* are capable of resisting the 1,500# lateral force. Assuming $AF_x = CH_x$, then

$$[\Sigma F_x = 0]\ AF_x + CH_x = 1{,}500\#$$

$$AF_x = CH_x = 750\#$$

$$AF = CH = \frac{750}{\sqrt{2}} = 1{,}061\#\ (\text{T})$$

Completing the analysis using the method of joints for trusses:

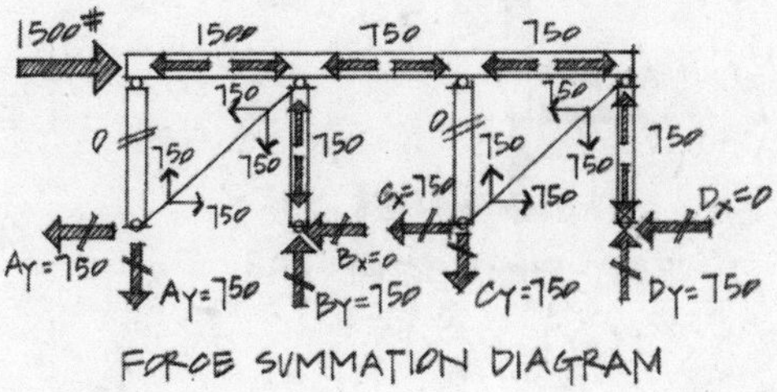

FORCE SUMMATION DIAGRAM

8 A simple carport is framed using knee-braced frames spaced at five feet on center. Assuming wind pressure at 20 psf, analyze a typical interior frame.

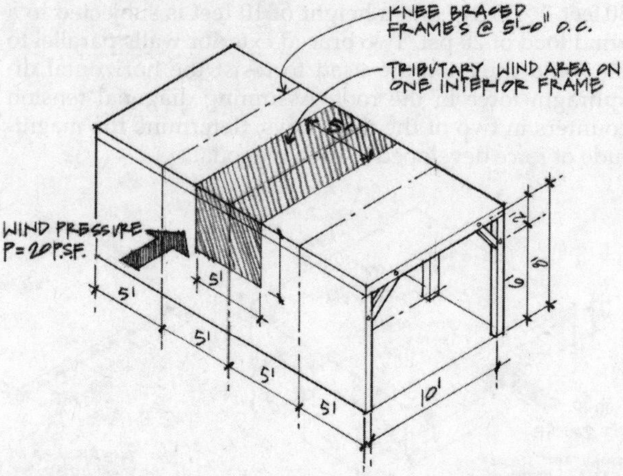

Solution:

Each interior knee-braced frame is required to resist a load applied to a tributary wall area of 20 square feet at 20 psf.

$$F = p \times A = 20\,\#/\text{ft.}^2 \times 20\,\text{ft.}^2 = 400\#$$

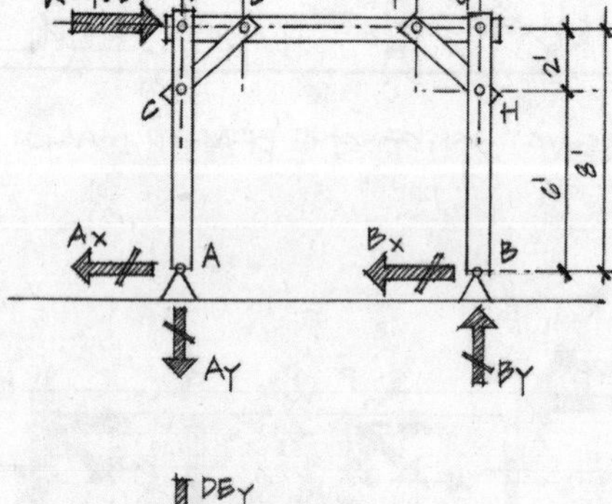

Notice that in the FBD of the frame, a total of four support reactions develop at *A* and *B*. Because only three equations of equilibrium are permitted, all support reactions cannot be solved unless an assumption(s) is made about the frame or its load distribution characteristics. In this case, only one assumption is necessary, because the external support condition is indeterminate to the first degree.

Assume

$$A_x = B_x.$$

Then,

$$[\Sigma F_x = 0]\, A_x + B_x = 400\#$$
$$\therefore A_x = B_x = 200\#$$

Writing the other equations of equilibrium, we get

$$[\Sigma M_A = 0] - 400\#(8') + B_y(10') = 0$$
$$B_y = 320\#$$
$$[\Sigma F_y = 0] - A_y + B_y = 0$$
$$A_y = 320\#$$

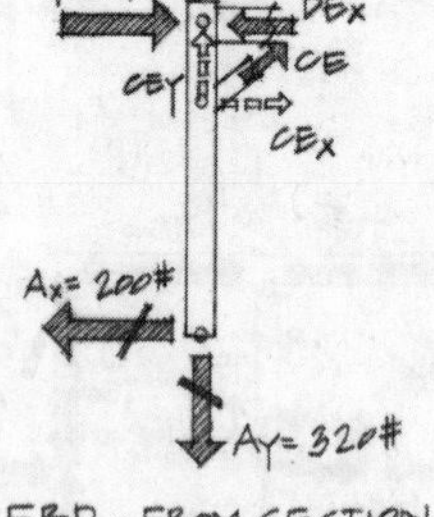

FBD - FROM SECTION a-a

Once the support reactions have been determined, pass a vertical section *a-a* through one knee-brace. Isolate the left column, and draw an FBD.

$$[\Sigma M_D = 0] + CE_x(2') - 200\#(8') = 0$$
$$\therefore CE_x = 800\#$$
$$CE = 800\sqrt{2}\#$$
$$CE_y = 800\#$$
$$[\Sigma F_x = 0] + 400\# - A_x + CE_x - DE_x = 0$$

Substituting for A_x and CE_x,

$$DE_x = 400\# - 200\# + 800\#$$
$$DE_x = +1{,}000\#$$
$$[\Sigma F_y = 0] - DE_y + CE_y - A_y = 0$$
$$DE_y = 800\# - 320\#$$
$$DE_y = +480\#$$

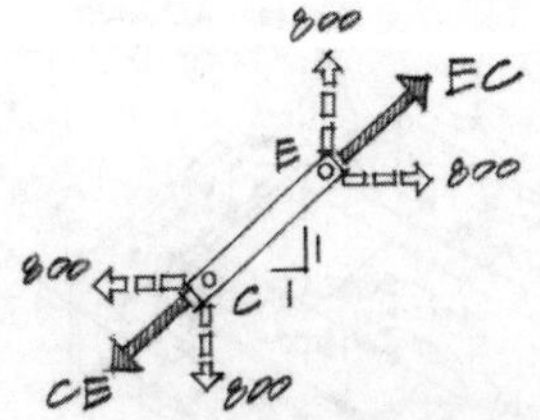

KNEE BRACE MEMBER CE
(TENSION)

In a similar manner, isolate the right column using section cut *b-b*.

$$[\Sigma M_G = 0] - 200\#(8') + FH_x(2') = 0$$
$$FH_x = +800\#$$
$$FH = 800\sqrt{2}\#$$
$$FH_y = 800\#$$
$$[\Sigma F_y = 0] + FG_y - FH_y + B_y = 0$$
$$FG_y = 800\# - 320\# = 480\#$$
$$[\Sigma F_x = 0] - FG_x + FH_x - B_x = 0$$
$$FG_x = 800\# - 200\# = 600\#$$

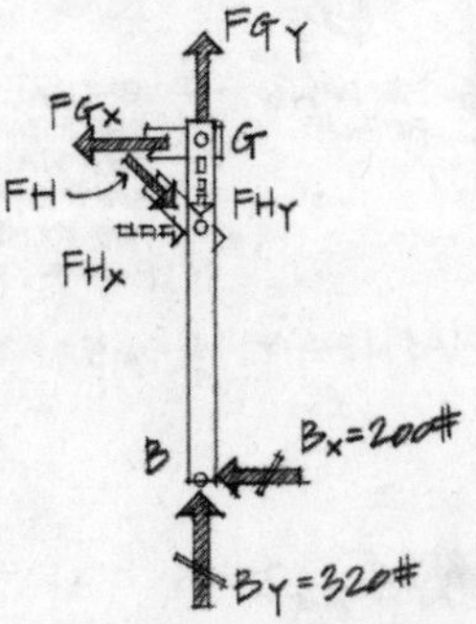

FBD-FROM SECTION b-b

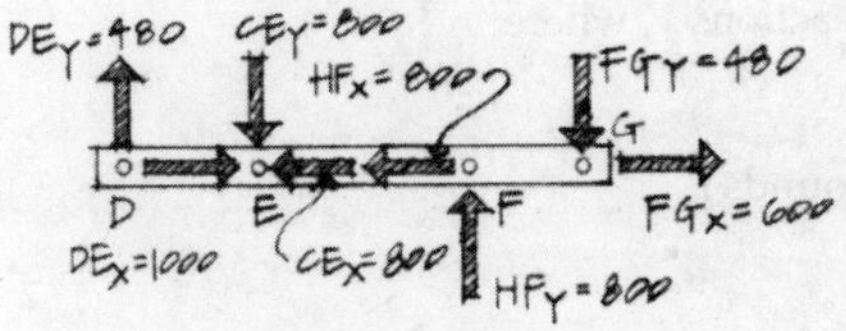

FBD - TOP BEAM

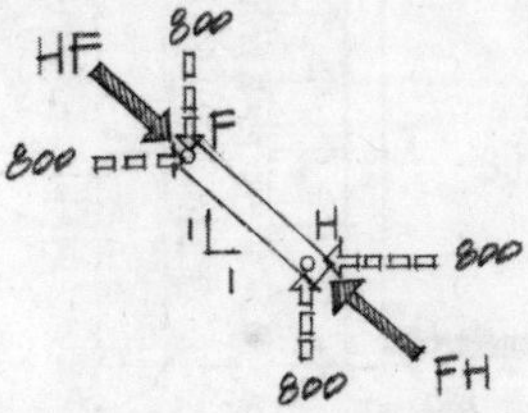

KNEE BRACE MEMBER FH
(COMPRESSION)

9 In this section, an analysis will be performed on a simple rectangular, one-story wood building, illustrating the load propagation and transfer that occurs in a roof diaphragm and shearwall resistive system.

Wood-framed roofs and walls are stiffened considerably by the use of plywood or OSB/waferboard sheathing acting as diaphragms and shearwalls.

Wind force (assumed as a uniform pressure on the windward front wall) is initially distributed to the roof and floor diaphragm (or foundation). Conventional wood stud framing in the walls functions as vertical beams and distributes half of the wind load to the roof and the other half to the floor construction.

Pressures on the windward wall and suction on the leeward wall convert into uniformly distributed loads ω along the windward and leeward boundary edges of the roof diaphragm. Often, the loads on the windward and leeward edges are combined as one load distribution along the windward edge.

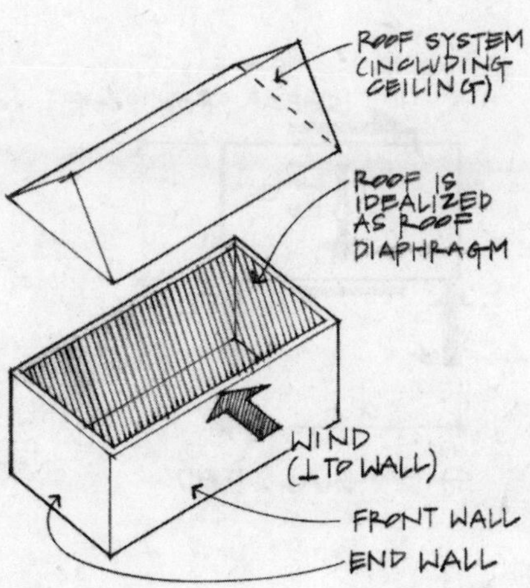

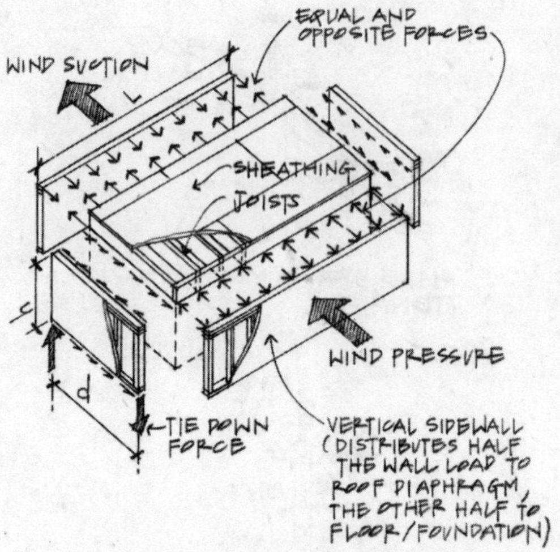

TYPICAL DIAPHRAGM & SHEARWALL

The $\frac{1}{2}$ wall height dimension represents the tributary wall dimension that loads the roof diaphragm. Uniform load ω carries the units of pounds per lineal foot, the same as a uniform load on a beam.

$$\omega = \text{wind pressure } p \times \tfrac{1}{2} \text{ the wall height}$$

In fact, roof diaphragms are essentially treated as flat, deep beams spanning from wall support to wall support.

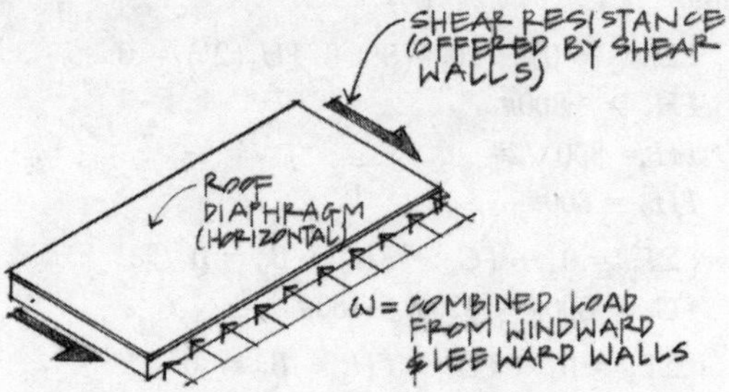

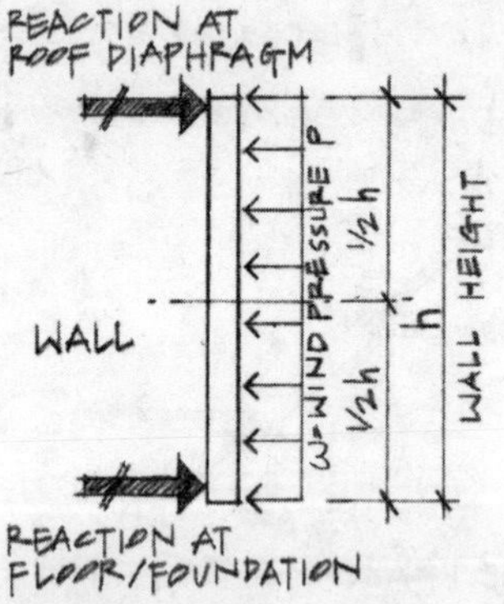

DIAGRAM OF WALL SECTION

Shearwalls represent supports for the roof diaphragm with resulting reactions V, where

$$V = \frac{\omega L}{2}(\text{pounds})$$

The intensity of the shear reaction is expressed as lowercase v, where

$$v = \frac{V}{d}(\text{pounds/ft.})$$

Shear load V is applied to the top edge of the shearwall. Wall equilibrium is established by developing an equal and opposite shear reaction V' at the foundation, accompanied by a tension (T) and compression (C) couple at the wall edges to counteract the overturning moment created by V. The tension T is normally referred to as the *tie-down force*.

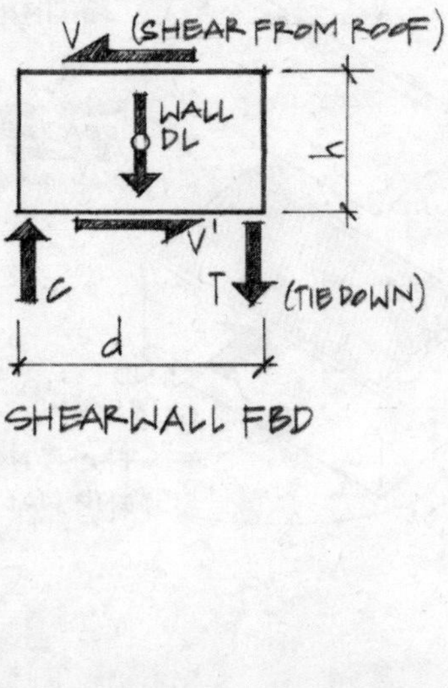

SHEARWALL FBD

Because wind cannot be assumed to act in a prescribed direction, another analysis is required with the wind pressure applied to the end walls, perpendicular in direction to the earlier analysis. Each wall is designed with the requisite wall sheathing thickness, nail size, and spacing to reflect the results of the wind analysis. Details of this design procedure are covered more thoroughly in subsequent courses on timber design. An excellent discussion, with examples of shearwalls in actual structures, can be found on the Internet at http://www.mcvicker.com/vwall/dti.htm.

10 A beach cabin on the Washington coast (100 mph wind velocity) is required to resist a wind pressure of 35 psf. Assuming wood-frame construction, the cabin utilizes a roof diaphragm and four exterior shearwalls for its lateral resisting strategy.

Draw an exploded view of the building, and perform a lateral load trace in the N-S direction. Show the magnitude of shear V and intensity of shear v for the roof and critical shearwall. Also, determine the theoretical tie-down force necessary to establish equilibrium of the shearwall. Note that the dead weight of the wall can be used to aid in the stabilizing of the wall.

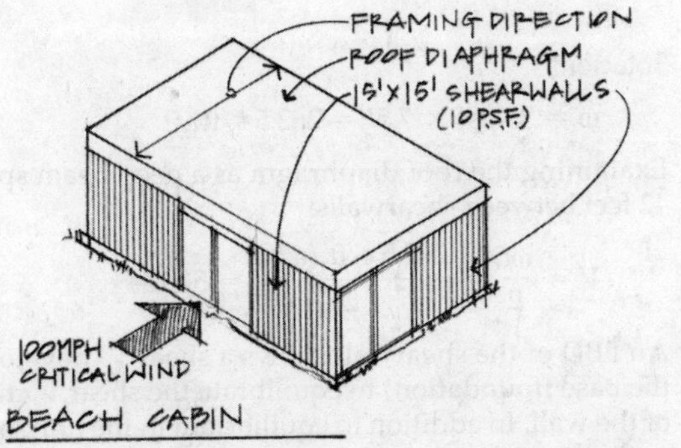

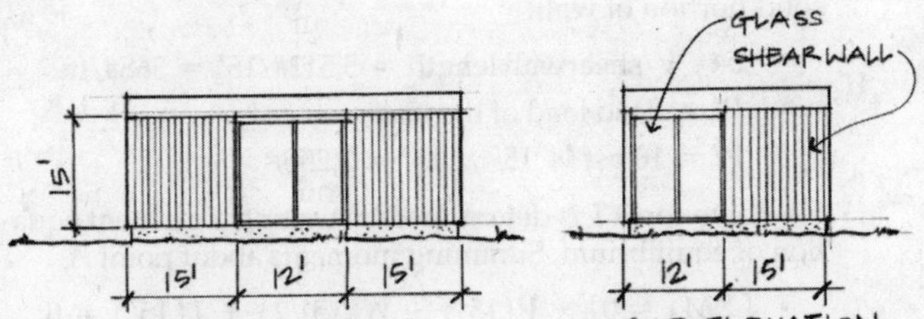

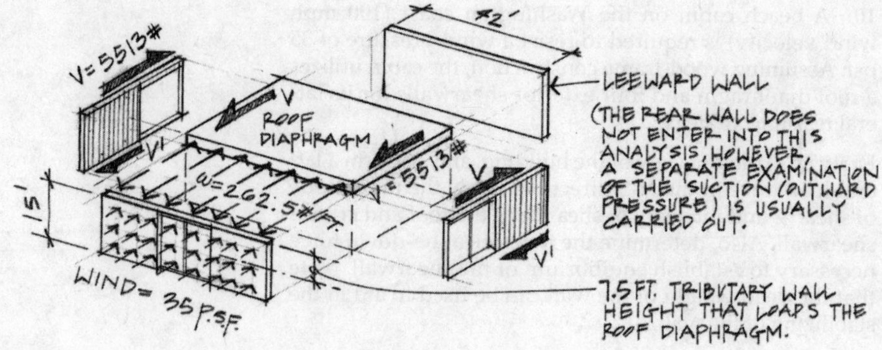

Solution:

$$\omega = 35 \text{ psf} \times 7.5' = 262.5\,\#/\text{ft.}$$

Examining the roof diaphragm as a deep beam spanning 42 feet between shearwalls:

$$V = \frac{\omega L}{2} = \frac{262.5\,\#/\text{ft.}(42')}{2} = 5{,}513\#$$

An FBD of the shearwall shows a shear V' developing at the base (foundation) to equilibrate the shear V at the top of the wall. In addition to equilibrium in the horizontal direction, rotational equilibrium must be maintained by the development of a force couple T and C at the edges of the solid portion of wall.

$$v = V/\text{shearwall length} = 5{,}513\#/15' = 368\#/\text{ft.}$$

$W =$ dead load of the wall

$$W = 10 \text{ psf} \times 15' \times 15' = 2{,}250\#$$

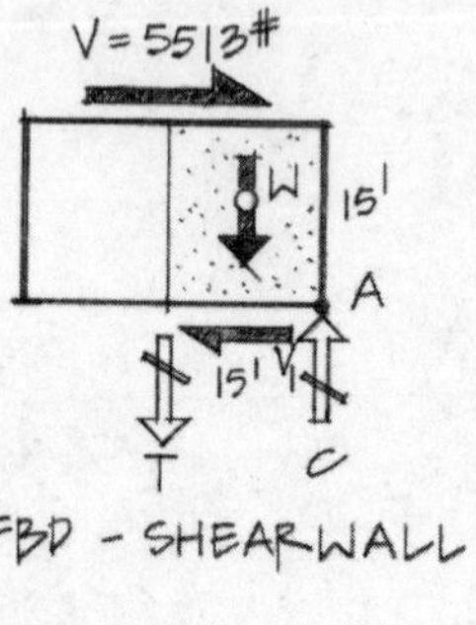

Tie-down force T is determined by writing a moment equation of equilibrium. Summing moments about point A,

$$[\Sigma M_A = 0] - V(15') + W(15'/2) + T(15') = 0$$

$$15T = 5{,}513\#(15') - 2{,}250\#(7.5')$$

$$T = \frac{(82{,}695\,\#\text{ft.}) - (16{,}875\,\#\text{-ft.})}{15}$$

$$T = 4{,}390\#$$

Problems

8 Determine the forces in each of the members, including the effective tension counters. Assume the lateral force to be resisted equally by each tension counter.

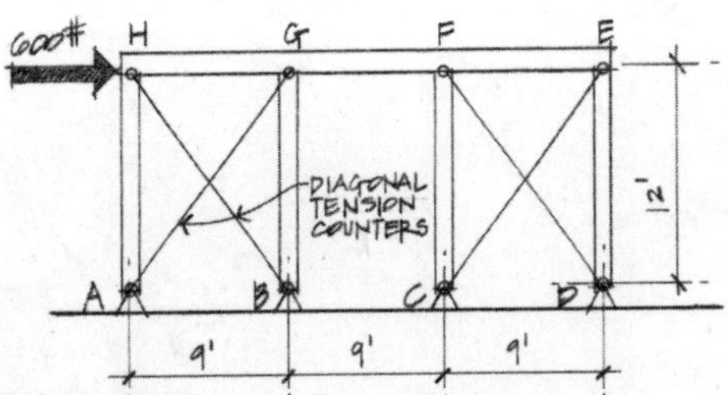

9 Determine the reaction forces A and B and all other member forces. Unlike the previous problem, knee-brace elements are capable of carrying both tension and compression forces. Assume $A_x = B_x$.

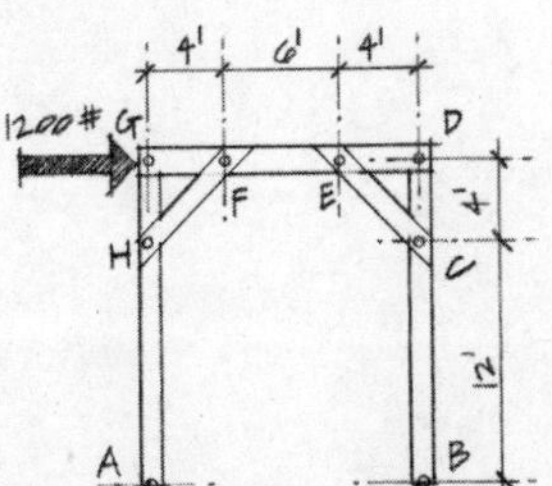

10 A two-story warehouse is subjected to lateral forces as shown. Determine the effective tension counters and forces in all other members. Assume the effective diagonal tension counters at the lower level share equally in resisting the horizontal forces.

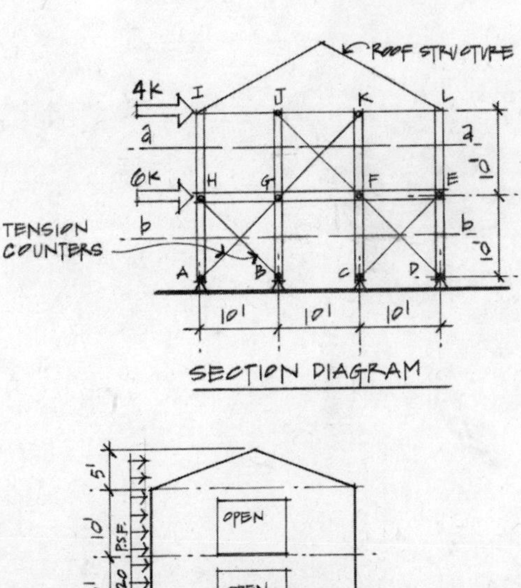

11 A barn structure is subjected to wind velocities with the equivalent of 20 psf pressure on the vertical projection (including the roof).
Analyze the diaphragm and shearwall forces assuming the wind hitting the long dimension of the barn. Use exploded-view FBDs in tracing the loads. Determine the shear reaction and hold-down forces at the base of the walls.

Note: *The dead load of the walls may be used in helping to stabilize against rotation due to overturning moments.*

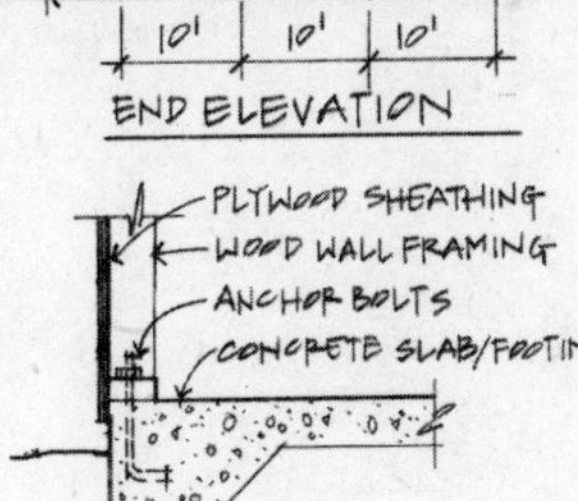

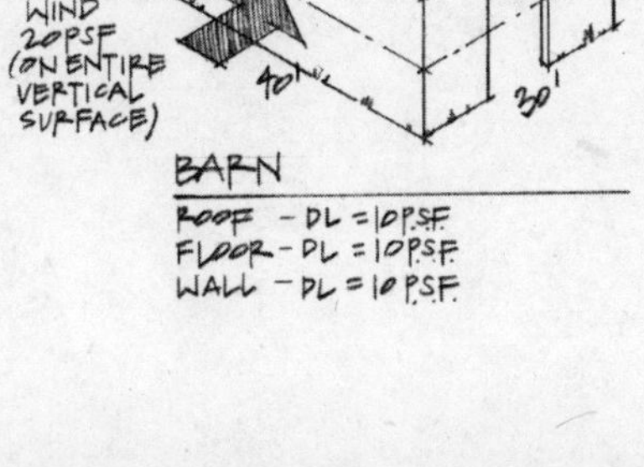

12 A small garage utilizes premanufactured trusses spaced at two feet, zero inches 2′ 0″ on center. One wall of the garage has a 22 foot opening, framed with a large glue-laminated girder. Trace the loads from the roof, and determine the load at each end of the header. Also, size the concrete footing that supports the header post (assume the footing is square, 10″ thick).

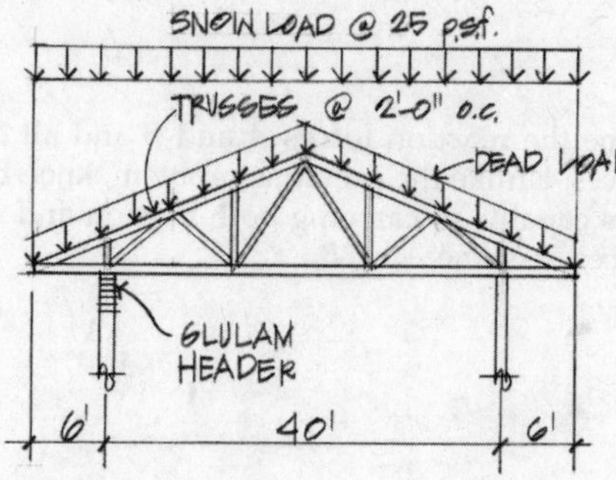

Summary

- Load tracing involves the systematic process of determining load and support reactions of individual structural members as they in turn affect the loading of other structural members. Simple determinate structures can be thoroughly analyzed using FBDs in conjunction with the basic equations of equilibrium for rigid bodies.
- Loads uniformly distributed over an area of roof or floor are assigned to individual members based on the concept of tributary (contributory) area. Member load areas are assumed to be halfway between the adjacent similar members.
- All building structures require a certain set(s) of elements (bracing system) that provides the necessary lateral stability for the entire structural geometry. Wind and seismic forces on buildings are assumed to act horizontally (laterally) and must be resisted in combination with gravity loads.

Answers to Selected Problems

1 ω = 50 psf × 5′ = 250 plf
B1: Reaction (R) = 1,250 lb.
B2: R = 1,250 lb.; B3: R = 1,250 lb.
G1: R = 1,250 lb.; G2: R = 3,750 lb.
G3: R = 1,250/2,500 lb.
Col. Loads: A1 = 3,750 lb.; D1 = 3,750 lb.;
B2 = 3,750 lb.; C2 = 3,750 lb.;
A3 = 5,000 lb.; D3 = 5,000 lb.

2 ω_{snow} = 50 plf (horizontal projection)
ω_{DL} = 20 plf (along the rafter length)
ω_{total} = 70.6 plf (equiv. horiz. proj.)
Wall reaction = 388 lb. per 2′
Ridge beam load = 777 lb. per 2′
Ceiling load ω = 30 plf
Third-floor level:
Load at top of left wall = 269 plf
Load at top of interior wall = 165 plf
Load at top of right wall = 284 plf
Second-floor level:
Load at top of left wall = 649 plf
Load at top of interior wall = 905 plf
Load at top of right wall = 724 plf
Load on exterior 'W' beam = 1,072 plf
Load on interior beam = 1,706 plf

3 Roof rafters (joists) = ω = 66 plf.
Reaction at front wall = 764 lb. per 2′
Reaction on roof beam = 820 lb. per 2′
Reaction at back wall = 396 lb. per 2′
Load at base of front wall = 446 plf
Load at base of back wall = 262 plf
Roof beam load = 410 plf
Floor joist reactions:
Reaction at front wall = 672 lb. per 2′
Reaction at back wall = 576 lb. per 2′
Reaction on floor bm. = 1,248 lb. per 2′
Top of front wall footing = 782 plf
Top of back wall footing = 550 plf
Critical inter footing load = 8,664 lb.

4 Beam B1: ω = 335 plf; wall/beam reaction = 4,020 lb.
Girder carries concentrated loads of 8,040 lb. every 8′ on center plus the girder weight of 50 plf
Critical column load = 42 kips
Beam B2: ω = 255 plf;
Wall/G2 reaction = 2,040 lb.
Girder supports a load = 2,040 lb. concentrated every 6′ o.c., and ω = 566 plf from truss joists.

5 Critical roof joist: ω_{SL} = 26.7 plf; ω_{DL} = 20 plf; and the equivalent total load on the horizontal projection of the roof joist = 51.7 plf. Rafter reaction = 439 lb. per 16″. The ridge beam supports a triangular load distribution with a peak value of 659 plf (12 ft. to the right of column A).
Column A load = 3,140 lb.;
Column B load = 9,420 lb.

6 Rafter loads:
ω_{SL} = 60 plf (horiz.); ω_{DL} = 36 plf
ω_{Total} = 98 plf (equiv. horiz. proj.)
Roof beam load = 759 plf
Top of left wall = 343 plf
Top of right wall = 396 plf
Floor joist load = 66.7 plf
Floor beam load = 750 plf with column loads spaced at 10′ o.c. directly over foundation posts.
Top of left continuous foundation wall load = 823 plf
Top of right continuous foundation load = 926 plf
Required pier footing size = 2′–10″ sq.

8 AH = 0; AG = 500 lb. (T);
BG = 400 lb. (C); CF = 0;
CE = 500 lb. (T); DE = 400 lb. (C)

10 GK = 5.66 k (T); AG = CE = 7.07 k (T);
IJ = JK = 4 k (C); KL = 0;
IH = JG = LE = 0; KF = 4 k (C);
HG = 6 k (C); GF = FE = 5 k (C);
HA = 0; BG = 1 k (C); FC = 4 k (C);
ED = 5 k (C).

11 Total load at roof diaphragm level = 8,000 lb. or 200 plf along the 40 ft. edge of the roof.

Second-floor diaphragm load = 8,000 lb. or 200 plf.
Shear at the top of the second-floor walls = 4,000 lb.; v = 200 plf through the second-story walls.
Shear at the top of the first-floor walls, V = 8,000 lb., and the wall shear, v = 400 plf
The tie-down force T = 5,000 lb.

Strength of Materials

Figure 1 Galileo Galilei (1564–1642).

Galileo, pushed by his mathematician father to study medicine, was purposely kept from the study of mathematics. Fate took a turn, however, and Galileo accidentally attended a lecture on geometry. He pursued the subject further, which eventually led him to the works of Archimedes. Galileo pleaded, and reluctantly, his father conceded and permitted him to pursue the study of mathematics and physics. Galileo's fundamental contribution to science was his emphasis on direct observation and experimentation rather than on blind faith in the authority of ancient scientists. His literary talent enabled him to describe his theories and present his quantitative method in an exquisite manner. Galileo is regarded as the founder of modern physical science, and his discoveries and the publication of his book Mechanics *served as the basis for the three laws of motion propounded by Isaac Newton a century later.*

Galileo is perhaps best known for his views on free-falling bodies. Legend has it that he simultaneously dropped two cannon balls, one 10 times heavier than the other, from the Leaning Tower of Pisa, both being seen and heard to touch the ground at the same time. This experiment has not been substantiated, but other experiments actually performed by Galileo were sufficient to cast doubt on Aristotelian physics.

Introduction

Statics is essentially force analysis: the determination of the total internal forces produced in members of a structural framework by externally applied loads. Statics in itself is not the design of any member, but it is a first step leading to structural design. The primary objective for a course of study in strength (mechanics) of materials is the development of the relationship between the loads applied to a nonrigid body and the resulting internal forces and deformations induced in the body. These internal forces, together with predetermined allowable unit stresses (usually expressed in pounds per square inch), are then used to determine the size of a structural element required to safely resist the externally applied loads. This forms the basis of structural design.

In his book *Dialogues Concerning Two New Sciences* (1638), Galileo Galilei (Figure 1) made reference to the strength of beams and the properties of structural materials. He became one of the early scholars who fostered the development of strength of materials as an area of study.

1 STRESS AND STRAIN

It is hoped that the study of the strength of materials will enable the reader to develop a logical rationale for the selection and investigation of structural members.

The subject matter covered in this chapter establishes the methodology for the solution of three general types of problems:

1. **Design.** Given a certain function to perform (the supporting of a roof system over a sports arena or the floors for a multistory office building), of what materials should the structure be constructed, and what should be the sizes and proportions of the various elements? This constitutes *structural design*, where there is often no single solution to a given problem, as there is in statics.

From Chapter 5 of *Statics and Strength of Materials for Architecture and Building Construction*, Fourth Edition, Barry Onouye, Kevin Kane.

2. **Analysis.** Given the completed design, is it adequate? That is, does it perform the function economically and without excessive deformation? What is the margin of safety allowed in each member? This we call *structural analysis*.

3. **Rating.** Given a completed structure, what is its actual load-carrying capacity? The structure may have been designed for some purpose other than the one for which it is now to be used. Is the structure or its members adequate for the proposed new use? This is called a *rating problem*.

Because the complete scope of these problems is obviously too comprehensive for coverage in a single text, this text will be restricted to the study of individual members and simple structural frameworks. Subsequent, more advanced books on structures will consider the entire structure and will provide essential background for more thorough analysis and design.

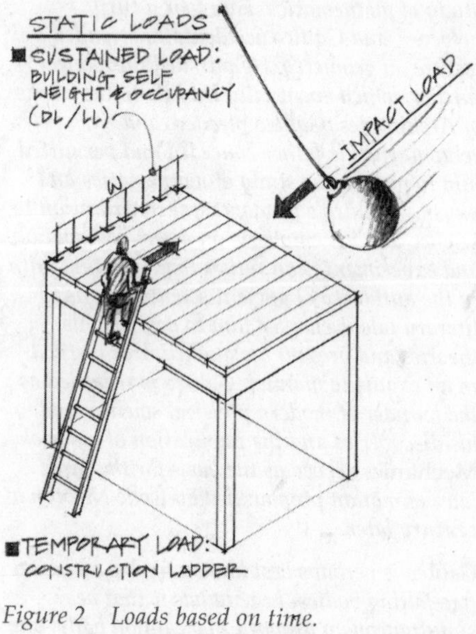

Figure 2 Loads based on time.

Structural Load Classification

Loads applied to structural elements may be of various types and sources. Their definitions are given below so that the terminology will be clearly understood.

Loads classified with respect to time (Figure 2)

1. **Static load.** A gradually applied load for which equilibrium is reached in a relatively short time. Live or occupancy loads are considered to be statically applied.

2. **Sustained load.** A load that is constant over a long period of time, such as the structure weight (dead load) or material and/or goods stored in a warehouse. This type of load is treated in the same manner as a static load.

3. **Impact load.** A load that is rapidly applied (an energy load). Vibration normally results from an impact load, and equilibrium is not established until the vibration is eliminated, usually by natural damping forces.

Loads classified with respect to the area over which the load is applied

1. **Concentrated load.** A load or force that is applied at a point. Any load that is applied to a relatively small area compared with the size of the loaded member is assumed to be a concentrated load.
2. **Distributed load.** A load distributed along a length or over an area. The distribution may be uniform or nonuniform.

Loads classified with respect to the location and method of application

1. **Centric load.** A load in which the resultant concentrated load passes through the centroid (geometrical center) of the resisting cross-section. If the resultant concentrated force passes through the centroids of all resisting sections, the loading is called *axial*. Force P in Figure 3 has a line of action that passes through the centroid of the column as well as the footing; therefore, load P is axial.

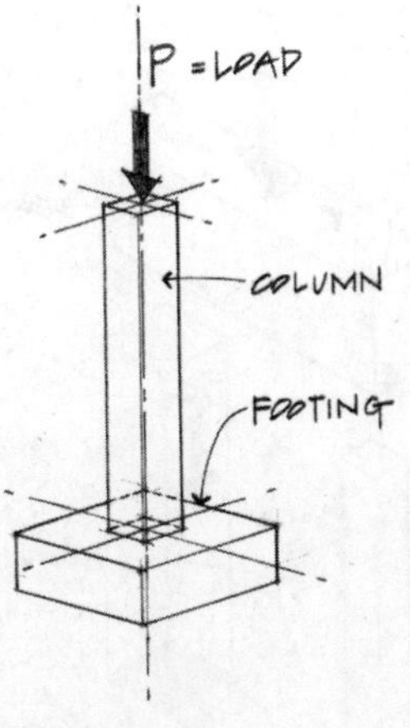

Figure 3 Centric loads.

2. **Bending or flexural load.** A load in which the loads are applied transversely to the longitudinal axis of the member. The applied load may include couples that lie in planes parallel to the axis of the member. A member subjected to bending loads deflects along its length. Figure 4 illustrates a beam subjected to flexural loading consisting of a concentrated load, a uniformly distributed load, and a couple.

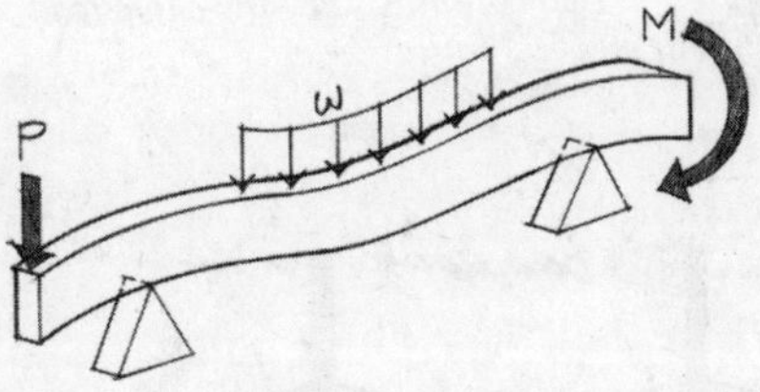

Figure 4 Bending (flexural) loads on a beam.

3. **Torsional load.** A load that subjects a member to couples or moments that twist the member spirally (Figures 5 and 6).
4. **Combined loading.** A combination of two or more of the previously defined types of loading.

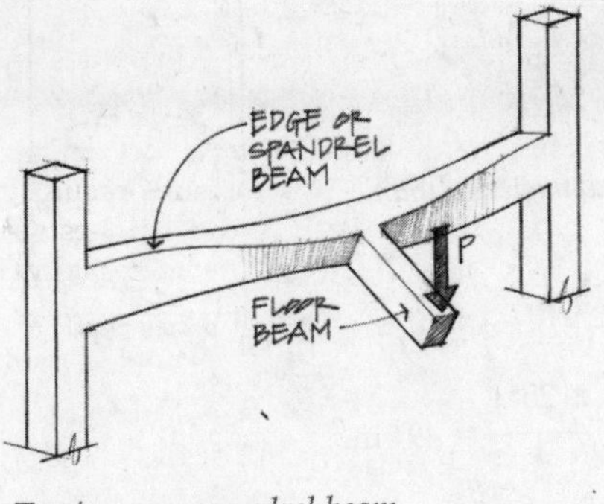

Figure 5 Torsion on a spandrel beam.

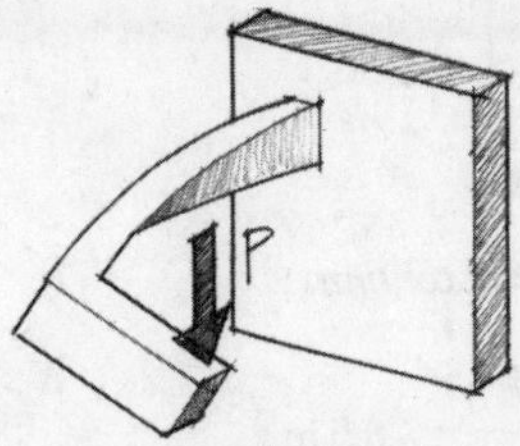

Figure 6 Torsion on a cantilever beam (eccentric loading).

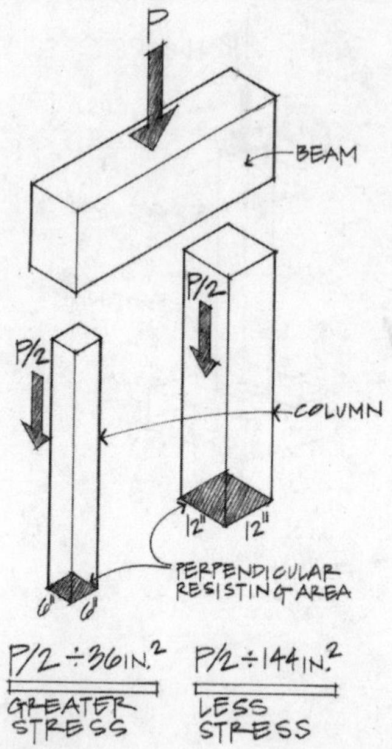

Figure 7 *Two columns with the same load, different stress.*

Concept of Stress

Stress, like pressure, is a term used to describe the *intensity of a force*—the quantity of force that acts on a unit of area. Force, in structural design, has little significance until something is known about the resisting material, cross-sectional properties, and size of the element resisting the force (Figure 7).

The unit stress, or the average value of the axial stress, may be represented mathematically as

$$f = \sigma = \frac{P}{A} = \frac{\text{axial force}}{\text{perpendicular resisting area}}$$

where

P = applied force or load (axial); units are expressed as #, kips (k), N, or kN

A = resisting cross-sectional area perpendicular to the load direction; units are expressed as in.^{2}, ft.^{2}, m^2, or mm^2

$f = \sigma$(sigma) = the symbol(s) representing unit stress (normal); units are expressed as #/in.^{2}, k/in.^{2}, k/ft.^{2}, and pascal (N/m^2) or N/mm^2

Example Problems: Stress

1 Assume two *short* concrete columns, each supporting a compressive load of 300,000#. Find the stress.

Column 1 has a diameter of 10 inches
Column 2 has a diameter of 25 inches } PLAIN CONCRETE

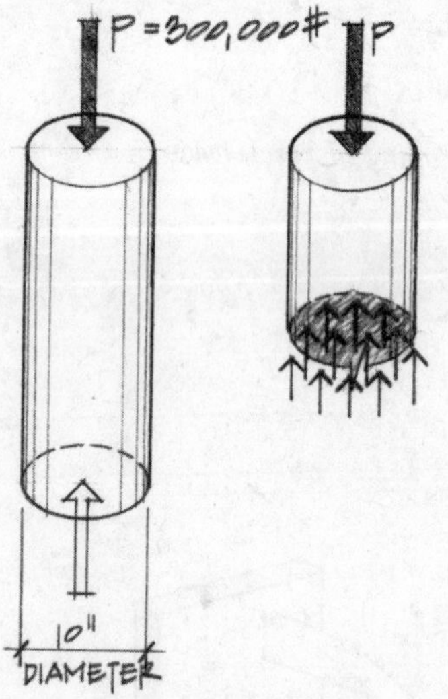

10"-diameter column.

$$A = \frac{\pi(10^2)}{4} = 78.5\text{ in.}^2$$

$$\text{stress} = \frac{\text{force}}{\text{resisting area}} = \frac{300{,}000\#}{78.5\text{ in.}^2} = 3{,}820\ \#/\text{in}$$

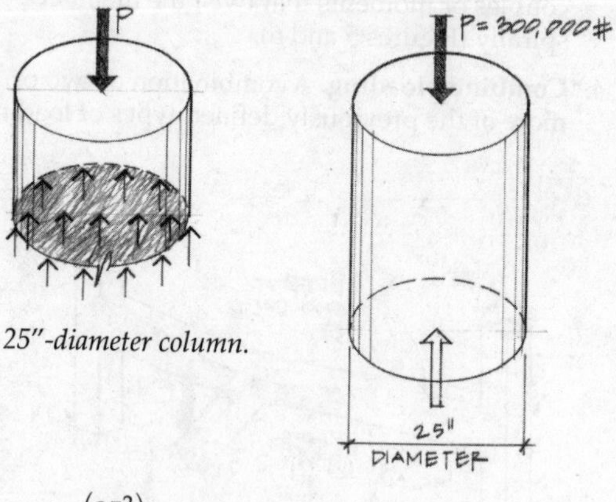

25"-diameter column.

$$A = \frac{\pi(25^2)}{4} = 491\text{ in.}^2$$

$$\text{stress} = \frac{300{,}000\#}{491\text{ in.}^2} = 611\ \#/\text{in.}^2$$

Solution:

Column 1 would probably approach a critical stress level in this example, whereas Column 2 is, perhaps, overdesigned for a 300,000# load.

The inference in Example Problem 1 is that every portion of the area supports an equal share of the load (i.e., the stress is assumed to be uniform throughout the cross-section). In elementary studies of the strength of materials, the unit stress on any cross-section of an axially loaded, two-force member is considered to be uniformly distributed unless otherwise noted.

Normal stress

A stress can be classified according to the internal reaction that produces it. As shown in Figures 8 and 9, axial tensile or compressive forces produce tensile or compressive stress, respectively. This type of stress is classified as a *normal stress,* because the stressed surface is normal (perpendicular) to the load direction.

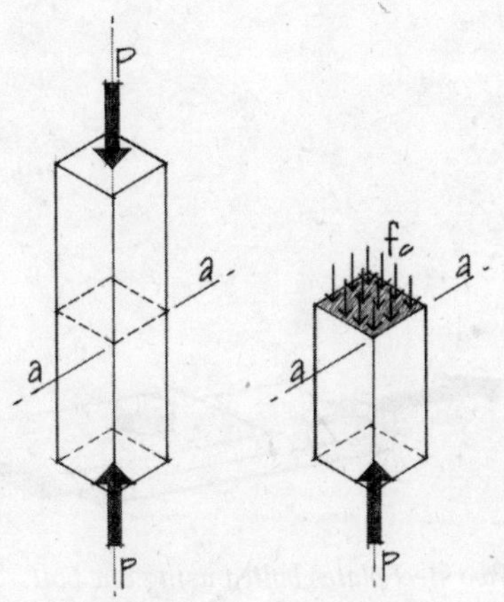

Figure 8 Normal compressive stress across section a-a.

The stressed area *a-a*, is perpendicular to the load.

In normal compressive stress,

$$f_c = \frac{P}{A}$$

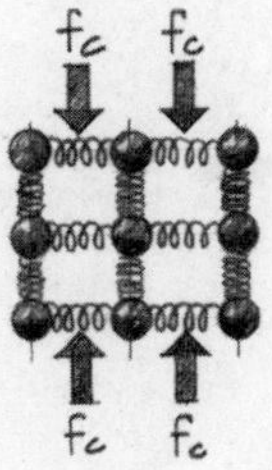

where

P = applied load
A = resisting surface normal (perpendicular) to P

In normal tensile stress,

$$f_t = \frac{P}{A}$$

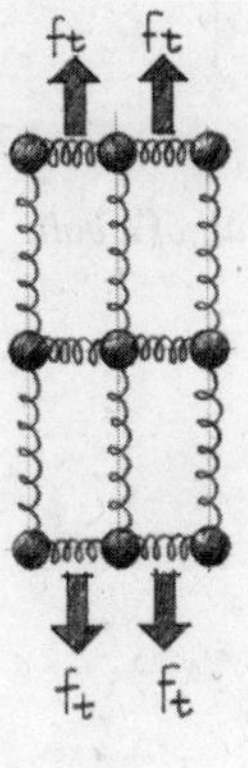

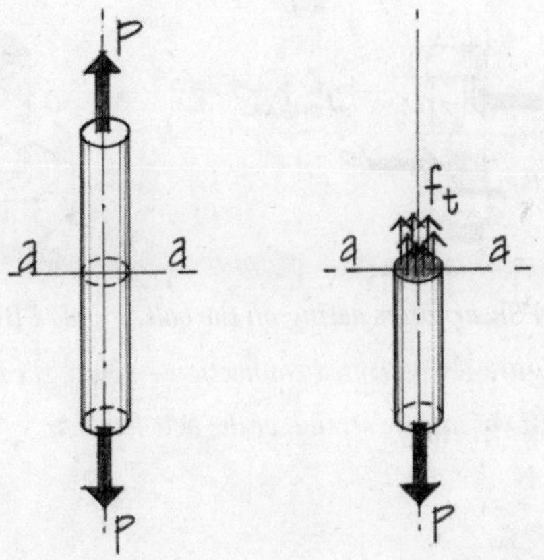

Figure 9 Normal tensile stress through section a-a.

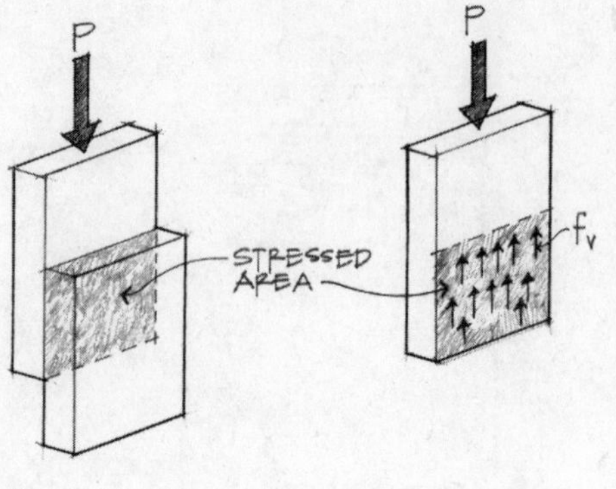

Figure 10 Shear stress between two glued blocks.

Shear stress

Shear stress, the second classification of stress, is caused by a tangential force in which the stressed area is a plane parallel to the direction of the applied load. (Figures 10 through 12). Average shear stress may be represented mathematically as

$$f_v = \tau = \frac{P}{A} = \frac{\text{axial force}}{\text{parallel resisting area}}$$

where

P = applied load (# or k, N or kN)

A = cross-sectional area parallel to load direction (in.^{2}, m^2, mm^2)

f_v or τ = average unit shear stress (psi or ksi, N/mm^2)

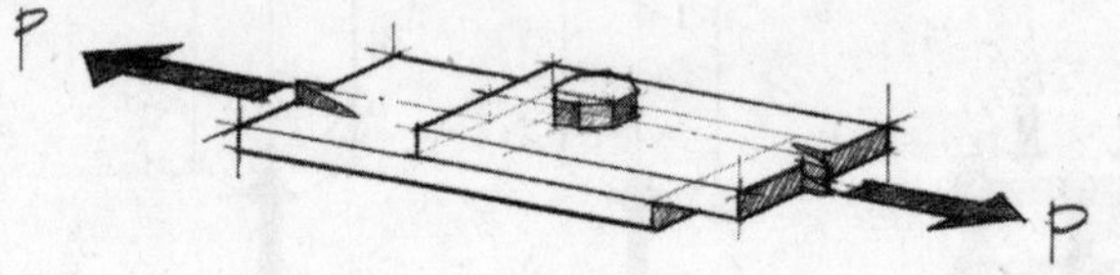

(a) Two steel plates bolted using one bolt.

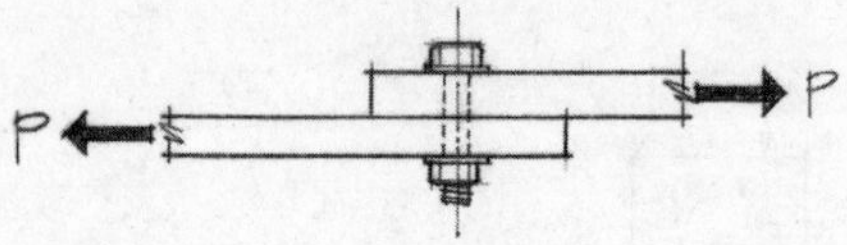

(b) Elevation showing the bolt in shear.

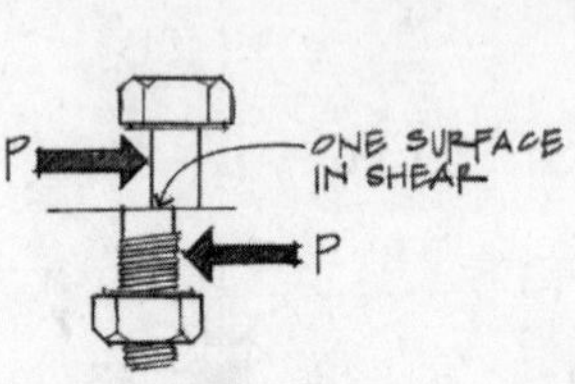

(c) Shear forces acting on the bolt.

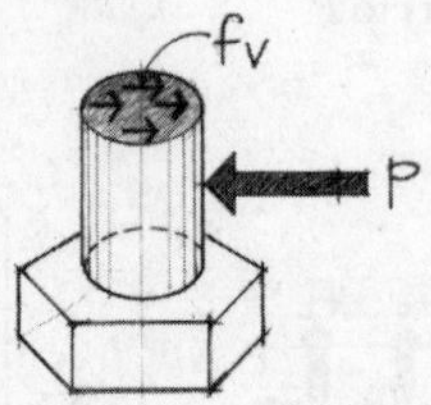

(d) FBD of half of a bolt.

f_v = average shear stress through bolt cross-section

A = bolt cross-sectional area

$$f_v = \frac{P}{A}$$

Figure 11 A bolted connection—single shear.

FBD of middle section of the bolt in shear.

$$f_v = \frac{P}{2A}$$

(two shear planes)

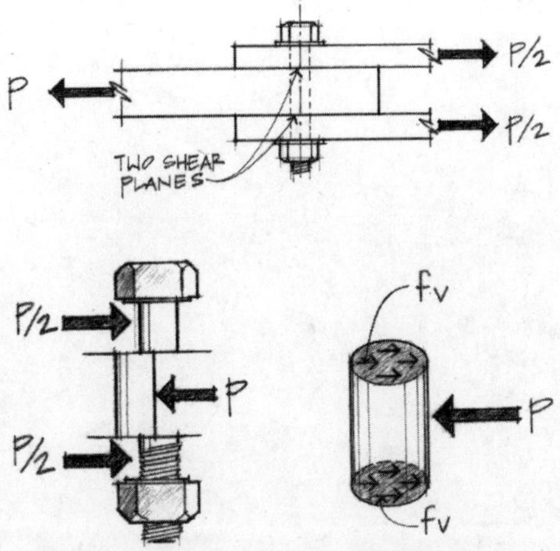

Free-body diagram of middle section of the bolt in shear.

Figure 12 A bolted connection in double shear.

Bearing stress

The third fundamental type of stress, *bearing stress* (Figure 13), is actually a type of normal stress, but it represents the intensity of force between a body and another body (i.e., the contact between beam and column, column and footing, footing and ground). The stressed surface is perpendicular to the direction of the applied load, the same as normal stress. Like the previous two stresses, the average bearing stress is defined in terms of a force per unit area

$$f_p = \frac{P}{A}$$

where

f_p = unit-bearing stress (psi, ksi, or psf; N/mm^2 or N/m^2)

P = applied load (# or k, N or kN)

A = bearing contact area ($in.^2$ or $ft.^2$, mm^2 or m^2)

Both the column and footing may be assumed to be separate structural members, and the bearing surface is the contact area between them. There also exists a bearing surface between the footing and the ground.

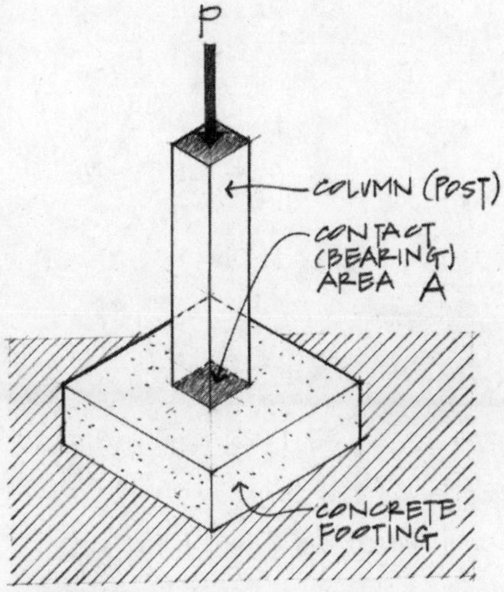

Figure 13 Bearing stress—post/footing/ground.

In the preceding three stress classifications, the basic equation of stress may be written in three different ways, depending on the condition being evaluated.

1. $f = P/A$ (Basic equation; used for analysis purposes in which the load, member size, and material are known.)
2. $P = f \times A$ (Used in evaluating or checking the capacity of a member when the material and member size are known.)
3. $A = P/f$ (Design version of the stress equation; member size can be determined if the load and material's allowable stress capability are known.)

Torsional stress

The fourth type of stress is called *torsional stress* (Figure 14). Members in torsion are subjected to twisting action along their longitudinal axes caused by a moment couple or eccentric load (see Figures 4 and 5). One of the most common examples of a building member subjected to torsional moments is a spandrel (edge) beam. Most building members subjected to torsional effects are also experiencing either bending, shear, tensile, and/or compressive stresses; therefore, it is relatively uncommon to design specifically for torsion. On the other hand, designs involving machinery and motors with shafts are extremely sensitive to the stresses resulting from torsion.

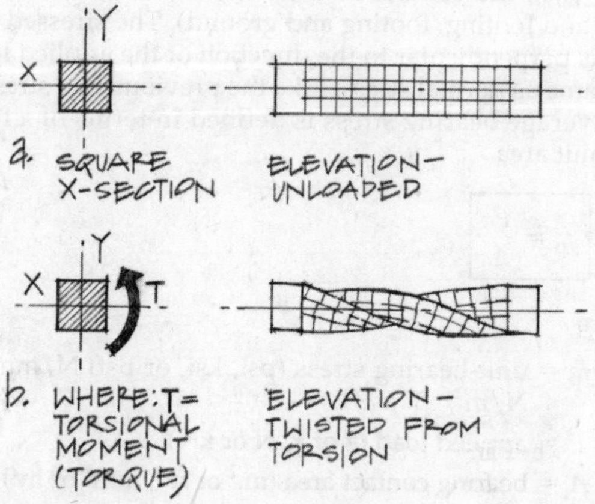

Figure 14 Member subjected to torsion.

Example Problems: Stress

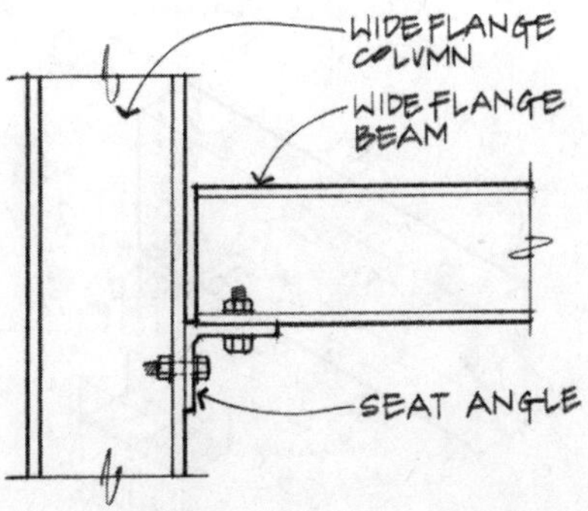

2 A typical method of temporarily securing a steel beam onto a column is by using a seat angle with bolts through the column flange. Two $\frac{1}{2}''$-diameter bolts are used to fasten the seat angle to the column. The bolts must carry the beam load of $P = 5$ k in single shear. Determine the average shear stress developed in the bolts.

Solution:

$$f_v = \tau = \frac{P}{A}$$

$$A = 2 \times \frac{\pi D^2}{4} = 2 \times \frac{3.14(0.5'')^2}{4} = 0.393 \text{ in.}^2$$

↑
(two bolts)

$$f_v = \tau = \frac{5\text{ k}}{0.393\text{ in.}^2} = 12.72\text{ ksi}$$

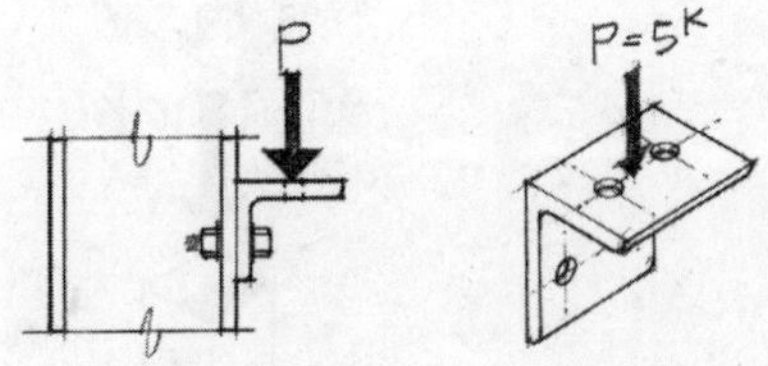

3 In a typical floor support, a short timber post is capped with a steel channel to provide a larger bearing area for the joists. The joists are 4″ × 12″ rough cut. The steel base plate is provided to increase the bearing area on the concrete footing. The load transmitted from each floor joist is 5.0 k.

Find the following:

a. The minimum length of channel required to support the joists if the maximum allowable bearing stress perpendicular to the grain is 400 psi.
b. The minimum size of post required to support the load if the maximum stress allowed in compression parallel to the grain is 1,200 psi.
c. The size of base plate required if the allowable bearing on concrete is 450 psi.
d. The footing size if allowable soil $f_p = 2{,}000$ psf.

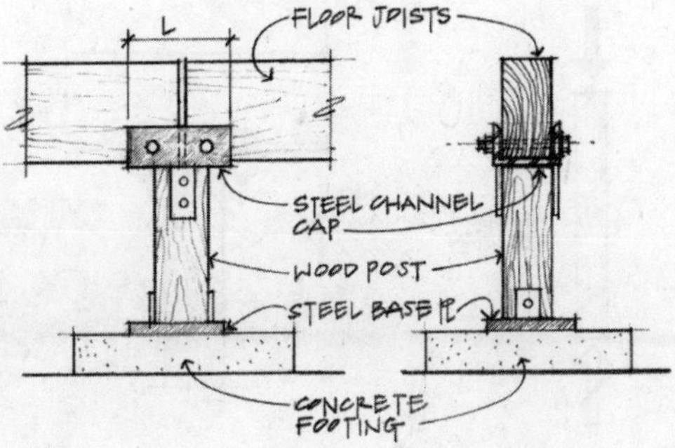

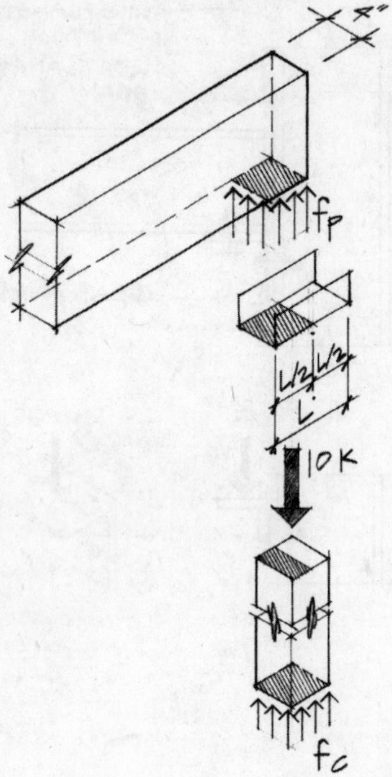

Solution

a. $f_p = \dfrac{P}{A}$ Examine one joist; $P = 5{,}000\#$

$f_{allowable} = 400\ \#/\text{in.}^2$

$A = \dfrac{P}{f} = \dfrac{5{,}000\#}{400\ \#/\text{in.}^2} = 12.5\ \text{in.}^2$

$A = 4'' \times L/2$

$4'' \times L/2 = 12.5\ \text{in.}^2$

$\therefore L = 6.25\ \text{in.}$

b. $f_c = \dfrac{P}{A}$; $P = 2 \times 5.0\ \text{k} = 10\ \text{k}$

$f_{allowable} = 1{,}200\ \#/\text{in.}^2$

$A_{required} = \dfrac{P}{f} = \dfrac{10{,}000\#}{1{,}200\ \#/\text{in.}^2} = 8.33\ \text{in.}^2, L = \sqrt{A}$

Minimum size requirement of square post is 2.89″ × 2.89″.

Practical to use at least a 4″ × 4″ post.

c. $A_{required} = \dfrac{P}{f} = \dfrac{10{,}000\#}{450\ \#/\text{in.}^2} = 22.2\ \text{in.}^2$

Minimum base plate = 4.72″ square

Use at least a 5″ × 5″ square plate.

d. $A_{required} = \dfrac{P}{f} = \dfrac{10{,}000\#}{2{,}000\ \#/\text{ft.}^2} = 5\ \text{ft.}^2$; $x = 2.24'$

Use a 2′−3″ × 2′−3″ footing size.

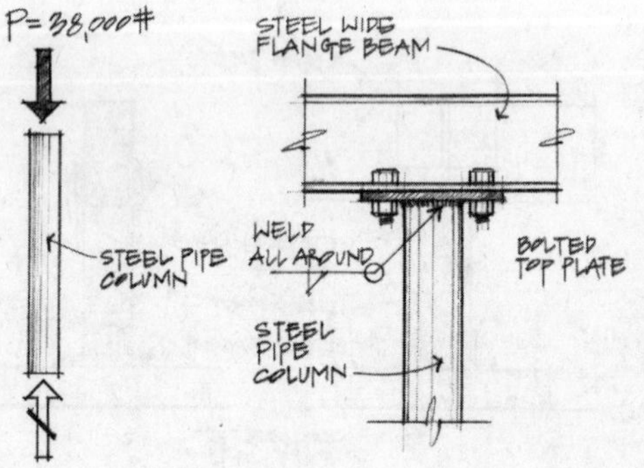

4 A piece of standard steel pipe is used as a structural steel column and supports an axial load of 38,000#. If the allowable unit stress in the column is 12,000 psi, what size pipe should be used?

Solution:

$F_{allowable} = 12{,}000\ \#/\text{in.}^2$

$f_c \dfrac{P}{A}$; $A_{required} = \dfrac{P}{f} = \dfrac{38{,}000\#}{12{,}000\ \#/\text{in.}^2} = 3.17\ \text{in.}^2$

See the Table A8 in the Appendix.

Use a 4″-diameter standard weight pipe. (Area = 3.17 in.^{2})

5 A timber roof truss is subjected to roof loads as shown. Because timber lengths are relatively restrictive, it is necessary to provide a glued splice on the bottom chord. Determine the tensile force in the bottom chord member (splice). Assuming the members and splice plate are 6″ deep and the glue has a shear capacity of 25 #/in.^{2} (with a lot of safety factor), determine the required length L of the splice.

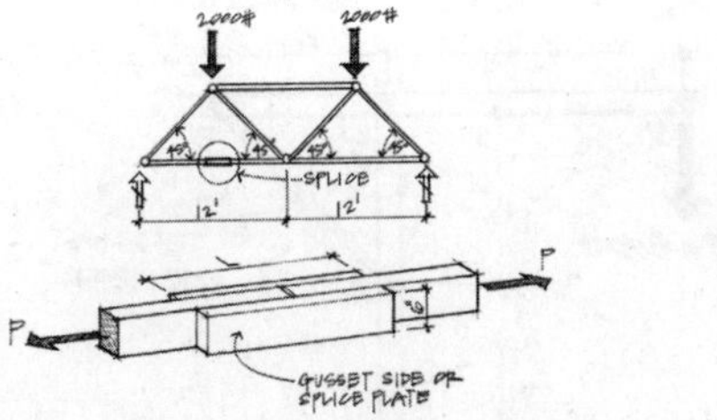

$P = 2{,}000\# \text{ @ splice}$

Solution:

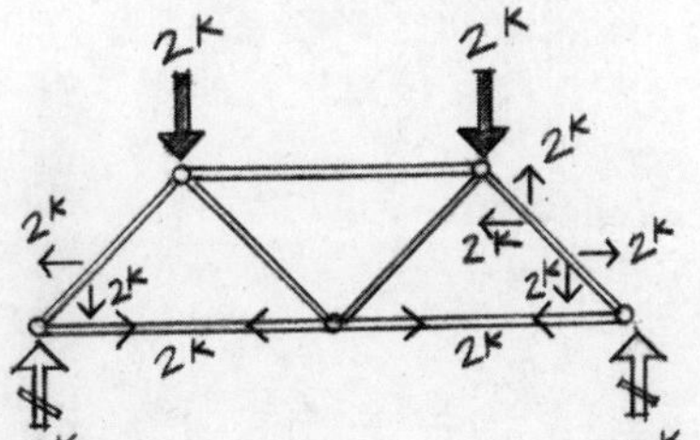

$$f_v = \tau = \frac{P}{A};$$

$$A_{\text{required}} = \frac{P}{f_{\text{allowable}}} = \frac{2{,}000\#}{25\,\#/\text{in.}^2} = 80\text{ in.}^2$$

Each side plate provides half of the resistance.

$$\therefore A_{\text{required}} = 40\text{ in.}^2\ (\text{per side plate})$$

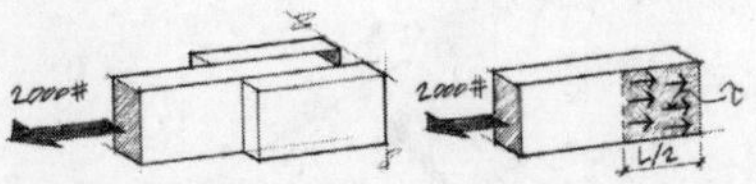

$$A = 6'' \times \frac{L}{2} = 3L$$

$$L = \frac{A}{3} = \frac{40\text{ in.}^2}{3\text{ in.}} = 13.3\text{ in.}$$

6 The figure shown is a connection of the lower joint on a single-member truss. If the reaction is 10,000# and the members are 8″ × 10″, determine the shearing stress developed on the horizontal plane *a-b-c*.

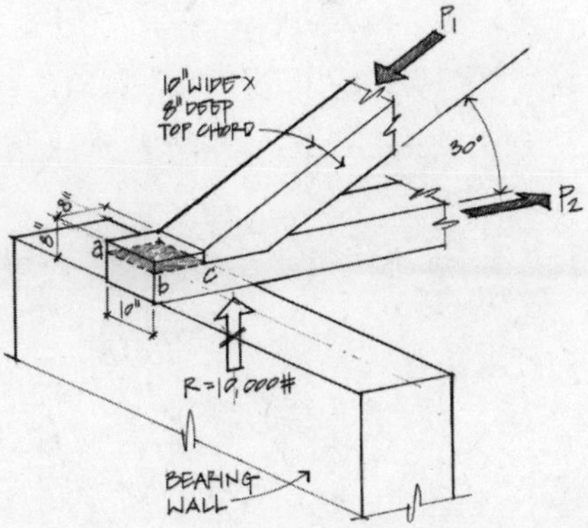

Solution:

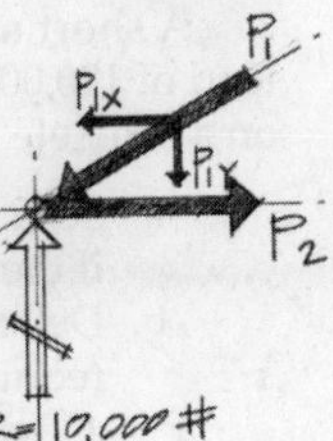

$$\left[\Sigma F_y = 0\right] - P_{1y} + 10{,}000 = 0$$

$$P_{1y} = 10{,}000\#$$

$$P_1 = \frac{P_{1y}}{\sin 30°} = \frac{10{,}000\#}{.5} = 20{,}000\#$$

$$P_{1x} = P_1 \cos 30° = 20\,\text{k}(.866)$$

$$= 17.32\,\text{k (horiz. thrust)}$$

$$f_v = \tau = \frac{P_{1x}}{A} = \frac{17{,}320\#}{8'' \times 10''} = 216.5\,\#/\text{in.}^2$$

Problems

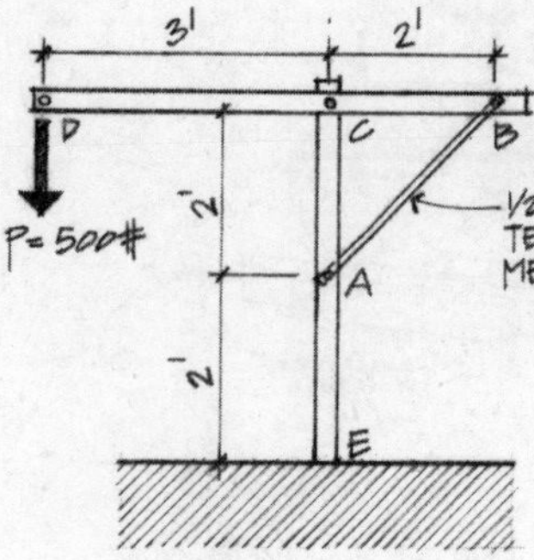

1 Determine the tensile stress developed in member *AB* due to a load of $P = 500\#$ at *D*. The member *AB* is $\frac{1}{2}''$ thick and 2″ wide.

2 A 10′ × 20′ hotel marquee hangs from two rods inclined at an angle of 30°. The dead load and snow load on the marquee add up to 100 psf. Design the two rods out of A36 steel that has an allowable tensile stress:

$$F_t = 22{,}000 \text{ psi (allowable stress)}$$

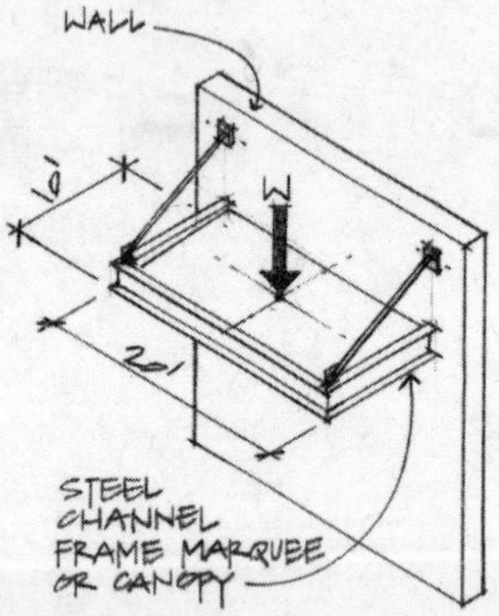

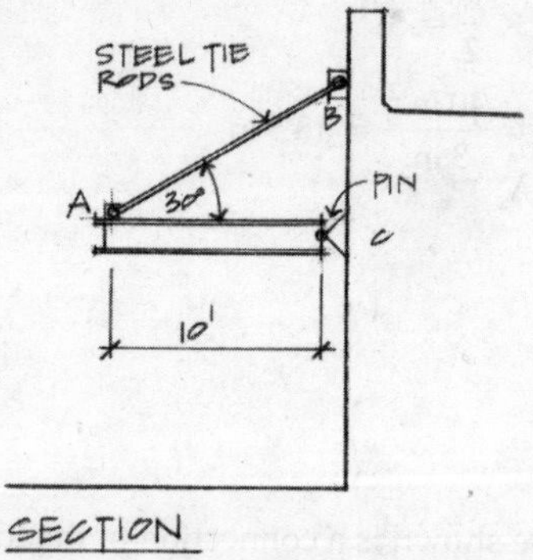

3 A short steel column supports an axial compressive load of 120,000# and is welded to a steel base plate resting on a concrete footing.

a. Select the lightest W8 (wide-flange) section to use if the unit stress is not to exceed 13,500 psi.
b. Determine the size of the base plate (square) required if the allowable bearing on concrete is 450 psi.
c. Calculate the required size of footing (square) if the allowable soil pressure is equal to 3,000 psf.

Neglect weights of column, base plate, and footing.

4 Assuming a density of 120 #/ft.^{3} for masonry brickwork, determine the maximum height of a brick wall if the allowable compressive stress is limited to 150 #/in.^{2} and the brick is (a) four inches wide and (b) six inches wide.

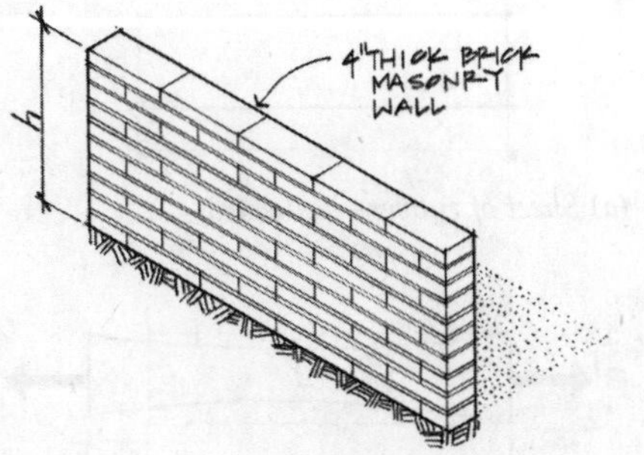

5 The accompanying figure shows part of a common type of roof truss, constructed mainly of timber and steel rods. Determine:

a. The average compressive stress in the 8″ × 8″ diagonal member if the load in it is 20 k.
b. The tensile stress in the $\frac{3}{4}$″ diameter threaded steel rod if the load in it is 4 k.
c. The bearing stress between the timber and the 4″ × 4″ square steel washer if the hole in it is $\frac{7}{8}$″ diameter.
d. The bearing stress between the brick wall column and the 8″ × 10″ timber if the load in the column is 15 k.
e. The length L required to keep the dashed portion of the 8″ × 10″ member from shearing off due to the horizontal thrust of 16 k against the steel shoe. The F_v = 120 psi allowable.

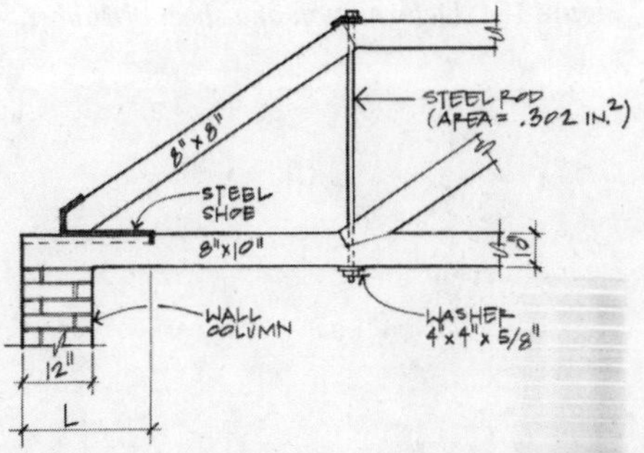

6 The turnbuckles in the diagram shown are tightened until the compression block DB exerts a force of 10,000# on the beam at B. Member DB is a hollow shaft with an inner diameter of 1.0 inch and outer diameter of 2 inches. Rods AD and CD each have cross-sectional areas of 1.0 in.^{2}. Pin C has a diameter of 0.75 inch. Determine:

a. The axial stress in BD.
b. The axial stress in CD.
c. The shearing stress in pin C.

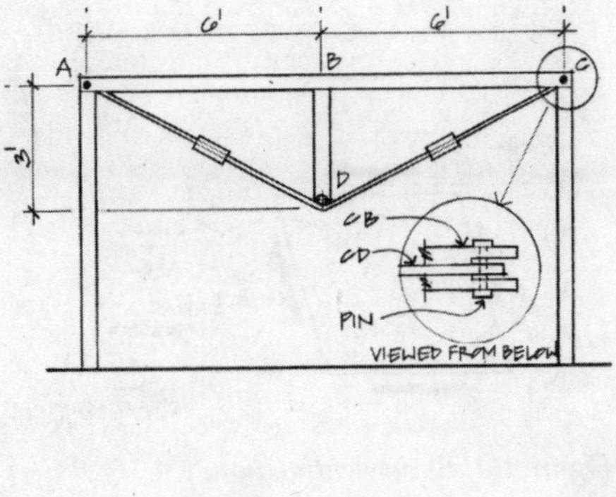

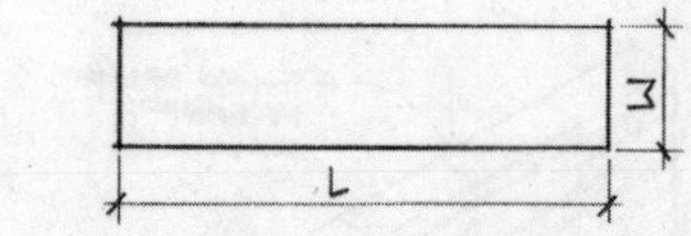

(a) Sheet of rubber—unloaded.

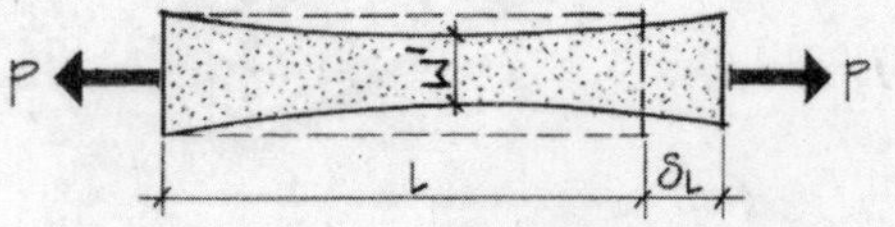

(b) Sheet of rubber—under load.

Figure 15 *Deformation of a sheet of rubber.*

Deformation and Strain

Most materials of construction deform under the action of loads. When the size or shape of a body is altered, the change in any direction is termed *deformation* and given the symbol δ (delta). *Strain,* which is given the symbol ε (epsilon) or γ (gamma), is defined as the deformation per unit length. The deformation or strain may be the result of a change of temperature or stress.

Consider a piece of rubber being stretched:

L = Original length

W = Original width

W' = New width

δ_L = Longitudinal change in length (deformation)

$W - W' = \delta_t$ = Transverse change in length

In Figure 15, the rubber tends to elongate in the direction of the applied load with a resultant deformation δ; correspondingly, a contraction of the width occurs. This deformation behavior is typical of most materials, because all solids deform to some extent under applied loads. No truly "rigid bodies" exist in structural design.

Strain resulting from a change in stress is defined mathematically as

$$\boxed{\varepsilon = \frac{\delta}{L}}$$

where

ε = unit strain (in./in.)

δ = total deformation (in.)

L = original length (in.)

Members subjected to a shear stress undergo a deformation that results in a change in shape.

Rather than an elongation or shortening, shearing stress causes an angular deformation of the body. The square shown in Figure 16 becomes a parallelogram when acted upon by shear stresses. Shearing strain, represented by γ, is

$$\boxed{\gamma = \frac{\delta_s}{L} = \tan\phi \cong \phi}$$

When the angle ϕ is small, $\tan\phi \cong \phi$, where ϕ is the angle expressed in radians.

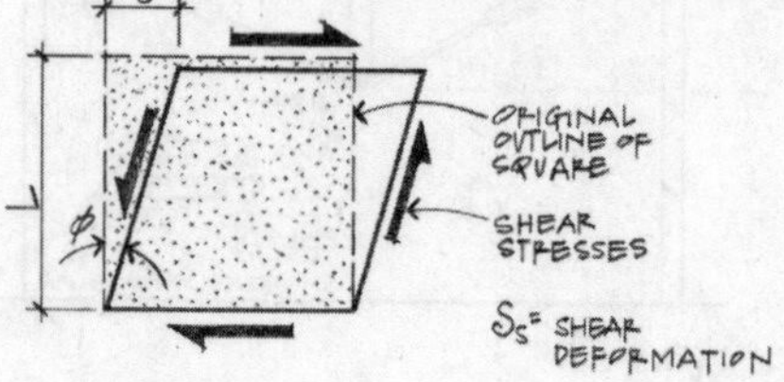

Figure 16 *Shear deformation.*

Example Problems: Deformation and Strain

7 A concrete test cylinder is loaded with $P = 100$ k and a resulting shortening of 0.036 inch. Determine the unit strain developed in the concrete.

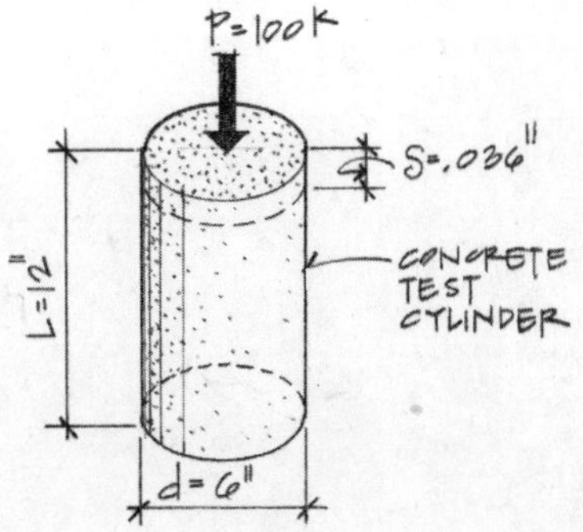

Solution:

$$\varepsilon = \frac{\delta}{L} = \frac{0.036''}{12''} = 0.003 \text{ in./in.}$$

Note that the value of unit strain is obtained by dividing a length by a length. The result is simply a ratio.

8 A truss tie rod has dimensions as shown. Upon loading, it is found that an elongation of 0.400 inch occurred in each tie rod assembly. If the unit strain on the rod portion equaled 0.0026, what was the unit strain on the two end clevises?

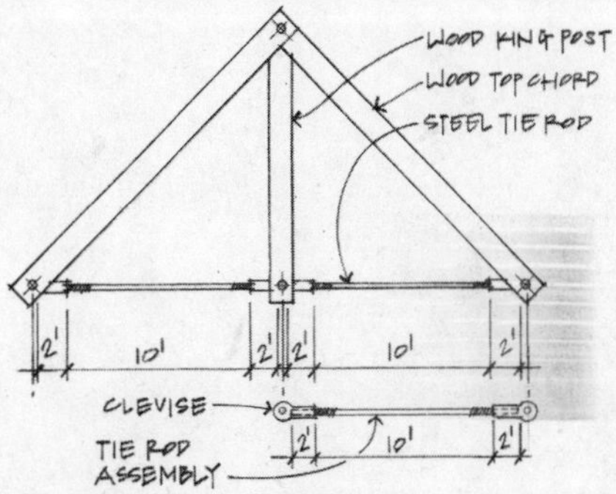

Solution:

$$\varepsilon = \frac{\delta_{\text{rod}}}{L};\ \delta_{\text{rod}} = \varepsilon L = 0.0026 \times 120'' = 0.312''$$

$$\text{Total } \delta = 0.400'' - 0.312'' = 0.088''$$

$$\varepsilon = \frac{\delta_e}{L} = \frac{0.088''}{48''} = 0.00183$$

$$(L = 2' \text{ at each end} = 4' = 48'')$$

9 The midpoint C of a cable drops to C' when a weight W is suspended from it. Find the strain in the cable.

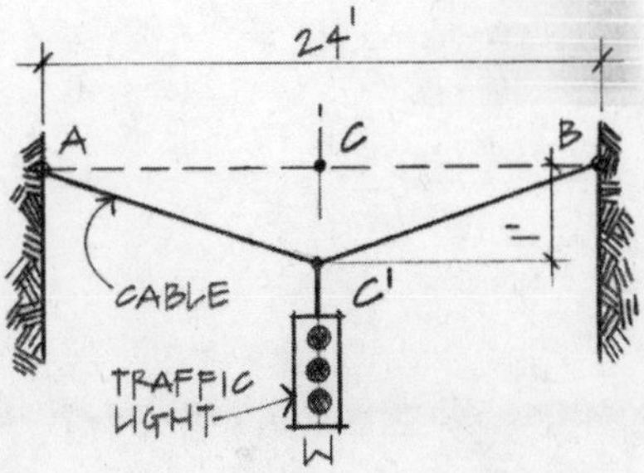

Solution:

$$\varepsilon = \frac{\delta}{L}$$

δ = Deformation = Change in length of the cable

L = Original length of the cable or $\frac{1}{2}$ cable

BC = Old length (before loading)

BC' = New length (after loading)

$$\therefore\ \delta = BC - BC'$$

$$= \sqrt{12^2 + 1^2} - 12'$$

$$= 12.04' - 12' = 0.04' = 0.48''$$

$$\varepsilon = \frac{0.48''}{12 \times 12} = 0.0033 \text{ in./in. or leave it unitless}$$

Problems

7 During the test of a specimen in a tensile testing machine, it is found that the specimen elongates 0.0024 inch between two punch marks that are initially two inches apart. Evaluate the strain.

8 A reinforced concrete column is 12 feet long, and under load, it shortens $\frac{1}{8}$ inches″. Determine its average unit strain.

9 A concrete test cylinder eight 8″ tall and 4″ in diameter is subjected to a compressive load that results in a strain of 0.003 in./in. Determine the shortening that develops as a result of this loading.

10 A 500-foot-long steel cable is loaded in tension and registers an average unit strain of 0.005. Determine the total elongation due to this load.

2 ELASTICITY, STRENGTH, AND DEFORMATION

Relationship Between Stress and Strain

A wide variety of materials are presently used in architectural structures: stone, brick, concrete, steel, timber, aluminum, plastics, etc. All have essential properties that make them applicable for a given purpose in a structure. The criterion for selection, at a very basic level, is the material's ability to withstand forces without excessive deformations or actual failures.

One major consideration in any structural design is deflection (deformation). Deformation in structures cannot increase indefinitely, and it should disappear after the applied load is removed. *Elasticity* is a material property in which deformations disappear with the disappearance of the load (Figure 17).

All structural materials are elastic to some extent. As loads are applied and deformations result, the deformations will vanish as the load is removed as long as a certain limit is not exceeded. This limit is called the *elastic limit.* Within the elastic limit, no permanent deformations result from the application and removal of the load. If this limit of loading is exceeded, however, a permanent deformation results. The behavior of the material is then termed *plastic* or *inelastic.*

In some materials, when the elastic limit is exceeded, the molecular bonds within the material are unable to re-form, thus causing cracks or separation of the material. Such materials are termed *brittle.* Cast iron, high-carbon steel, and ceramics are considered to be brittle; low-carbon steel, aluminum, copper, and gold exhibit properties of *ductility,* which is a measure of *plasticity.*

Materials that have molecular bonds re-forming after exceeding the elastic limit will result in permanent deformations; however, the material still remains in one piece without any significant loss in strength. This type of material behavior is termed *ductile.*

Ductile materials give warning of impending failure. Brittle materials do not.

One of the most important discoveries in the science of mechanics of materials was undoubtedly that pertaining to the elastic character of materials. This discovery in 1678 by Robert Hooke, an English scientist, mathematically relates stress to strain. The relationship, known as Hooke's law, states that in elastic materials, stress and strain are proportional. Hooke observed this stress-strain relationship by experimentally loading various materials in tension and then measuring the subsequent deformations. Although Hooke's initial experiment, techniques, and testing equipment have improved, the relationship between stress and strain and the determination of elastic and plastic properties of materials still use Hooke's basic concept.

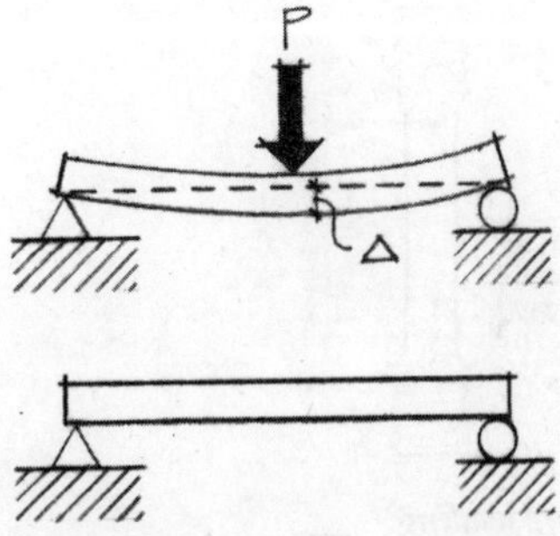

(a) Elastic behavior.

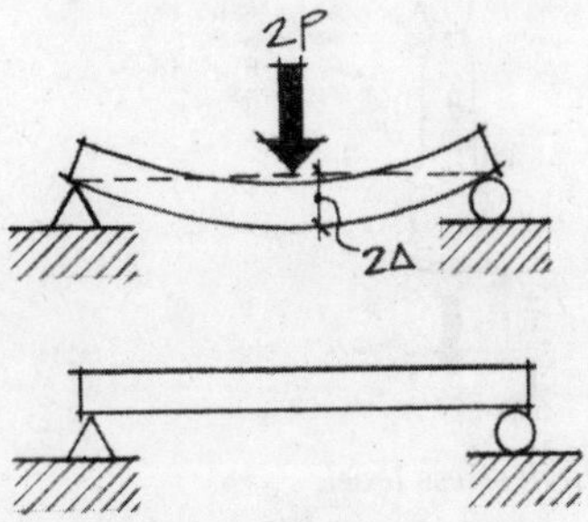

(b) Linearly elastic behavior.

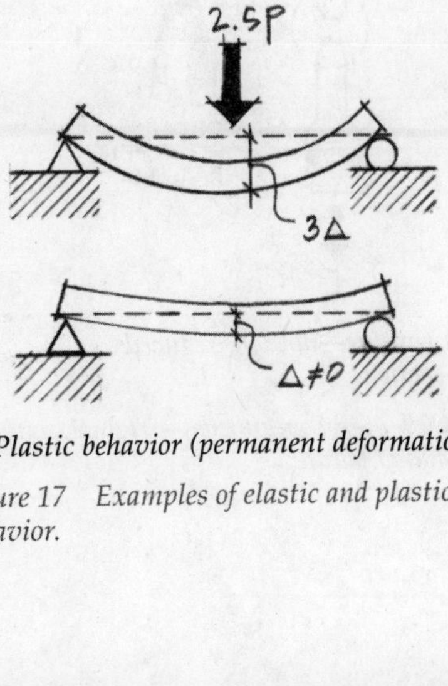

(c) Plastic behavior (permanent deformation).

Figure 17 Examples of elastic and plastic behavior.

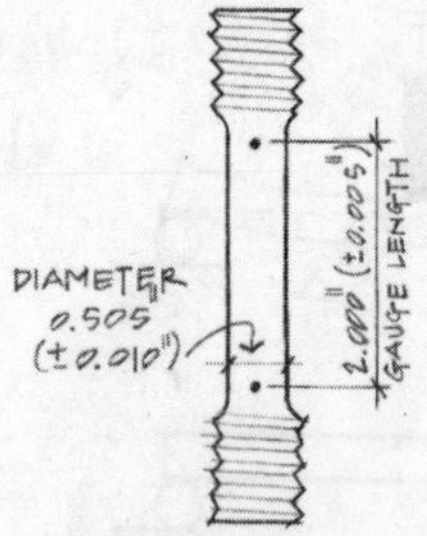

(a) Before loading.

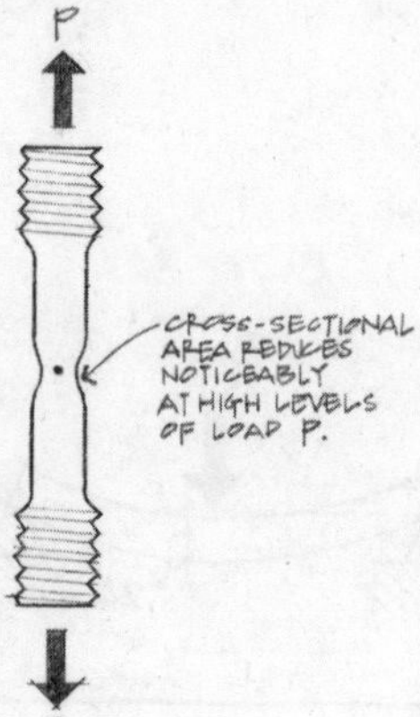

(b) At high stress level.

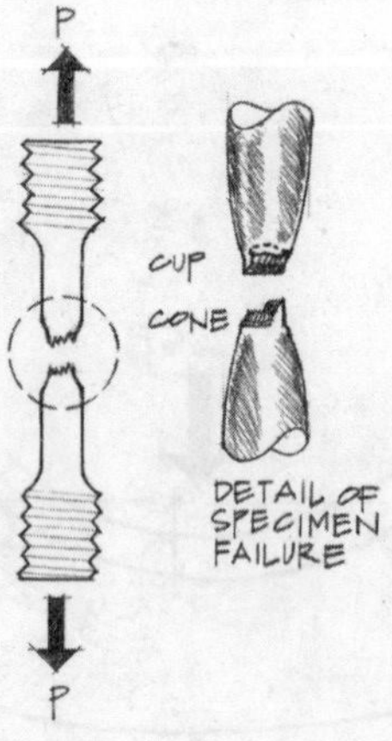

(c) At rupture—note the reduced cross-section.

Figure 19 Steel specimens—original, with load, and at failure.

Today, universal testing machines, similar to the one shown in Figure 18, are employed to apply precise loads at precise rates to standardized tensile and compressive specimens (Figure 19). The tensile test is the most common test applied to materials. A variety of devices for measuring and recording strain or deformation can be attached to the test specimen to obtain data for plotting stress-strain diagrams (or load-deformation curves).

The stress-strain curves obtained from tension or compression tests conducted on various materials reveal several characteristic patterns (Figure 20). Ductile rolled steels, such as ordinary, low-carbon structural steel, stretch considerably after following a straight-line variation of stress and strain. For steels alloyed with increasing amounts of carbon and other strengthening materials, such as chromium, nickel, silicon, manganese, and so forth, the tendency to produce such an intermediate stretching point becomes increasingly remote. The stress-strain curves for heavily alloyed steels are generally straight to a point a short distance from the rupture point.

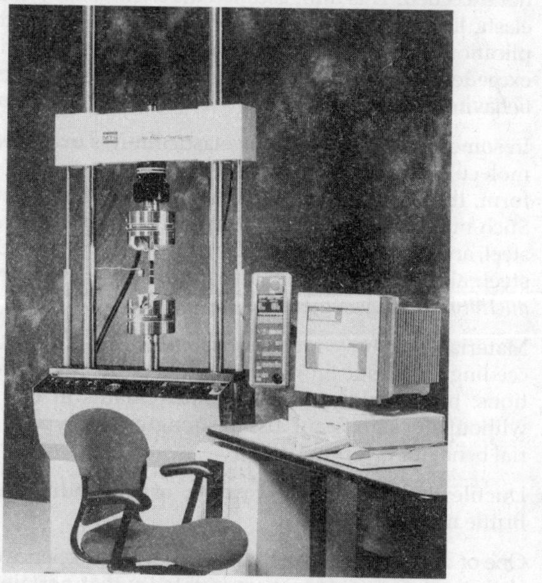

Figure 18 Universal testing machine. Photo courtesy of MTS Systems Corporation.

In contrast to such straight-line, stress-strain curves are those obtained for materials such as cast iron, brass, concrete, wood, and so forth, which are often curved throughout most of their length.

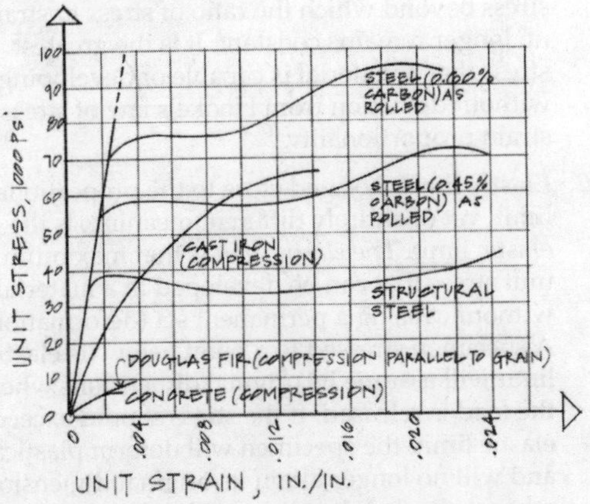

Figure 20 Stress-strain diagram for various materials.

The stress-strain curve for low-carbon (less than 0.30% carbon) steel (Figure 21) will form the basis for the ensuing remarks concerning several familiar strength values. This diagram plots strain along the abscissa and stress along the ordinate. The stress is defined as the load in pounds or kips divided by the original cross-sectional area of the specimen.

As the test proceeds, with larger loads being applied at a specified rate, the actual cross-sectional area of the specimen decreases. At high stresses, this reduction in area becomes appreciable.

The stress based on the initial area is not the *true stress*, but it is generally used (and is called the *indicated stress*). The calculated stress in load-carrying members is almost universally based on this original area. The strain used is the elongation of a unit length of the test specimen taken over the gauge length of two inches.

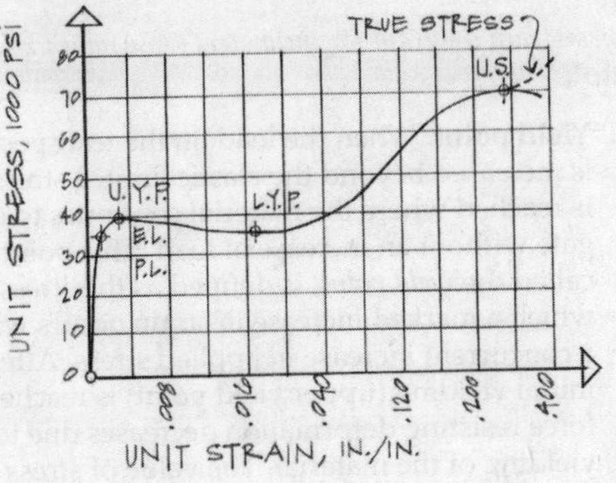

Figure 21 Stress-strain diagram for low-carbon structural steel.

Using an exaggerated scale on the stress-strain data for mild steel, as shown in Figure 22, the significant points on the curve are defined as follows:

1. **Proportional limit.** The *proportional limit* is that stress beyond which the ratio of stress to strain no longer remains constant. It is the greatest stress that a material is capable of developing without deviation from Hooke's law of stress-strain proportionality.

2. **Elastic limit.** Located close to the proportional limit, yet of entirely different meaning, is the elastic limit. The *elastic limit* is that maximum unit stress that can be developed in a material without causing a permanent set (deformation). A specimen stressed to a point below its elastic limit will assume its original dimensions when the load is released. If the stress should exceed its elastic limit, the specimen will deform plastically and will no longer attain its original dimensions when unloaded. It is then said to have incurred a *permanent set*.

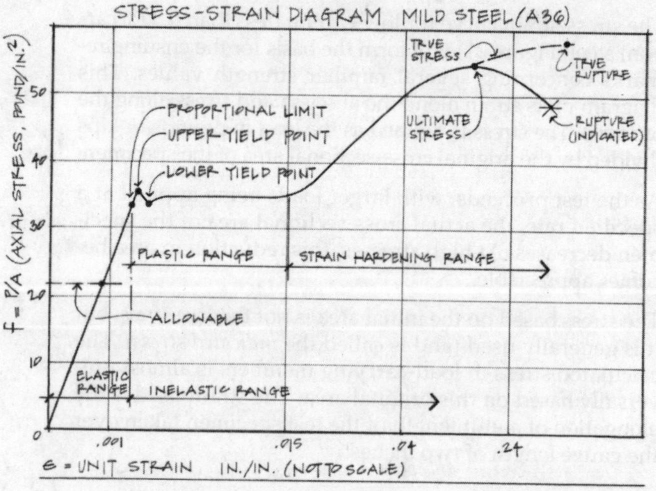

Figure 22 Stress-strain diagram for mild steel (A36) with key points highlighted.

3. **Yield point.** When the load on the test specimen is increased beyond the elastic limit, a stress level is reached where the material continues to elongate without an increase of load. This point, called the *yield point*, is defined as the stress at which a marked increase in strain occurs without a concurrent increase in applied stress. After the initial yielding (upper yield point) is reached, the force resisting deformation decreases due to the yielding of the material. The value of stress after initial yielding (the lower yield point) is usually

taken to be the true material characteristic to be used as the basis for the determination of allowable stress (for design purposes).

Many materials do not exhibit well-defined yield points, and the yield strength is defined as the stress at which the material exhibits a specified limiting permanent set. The specified set (or offset) most commonly used is 0.2%, which corresponds to a strain of 0.002 in./in. (Figure 23).

When a test specimen is stressed beyond its elastic limit and then has its load released, a plot of the data shows that during the load-reducing stage, the stress-strain curve parallels the initial portion of the curve. The horizontal intercept along the x axis is the permanent set. Such a load cycle does not necessarily damage a material even if the imposed stress exceeds the elastic limit. *Ductility* may be lowered, but the *hardness* (ability of a material to resist indentation) and elastic stress limit of the material will generally increase.

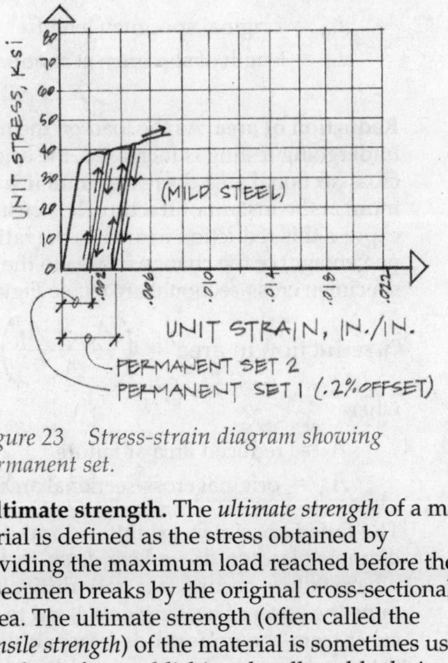

Figure 23 Stress-strain diagram showing permanent set.

4. **Ultimate strength.** The *ultimate strength* of a material is defined as the stress obtained by dividing the maximum load reached before the specimen breaks by the original cross-sectional area. The ultimate strength (often called the *tensile strength*) of the material is sometimes used as a basis for establishing the allowable design stresses for a material.

5. **Rupture strength** (*breaking strength, fracture strength*). In a ductile material, rupture does not usually occur at the ultimate unit stress. After the ultimate unit stress has been reached, the material will generally "neck down," as shown in Figure 24(b), and its rapidly increasing elongation will be accompanied by a decrease in

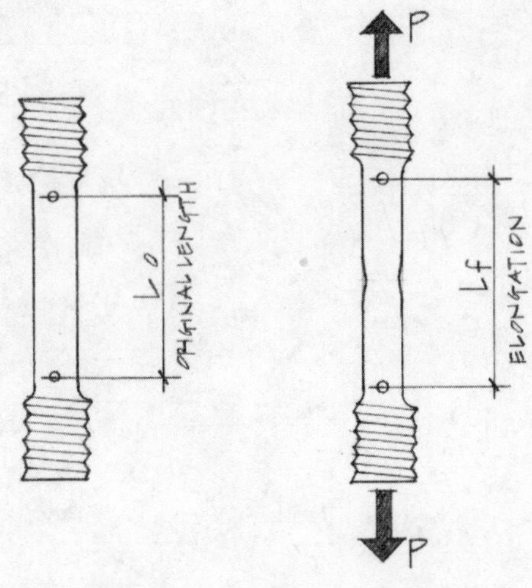

(a) Unloaded. (b) Under load.

Figure 24 Elongation of specimen under loading.

load. This decrease becomes more rapid as the rupture point is approached. The *rupture strength*, obtained by dividing the load at rupture by the original area (indicated rupture), has little or no value in design. A more correct evaluation of the variation of stress following attainment of the ultimate unit stress is obtained by dividing the loads by the simultaneously occurring decreasing areas (true rupture strength).

6. **Elongation.** *Elongation* (Figure 24) is a measure of the ability of a material to undergo deformation without rupture. *Percentage elongation*, defined by the equation below, is a measure of the ductility of a material. Ductility is a desirable and necessary property, and a member must possess it to prevent failure due to local overstressing.

$$\left(\frac{L_f - L_o}{L_o}\right) \times 100\% = \%\text{ of elongation}$$

where

L_o = original specimen length
L_f = length of specimen at rupture (fracture)

7. **Reduction of area.** As the load on the material undergoing testing is increased, the original cross-sectional area decreases until it is at a minimum at the instant of fracture. It is customary to express this reduction in area as the ratio (as a percentage) of the change in area to the original specimen cross-sectional area. (See Figure 24.)

$$\%\text{ reduction in area} = \left(\frac{A_o - A_f}{A_o}\right) \times 100\%$$

where

A_f = reduced area at failure
A_o = original cross-sectional area

The failed specimen exhibits a local decrease in diameter known as *necking down* in the region where failure occurs. It is very difficult to determine the onset of necking down and to differentiate it from the uniform decrease in diameter of the specimen. Failure in a structural steel test specimen commences when the material is sufficiently reduced in cross-sectional area and molecular bonds within the material begin breaking down. Eventually, the ultimate tensile strength of the material is reached, and actual separation of the material starts, with shear failure occurring at the periphery of the specimen at 45° angles. Then, complete separation results in the center portion in which the plane of failure is normal to the direction of the tensile force.

The percentage reduction in area can be used as a measure of ductility. Brittle materials exhibit almost no reduction in area, whereas ductile materials exhibit a high percentage reduction in area.

Table 1 shows the average strength values for selected engineering materials.

Table 1 Average strength values for selected engineering materials.

	Yield Stress or Proportional Limit (ksi)			**Ultimate Strength (ksi)**			**Modulus of Elasticity (ksi)**	
Materials	**Tension**	**Compression**	**Shear**	**Tension**	**Compression**	**Shear**	**Tens. or Comp.**	**Shear**
Steel:								
A-36 Structural	36	36	22	58		40	29,000	12,000
A572 Grade 50* (also A992)	50	50	30	65		45	30,000	12,000
Iron:								
Malleable	25	25	12	50		40	24,000	11,000
Wrought	30	30	18	58		38	25,000	10,000
Aluminum Alloy:								
6061-T6 Rolled/extruded	35	35	20	38		24	10,000	3,800
6063-T6 Extruded tubes	25	25	14	30		19	10,000	3,800
Other Metals:								
Brass: 70% Cu, 30% Zinc	25		15	55		48	14,000	6,000
Bronze, cast heat treated	55		37	75		56	12,000	5,000
Timber, Air Dry:								
Yellow Pine		6.2			8.4	1.0	1,600	
Douglas Fir		5.4			6.8	0.8	1,600	
Spruce		4.0			5.0	0.75	1,200	
Concrete:								
Concrete: 1:2:4 mix, 28 days					3.0		3,000	

*With special requirements per *AISC Technical Bulletin #3*.

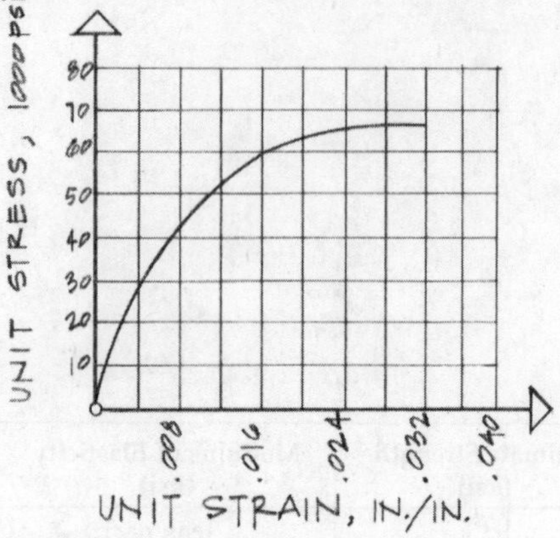

Figure 25 Stress-strain diagram for cast iron (compression test).

3 OTHER MATERIAL PROPERTIES

Compression Tests

The compression test is used primarily to test brittle materials, such as cast iron and concrete (Figure 25). The universal testing machine is used for this purpose, and data are taken in a manner similar to that discussed for the tension test. The results of the compression test generally define an elastic range, a proportional limit, and a yield strength. In the compression test, the cross-sectional area of the specimen increases as loads increase, which produces a continuously rising stress-strain curve.

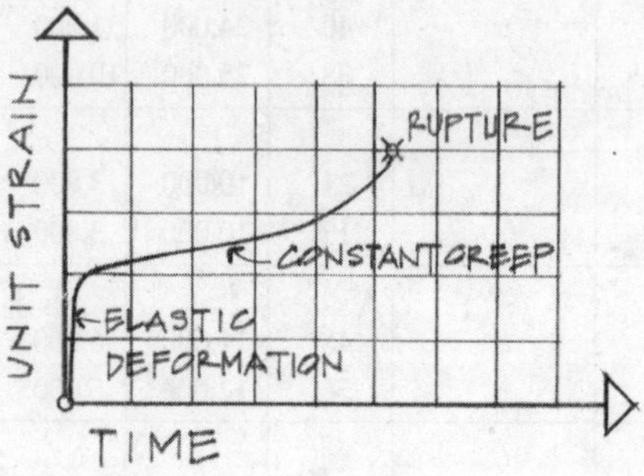

Figure 26 Strain with respect to time (creep).

Creep

The deformation that most structural materials undergo when stressed to their allowable limit at room temperature is a completed deformation and will not increase no matter how long the stress is applied. At some higher temperature, however, these same materials will reveal a continuing deformation or creep that, if permitted to continue, will ultimately lead to excessive displacements or rupture (Figure 26).

Cyclic Stress (Fatigue)

Members subjected to repeated conditions of loading or unloading, or to repeated stress reversals, will fail at a stress considerably lower than the ultimate stress obtained in a simple tension test. Failures that occur as a result of this type of repeated loading are known as *fatigue* failures.

A theory of fatigue failure assumes a sudden change in shape of the loaded member. Inconsistencies in the material cause localized stresses to develop that are far greater than the average stress in the material. These localized stresses exceed the material's yield strength and cause permanent deformations to occur locally. Repeated permanent deformations in a small area eventually cause hairline cracks to develop. This cracking process continues until the average stress on the resisting area reaches the ultimate strength of the material.

Poisson's Ratio

The cross-sectional reduction (necking down) during a steel tensile test has a definite relationship to the increase in length (elongation) experienced by the specimen. When a material is loaded in one direction, it will undergo strains both perpendicular as well as parallel to the direction of the load (see Figure 15). The ratio of the lateral or perpendicular strain to the longitudinal or axial strain is called *Poisson's ratio*. Poisson's ratio varies from 0.2 to 0.4 for most metals. Most steels have values in the range of 0.283 to 0.292. The symbol μ (mu) is used for Poisson's ratio, which is given by the equation

$$\mu = \frac{\varepsilon_{\text{lateral}}}{\varepsilon_{\text{longitudinal}}}$$

Allowable Working Stress—Factor of Safety

A *working stress* or *allowable stress* (Table 2) is defined as the maximum stress permitted in a design computation. It is the stress derived from the results of many tests and the accumulated experience obtained from many years of firsthand observation in the performance of members in actual service.

The *factor of safety* may be defined as the ratio of a failure-producing load to the estimated actual load. The ratio may be calculated as the *ultimate stress* (or *yield-point stress*) to the allowable working stress.

Load resistance factor design (LRFD), also known as limit state or the strength method, represents another philosophy used in the design of concrete and steel and, more recently, timber.

Modulus of Elasticity (Young's Modulus)

In 1678, Sir Robert Hooke observed that when rolled materials were subjected to equal increments of stress, they suffered equal increments of strain—in other words, stress is proportional to strain. The ratio formed by dividing a unit stress by its corresponding value of strain was suggested by Thomas Young in 1807 as a means of evaluating the relative stiffness of various materials (Figure 27). This ratio is called *Young's modulus*, or the *modulus of elasticity*, and it is the slope of the straight-line portion of the stress-strain diagram:

$$E = \frac{f}{\varepsilon}$$

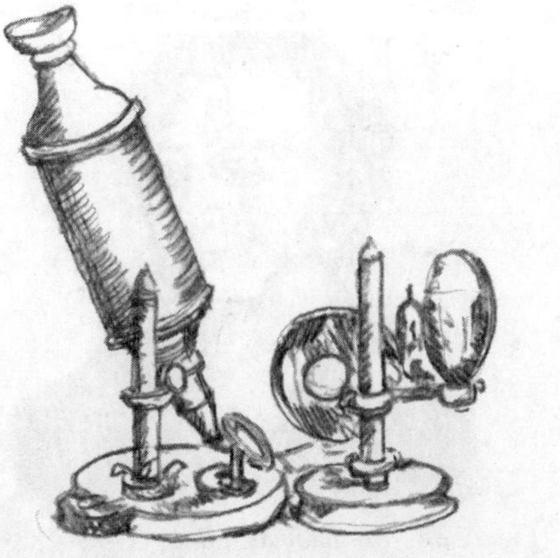

Although no portrait of Robert Hooke survives and his name is somewhat obscure today, he was perhaps the greatest experimental scientist of the 17th century. An earthy, albeit cantankerous, fellow, Hooke was occupied with an enormous number of practical problems. Among Hooke's inventions that are still in use today are the universal joint used in cars and the iris diaphragm, which was used in most early cameras.

Hooke experimented in a wide variety of fields, ranging from physics, astronomy, chemistry, geology, and biology to microscopy. He is credited with the discovery of one of the most important laws in the science of mechanics pertaining to the elastic character of materials. By experimenting with the behavior of elastic bodies, especially spiral springs, Hooke saw clearly that not only do solids resist mechanical loads by pushing back, they also change shape in response to the loads. It is this change in shape that enables the solid to do the pushing back.

Unfortunately, Hooke's personality hindered the application of his theories on elasticity. He was reputed to be a most nasty and argumentative individual, and he reportedly used his power in the Royal Society against those he perceived as his enemies. Isaac Newton had the misfortune of heading that list. So fierce was the hatred that grew between these two men that Newton, who lived for 25 years after Hooke's death, devoted a good deal of time to denigrating Hooke's memory and the importance of applied science. As a result, subjects such as structures suffered in popularity, and Hooke's work was not much followed or exploited, for some years after Newton's death.

Figure 27 Sir Thomas Young (1773–1829).

Young was a prodigy in his infancy who purportedly could read at the age of two and had read the entire Bible twice before the age of four. At Cambridge, his incredible abilities earned him the nickname "Phenomenon Young." He matured into an adult prodigy and was knowledgeable in 12 languages and could play a variety of musical instruments. As a physician, he was interested in sense perception. From the eye and then to light itself, it fell to Young to demonstrate the wave nature of light. Turning more and more to physics, he introduced the concept of energy in its modern form in 1807. In the same year, he suggested the ratio formed by dividing a unit stress by its corresponding value of strain (Young's modulus) as a means of evaluating the stiffness of various materials. He was also an accomplished Egyptologist, instrumental in deciphering the Rosetta Stone, the key to Egyptian hieroglyphics.

Appointed to the Chair of Natural Philosophy at the Royal Institution in London, Young was expected to deliver scientific lectures to popular audiences. Young took this mission seriously and launched into a series of lectures about the elasticity of various structures, with many useful and novel observations on the behaviors of walls and arches. Unfortunately for Young, he lacked the flair and oratory skill of his colleague Humphrey Davy, and he might as well have been reciting hieroglyphics as far as his audiences were concerned. Disappointed, Young resigned his chair and returned to medical practice.

where

E = modulus of elasticity (ksi or psi, N/m^2 pascal or N/mm^2)

f = stress (ksi or psi, N/m^2 pascal or N/mm^2)

ε = strain (in./in., mm/mm)

This ratio of stress to strain remains constant for all steels and many other structural materials within their useful range.

Generally, a high modulus of elasticity is desirable, because E is often referred to as a stiffness factor. Materials exhibiting high E values are more resistant to deformation and, in the case of beams, suffer much less deflection under load. Note in Figure 28 that of the three materials shown, the steel specimen has a much steeper slope in the elastic range than aluminum or wood and, therefore, will be much more resistant to deformation.

The Young's modulus equation may also be written in a very useful expanded form whenever the stress and deformation are caused by *axial loads.*

$$f = \frac{P}{A};\ \varepsilon = \frac{\delta}{L}$$

$$E = \frac{P/A}{\delta/L} = \frac{PL}{\delta A'}$$

$$\boxed{\therefore \delta = \frac{PL}{AE}} \quad \text{(Elastic equation)}$$

where

δ = deformation (in., mm)

P = applied axial load (# or k, N or kN)

L = length of member (in., mm)

A = cross-sectional area of member (in.^{2}, mm^2)

E = modulus of elasticity of material (#/in.^{2} or k/in.^{2}, N/m^2pascal or N/mm^2)

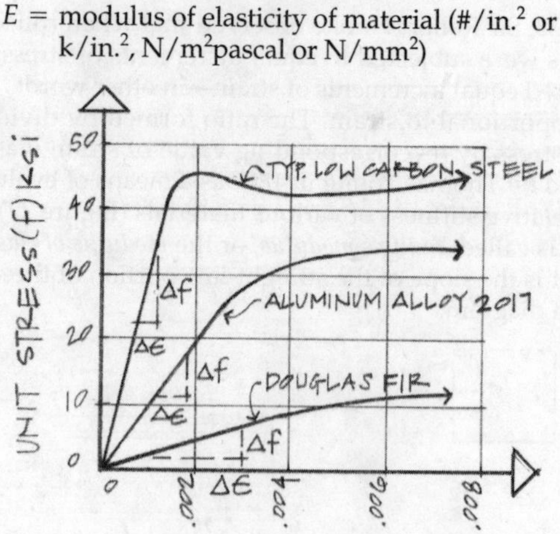

Figure 28 E—ratio of stress to strain for various materials.

Toughness

The area under the stress-strain curve (Figure 29) is a measure of the work required to cause a fracture. This ability of a material to absorb energy up to fracture is also used by designers as a characteristic property of a material and is called *toughness*. Toughness may be important in applications where stresses in the plastic range of the material may be approached but the resulting permanent set is not critical—and is sometimes even desirable. An example would be die-forming sheetmetal for automobile bodies. The stress-strain diagrams indicate that low-carbon (mild) steels are much "tougher" than high-carbon (higher-strength) steels. This concept is sometimes in opposition to the instinct of the engineer to specify the use of a "stronger" steel when a structure fails or seems in danger of failing. This could be a mistake in larger structures, because even in mild steel, much of the strength is not really being used. Failure of a structure may be controlled by the *brittleness* of the material, not by its strength.

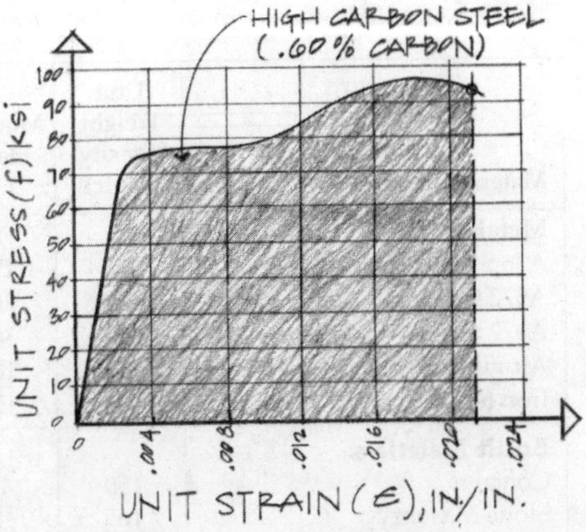

Figure 29 Toughness—area under the stress-strain diagram.

Table 2 Allowable stresses for selected engineering materials.

Materials	Unit Weight (density) γ (pfc)	Modules of Elasticity *E* (ksi)	Allowable Tension Stress F_t	Allowable Axial Compress F_c	Allowable Compress Bearing $F_{c\perp}$	Allowable Bending Stress F_b	Allowable Shear Stress F_v
Metals:							
A36 Steel $F_y = 36$ ksi	490	29,000	22 ksi	22 ksi		22 ksi	14.5 ksi
A572 Grade 50/A992	490	30,000	30 ksi	30 ksi		30 ksi	20 ksi
A572 Steel $F_y = 65$ ksi	490	30,000	39 ksi	39 ksi		39 ksi	26 ksi
Aluminum	165	10,000	16 ksi	16 ksi		16 ksi	10 ksi
Iron (cast)	450	15,000	5 ksi	20 ksi		5 ksi	7.5 ksi
Brittle Materials:							
Concrete	150	3,000	100 psi	1,350 psi			100 psi
Stone Masonry	165	1,000	10 psi	100 psi			10 psi
Brick Masonry	120	1,500	20 psi	300 psi			30 psi
Wood:							
Doug-Fir Larch North*							
• Joist & Rafters (No. 2)	35	1,700	650 psi	1,050 psi	625 psi	1,450 psi	95 psi
• Beams & Posts (No. 1)	35	1,600	700 psi	1,000 psi	625 psi	1,300 psi	85 psi
Southern Pine*							
• Joists & Rafters (No. 2)	35	1,600	625 psi	1,000 psi	565 psi	1,400 psi	90 psi
• Beams & Posts (D-No. 1)	35	1,600	1,050 psi	975 psi	440 psi	1,550 psi	110 psi
Hem-Fir*							
• Joists & Rafters (No. 2)	30	1,400	800 psi	1,050 psi	405 psi	1,150 psi	75 psi
• Beams & Posts (No. 1)	30	1,300	600 psi	850 psi	405 psi	1,000 psi	70 psi
Wood Products:							
Glu-Lam Beams	35	1,800	1,100 psi	1,650 psi	650 psi	2,400 psi	165 psi
Micro-Lam Beams	37	1,800	1,850 psi	2,460 psi	750 psi	2,600 psi	285 psi
Parallam Beams	45	2,000	2,000 psi	2,900 psi	650 psi	2,900 psi	290 psi

**Averaged stress values for design.*

Example Problems: Material Properties

10 The following data were obtained during a tensile test on a mild steel specimen having an initial diameter of 0.505 inch. At failure, the reduced diameter of the specimen was 0.305 inch. Plot the data, and determine the following:

a. Modulus of elasticity.
b. Proportional limit.
c. Ultimate strength.
d. Percentage reduction in area.
e. Percentage elongation.
f. Indicated strength at rupture.
g. True rupture strength.

Axial Load (#)	Stress f (#/in.^{2})	Elongation per 2″ Length (in.)	Strain δ/L (in./in.)
0	0	0	0
1,640	8,200	.00050	.00025
3,140	15,700	.0010	.00050
4,580	22,900	.0015	.00075
6,000	30,000	.0020	.00100
7,440	37,200	.0025	.00125
8,000	40,000	.0030	.00150
7,980	39,900	.00375	.001875
7,900	39,500	.00500	.00250
8,040	40,200	.00624	.00312
8,040	40,200	.00938	.00469
8,060	40,300	.0125	.00625
9,460	47,300	.050	.0250
12,000	60,000	.125	.0625
13,260	66,300	.225	.1125
13,580	67,900	.325	.1625
13,460	67,300	.475	.2375
13,220	66,100	.535	.2675
9,860	49,300	.625	.3125

Solution:

Initial diameter = 0.505″

$L_{orig} = 2.00''$

$A_{orig} = 0.20 \text{ in.}^2$

Reduced diameter at failure = 0.305″

$A_{fail} = 0.073 \text{ in.}^2$

a. Modulus of elasticity:

$$E = \frac{\Delta f}{\Delta \varepsilon} = \frac{(30{,}000\ \#/\text{in.}^2)}{0.0010} = 30{,}000{,}000\ \#/\text{in.}^2$$

b. Proportional limit is the last point of the linear part of the diagram.

$\therefore f_{prop} = 30{,}000$ psi

c. Ultimate strength is the absolute highest stress magnitude.

$\therefore f_{ult} = 67{,}900$ psi

d. Percentage area reduction equals

$$\frac{A_{orig} - A_{fail}}{A_{orig}} = \frac{0.20 - 0.073}{0.20} \times 100\% = 63.5\%$$

e. Percentage elongation equals

$$\frac{\delta_{total}}{L_{original}} = \frac{0.625''}{2.00''} \times 100\% = 31.25\%$$

f. Indicated strength of rupture:

$f_{rupture} = 49{,}300$ psi

g. True rupture strength:

$$f_{rupture} = \frac{9{,}860\#}{0.073 \text{ in.}^2} = 135{,}068 \text{ psi}$$

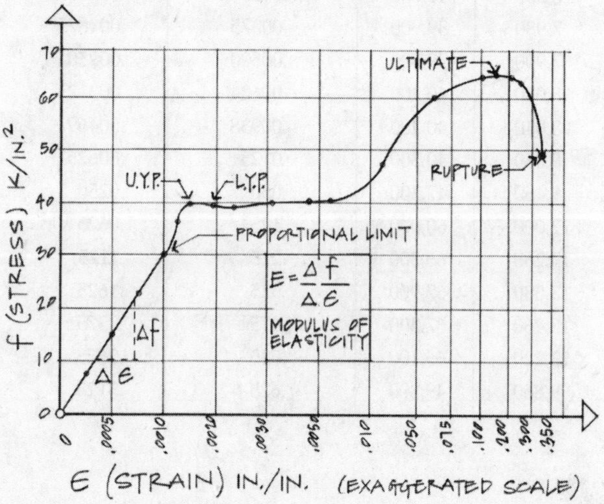

Plot of data for steel tensile test.

11 A one-inch-diameter manganese bronze test specimen was subjected to an axial tensile load, and the following data were obtained.

Gauge length	10 inches
Final gauge length	12.25 inches
Load at proportional limit	18,500#
Elongation at proportional limit	0.016 inch
Maximum load	55,000#
Load at rupture	42,000#
Diameter at rupture	0.845 inch

Find the following:

a. Proportional limit.
b. Modulus of elasticity.
c. Ultimate strength.
d. Percentage elongation.
e. Percentage reduction in area.
f. Indicated rupture strength.
g. True rupture strength.

Solution:

$A_{orig.} = 0.785 \text{ in.}^2; A_{rupture} = 0.560 \text{ in.}^2$

a. $f_{prop.} = \dfrac{18{,}500\#}{0.785 \text{ in.}^2} = 23{,}567 \text{ psi}$

$\varepsilon_{prop.} = \dfrac{0.016 \text{ in.}^2}{10 \text{ in.}} = 0.0016 \text{ in./in.}$

b. $E = \dfrac{\Delta f}{\Delta \varepsilon} = \dfrac{f_{prop.}}{\varepsilon_{prop.}}$

$E = \dfrac{23{,}567 \text{ \#/in.}^2}{0.0016 \text{ in./in.}} = 14{,}729{,}375 \text{ psi}$

c. $f_{ult} = \dfrac{\text{max. load}}{A_{orig.}} = \dfrac{55{,}000\#}{0.785 \text{ in.}^2} = 70{,}100 \text{ psi}$

d. $\% \text{ elongation} = \dfrac{2.25''}{10''} \times 100\% = 22.5\%$

e. $\% \text{ reduction of area} = \dfrac{0.785 \text{ in.}^2 - 0.560 \text{ in.}^2}{0.785 \text{ in.}^2} \times 100\% = 28.7\%$

f. $f_{rupture} = \dfrac{\text{load at rupture}}{A_{original}} = 53{,}503 \text{ psi (indicated)}$

g. $f_{rupture} = \dfrac{\text{load at rupture}}{A_{rupture}} = 75{,}000 \text{ psi (true)}$

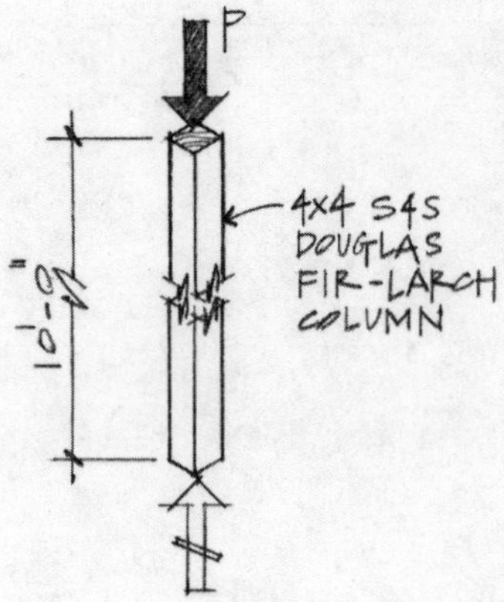

12 Determine the allowable load capacity of the column shown, assuming that the allowable compressive stress ($F_c = 600$ psi) accounts for the buckling potential. Refer to the standard wood tables in Table A1 of the Appendix for information on cross-sectional properties.

Solution:

$$P_{allow} = F_c \times A = 600 \text{ psi} \times \left(3\frac{1}{2}'' \times 3\frac{1}{2}''\right) = 7{,}350\#$$

What is the deformation for P_{allow}?

$$\delta = \frac{PL}{AE} = \frac{7{,}350\# \,(10' \times 12 \text{ in./ft.})}{(12.25 \text{ in.}^2)(1.6 \times 10^6 \#/\text{in.}^2)} = 0.045''$$

13 A 600-foot-long roof cable cannot be permitted to stretch more than three feet when loaded, or the roof geometry will be affected too drastically. If $E_s = 29 \times 10^3$ ksi and the load is 1,500 k, determine the required cable diameter needed to avoid excessive elongation or overstress. $F_t = 100$ ksi (allowable tensile stress).

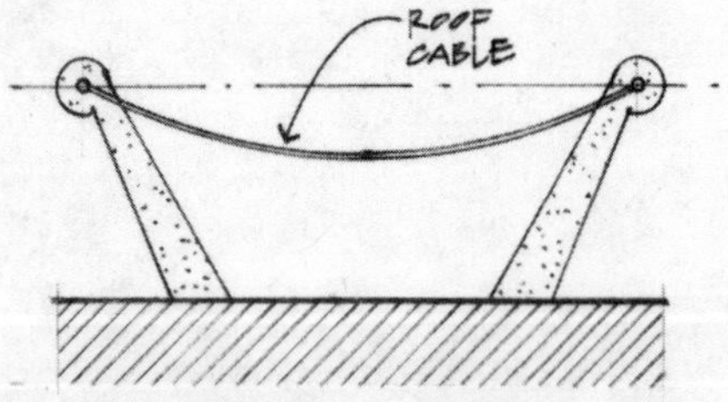

Section cut through a cable roof structure.

Solution:

$$\delta = \frac{PL}{AE};\ A = \frac{PL}{\delta E} = \frac{1{,}500 \text{ k}(600')}{3'(29 \times 10^3 \text{ k/in.}^2)} = 10.34 \text{ in.}^2$$

$$A = \frac{\pi D^2}{4};\ D = \sqrt{\frac{4(10.34 \text{ in.}^2)}{\pi}} = 3.63''$$

(diameter based on the deformation requirement)

$$f = \frac{P}{A};\ A = \frac{P}{f_t} = \frac{1{,}500 \text{ k}}{100 \text{ k/in.}^2} = 15 \text{ in.}^2 \Leftarrow \text{governs}$$

$$D = \sqrt{\frac{4(15 \text{ in.}^2)}{\pi}} = 4.37'' \Leftarrow \text{governs}$$

(diameter based on tensile stress)

14 A heavy chandelier weighing 1,500# is suspended from the roof of a theater lobby. The steel pipe from which it hangs is 20 feet long. Determine the size of pipe necessary to carry the chandelier safely. Use A36 steel. What is the resulting elongation of the pipe?

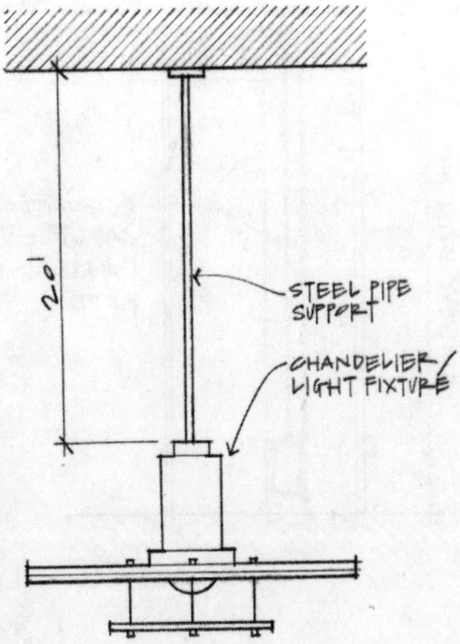

Again, we're looking for a required size; therefore, this is a design problem.

Solution:

$$f_t = \frac{P}{A}$$

$$A_{required} = \frac{P}{f_t}$$

For A36 steel, $F_t = 22{,}000$ psi

$$A_{required} = \frac{1{,}500\#}{22{,}000\ \#/\text{in.}^2} = 0.0682\ \text{in.}^2$$

Refer to the Table A6 in the Appendix.

A $\frac{1}{2}$-inch-diameter standard weight pipe has the following cross-section properties:

Nominal Diameter	Outer Diameter	Inner Thickness	Wall Foot	Weight per Area	Diameter
0.5″	84″	0.622″	0.109″	0.85 #/ft.	0.25 in.²

$$A_{required} = 0.0682\ \text{in.}^2 < 0.25\ \text{in.}^2\ \text{OK}$$

To determine elongation,

$$\delta = \frac{PL}{AE} = \frac{1{,}500\#(20' \times 12\ \text{in./ft.})}{(0.25\ \text{in.}^2)(29{,}000{,}000\ \#/\text{in.}^2)} = 0.05''$$

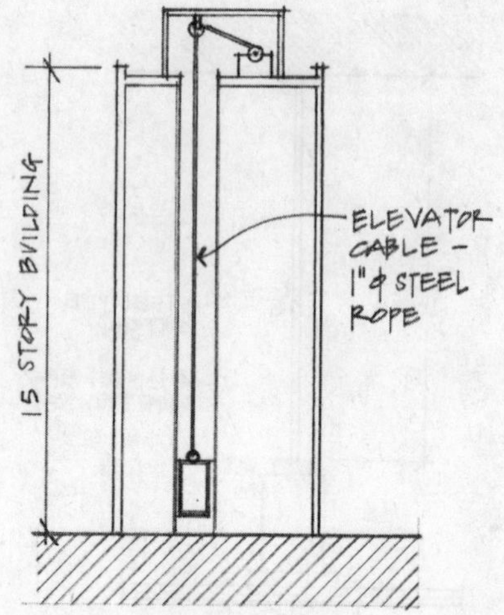

15 A 15-passenger elevator in a 15-story building is raised by using a one-inch-diameter 1″ steel rope. Assuming that the city code requires a factor of safety of 11 against the ultimate strength of the rope, check the adequacy of the rope and its elongation.

Solution

One-inch 1″-diameter rope:

Net resisting area = 0.523 in.^{2}
Ultimate strength = 27 tons = 54 k
Rope wt. = 2.0 #/ft.
Rope length = 14 stories of rope plus 10′ to pulley

Loads on rope:

15 passengers @ 150# ea.	= 2,250#
15-passenger elevator cab	= 1,250#
Rope length = 14 × 10′ per story + 10′ (to pulley) = 150′ × 2.0 #/ft.	= 300#
	P = 3,800#

Ultimate strength = 54,000#

$$\text{safe strength (working)} = \frac{\text{ultimate strength}}{\text{safety factor}} = \frac{54{,}000\#}{11} = 4{,}909\#$$

$$P_{actual} = 3{,}800\# < 4{,}909\# \text{ allowable OK}$$

$$\delta = \frac{PL}{AE} = \frac{(3.8\text{ k})(150' \times 12\text{ in./ft.})}{(0.523\text{ in.}^2)(29{,}000\text{ k/in.}^2)} = 0.45''$$

Problems

11 Two 4″-wide by 12-feet-high brick walls of a garage support a roof slab 20 feet wide. The roof weighs 100 psf and carries a snow load of 30 psf. Check the compressive stress at the base of the wall assuming brick (for this problem) has a capacity of 125 psi. Brick weighs 120 #/ft.^{3}

Hint: Analyze a typical one foot strip of wall.

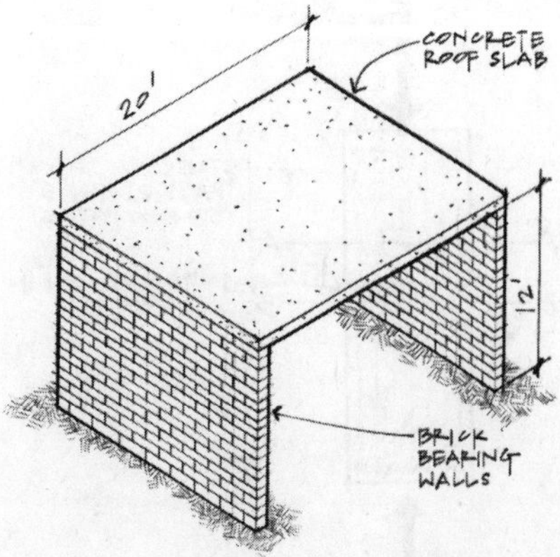

12 A steel wire 300 feet long and $\frac{1}{8}$ inch in diameter weighs 0.042 #/ft. If the wire is suspended vertically from its upper end, calculate (a) the maximum tensile stress due to its own weight and (b) the maximum weight W that can be safely supported assuming a safety factor of three and an ultimate tensile stress of 65 ksi.

13 A structural steel rod $1\frac{1}{2}$ inches in diameter and 25 feet long, in supporting a balcony, carries a tensile load of 29 k; $E = 29 \times 10^3$ ksi.

a. Find the total elongation δ of the rod.
b. What diameter d is necessary if the total δ is limited to 0.1 inch?

14 A 100-foot-long surveyor's steel tape with a cross-sectional area of 0.006 square inch must be stretched with a pull of 16# when in use. If the modulus of elasticity of this steel is $E = 30{,}000$ ksi, (a) what is the total elongation δ in the 100 foot tape and (b) what unit tensile stress is produced by the pull?

15 The ends of the laminated-wood roof arch shown are tied together with a horizontal steel rod 90 feet, "10 inches" long, which must withstand a total load of 60 k. Two turnbuckles are used. All threaded rod ends are upset.

a. Determine the required diameter D of the rod if the maximum allowable stress is 20 ksi.
b. If the unstressed length of the rod is 90 feet, "10 inches" and there are four threads per inch on the upset ends, how many turns of one turnbuckle will bring it back to its unstressed length after it has elongated under full allowable tensile stress? $E = 29 \times 10^3$ ksi.

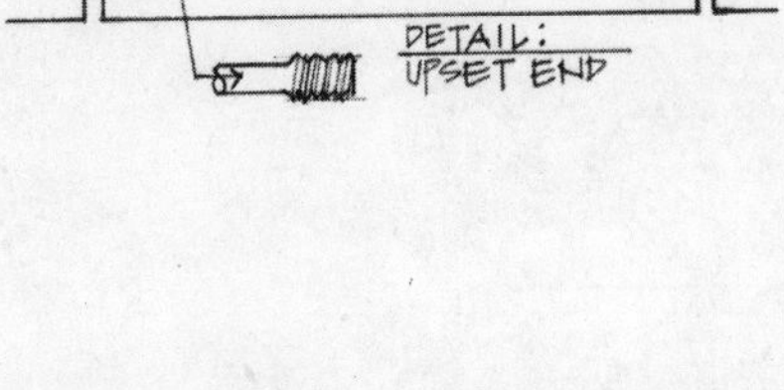

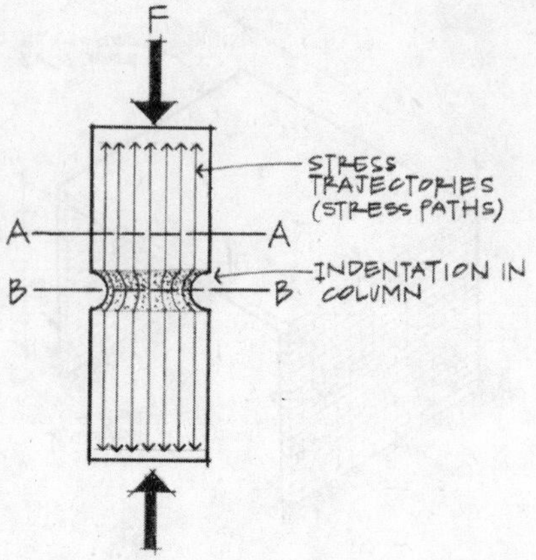

Figure 30 Normal stress.

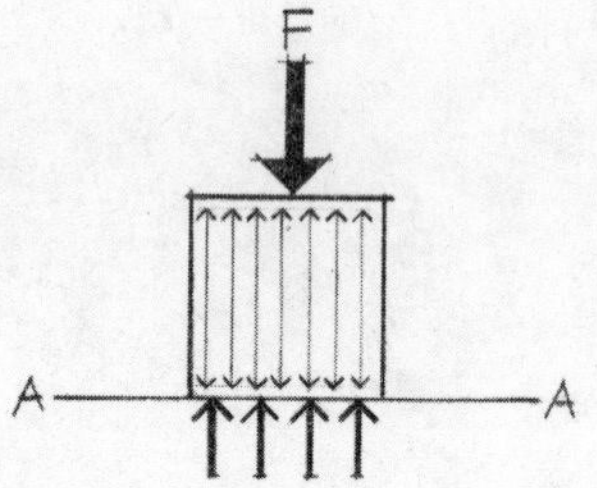

Figure 31 Uniform stress distribution.

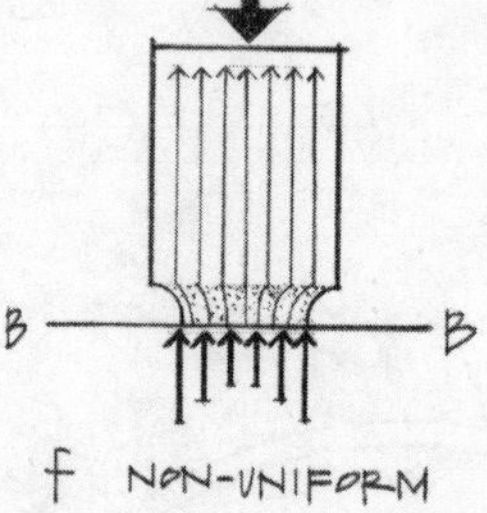

Figure 32 Nonuniform stress distribution.

Stress Concentration

In our initial discussion on normal stress (Figure 30), we made the assumption that if a load is applied centrically (through the axis of the member), the stress developed on the normal plane could be assumed to be uniform (Figure 31). For most cases of normal stress, this is a practical assumption to make for a *static* load condition.

If, however, the geometry of the member is changed to include discontinuities or changing cross-sections, stress can no longer be assumed to be uniform across the surface.

Stress trajectories, also called *isostatic lines,* connect points of equal principal stress and represent stress paths through a member. This concept provides a visual picture of the stress distribution of a member or structure under various loading conditions.

Stress trajectories are normally drawn at equal increments of stress to denote a uniform stress. A crowding of the stress trajectory lines indicates stress concentration, or high stress, just as contour lines on a topographic map indicate steep grades (Figures 32 and 33).

A French mathematician named Barre de Saint-Venant (1797–1886) observed that localized distortions occurred in areas of discontinuity and that stress concentrations developed, causing an uneven distribution of stress across the stressed surface. However, these localized effects disappeared at some distance from such locations. This is known as *Saint-Venant's principle.*

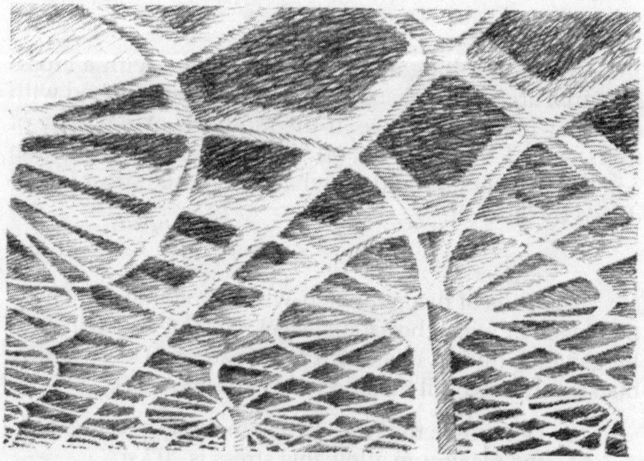

Figure 33 Column under compressive load.

Load concentrations, reentrant corners, notches, openings, and other discontinuities will cause stress concentrations. These, however, do not necessarily produce structural failures, even if the maximum stress exceeds the allowable working stress. For example, in structural steel, extreme stress conditions may be relieved, because steel has a tendency to yield (give), thus causing a redistribution of some of the stress across more of the cross-section. This redistribution of stress enables the greater part of the structural member to be within the permissible stress range.

A stress concentration in concrete is a serious matter. Excessive tensile stresses, even though localized, cause cracks to appear in the concrete. Over a period of time, the cracks become more pronounced because of the high-stress concentration at the end of the cracks. Cracking in reinforced concrete can be minimized by placing the reinforcing steel across potential crack lines. Timber behaves in much the same way, as cracks appear along the grain (Figure 34).

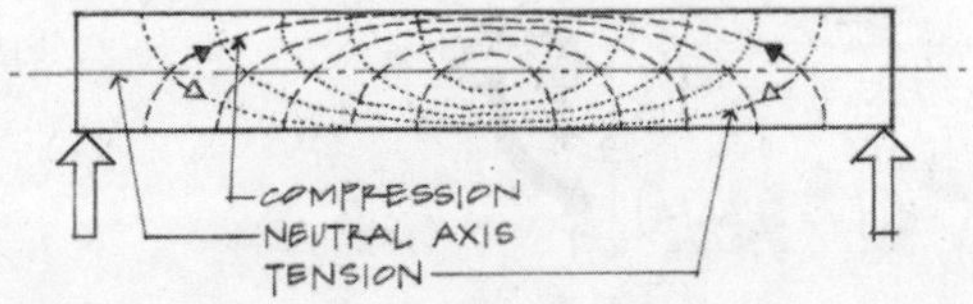

Figure 34 *Stress trajectories in a beam (flexure).*

In the past, photoelasticity (the shining of a polarized light on a transparent material) was often used to produce stress patterns for various structural members under loading. Today, computer modeling and analysis software are capable of generating colorful stress contour mapping, visually representing the stress intensity for both individual members and the structure as a whole.

Often, structural elements will have discontinuities (holes in a beam for mechanical ducts, window openings in walls) that interrupt the stress paths (called *stress trajectories*). The stress at the discontinuity may be considerably greater than the average stress due to centric loading; thus, there exists a stress concentration at the discontinuity (Figure 35).

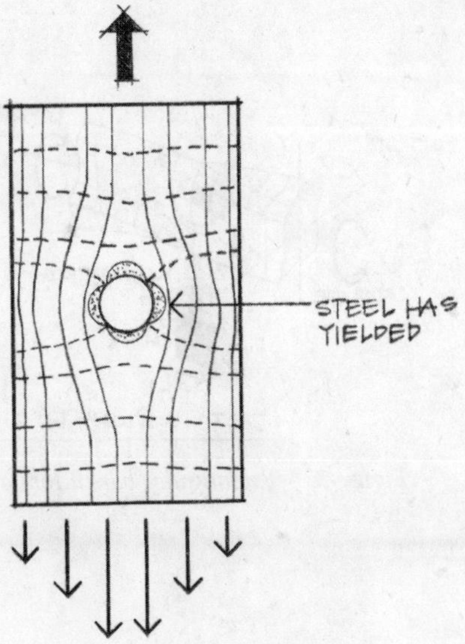

Figure 35 *Stress trajectories around a hole.*

Stress concentrations are usually not significantly critical in the case of static loading of ductile material, because the material will yield inelastically in the high-stress areas and redistribution of stress results. Equilibrium is established, and no harm is done. However, in cases of dynamic or impact loading, or of static loading of brittle material, stress concentrations become very critical and cannot be ignored. Stress redistribution does not result to such an extent that equilibrium is maintained.

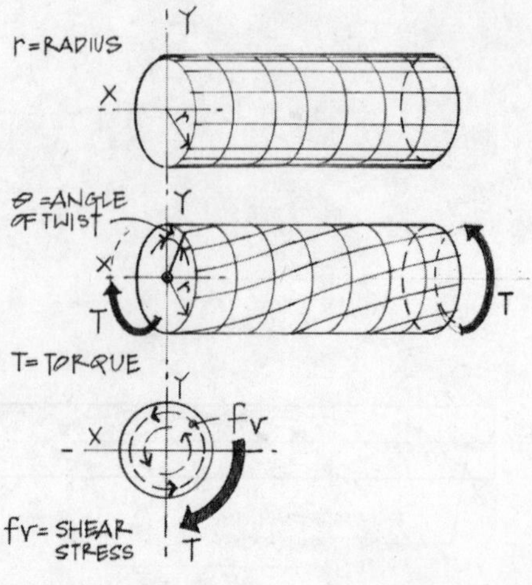

Figure 36 Circular cross section in torsion.

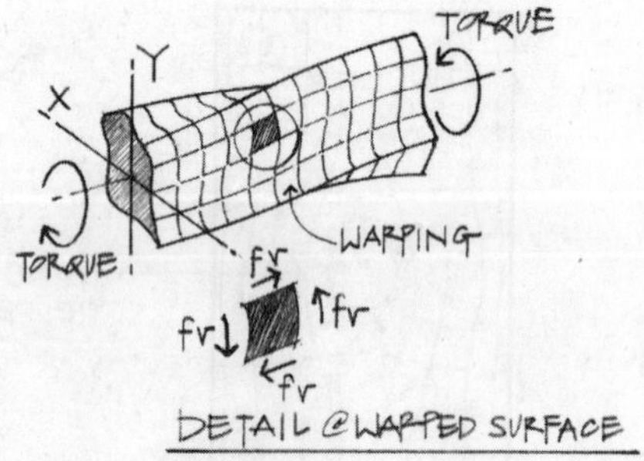

Figure 37 Rectangular bar in torsion.

Torsional Stress

Charles-Augustin de Coulomb, a French engineer of the 18th century, was the first to explain torsion in a solid or hollow circular shaft. He experimentally developed a relationship between the applied *torque* (T) and the resulting deformation (angle of twist) of circular rods.

From the distortion of the rod shown in Figure 36, it is clear that shearing stresses f_v must exist. In an elastic material, such as steel, the stresses increase in magnitude proportionately to the distance from the center of the circular cross-section and flow circularly around the area. Coulomb derived by means of equilibrium concepts the relationship

$$\boxed{T = \frac{\pi r^3 f_v}{2}}$$

where

$T =$ externally applied torsional moment (torque)

$\pi r^2 =$ cross-sectional area of the rod (shaft)

$r =$ radius of the rod

$f_v =$ internal shear stress on the transverse plane off the rod

Hollow, circular cross-sections (pipes) offer the greatest torque resistance per unit volume of material, because material located near the center is at a low stress level and, thus, is less effective.

Noncircular cross-sectioned members, such as rectangular or I-shaped beams, develop a completely different distribution of shear stress when subjected to torsion.

A full century after Coulomb, Barre de Saint-Venant developed the theory to explain the difference between circular torsion and noncircular torsion. Circumferential lines of a circular rod remain in their original cross-sectional plane under torsional forces (see Figure 36), whereas the corresponding lines of a rectangular bar warp out of their original plane (Figure 37). This warping significantly alters the simple linear stress distribution assumed by Coulomb.

4 THERMAL EFFECTS

Most structural materials increase in volume when subjected to heat and contract when cooled. Whenever a design prevents the change in length of a member subjected to temperature variation, internal stresses develop. Sometimes these thermal stresses may be sufficiently high to exceed the elastic limit and cause serious damage. Free, unrestrained members experience no stress changes with temperature changes, but dimensional change results. For example, it is common practice to provide expansion joints between sidewalk pavements to allow movement during hot summer days. Prevention of expansion on a hot day would undoubtedly result in severe buckling of the pavement.

The dimensional change due to temperature changes is usually described in terms of the change in a linear dimension. The change in length of a structural member ΔL is directly proportional to both the temperature change ΔT and the original length of the member L_o. Thermal sensitivity, called the *coefficient of linear expansion* (α), has been determined for all engineering materials (Table 3). Careful measurements have shown that the ratio of strain ε to temperature change ΔT is a constant:

$$\alpha = \frac{\text{strain}}{\text{temperature change}} = \frac{\varepsilon}{\Delta T} = \frac{\delta/L}{\Delta T}$$

Solving this equation for the deformation,

$$\boxed{\delta = \alpha L \Delta T}$$

where

α = coefficient of thermal expansion
L = original length of member (in.)
ΔT = change in temperature (°F)
δ = total change in length (in.)

Table 3 Linear coefficients of thermal expansion (contraction).

Material	Coefficients (α) [in./in./°F]
Wood	3.0×10^{-6}
Glass	4.4×10^{-6}
Concrete	6.0×10^{-6}
Cast iron	6.1×10^{-6}
Steel	6.5×10^{-6}
Wrought iron	6.7×10^{-6}
Copper	9.3×10^{-6}
Bronze	10.0×10^{-6}
Brass	10.4×10^{-6}
Aluminum	12.8×10^{-6}

Of perhaps even greater importance in engineering design are the stresses developed by restraining the free expansion and contraction of members subjected to temperature variations. To calculate these temperature stresses, it is useful to determine first the free expansion or contraction of the member involved and then the force and unit stress developed in forcing the member to attain its original length. The problem from this point on is exactly the same as those solved in the earlier portions of this chapter dealing with axial stresses, strains, and deformations. The amount of stress developed by restoring a bar to its original length L is

$$f = \varepsilon E = \frac{\delta}{L}E = \frac{\alpha L \Delta T E}{L} = \alpha \Delta T E$$

$$\therefore \boxed{f = \alpha \Delta T E}$$

Example Problems: Thermal Effects

16 A surveyor's steel tape measures exactly 100 feet between the end markings when the temperature is 70°F. What is the total error that results when measuring a traverse (route of a survey) of 5,000 feet when the temperature of the tape is 30°F?

Solution:

$$\delta = \alpha L \Delta T$$

$$\alpha_s = 6.5 \times 10^{-6}$$

$$\Delta T = 70°\text{F} - 30°\text{F} = 40°\text{F}$$

$$\delta = (6.5 \times 10^{-6}\ \text{in./in./°F})(100' \times 12\ \text{in./ft.})(40°\text{F}) = 0.312\ \text{in. (per } 100'\text{)}$$

Total length of the traverse = 5,000′

$$\frac{5{,}000'}{100'/\text{measurement}} = 50 \text{ tape lengths}$$

$$\therefore \delta_{\text{total}} = 50 \times 0.312'' = 15.6'' = 1.3'$$

17 A W18 × 35 wide-flange beam (see Table A3 in the Appendix) is used as a support beam for a bridge. If a temperature change (rise) of 40°F occurs, determine the deformation that results.

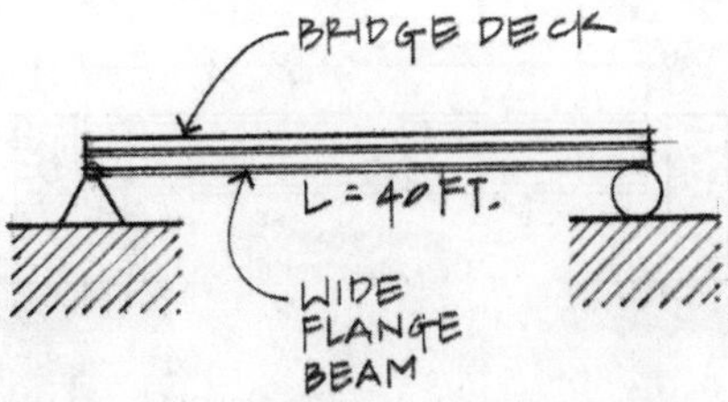

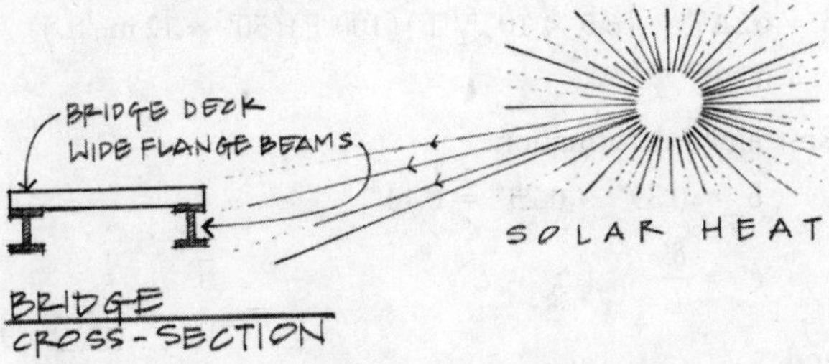

Solution:

$$\delta = \alpha L \Delta T = (6.5 \times 10^{-6}\,\text{in./in./°F})(40' \times 12\,\text{in./ft.})(40°)$$

$$= 1.25 \times 10^{-1}\,\text{in.} = 0.125''$$

What would happen if both ends of the beam were solidly imbedded in concrete foundations on both sides? Assume it is initially unstressed axially.

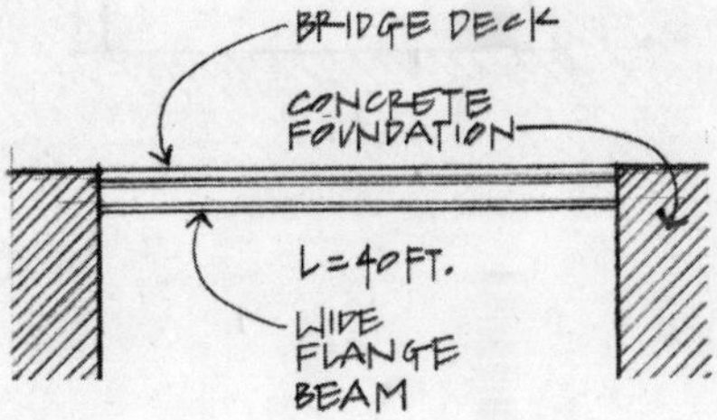

Solution:

Because the support restricts any deformation from occurring, stresses will be induced.

$$\Delta f = \varepsilon E = \frac{\alpha L \Delta TE}{L} = \alpha \Delta TE$$

$$f = (6.5 \times 10^{-6}\,\text{in./in./°F})(40°\text{F})(29 \times 10^{6}\,\text{k/in.}^3) = 7{,}540\,\#/\text{in.}^2$$

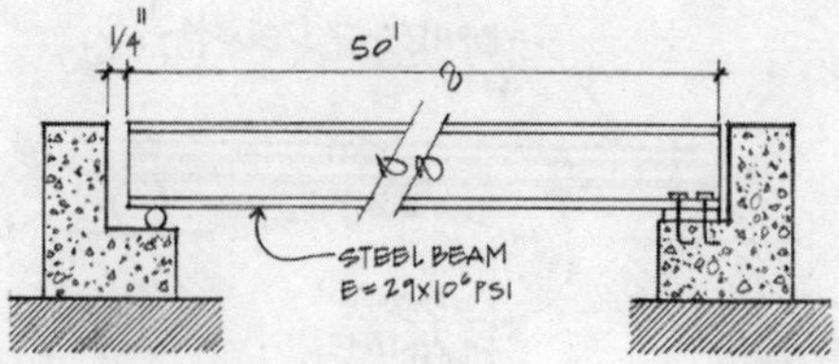

18 Compute the thermal stress induced due to a temperature change of 100°F, assuming that the beam is able to expand freely for $\frac{1}{4}$ inch.

Solution

$$\delta = \alpha L \Delta T = (6.5 \times 10^{-6}/°\text{F})(100°\text{F})(50' \times 12\,\text{in./ft.})$$
$$= 0.39''$$

Restrained deformation:

$$\delta' = 0.39'' - 0.25'' = 0.14''$$
$$\varepsilon' = \frac{\delta'}{L}$$

and

$$f = \varepsilon' E$$

$$\therefore \Delta f = \varepsilon' E = \frac{\delta'}{L}(E) = \frac{0.14''}{600''}(29 \times 10^6\,\text{psi}) = 6{,}767\,\text{psi}$$

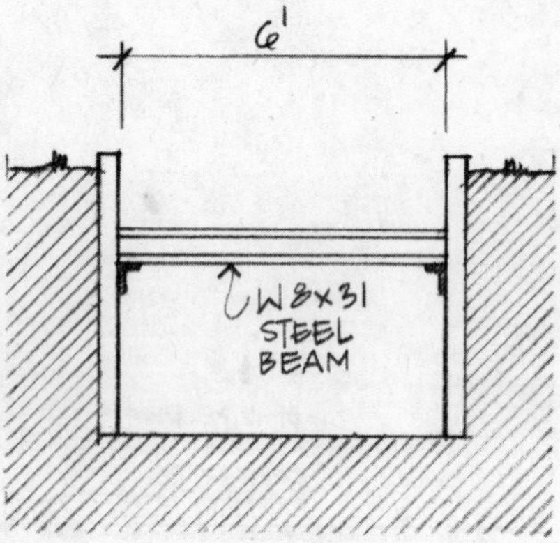

19 A steel wide-flange beam (W8 × 31) is used to brace two shoring walls as shown. If the walls move 0.01 inch outward when the beam is subjected to a 100°F temperature change, determine the stress in the beam.

Solution

The total elongation of the beam if it is unrestrained is

$$\delta = \alpha L \Delta T = (6.5 \times 10^{-6}/°\text{F})(72'')(100°\text{F}) = 0.0468''$$

Because the walls move 0.01 inch, the beam must be compressed by a force causing a deformation of

$$\delta' = 0.0468'' - 0.01'' = 0.0368''$$

Therefore,

$$f = \varepsilon E = \frac{\delta'(E)}{L} = \frac{0.0368''(29 \times 10^6\,\text{psi})}{72''} = 14{,}822\,\text{psi}$$

Problems

16 A long concrete bearing wall has vertical expansion joints placed every 40 feet. Determine the required width of the gap in a joint if it is wide open at 20°F and just barely closed at 80°F. Assume $\alpha = 6 \times 10^{-6}$/°F.

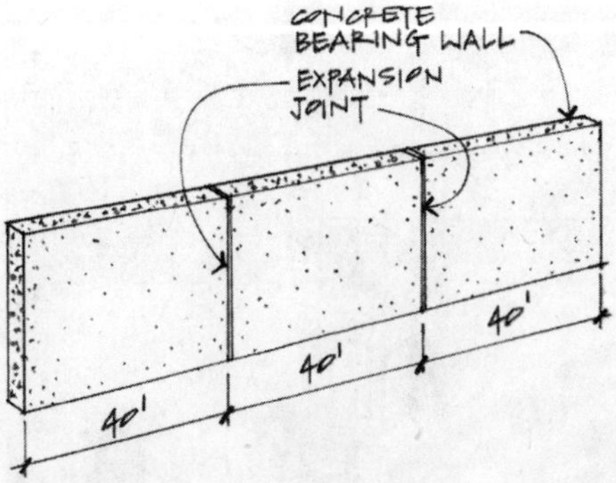

17 An aluminum curtain wall panel 12 feet high is attached to large concrete columns (top and bottom) when the temperature is 65°F. No provision is made for differential thermal movement vertically. Because of insulation between them, the sun heats up the wall panel to 120°F but the column to only 80°F. Determine the consequent compressive stress in the curtain wall.

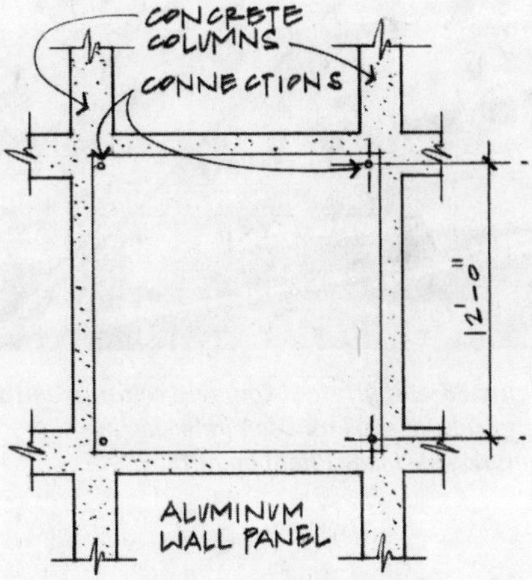

18 The steel rails of a continuous, straight railroad track are each 60 feet long and are laid with spaces between their ends of 0.25 inch at 70°F.

a. At what temperature will the rails touch end to end?
b. What compressive stress will be produced in the rails if the temperature rises to 150°F?

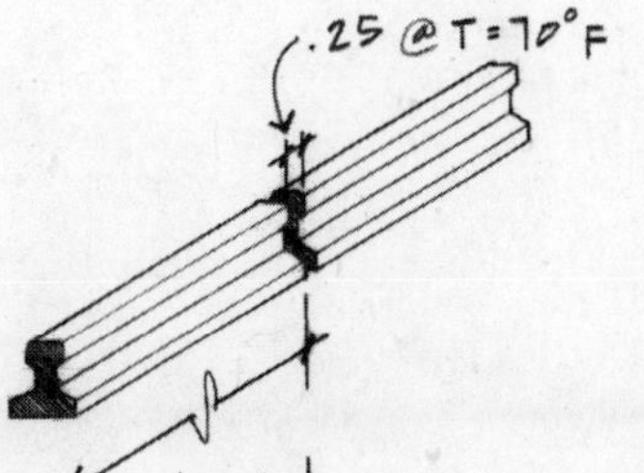

Figure 38 Reinforced concrete columns with longitudinal steel and concrete sharing the compressive load. Photo by author.

5 STATICALLY INDETERMINATE MEMBERS (AXIALLY LOADED)

In the work thus far, it has always been possible to find the internal forces in any member of a structure by means of the equations of equilibrium; that is, the structures were statically determinate. If, in any structure, the number of unknown forces and distances exceeds the number of independent equations of equilibrium that are applicable, the structure is said to be statically indeterminate. A reinforced concrete column, as shown in Figure 38, is an example of a statically indeterminate system in which it is necessary to write an additional equation(s) involving the geometry of the deformations in the members of the structure to supplement the equations of equilibrium. The following outline is a procedure that might be helpful in the analysis of some problems involving axially loaded, statically indeterminate members.

1. Draw an FDB.
2. Note the number of unknowns involved (magnitudes and positions).
3. Recognize the type of force system on the FBD, and note the number of independent equations of equilibrium available for this system.
4. If the number of unknowns exceeds the number of equilibrium equations, a deformation equation must be written for each extra unknown.
5. When the number of independent equilibrium equations and deformation equations equals the number of unknowns, the equations can be solved simultaneously. Deformations and forces must be related to solve the equations simultaneously.

It is recommended that a displacement diagram be drawn showing deformations to assist in obtaining the correct deformation equation.

Example Problems: Statically Indeterminate Members (Axially Loaded)

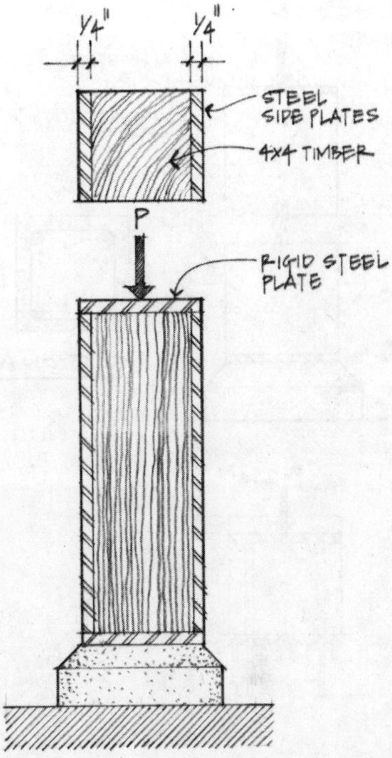

20 A short, built-up column made up of a rough-cut 4″ × 4″ timber member, reinforced with steel side plates, must support an axial load of 20 k. Determine the stress that develops in the timber and in the steel plates if

$$E_{\text{timber}} = 1.76 \times 10^3 \text{ ksi};\ E_{\text{steel}} = 29 \times 10^3 \text{ ksi}$$

The rigid plates at the top and bottom allow the timber and steel side plates to deform uniformly under the action of *P*.

Solution:

From the condition of equilibrium:

$f_t =$ Stress developed in the timber

$f_s =$ Stress developed in the steel

$$\left[\Sigma F_y = 0\right] - 20\text{ k} + f_s A_s + f_t A_t = 0$$

where

$$A_s = 2 \times \tfrac{1}{4}'' \times 4'' = 2 \text{ in.}^2$$

$$A_t = 4'' \times 4'' = 16 \text{ in.}^2$$

$$2 \text{ in.}^2 (f_s) + 16 \text{ in.}^2 (f_t) = 20\text{ k}$$

Obviously, the equation of equilibrium alone is insufficient to solve for the two unknowns. Therefore, another equation, involving a deformation relationship, must be written.

$$\delta = \delta_t = \delta_s$$

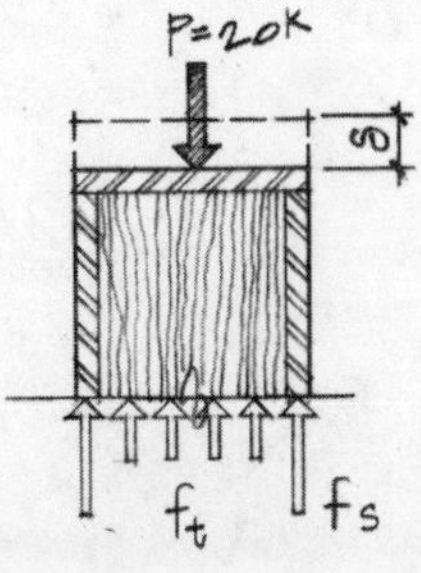

Because both the timber and the steel members are of equal length, $L_t = L_s$; then,

$$\varepsilon = \frac{\delta_t}{L_t} = \frac{\delta_s}{L_s};\quad \varepsilon_t = \varepsilon_s$$

$$\text{but } E = \frac{f}{\varepsilon} \text{ or } \varepsilon = \frac{f}{E}$$

$$\therefore \frac{f_t}{E_t} = \frac{f_s}{E_s};\quad f_t = f_s \frac{E_t}{E_s}$$

$$f_t = \frac{1.76 \times 10^3 \text{ ksi}}{29 \times 10^3 \text{ ksi}}(f_s) = 0.061(f_s)$$

Substituting into the equilibrium equation,

$$2 \text{ in.}^2 (f_s) + 16 \text{ in.}^2 (0.061 f_s) = 20\text{ k}$$

$$2f_s + 0.976 f_s = 20 \text{ ksi};\ 2.976 f_s = 20 \text{ ksi}$$

$$f_s = 6.72 \text{ ksi}$$

$$f_t = 0.061(6.72 \text{ ksi}) = 0.41 \text{ ksi}$$

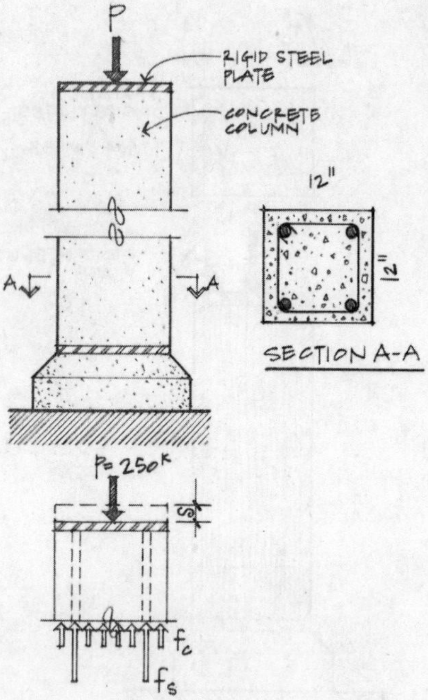

21 A short concrete column measuring 12 square inches is reinforced with four #8 bars ($A_s = 4 \times 0.79\ \text{in.}^2 = 3.14\ \text{in.}^2$) and supports an axial load of 250 k. Steel bearing plates are used top and bottom to ensure equal deformations of steel and concrete. Calculate the stress developed in each material if

$$E_c = 3 \times 10^6\ \text{psi and}$$
$$E_s = 29 \times 10^6\ \text{psi}$$

Solution

From equilibrium,

$$[\Sigma F_y = 0] - 250\ \text{k} + f_s A_s + f_c A_c = 0$$
$$A_s = 3.14\ \text{in.}^2$$
$$A_c = (12'' \times 12'') - 3.14\ \text{in.}^2 \cong 141\ \text{in.}^2$$
$$3.14 f_s + 141 f_c = 250\ \text{k}$$

From the deformation relationship,

$$\delta_s = \delta_c; \quad L_s = L_c$$
$$\therefore \frac{\delta_s}{L} = \frac{\delta_c}{L}$$

and

$$\varepsilon_s = \varepsilon_c$$

Because

$$E = \frac{f}{\varepsilon}$$

and

$$\frac{f_s}{E_s} = \frac{f_c}{E_c}$$

$$f_s = f_c \frac{E_s}{E_c} = \frac{29 \times 10^3 (f_c)}{3 \times 10^3} = 9.67 f_c$$

Substituting into the equilibrium equation,

$$3.14(9.76 f_c) + 141 f_c = 250$$
$$30.4 f_c + 141 f_c = 250$$
$$171.4 f_c = 250$$
$$f_c = 1.46\ \text{ksi}$$
$$\therefore f_s = 9.67(1.46)\ \text{ksi}$$
$$f_s = 14.1\ \text{ksi}$$

Problems

19 The column shown consists of a number of steel reinforcing rods imbedded in a concrete cylinder. Determine the cross-sectional area of the concrete and the steel and the stresses in each if the column deforms 0.01 inch while carrying a 100 k load.

$E_{steel} = 29 \times 10^6$ psi

$E_{concrete} = 3 \times 10^6$ psi

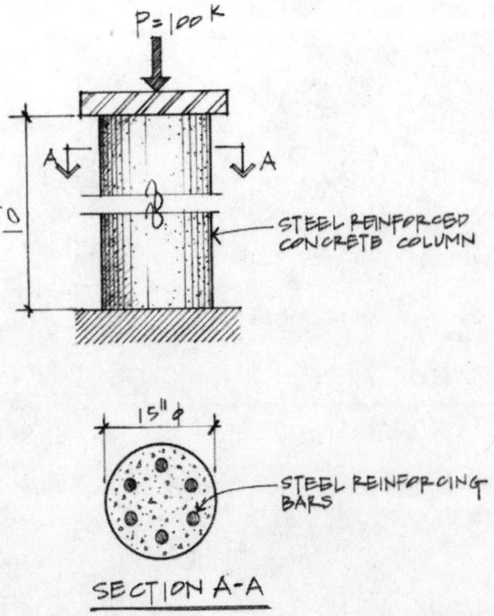

20 A short, hollow steel tube ($L = 30''$) is filled with concrete. The outside dimension of the tube is 12.75 inches, and the wall thickness is 0.375 inch. The assembly is compressed by an axial force $P = 180$ k applied to infinitely rigid cover plates. Determine the stress developed in each material and the shortening in the column.

$E_{concrete} = 3 \times 10^3$ ksi

$E_{steel} = 29 \times 10^3$ ksi

21 Two steel plates $\frac{1}{4}$ inch thick by eight inches wide are placed on either side of a block of oak four inches thick by eight inches wide. If $P = 50{,}000\#$ is applied in the center of the rigid top plate, determine the following:

a. Stress developed in the steel and oak.
b. Deformation resulting from the applied load P.

$E_{steel} = 30 \times 10^6$ psi; $E_{oak} = 2 \times 10^6$ psi

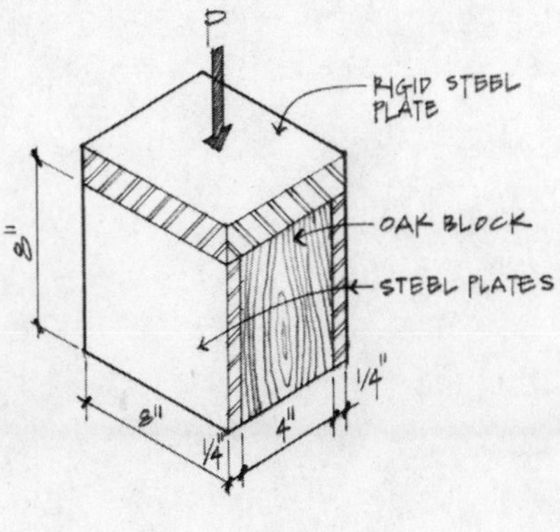

22 A surveyor's tape of hard steel having a cross-sectional area of 0.004 square inch is exactly 100 feet long when a pull of 15# is exerted on it at 80°F.

a. Using the same pull on it, how long will the tape be at 40°F?
b. What pull P is required to maintain its length of 100 feet at 40°F?

$E_s = 29 \times 10^3$ ksi

Summary

- Stress is the intensity of a force—the quantity of force that acts on a unit area. Mathematically, stress is written as

$$f = \frac{P}{A} = \frac{\text{axial force}}{\text{resisting force}}$$

- Two basic stresses are normal (tensile or compressive) and shearing stress.
- Tensile stresses tend to elongate a member, whereas compressive stresses shorten the element. Both are forms of normal stress where the resisting area (the member's cross-sectional area) is perpendicular to the load direction.

$$f_{\text{compression}} = f_c = \frac{P}{A} \quad f_{\text{tension}} = f_t = \frac{P}{A}$$

- Shear stresses develop over an area that is parallel to the direction of the applied forces. The shear stress equation is identical with that for normal stress except for the resisting area used.

$$f_{\text{shear}} = f_c = \frac{P}{A}$$

- Strain is a measure of deformation per unit length. Axial strain (due to tension, compression, or thermal change) is defined by the equation:

$$\varepsilon = \frac{\delta}{L} = \frac{\text{deformation}}{\text{member length}}$$

- Elasticity is a material property in which deformations disappear with the removal of the load. All structural materials are elastic to some extent. If loads remain below the elastic limit of the material, no permanent deformation results from the application and removal of the load.
- When loads exceed the elastic limit in a material like steel, a permanent deformation results, and the behavior is called plastic or inelastic.
- Structural steels exhibit a number of key points when seen in a graph depicting stress versus strain.
    - **Elastic limit.** The maximum stress that can be developed without causing permanent deformation.
    - **Yield point.** The stress at which a significant strain occurs without a concurrent increase in stress. This stress value is used in determining the allowable stress (safe, working levels) used in the design of structural steel members.
    - **Ultimate stress.** The highest level of stress attained before failure.
    - **Rupture.** The stress level at the time of physical failure.

- The measure of elasticity of a material is referred to as the modulus of elasticity, or Young's modulus.

$$E = \frac{f}{\varepsilon} = \frac{\text{stress}}{\text{strain}} \text{ (in the elastic range)}$$

This ratio (E) represents the slope of the elastic portion of the stress-strain diagram. High E values are generally desirable, because the material is more resistant to deformation. The modulus of elasticity is a measure of material stiffness.

- Stress concentrations occur when a member's geometry is changed to include discontinuities or changing cross-sections.

- Unrestrained structural members will experience dimensional changes due to temperature change.

$$\delta = \alpha L \Delta T = \text{(coefficient of thermal expansion)} \times \text{(length)} \times \text{(change in temperature)}$$

- If a structural member is fully restrained and no deformation can occur due to thermal change, internal stresses will result. Internal stress is computed as

$$f = \alpha \Delta T E = \text{(coefficient of thermal expansion)} \times \text{(change in temperature)} \times \text{(modulus of elasticity)}$$

Answers to Selected Problems

1 $f_t = 1{,}060.7$ psi

2 $T_{AB} = 10$ k; $A_{req'd.} = 0.46$ in.^{2};
for a $\frac{13}{16}''$ dia. rod; $A = 0.5185$ in.^{2}

4 $h = 180'$

5 (a) $f_c = 312.5$ psi; (b) $f_t = 13{,}245$ psi;
(c) $f_{brg} = 259.7$ psi; (d) $f = 156.3$ psi;
(e) $L = 16.7$ in.

7 $\varepsilon = 0.0012$ in./in.

9 $\delta = 0.0264$ in.

11 $f_{bearing} = P/A = 1{,}780$ lb./48 in.^{2} =
37.1 psi < 125 psi $\therefore$ OK

13 (a) $\delta = PL/AE = 0.17''$
(b) $A_{req'd.} = 3$ in.^{2}; $D = 1.95'' \approx 2''$ rod

15 (a) $A_{req'd.} = 3$ in.^{2}; $D = 1.95''$
(b) $\delta = 0.75''$
One turn on the turnbuckle = $\frac{1}{2}''$ Number of turns required = 1.5

17 $f = 6{,}140$ psi

18 (a) $\Delta T = 53.4°F$; $T_{final} = 123.4°F$;
(b) $f = 4{,}994$ psi

19 $f_s = 2.42$ ksi; $f_c = 0.25$ ksi;
$A_s = 25.8$ in.^{2}; $A_c = 150.8$ in.^{2}

20 $f_s = 6.87$ ksi; $f_c = 0.71$ ksi; $\delta = 0.0071''$

21 (a) $f_o = .543$ ksi; $f_s = 8.15$ ksi;
(b) $\delta_s = 0.002''$

Cross-Sectional Properties of Structural Members

Cross-Sectional Properties of Structural Members

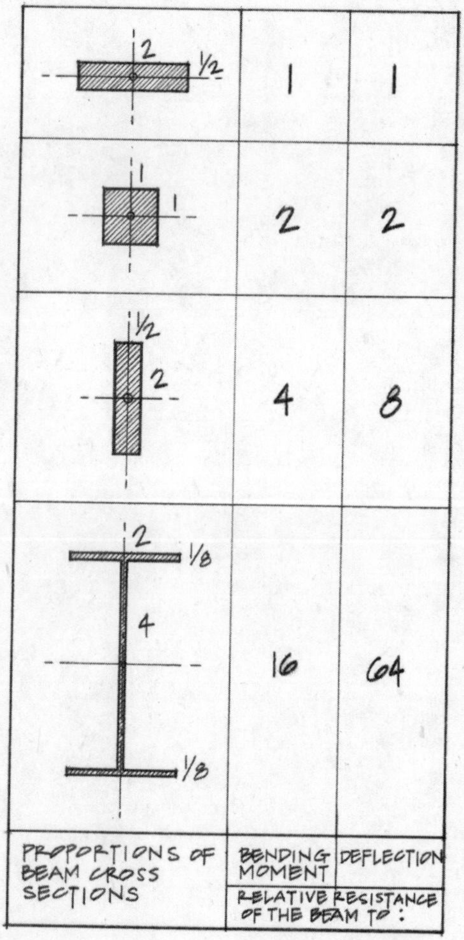

Figure 1 Relative resistance of four beam cross-sections (with the same cross-sectional areas) to bending stress and deflection.

Introduction

Beam design requires the knowledge of material strengths (allowable stresses), critical shear and moment values, and information about their cross-section. The shape and proportion of a beam cross-section is critical in keeping bending and shear stresses within allowable limits and moderating the amount of deflection that will result from the loads. Why does a 2″ × 8″ joist standing on edge deflect less when loaded at midspan than the same 2″ × 8″ used as a plank? Columns with improperly configured cross-sections may be highly susceptible to buckling under relatively moderate loads. Are circular pipe columns, then, better at supporting axial loads than columns with a cruciform cross-section? (Figure 1)

It will be necessary to calculate two cross-sectional properties crucial to the design of beams and columns. The two properties are the *centroid* and the *moment of inertia*.

1 CENTER OF GRAVITY—CENTROIDS

Center of gravity, or *center of mass,* refers to masses or weights and can be thought of as a single point at which the weight could be held and be in balance in all directions. If the weight or object were homogeneous, the center of gravity and the centroid would coincide. In the case of a hammer with a wooden handle, its center of gravity would be close to the heavy steel head, and the *centroid,* which is found by ignoring weight and considering only volume, would be closer to the middle of the handle. Because of varying densities, the center of gravity and the centroid do not coincide.

Centroid usually refers to the centers of lines, areas, and volumes. The centroid of cross-sectional areas (of beams and columns) will be used later as the *reference origin* for computing other section properties.

The method of locating the center of gravity of a mass or an area is based on the method of determining the resultants of parallel force systems. If an area or mass is divided into a large number of small, equal areas, each of which is represented by a vector (weight) acting at its centroid, the resultant vector of the entire area would act through the center of gravity of the total mass area.

The center of gravity of a mass or an area is the theoretical point at which the entire mass or area can be considered to be concentrated.

To develop the equations necessary for calculating the centroidal axes of an area, consider a simple, square plate of uniform thickness (Figure 2).

$\bar{x}$ = centroidal x distance = 2′ from the reference y axis

$\bar{y}$ = centroidal y distance = 2′ from the reference x axis

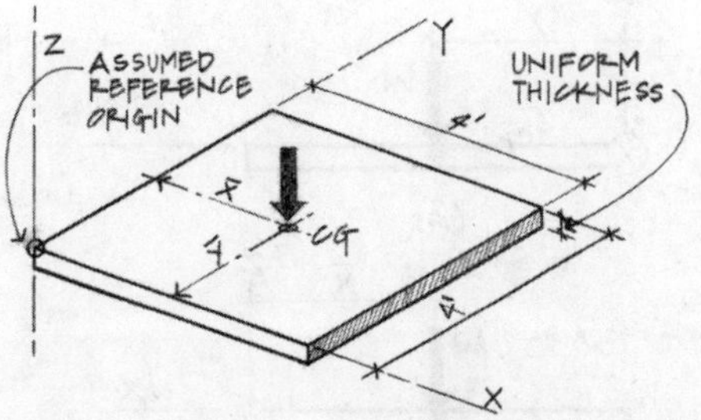

Figure 2 Centroid of the entire plate.

It may be obvious that the centroid is located at $\bar{x}$ = 2′ and $\bar{y}$ = 2′, but a methodology may be necessary to handle odd-shaped or complicated areas.

The first step, using the method described below, is to divide the area into smaller increments called *components* (Figure 3).

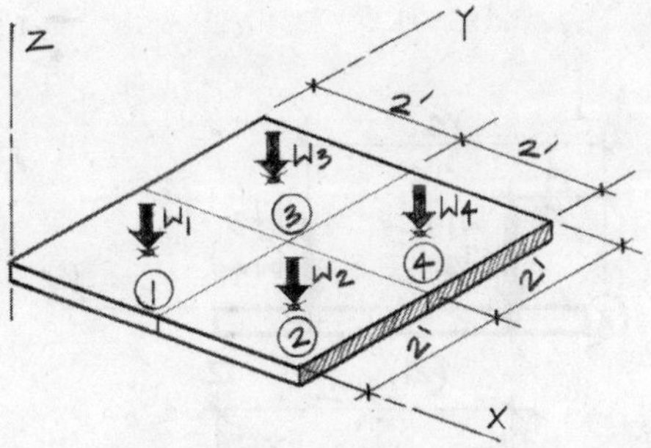

Figure 3 Plate divided into four components.

Each component has its own weight and centroid, with all weights directed perpendicular to the surface area (x-y plane). The magnitude of the resultant is equal to the algebraic sum of the component weights.

$$W = \Sigma \Delta W$$

where

W = total weight of the plate
ΔW = component weight

Centroids are obtained by taking moments about the x and y axes, respectively. The principle involved may be stated as

The moment of an area about an axis equals the algebraic sum of the moments of its component areas about the same axis.

Using the diagrams in Figures 4 and 5, write the moment equations:

$$\Sigma M_y: \bar{x}W = W_1x_2 + W_2x_1 + W_3x_2 + W_4x_1$$

and

$$\Sigma M_x: \bar{y}W = W_1y_1 + W_2y_1 + W_3y_2 + W_4y_2$$

$$\bar{x} = \frac{\Sigma(x\Delta W)}{W}$$

$$\bar{y} = \frac{\Sigma(y\Delta W)}{W}$$

If the plate is divided into an infinite number of elemental pieces, the centroidal expressions may be written in calculus form as

$$\bar{x} = \frac{\int xdW}{W}$$

$$\bar{y} = \frac{\int ydW}{W}$$

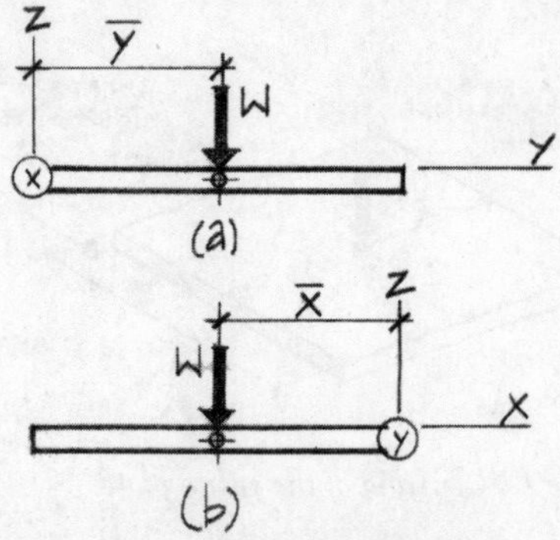

Figure 4 Elevations of the whole plate.

Assuming that the plate is of uniform thickness t,

$W = \gamma t A$

where

W = total weight of the plate

γ = density of the plate material

t = plate thickness

A = surface area of the plate

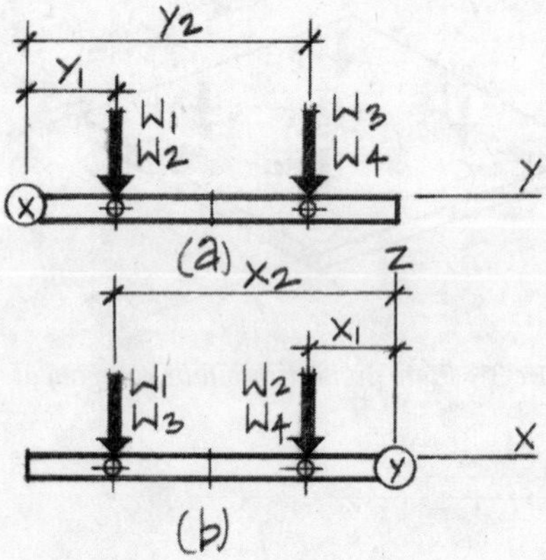

Figure 5 Elevations of the quartered plate.

Correspondingly, for the component parts (areas) of the plate with uniform thickness t,

$\Delta W = \gamma t \Delta A$

where

ΔW = weight of component plate area

ΔA = surface area of component

If we return to the moment equations written above and substitute the values $\gamma t A$ for W and $\gamma t \Delta A$ for ΔW, we find that if the plate is homogeneous and of constant thickness, γt cancels out of the equation(s).

The resulting moment equation would then be written as

$$\Sigma M_y: \bar{x}W = x_2\Delta A_1 + x_1\Delta A_2 + x_2\Delta A_3 + x_1\Delta A_4$$

$$\Sigma M_x: \bar{y}W = y_1\Delta A_1 + y_1\Delta A_2 + y_2\Delta A_3 + y_2\Delta A_4$$

$$\bar{x} = \frac{\Sigma(x\Delta A)}{A}$$

$$\bar{y} = \frac{\Sigma(y\Delta A)}{A}$$

where

$$A = \Sigma\Delta A$$

The moment of an area is defined as the product of the area multiplied by the perpendicular distance from the moment axis to the centroid of the area.

The centroids of some of the more common areas have been derived and are shown in Table 1.

The derivation above shows how the centroid of an area can be located by dividing an area into elemental areas and summing the moments of the elemental areas about an axis. In finding the centroid of a more complex area (i.e., a composite area), a similar methodology is used.

Composite or more complex areas are first divided into simpler geometric shapes (as shown in Table 1) with known centroids. A reference origin is chosen (usually the lower left corner) to establish the reference x and y axes. Then, moments of area are summed about the reference x and y axes, respectively. The centroid locates the *new* reference origin for subsequent computations of other cross-sectional properties (moment of inertia and radius of gyration).

Table 1 Centroids of simple areas.

Shape	Drawing	$\bar{x}$	$\bar{y}$	Area
Rectangle	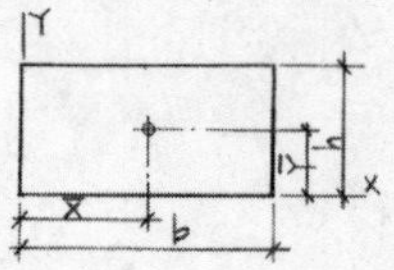	$b/2$	$h/2$	bh
Triangle	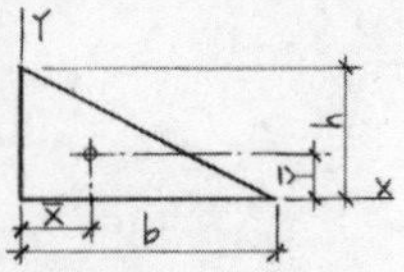	$b/3$	$h/3$	$bh/2$
Semicircle	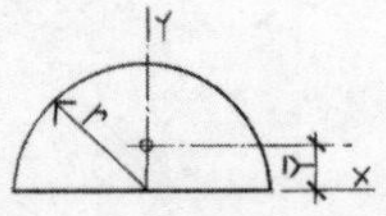	0	$4r/3\pi$	$\pi r^2/2$
Quarter Circle	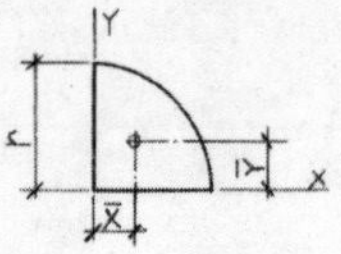	$4r/3\pi$	$4r/3\pi$	$\pi r^2/4$
Parabolic Segment	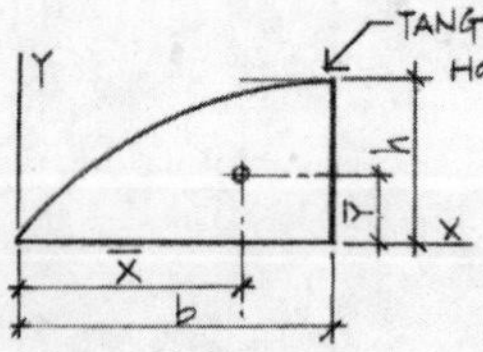	$5b/8$	$2h/5$	$2bh/3$
Complement of a Parabolic Segment	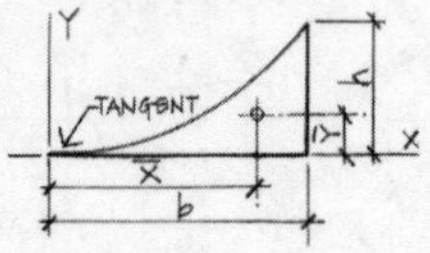	$3b/4$	$3h/10$	$bh/3$

Example Problems: Centroids

1 Determine the centroidal x and y distances for the area shown. Use the lower left corner of the trapezoid as the reference origin.

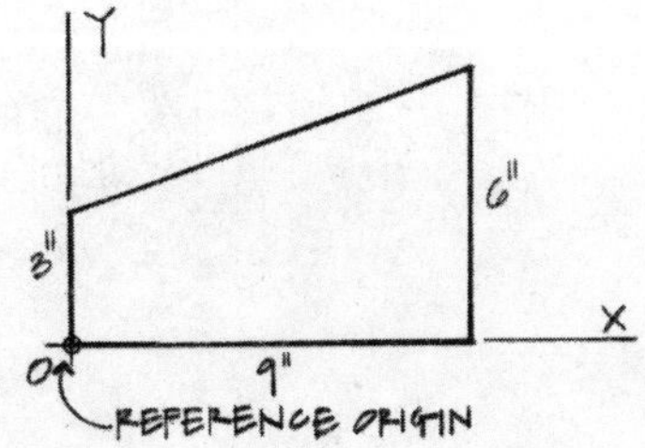

Solution:

Select a convenient reference origin. It is usually advantageous to select a reference origin such that x and y distances are measured in the positive x and y directions to avoid dealing with negative signs.

Divide the trapezoid into simpler geometric shapes: a rectangle and a triangle.

As composite areas become more complex, it may be convenient to use a tabular format for centroidal axis calculations.

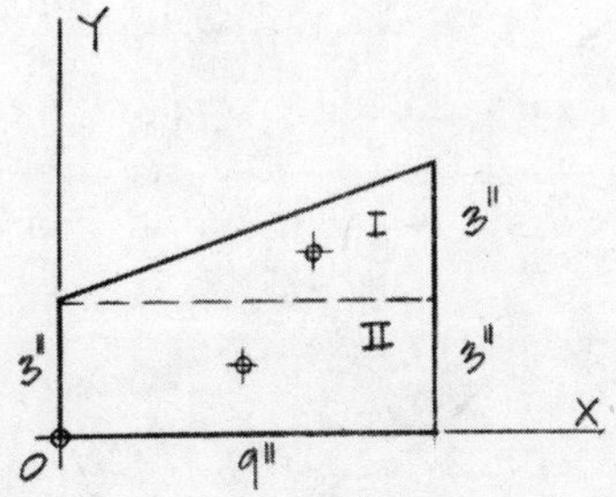

Component	Area (ΔA)	x	$x\Delta A$	y	$y\Delta A$
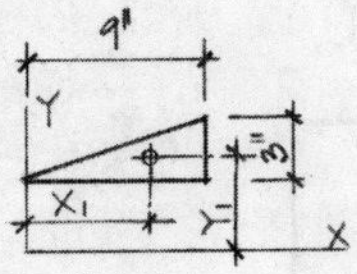	$\frac{9''(3'')}{2} = 13.5\text{ in.}^2$	6″	81 in.^{3}	4″	54 in.^{3}
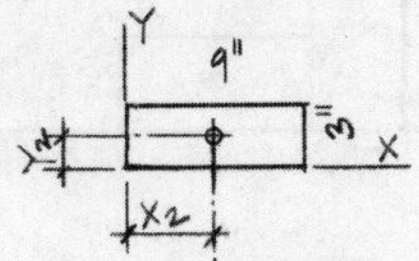	$9''(3'') = 27\text{ in.}^2$	4.5″	121.5 in.^{3}	1.5″	40.5 in.^{3}
	$A = \Sigma\Delta A = 40.5\text{ in.}^2$		$\Sigma x\Delta A =$ 202.5 in.^{3}		$\Sigma y\Delta A =$ 94.5 in.^{3}

The centroidal distances x and y from the reference origin are

$$\bar{x} = \frac{\Sigma x\Delta A}{A} = \frac{202.5\text{ in.}^3}{40.5\text{ in.}^2} = 5''$$

$$\bar{y} = \frac{\Sigma y\Delta A}{A} = \frac{94.5\text{ in.}^3}{40.5\text{ in.}^2} = 2.33''$$

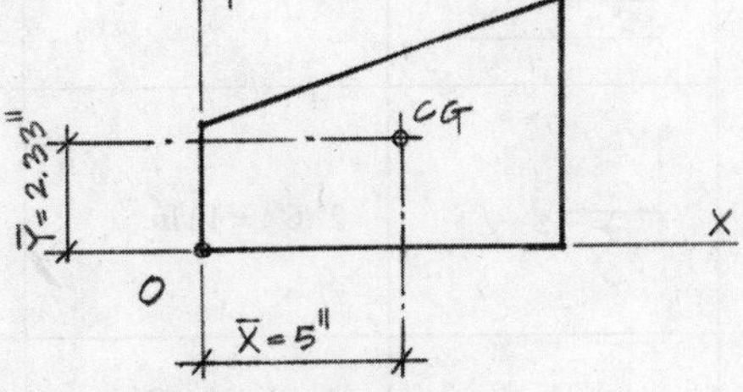

2 Find the centroid of the L-shaped area shown. Use the reference origin shown.

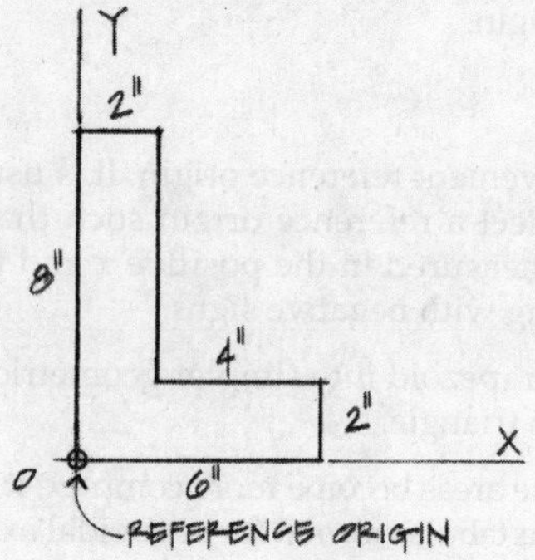

Solution:

Again, the composite area will be sectioned into two simple rectangles. The solution below is based on the diagram in Figure (a).

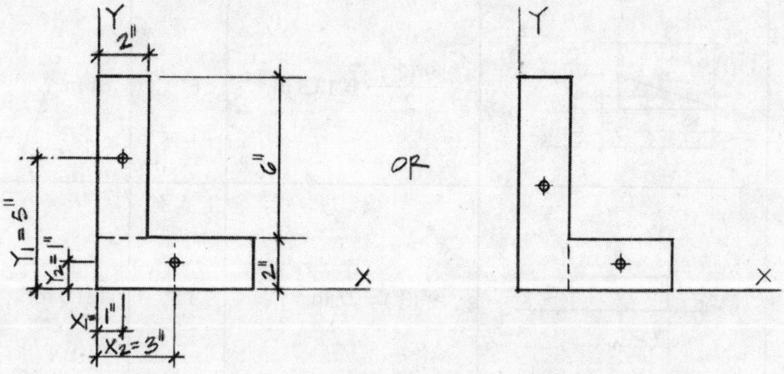

(a) (b)

Component	Area (ΔA)	x	$x\Delta A$	y	$y\Delta A$
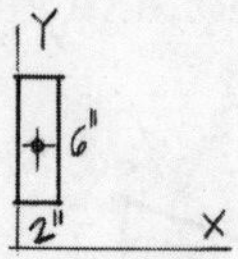	$2''(6'') = 12$ in.^{2}	$1''$	12 in.^{3}	$5''$	60 in.^{3}
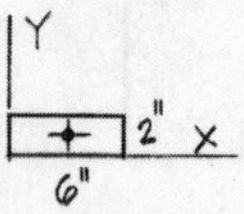	$2''(6'') = 12$ in.^{2}	$3''$	36 in.^{3}	$1''$	12 in.^{3}
	$A = \Sigma\Delta A = 24$ in.^{2}		$\Sigma x\Delta A = 48$ in.^{3}		$\Sigma y\Delta A = 72$ in.^{3}

The centroidal axis from the reference origin is

$$\bar{x} = \frac{\Sigma x\Delta A}{A} = \frac{48 \text{ in.}^3}{24 \text{ in.}^2} = 2''$$

$$\bar{y} = \frac{\Sigma y\Delta A}{A} = \frac{72 \text{ in.}^3}{24 \text{ in.}^2} = 3''$$

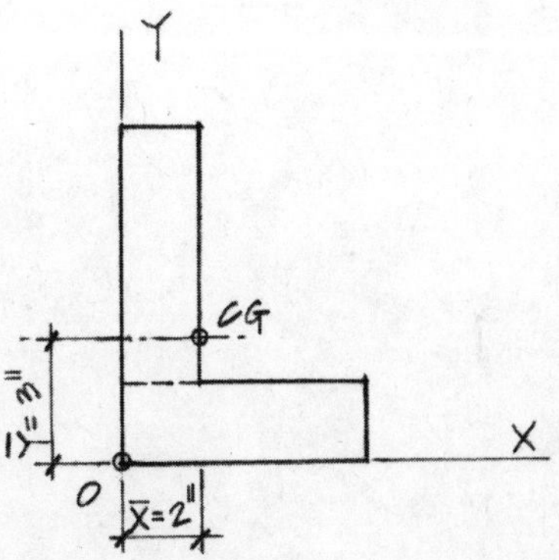

3 Determine the center of gravity (centroid) of the triangle with the cutout shown. This particular problem will utilize the concept of negative areas in the solution.

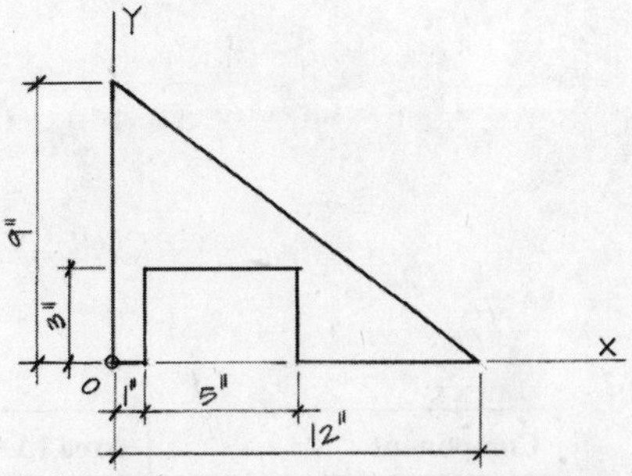

Solution:

The reference origin is again located in the lower left corner for convenience (avoiding the negative distances).

Component	**Area (ΔA)**	x	$x\Delta A$	y	$y\Delta A$
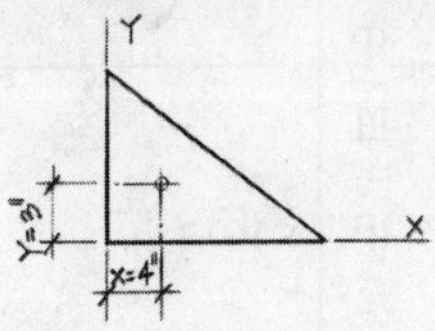	$\frac{12''(9'')}{2} = 54 \text{ in.}^2$	4"	216 in.^{3}	3"	162 in.^{3}
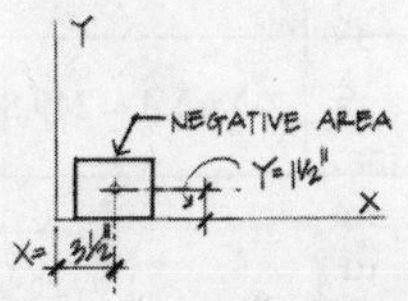	$-3''(5'') = -15 \text{ in.}^3$	3.5"	− 52.5 in.^{3}	1.5"	− 22.5 in.^{3}
	$\Sigma\Delta A = 39 \text{ in.}^2$		$\Sigma x\Delta A = 163.5 \text{ in.}^3$		$\Sigma y\Delta A = 139.5 \text{ in.}^3$

$$\bar{x} = \frac{\Sigma x\Delta A}{A} = \frac{163.5 \text{ in.}^3}{39 \text{ in.}^2} = 4.2''$$

$$\bar{y} = \frac{\Sigma y\Delta A}{A} = \frac{139.5 \text{ in.}^3}{39 \text{ in.}^2} = 3.6''$$

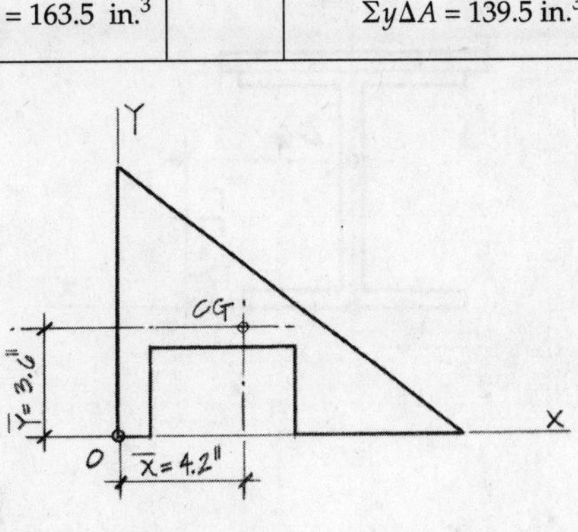

4 Find the centroid of the built-up steel section composed of a W12 × 87 (wide flange) with a $\frac{1}{2}'' \times 14''$ cover plate welded to the top flange. See Table A3 in the Appendix for information about the wide flange.

Solution:

W12 × 87:
$d = 12.53''$
$b_f = 12.13''$
$A = 25.6 \text{ in.}^2$

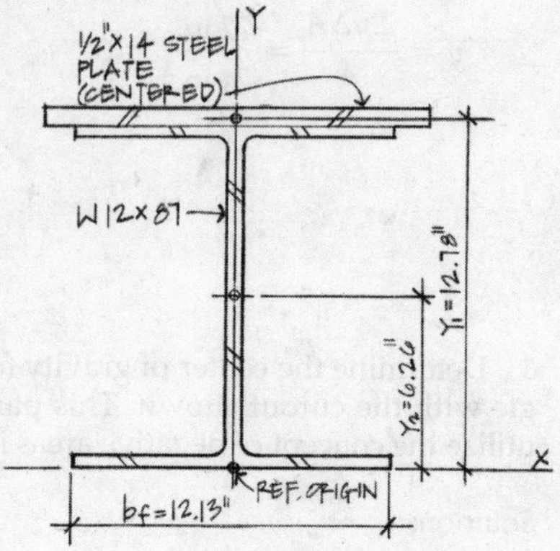

Component	Area (ΔA)	x	$x\Delta A$	y	$y\Delta A$
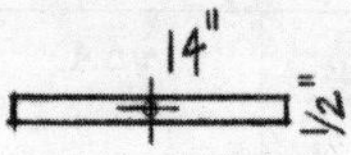	7 in.^{2}	0″	0	12.78″	89.5 in.^{3}
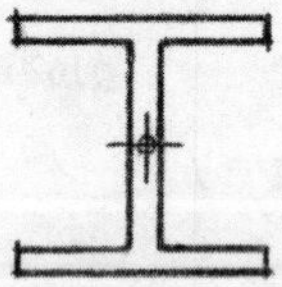	25.6 in.^{2}	0″	0	6.26″	160.3 in.^{3}
	$A = \Sigma\Delta A = 32.6 \text{ in.}^2$		$\Sigma x\Delta A = 0$		$\Sigma y\Delta A = 249.8 \text{ in.}^3$

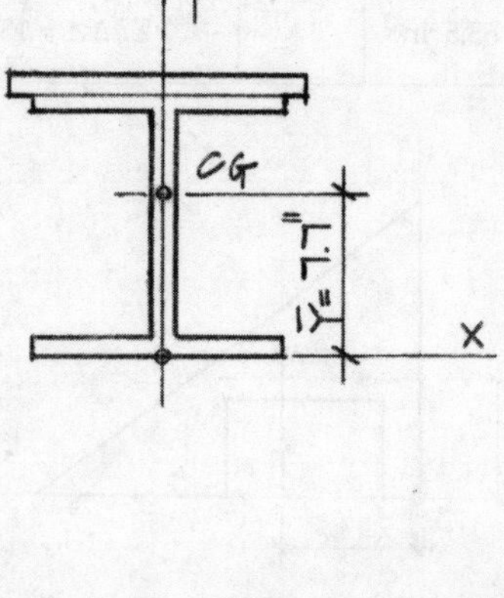

$$\bar{x} = \frac{\Sigma x\Delta A}{A} = \frac{0}{32.6 \text{ in.}^2} = 0$$

$$\bar{y} = \frac{\Sigma y\Delta A}{A} = \frac{249.8 \text{ in.}^3}{32.6 \text{ in.}^2} = 7.7''$$

The centroid, or center of gravity (CG), now becomes the new reference origin for evaluating other cross-sectional properties.

Problems

Find the centroid of the following cross-sections and planes.

1

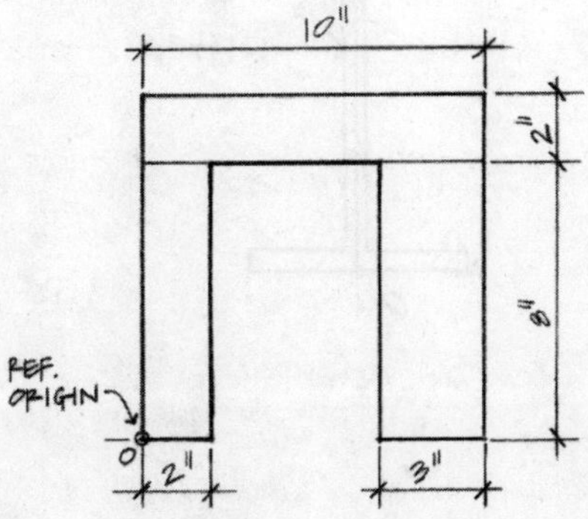

2

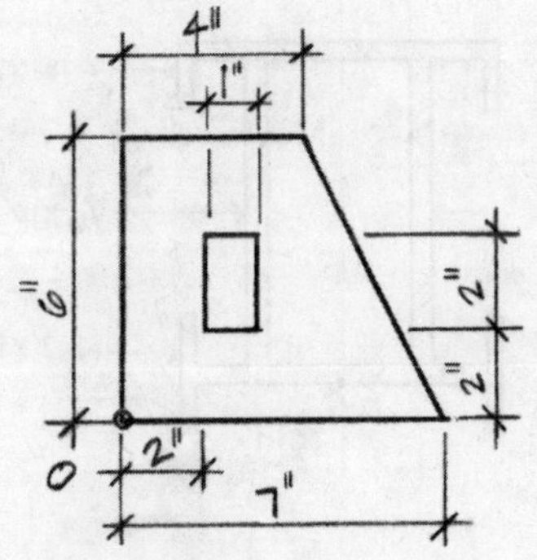

3

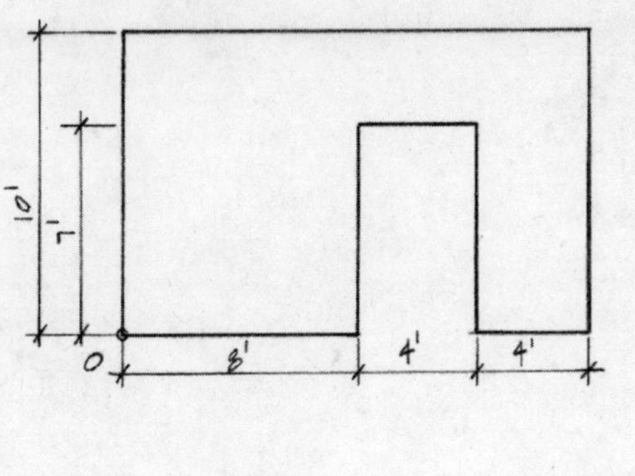

4

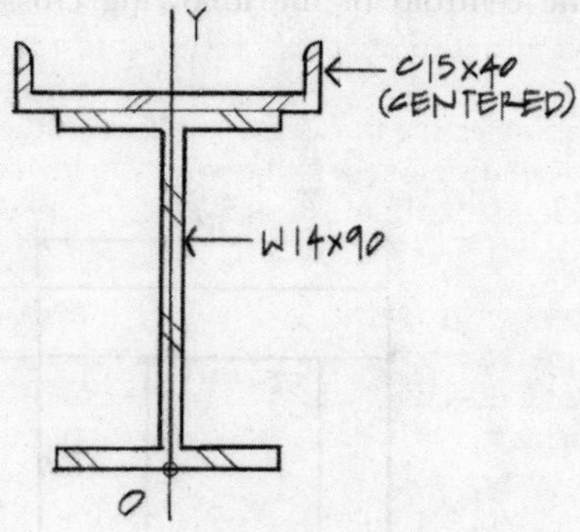
Y
C15×40
(CENTERED)
W14×90
O

5

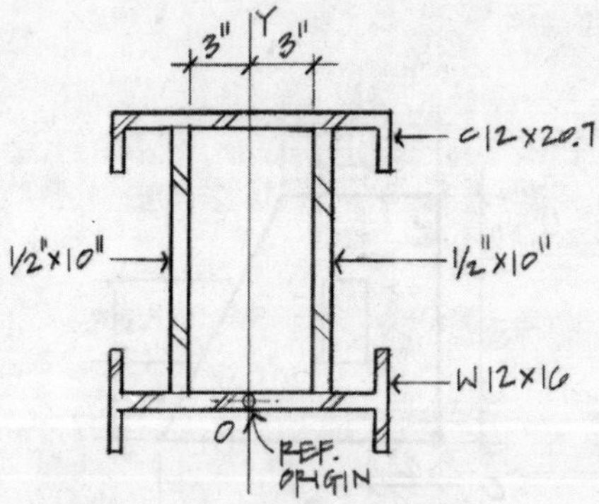
3"
Y
3"
C12×20.7
1/2"×10"
1/2"×10"
W12×16
O
REF.
ORIGIN

2 MOMENT OF INERTIA OF AN AREA

The *moment of inertia*, or *second-moment* as it is sometimes called, is a mathematical expression used in the study of the strength of beams and columns. It measures the effect of the cross-sectional shape of a beam on the beam's resistance to bending stress and deflection. Instability or buckling of slender columns is also affected by the moment of inertia of its cross-section.

The moment of inertia, or *I*-value, is a shape factor that quantifies the relative location of material in a cross-section in terms of effectiveness. A beam section with a large moment of inertia will have smaller stresses and deflections under a given load than one with a lesser *I*-value. A long, slender column will not be as susceptible to buckling laterally if the moment of inertia of its cross-section is sufficient. Moment of inertia is a measure of cross-sectional stiffness, whereas the modulus of elasticity E is a measure of material stiffness.

The concept of moment of inertia is vital to understanding the behavior of most structures, and it is unfortunate this concept has no accurate physical analogy or description. The dimensional unit for moment of inertia I is inches to the fourth power (in.^{4}).

Assuming the rectangular cross-section shown in Figure 6, a physical description can be given as follows:

area $= b \times h$ (in.^{2})
perimeter $= 2b + 2h$ (in.)

However, the moment of inertia for the cross-section is

$$I = \frac{bh^3}{12} \text{ in.}^4$$

for a rectangular cross-section.

The second moment of an area (area times a distance squared) is quite abstract and difficult to visualize as a physical property.

If we consider two prismatic beams made of the same material but with different cross-sections, the beam whose cross-sectional area had the greater moment of inertia would have the greater resistance to bending. To have a greater moment of inertia does not necessarily imply, however, a greater cross-sectional area. Orientation of a cross-section with respect to its bending axis is crucial in obtaining a large moment of inertia.

A 2″ × 6″ rectangular cross-section is used as a joist in Figure 7(a) and as a plank in Figure 7(b). From experience, it is already known that the joist is much more resistant to bending than the plank. Like many structural elements, the rectangle has a strong axis (orientation) and a weak axis. It is far more efficient to load a cross-section so that bending occurs about its strong axis.

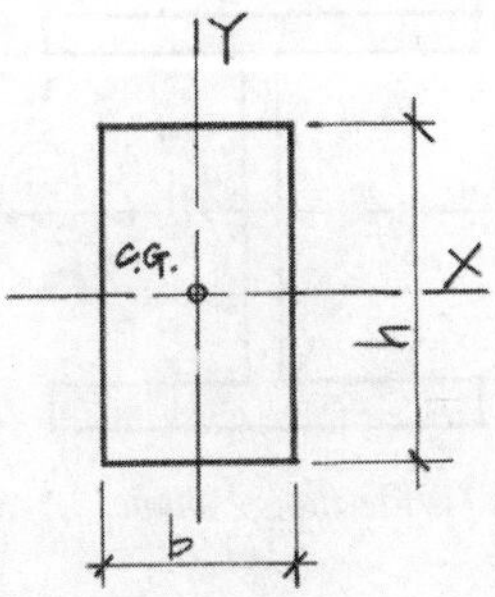

Area $= b \times h$ (in.^{2})

Perimeter $= 2b + 2h$ (in.)

Figure 6 Rectangular beam cross-section.

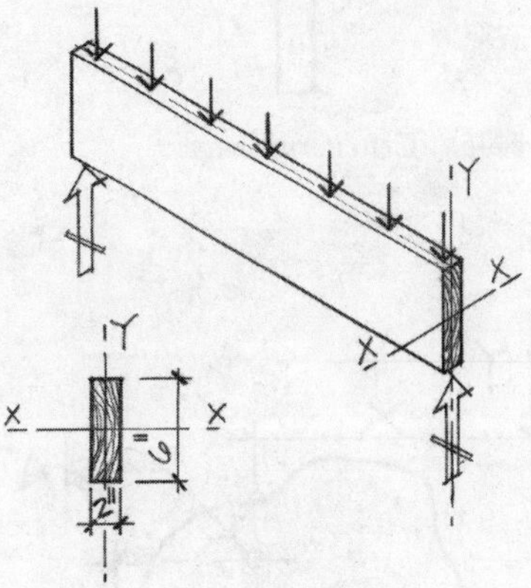

Figure 7(a) 2″ × 6″ joist.

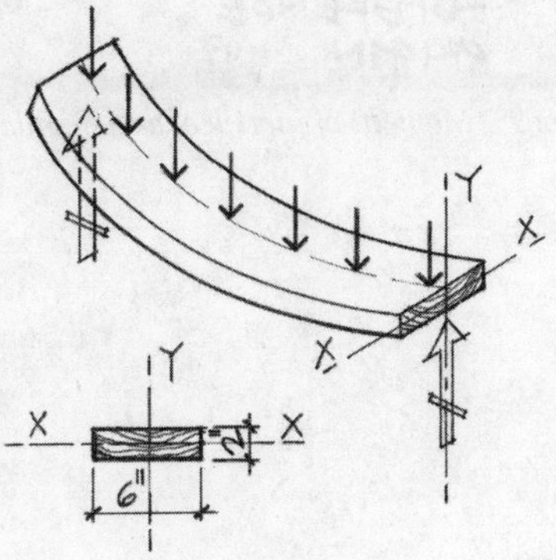

Figure 7(b) 6″ × 2″ plank.

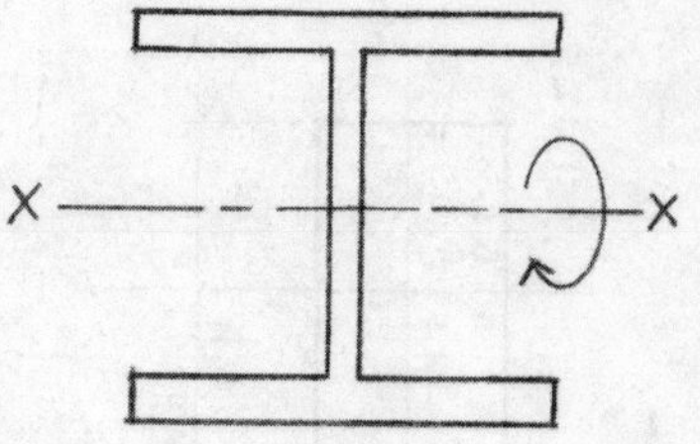

Figure 8(a) *Wide-flange shape.*

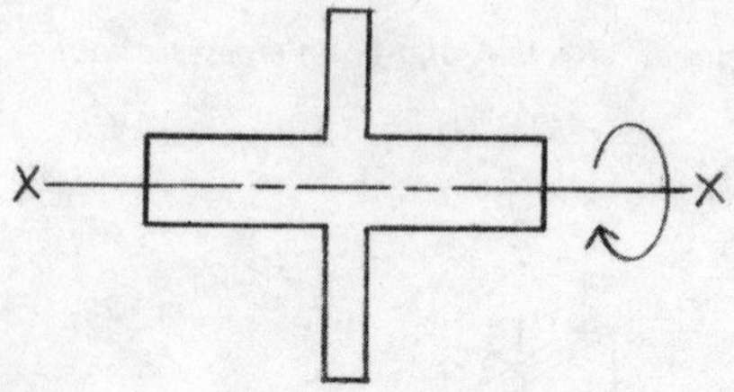

Figure 8(b) *Cruciform shape.*

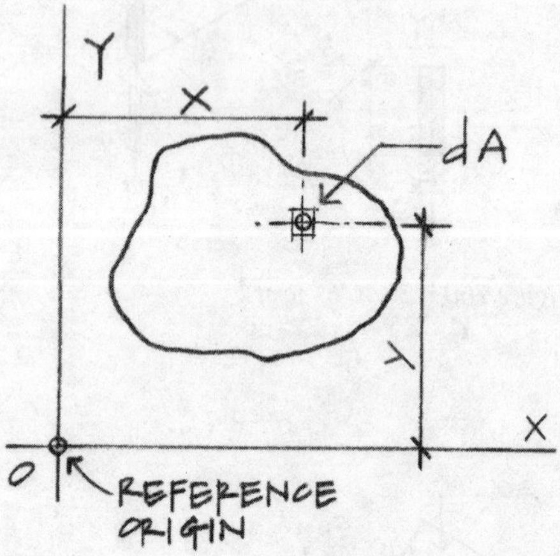

Figure 9 *Moment of inertia of an irregular area.*

It may help to understand the concept of moment of inertia if we draw an analogy based upon real inertia due to motion and mass. Imagine the two shapes shown in Figure 8 to be cut out of a $\frac{1}{2}$-inch steel plate and placed and spun about axis x-x. The two shapes have equal areas, but the one in Figure 8(a) has a much higher moment of inertia $I_{x\text{-}x}$ with respect to the axis of spin. It would be much harder to start it spinning, and once moving, it would be much harder to stop. The same principle is involved when a figure skater spins on ice. With arms held close in, the skater will rotate rapidly; with arms outstretched (creating increased resistance to spin and/or more inertia), the skater slows down.

In our discussion about the method of finding the center of gravity for areas, each area was subdivided into small elemental areas that were multiplied by their respective perpendicular distances from the reference axis. The procedure is somewhat similar for determining the moment of inertia. The moment of inertia about the same axis would require, however, that each elemental area be multiplied by the square of the respective perpendicular distances from the reference axis.

A moment of inertia value can be computed for any shape with respect to any reference axis (Figure 9).

Suppose we wanted to find the moment of inertia of an irregular area, as shown in Figure 9, about the x axis. We would first consider the area to consist of many infinitely small areas dA (where dA is a much smaller area than ΔA). Considering the dA shown, its moment of inertia about the x axis would be y^2dA. However, this product is only a minute portion of the whole moment of inertia. Each dA making up the area, when multiplied by the square of its corresponding moment arm y and added together, will give the moment of inertia of the entire area about the x axis.

The moment of inertia of an area about a given axis is defined as the sum of the products of all the elemental areas and the square of their respective distances to that axis. Therefore, the following two equations from Figure 9 are

$$I_x = \int_0^A y^2 dA$$

$$I_y = \int_0^A x^2 dA$$

The difficulty of this integration process is largely dependent on the equation of the outline of the area and its limits. When the integration becomes too difficult or a more simple, approximate solution is permissible, the moment of inertia may be expressed in finite terms by

$$I_x = \Sigma y^2 \Delta A$$

$$I_y = \Sigma x^2 \Delta A$$

The solution becomes less accurate as the size of ΔA is increased.

An I-value has the units of length to the fourth power, because the distance from the reference axis is squared. For this reason, the moment of inertia is sometimes called the *second moment of an area*. More importantly, it means that elements or areas that are relatively far away from the axis will contribute substantially more to an I-value than those that are close by.

Example Problems: Moment of Inertia by Approximation

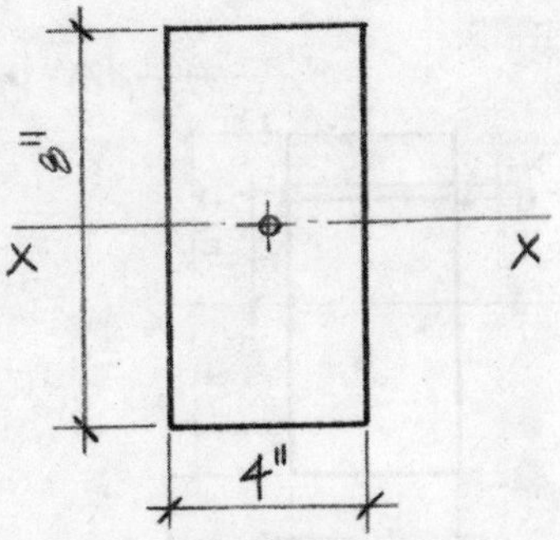

Beam cross section (4" × 8").

5 To illustrate the approximate method of moment of inertia calculation, we will examine a 4" × 8" beam cross-section.

The moment of inertia I is always computed relative to a reference point or axis. The most useful, and often-used, reference axis is the centroidal axis. (Now you see the reason for finding the centroid of an area.)

In the first approximate calculation for I_x, let's assume the cross-section above is divided into two elemental areas. Each elemental area measures 4" × 4", and the component centroidal y distance is two inches.

$$A_1 = 16 \text{ in.}^2; \quad y_1 = 2''$$

$$A_2 = 16 \text{ in.}^2; \quad y_2 = 2''$$

$$I_x = \Sigma y^2 \Delta A = (16 \text{ in.}^2)(2'')^2 + (16 \text{ in.}^2)(2'')^2 = 128 \text{ in.}^4$$

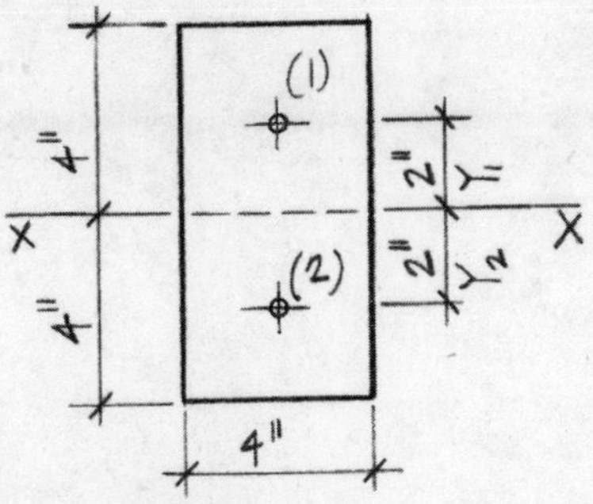

I_x based on two elemental areas.

The smaller the elements selected, the more accurate the approximation will be. Therefore, let's examine the same cross-section and subdivide it into four equal elements.

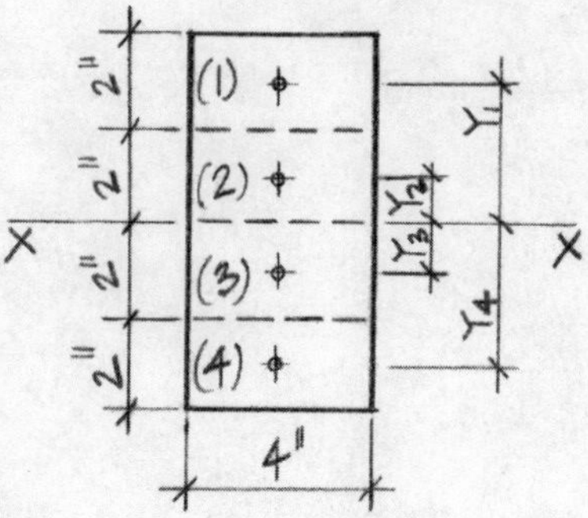

I_x *based on four elemental areas.*

$$A_1 = 8\text{ in.}^2;\quad y_1 = +3''$$
$$A_2 = 8\text{ in.}^2;\quad y_2 = +1''$$
$$A_3 = 8\text{ in.}^2;\quad y_3 = -1''$$
$$A_4 = 8\text{ in.}^2;\quad y_4 = -3''$$

$$I_x = \Sigma y^2 \Delta A = (8\text{ in.}^2)(+3'')^2 + (8\text{ in.}^2)(+1'')^2 + (8\text{ in.}^2)(-1'')^2 + (8\text{ in.}^2)(-3'')^2$$

$$I_x = 72\text{ in.}^4 + 8\text{ in.}^4 + 8\text{ in.}^4 + 72\text{ in.}^4 = 160\text{ in.}^4$$

Notice that the value of I_x is different from that in the previous calculation.

If the cross-section is subdivided into even smaller areas, I_x will approach an exact value. To compare the two computations above with the exact value of I_x for a rectangular cross-section, the rectangle will be subdivided into infinitely small areas dA.

$$I_x = \int y^2 dA; \qquad dA = bdy$$

$$I_x = \int y^2 dA = \int_{-h/2}^{+h/2} y^2 bdy = b\int_{-h/2}^{+h/2} y^2 dy = \left.\frac{by^3}{3}\right|_{-h/2}^{+h/2}$$

$$I_x = \frac{b}{3}\left[\left(\frac{h}{2}\right)^3 - \left(\frac{-h}{2}\right)^3\right] = \frac{b}{3}\left[\frac{h^3}{8} + \frac{h^3}{8}\right] = \frac{bh^3}{12}$$

Substituting $b = 4''$ and $h = 8''$,

$$I_{\text{exact}} = \frac{(4'')(8'')^3}{12} = 171\text{ in.}^4$$

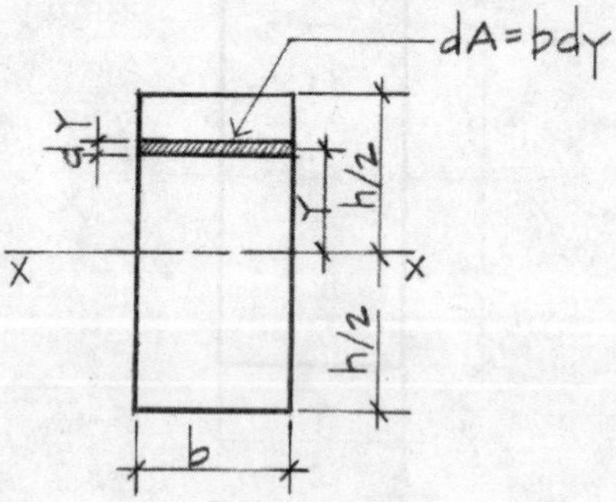

I_x *based on integration of areas dA.*

The moment of inertia can be determined about the y axis in the same manner as was done for the x axis.

Moments of inertia calculated by the integration method (exact) for some basic geometric shapes are shown in Table 2.

Table 2 Moments of inertia for simple geometric shapes.

Shape	Moment of Inertia (I_x)
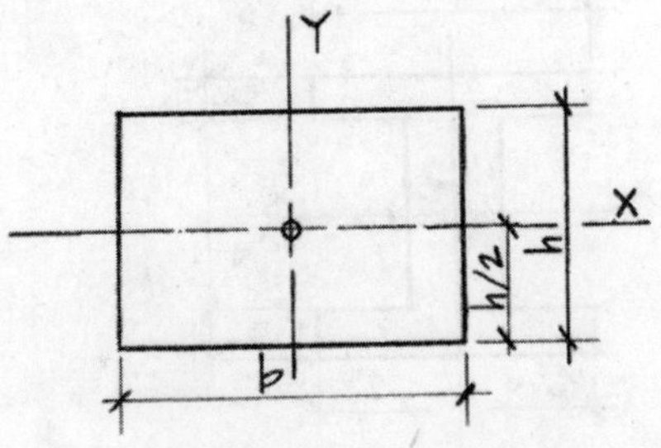	$I_x = \frac{bh^3}{12}$
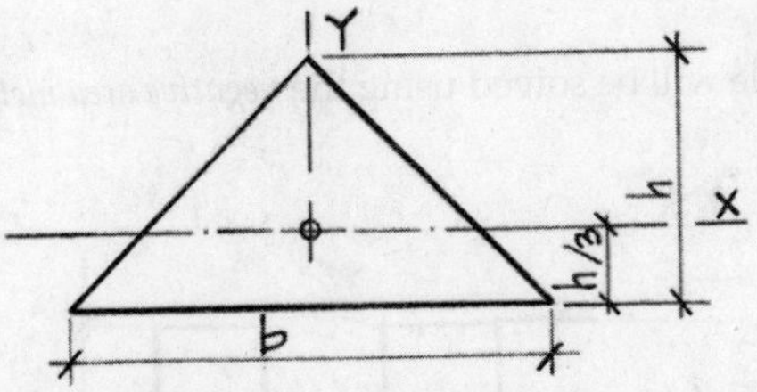	$I_x = \frac{bh^3}{36}$
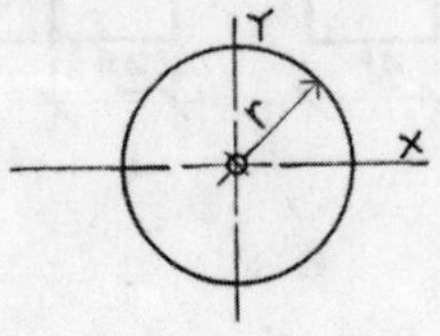	$I_x = \frac{\pi r^4}{4} = \frac{\pi d^4}{64}$
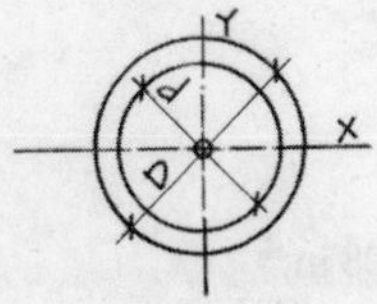	$I_x = \frac{\pi(D^4 - d^4)}{64}$
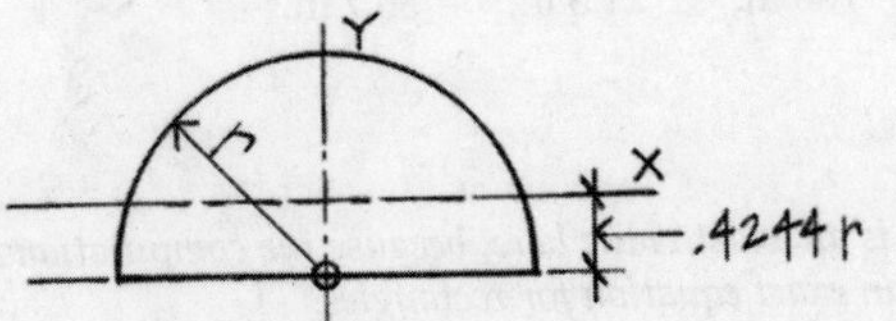	$I_x = r^4\left(\frac{\pi}{8} - \frac{8}{9\pi}\right) = 0.11r^4$

6 Determine the value of I about the x axis (centroidal).

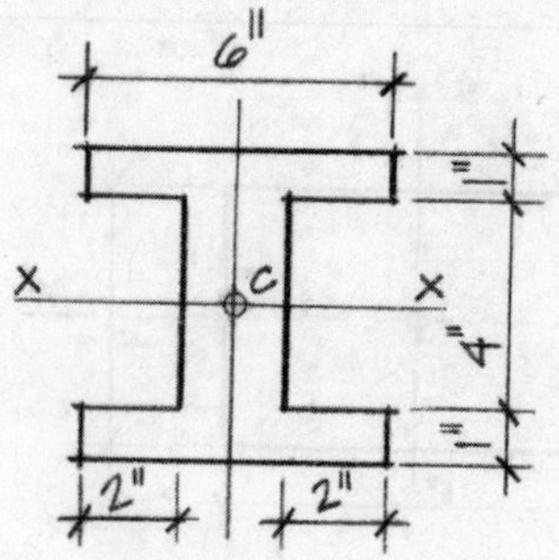

Solution:

This example will be solved using the *negative area method.*

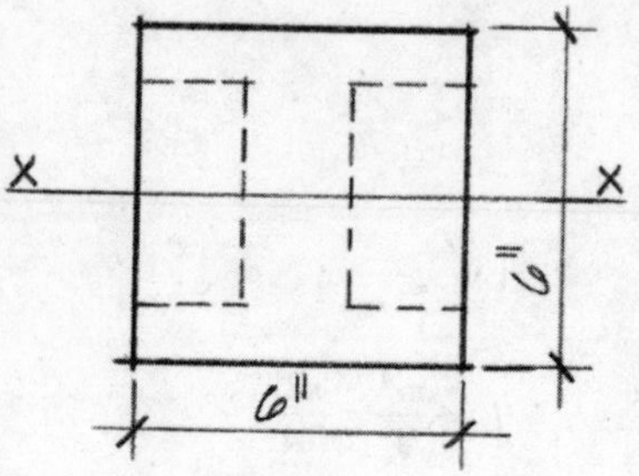

Solid

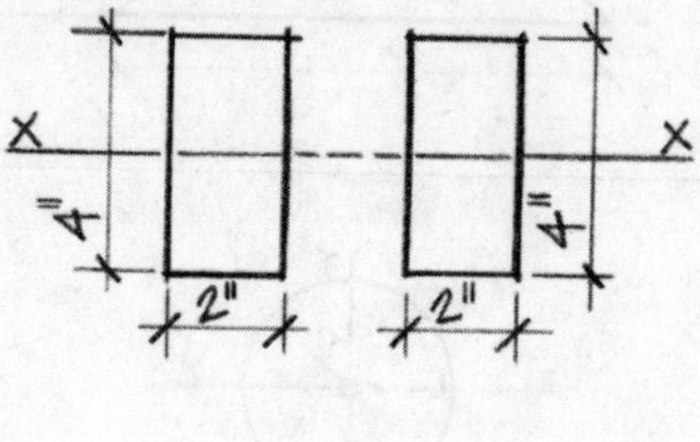

Voids

$$I_{\text{solid}} = \frac{bh^3}{12}$$

$$I_{\text{openings}} = 2 \times \frac{bh^3}{12}$$

$$I_{\text{solid}} = \frac{(6'')(6'')^3}{12} = 108 \text{ in.}^4$$

$$I_{\text{openings}} = 2 \times \frac{(2'')(4'')^3}{12} = 21.3 \text{ in.}^4$$

$$I_x = 108 \text{ in.}^4 - 21.3 \text{ in.}^4 = 86.7 \text{ in.}^4$$

Note: *I_x is an exact value here, because the computations were based on an exact equation for rectangles.*

Moment of Inertia by Integration:

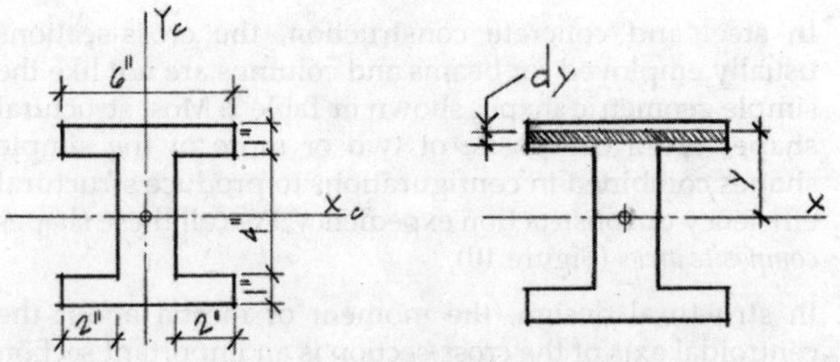

$$I_{x_c} = \int y^2 dA$$

where

$dA = bdy$ (b = base)

y varies from

$\left.\begin{matrix} 0 \rightarrow +2'' \\ 0 \rightarrow -2'' \end{matrix}\right\}$ while $b = 2''$

and from:

$\left.\begin{matrix} +2'' \rightarrow +3'' \\ -2'' \rightarrow -3'' \end{matrix}\right\}$ while $b = 6''$

$$I_{x_c} = \int_A y^2 bdy$$

Treat b as a constant within its defined boundary lines.

$$I_{x_c} = \int_{-2}^{+2} (2)y^2 dy + \int_{+2}^{+3} (6)y^2 dy + \int_{-3}^{-2} (6)y^2 dy$$

$$I_{x_c} = \left.\frac{2y^3}{3}\right|_{-2}^{+2} + \left.\frac{6y^3}{3}\right|_{+2}^{+3} + \left.\frac{6y^3}{3}\right|_{-3}^{-2}$$

$$I_{x_c} = \frac{2}{3}(8 - [-8]) + 2(27 - 8) + 2(-8 - [-27])$$

$$I_{x_c} = 10.67 + 38 + 38 = 86.67 \text{ in.}^4$$

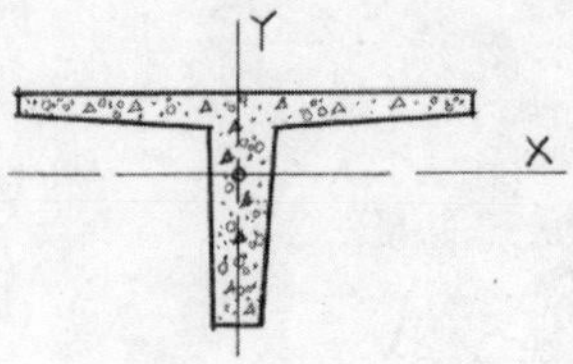

(a) *Precast concrete T-section.*

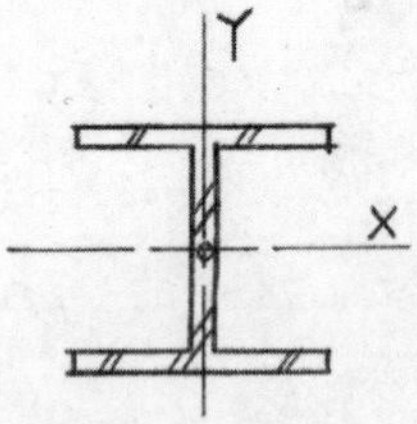

(b) *Steel wide-flange section.*

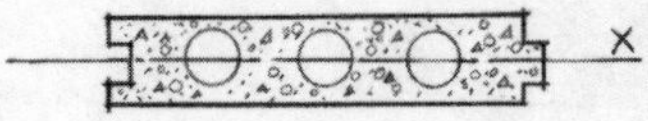

(c) *Precast concrete plank.*

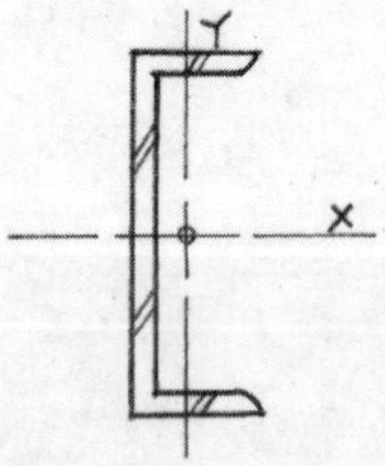

(d) *Steel channel section.*

Figure 10 Column composite shapes for beams.

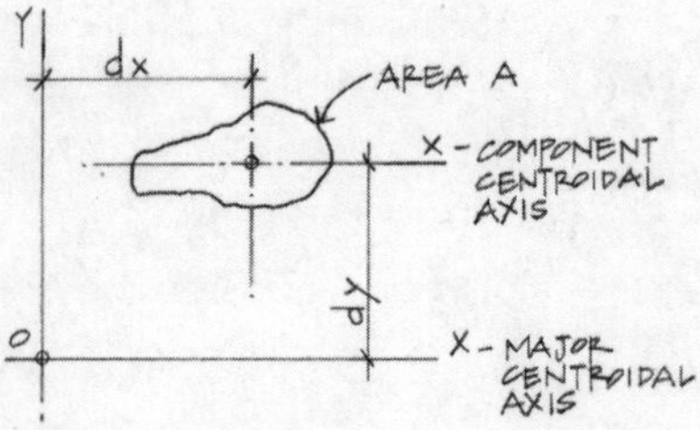

Figure 11 Transfer area about axes x and y.

3 MOMENT OF INERTIA OF COMPOSITE AREAS

In steel and concrete construction, the cross-sections usually employed for beams and columns are not like the simple geometric shapes shown in Table 2. Most structural shapes are a composite of two or more of the simple shapes combined in configurations to produce structural efficiency or construction expediency. We call these shapes *composite areas* (Figure 10).

In structural design, the moment of inertia about the centroidal axis of the cross-section is an important section property. Because moments of inertia can be computed with respect to any reference axis, a standard reference was necessary in developing consistency when comparing the stiffness of one cross-section relative to another.

The *parallel axis theorem* provides a simple way to compute the moment of inertia of a shape about any axis parallel to the centroidal axis (Figure 11). The principle of the parallel axis theorem may be stated as follows:

> *The moment of inertia of an area with respect to any axis not through its centroid is equal to the moment of inertia of that area with respect to its own parallel centroidal axis plus the product of the area and the square of the distance between the two axes.*

The parallel axis theorem expressed in equation form is

$$\boxed{I_x = \Sigma I_{x_c} + \Sigma A d_y^2}$$

which is the transfer formula about the major x axis and where

I_x = moment of inertia of the total cross-section about the major centroidal x axis (in.^{4})

I_{x_c} = moment of inertia of the component area about its own centroidal x axis (in.^{4})

A = area of the component (in.^{2})

dy = perpendicular distance between the major centroidal x axis and the parallel axis that passes through the centroid of the component (in.)

The transfer formula for the major y axis is expressed as

$$\boxed{I_y = \Sigma I_{y_c} + \Sigma A d_x^2}$$

Example Problems: Moment of Inertia of Composite Areas

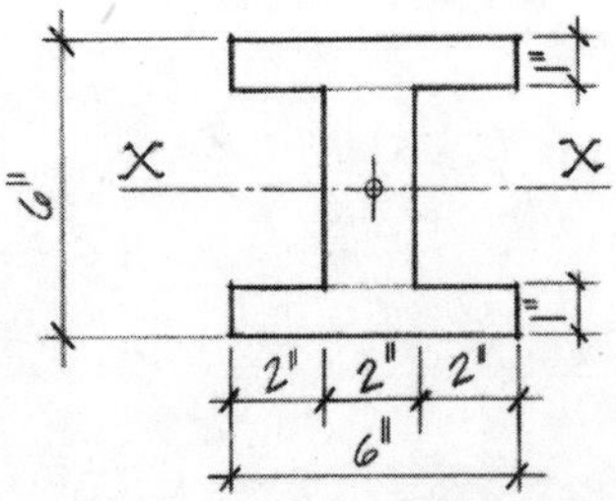

7 Determine the moment of inertia I_x about the centroidal x axis.

Note: *This is identical to Example Problem 6.*

Solution:

Instead of the negative area method, the transfer formula will be used, employing the parallel axis theorem.

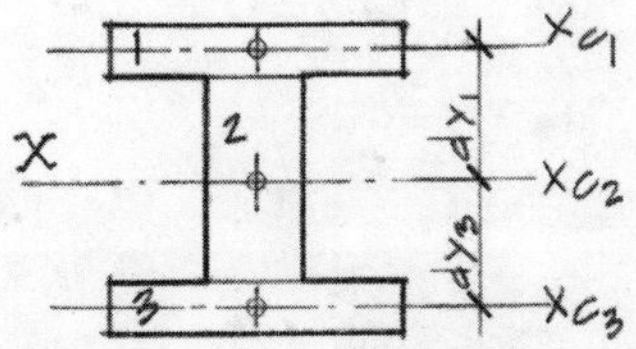

The cross-section will be divided into three components as shown (two flanges and the web).

Each component of the composite area has its own centroid and is denoted as x_c. The major centroidal axis of the entire cross-section is X. Note that the major centroidal axis X coincides with the component axis x_{c_2}.

As composite areas become more complex, it may be advisable to use a tabular format to minimize error and confusion.

Component	I_{x_c} (in.^{4})	A (in.^{2})	d_y (in.)	Ad_y^2 (in.^{4})
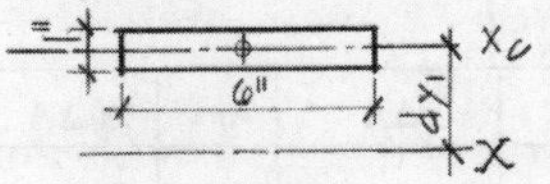	$\frac{bh^3}{12} = \frac{6''(1'')^3}{12} = 0.5$ in.^{4}	6 in.^{2}	2.5″	37.5 in.^{4}
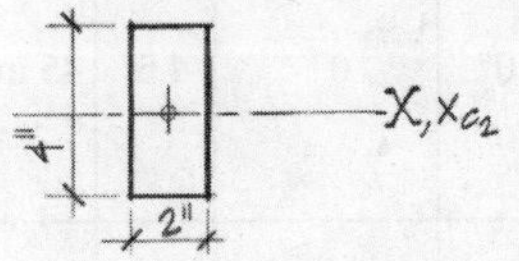	$\frac{2''(4'')^3}{12} = 10.67$ in.^{4}	8 in.^{2}	0″	0
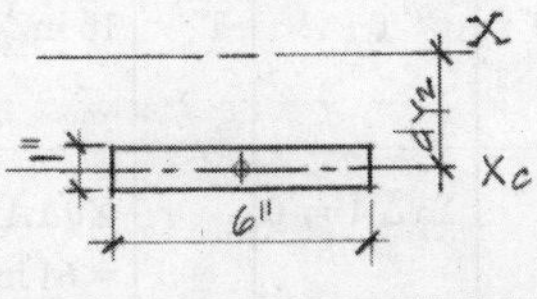	= 0.5 in.^{4}	6 in.^{2}	–2.5″	37.5 in.^{4}
	$\Sigma I_{x_c} = 11.67$ in.^{4}			$\Sigma Ad_y^2 = 75$ in.^{4}

The moment of inertia of the entire composite area is

$$I_X = \Sigma I_{x_c} + \Sigma Ad_y^2 = 11.67 \text{ in.}^4 + 75 \text{ in.}^4 = 86.67 \text{ in.}^4$$

The concept of the transfer formula involves the additional inertia required to merge or transfer an axis from one location to another. The term Ad_y^2 represents the additional inertia developed about the major axis X due to components l and 2.

8 Determine the moment of inertia about the centroidal x and y axes for the composite area shown.

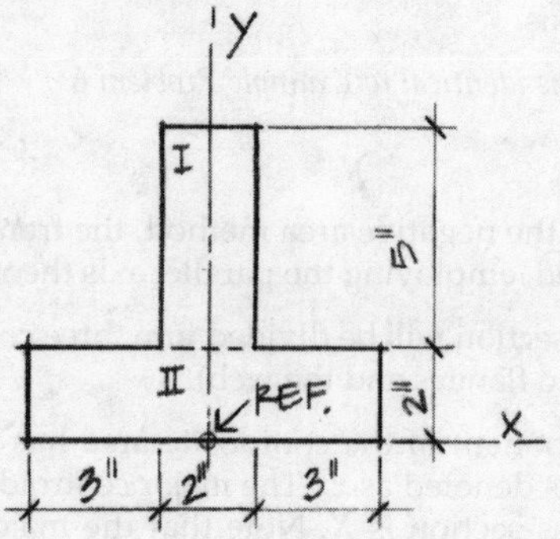

Solution:

Usually the first step in determining the moment of inertia about the major or centroidal axis requires the determination of the centroid (particularly in unsymmetrical cross-sections).

Component	ΔA	x	$x\Delta A$	y	$y\Delta A$
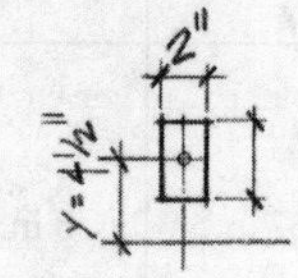	10 in.^{2}	0″	0	4.5″	45 in.^{3}
	16 in.^{2}	0″	0	1″	16 in.^{3}
	$A = \Sigma\Delta A$ = 26 in.^{2}		$\Sigma x\Delta A = 0$		$\Sigma y\Delta A$ = 61 in.^{3}

$$\bar{x} = 0$$

$$\bar{y} = \frac{\Sigma y\Delta A}{A} = \frac{61 \text{ in.}^3}{26 \text{ in.}^2} = 2.35''$$

$d_{y1} = y_1 - \bar{y} = 4.5'' - 2.35'' = 2.15''$

$d_{y2} = \bar{y} - y_2 = 2.35'' - 1'' = 1.35''$

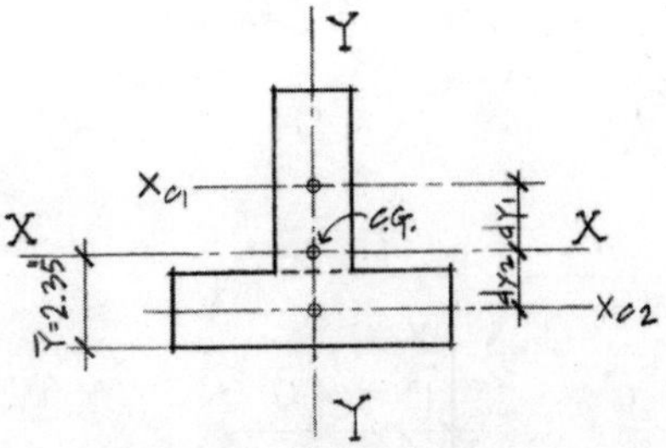

Component	A	I_{x_c}	d_y	Ad_y^2	I_{y_c}	d_x	Ad_x^2
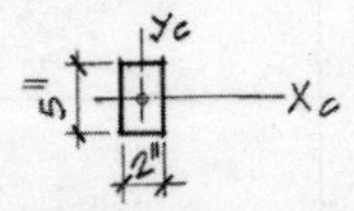	10 in.^{2}	$\frac{2''(5'')^3}{12}$ = 20.8 in.^{4}	2.15″	46.2 in.^{4}	$\frac{5''(2'')^3}{12}$ = 3.3 in.^{4}	0″	0
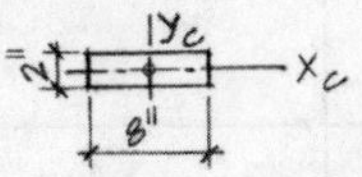	16 in.^{2}	$\frac{8''(2'')^3}{12}$ = 5.3 in.^{4}	1.35″	29.2 in.^{4}	$\frac{2''(8'')^3}{12}$ = 85.3 in.^{4}	0″	0
		ΣI_{x_c} = 26.1 in.^{4}		ΣAd_y^2 = 75.4 in.^{4}	ΣI_{y_c} = 88.6 in.^{4}		$\Sigma Ad_x^2 = 0$

$I_x = \Sigma I_{x_c} + \Sigma Ad_y^2 = 26.1 \text{ in.}^4 + 75.4 \text{ in.}^4 = 101.5 \text{ in.}^4$

$I_y = \Sigma I_{y_c} + \Sigma Ad_x^2 = 88.6 \text{ in.}^4 + 0 \text{ in.}^4 = 88.6 \text{ in.}^4$

9 Find I_x and I_y for the L-shaped cross-section shown.

Solution:

It may be convenient to set up a table for solving the centroid as well as the moment of inertia.

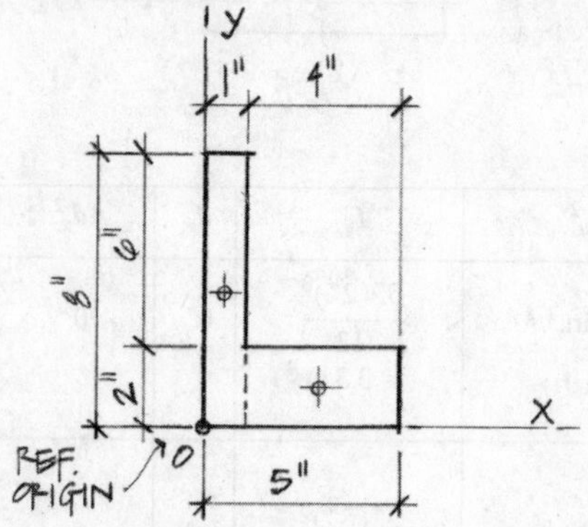

Component	Area	x	Ax	y	Ay
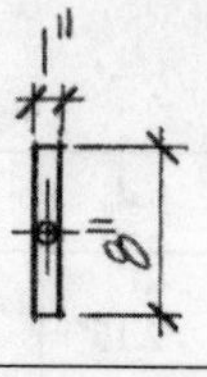	8 in.^{2}	0.5″	4 in.^{3}	4″	32 in.^{3}
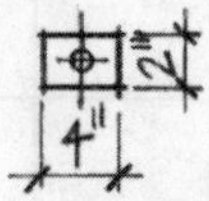	8 in.^{2}	3″	24 in.^{3}	1″	8 in.^{3}
	$\Sigma A =$ 16 in.^{2}		$\Sigma Ax =$ 28 in.^{3}		$\Sigma Ay =$ 40 in.^{3}

$$\bar{x} = \frac{28 \text{ in.}^3}{16 \text{ in.}^2} = 1.75''; \qquad \bar{y} = \frac{40 \text{ in.}^3}{16 \text{ in.}^2} = 2.5''$$

Component	A	I_{x_c}	d_y	Ad_y^2	I_{y_c}	d_x	Ad_x^2
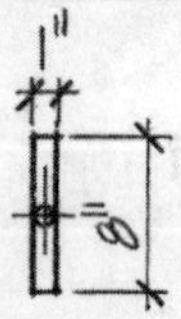	8 in.^{2}	$\frac{1''(8'')^3}{12}$ = 42.67 in.^{4}	1.5″	18 in.^{4}	$\frac{8''(1'')^3}{12}$ = 0.67 in.^{4}	1.25″	12.5 in.^{4}
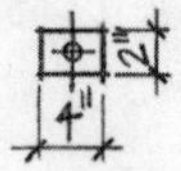	8 in.^{2}	$\frac{4''(2'')^3}{12}$ = 2.67 in.^{4}	1.5″	18 in.^{4}	$\frac{2''(4'')^3}{12}$ = 10.67 in.^{4}	1.25″	12.5 in.^{4}

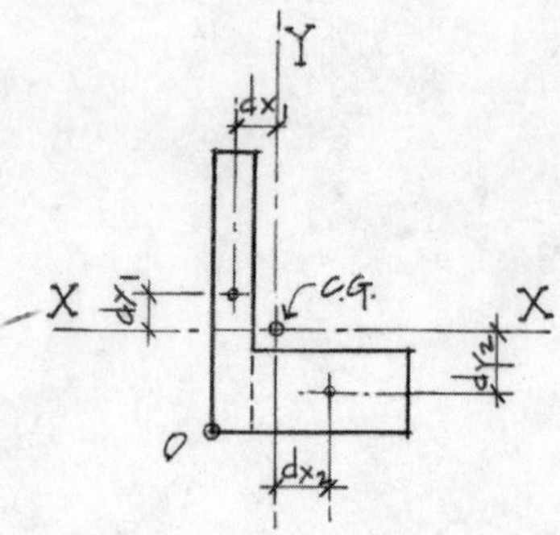

$$\Sigma I_{x_c} = 45.34 \text{ in.}^4; \quad \Sigma I_{y_c} = 11.34 \text{ in.}^4$$

$$\Sigma Ad_y^2 = 36 \text{ in.}^4; \quad \Sigma Ad_x^2 = 25 \text{ in.}^4$$

$$I_x = \Sigma I_{x_c} + \Sigma Ad_y^2; \quad I_x = 81.34 \text{ in.}^4$$

$$I_y = \Sigma I_{y_c} + \Sigma Ad_x^2; \quad I_y = 36.34 \text{ in.}^4$$

Problems

Determine I_x and I_y for the cross-sections in Problems 6 through 8 and I_x for Problems 9 through 11.

6

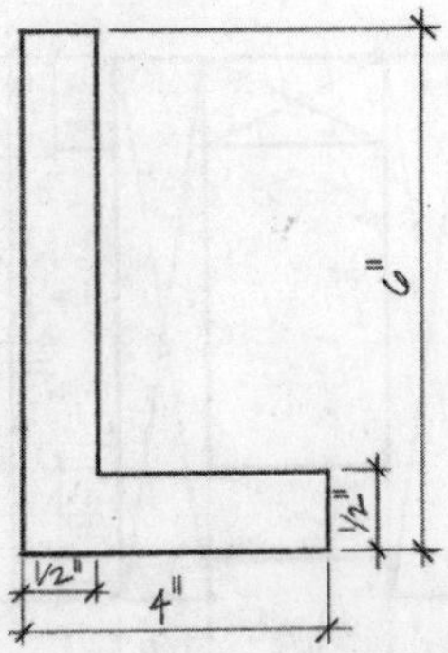

7

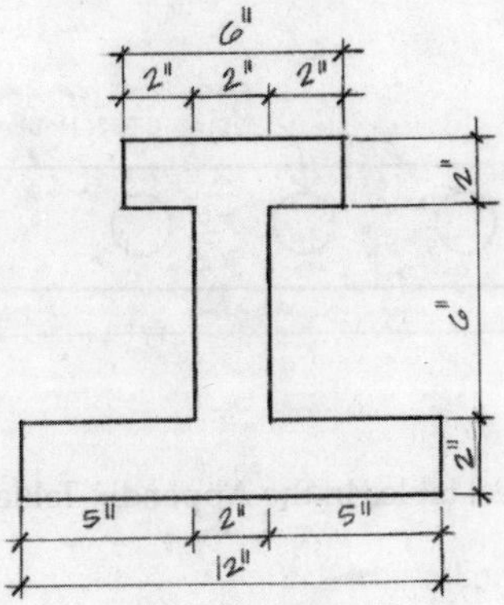

8

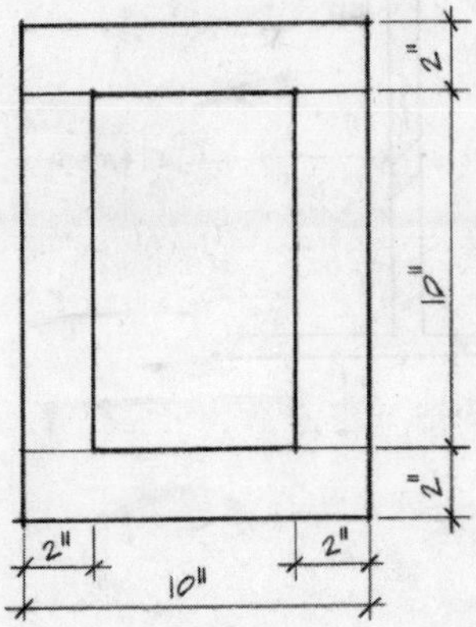

9 All members are S4S (surfaced on four sides). See Table A1 in the Appendix.

2 × 4 S4S; 1.5″ × 3.5″; A = 5.25 in.^{2}

2 × 12 S4S; 1.5″ × 11.25″; A = 16.88 in.^{2}

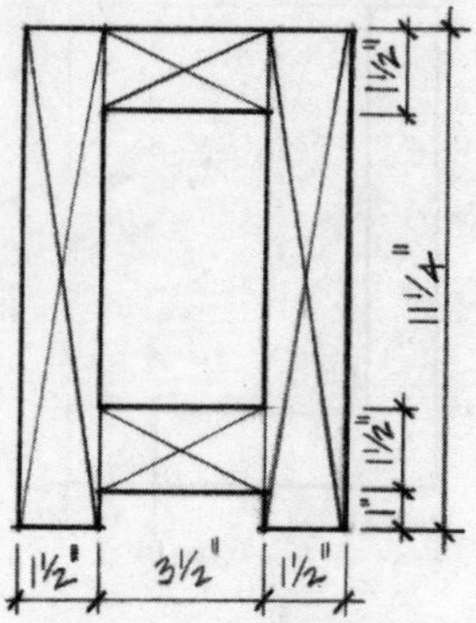

10

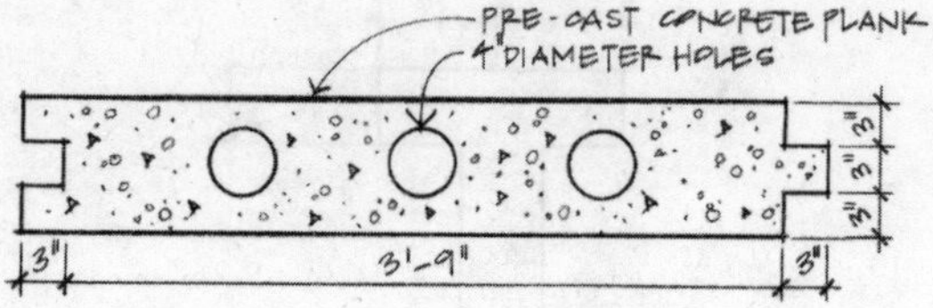

11 See the steel tables in the Appendix Table A3.

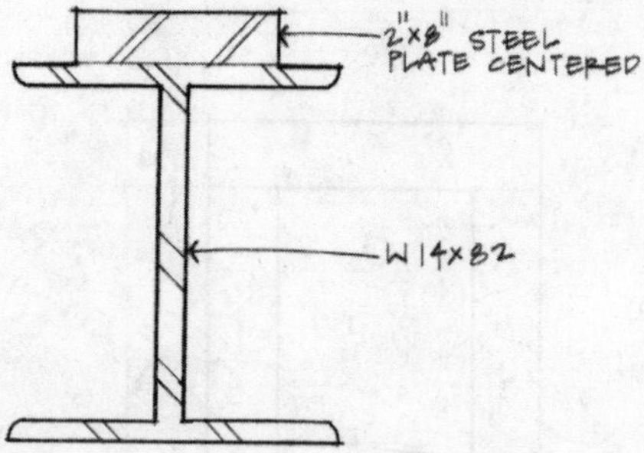

Example Problems

10 A built-up steel beam uses a W18 × 97 on its side with a 1″ × 32″ vertical plate and a 2″ × 16″ horizontal plate. Assuming the vertical plate is centered on the wide flange's web, calculate I_x and I_y about the major centroidal axes of the cross-section.

Solution:

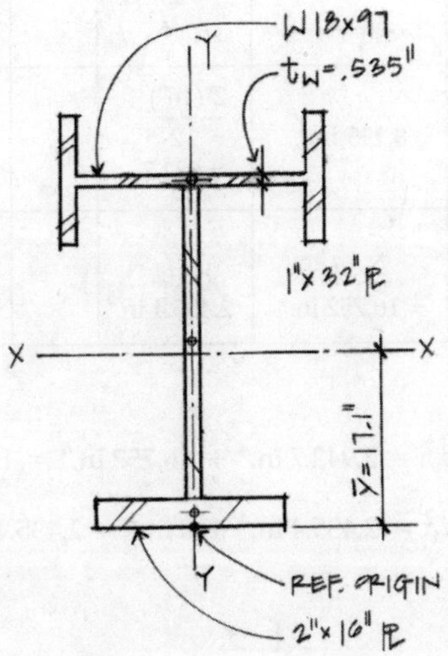

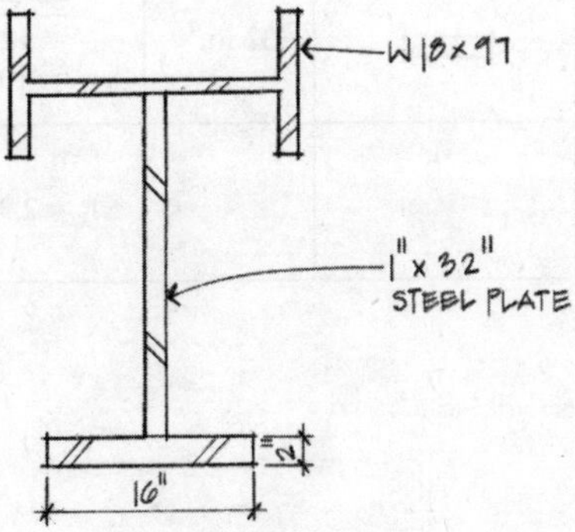

Component	Area	y	Ay
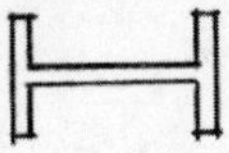	28.5 in.^{2}	$2'' + 32'' + \frac{0.532''}{2} = 34.27''$	976.7 in.^{3}
	1″ × 32″ = 32 in.^{2}	2″ + 16″ = 18″	576 in.^{3}
	2″ × 16″ = 32 in.^{2}	1″	32 in.^{3}
	ΣA = 92.5 in.^{2}		ΣAy = 1,585 in.^{3}

$$\bar{y} = \frac{\Sigma y \Delta A}{A} = \frac{1{,}584.6 \text{ in.}^3}{92.5 \text{ in.}^2} = 17.1''$$

Component	A	I_{x_c} (in.^{4})	d_y	Ad_y^2	I_{y_c} (in.^{4})	d_x	Ad_x^2
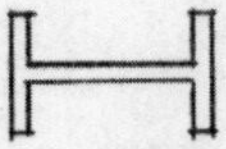	28.5 in.^{2}	201	17.2″	8,431 in.^{4}	1,750	0″	0
	32 in.^{4}	$\frac{1''(32'')^3}{12} = 2{,}731$	0.9″	26 in.^{4}	$\frac{32''(1'')^3}{12} = 2.7$	0″	0
	32 in.^{4}	$\frac{16''(2'')^3}{12} = 10.7$	16.1″	8,295 in.^{4}	$\frac{2''(16'')^3}{12} = 682.7$	0″	0
		$\Sigma I_{x_c} = 2{,}942.7$ in.^{4}		$\Sigma Ad_y^2 = 16{,}752$ in.^{4}	$\Sigma I_{y_c} = 2{,}435.4$ in.^{4}		$\Sigma Ad_x^2 = 0$

$$I_x = \Sigma I_{x_c} + \Sigma Ad_y^2 = 2{,}942.7 \text{ in.}^4 + 16{,}752 \text{ in.}^4 = 19{,}694.7 \text{ in.}^4$$

$$I_y = \Sigma I_{y_c} + \Sigma Ad_x^2 = 2{,}435.4 \text{ in.}^4 + 0 \text{ in.}^4 = 2{,}435.4 \text{ in.}^4$$

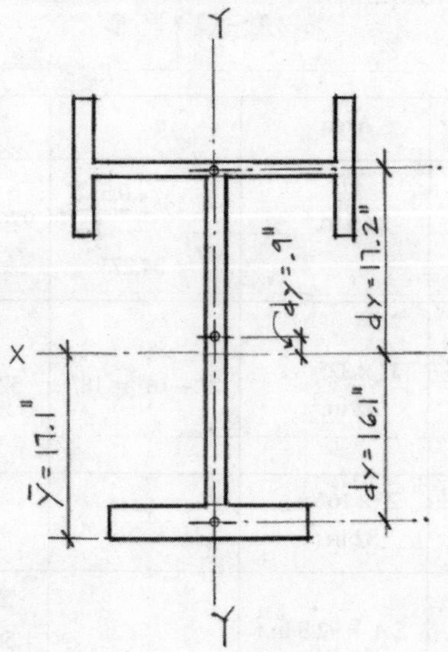

11 A heavily loaded floor system uses a composite steel section as shown. A C15 × 40 channel section is attached to the top flange of the W18 × 50. Determine I_x and I_y about the major centroidal axes using the cross-sectional properties given in the steel tables for standard rolled shapes (see Appendix Tables A3 and A4).

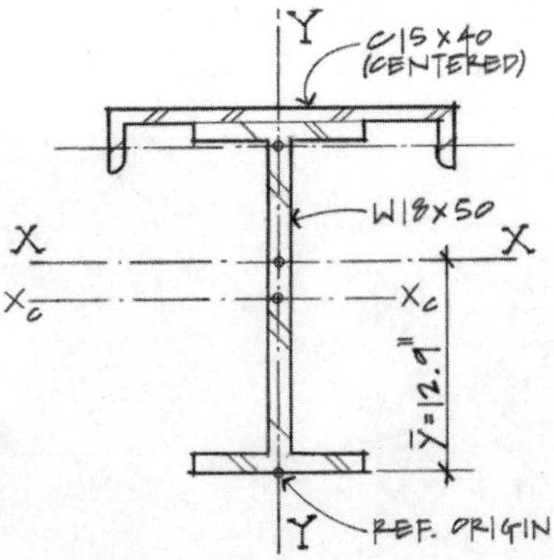

Solution:

Determine the major centroidal axes as the first step.

Component	Area	y	Ay
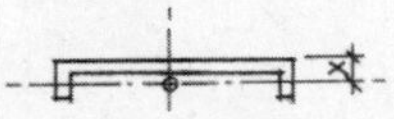	11.8 in.^{2}	$d + t_w - x =$ $18 + 0.52 - 0.78 =$ 17.74″	209.3 in.^{3}
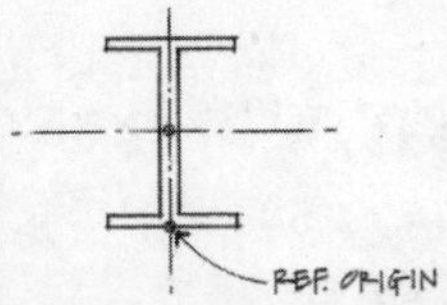	14.7 in.^{2}	$\frac{d}{2} = \frac{18''}{2} = 9''$	132.3 in.^{3}
	$\Sigma A = 26.5$ in.^{2}		$\Sigma Ay = 341.6$ in.^{3}

$$\bar{y} = \frac{\Sigma y \Delta A}{A} = \frac{341.6 \text{ in.}^3}{26.5 \text{ in.}^2} = 12.9''$$

Component	A	I_{x_c}	d_y	Ad_y^2	I_{y_c}	d_x	Ad_x^2
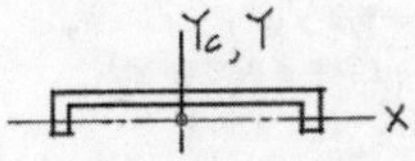	11.8 in.^{2}	9.23	$y_1 - \bar{y}$ $= (17.7 - 12.9)$ $= 4.8''$	272 in.^{4}	349 in.^{4}	0″	0
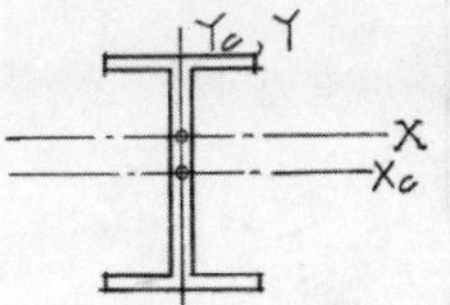	14.7 in.^{2}	800	$\bar{y} - y_2$ $= (12.9 - 9)$ $= 3.9''$	224 in.^{4}	40.1 in.^{4}	0″	0
		ΣI_{x_c} $= 809$ in.^{4}		ΣAd_y^2 $= 496$ in.^{4}	ΣI_{y_c} $= 389$ in.^{4}		ΣAd_x^2 $= 0$

$$I_x = \Sigma I_{x_c} + \Sigma Ad_y^2 = 809 \text{ in.}^4 + 496 \text{ in.}^4 = 1{,}305 \text{ in.}^4$$

$$I_y = \Sigma I_{y_c} + \Sigma Ad_x^2 = 389 \text{ in.}^4 + 0 \text{ in.}^4 = 389 \text{ in.}^4$$

Problems

Determine the moments of inertia for the composite areas using the standard rolled sections shown below.

12

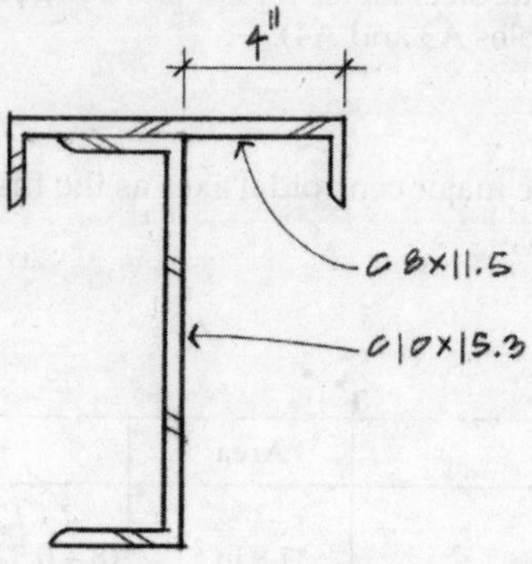

13

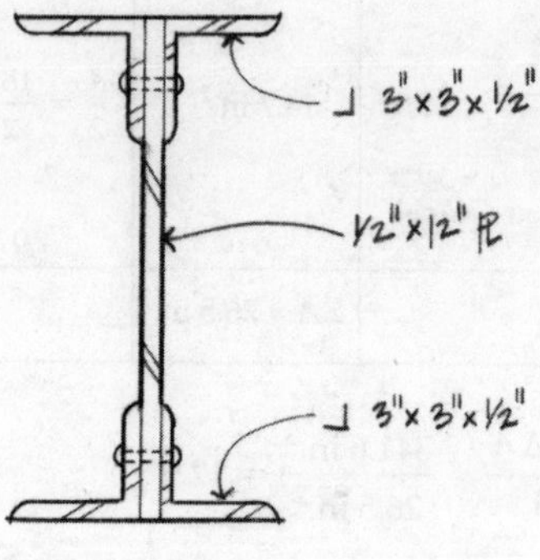

14

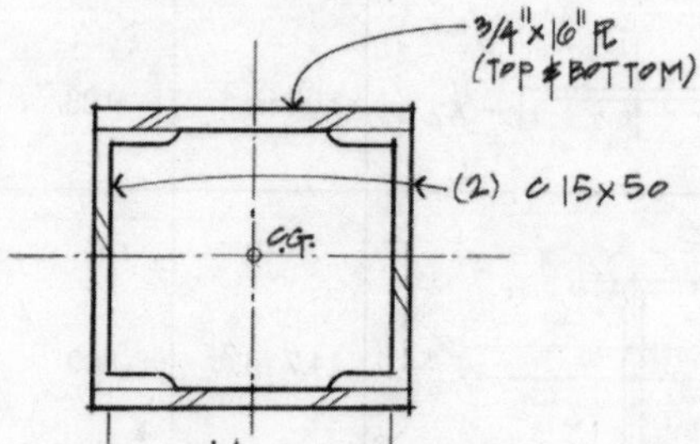

A built-up box column is made by welding two $\frac{3}{4}'' \times 16''$ plates to the flanges of two C15 × 50. For structural reasons, it is necessary to have I_x equal to I_y. Find the distance W required to achieve this.

4 RADIUS OF GYRATION

In the study of column behavior, we will be using the term *radius of gyration* (r). The radius of gyration expresses the relationship between the area of a cross-section and a centroidal moment of inertia. It is a shape factor that measures a column's resistance to buckling about an axis.

Assume that a W14 × 90 steel column (Figure 12) is axially loaded until it fails in a buckling mode (Figure 13).

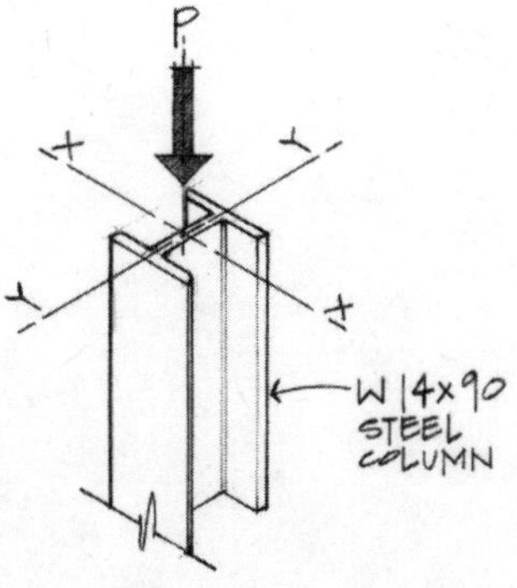

Figure 12 Axially loaded wide-flange column.

An examination of the buckled column will reveal that failure occurs about the y axis. A measure of the column's ability to resist buckling is its radius of gyration (r) value. For the W14 × 90, the radius of gyration values about the x and y axes are

W14 × 90: $r_x = 6.14''$

$r_y = 3.70''$

The larger the r value, the more resistance offered against buckling.

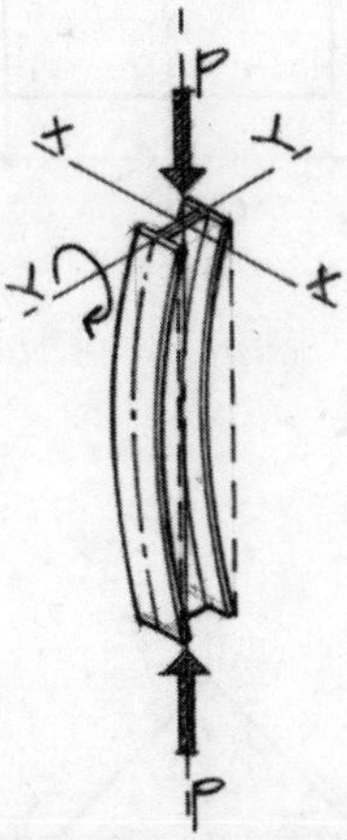

Figure 13 Column buckling about the weak (y) axis.

The radius of gyration of a cross-section (area) is defined as that distance from its moment of inertia axis at which the entire area could be considered as being concentrated (like a black hole in space) without changing its moment of inertia (Figure 14).

If

$$A_1 = A_2$$

and

$$I_{x1} = I_{x2}$$

then

$$I_x = Ar^2$$

$$\therefore r_x^2 = \frac{I_x}{A}$$

and

$$\boxed{r_x = \sqrt{\frac{I_x}{A}} \qquad r_y = \sqrt{\frac{I_y}{A}}}$$

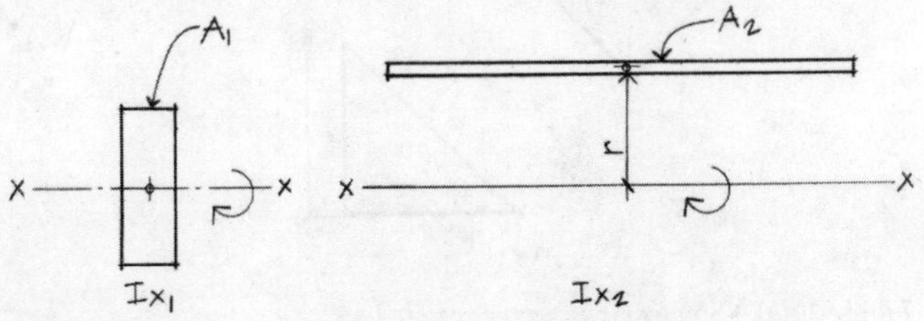

Figure 14 Radius of gyration for A_1 and A_2.

For all standard rolled shapes in steel, the radius of gyration values are given in the steel section properties table in the Appendix (Tables A3 through A6).

Example Problems: Radius of Gyration

12 Using the cross-section shown in Example Problem 11, we found that

$$I_x = 1{,}305 \text{ in.}^4; \quad A = 26.5 \text{ in.}^2$$
$$I_y = 389 \text{ in.}^4$$

The radii of gyration for the two centroidal axes are computed as

$$r_x = \sqrt{\frac{I_x}{A}} = \sqrt{\frac{1{,}305 \text{ in.}^4}{26.5 \text{ in.}^2}} = 7.02''$$
$$r_y = \sqrt{\frac{I_y}{A}} = \sqrt{\frac{389 \text{ in.}^4}{26.5 \text{ in.}^2}} = 3.83''$$

13 Two identical square cross-sections are oriented as shown in Figure 15. Which of these has the larger I value? Find the radius of gyration r for each.

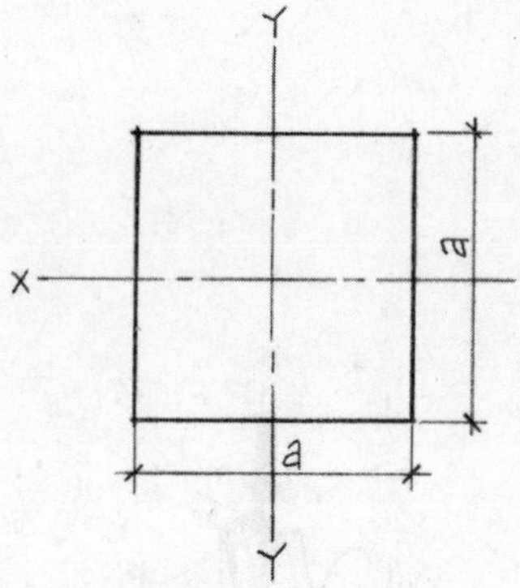

Figure 15(a) Square cross-section (a)x(a).

Solution:

Figure (a): $I_x = \dfrac{bh^3}{12} = \dfrac{a(a)^3}{12} = \dfrac{a^4}{12}$

Figure (b): Made up of four triangles

$$\therefore I_x = \frac{4(bh^3)}{36} + 4(Ad_y^2)$$

$$b = 0.707a; \quad h = 0.707a; \quad d_y = \frac{h}{3} = \frac{0.707a}{3}$$

$$I_x = \frac{4(0.707a \times [0.707a]^3)}{36} + 4\left(\frac{1}{2} \times 0.707a \times 0.707a\right)\left(\frac{0.707a}{3}\right)^2$$

$$I_x = \frac{a^4}{36} + \frac{a^4}{18} = \frac{3a^4}{36} = \frac{a^4}{12}$$

Both cross-sections have equal radii of gyration.

$$r_x = \sqrt{\frac{I_x}{A}} = \sqrt{\frac{\frac{a^4}{12}}{a^2}} = \sqrt{\frac{a^2}{12}} = \frac{a}{2}\sqrt{\frac{1}{3}} = \frac{a}{2\sqrt{3}}$$

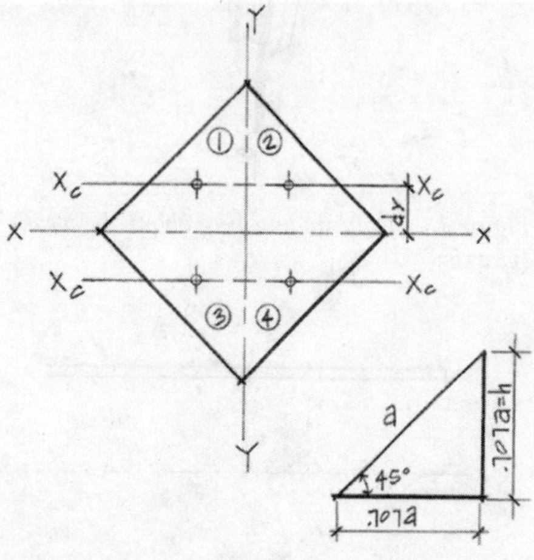

Figure 15(b) Square cross-section rotated 45°.

Summary

- *Center of gravity (C.G.)*, or *center of mass*, refers to masses or weights idealized as a single point at which the weight could be held and be in balance in all directions.
- *Centroid* refers to the geometric center of lines, areas, and volumes. Beam and column design utilizes the centroid of cross-sectional areas for computing other section properties.
- Composite areas are made up of simpler areas.

  $(A = \Sigma \Delta A)$

- The moment of a area about an axis equals the algebraic sum of the moments of its component areas about the same axis.

  $$\bar{x} = \frac{\Sigma x \Delta A}{A}; \qquad \bar{y} = \frac{\Sigma y \Delta A}{A}$$

- The moment of an area is defined as the product of the area multiplied by the perpendicular distance from the moment axis to the centroid of the area.
- Moment of inertia (I), or second moment, is a factor that quantifies the effect of the beam or column's cross-sectional shape in resisting bending, deflection, and buckling. The moment of inertia is a measure of cross-sectional stiffness.

  $$I_x = \Sigma y^2 \Delta A; \quad I_y = \Sigma x^2 \Delta A;$$

- When cross-sectional shapes are not simple geometric shapes but a composite of two or more simple shapes combined, the parallel axis theorem is used for determining the moment of inertia about any axis parallel to the centroidal axis.

  $$I_x = \Sigma I_{x_c} + \Sigma A d_y^2; \quad I_y = \Sigma I_{y_c} + \Sigma A d_x^2$$

- The radius of gyration expresses the relationship between the area of a cross-section and a centroidal moment of inertia. This shape factor is used in measuring a column's slenderness and its resistance to buckling.

  $$r_x = \sqrt{\frac{I_x}{A}}; \quad r_y = \sqrt{\frac{I_y}{A}}$$

Answers to Selected Problems

1 $x = 5.33''$; $y = 5.67''$

3 $x = 7.6'$; $y = 5.3'$

4 $x = 0$; $y = 9.4''$

6 $y = 2.0''$; $I_x = 17.4$ in.^{4}

$x = 0.99''$; $I_y = 6.2$ in.^{4}

8 $I_x = 1{,}787$ in.^{4}; $I_y = 987$ in.^{4}

9 $y = 5.74''$; $I_x = 561$ in.^{4}

11 $y = 10.4''$; $I_x = 1{,}518$ in.^{4}

12 $x = -.036''$; $y = 7.0''$,
$I_x = 110.4$ in.^{4}; $I_y = 35.7$ in.^{4}

14 $I_x = 2{,}299$ in.^{4}; $W = 15.8''$

Bending and Shear in Simple Beams

Bending and Shear in Simple Beams

Introduction

A beam is a long, slender structural member that resists loads that are usually applied transverse (perpendicular) to its longitudinal axis. These transverse forces cause the beam to bend in the plane of the applied loads, and internal stresses develop in the material as it resists these loads.

Beams are probably the most common type of structural member used in the roof and floors of a building of any size, as well as for bridges and other structural applications. Not all beams need to be horizontal; they may be vertical or on a slant. In addition, they may have either one, two, or several reactions.

1 CLASSIFICATION OF BEAMS AND LOADS

The design of a beam entails the determination of size, shape, and material based on the bending stress, shear stress, and deflection due to the applied loads (Figure 1).

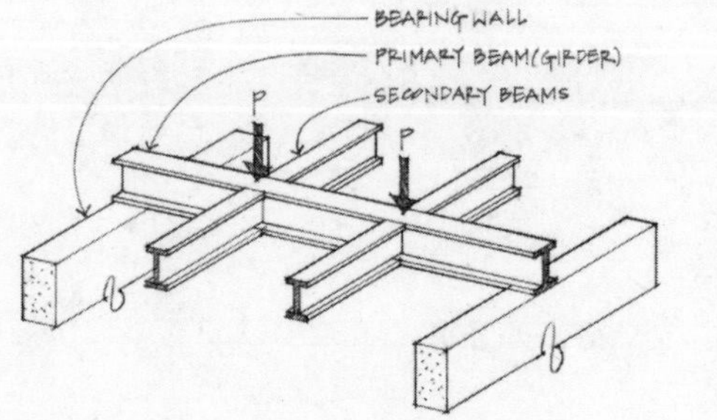

(a) Pictorial diagram of a loaded beam.

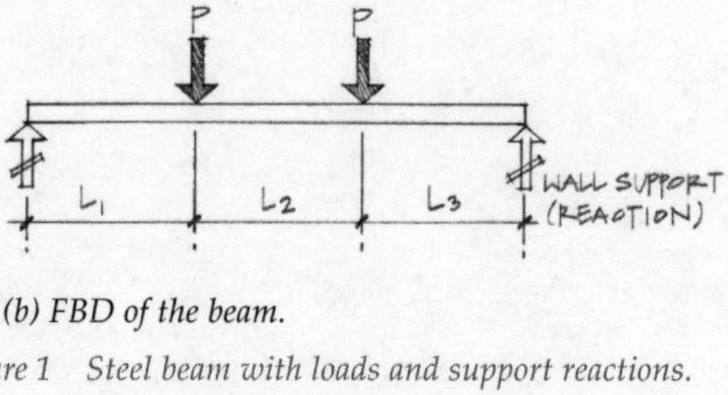

(b) FBD of the beam.

Figure 1 Steel beam with loads and support reactions.

Beams are often classified according to their support conditions. Figure 2 illustrates six major beam classifications.

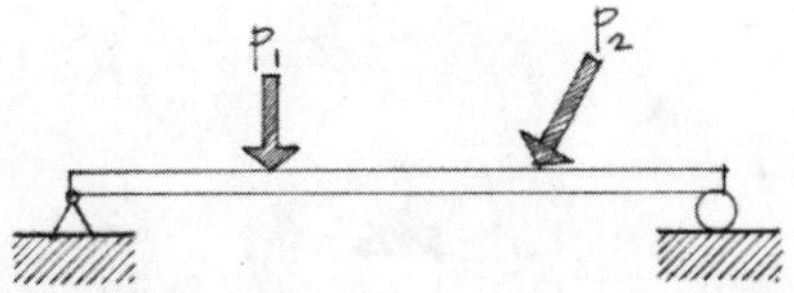

(a) Simply supported: two supports.

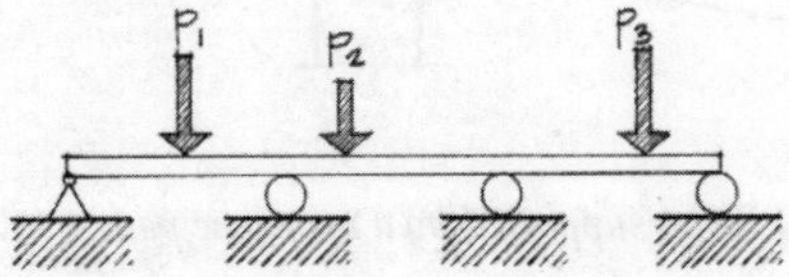

(b) Continuous: three or more supports.

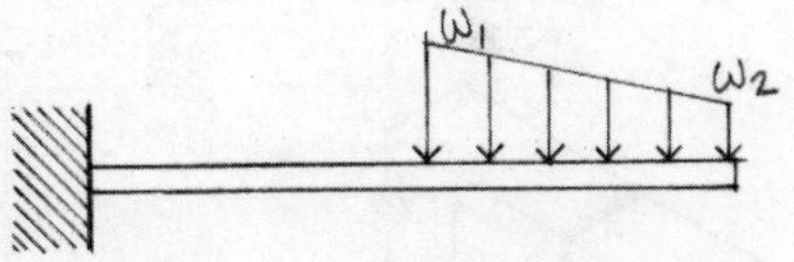

(c) Cantilever: one end supported rigidly.

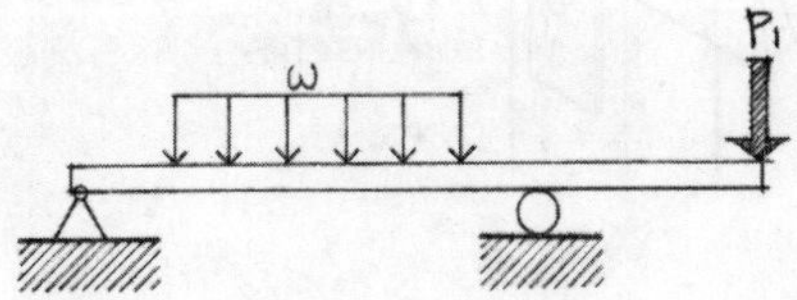

(d) Overhang: two supports—one or both supports not located at the end.

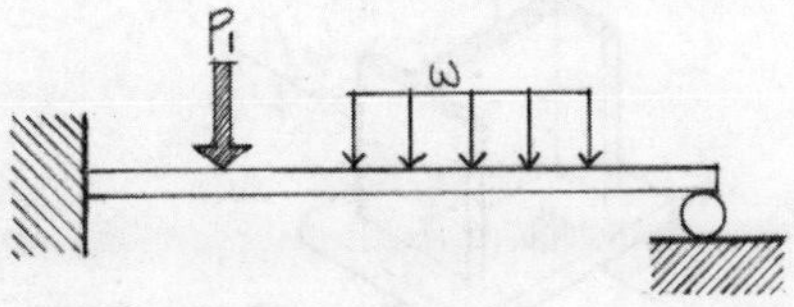

(e) Propped: two supports—one end is fixed.

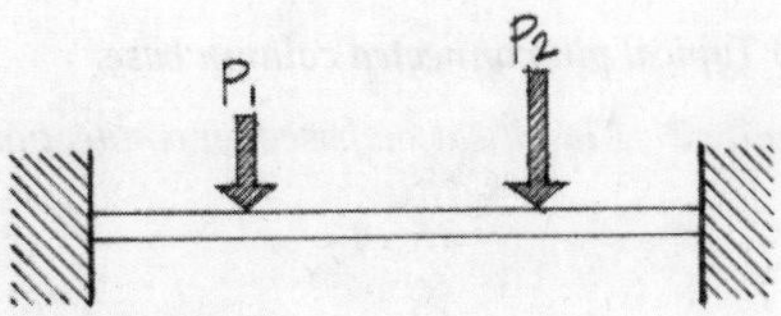

(f) Restrained or fixed: both supports are fixed, allowing no rotation at the restrained ends.

Figure 2 Classification based on support conditions.

Types of Connections

Actual support and connection conditions for beams and columns are idealized as rollers, hinges (pins), or fixed. Figure 3 illustrates examples of common support/connection conditions found in practice.

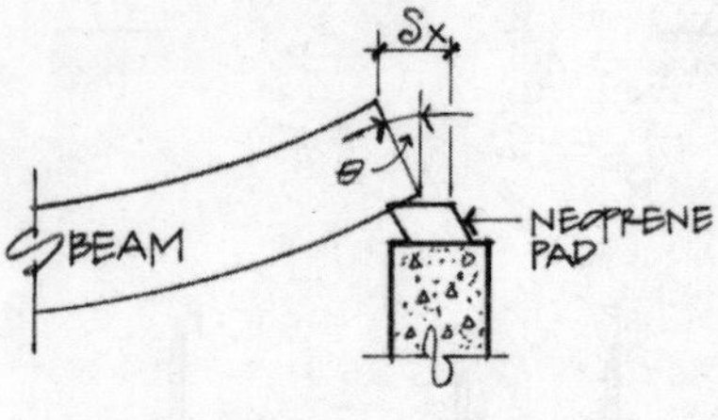

(a) Beam supported by a neoprene pad.

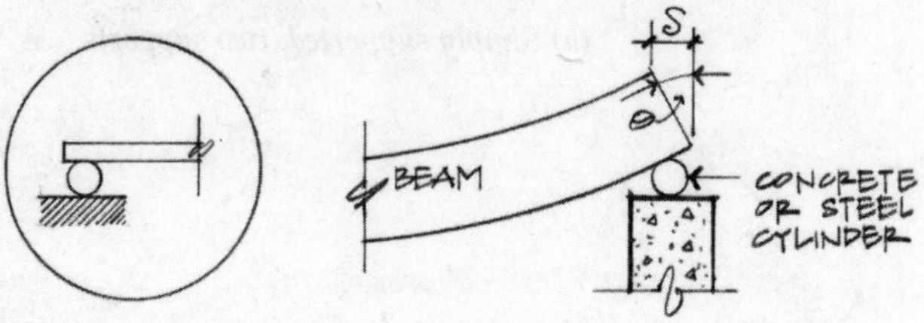

(b) Beam supported by a concrete or steel cylinder.

Examples of roller supports (a, b). Horizontal displacement and rotation are permitted; may be due to loads or thermal conditions.

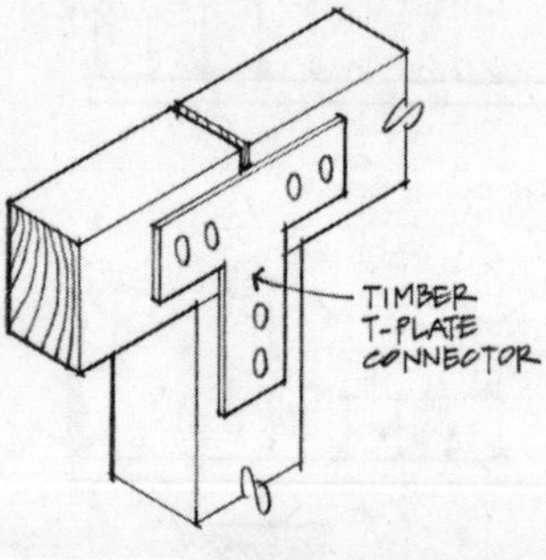

(c) Timber beam-column connection with T-plate.

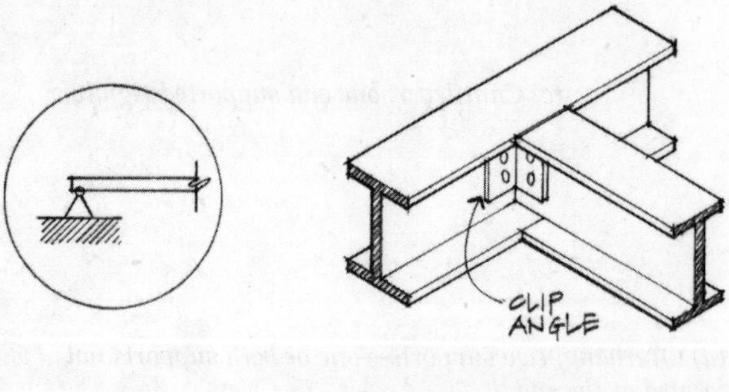

(d) Steel beam connected to a steel girder.

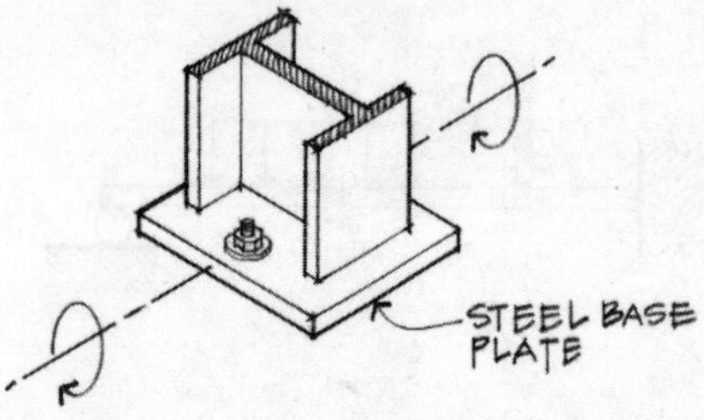

(e) Typical pin-connected column base.

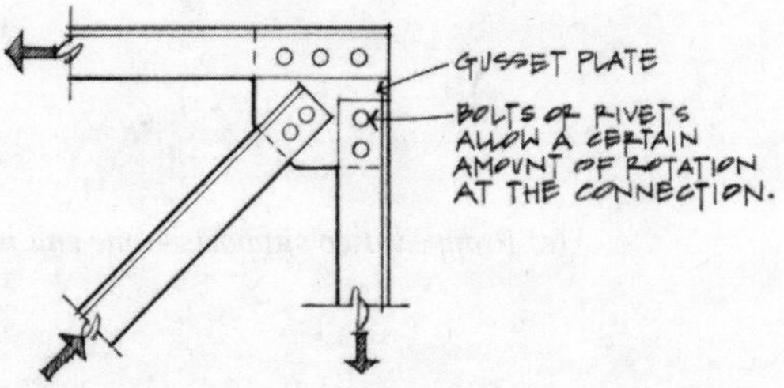

(f) Truss joint—three steel angles with gusset plate.

Figure 3 Classification based on connection types (continues on next page).

Examples of hinge or pin supports (c, d, e, f). Allows a certain amount of rotation at the connection.

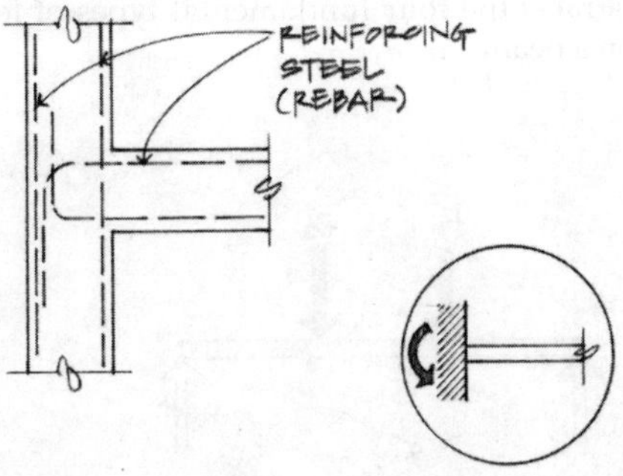

(g) Reinforced concrete floor-wall connection.

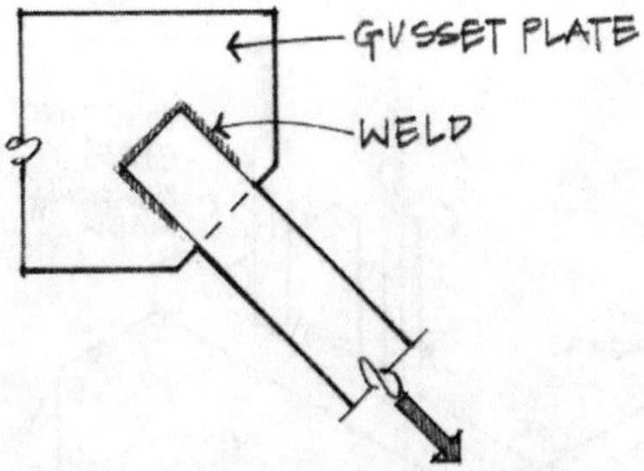

(h) Steel strap welded to a gusset plate.

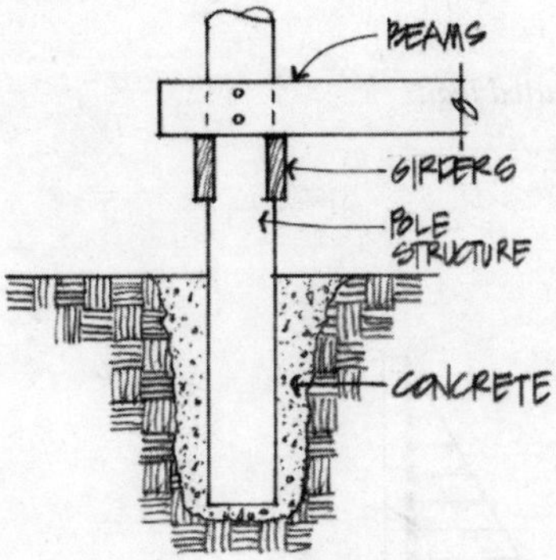

(i) Timber pole structure—embedded base.

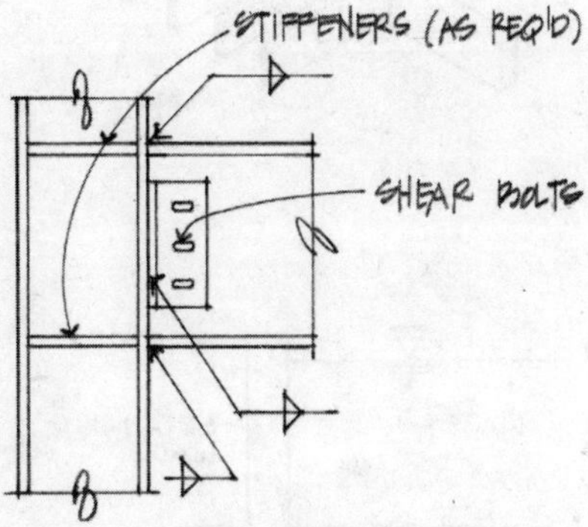

(j) Beam-column moment connection.

Examples of fixed support (g, h, i, j). No rotation at the connection.

Figure 3 Classification based on connection types (Con't.)

Figure 4 illustrates the four fundamental types of loads that can act on a beam.

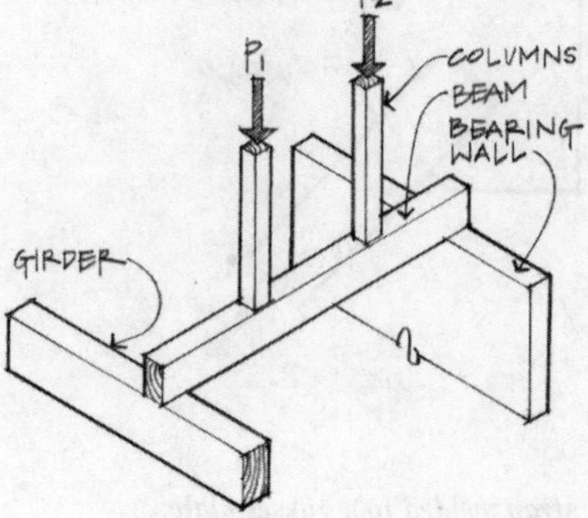

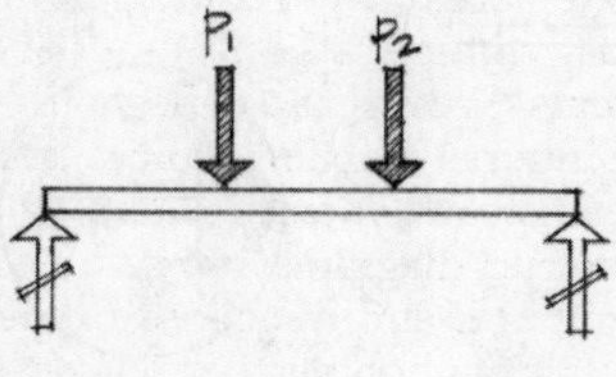

(a) Concentrated load.

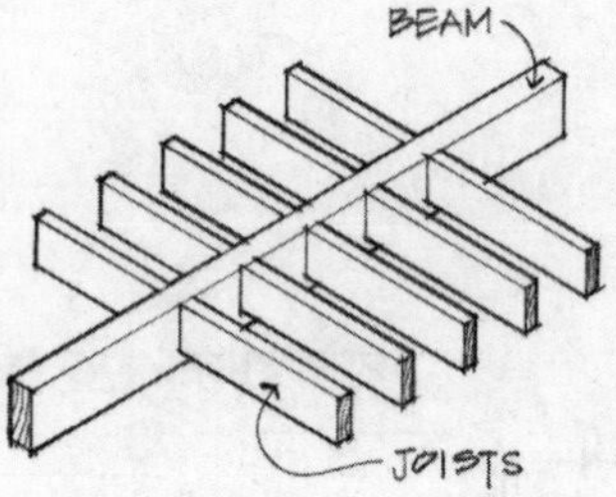

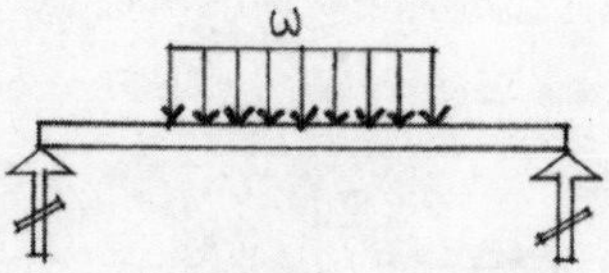

(b) Uniformly distributed load.

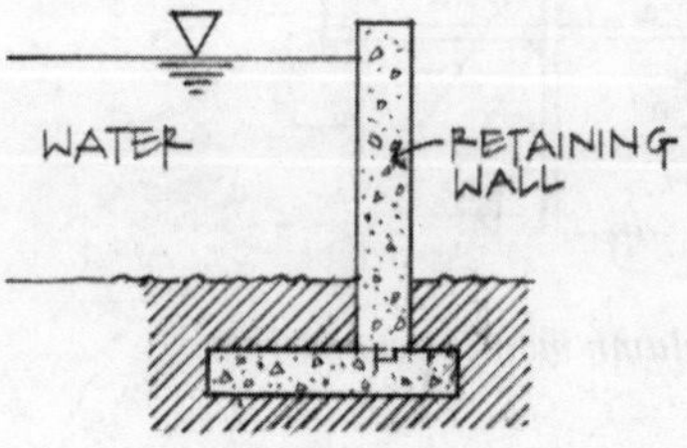

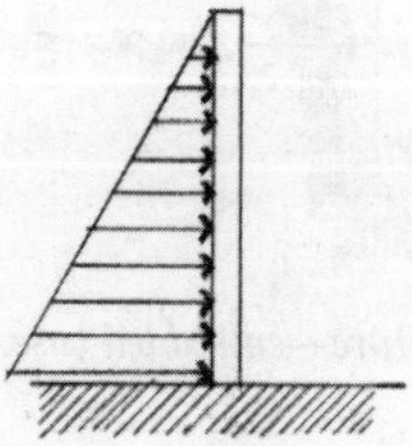

(c) Nonuniformly distributed load.

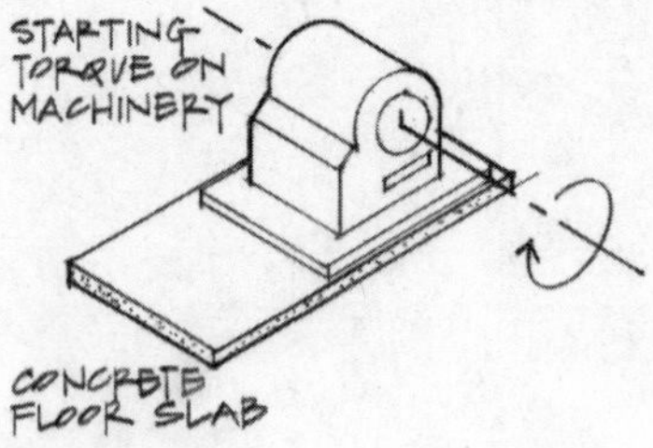

(d) Pure moment.

Figure 4 Classification based on load type.

2 SHEAR AND BENDING MOMENT

When a beam is subjected to any of the loadings previously discussed, either singly or in any combination, the beam must resist these loads and remain in equilibrium. For the beam to remain in equilibrium, an internal force system must exist within the beam to resist the applied forces and moments. Stresses and deflections in beams are functions of the internal reactions, forces, and moments. For this reason, it is convenient to "map" these internal forces and to construct diagrams that give a complete picture of the magnitudes and directions of the forces and moments that act throughout the beam length. These diagrams are referred to as *load*, *shear* (*V*), and *moment* (*M*) *diagrams* (Figure 5).

- The *load diagram* shown in Figure 5 is for a point load at the free end of a cantilever beam. (The load diagram is essentially the FBD of the beam.)
- The *shear diagram* shown in Figure 5 is a graph of the transverse shear along the beam length.
- The *moment diagram* shown in Figure 5 is a graph of the bending moment along the beam length.

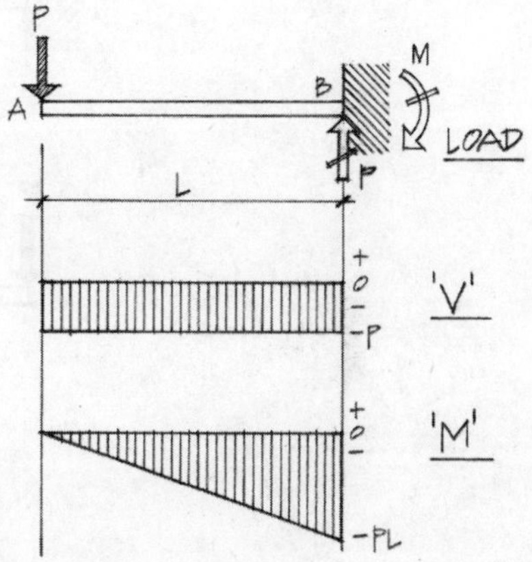

Figure 5 Load, shear (V), and moment (M) diagrams.

A *shear diagram* is a graph in which the *abscissa* (horizontal reference axis) represents distances along the beam length and the *ordinates* (vertical measurements from the abscissa) represent the transverse shear at the corresponding beam sections. A *moment diagram* is a graph in which the abscissa represents distances along the beam and the ordinates represent the bending moment at the corresponding sections.

Shear and moment diagrams can be drawn by calculating values of shear and moment at various sections along the beam and plotting enough points to obtain a smooth curve. Such a procedure is rather time-consuming, however, and although it may be desirable for graphical solutions of certain structural problems, two more rapid methods will be developed in Sections 3 and 5.

A sign convention is necessary for shear and moment diagrams if the results obtained from their use are to be interpreted conveniently and reliably.

By definition, the shear at a section is considered to be positive when the portion of the beam to the left of the section cut (for a horizontal beam) tends to be in the up position with respect to the portion to the right of the section cut, as shown in Figure 6.

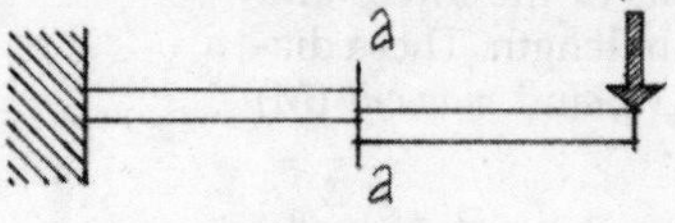

(+) Shear.

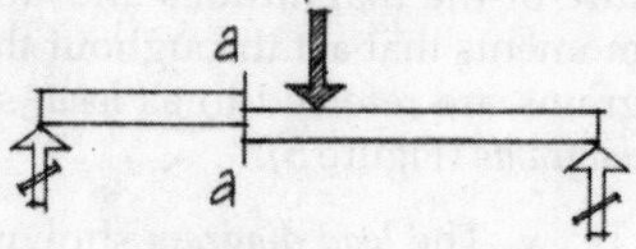

(+) Shear.

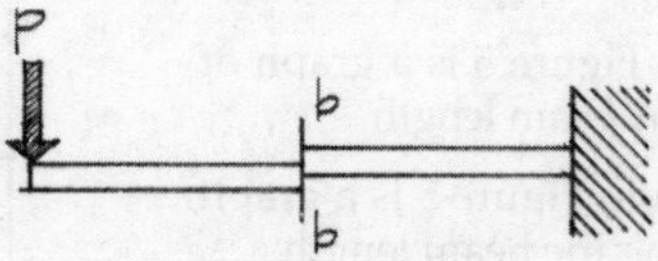

(–) Shear.

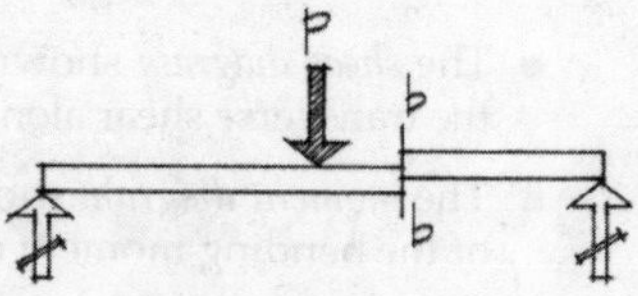

(–) Shear.

Figure 6 Sign convention for shear.

Also by definition, the bending moment in a horizontal beam is positive at sections for which the top fibers of the beam are in compression and the bottom fibers are in tension, as shown in Figure 7.

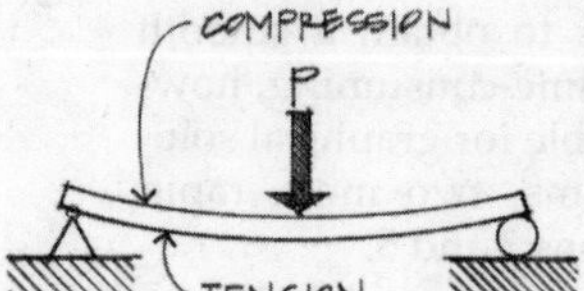

(+) Moment.

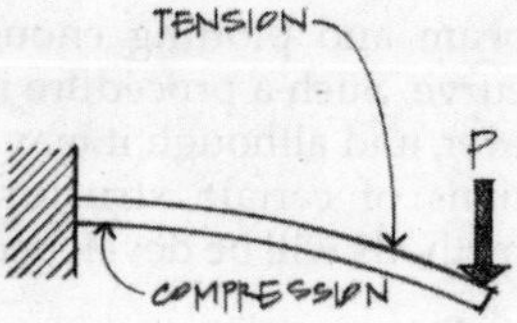

(–) Moment.

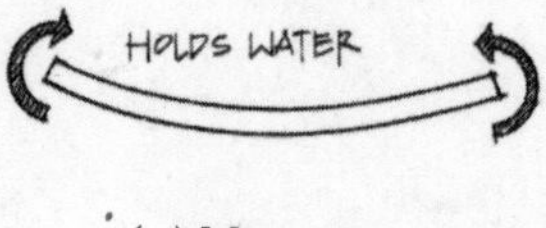

(+) Moment.

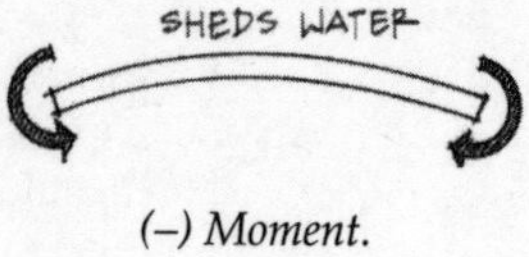

(–) Moment.

Figure 7 Sign convention for moment.

Positive moment generates a curvature that tends to hold water (concave-upward curvature), whereas *negative moment* causes a curvature that sheds water (concave-downward curvature).

This convention is a standard one for mathematics and is universally accepted. Because the convention is related to the probable deflected shape of the beam for a prescribed loading condition, it may be helpful to sketch intuitively the beam's deflected shape to assist in determining the appropriate moment signs (Figure 8).

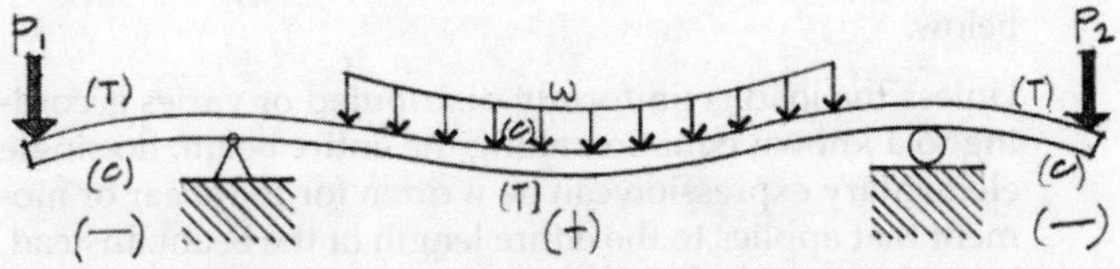

Figure 8 Deflected shape due to loads on overhang beam.

The overhang beam shown in Figure 8 exhibits a changing curvature that results in negative to positive to negative moments. The implication here is that the beam span includes one or more transverse sections where the bending moment is zero to accommodate the required sign change. Such a section, termed the *inflection point* or *point of inflection*, is almost always present in overhang and multiple-span beams.

An important feature of the sign convention used for shear and moment diagrams is that it differs from the conventions used in statics. When using the equations of equilibrium, forces directed up and to the right are positive, and counterclockwise moment tendencies are positive. The new sign convention is used specifically for plotting the shear and moment diagrams. Make sure you do not confuse the two conventions.

3 EQUILIBRIUM METHOD FOR SHEAR AND MOMENT DIAGRAMS

One basic method used in obtaining shear and moment diagrams is referred to as the *equilibrium method*. Specific values of V and M are determined from statics equations that are valid for appropriate sections of the member. In the explanations that follow, we shall assume that the member is a beam acted upon by downward loads, but the member could be turned at any angle.

A convenient arrangement for constructing shear and moment diagrams is to draw an FBD of the entire beam and then construct shear and moment diagrams directly below.

Unless the load is uniformly distributed or varies according to a known equation along the entire beam, no single elementary expression can be written for the shear or moment that applies to the entire length of the beam. Instead, it is necessary to divide the beam into intervals bounded by abrupt changes in the loading.

An origin should be selected (different origins may be used for different intervals), and positive directions should be indicated for the coordinate axes. Because V and M vary as a function of x along the beam length, equations for V and M can be obtained from FBDs of portions of the beam (see Example Problem 1). Complete shear and moment diagrams should indicate values of shear and moment at each section where they are maximum positive and maximum negative. Sections where the shear and/or moment are zero should also be located.

Example Problems: Equilibrium Method for Shear and Moment Diagrams

1 Using the equilibrium method, draw the shear and moment diagrams for a simply supported beam with a single concentrated load.

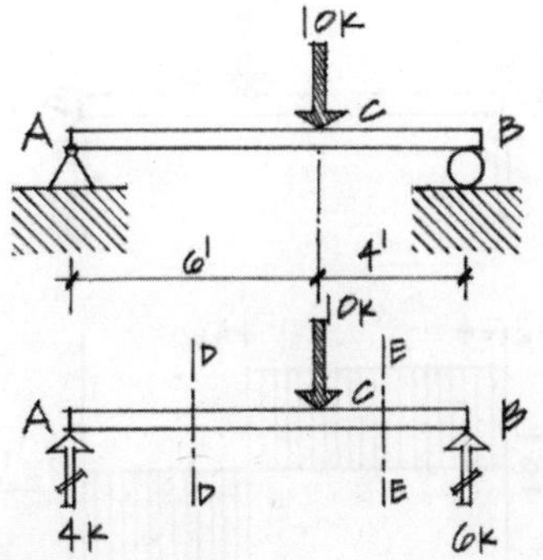

FBD of entire beam (often referred to as the load *diagram).*

Solution:

Solve for external reactions at *A* and *B*. Cut the beam through section *D-D*. Draw an FBD for each half of the beam.

Examine segment *AD* from the FBD cut through *D*.

$[\Sigma F_y = 0] V = 4\,\text{k}$
$[\Sigma M_D = 0] M = 4\,\text{k}(x)$

Note: *Shear* V *is a constant between* A *and* C. *The moment varies as a function of* x *(linearly) between* A *and* C.

$@\, x = 0, M = 0$
$@\, x = 6', M = 24\,\text{k-ft.}$

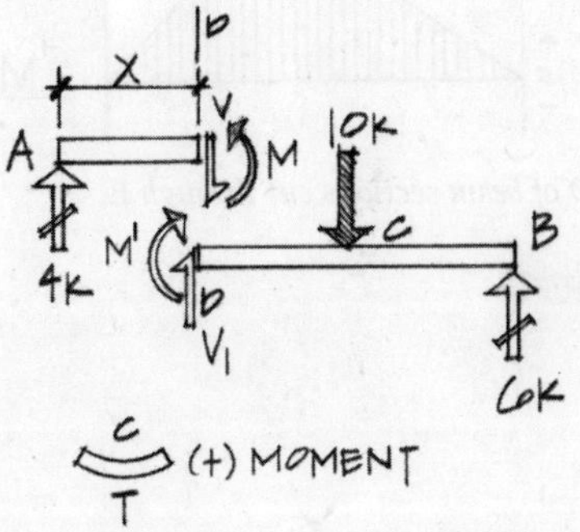

FBD of beam sections cut through D.

Examine segment *AE* from the FBD cut through *E*.

$[\Sigma F_y = 0]\ V = 10\,\text{k} - 4\,\text{k} = 6\,\text{k}$

$[\Sigma M = 0] + M + 10\,\text{k}\,(x - 6') - 4\,\text{k}(x) = 0$
$M = 60\,\text{k-ft.} - 6x$

$@\, x = 6', M = 24\,\text{k-ft.}$

$@\, x = 10', M = 0$

Note: *Shear* V $= 6\,k$ *remains constant between* C *and* B. *The moment varies linearly, decreasing as* x *increases from* C *to* B.

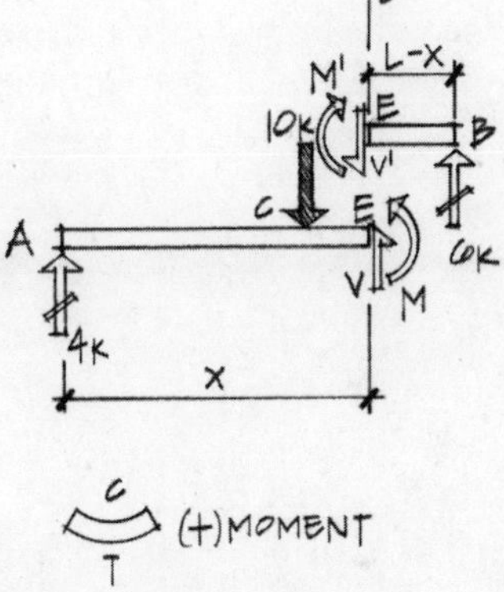

FBD of beam sections cut through E.

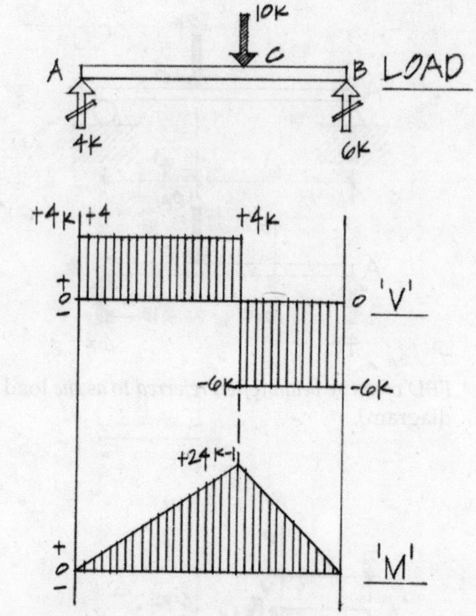

Load diagram (FBD).

Shear (V) diagram.

Shear constant *A* to *C* (positive).

Shear constant C to *B* (negative).

$V_{max} = 6\text{ k }(-)$ shear

Moment (M) diagram.

FBD of beam sections cut through E.

Moments are all positive.

Moment increases linearly from *A* to *C* ($x = 0$ to $x = 6'$).

Moment decreases linearly from C to *B* ($x = 6'$ to $x = 10'$).

2 Draw shear and moment diagrams for an overhang beam loaded as shown. Determine the critical V_{max} and M_{max} locations and magnitudes.

Draw an FBD. Solve for external reactions. Based on intuition, sketch the deflected shape of the beam to assist in determining the signs for moment.

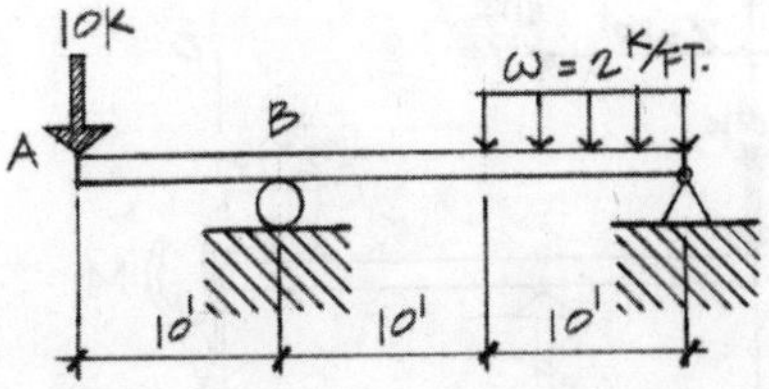

Loaded beam.

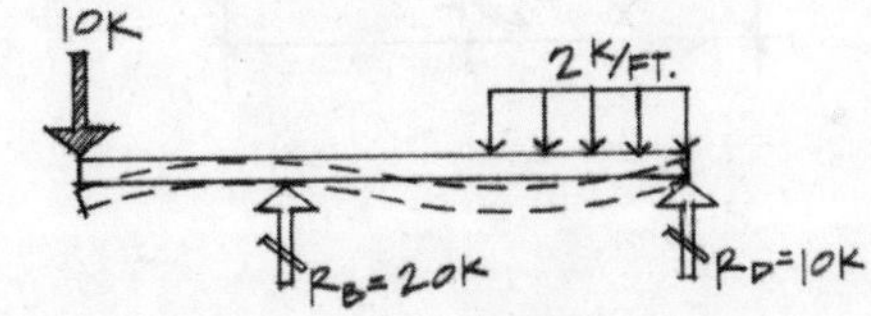

Load diagram (FBD).

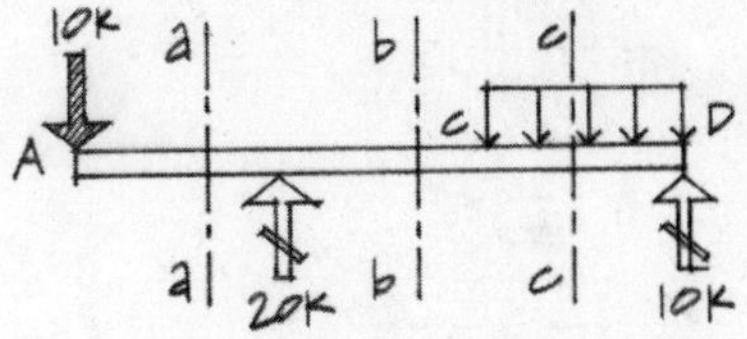

Cut sections a, b, *and* c *between loads and reactions.*

Solution:

To find $V_{critical}$, examine section (a) left and right of concentrated loads and section (b) at the beginning and end of distributed loads.

FBD at section cut a-a.

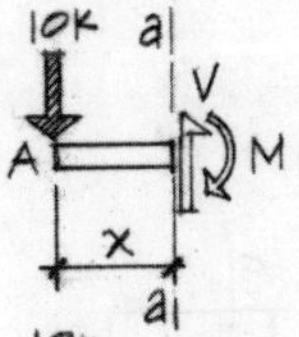

Section *a-a*, $x = 0$ to $x = 10'$

$[\Sigma F_y = 0] V = 10\,\text{k}\,(-)$ shear

Just right of *A*, $V = 10\,\text{k}$

At $x = 10'$, $V = 10\,\text{k}$

FBD at section cut b-b.

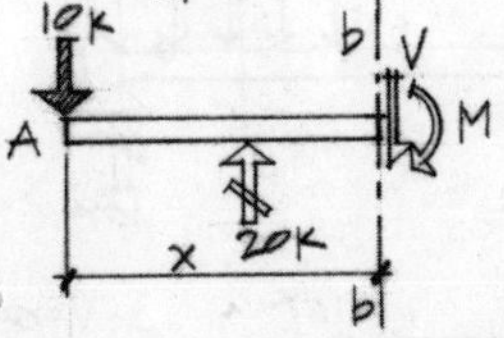

Section *b-b*, $x = 10'$ to $x = 20'$

Just right of *B*, $[\Sigma F_y = 0] V = 10\,\text{k}$

$(+)$ shear (constant)

Just left of *C*, at $x = 20'$, $[\Sigma F_y = 0]$ and $V = 10\,\text{k}$

FBD at section cut c-c.

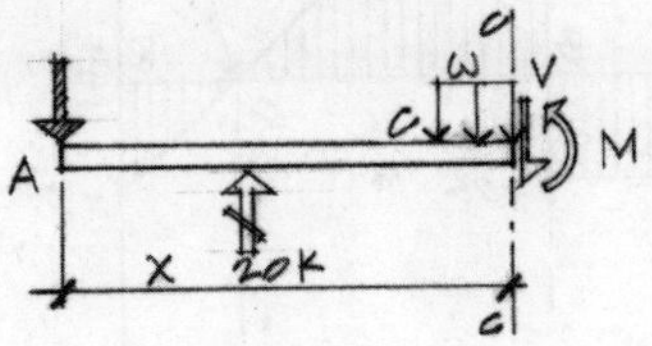

Section *c-c*, $x = 20'$ to $x = 30'$

Just right of *C*, $[\Sigma F_y = 0] V = 10\,\text{k}\,(+)$ shear

Just left of *D*, at $x = 30'$, $[\Sigma F_y = 0]$ and

$V = 20\,\text{k} - 10\,\text{k} - 2\,\text{k/ft.}(x - 20)'$

$V = 50\,\text{k} - 2x$

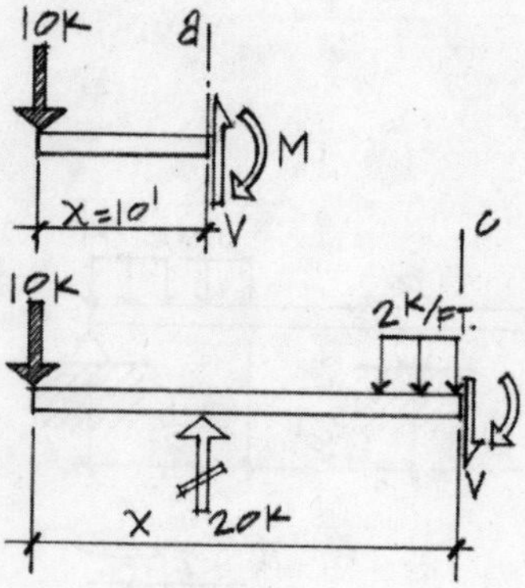

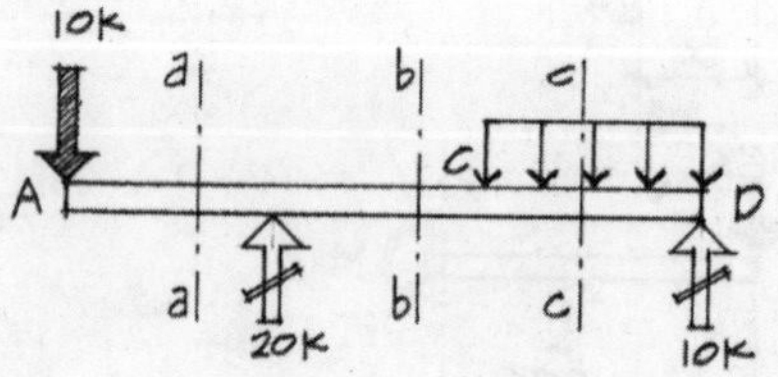

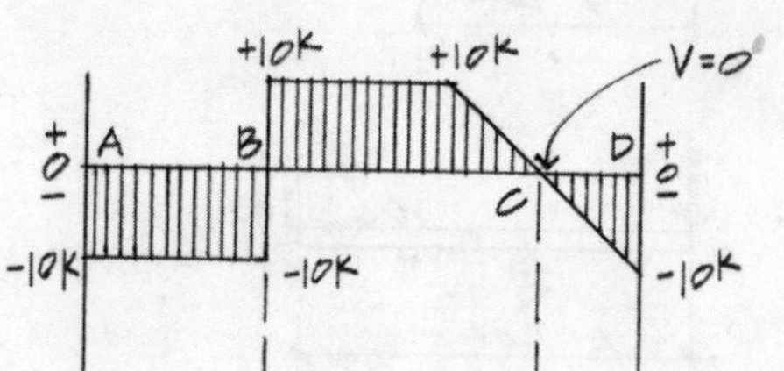

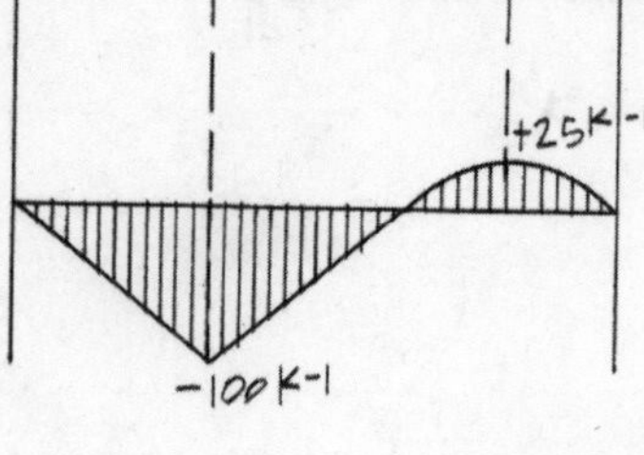

M_{max} occurs at places where $V = 0$ or V changes sign. This occurs twice, at B and between C and D.

For M_{max} at B:

Examine a section cut just to the left or right of the concentrated load.

$M = (10\text{ k})(10') = 100\text{ k-ft.}\ (-)$ moment

For M_{max} between C and D:

Examine the equation of section cut c-c.

$[\Sigma F_y = 0]\ -10\text{ k} + 20\text{ k} - 2\text{ k/ft.}(x - 20') - V = 0$

$-10\text{ k} + 20\text{ k} - 2x + 40 - V = 0$

$\therefore\ V = 50 - 2x$

But, M_{max} occurs at $V = 0$.

$\therefore\ 0 = 50 - 2x, \quad x = 25'$

$[\Sigma M_c = 0]$ at $x = 25'$

$+10\text{ k}(25') - 20\text{ k}(15') + 2\text{ k/ft.}(5')(2.5') + M = 0$

$M_{max} = 25\text{ k-ft.}\ (+)$ moment

***Note:** Beams with one overhang end develop two possible* M_{max} *values.*

$\therefore\ M_{critical} = 100\text{ k-ft. at } B\ (-)$ moment

Construct the resulting shear and moment diagrams.

Load diagram.

Shear diagram.

Moment diagram.

Problems

Construct shear and moment diagrams using the equilibrium method. Indicate the magnitudes of V_{max} and M_{max}.

1

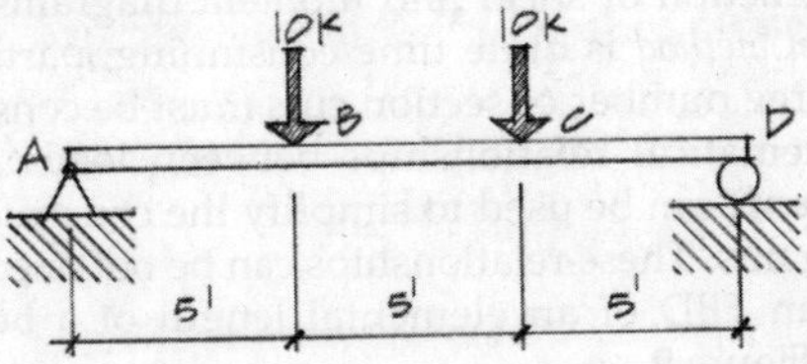

2

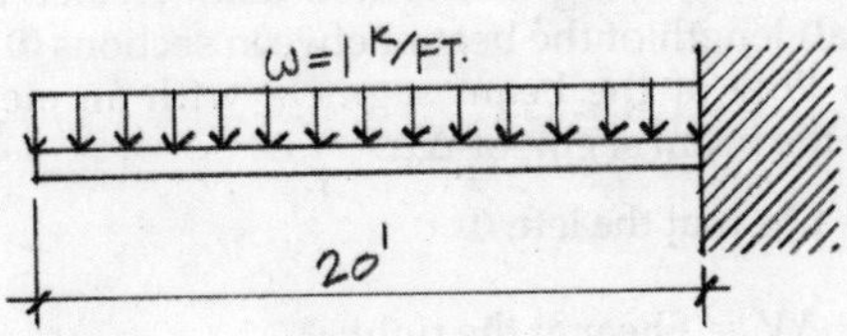

3

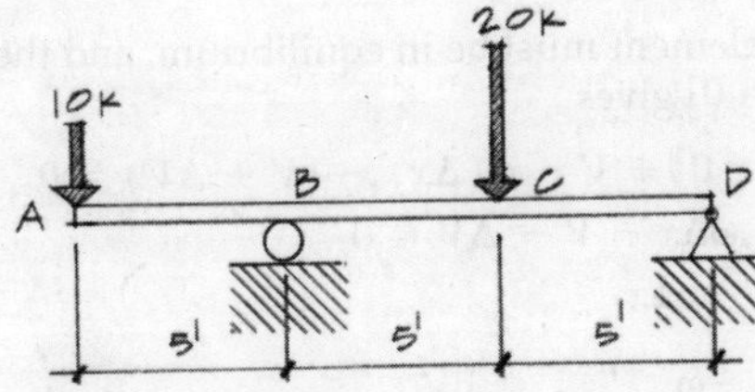

4

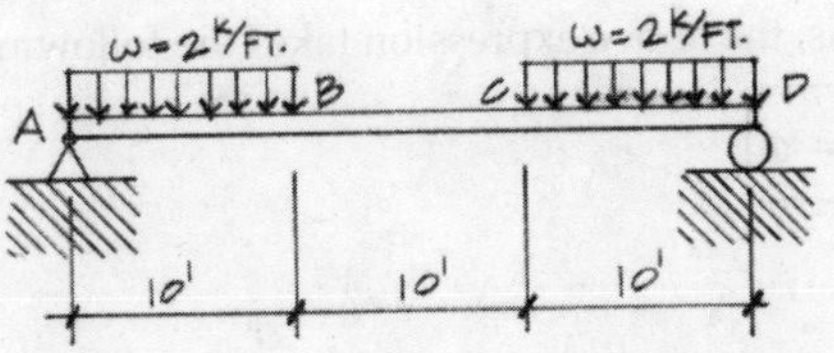

4 RELATIONSHIP BETWEEN LOAD, TRANSVERSE SHEAR, AND BENDING MOMENT

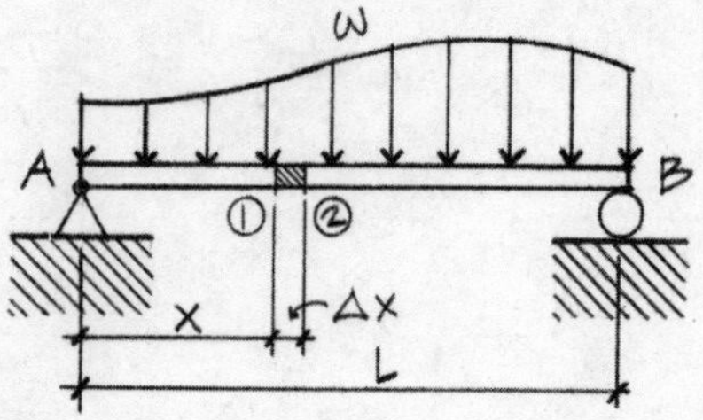

Figure 9(a) Beam with a generalized load.

The construction of shear and moment diagrams by the *equilibrium method* is quite time-consuming, particularly when a large number of section cuts must be considered. The mathematical relationships between loads, shears, and moments can be used to simplify the construction of such diagrams. These relationships can be obtained by examining an FBD of an elemental length of a beam, as shown in Figure 9.

In this example, we will assume a simply supported beam loaded with a varying distributed load. Detach a small (elemental) length of the beam between sections ① and ②. Draw an FBD of the beam segment with an elemental length of the beam segment Δx.

$V =$ Shear at the left; ①

$V + \Delta V =$ Shear at the right; ②

$\Delta V =$ Change in shear between sections ① and ②

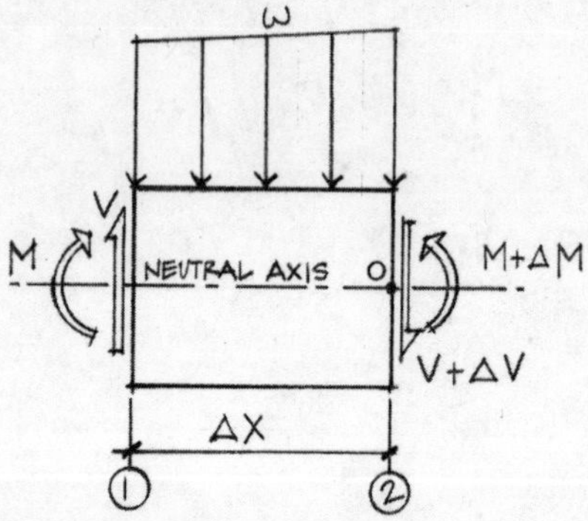

Figure 9(b) An elemental section of the beam.

The beam element must be in equilibrium, and the equation $[\Sigma F_y = 0]$ gives

$$[\Sigma F_y = 0] + V - \omega(\Delta x) - (V + \Delta V) = 0$$
$$+V - \omega\Delta x - V - \Delta V = 0$$
$$\Delta V = -\omega\Delta x$$
$$\frac{\Delta V}{\Delta x} = -\omega$$

Note: *The negative sign represents a negative slope for this particular load condition.*

In calculus, the above expression takes the following form:

$$\boxed{\frac{dV}{dx} = \omega}$$

The preceding equation indicates that at any section in the beam, the slope of the shear diagram is equal to the intensity of the loading.

If we examine the shear on the beam between points x_1 and x_2 (Figure 10), we obtain

$$V = \omega \Delta x$$
$$\text{but } \Delta V = V_2 - V_1$$
$$\text{and } \Delta x = x_2 - x_1$$
$$\therefore V_2 - V_1 = \omega(x_2 - x_1)$$

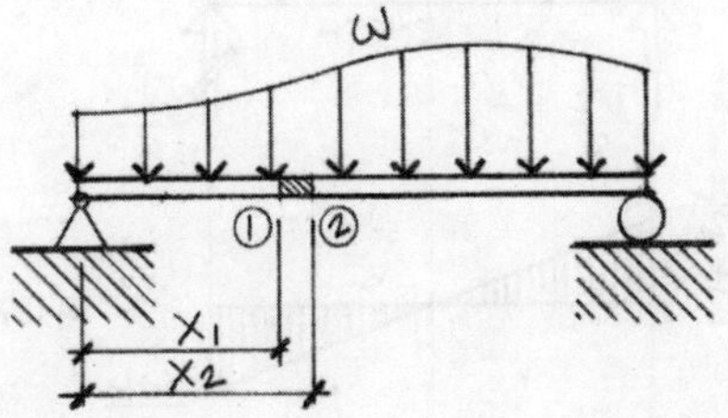

Figure 10 Section of beam between points ① and ②.

When $dV/dx = \omega$ is known as a function of x, the equation can be integrated between definite limits as follows:

$$\int_{v_1}^{v_2} dV = \int_{x_1}^{x_2} \omega dx$$

$$\boxed{V_2 - V_1 = \omega(x_2 - x_1)}$$ ***(Note:** Same equation as above.)*

That is, the change in shear between sections at x_1 and x_2 is equal to the area under the load diagram between the two sections.

Another equation of equilibrium about point 0 for Figure 9(a) can be written as

$$[\Sigma M_0 = 0] - V(\Delta x) - M + (M + \Delta M) + \omega(\Delta x)\left(\frac{\Delta x}{2}\right) = 0$$

$$-V\Delta x - M + M + \Delta M + \frac{\omega \Delta x^2}{2} = 0$$

If Δx is a small value, the square of Δx becomes negligible.

$$\therefore \Delta M = V\Delta x \text{ or } dM = Vdx$$

$$\boxed{\frac{dM}{dx} = V}$$

The preceding equation indicates that at any section in the beam, the slope of the moment diagram is equal to the shear. Again, examining the beam between points ① and ② of Figure 10:

$$\Delta M = M_2 - M_l;\ \Delta x = x_2 - x_l$$

$$\therefore M_2 - M_l = V(x_2 - x_l)$$

$$\text{or } \int_{M_1}^{M_2} dM = \int_{x_1}^{x_2} Vdx$$

$$\boxed{M_2 - M_1 = V(x_2 - x_1)}$$

5 SEMIGRAPHICAL METHOD FOR LOAD, SHEAR, AND MOMENT DIAGRAMS

The two expressions developed in the previous section can be used to draw shear and moment diagrams and compute values of shear and moment at various sections along the beam as needed. This method is often referred to as the *semigraphical method*.

Before illustrating the semigraphical method for shear and moment diagrams, it might be helpful to see the relationship that exists between all of the diagrams (Figure 11). The example shown is for a simply supported beam with a uniform load over the entire span.

Also necessary before attempting the semigraphical method is an understanding of basic curves and curve relationships (Figures 12 and 13).

$$\text{Load: } \omega = \frac{dV}{dx} = \frac{d^2M}{dx^2} = \frac{EId^4y}{dx^4}$$

where

E = modulus of elasticity

I = moment of inertia

$$\text{Shear: } V = \frac{dM}{dx} = EI\frac{d^3y}{dx^3}$$

$$\text{Moment: } M = \frac{d^2y}{dx^2}EI$$

$$\frac{M}{EI} = \frac{d^2y}{dx^2} = \frac{d\theta}{dx}$$

$$\text{Slope: } \theta = \frac{dy}{dx}$$

Deflection: y

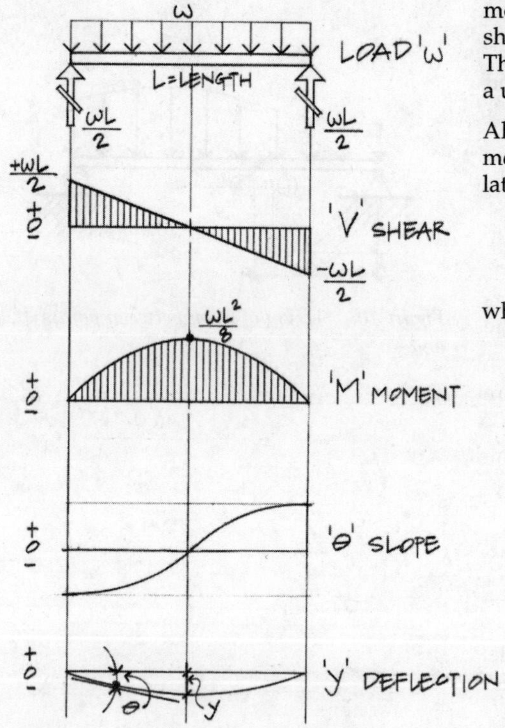

Figure 11 Relationship of load, shear, moment, slope, and deflection diagrams.

Zero-degree curve

$y = c$

c = constant

First-degree curve

Straight line—may be uniformly increasing or decreasing.

$$\text{Slope} = \frac{\Delta y}{\Delta x}$$

$y = cx$

c = constant

Second-degree curve

Parabolic—increasing (approaching verticality) or decreasing (approaching horizontality).

$y = kx^2 + c$

Third-degree curve

Generally steeper than a second-degree curve.

$y = kx^3 + k'x^2 + \ldots$

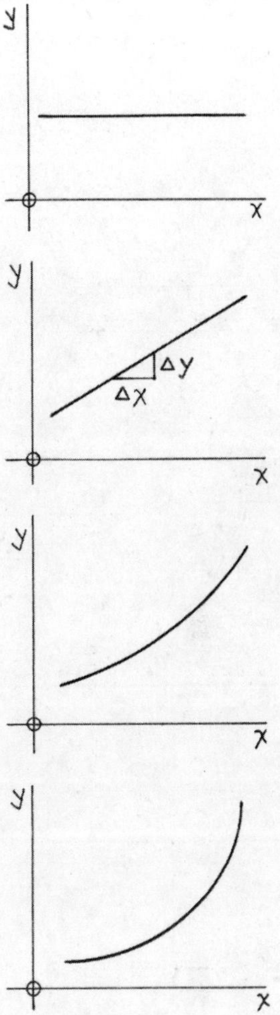

Figure 12 Basic curves.

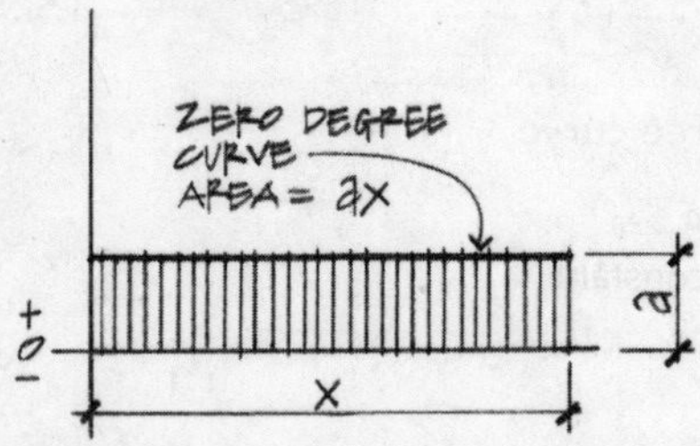

Zero-degree curve

A zero-degree curve may represent a uniformly distributed load or the area of a shear diagram. x = any point x along the beam.

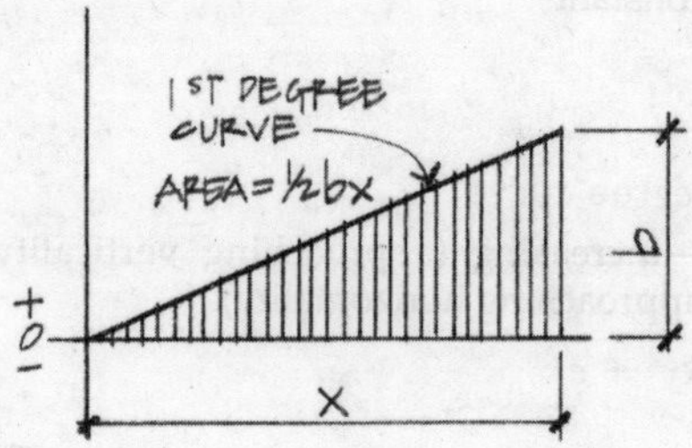

First-degree curve

A first-degree curve may represent triangular loading, the area under the shear diagram for a uniform load, or the area under the moment diagram for a concentrated load.

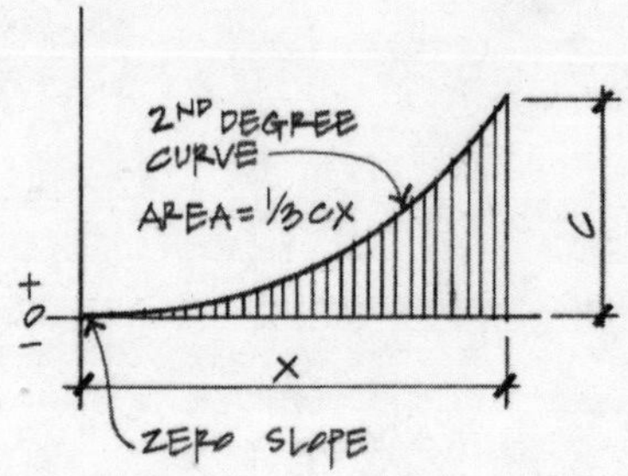

Second-degree curve

A second-degree curve usually represents the area of a shear diagram due to a triangular load distribution, or it could represent the moment diagram for a uniform load distribution.

Figure 13 Basic curves and their properties.

Load, Shear, and Moment Diagrams (Semigraphical Method)

General considerations for drawing shear and moment diagrams:

1. When all loads and reactions are known, the shear and moment at the ends of the beam can be determined by inspection.
2. At a simply supported or pinned end, the shear must equal the end reaction, and the moment must be zero.
3. Both shear and moment are zero at a free end of a beam (cantilever beam or overhang beam).
4. At a built-in or fixed-end beam, the reactions are equal to the shear and moment values.
5. Load, shear, and moment diagrams are usually drawn in a definite sequence, with the load diagram on top, the shear diagram directly beneath the load diagram, and the moment diagram below the shear diagram.
6. When positive directions are chosen as upward and to the right, a uniformly distributed load acting downward will give a negative slope in the shear diagram, and a positive distributed load (one acting upward) will result in a positive slope.
7. A concentrated force produces an abrupt change in shear.
8. The change in shear between any two sections is given by the area under the load diagram between the same two sections: $(V_2 - V_1) = \omega_{\text{ave}}(x_2 - x_1)$.
9. The change of shear at a concentrated force is equal to the concentrated force.
10. The slope at any point on the moment diagram is given by the shear at the corresponding point on the shear diagram: A positive shear represents a positive slope, and a negative shear represents a negative slope.
11. The rate of increase or decrease in the moment diagram slope is determined by the increasing or decreasing areas in the shear diagram.
12. The change in moment between any two sections is given by the area under the shear diagram between corresponding sections: $(M_2 - M_1) = V_{\text{ave}}(x_2 - x_1)$
13. A moment couple applied to a beam will cause the moment to change abruptly by an amount equal to the moment of the couple.

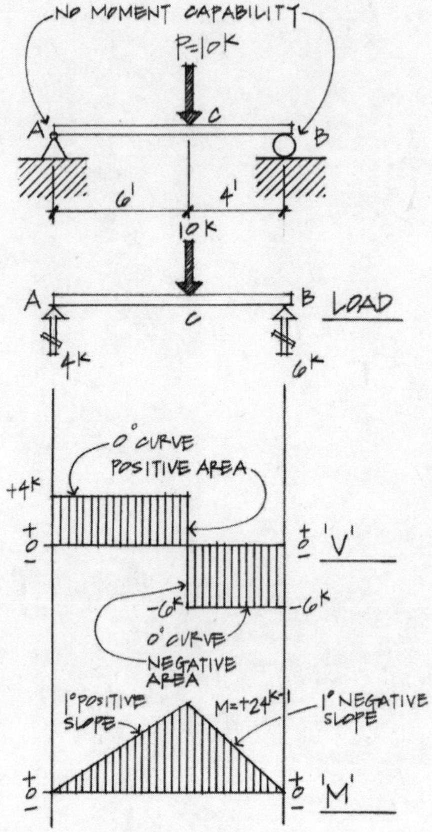

Example Problems: Shear and Moment Diagrams

3 Beam *ABC* is loaded with a single concentrated load as shown. Construct the shear and moment diagrams.

Solution:

Load, shear, and moment diagrams come in a definite order because of their mathematical relationships (see Figure 11).

Draw an FBD of the beam, and solve for the external support reactions. This FBD is the load diagram.

By inspection, the shear at end *A* is +4 k.

Between *A* and *C*, there is no load shown on the load diagram. Therefore,

$$\omega = 0$$

$$V_2 - V_1 = \omega(x_2 - x_1)$$

$$\therefore\ V_2 - V_1 = 0$$

There is no change in shear between *A* and *C* (the shear is constant).

At *C*, the 10 k concentrated load causes an abrupt change in shear from +4 k to −6 k. The total shear change equals the magnitude of the concentrated load.

Between *C* and *B*, no load exists; therefore, there is no shear change. The shear remains a constant −6 k.

At support *B*, an upward 6 k force returns the shear to zero. There is no resultant shear at the very end of the beam.

The moment at pin and roller supports is zero; pins and rollers have no capacity to resist moment.

The change in moment between any two points on a beam equals the area under the shear curve between the same two points:

$$M_2 - M_1 = V(x_2 - x_1)$$

Between *A* and *C*, the area under the shear curve is the area of a rectangle:

$$\text{area} = 6' \times 4\,\text{k} = 24\,\text{k-ft.}$$

Because the shear area is positive, the change in moment will occur along a positive, increasing curve. The change in moment is uniform (linearly increasing).

Shear diagram → Moment diagram
$0°$ curve $1°$ curve
$(+)$ area $(+)$ slope

From C to B, the area of the shear diagram is

$$\text{Area} = 4' \times 6\,\text{k} = 24\,\text{k-ft.}$$

The change in moment from C to B is 24 k-ft.

Shear area → Moment diagram
$0°$ curve $1°$ curve
$(-)$ area $(-)$ slope

Because the shear area is negative, the slope of the moment curve is negative.

The moment at B should go back to zero, because no moment capability exists at the roller support.

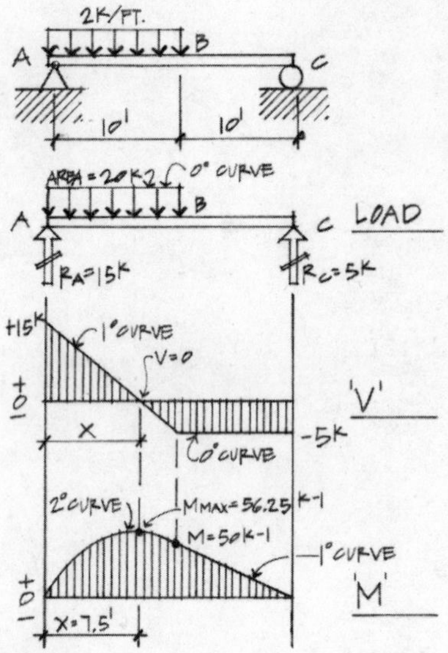

4 Construct shear and moment diagrams for the simply supported beam *ABC*, which is subjected to a partial uniform load.

Solution:

Draw an FBD of the beam, and solve for the external reactions. This is the *load diagram.*

By inspection, we see that at *A*, the reaction of 15 k is the shear. The shear at the end reaction point is equal to the reaction itself. Between *A* and *B* is a *downward* (−) uniform load of 2 k/ft. The change in shear between *A* and *B* equals the area under the load diagram between *A* and *B*. Area = 2 k/ft.(10 ft.) = 20 k. Therefore, shear changes from +15 k to −5 k.

V goes to zero at some distance from *A*.

$$\underbrace{V_2 - V_1}_{15\,k\to 0} = \underbrace{\omega}_{2\,k/ft.}\ \underbrace{(x_2 - x_1)}_{x};\ \therefore 15\,k = 2\,k/ft.\,(x);\quad x = 7.5'$$

Between *B* and *C*, no load exists on the beam, so no change in shear occurs. Shear is constant between *B* and *C*.

The moment at the pin and roller is zero.

Compute the area under the shear diagram between *A* and *x*.

$$\text{area} = \left(\tfrac{1}{2}\right)(7.5\,\text{ft.})(15\,\text{k}) = 56.25\,\text{k-ft.}$$

The change in moment between *A* and *x* equals 56.25 k-ft., and because the shear area is (+), the slope of moment curve is (+). A first-degree shear curve results in a second-degree moment curve. The shear curve is positive, but because the area is decreasing, the corresponding moment slope is positive but decreasing.

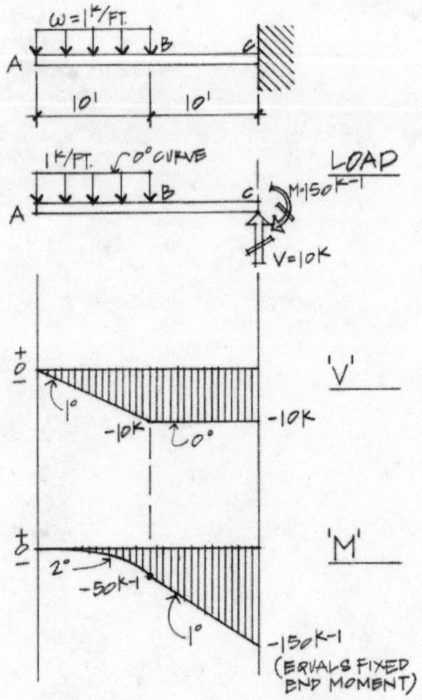

5 Draw the shear and moment diagrams for the partial uniform load on a cantilever beam.

Solution:

Solve for the external reactions.

The load diagram has a uniform load, which is a zero-degree curve. Because the force is acting downward, it constitutes a negative area, thus producing a negative slope in the shear diagram. The resulting shear area is drawn as a first-degree curve with a negative slope. No load exists between *B* and *C* in the load diagram; therefore, no change in shear results between *B* and *C*.

The area under the shear diagram between *A* and *B* equals 50 k-ft. Because the shear area is negative, it produces a moment with a negative slope. As the shear area increases from *A* to *B* (becoming more negative), the moment curve develops an increasing (steeper) negative slope.

The shear area is uniform between *B* and *C*; therefore, it produces a first-degree curve in the moment diagram. The shear area is still negative; therefore, the moment diagram is drawn with a negative first-degree slope.

6 Draw the load, shear, and moment diagrams for the illustrated single overhang beam with a uniform and concentrated load. (***Note:*** *Single overhangs develop two points of possible* M_{max}.)

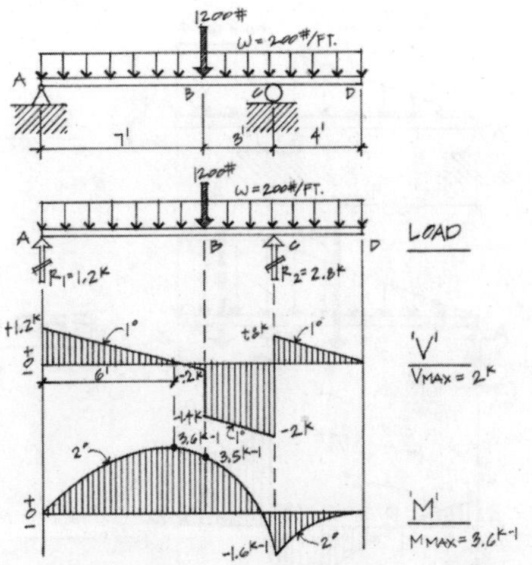

Solution:

Solve for the support reactions. Then, using the load diagram, work from the left end to the right end of the beam. The shear diagram is a first-degree curve with a negative slope between *A* and *B* and crosses the zero axis six feet to the right of support *A*. At the concentrated 1,200# load, an abrupt change in *V* results. The shear diagram continues with a first-degree negative slope between *B* and *C*, and again, a concentrated reaction force at *C* causes an abrupt change of *V*. From *C* to *D*, the shear diagram changes linearly from 0.8 k to zero.

The moment diagram develops two peak points, at a distance six feet to the right of support ω (where $V = 0$) and also at reaction support ω (where the shear diagram crosses the zero axis). The first-degree curves of the shear diagram generate second-degree curves in the moment diagram. Moments are at both the hinge at *A* and the free overhang end at *D*. Note that the moment at the roller support *C* is not zero, because the beam continues on as an overhang.

7 For a cantilever beam with an upturned end, draw the load, shear, and moment diagrams.

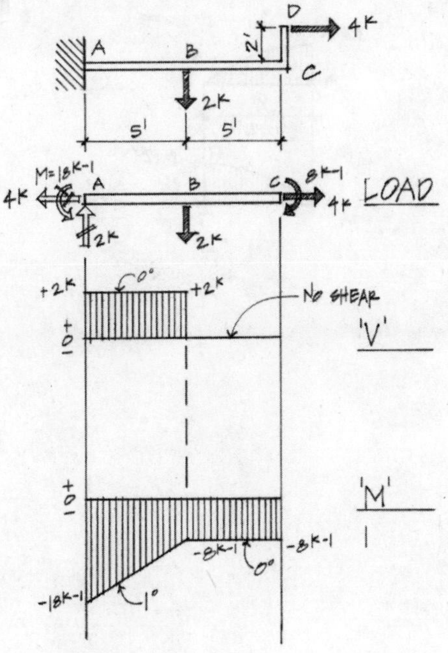

Solution:

Determine the support reactions. Then, move the horizontal 4 k force at *C* to align with the beam axis *A-B-C*.

Because the 4 k force is moved to a new line of action, a moment $M = 8$ k-ft. must be added to point *C*.

The shear diagram is very simple in this example. The left support pushes up with a force of 2 k and remains constant until *B*, because no other loads are present between *A* and *B*.

At *B*, a 2 k downward-acting force brings *V* back to zero, and *V* remains zero all the way to *C* (no vertical loads occur between *B* and *C*).

The moment diagram starts with a moment at the left end because of the presence of the support moment $M = 18$ k-ft.

Imagine the beam curvature in determining whether $M =$ 18 k-ft. is plotted in the positive or negative direction. Because the curvature due to bending results in tension on the top surface of the beam, the sign convention says this is a negative moment condition. Between *A* and *B*, the moment remains negative, but with a positive slope of the first degree. There is no change in moment between *B* and *C*; therefore, the magnitude remains −8 k-ft., which corresponds to the applied moment at *C*.

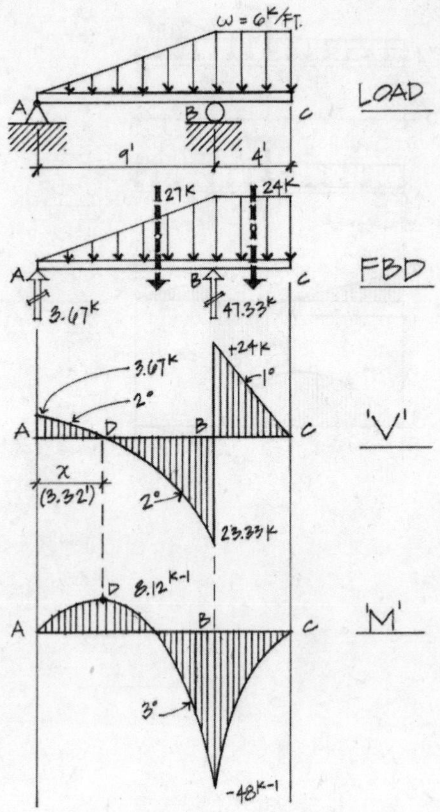

8 Draw the load, shear, and moment diagrams for an overhang beam with a triangular and uniform load.

Solution:

It is necessary to determine the distance x in the shear diagram where $V = 0$.

From A to D, the shear changes from +3.67 k to zero.

$$\therefore\ V_2 - V_1 = +3.67\text{ k}$$

$$\omega(x_2 - x_1) = \text{area under the load diagram between } A \text{ and } D.$$

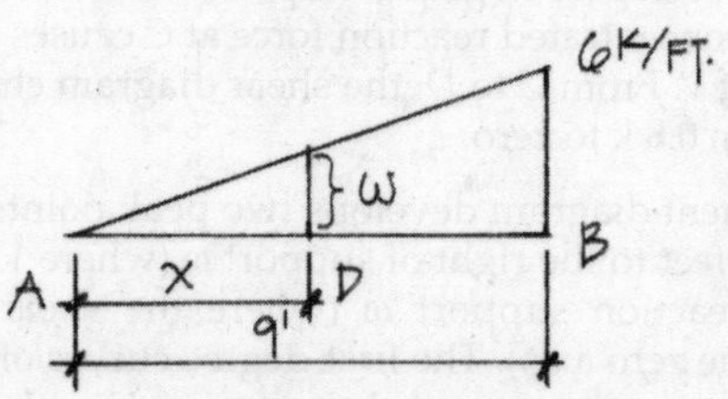

If we study the load diagram, we find that ω varies from A to B. Therefore, ω must be a function of the distance x.

Using similar triangles,

$$\frac{\omega}{x} = \frac{6\text{ k/ft.}}{9'} \qquad \therefore\ \omega = \frac{2}{3}x$$

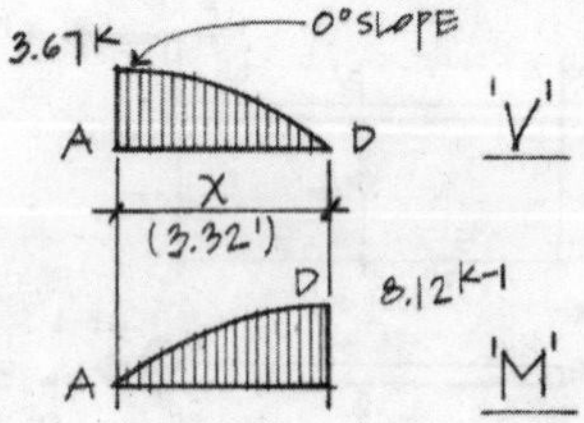

The area under the load diagram between A to D equals

$$\omega(x_2 - x_1) = \left(\frac{1}{2}\right)(x)\left(\frac{2}{3}x\right) = \frac{x^2}{3}$$

$$V_2 - V_1 = \omega(x_2 - x_1)$$

Equating:

$$3.67\text{ k} = \frac{x^2}{3}; \quad x = 3.32\text{ ft.}$$

The change in moment from A to D is found by

$$M_2 - M_1 = V(x_2 - x_1)$$

(area under the shear diagram)

$$\text{Area} = \left(\frac{2}{3}\right)bh = \left(\frac{2}{3}\right)(3.32')(3.67\text{ k}) = 8.12\text{ k-ft.}$$

The calculated change in moment between D and B (shear area DBE) cannot be calculated as the area of a spandrel, because there is no zero slope anywhere along curve DE.

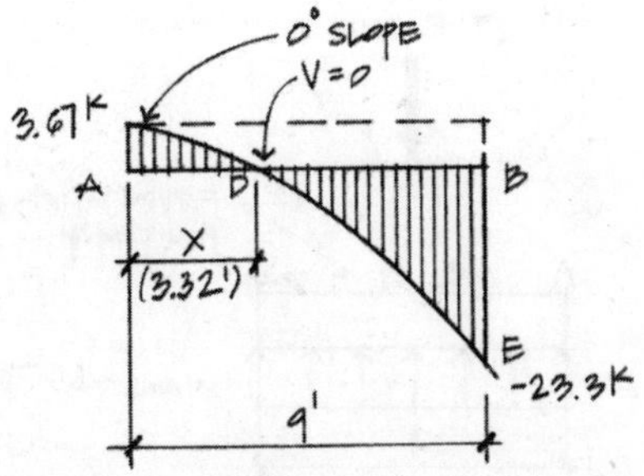

Instead, the area must be determined by using the concept of calculating the area of the spandrel ABE and subtracting the section ADB.

area ABE (spandrel) $= A = \frac{1}{3}(9')(27\,\text{k}) = 81$ k-ft.

total area of $ADB = 3.67\,\text{k} \times (9') = 33$ k-ft.

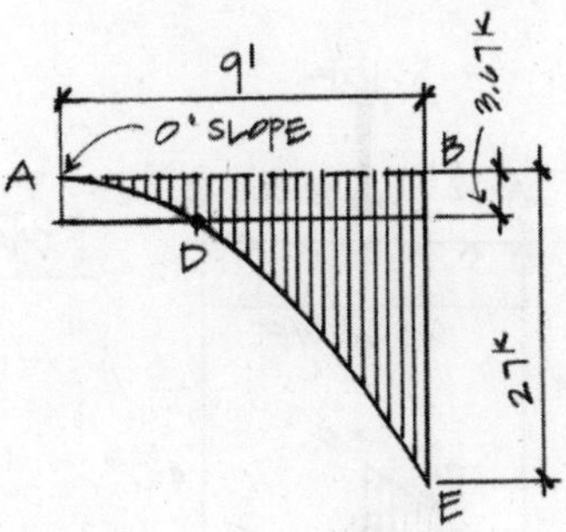

area $(AD) = \frac{2}{3}(3.32')(3.67\,\text{k}) = 8.12$ k-ft.

area $(DB) = 33$ k-ft. $- 8.12$ k-ft. $= 24.87$ k-ft.

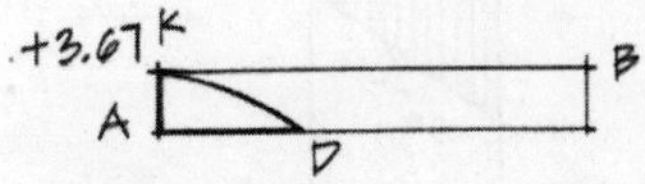

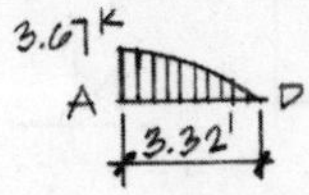

area $DBE = 81$ k-ft. $- 24.87$ k-ft. $= 56.13$ k-ft.

Between D and B, the moment changes by

$M_2 - M_1 = 56.13$ k-ft. $- 8.12$ k-ft. $= 48$ k-ft.

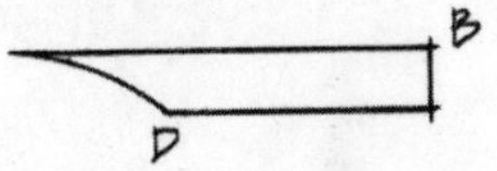

The change in moment between B and C is equal to the triangular shear area:

area $(BC) = \left(\frac{1}{2}\right)(4')(24\,\text{k}) = 48$ k-ft.

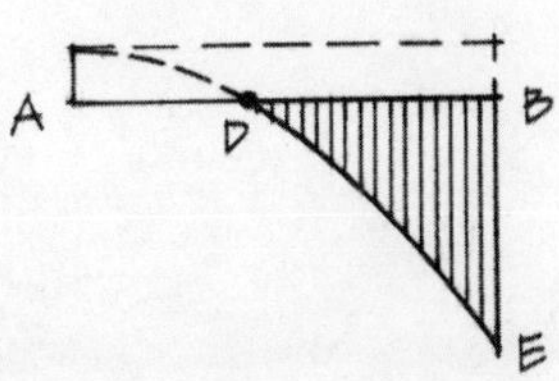

The positive shear area produces a decreasing second-degree curve.

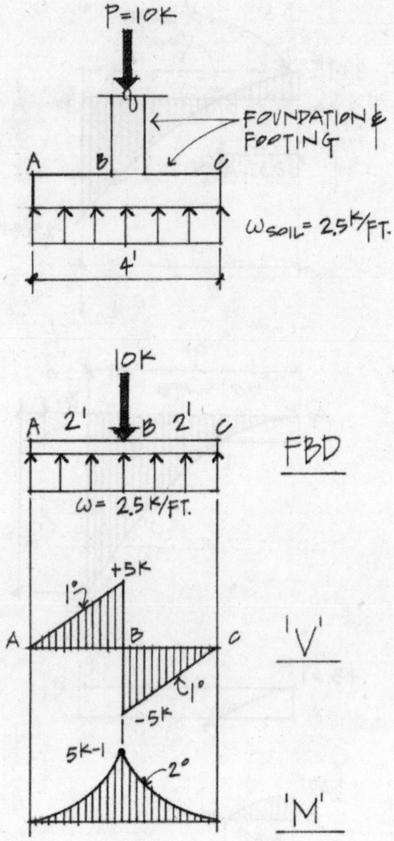

9 The diagram shows a bearing load on a spread footing. Draw the load, shear, and moment diagrams of the figure shown.

Solution:

A typical spread footing supporting a column load develops unique shear and moment diagrams.

Between *A* and *B*, the shear changes from zero to 5 k (which is the area under the upward-acting load of the soil bearing from *A* to *B*). Because the load envelope is positive, the slope of the shear diagram is positive. The column load at *B* causes an abrupt change to occur in the shear diagram. A positive load envelope between *B* and *C* again generates a first-degree positive slope to zero.

The moment at the left end of the footing is zero and increases positively to a magnitude of 5 k-ft. at *B*. A decreasing negative slope is generated between *B* and *C* as the curve diminishes to zero at C.

$$M_2 - M_1 = V(x_2 - x_1)$$

Area of triangle:

$$\frac{1}{2}(2')(5\,\text{k}) = 5\,\text{k-ft.}$$

(shear diagram)

10 A compound beam with internal hinges is loaded as shown.

Solution:

The problem illustrated here represents a compound beam, which is essentially several simpler beams linked together by hinges.

Beam *CD* represents a simple beam with two pin supports, and beams *ABC* and *DEF* are single overhang beams.

In solving for the support reactions at *A*, *B*, *E*, and *F*, detach each beam section, and draw an individual FBD for each.

Once support reactions have been determined, reassemble the beam into its original condition, and begin construction of the shear and moment diagrams.

Remember, the hinges at C and *D* have no moment capability ($M = 0$).

The shear diagram crosses the zero axis in five places; therefore, five peak points develop in the moment diagram. Moment is most critical at the support points *B* and *E*.

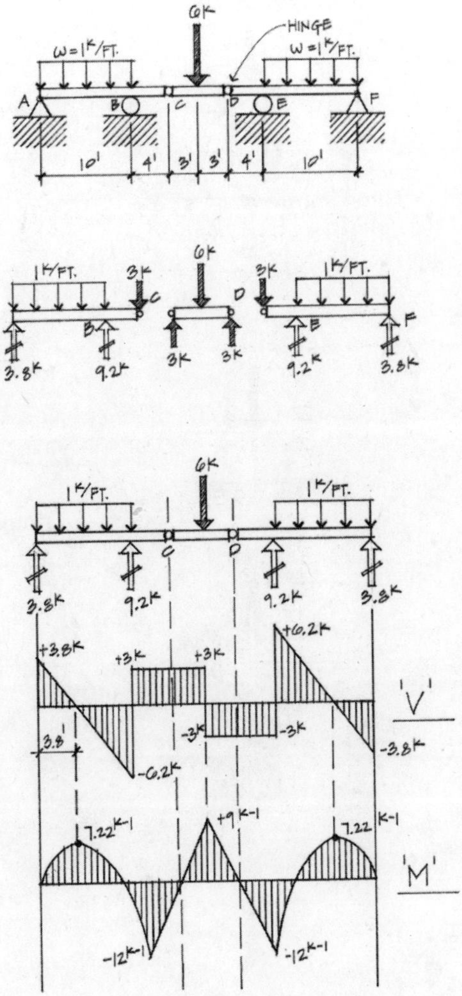

Problems

Construct the load, shear, and moment diagrams for the following beam conditions using the semigraphical approach.

5

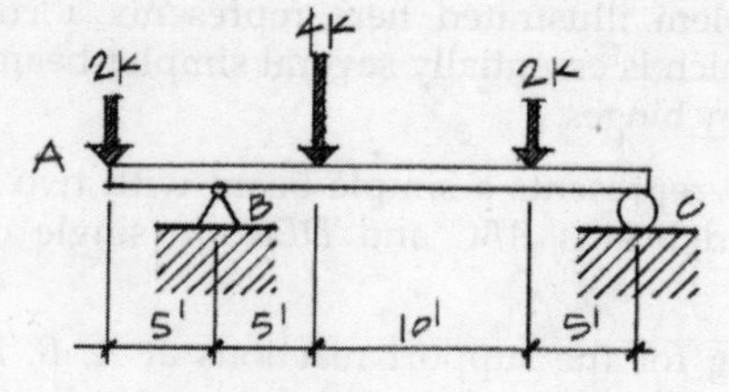

6

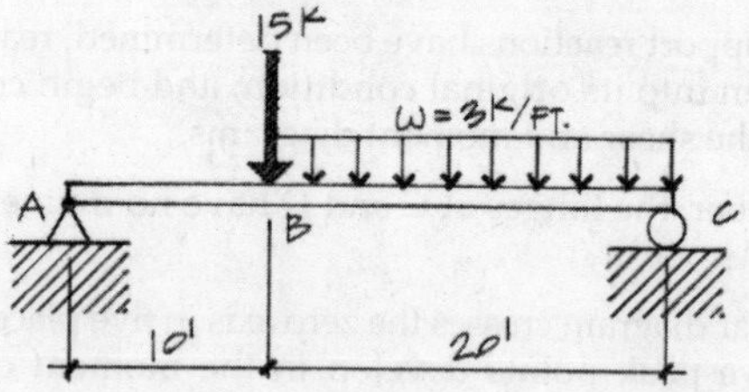

7

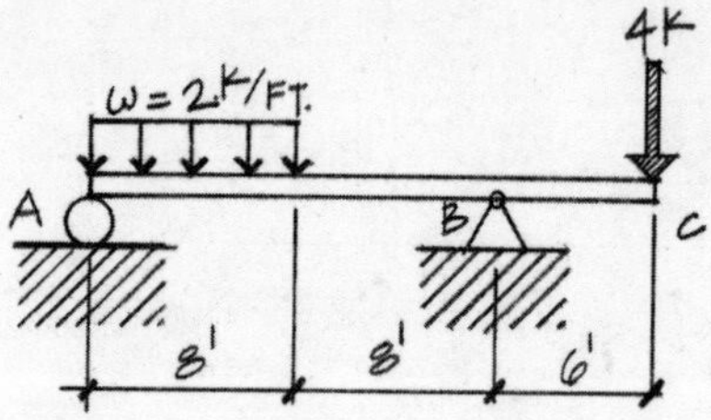

8

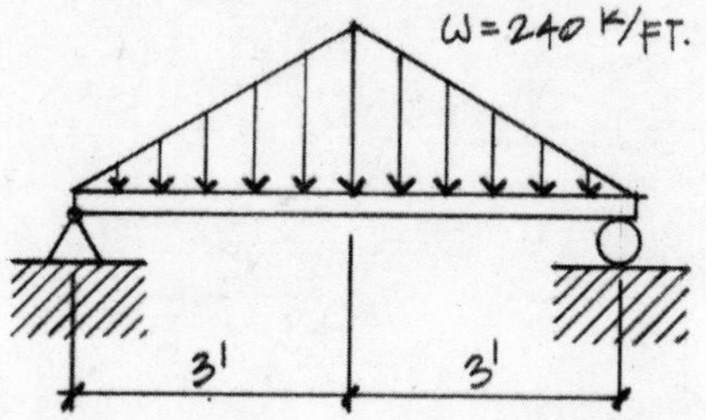

9

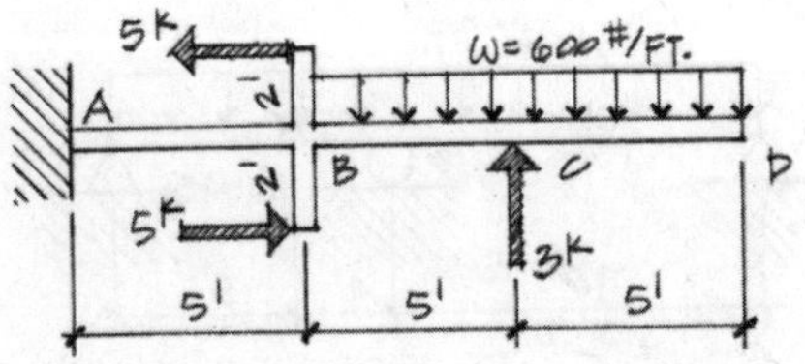
5K
ω=600#/FT.
2"
2"
A
B
C
D
5K
3K
5'
5'
5'

10

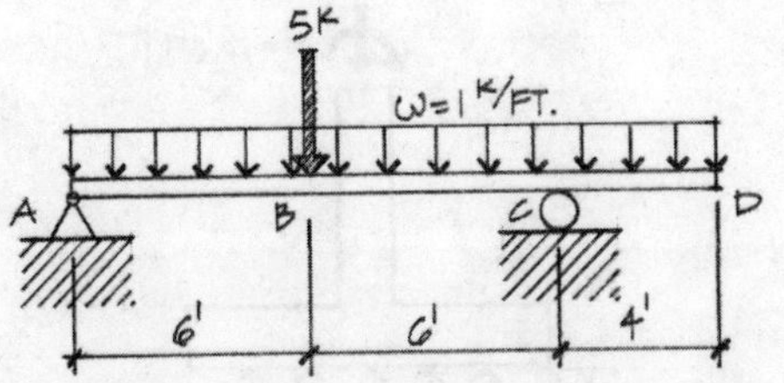
5K
ω=1K/FT.
A
B
C
D
6'
6'
4'

11

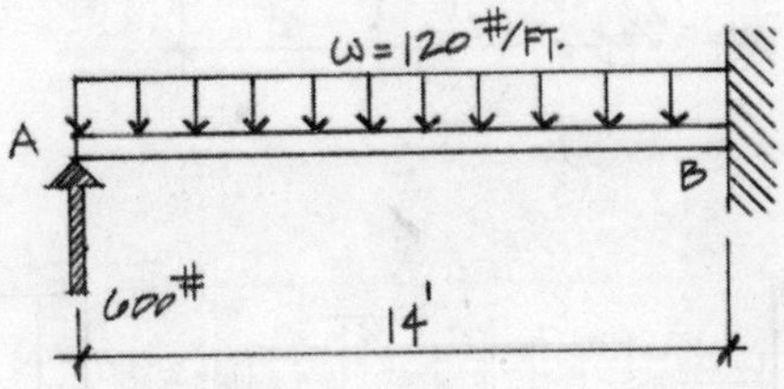
ω=120#/FT.
A
B
600#
14'

12

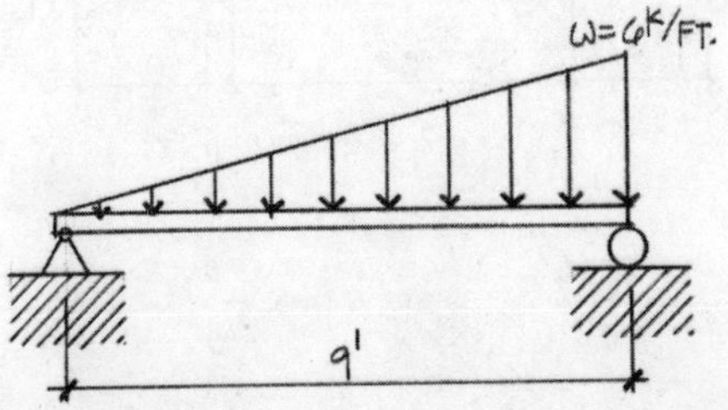
ω=6K/FT.
9'

13

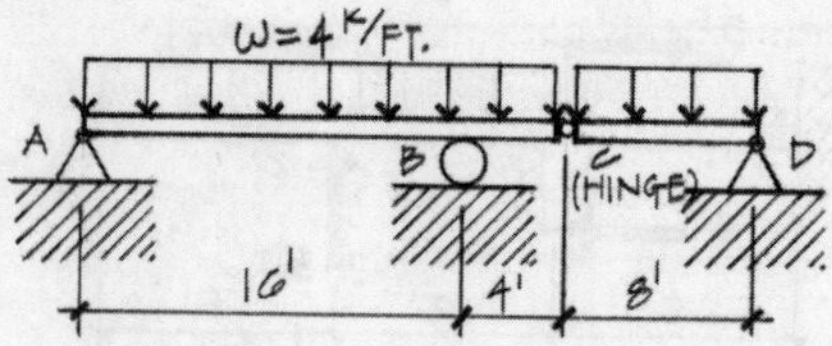
w=4K/FT.
A
B
C
(HINGE)
D
16'
4'
8'

14

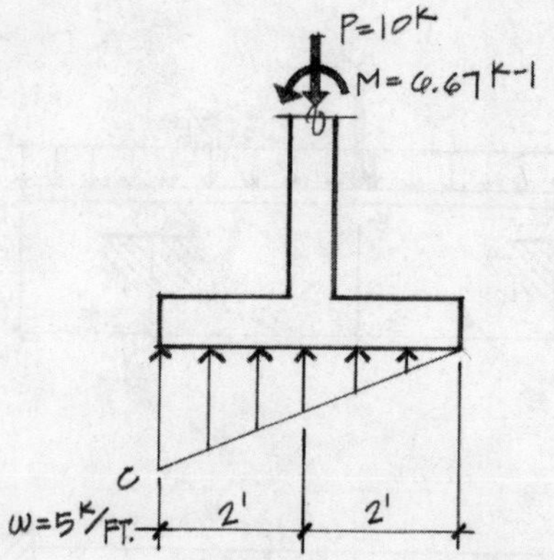
P=10K
M=6.67K-1
C
w=5K/FT.
2'
2'

15

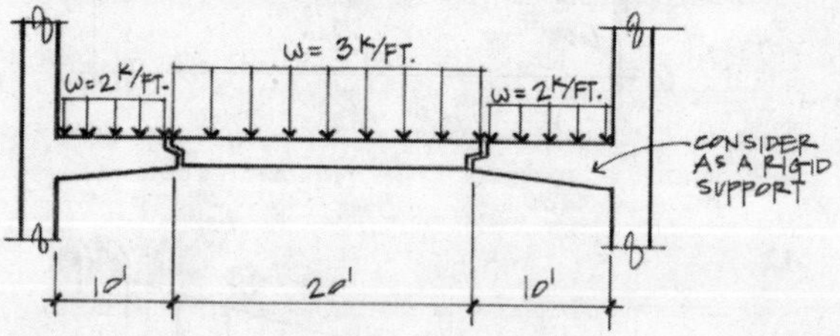
w= 3K/FT.
w=2K/FT.
w=2K/FT.
CONSIDER
AS A RIGID
SUPPORT
10'
20'
10'

Most commercially available structural software will visually and numerically display load, shear, and moment diagrams for beam and frame systems. Figure 14 is an example of the shear and moment diagrams generated for a rigid frame with filler beams.

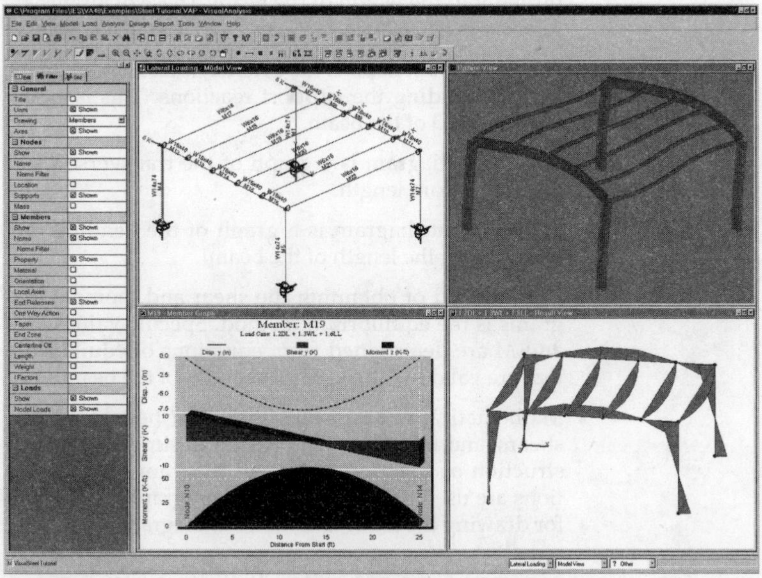

Figure 14 Shear, moment, and deflection diagrams for a frame and beams. Image is reprinted with permission and courtesy of Integrated Engineering Software, Inc., Bozeman, Montana.

Free, downloadable software capable of generating shear, moment, and deflection diagrams can be found on the Internet at:

http://www.eas.asu.edu/~ece313/beams/beams.html

http://www.iesweb.com*

***Note:** This vendor offers educational use of a substantial structural software package if arranged through your professor.*

Summary

- Stresses and deflections in beams are functions of the internal reactions, forces, and moments. Therefore, it is convenient to "map" these internal forces and show, in a diagrammatic form, the shears and moments that act throughout the length of the beam. These diagrams are referred to as *load, shear* (V), and *moment* (M) *diagrams.*
- A load diagram depicts the external forces acting on the beam, including the support reactions. This is essentially an FBD of the beam.
- The shear diagram is a graph of the transverse shear along the beam length.
- The moment diagram is a graph of the bending moments along the length of the beam.
- One method of obtaining the shear and moment diagrams is the equilibrium method. Specific values of V and M are determined from equations of equilibrium that are valid for appropriate sections of the beam.
- Mathematical relationships that exist between loads, shears, and moments can be used to simplify the construction of shear and moment diagrams. Two equations are used in generating the semigraphical method for drawing the shear and moment diagrams.

$$\frac{dV}{dx} = \omega; \quad \int_{V_1}^{V_2} dV = \int_{x_1}^{x_2} \omega dx; \quad V_2 - V_1 = \omega(x_2 - x_1)$$

The change in shear between sections x_1 and x_2 is equal to the area under the load diagram between the two sections.

$$\frac{dM}{dx} = V; \quad \int_{M_1}^{M_2} dM = \int_{x_1}^{x_2} V dx; \quad M_2 - M_1 = V(x_2 - x_1)$$

The change in moment between sections at x_1 and x_2 is equal to the area under the shear diagram between the two sections.

Answers to Selected Problems

1 $V_{max} = 10$ k; $M_{max} = 50$ k-ft.

2 $V_{max} = -20$ k; $M_{max} = -200$ k-ft.

3 $V_{max} = +15$ k; $M_{max} = -50$ k-ft.

4 $V_{max} = \pm 20$ k; $M_{max} = +100$ k-ft.

5 $V_{max} = +4$ k; $M_{max} = \pm 10$ k-ft.

6 $V_{max} = -45$ k; $M_{max} = +337.5$ k-ft.

7 $V_{max} = +10.5$ k; $M_{max} = +27.6$ k-ft.

8 $V_{max} = \pm 360$ lb.; $M_{max} = +720$ lb.-ft.

9 $V_{max} = +3$ k; $M_{max} = -15$ k-ft.

10 $V_{max} = -9.2$ k; $M_{max} = +28.8$ k-ft.

11 $V_{max} = -1{,}080$ lb.; $M_{max} = -3{,}360$ lb.-ft.

12 $V_{max} = -18$ k; $M_{max} = +31.2$ k-ft.

13 $V_{max} = -38$ k; $M_{max} = -96$ k-ft.

14 $V_{max} = +7.5$ k; $M_{max} = +8.33$ k-ft.

Bending and Shear Stresses in Beams

Introduction

One of the earliest studies concerned with the strength and deflection of beams was carried out by Galileo Galilei. Galileo was the first to discuss the bending strength of a beam. He thus became the founder of an entirely new branch of science: the theory of the strength of materials, which has played a vital part in modern engineering science.

Figure 1 *Cantilever beam loaded at the free end. From Galileo Galilei,* Discorsi e Demostrazioni Matematiche, *Leyden, 1638. Drawing based on the illustration in* Schweizerische Bauzeitung, *Vol. 119.*

Galileo started with the observation of a cantilever beam (Figure 1) subjected to a load at the free end. He equated the statical moments of the external load with that of the resultant of the tensile stresses in the beam (assumed to be uniformly distributed over the entire cross-section of the beam, as shown in Figure 2) in relation to the axis of rotation (assumed to be located at the lower edge of the embedded cross-section). Galileo concluded that the bending strength of a beam was not directly proportional to its width but, instead, was proportional to the square of its height. However, as he based his proposition merely on considerations of statics and did not yet introduce the notion of elasticity—an idea propounded by Robert Hooke a half-century later—Galileo had erred in the evaluation of the magnitude of the bending strength in relation to the tensile strength of the beam.

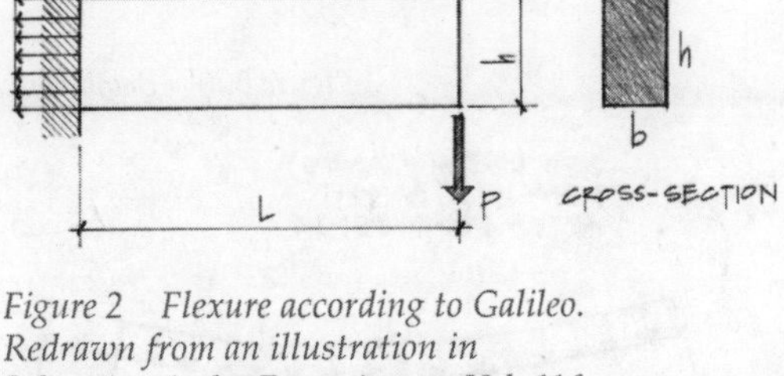

Figure 2 *Flexure according to Galileo. Redrawn from an illustration in* Schweizerische Bauzeitung, *Vol. 116.*

Expressed in modern terms, the moment of resistance (inertia) of the rectangular beam would, according to Galileo, amount to

$$\frac{bh^3}{4}$$

which is three times as great as the correct value:

$$\frac{bh^3}{12}$$

About 50 years after Galileo's observations, a French physicist, Edme Mariotte (1620–1684), still retaining the concept of the fulcrum at the compression surface of the

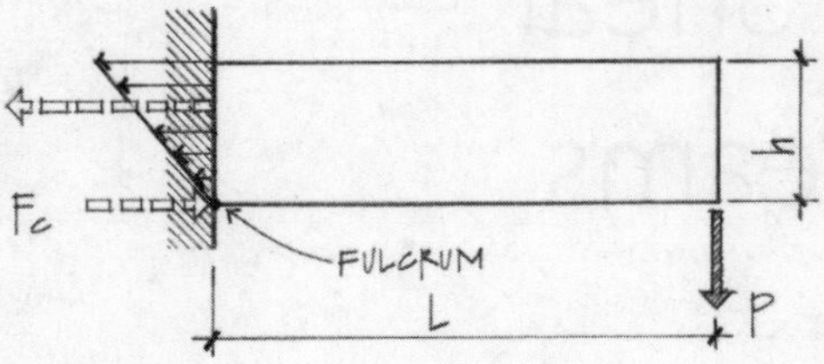

Figure 3 Flexure according to Mariotte.

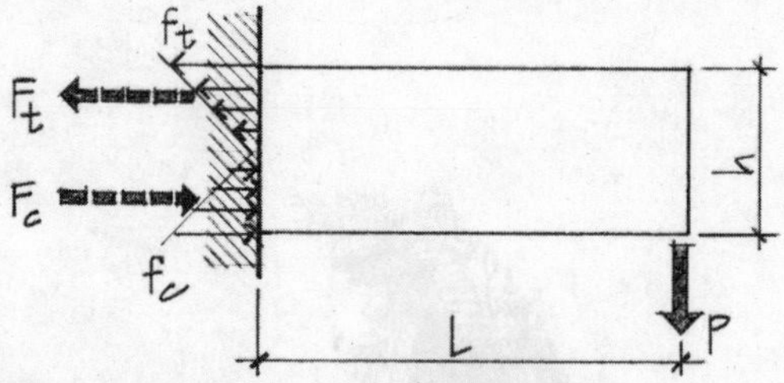

Figure 4 Flexure according to Coulomb.

beam but reasoning that the extensions of the longitudinal elements of the beam (sometimes called *fibers*) would be proportional to the distance from the fulcrum, suggested that the tensile stress distribution was as shown in Figure 3.

Mariotte later rejected the concept of the fulcrum and observed that part of the beam on the compression side was subjected to compressive stress having a triangular distribution. However, his expression for the ultimate load was still based on his original concept.

Two centuries after Galileo Galilei's initial beam theory, Charles-Augustin de Coulomb (1736–1806) and Louis-Marie-Henri Navier (1785–1836) finally succeeded in finding the correct answer. In 1773, Coulomb published a paper that discarded the fulcrum concept and proposed the triangular distribution shown in Figure 4, in which both the tensile and compressive stresses have the same linear distribution.

I FLEXURAL STRAIN

The accuracy of Coulomb's theory can be demonstrated by examining a simply supported beam subjected to bending. The beam is assumed (a) to be initially straight and of constant cross-section, (b) to be elastic and have equal moduli of elasticity in tension and compression, and (c) to be homogeneous—that is, of the same material throughout. It is further assumed that a plane section before bending remains a plane after bending [Figure 5(a) and 5(b)].

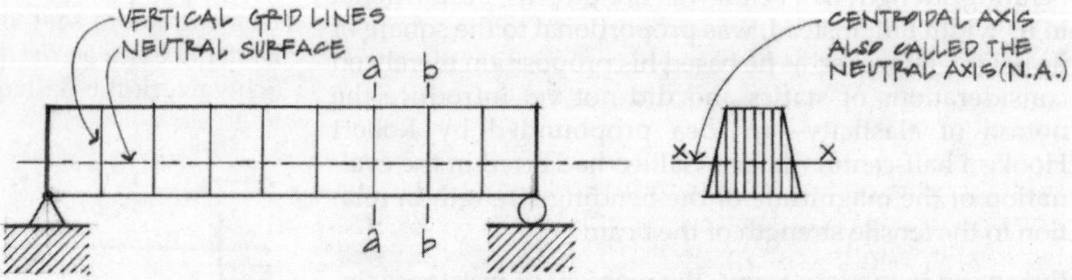

Figure 5(a) Beam elevation before loading. *Beam cross-section.*

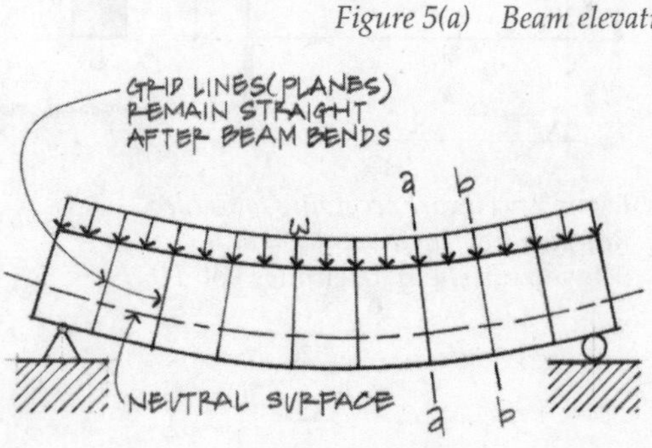

Figure 5(b) Beam bending under load.

For this to be strictly true, the beam needs to be bent only with couples (no shear on transverse planes). The beam must be proportioned so that it will not buckle, and the loads must be applied so that no twisting (torsion) occurs.

Examining a portion of the bent beam between sections *a-a* and *b-b* (Figure 6), one observes that at some distance C above the bottom of the beam, the longitudinal elements (fibers) undergo no change in length.

The curved surface (①–②) formed by these elements is referred to as the *neutral surface*, and the intersection of this surface with any cross-section is called the *neutral axis of the cross-section*. The neutral axis corresponds to the centroidal axis of a cross-section. All elements (fibers) on one side of the neutral surface are compressed, and those on the opposite side are in tension. For the simple beam shown in Figure 5, the portion of the beam above the neutral surface experiences compression, whereas the lower portion is undergoing tensile stressing.

The assumption is made that all longitudinal elements (fibers) have the same initial length before loading.

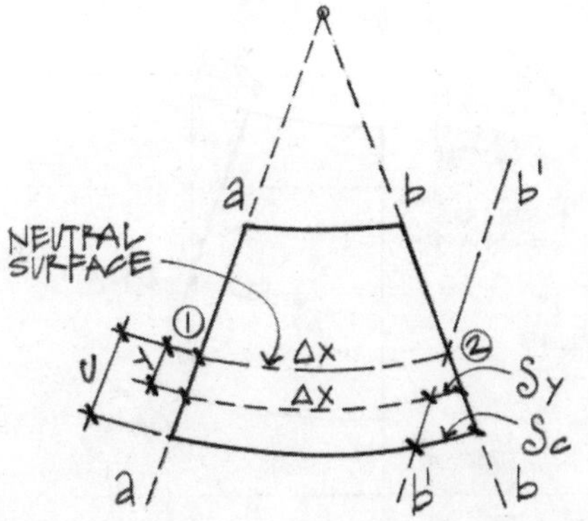

Figure 6 *Beam section after loading.*

Referring again to Figure 6,

$$\frac{\delta_y}{y} = \frac{\delta_c}{c}$$

or

$$\delta_y = \frac{y}{c}\delta_c$$

where

δ_y = deformation developed along fibers located a distance y below neutral surface

δ_c = deformation at the bottom surface of the beam located a distance c below the neutral surface

Because all elements had the same initial length Δx, the strain of any element can be determined by dividing the deformation by the length of the element; therefore, the strain becomes

$$\varepsilon_y = \frac{y\varepsilon_c}{c}$$

which indicates that the strain of any fiber is directly proportional to the distance of the fiber from the neutral surface.

With the premise that the longitudinal strains are proportional to the distance from the neutral surface accepted, the assumption is now made that Hooke's law applies, which restricts stresses to magnitudes within the proportional limit of the material. Then, the equation becomes

$$\frac{\varepsilon_y}{y} = \frac{f_y}{E_y y} = \frac{f_c}{E_c c}$$

The final result, if $E_c = E_y$ (constant), is

$$\frac{f_y}{y} = \frac{f_c}{c}$$

which verifies Coulomb's conclusion.

Redrawing the diagram shown in Figure 6 to include the compressive as well as the tensile deformations due to bending stress, we can use Hooke's law to explain the stress variations occurring on the cross-section (Figure 7).

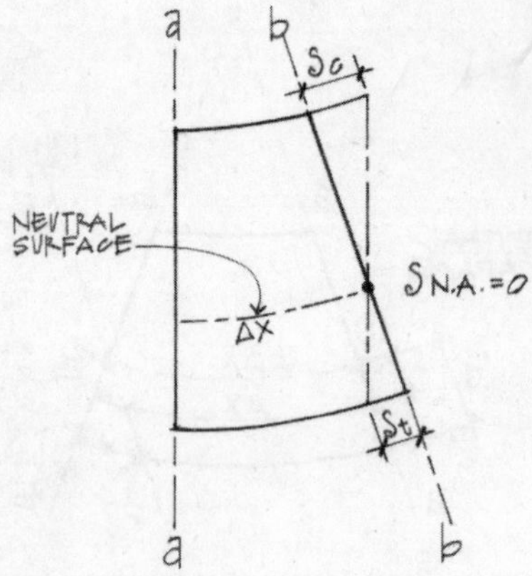

Figure 7 Deformed section on beam due to bending.

The deformation at the neutral axis is zero after bending; therefore, the stress at the neutral axis is zero. At the top fiber, the maximum shortening (compressive deformation) occurs from the development of maximum compressive stresses. Conversely, the maximum tensile stress occurs at the bottom fibers, resulting in a maximum elongation deformation (Figure 8).

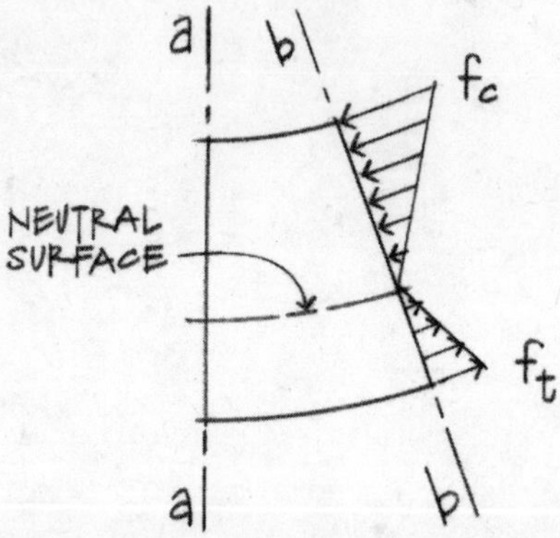

Figure 8 Bending stresses on section b-b.

2 FLEXURAL (BENDING) STRESS EQUATION

Consider a portion of a beam that is subjected to pure bending only by couples (designated by *M*) at each end, as shown in Figure 9. Because the beam is in equilibrium, the moments at each end will be numerically equal but of opposite sense. Due to the moment couples, the beam is bent from its original straight position to the curved (deformed) shape indicated in Figure 9.

Elevation of beam in bending. *Beam cross section.*

Figure 9 Beam curvature due to bending moment.

Because of this bending action, we find that the lengths of the upper parts of the beam decrease, while the bottom parts of the beam lengthen. This action has the effect of placing the upper portion of the beam in compression and the lower portion of the beam in tension. An equation must be obtained that will relate bending stress to the external moment and the geometric properties of the beam. This can be done by examining a segment of the beam whose internal force system at any given transverse section is a moment M, as shown in Figure 10, where

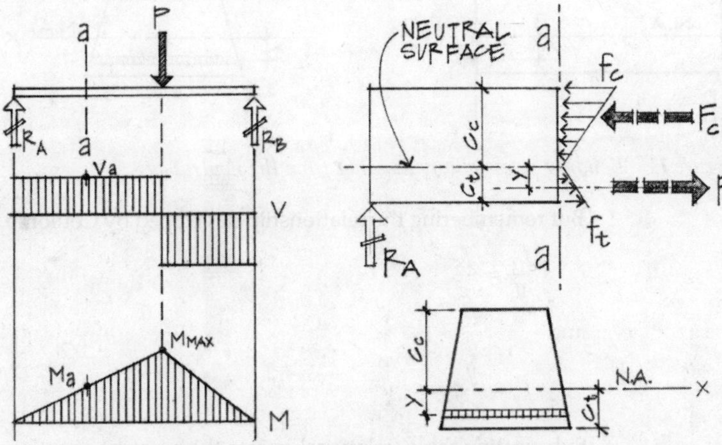

Figure 10 Bending stresses on a beam cross-section.

c_c = distance from neutral axis (N.A.) to the extreme compressive fiber

c_t = distance from N.A. to the extreme tensile fiber

y = distance from N.A. to some area ΔA

ΔA = small strip of area on the beam cross-section

If we denote the element of area at any distance y from the neutral axis (see Figure 10) as ΔA and the stress on it as f, the requirement for equilibrium of forces yields

$$[\Sigma F_x = 0]\Sigma f_t \Delta A + \Sigma f_c \Delta A = 0$$

where

f_t = tensile stress below the N.A.

f_c = compressive stress above the N.A.

Therefore,

$$\Sigma f_t \Delta A = F_t$$

and

$$\Sigma f_c \Delta A = F_c$$

If each $f_y \Delta A$ is multiplied by its y distance above or below the neutral axis,

$$M = \Sigma f_y y \Delta A$$

where

M = internal bending moment (Figure 11)

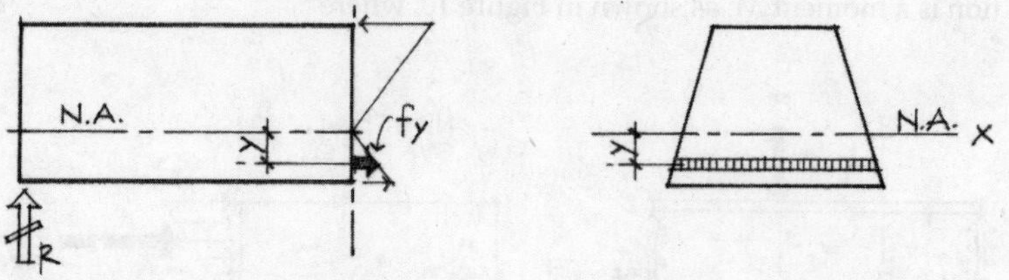

Figure 11 Bending stress at any distance from the neutral axis.

But remembering the relationship developed by Coulomb,

$$\frac{f_y}{y} = \frac{f_c}{c}$$

and

$$f_y = \frac{y}{c} f_c$$

Substituting the f_y relationship into the moment equation:

$$M = \Sigma f_y y \Delta A = \Sigma \frac{y}{c} f_c y \Delta A = \frac{f_c}{c} \Sigma y^2 \Delta A$$

We developed the relationship for moment of inertia, where

$$I = \Sigma y^2 \Delta A \text{ (moment of inertia)}$$

$$\therefore M = \frac{f_c I}{c}$$

or

$$\boxed{f_b = \frac{Mc}{I}} \leftarrow \text{flexure formula}$$

where

f_b = bending stress at the extreme fiber, top or bottom

c = distance from the N.A. to the extreme fiber

I = moment of inertia of the cross-section about its centroidal axis (or N.A.)

M = moment at some point along the beam length

Note: *Bending stress f is directly proportional to the value c; therefore, the largest bending stress on a cross-section is obtained by selecting the largest c value for unsymmetrical cross-sections (Figure 12).*

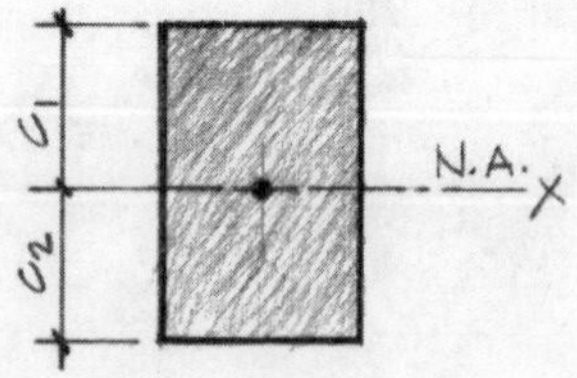

(a) Rectangular cross section.

$c_1 = c_2$; $f_{top} = f_{bottom}$

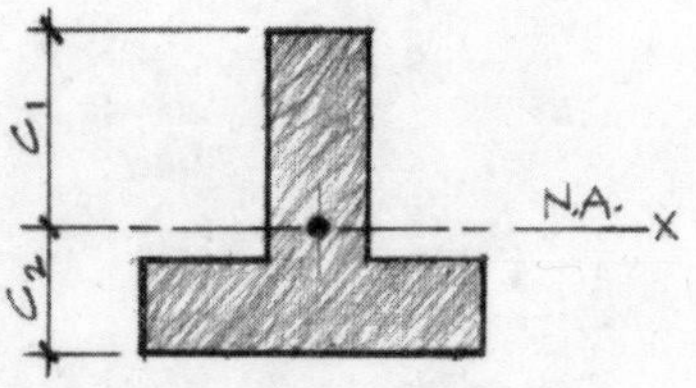

(b) Unsymmetrical cross section.

$c_1 > c_2$; $f_{top} > f_{bottom}$

Figure 12 Distances to the extreme fiber for beam cross-sections.

Example Problems: Bending Stress

1 A 4 × 12 S4S Douglas fir beam is loaded and supported as shown.

a. Calculate the maximum bending stress developed in the beam.
b. Determine the magnitude of the bending stress developed three feet to the left of support *B*.

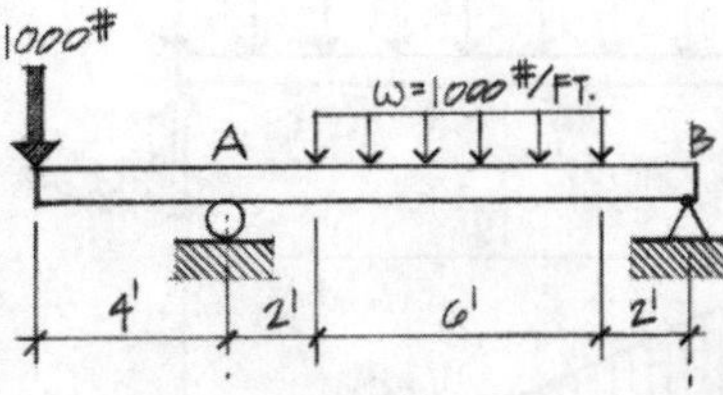

Solution:

The maximum bending stress developed in the beam occurs where the bending moment is largest. To determine the maximum moment, plot the shear (V) and moment (M) diagrams.

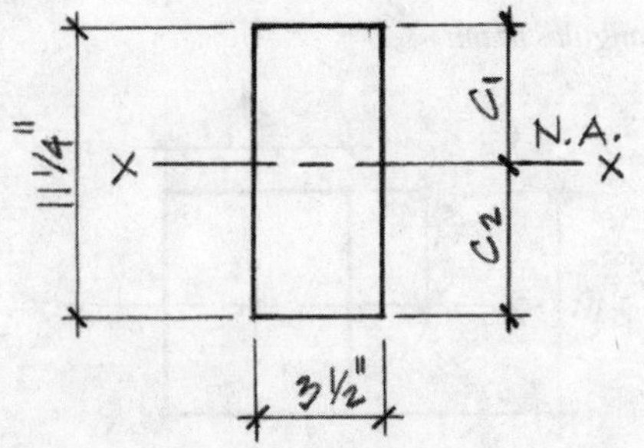

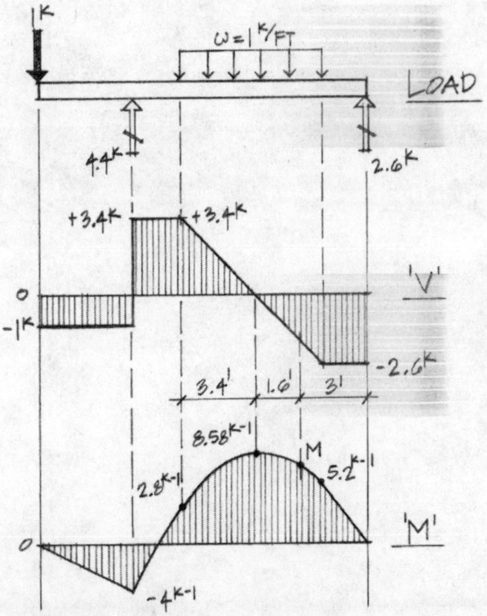

V at three feet to the left of B:

$V = w(1.6')$

$V = 1.6\text{ k}$

4 × 12 S4S

$A = 39.4\text{ in.}^2$

(a) $M_{max} = 8.58\text{ k-ft.}$

$$f_b = \frac{Mc}{I_x} = \frac{(8.58\text{ k-ft.} \times 12\text{ in./ft.})(5.63'')}{415.3\text{ in.}^4} = 1.4\text{ ksi}$$

(b) Moment at three feet to the left of B:

$M = 8.58\text{ k-ft.} - \frac{1}{2}(1.6')(1.6\text{ k})$

$M = 8.58\text{ k-ft.} - 1.28\text{ k-ft.}$

$M = 7.3\text{ k-ft.}$

$$f = \frac{(7{,}300\text{ \#-ft.} \times 12\text{ in./ft.})(5.63'')}{415.3\text{ in.}^4} = 1{,}188\text{ psi}$$

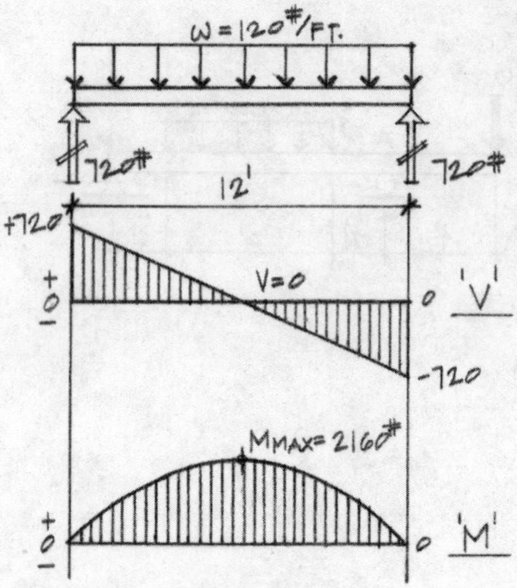

2 A beam must span a distance of 12 feet and carry a uniformly distributed load of 120 #/ft. Determine which cross-section would be the least stressed: (a), (b), or (c).

Solution:

(a) *Plank.*

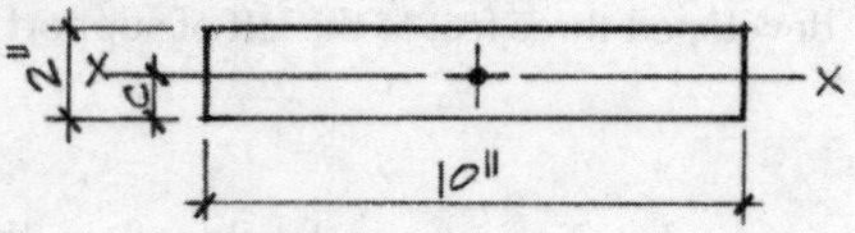

$A = 20 \text{ in.}^2; \quad I_x = 6.7 \text{ in.}^4; \quad c = 1''$

$$f_{max} = \frac{Mc}{I} = \frac{(2{,}160 \text{ \#-ft.} \times 12 \text{ in./ft.})(1'')}{6.7 \text{ in.}^4} = 3{,}869 \text{ \#/in.}^2$$

(b) *Rectangular beam.*

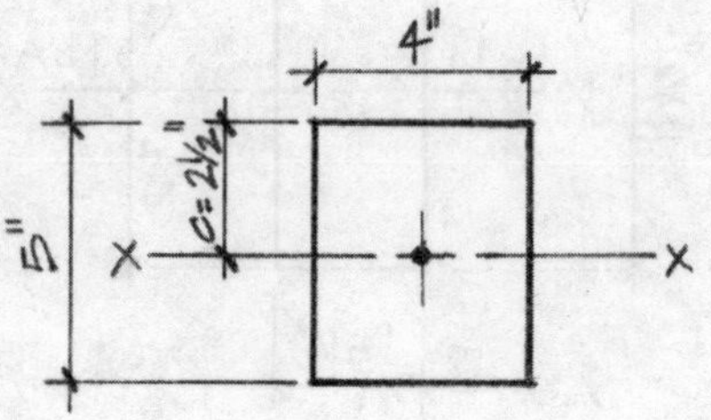

$A = 20 \text{ in.}^2; \quad I_x = 41.7 \text{ in.}^4; \quad c = 2.5''$

$$f_{max} = \frac{Mc}{I} \frac{(2{,}160 \text{ \#-ft.} \times 12 \text{ in./ft.})(2.5'')}{(41.7 \text{ in.}^4)} = 1{,}554 \text{ \#/in.}^2$$

(c) *I-beam.*

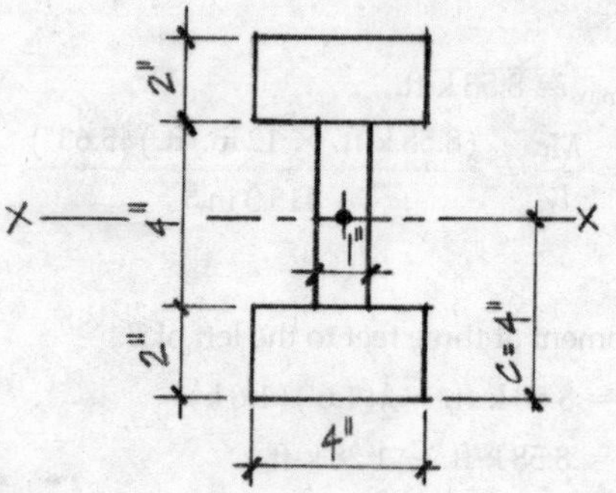

$A = 20 \text{ in.}^2; \quad I_x = 154.7 \text{ in.}^4; \quad c = 4''$

$$f_{max} = \frac{Mc}{I} = \frac{(2{,}160 \text{ \#-ft.} \times 12 \text{ in./ft.})(4'')}{154.7 \text{ in.}^4} = 670 \text{ \#/in.}^2$$

3 A W8 × 28 steel beam is loaded and supported as shown. Determine the maximum bending stress.

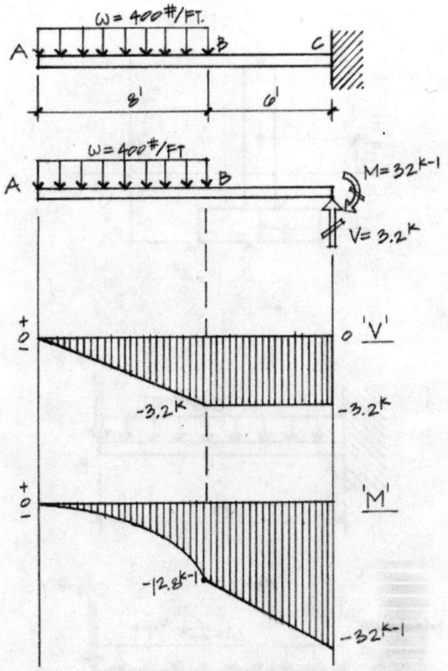

Solution:

$$V = w \times 8' = 400\,\#/\text{ft.} \times 8' = 3{,}200\,\#$$

$$M = 3.2\,\text{k}(10') = 32\,\text{k-ft.}$$

$$f_{max} = \frac{Mc}{I} \text{ (using } M_{max} \text{ from the moment diagram)}$$

$$I = 98.0\,\text{in.}^4$$

$$c = \frac{d}{2} = \frac{8.06''}{2} = 4.03''$$

$$M = 32\,\text{k-ft.} \times 12\,\text{in./ft.} = 384\,\text{k-in.}$$

$$f = \frac{(384\,\text{k-in.})(4.03'')}{98.0\,\text{in.}^4} = 15.8\,\text{ksi}$$

$$F_{allow} = 22\,\text{ksi} \quad \therefore \text{OK}$$

What is the bending stress that would result if the steel beam were replaced by a 6 × 16 S4S Southern Pine No. 1 beam? (Obtain section properties from timber tables in Appendix Table A1.)

Solution:

$$f = \frac{Mc}{I}$$

$$I = 1{,}707\,\text{in.}^4$$

$$c = \frac{d}{2} = \frac{15.5''}{2} = 7.75''$$

$$f = \frac{(384{,}000\,\#\text{-in.})(7.75'')}{1{,}707\,\text{in.}^4} = 1{,}743\,\text{psi}$$

$$F_{allow} = 1{,}550\,\text{psi} \quad \therefore \text{Not Good}$$

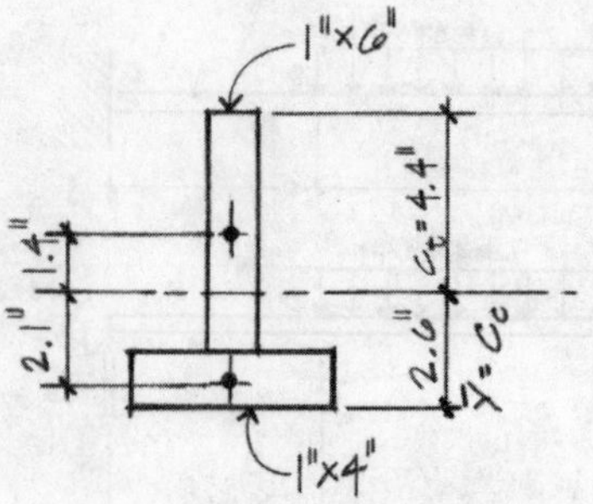

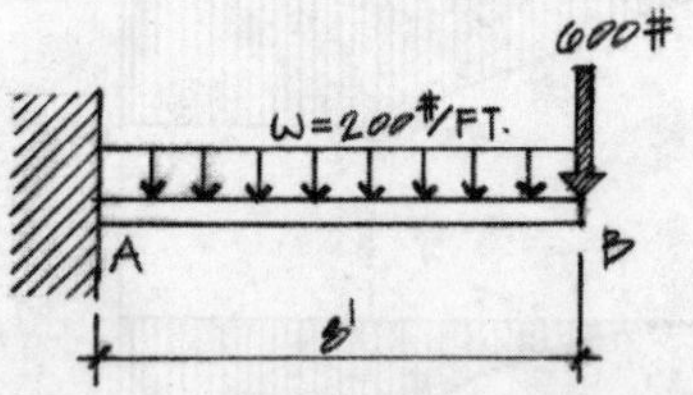

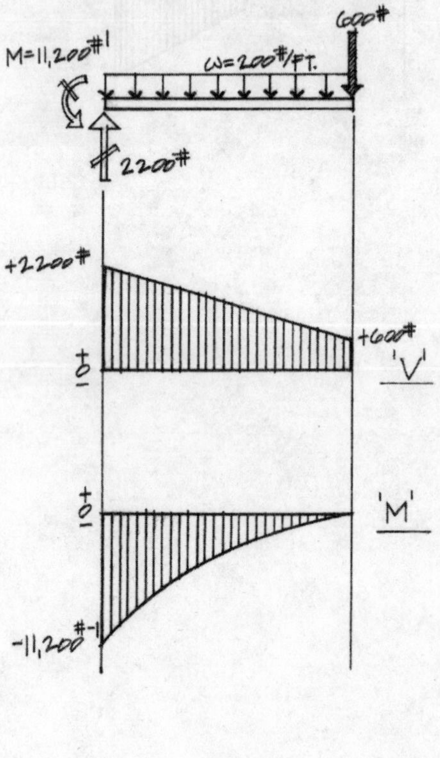

4 Determine the maximum tensile and compressive bending stresses in the beam shown.

Solution:

Component	A	y	Ay
	6 in.^{2}	4″	24 in.^{3}
	4 in.^{2}	0.5″	2 in.^{3}

$$\Sigma A = 10 \text{ in.}^2; \quad \Sigma Ay = 26 \text{ in.}^3$$

$$\bar{y} = \frac{\Sigma Ay}{\Sigma A} = \frac{26 \text{ in.}^3}{10 \text{ in.}^2} = 2.6''$$

Component	I_{x_c} (in.^{4})	dy (in.)	Ay^2 (in.^{4})
	18	1.4	11.76
	0.33	2.1	17.64

$$\Sigma I_{x_c} = 18.33 \text{ in.}^4; \quad \Sigma A d_y^2 = 29.4 \text{ in.}^4$$

$$I_x = 18.33 \text{ in.}^4 + 29.4 \text{ in.}^4 = 47.73 \text{ in.}^4$$

$$\underset{\text{(top)}}{f_b} = \frac{Mc_t}{I} = \frac{(11{,}200 \text{ \#-ft.} \times 12 \text{ in./ft.})(4.4'')}{47.73 \text{ in.}^4}$$

$$= 12{,}390 \text{ \#/in.}^2$$

$$\underset{\text{(bottom)}}{f_b} = \frac{Mc_c}{I} = \frac{(11{,}200 \text{ \#-ft.} \times 12 \text{ in./ft.})(2.6'')}{47.73 \text{ in.}^4}$$

$$= 7{,}321 \text{ \#/in.}^2$$

Section Modulus

The majority of the structural shapes used in practice (structural steel, timber, aluminum, etc.) are standard shapes that are normally available in industry. Cross-sectional properties such as area (A), moment of inertia (I), and dimensional size (depth and width) for standard shapes are usually listed in handbooks and tables.

As a means of expanding the basic flexure equation into a design form, the two section properties I and c are combined as I/c, which is called the *section modulus*.

$$f_b = \frac{Mc}{I} = \frac{M}{I/c}$$

Section modulus: $S = I/c$

Therefore,

$$\boxed{f_b = \frac{Mc}{I} = \frac{M}{S}}$$

where

S = section modulus, usually about the x axis (in.^{3})

M = bending moment in the beam, usually M_{max}

Because I and c of standard sections are known, their section moduli (S) are also listed in handbooks. For nonstandard sections and for regular geometric shapes, the section modulus may be obtained by calculating the moment of inertia I of the area and then dividing I by c, the distance from the neutral axis to the extreme fiber. In symmetrical sections, c has only one value, but in unsymmetrical sections, c will have two values, as shown in Figure 12(b). In the analysis and design of beams, however, we are usually interested in the maximum stress that occurs in the extreme fiber. In all such problems, the greatest value of c must be used.

If we rewrite the basic flexure equation into a design form,

$$\boxed{S_{required} = \frac{M}{F_b}}$$

where

F_b = allowable bending stress (ksi or psi)

M = maximum bending moment in the beam (k-in. or #-in.)

the usefulness of the section modulus becomes quite apparent, because only one unknown exists rather than two (I and c).

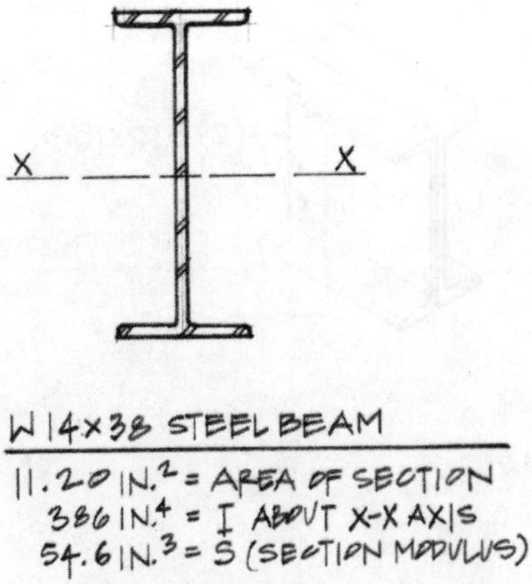

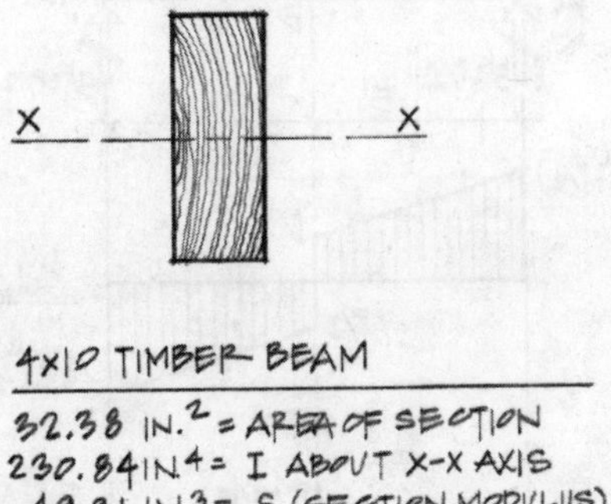

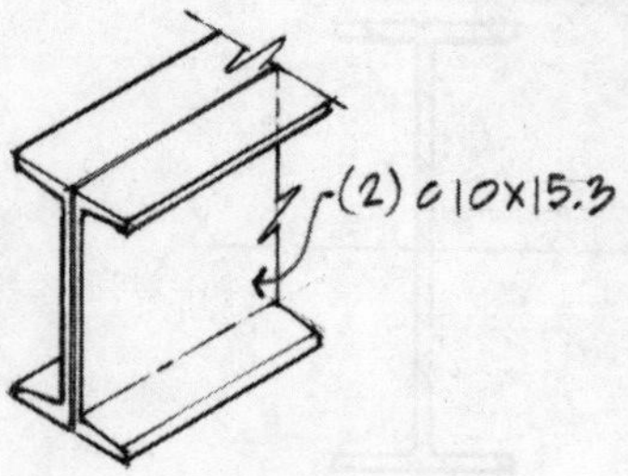

Example Problems: Section Modulus

5 Two C10 × 15.3 steel channels are placed back to back to form a 10-inch-deep beam. Determine the permissible P if $F_b = 22$ ksi. Assume A36 grade steel.

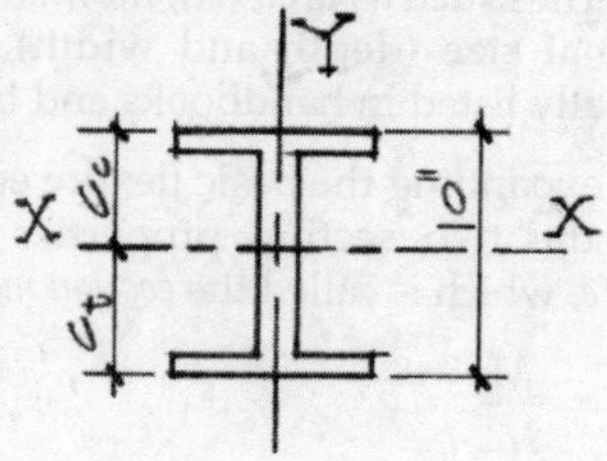

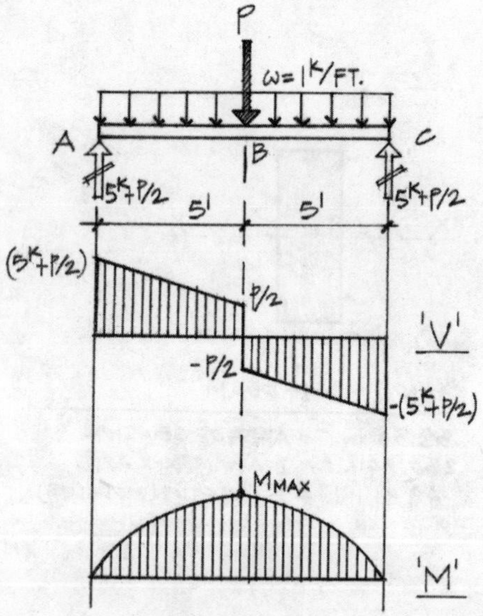

Solution:

$$I_x = 67.4 \text{ in.}^4 \times 2 = 134.8 \text{ in.}^4$$

$$M_{max} = \tfrac{1}{2}(5)(5) + (P/2)(5)$$

$$M_{max} = 12.5 + 2.5P = (12.5 \text{ k-ft.} + 2.5P) \times 12 \text{ in./ft.}$$

$$f = \frac{Mc}{I} = \frac{M}{S}$$

$$M = F_b S$$

$$S = 2 \times 13.5 \text{ in.}^3 = 27 \text{ in.}^3$$

Equating both M_{max} equations,

$$M = 22 \text{ ksi} \times 27 \text{ in.}^3 = 594 \text{ k-in.}$$

$$(12.5 \text{ k-ft.} + 2.5P)(12 \text{ in./ft.}) = 594 \text{ k-in.}$$

Dividing both sides of the equation by 12 in./ft.,

$$12.5 \text{ k-ft.} + 2.5'(P) = 49.5 \text{ k-ft.}$$

$$2.5P = 37 \text{ k}$$

$$P = 14.8 \text{ k}$$

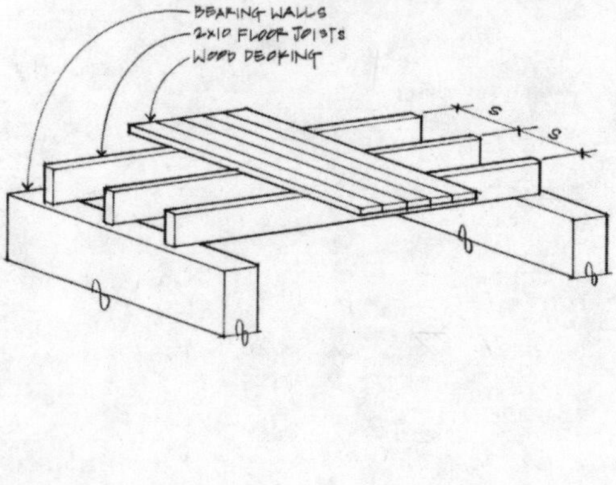

6 A timber floor system utilizing 2 × 10 S4S joists spans a length of 14 feet (simply supported). The floor carries a load of 50 psf (dead load plus live loadDL + LL). At what spacing should the joists be placed? Assume Douglas fir-Larch No. 2 ($F_b = 1{,}450$ psi).

Solution:

Based on the allowable stress criteria,

$$f = \frac{Mc}{I} = \frac{M}{S}$$

$$M_{max} = S \times f_b = (21.4 \text{ in.}^3)(1.45 \text{ k/ in.}^3) = 31 \text{ k-in.}$$

$$M = \frac{31 \text{ k-in}}{12 \text{ in./ft.}} = 2.58 \text{ k-ft.}$$

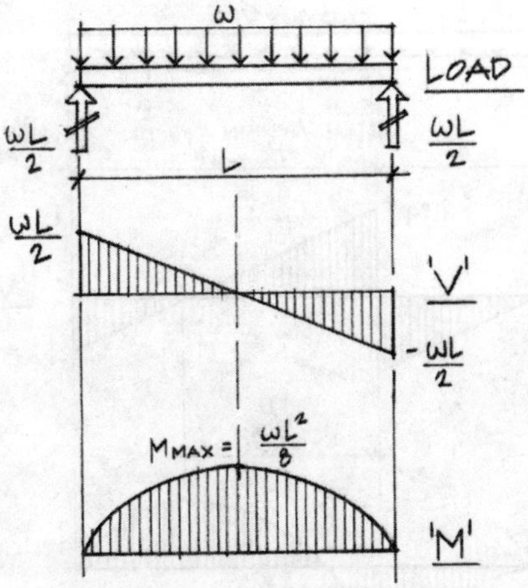

Based on the bending moment diagram,

$$M_{max} = \frac{\omega L^2}{8}$$

Therefore,

$$\omega = \frac{8M}{L^2}$$

Substituting for M obtained previously,

$$\omega = \frac{3(2.58\text{ k ft})}{(14')^2} = 0.105\text{ k/ft.}$$
$$= 105\#/\text{ft.}$$

but

$$\omega = \#/\text{ft.}^2 \times \text{tributary width (joist spacing } s)$$

$$s = \frac{\omega}{50\text{ psf}} = \frac{105\ \#/\text{ft.}}{50\ \#/\text{ft.}^2} = 2.1'$$

$$s = 25''\text{ spacing}$$

Use 24″ on center (o.c.) spacing.

Note: *Spacing is more practical for plywood subflooring, based on a four foot module of the sheet.*

7 Design the roof and second-floor beams if $F_b = 1{,}550$ psi (Southern Pine No. 1).

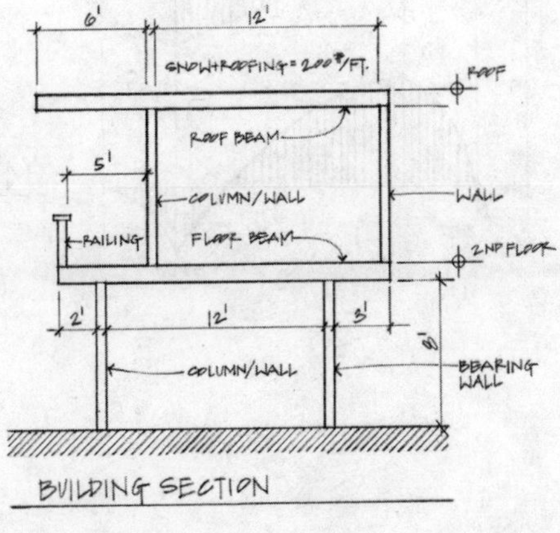

Solution:

Load conditions:

Roof: SL + DL (roof) = 200 #/ft.

Walls: 400# concentrated load on beams at second floor

Railing: 100# concentrated load on beam overhang

Second Floor: DL + LL = 300 #/ft. (also on deck)

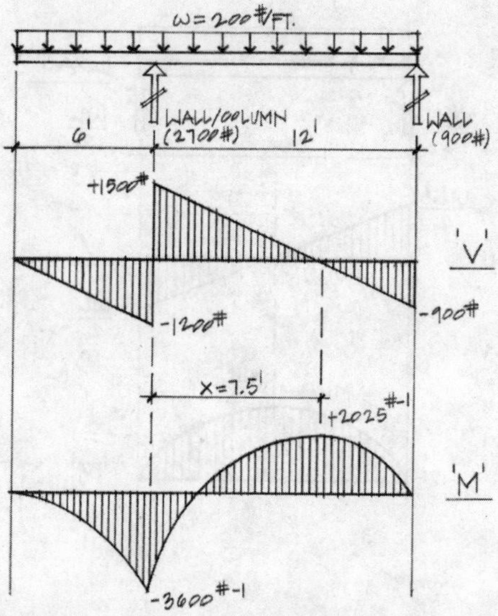

Roof beam design:

$$M_{\text{max}} = 3{,}600 \text{ \#-ft.}$$

$$S_{\text{required}} = \frac{(3.6 \text{ k-ft.})(12 \text{ in./ft.})}{1.55 \text{ k/in.}^2} = 27.9 \text{ in.}^3$$

From timber table in the Appendix: Use 4 × 8 S4S. $(S = 30.7 \text{ in.}^3)$

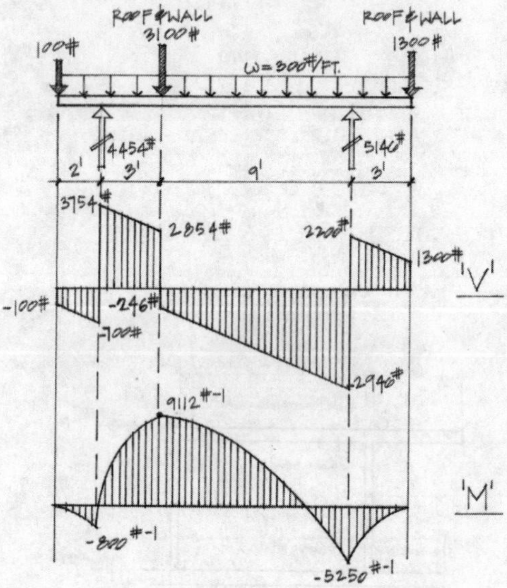

Second-floor beam design:

$$M_{\text{max}} = 9{,}112 \text{ \#-ft.}$$

$$S_{\text{required}} = \frac{M}{F_b}$$

$$S_{\text{required}} = \frac{(9.112 \text{ k-ft.})(12 \text{ in./ft.})}{1.55 \text{ k/in.}^2} = 70.5 \text{ in.}^3$$

From timber table in the Appendix: Use 4 × 12 S4S. $(S = 73.8 \text{ in.}^3)$

Problems

1 A cantilever beam has a span of nine feet with a concentrated load of 2,000# at its unsupported end. If a W8 × 18 is used (F_b = 22 ksi), is it safe?

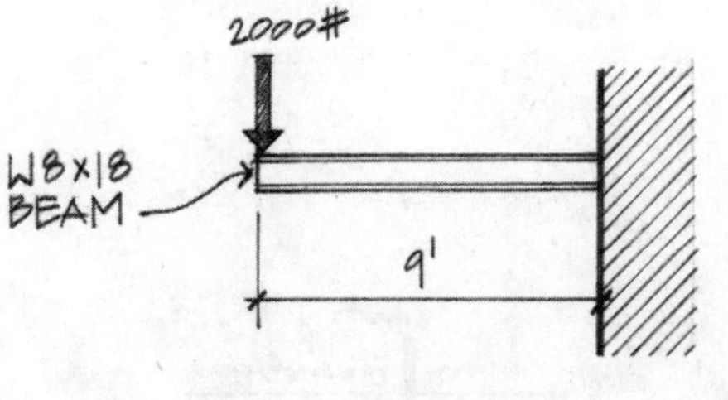

2 The single overhang beam uses a 4 × 12 S4S Douglas fir–Larch No. 1 member. Determine the maximum bending strength developed. Is it safely designed? (F_b = 1,300 psi)

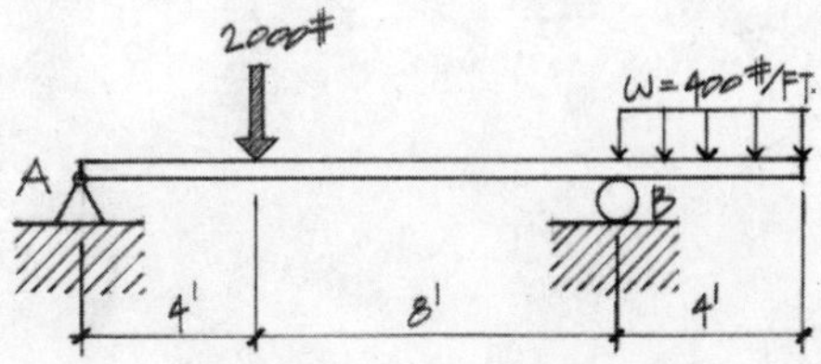

3 A 16-foot-long single overhang beam is loaded as shown. Assuming a W8 × 35, determine the maximum bending stress developed. (A992 steel, F_b = 30 ksi)

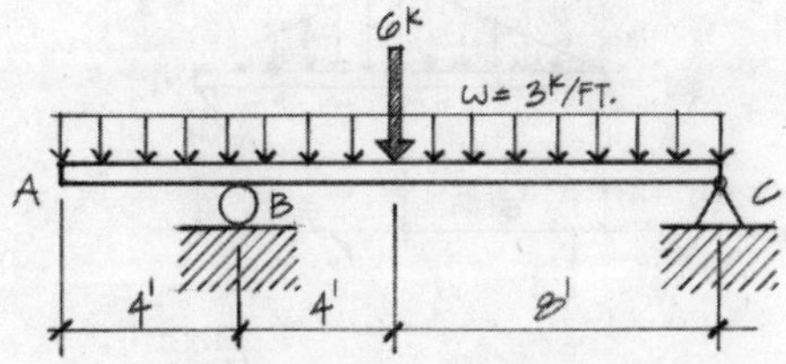

4 A beam as shown supports a floor and partition where the floor load is assumed to be uniformly distributed (500 #/ft.) and the partition contributes a 1,000# concentrated load. Select the lightest W8 steel section if F_b = 22 ksi.

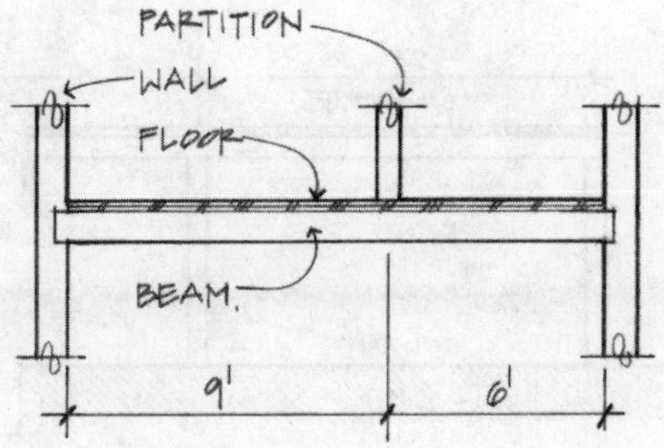

5 A W8 × 18 floor beam supports a concrete slab and a machine weighing 2,400#. Draw shear V and moment M diagrams, and determine the adequacy of the beam based on bending stress. (F_b for A992 steel is 30 ksi.)

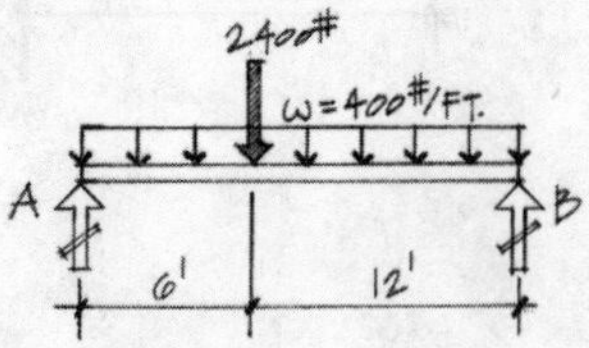

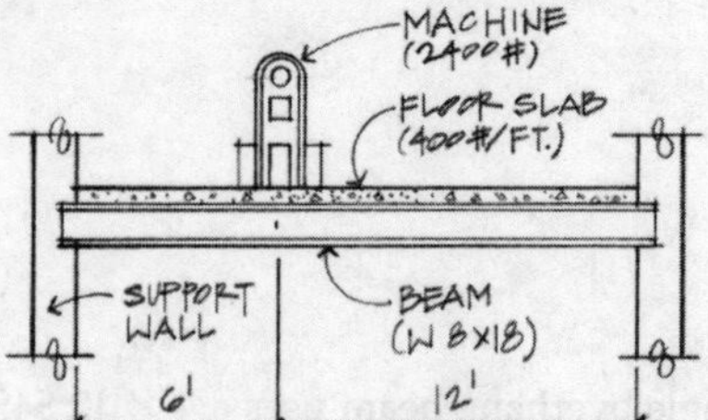

6 A lintel beam over a doorway opening 10 feet wide supports a triangular load as shown. Assuming the lintel beam to be a W8 × 15 (A36 steel), determine the bending stress developed. What size timber beam, eight inch nominal width, could be used if F_b = 1,600 psi?

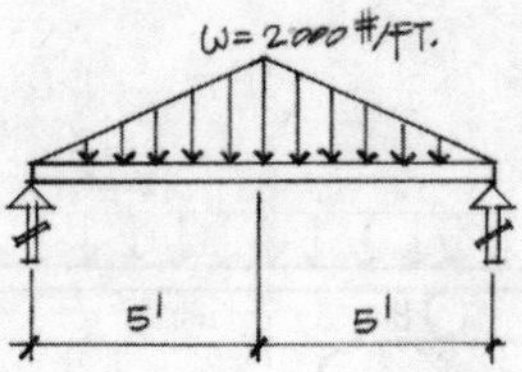

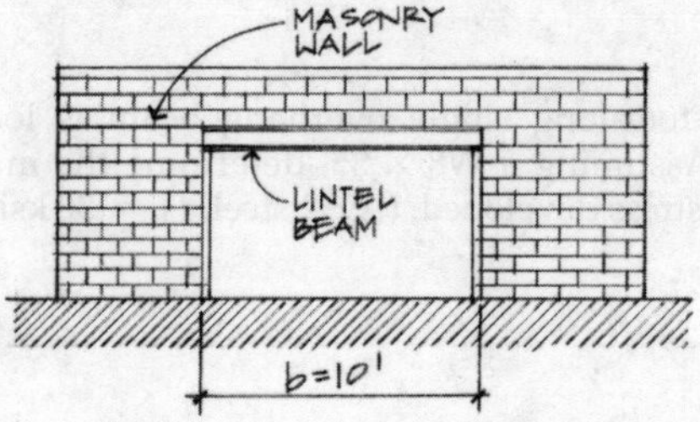

7 Glu-laminated beams are used to support the roof and pulley load at a warehouse. Beams span 24 feet plus an eight foot overhang over the loading area. Determine the bending stress adequacy of the beam.

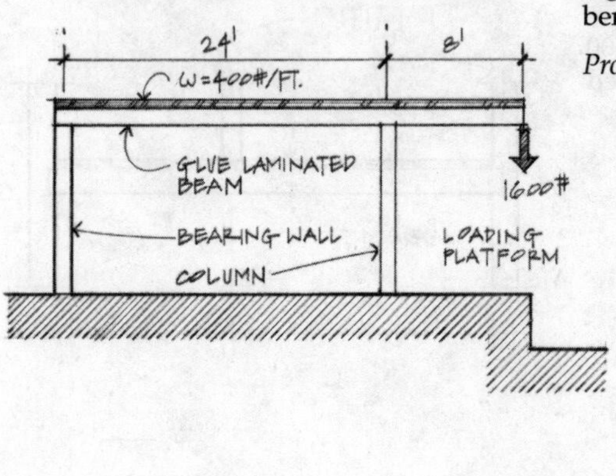

Properties of Glu-lam:

$b = 6.75''$

$h = 12''$

$S = 162 \text{ in.}^3$

$\bar{I} = 974 \text{ in.}^4$

$F_b = 2{,}400$ psi

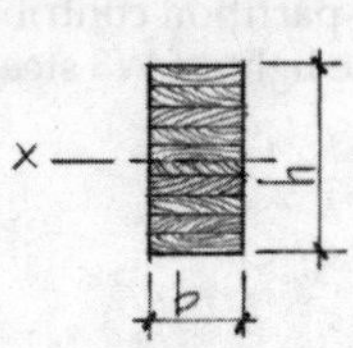

8 A W8 × 28 steel beam is loaded and supported as shown. Determine the maximum bending stress developed at the wall. What is the bending stress at a point four feet to the right of the free end of the beam? (Construct the shear V and moment M diagrams.)

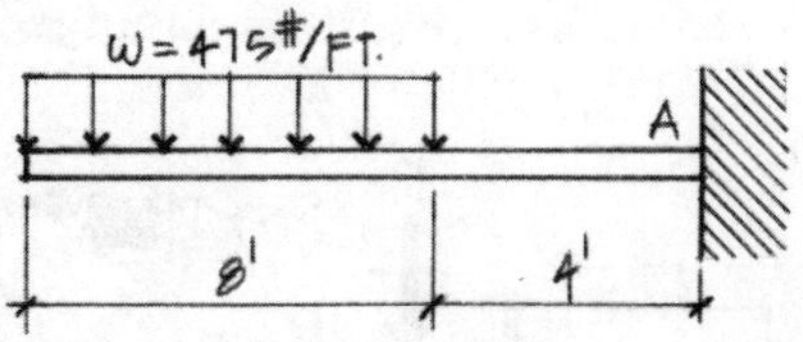

9 Select the lightest 14-inch-nominal-depth W beam to carry the load shown. Assume A992 steel. (F_b = 30 ksi.)

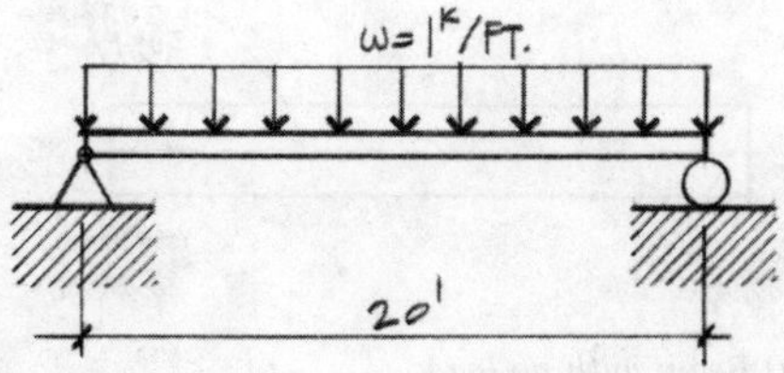

10 A W18 × 40 (A36) beam is used to support three concentrated loads of magnitude P. Determine the maximum permissible P. Draw shear V and moment M diagrams as an aid.

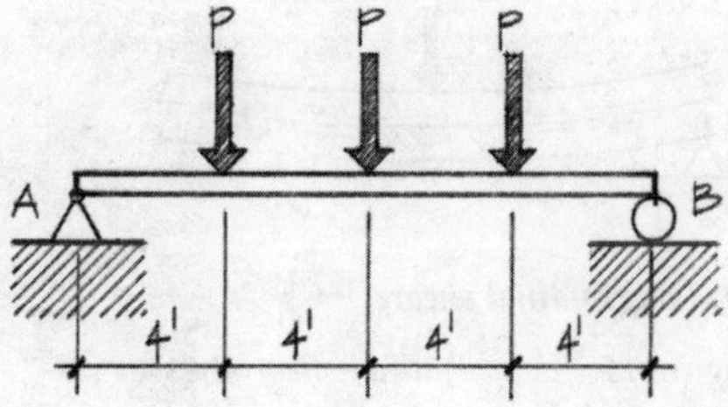

3 SHEARING STRESS—LONGITUDINAL AND TRANSVERSE

In addition to the internal bending moment present in beams, a second important factor to be considered when determining the strength of beams is shear. An internal shear force V generally is present and, in some cases, may govern the design of beams. Many materials (e.g., wood) are primarily weak in shear; for this reason, the load that can be supported may depend on the ability of the material (beam) to resist shearing forces.

Because beams are normally horizontal and the cross-sections upon which bending stresses are investigated are vertical, these shearing stresses in beams are generally referred to as *vertical* (transverse) and *horizontal* (longitudinal).

Transverse shear action (Figure 13) is a pure shearing condition and occurs even where there is no bending of the beam. However, beams do bend, and when they do, fibers on one side of the neutral axis are placed in compression and those on the other side are placed in tension. In effect, the fibers on either side of the neutral surface tend to slip in directions opposite to one another.

The existence of horizontal (longitudinal) shearing stresses in a bent beam can readily be visualized by bending a deck of cards. The sliding of one surface over another, which is plainly visible, is a shearing action that, if prevented, will set up horizontal shearing stresses on those surfaces (Figure 14).

If one constructs a beam by stacking one 4″ × 4″ member on top of another without fastening them together and then loads this beam in a direction normal to the beam length, the resulting deformation will appear somewhat like that shown in Figure 15(a). The fact that a solid beam does not exhibit this relative movement of longitudinal elements, as shown in Figure 15(b), indicates the presence of shearing stresses on longitudinal planes. The evaluation of these shearing stresses will now be studied by means of FBDs and the equilibrium approach.

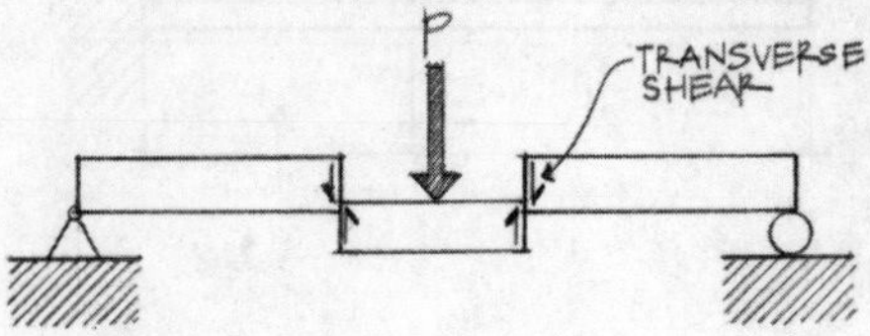

Figure 13 Transverse shear of a beam (see Section 7.2).

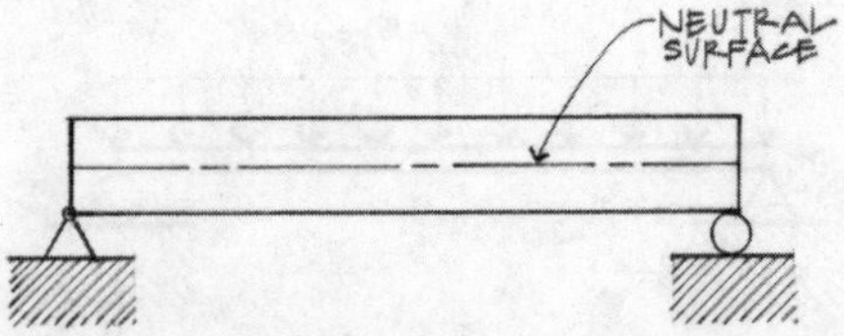

(a) Beam with no load.

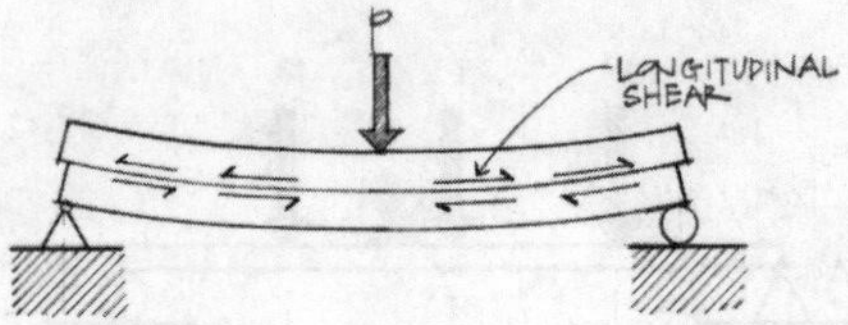

(b) Longitudinal shear.

Figure 14 Longitudinal shear stresses in beams.

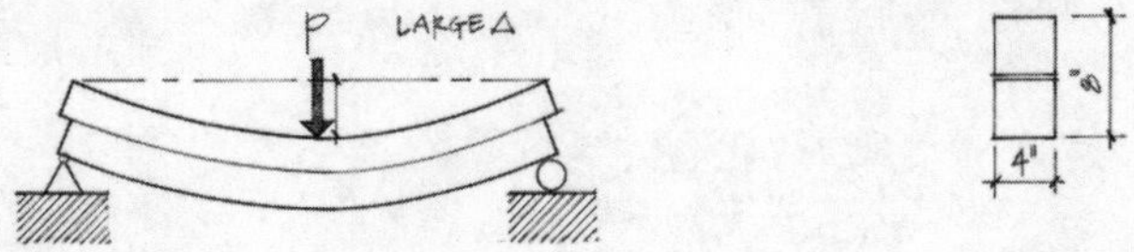

(a) Two 4″ × 4″s unfastened (large deflection).

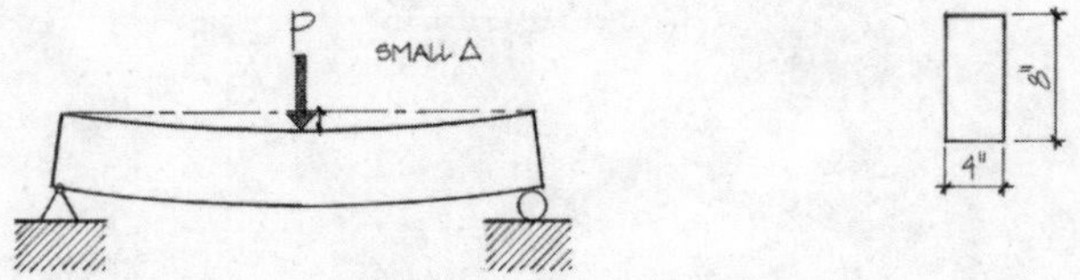

(b) Solid section (smaller deflection under load).

Figure 15 The effect of shearing stresses.

Relationship Between Transverse and Longitudinal Shearing Stress

We previously developed a method of plotting shear diagrams based on beams experiencing transverse shearing action. This section will now show that at any point in a deflected beam, the vertical and horizontal shearing stresses are equal. Therefore, the shear V diagram is a representation of both transverse and longitudinal shear along the beam.

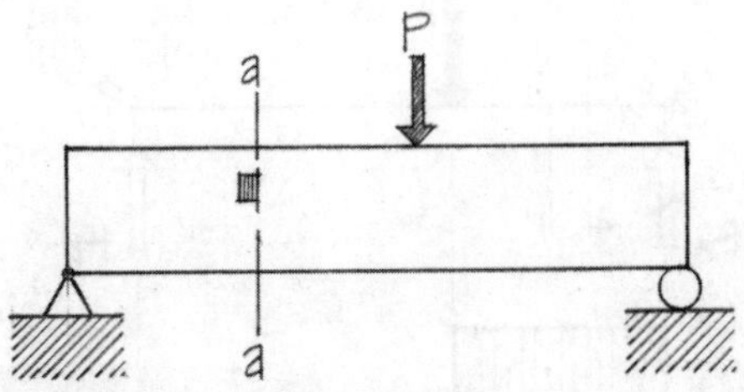

(a) Simply supported beam.

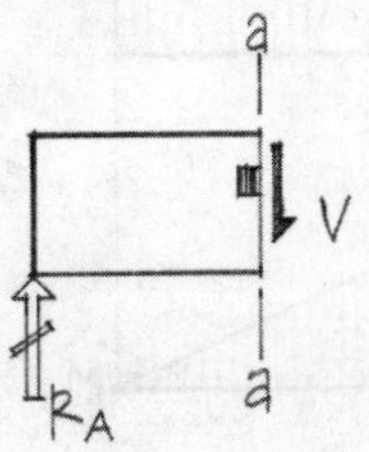

(b) Transverse shear force (V).

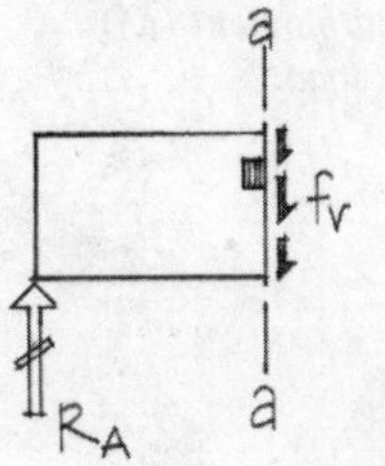

(c) Transverse shearing stress.

Figure 16 Transverse shear stress at section a-a.

Consider a simply supported beam as shown in Figure 16(a). When a section *a-a* is passed through the beam, a shear force *V*, representing the sum total of all unit transverse shearing stresses on the cut section, develops as shown in Figure 16(b). If we now isolate a small, square element of this beam, the following relationship develops:

$$V = \Sigma f_v A$$

where

f_v = unit shearing stress

A = cross-sectional area of beam

Removing the small elemental square from the beam, we draw an FBD showing the forces acting on it (Figure 17).

shear stress along section cut *a-a*

Assume that

$$\Delta y = \Delta x$$

and that the elemental square is very small.

f_v = transverse shear stress

For equilibrium vertically,

$$[\Sigma F_y = 0] f_{v_1} = f_{v_2} \text{ (forms a moment couple)}$$

To place the elemental square in rotational equilibrium, sum moments about point *O*.

$$[\Sigma M_o = 0] f_{v_1}(\Delta x) = f_{v_3}(\Delta y)$$

But

$$\Delta x = \Delta y$$

Therefore,

$$f_{v_1} = f_{v_2} = f_{v_3} = f_{v_4}$$

Shears f_{v_3} and f_{v_4} form a counterclockwise couple.

From the preceding example, we can conclude that

$$f_{\text{transverse}} = f_{\text{longitudinal}}$$

at a given point along the beam length.

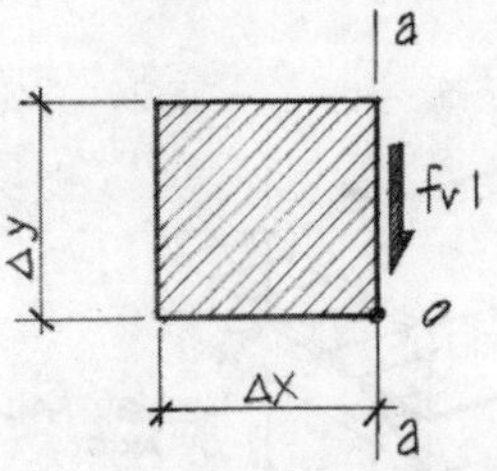

(a) Elemental square.

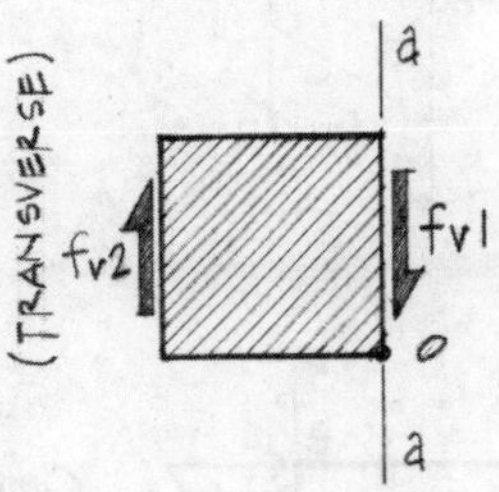

(b) Transverse shear stresses.

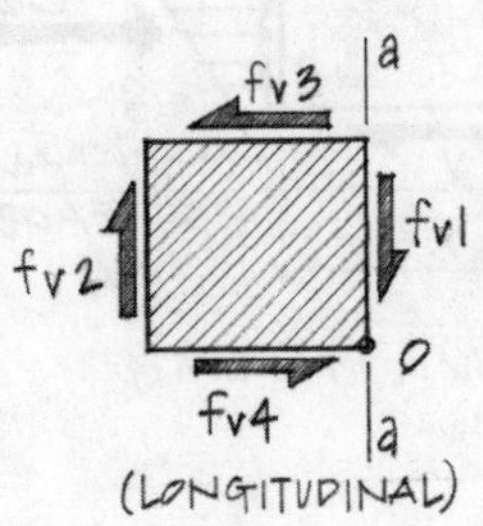

(c) Longitudinal shear stresses.

Figure 17 Shear stresses on a unit stress block.

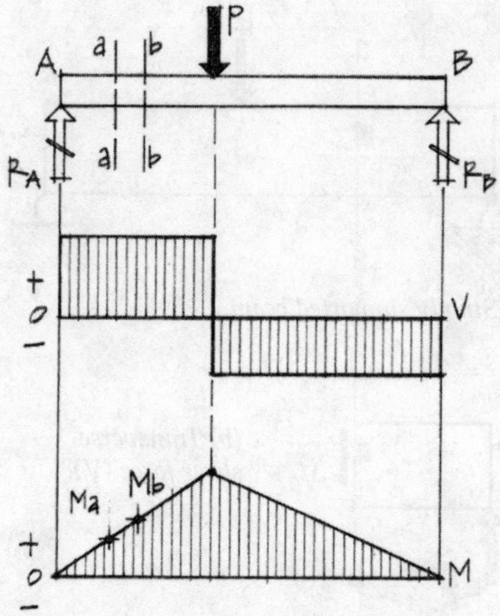

Figure 18 Shear (V) and moment (M) diagram of a beam under load.

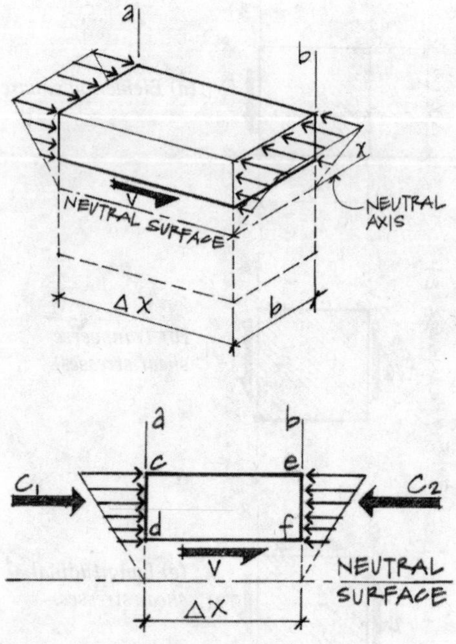

Figure 20 FBD of the upper portion of the beam between sections a-b.

4 DEVELOPMENT OF THE GENERAL SHEAR STRESS EQUATION

To arrive at a relationship for the shearing stress, consider the beam shown in Figure 18. At section *a-a* the moment is M_a, and at section *b-b*, an incremental distance to the right, the moment is M_b.

From the moment diagram in Figure 18, we see that

$$M_b > M_a$$

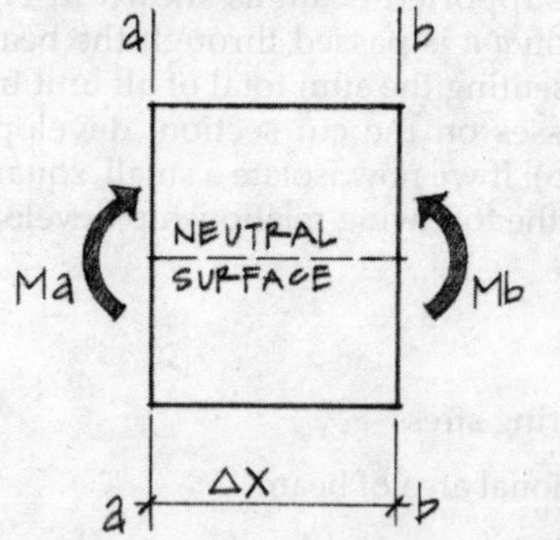

(a) Beam section between sections a *and* b.

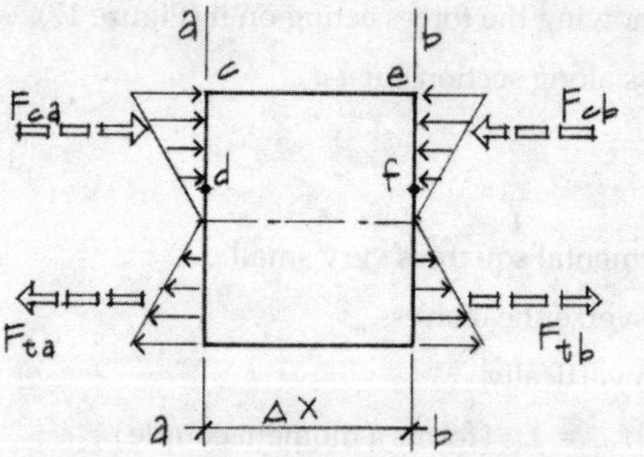

(b) Bending stresses on the beam section a-b.

Figure 19 Bending stress on a beam section.

Therefore,

$$F_{ca} < F_{cb} \text{ and } F_{ta} < F_{tb}$$

Isolating a small section of incremental beam (between sections *a-a* and *b-b* shown in Figures 19a and 19b) above the neutral surface, Figure 20 shows the distribution of tensile and compressive bending stresses. In the element *cdef*, the forces C_1 and C_2 are the resultants of the compressive stresses that act on the transverse planes *cd* and *ef*. Shear force *V* on plane *df* is required for horizontal equilibrium.

$$C_2 > C_1$$

$$\Sigma F_x = 0; \quad C_1 + V - C_2 = 0$$

$$\therefore \; V = C_2 - C_1 = (f_v)(b)(\Delta x)$$

Examine the cross-section of this isolated beam segment (Figure 21).

ΔA = small increment of area

y = distance from the N.A. to the area A

From the flexure formula,

$$f_y = \frac{My}{I}$$

The force against the area ΔA equals

$$\Delta A f_y = \frac{My\Delta A}{I}$$

But if we sum all of the ΔA values in the shaded cross-section shown in Figure 21,

$$\begin{bmatrix}\text{Area of the shaded} \\ \text{cross section}\end{bmatrix} = \Sigma \Delta A$$

$$\begin{bmatrix}\text{Total force on the shaded} \\ \text{cross-sectional area at} \\ \text{section } b\text{-}b\end{bmatrix} = C_2$$

$$C_2 = \frac{\Sigma M_b y \Delta A}{I} = \frac{M_b}{I} \Sigma \Delta A_y$$

where

M_b = internal bending moment at section *b-b*, obtained from the moment diagram (Figure 18)

I = moment of inertia of the *entire* beam cross-section, a constant

$\Sigma \Delta A y$ = Sum of all the ΔA values that compose the shaded area times the respective y distance from the N.A.

$$\Sigma \Delta A y = \Delta A \bar{y}$$

where

$\bar{y}$ = distance from the N.A. to the centroid of the shaded cross-section

$A\bar{y}$ is normally referred to as the statical or first moment. The symbol Q will be used to represent the value $A\bar{y}$:

$$Q = A\bar{y}$$

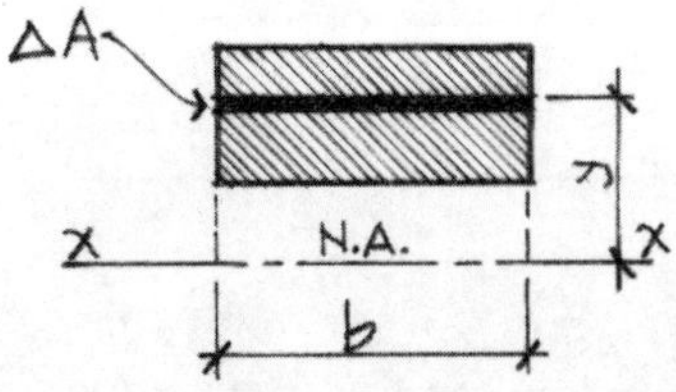

Figure 21 Upper portion of the beam cross-section.

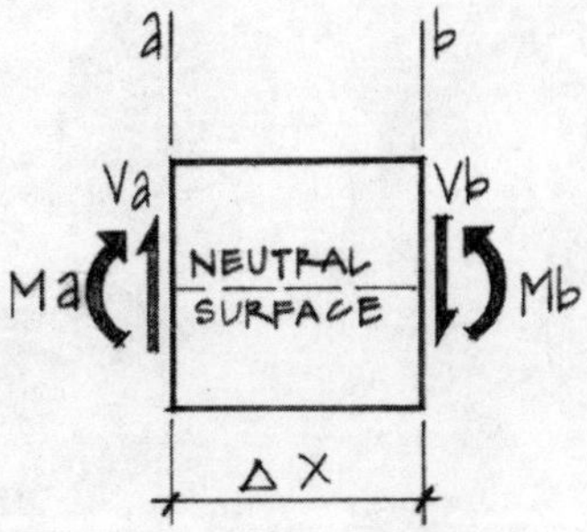

Figure 22 Beam segment between a-b.

Next, substituting:

$$C_2 = \frac{M_b Q}{I}; \text{ and } C_1 = \frac{M_a Q}{I}$$

But

$$V = C_2 - C_1$$

Therefore,

$$V = \frac{M_b Q}{I} - \frac{M_a Q}{I} = \frac{Q}{I}(M_b - M_a)$$

For beams of constant cross-section:

$$Q = \text{constant}, \ I = \text{constant}$$

Looking again at the section of the beam between section *a-a* and *b-b* shown in Figure 22, where $M_b > M_a$, the condition of vertical and moment equilibrium must be established:

$$[\Sigma F_y = 0] V_a = V_b = V_T \text{ (transverse)}$$

$$[\Sigma M_o = 0] + M_b - M_a - V_T \Delta x = 0$$

$$M_b - M_a = V_T \Delta x$$

Substituting $(M_b - M_a)$ into the earlier equation,

$$V_{\text{longitudinal}} = \frac{Q}{I}(V_T \Delta x)$$

where

V_L = shear force acting on the longitudinal beam surface (area = $b\Delta x$)

$$f_v = \text{shear stress (longitudinal)} = \frac{V}{\text{shear area}}$$

$$f_v = \frac{V}{b\Delta x}$$

$$f_v = \frac{Q}{I}\frac{(V_T \Delta x)}{b\Delta x}$$

Simplifying, the resulting equation represents the general shear formula:

$$f_v = \frac{VQ}{Ib}$$

where

f_v = unit shearing stress; transverse or longitudinal

V = shear in the beam at a given point along the beam length, usually obtained from the shear diagram

$Q = A\bar{y}$ = first moment

A = area above or below the level at which the shear stress is desired

$\bar{y}$ = distance from the beam cross-section's N.A. to the centroid of the area above or below the desired plane where shear stress is being examined

I_x = moment of inertia of the entire beam cross-section

b = width of the beam at the plane where the shear stress is being examined

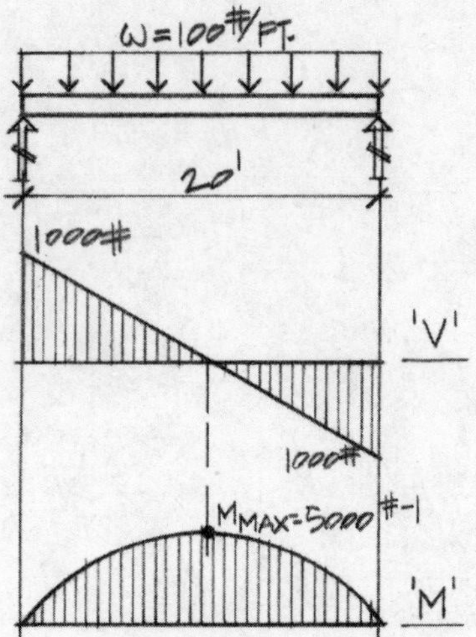

Example Problems: Shear Stress

8 Calculate the maximum bending and shear stress for the beam shown.

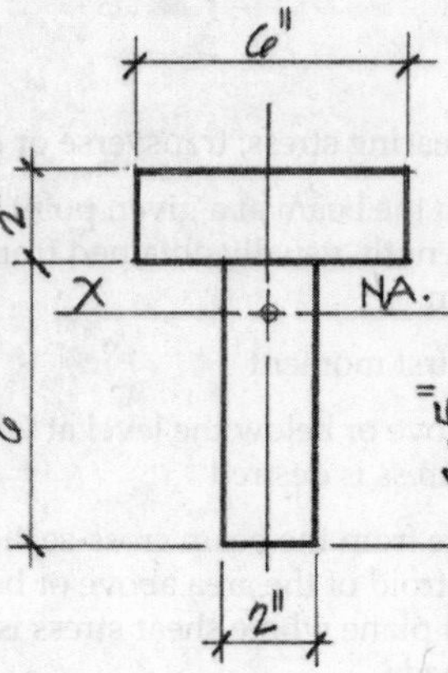

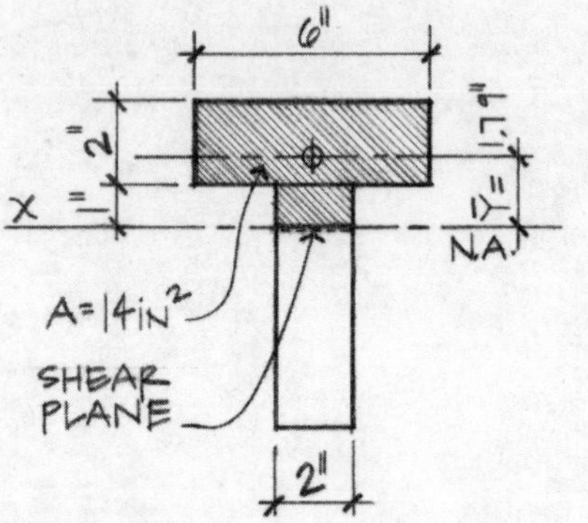

(a) Section above the neutral axis.

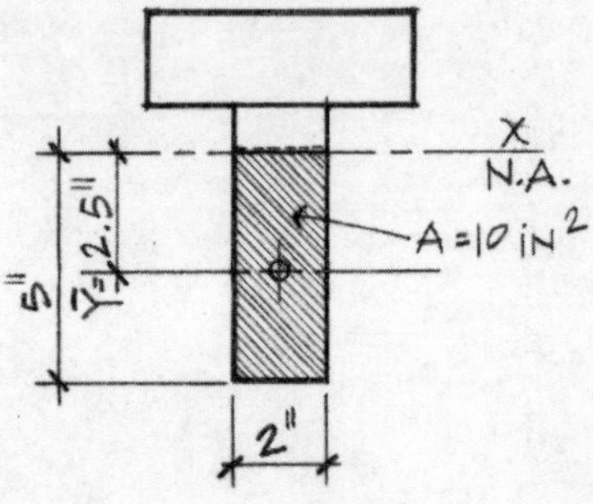

(b) Section below the neutral axis.

Solution:

Component	I_{x_c}	A	dy	Ady^2
▭	4 in.^{4}	12 in.^{2}	2″	48 in.^{4}
▯	36 in.^{4}	12 in.^{2}	2″	48 in.^{4}
	ΣI_{x_c} = 40 in.^{4}			ΣAd_y^2 = 96 in.^{4}

$I_x = 136 \text{ in.}^4$

Component	A	y	Ay
▭	12 in.^{2}	2″	24 in.^{3}
▯	2 in.^{2}	1/2″	1 in.^{3}
	ΣA = 14 in.^{2}		$\Sigma Ay = Q$ = 25 in.^{3}

$$\bar{y} = \frac{25 \text{ in.}^3}{14 \text{ in.}^2} = 1.79''$$

$$f_{b_{\max}} = \frac{Mc}{I} = \frac{(5{,}000 \text{ \#-ft.} \times 12 \text{ in./ft.})(5'')}{136 \text{ in.}^4} = 2{,}200 \text{ \#/in.}^2$$

From (a):

$V_{max} = 1{,}000\#$ (from shear diagram)

$Q = \Sigma Ay = A\bar{y} = 14 \text{ in.}^2(1.79'') = 25 \text{ in.}^3$

$I_x = 136 \text{ in.}^4$ (for the entire cross-section)

$b = 2''$

$$\therefore f_v = \frac{VQ}{Ib} = \frac{1{,}000\#(25 \text{ in.}^3)}{136 \text{ in.}^4(2 \text{ in.})} = 92 \text{ psi}$$

From (b):

$V = 1{,}000\#$

$Q = A\bar{y} = 25 \text{ in.}^3$

$I_x = 136 \text{ in.}^4$

$b = 2''$

$$\therefore f_v = \frac{1{,}000\#(25 \text{ in.}^3)}{136 \text{ in.}^4(2 \text{ in.})} = 92 \text{ psi}$$

Note: *Pick the easier half of the cross-section in calculating* $Q = A\bar{y}$.

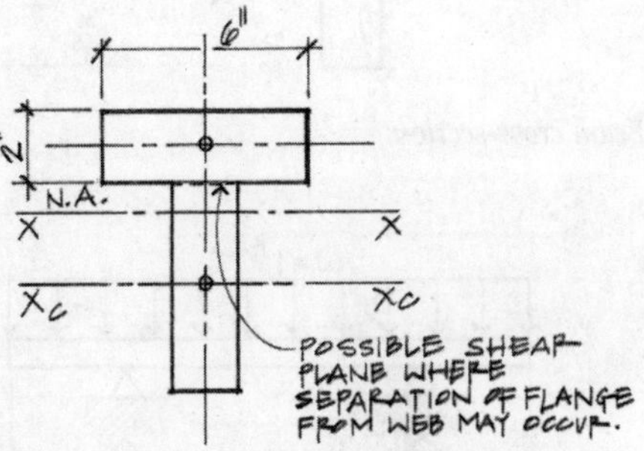

(c) Shear plane between flange and web.

What shear stress develops at the base of the flange? (This calculation would give an indication as to what kind of shear stress must be resisted if glue, nails, or any other fastening device is used to join the flange to the stem.)

$V = 1{,}000\#$

$I = 136 \text{ in.}^4$

$b = 2''$ or $6''$ (but a smaller b gives a larger f_v $\therefore$ Use $b = 2''$)

$Q = Ay = (12 \text{ in.}^2)(2'') = 24 \text{ in.}^3$

$$\therefore f_v = \frac{1{,}000\#(24 \text{ in.}^3)}{136 \text{ in.}^4(2 \text{ in.})} = 88.3 \text{ psi}$$

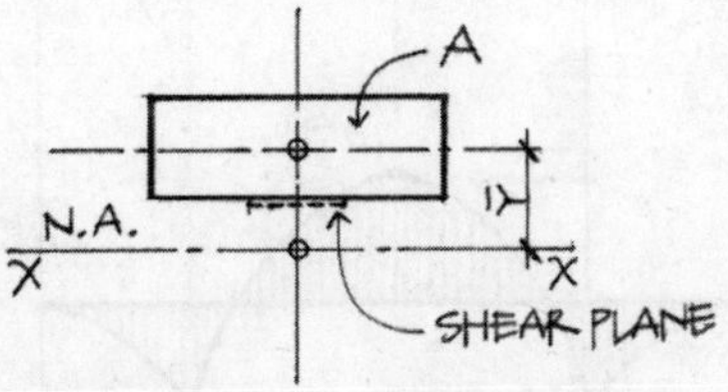

(d) Shear plane above the shear plane.

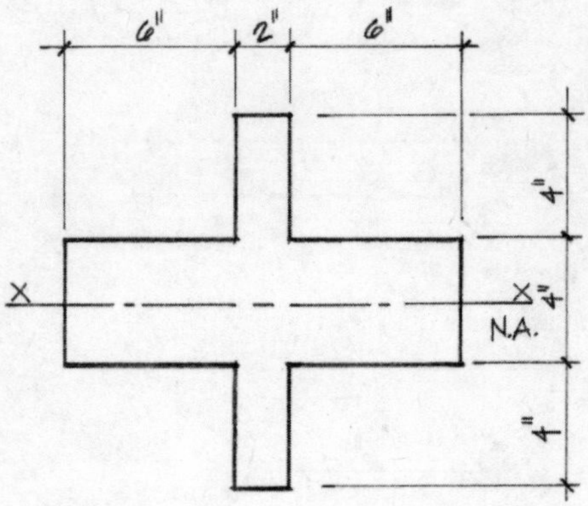

Beam cross-section.

9 Determine the maximum shear stress developed on the beam cross-section shown below.

Solution:

Component	I_{x_c}
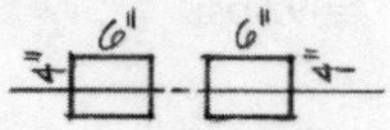	$\frac{2(6)(4)^3}{12} = 64 \text{ in.}^4$
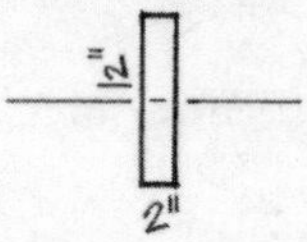	$\frac{2(12)^3}{12} = 288 \text{ in.}^4$
	$I_x = \Sigma I_{x_c} = 352 \text{ in.}^4$

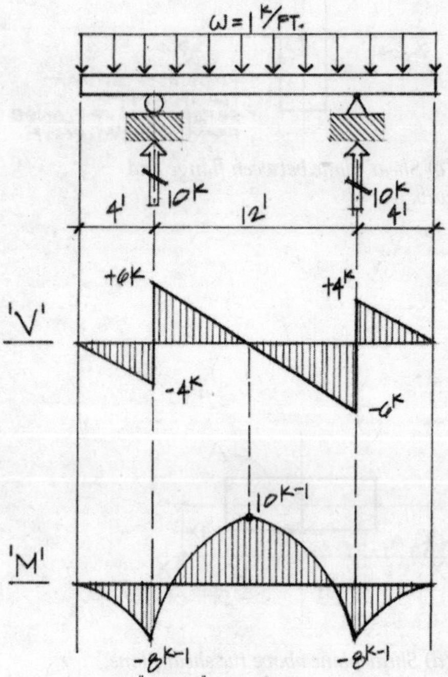

Two locations will be examined to determine the maximum shear stress. One shear plane will be through the neutral axis (normally the critical location), and the other will be where the section necks down to two inches.

Component	A	y	Ay
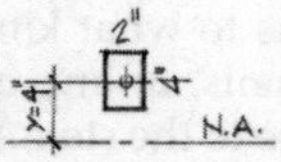	8 in.^{2}	4″	32 in.^{3}
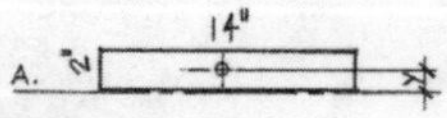	28 in.^{2}	1″	28 in.^{3}

$$\Sigma Ay = 60 \text{ in.}^3$$

$$Q = A\bar{y} = \Sigma Ay = 60 \text{ in.}^3$$

$$f_v = \frac{VQ}{Ib} = \frac{6{,}000\#(60 \text{ in.}^3)}{352 \text{ in.}^4(14 \text{ in.})} = 73.1 \text{ psi}$$

(at N.A.)

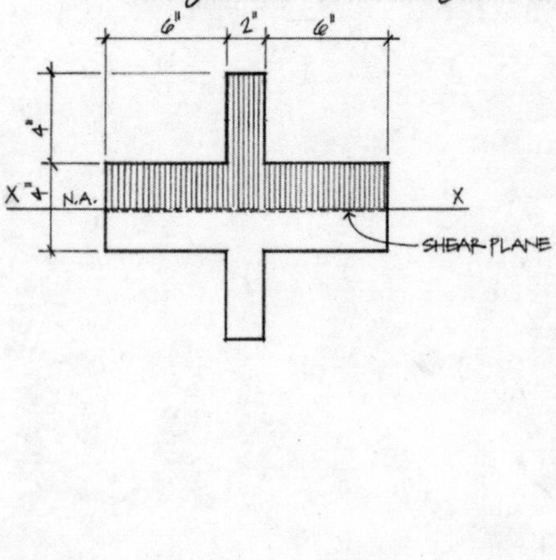

Component	A	y	Ay
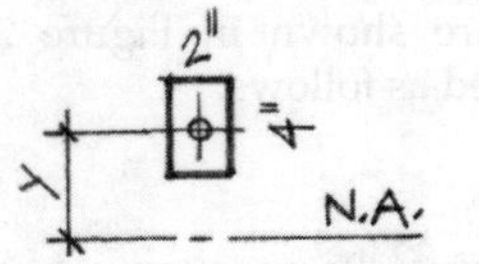	8 in.^{2}	4″	32 in.^{3}

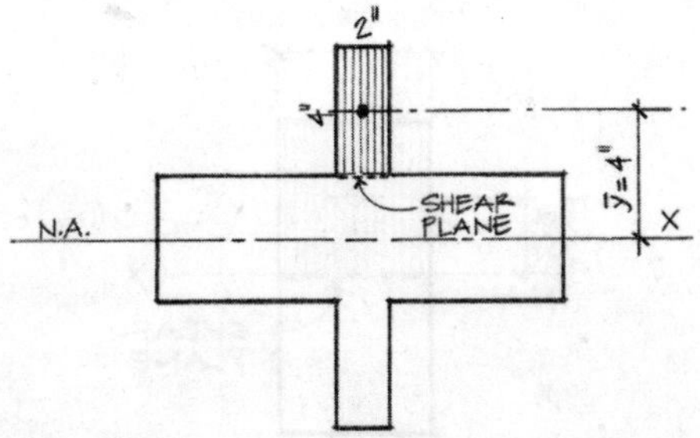

$$\Sigma Ay = 32 \text{ in.}^3$$

$$Q = \Sigma Ay = 32 \text{ in.}^3$$

$$f_v = \frac{VQ}{Ib} = \frac{6{,}000\#(32 \text{ in.}^3)}{352 \text{ in.}^4 (2 \text{ in.})} = 272.7 \text{ psi}$$

$$\therefore f_{v_{\max}} = 272.7 \text{ psi}$$

This is where longitudinal shear failure would probably occur.

10 For the beam cross-section shown, determine the longitudinal shear stress that develops at the neutral axis and at one inch increments above the neutral axis. Use $V_{\max}$ for your calculations.

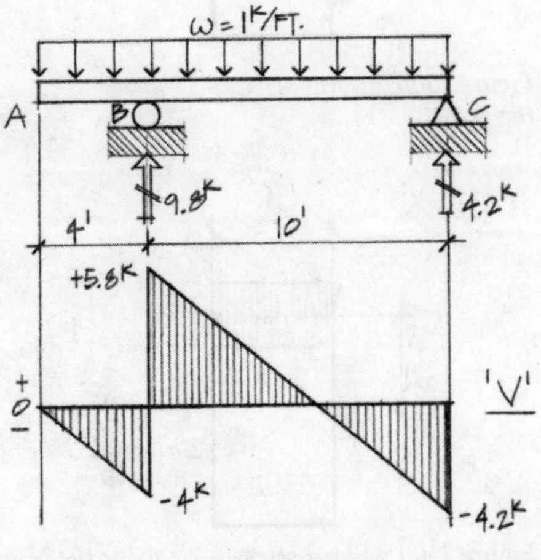

Solution:

For the general shear stress equation, a determination must be made for the $V_{\max}$ and the cross-sectional properties I, b, and Q. The $V_{\max}$ value is most conveniently obtained directly from the shear diagram.

Because the moment of inertia I is constant for a given cross-section, it may be calculated as

$$I_x = \frac{bh^3}{12} = \frac{(4'')(8'')^3}{12} = 171 \text{ in.}^4$$

The width of the cross-section (shear plane) is also constant; therefore, $b = 4''$.

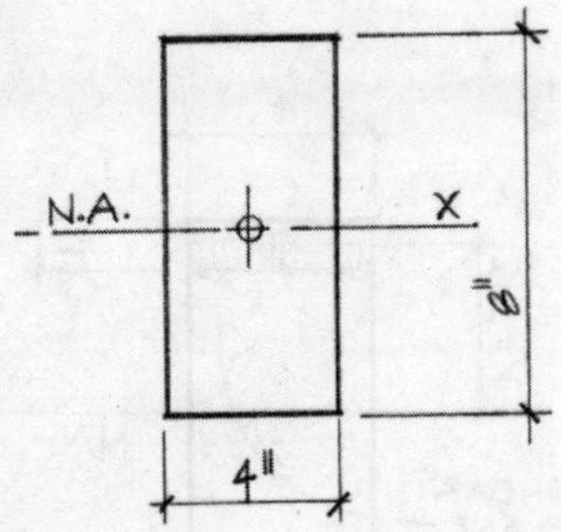

Beam cross-section.

The values of $Q = A\bar{y}$ for each of the four shear planes, including the neutral axis at which the horizontal (longitudinal) shear is desired, are shown in Figure 23(a) through 23(d) and are tabulated as follows:

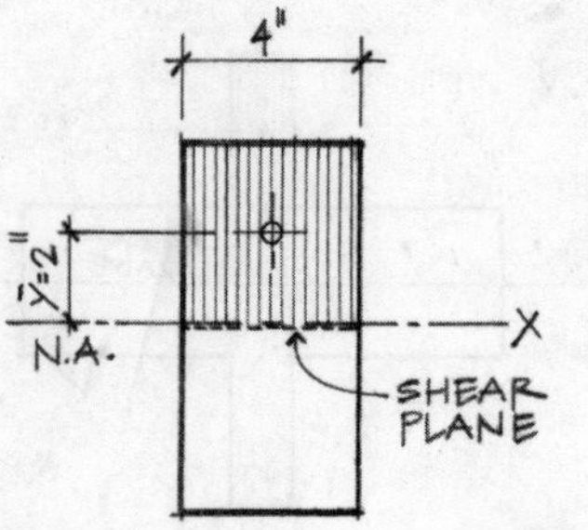

Figure 23(a) *Shear stresses at the neutral axis (N.A.)*

$$I_x = 171 \text{ in.}^4, \quad b = 4''$$
$$Q = A\bar{y} = (16 \text{ in.}^2)(2'') = 32 \text{ in.}^3$$
$$f_v = \frac{VQ}{Ib} = \frac{(5{,}800\#)(32 \text{ in.}^3)}{171 \text{ in.}^4(4 \text{ in.})} = 271 \text{ psi}$$

(N.A.)

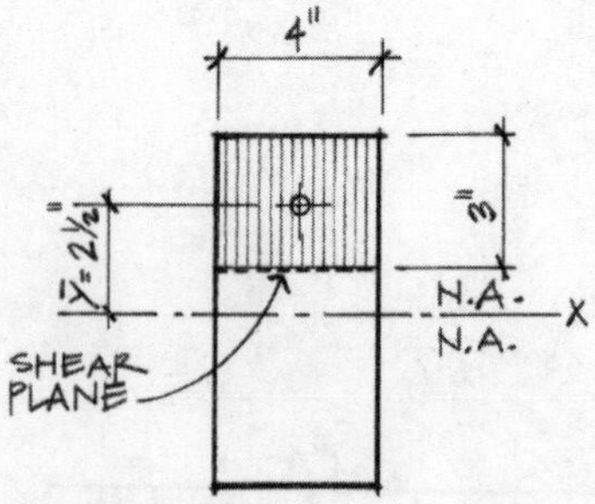

Figure 23(b) *Shear stresses 1″ above the N.A.*

$$I_x = 171 \text{ in.}^4, \quad b = 4''$$
$$Q = A\bar{y} = (4'')(3'')(2.5'') = 30 \text{ in.}^3$$
$$f_v = \frac{VQ}{Ib} = \frac{(5{,}800\#)(30 \text{ in.}^3)}{171 \text{ in.}^4(4 \text{ in.})} = 254 \text{ psi}$$

(1″ above N.A.)

$$I_x = 171 \text{ in.}^4, \quad b = 4''$$
$$Q = A\bar{y} = (8 \text{ in.}^2)(3'') = 24 \text{ in.}^3$$
$$f_v = \frac{VQ}{Ib} = \frac{(5{,}800\#)(24 \text{ in.}^3)}{171 \text{ in.}^4(4 \text{ in.})} = 204 \text{ psi}$$

(2″ above N.A.)

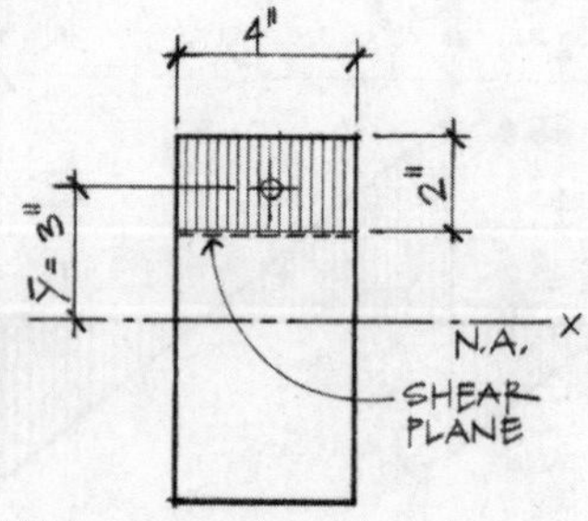

Figure 23(c) *Shear stresses 2″ above the N.A*

$$I_x = 171 \text{ in.}^4, \quad b = 4''$$
$$Q = A\bar{y} = (4 \text{ in.}^2)(3.5'') = 14 \text{ in.}^3$$
$$f_v = \frac{VQ}{Ib} = \frac{(5{,}800\#)(14 \text{ in.}^3)}{171 \text{ in.}^4(4 \text{ in.})} = 119 \text{ psi}$$

(3″ above N.A.)

Plotting the shear stress values on a graph adjacent to the beam cross-section, we obtain a parabolic curve as shown in Figure 24. Had the values of shearing stress been obtained for the corresponding points below the neutral axis, we should have found corresponding magnitudes. By completing the curve, it will be noted that the maximum value of horizontal shearing stress occurs at the neutral plane (surface), where Ay is a maximum and the bending stresses are equal to zero.

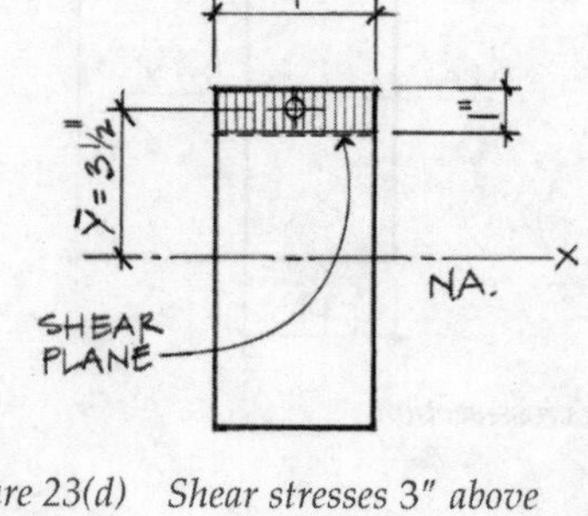

Figure 23(d) *Shear stresses 3″ above the N.A.*

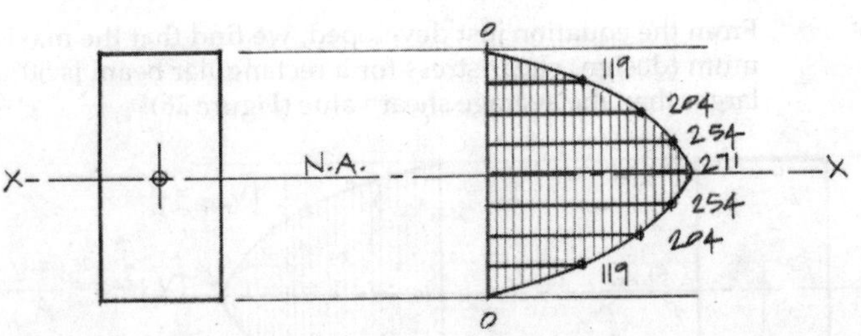

Beam cross-section. *Graph of stress intensities at various locations on the beam cross-section.*

Figure 24 *Shear stress distribution on a rectangular cross-section.*

Because of its frequent use in design, an expression for the maximum horizontal shearing stress occurring in solid rectangular beams (primarily timber beams) may be derived (Figure 25).

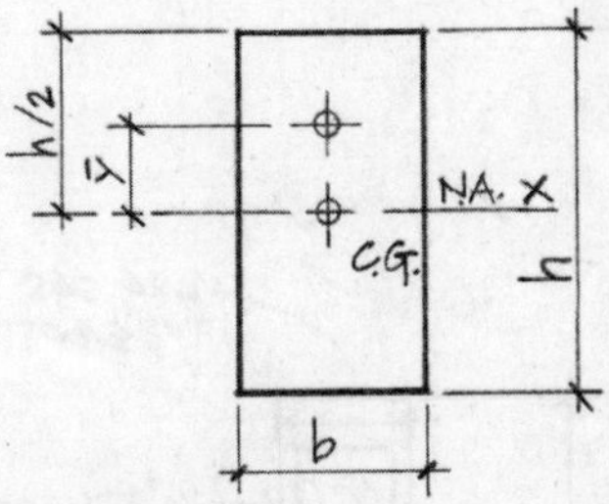

Figure 25 *Beam cross-section.*

Shear plane is maximum at the neutral axis, as found in Figure 24.

$$f_v = \frac{VQ}{Ib}; \quad I_x = \frac{bh^3}{12}; \quad A = b \times \frac{h}{2} = \frac{bh}{2}$$

$$b = b; \quad \bar{y} = \frac{h}{4}$$

$$Q = A\bar{y}$$

Therefore,

$$f_v = \frac{V\left(\frac{bh}{2} \times \frac{h}{4}\right)}{\left(\frac{bh^3}{12}\right)(b)} = \frac{12Vbh^2}{8b^2h^3} = \frac{3V}{2bh}$$

However, bh = area of the *entire* beam cross-section.

Simplifying,

$$\boxed{f_{v_{\max}\,(N.A.)} = \frac{3V}{2A} = \frac{1.5V}{A} \quad \text{for solid rectangular cross-sections}}$$

where

$f_{v_{\max}\,(N.A.)}$ = maximum shearing stress at the N.A.

V = maximum shear on the loaded beam

A = cross-sectional area of the beam

From the equation just developed, we find that the maximum (design) shear stress for a rectangular beam is 50% larger than the average shear value (Figure 26).

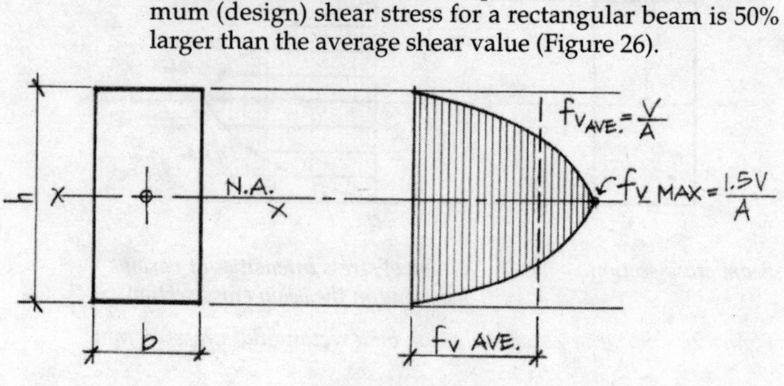

Cross Section. *Shear stress graph of a rectangular cross section.*

Figure 26 Shear stress distribution—key points.

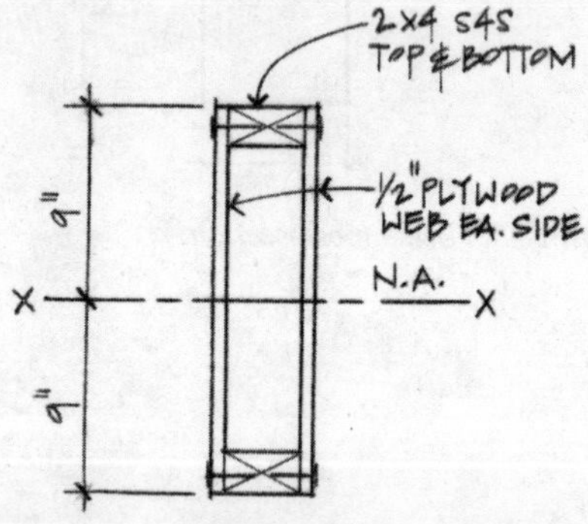

Built-up plywood box beam cross section.

11 A built-up plywood box beam with 2 × 4 S4S top and bottom flanges is held together by nails. Determine the pitch (spacing) of the nails if the beam supports a uniform load of 200 #/ft. along the 26 foot span. Assume the nails have a shear capacity of 80# each.

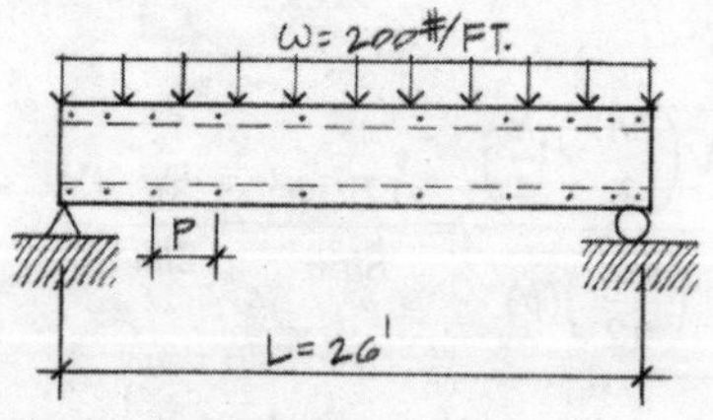

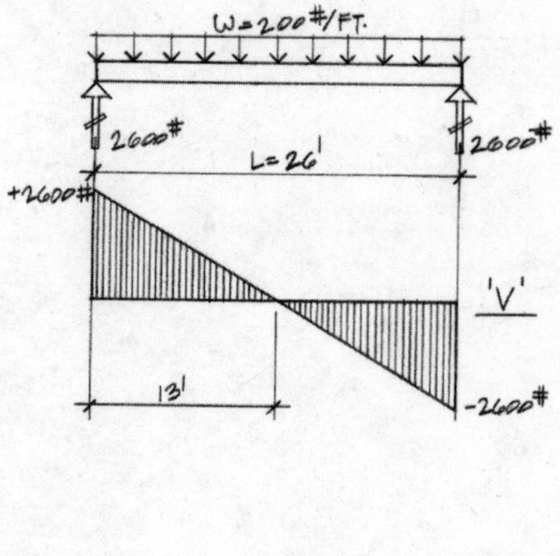

Solution:

Construct the shear diagram to obtain the critical shear condition and its location.

Note that the condition of shear is critical at the supports and that the shear intensity decreases as you approach the centerline of the beam. This would indicate that the nail spacing P varies from the support to midspan. Nails are closely spaced at the support, but increasing spacing occurs toward midspan, following the shear diagram.

$$f_v = \frac{VQ}{Ib}$$

$$I_x = \frac{(4.5'')(18'')^3}{12} - \frac{(3.5'')(15'')^3}{12} = 1{,}202.6 \text{ in.}^4$$

$$Q = A\bar{y} = (5.25\text{ in.}^2)(8.25'') = 43.3\text{ in.}^3$$

Shear force $= f_v \times A_v$

where

$A_v =$ shear area

Assume the following:

$F =$ capacity of two nails (one each side) at the flange, representing two shear surfaces

$$F = f_v \times b \times p = \frac{VQ}{Ib} \times bp$$

$$\therefore F = p \times \frac{VQ}{I} \quad p = \frac{FI_x}{VQ}$$

At the maximum shear location (support) wl $V = 2{,}600\#$,

$$p = \frac{(2\text{ nails} \times 80\,\#/\text{nail})(1{,}202.6\text{ in.}^4)}{(2{,}600\#)(43.3\text{ in.}^3)} = 1.71''$$

Checking the spacing requirement p at different locat along the beam, we obtain a graphical plot (like the sl diagram) of the spacing requirements.

At the support,

$V_0 = 2{,}600\#, p_0 = 1.36''$

$$V_2 = 2{,}200\#; p_2 = \frac{(2 \times 80\,\#/\text{nail})(1{,}202.6\text{ in.}^4)}{(2{,}200\#)(43.3\text{ in.}^3)} = 2$$

$$V_4 = 1{,}800\#; p_4 = \frac{(2 \times 80\,\#/\text{nail})(1{,}202.6\text{ in.}^4)}{(1{,}800\#)(43.3\text{ in.}^3)} = 2.4$$

$$V_6 = 1{,}400\#; p_6 = \frac{(2 \times 80\,\#/\text{nail})(1{,}202.6\text{ in.}^4)}{(1{,}400\#)(43.3\text{ in.}^3)} = 3.17''$$

$$V_8 = 1{,}000\#; p_8 = \frac{(2 \times 80\,\#/\text{nail})(1{,}202.6\text{ in.}^4)}{(1{,}000\#)(43.3\text{ in.}^3)} = 4.44''$$

$$V_{10} = 600\#; p_{10} = \frac{(2 \times 80\,\#/\text{nail})(1{,}202.6\text{ in.}^4)}{(600\#)(43.3\text{ in.}^3)} = 7.04''$$

In practical nail spacing, increments of half an inch or one inch should be used.

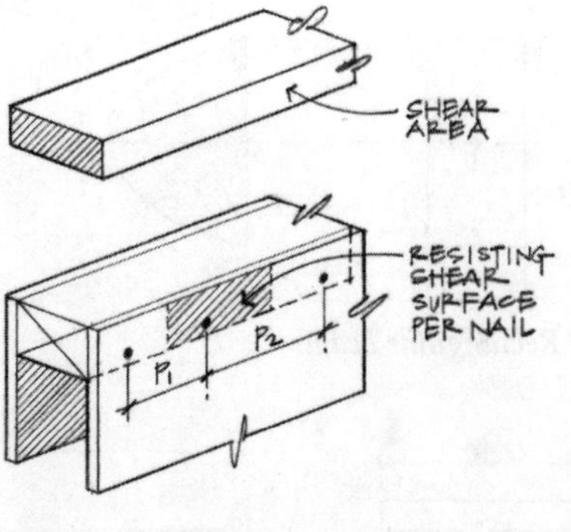

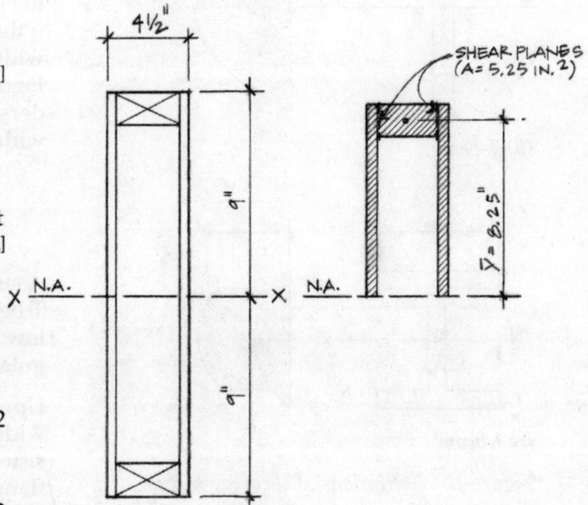

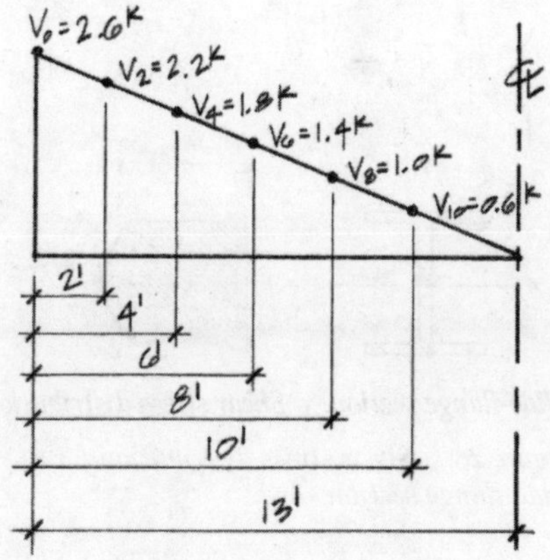

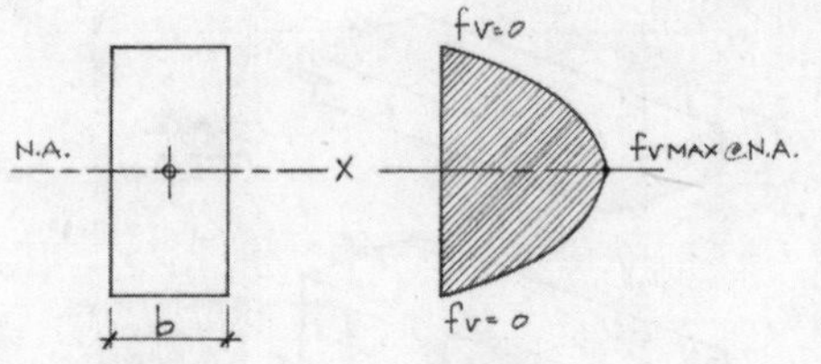

(a) Rectangular beam.

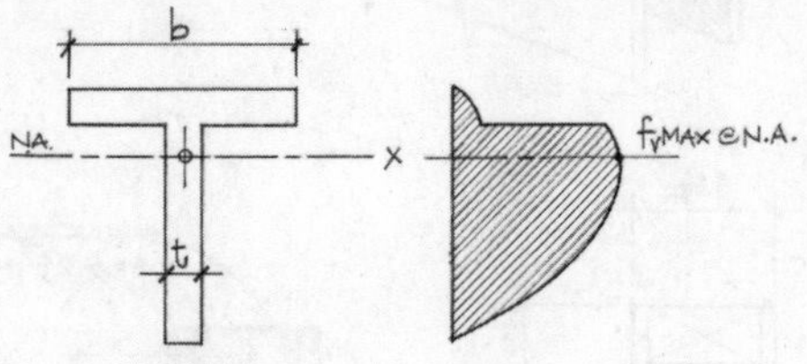

(b) T-beam.

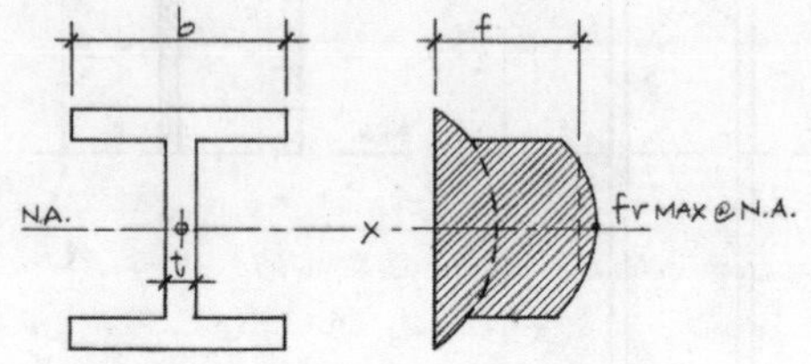

(c) I-beam.

Figure 27 Variations of shearing stress.

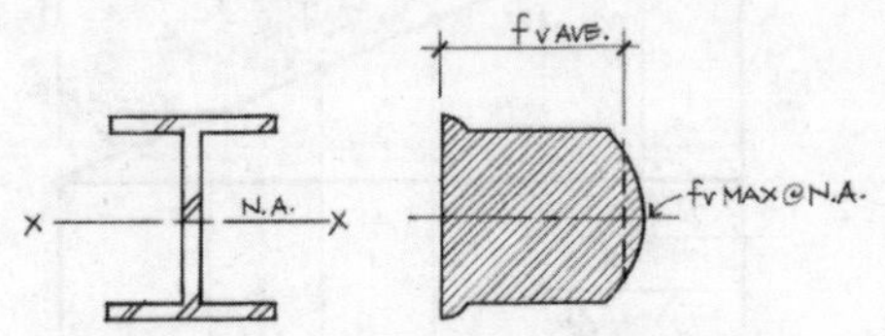

Wide-flange section. *Shear stress distribution.*

Figure 28 Shear stress distribution for a wide-flange section.

Shearing Stress Variations in Beams

Beams must be designed to safely withstand the maximum stresses due to bending and shear. The variation of tensile and compressive bending stresses over a cross-sectional area was discussed in Section 2. As in bending stress, shear stress also varies on a cross-section, as illustrated for a rectangular cross-section in Figure 26. With few exceptions, the maximum shearing stress generally occurs at the neutral axis.

Shearing stress variation over the cross-section of a T-beam, I-beam, and wide-flange section is illustrated in Figure 27(b), Figure 27(c), and Figure 28. The dashed curve in Figure 27(c) indicates what the stress variation would be if the beam area had remained rectangular with a constant width b. This variation would be similar to that shown in Figure 27(a). The sudden increase in shear stress at the underside of the top flange comes from the change of the width from b to t in

$$f_v = \frac{VQ}{Ib}$$

A similar change occurs at the flange-to-web transition of a T-beam, as shown in Figure 27(b), but here, the curve below the neutral axis follows the usual pattern for a rectangular beam.

Upon examination of the shear stress distribution for a wide-flange section, we find that most of the shear is resisted by the web, and very little resistance is offered by the flanges. The opposite is true in the case for flexural stresses—the flanges resist most of the bending stress, and the web offers little resistance to bending (Figure 28).

The calculation of the exact maximum stress magnitude using VQ/Ib can become difficult because of the presence of fillets (rounding) where the flange joins the web. A high level of accuracy is even harder to achieve in channels or standard I-shapes that have sloping flange surfaces. Accordingly, the American Institute of Steel Construction (AISC) recommends the use of a much simpler, approximate formula for the common steel shapes:

$$f_{v_{\text{average}}} = \frac{V}{t_w d}$$

where

V = shear force

d = beam depth

t_w = web thickness

This formula gives the *average* unit shearing stress for the web over the full depth of the beam, ignoring the contribution of the flange (Figure 29).

Webs resist approximately 90% of the total shear for structural shapes, as shown in Figure 29. In contrast, flanges resist 90% of the bending stresses.

Depending on the particular steel shape, the average shear stress formula

$$f_{v_{\text{average}}} = \frac{V}{t_w d}$$

can be as much as 20% in error in the nonconservative direction. This means that when a shearing stress computed from this equation gets within 20% of the maximum allowable shear stress, the actual maximum stress (VQ/Ib) might exceed the allowable stress by a small amount.

Fortunately, this low level of accuracy is seldom a problem for two reasons:

1. Structural steels are very strong in shear.
2. Most beams and girders in buildings, unlike those in some machines, have low shearing stresses.

High shearing stress may be present in short-span, heavily loaded beams or if large concentrated loads are applied adjacent to a support. In determining the size of a steel beam, flexural stresses or deflection will usually govern.

When shearing stresses do become excessive, steel beams do not fail by ripping along the neutral axis, as might occur in timber beams. Rather, it is the compression buckling of the relatively thin web that constitutes a shear failure (Figure 30). The AISC has provided several design formulas for determining when extra bearing area must be provided at concentrated loads or when web stiffeners are needed to prevent such failures (Figure 31).

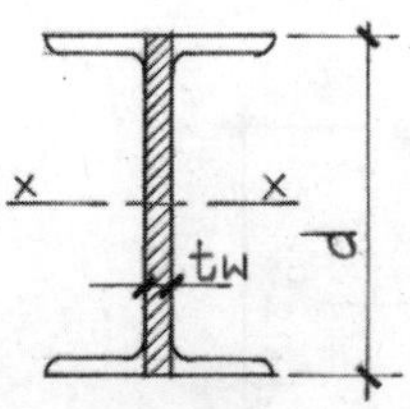

Wide-flange shape.

Figure 29(a)

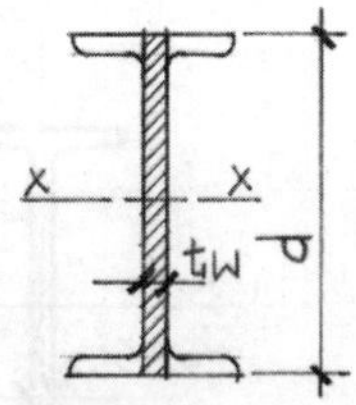

Standard shape.

Figure 29(b)

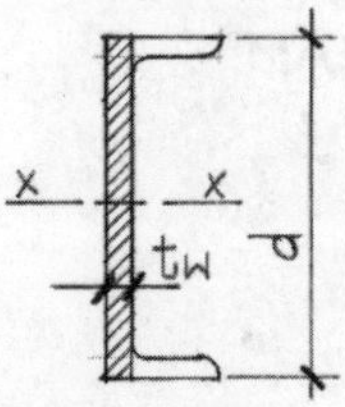

Channel shape.

Figure 29(c)

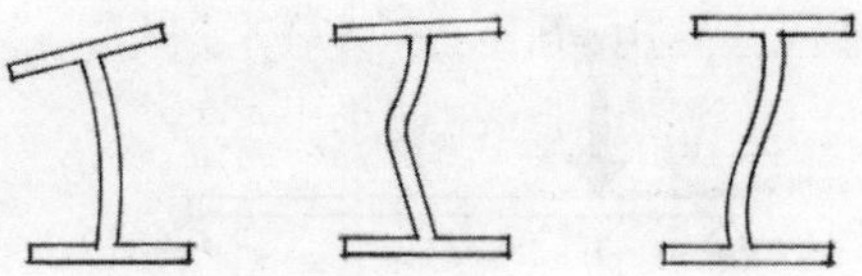

Figure 30 Web buckling in steel beams.

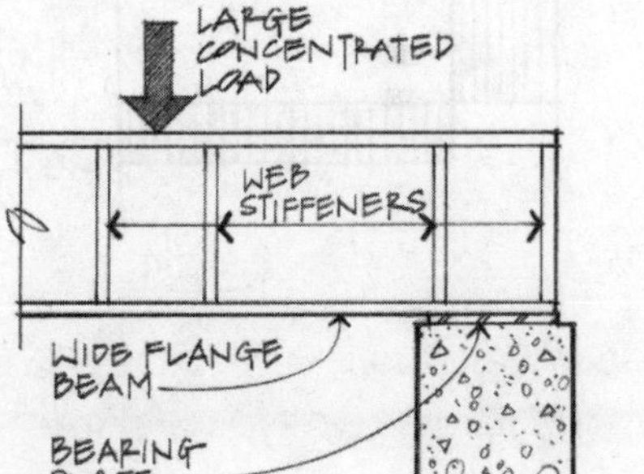

Figure 31 Web stiffeners.

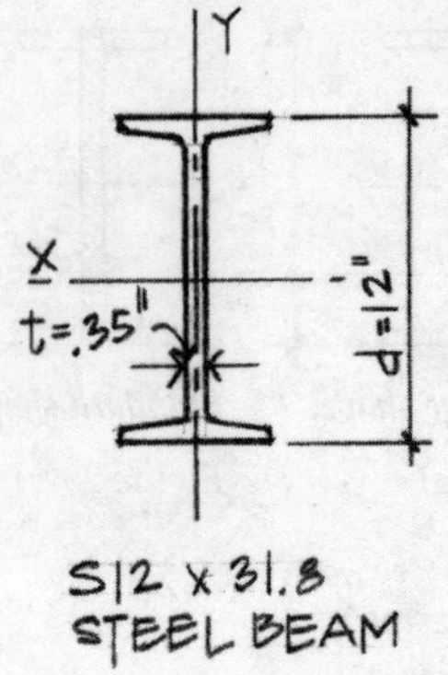

Example Problems: Shearing Stress

12 An American Standard S12 × 31.8 beam resists a shear $V = 12$ k at the supports. Determine the average web shear stress. $F_v = 14.5$ ksi (A36 steel).

Solution:

$$f_{v_{average}} = \frac{V}{t_w d}$$

$V = 12\text{ k}$

$t_w = 0.35''$

$d = 12''$

$$f_{v_{average}} = \frac{12\text{ k}}{(0.35'')(12'')} = 2.86\text{ ksi} < F_v = 14.5\text{ ksi}$$

∴OK

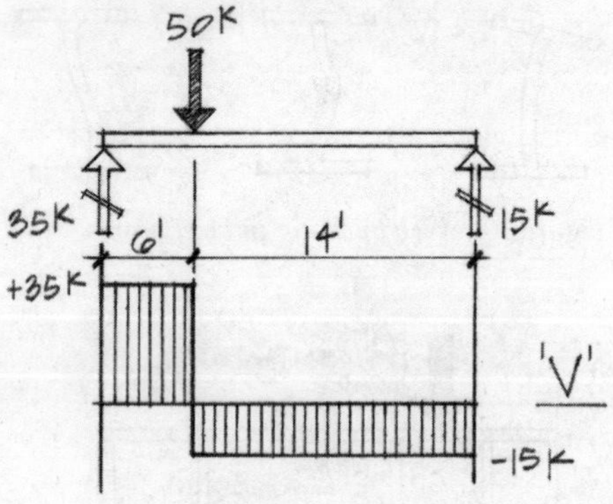

13 An (A36) W12 × 50 beam is loaded as shown. Calculate the critical $f_{v_{average}}$.

Solution:

$F_v = 14.5\text{ ksi}$ (A36 steel)

$V = 35\text{ k}$

$t_w = 0.37''$

$d = 12.19''$

$$f_{v_{average}} = \frac{V}{t_w d} = \frac{35\text{ k}}{(0.37'')(12.19'')} = 7.76\text{ ksi} < F_v = 14.5\text{ ksi}$$

∴OK

Problems

11 Two steel plates (A572, F_y = 50 ksi) are welded together to form an inverted T-beam. Determine the maximum bending stress developed. Also determine the maximum shear stress at the neutral axis of the cross-section and at the intersection where the stem joins the flange.

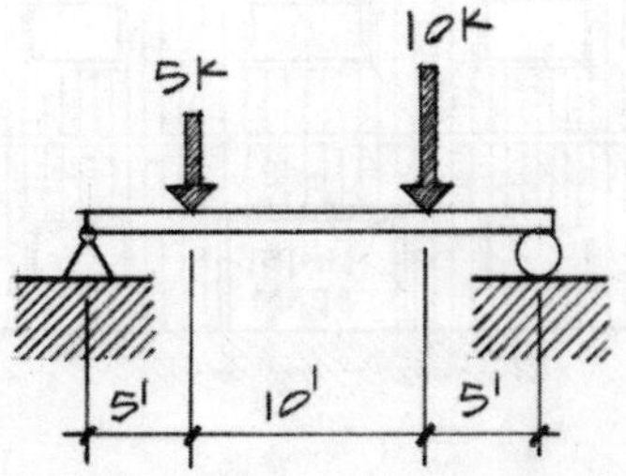

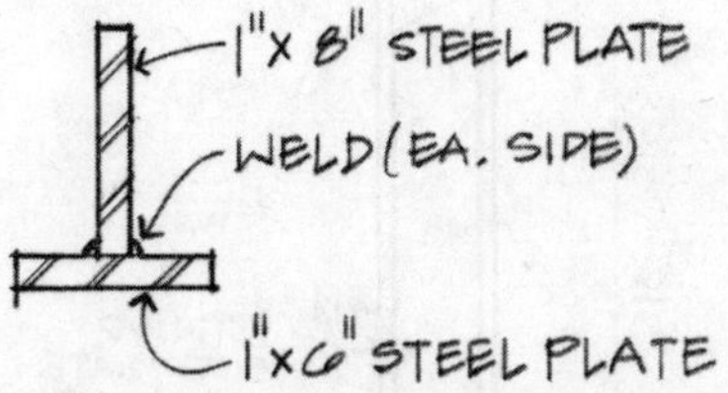

12 A log of diameter D is available to be used as a beam carrying a uniformly distributed load of 400 #/ft. over a length of 32 feet. Determine the required diameter D necessary if F_b = 1,200 psi and F_v = 100 psi.

13 The 20-foot beam shown has a cross-section built up from a 1″ × 10″ steel plate welded onto the top of a W8 × 31 section. Determine the maximum load w the beam can sustain when the steel section reaches a maximum allowable bending stress of F_b = 22 ksi. For the w calculated, determine the shear stress f_v developed between the plate and the top flange surface (use the flange width for b).

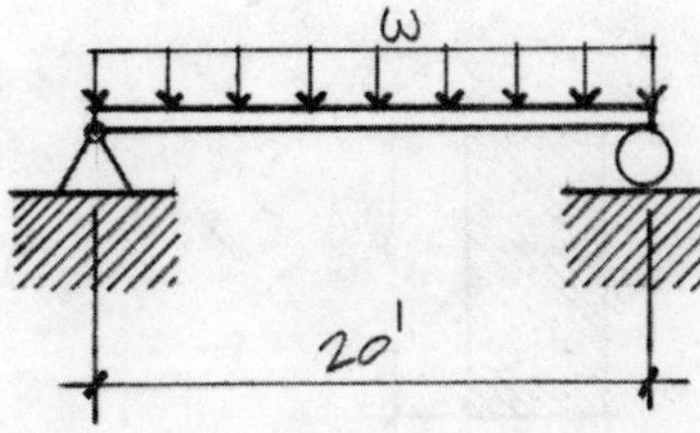

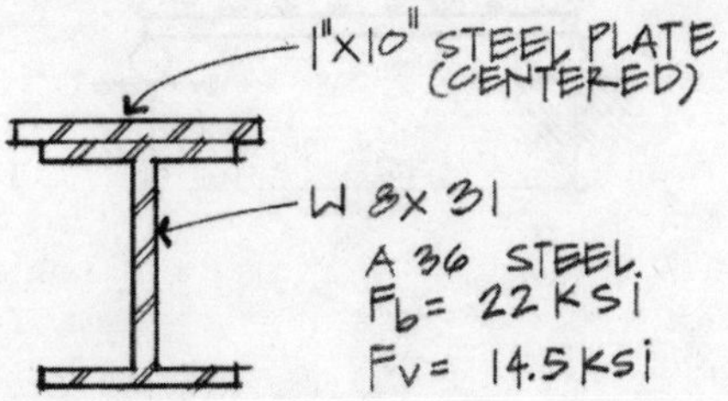

14 A lintel beam 12 feet long is used in carrying the imposed loads over a doorway opening. Assuming that a built-up box beam is used with a 12 inch overall depth as shown, determine the maximum bending stress and shear stress developed.

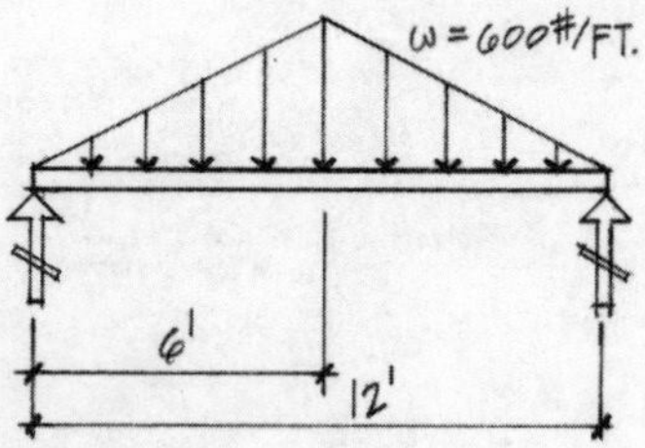

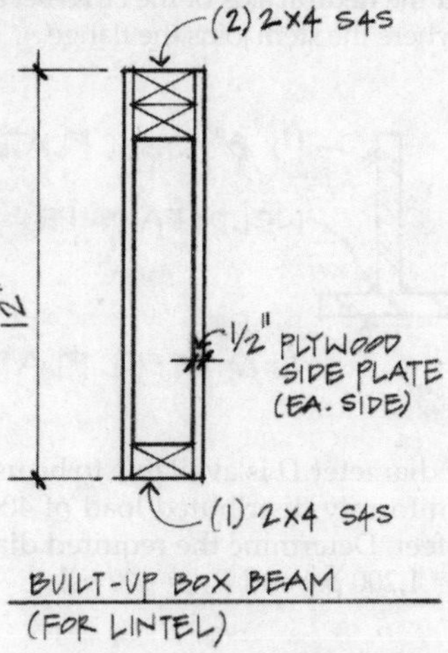

15 The cross-section of the rough-cut timber beam shown is loaded with w over six feet of the span. Determine the maximum value of w if the allowable bending stress is $F_b = 1{,}600$ psi and the allowable shear stress is $F_v = 85$ psi.

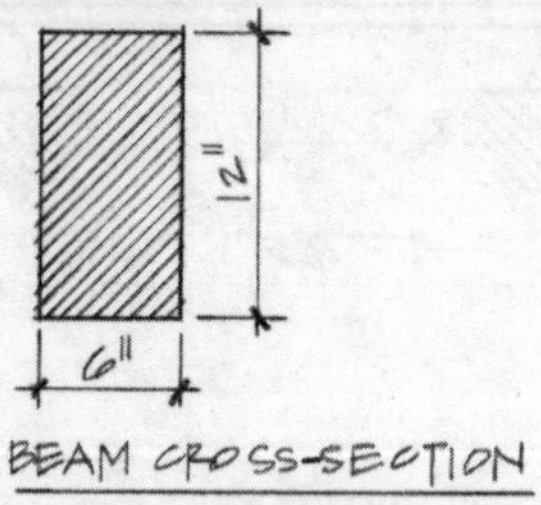

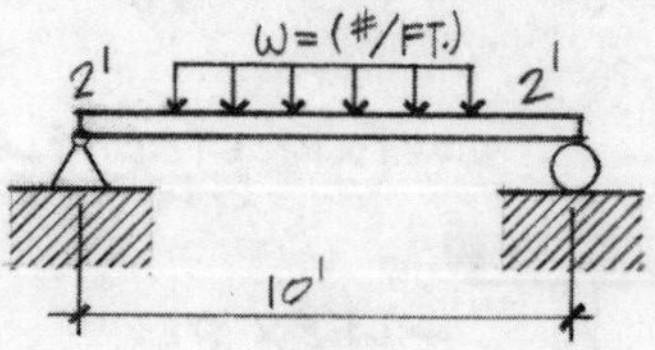

16 A 4 × 12 S4S beam carries two concentrated loads as shown. Assuming $F_b = 1{,}600$ psi and $F_v = 85$ psi, determine:

a. The maximum permissible load P.

b. The bending and shear stress four feet to the right of support A.

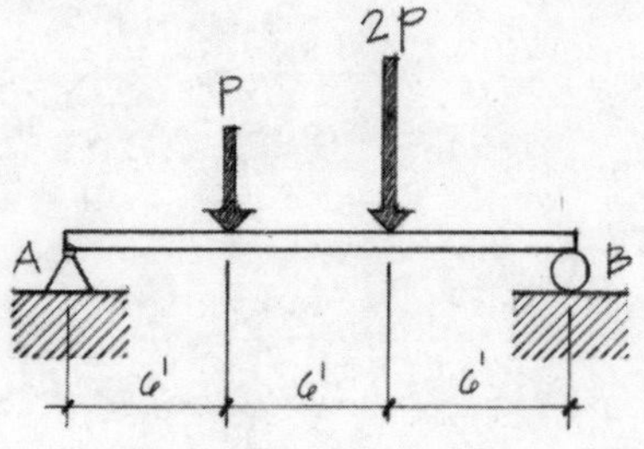

17 The beam shown is constructed by welding cover plates to two channel sections. What maximum uniformly distributed load can this beam support on a 20 foot span if $F_b = 22$ ksi?

Check the shear stress where the plate attaches to the channel flange.

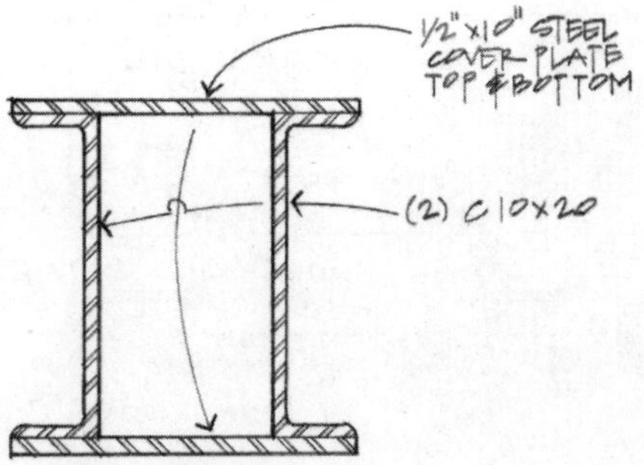

18 Select the lightest *W* section steel beam based on the bending condition. Check $f_{v_{average}}$ for the beam selected.

$F_b = 22$ ksi
$F_v = 14.5$ ksi } A36 Steel

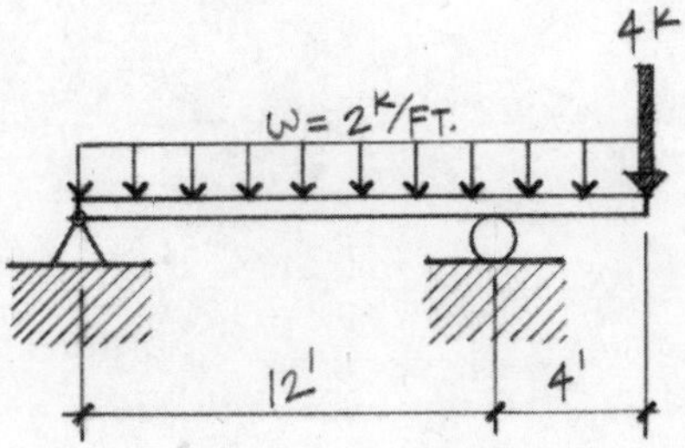

19 A plank is being used to support a triangular load as shown. Assuming the plank measures 12 inches wide, determine the required plank thickness if $F_b = 1{,}200$ psi and $F_v = 100$ psi.

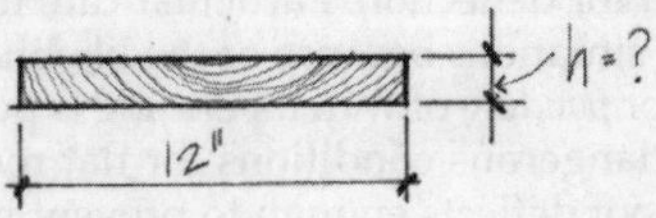

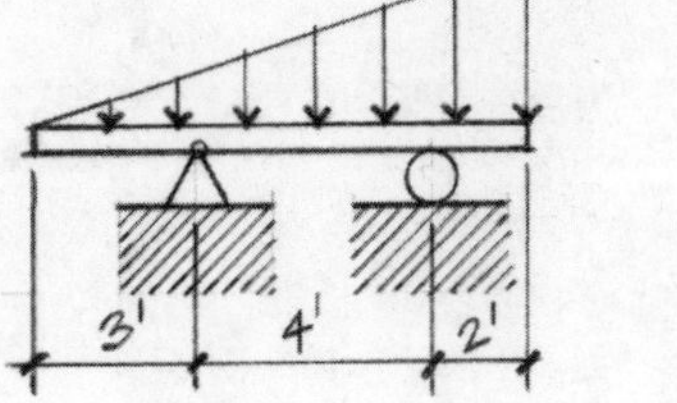

20 A built-up plywood box beam with 2" × 4" blocking top and bottom is held together by nails along the top and bottom chords. Determine the pitch (spacing) of the nails if the beam supports a 5 k concentrated load at midspan. The nails are capable of resisting 80# each in shear.

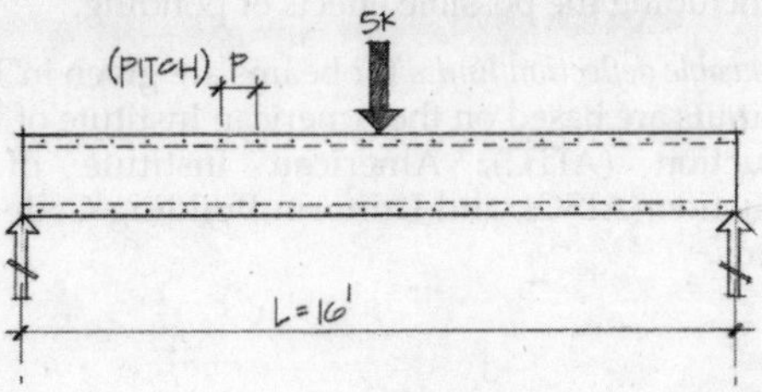

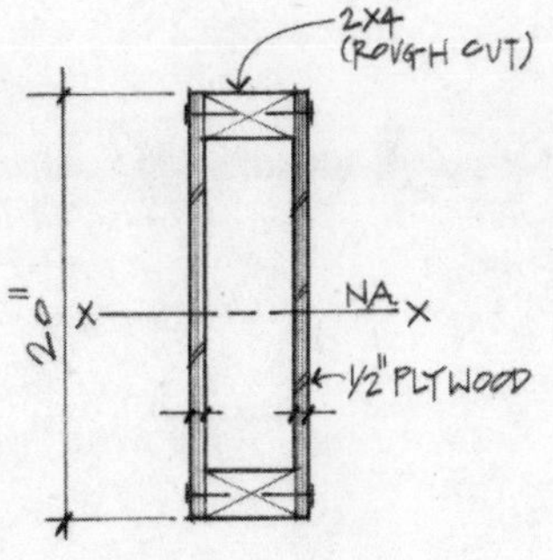

5 DEFLECTION IN BEAMS

As discussed in earlier sections of this chapter, the design of beams for a particular load and support condition requires the strength investigation of bending stress and shear stress. Quite frequently, however, the design of a beam is governed by its permissible *deflection*. In design, deformation (called *deflection* in beams) often shares an equivalent importance with strength considerations, especially in long-span structures.

Deflection, a *stiffness* requirement, represents a change in the vertical position of a beam due to the applied loads. Load magnitude, beam-span length, moment of inertia of the beam cross-section, and the beam's modulus of elasticity are all factors in the amount of deflection that results. Generally, the amount of *allowable deflection*, or *permissible deflection*, is limited by building codes or by practical considerations, such as minimizing plaster cracking in ceiling surfaces or reducing the springiness of a floor.

Wood, as a structural material, is less stiff (has a lower E-value) than steel or concrete; hence, deflection is always a concern. Detrimental effects from large deflections can include nail popping in gypsum ceilings, cracking of horizontal plaster surfaces, and visible sagging of ceilings and floors. In some design situations, primarily longer spans, a wood member satisfying the strength requirements will not necessarily satisfy deflection criteria.

Steel beams, although stronger relative to wood, still need to be checked for deflection. Particular care must be given in long-span situations because of the likelihood of objectionable sag or *ponding* of water. Ponding is potentially one of the most dangerous conditions for flat roofs. It occurs when a flat roof deflects enough to prevent normal water runoff. Instead, some water collects in the midspan, and with the added weight of accumulated water, the roof deflects a little more, allowing even more water to collect, which in turn causes the roof to deflect more. This progressive cycle continues until structural damage or collapse occurs. Building codes require that all roofs be designed with sufficient slope to ensure drainage after long-term deflection or that roofs be designed to support maximum roof loads, including the possible effects of ponding.

The *allowable deflection limits* for beams are given in Table 1. These limits are based on the American Institute of Timber Construction (AITC), American Institute of Steel Construction (AISC), and Uniform Building Code (UBC) standards.

Table 1 Recommended allowable deflection limits.

Use Classification	Live Load	Dead and Live Loads
Roof Beams:		
Industrial	l/180	l/120
Commercial and institutional		
Without plaster ceiling	l/240	l/180
With plaster ceiling	l/360	l/240
Floor Beams:		
Ordinary usage*	l/360	l/240

**Ordinary usage refers to floors intended for construction in which walking comfort and the minimizing of plaster cracking are primary considerations.*

The calculation of *actual* beam deflections is often approached from a mathematical viewpoint that requires the solution of a second-order differential equation subject to the loading and the type of end supports of the beam. This method is mathematically straightforward, but it presents formidable problems associated with evaluation of the proper boundary conditions as well as in the mathematics required to obtain the solution.

There are many ways to approach the problem of beam deflections: the moment-area method, conjugate beam, double integration, and formulas. This section will deal exclusively with the use of established deflection formulas found in standard handbooks, such as the AISC manual, timber design manuals, and the like.

Today, deflections are automatically calculated for most beam designs done on a computer. The intent of this section is to present a few fundamental concepts dealing with deflection and its role in beam design rather than to explore the many sophisticated mathematical techniques that may be employed in obtaining deflection values. An understanding of the basics of deflection will enable the user of computer software to better understand the results obtained.

The Elastic Curve—Radius of Curvature of a Beam

When a beam deflects, the neutral surface of the beam assumes a curved position, which is known as the *elastic curve* (Figure 32).

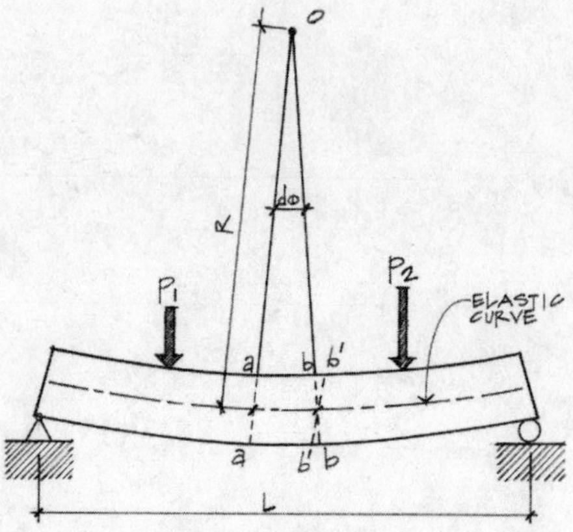

Figure 32(b) *After loading.*

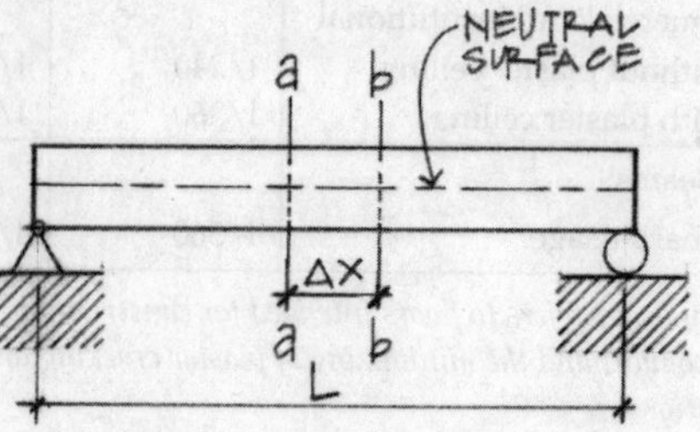

Figure 32(a) *Before loading.*

It is assumed from beam theory that planes *a* and *b* [Figure 32(a)], which were parallel before loading, will remain plane after bending so as to include a small angle dq [Figure 32(b)]. If the curvature is small, we may assume that $R_a = R_b = R$, the radius of curvature of the neutral surface (elastic curve).

The length of the segment between sections *a* and *b* is designated as Δx. If $d\theta$ is very small and R is very large, then $\Delta x = Rd\theta$, because for very small angles $\sin\theta = \tan\theta = \theta$. From Figure 33, $\Delta x' = (R + c)d\theta$ by the same reasoning.

$$\text{Length: } ab = \Delta x$$
$$a'b' = \Delta x'$$

The total elongation that the bottom fiber undergoes is

$$\delta_c = \Delta x' - \Delta x$$

Substituting the values given above, we get

$$\delta_c = (R + c)d\theta - Rd\theta = Rd\theta + cd\theta - Rd\theta$$
$$\therefore \delta_c = cd\theta$$

From $\varepsilon = \delta/L$, we get

$$\varepsilon_c = \frac{\Delta x' - \Delta x}{\Delta x} = \frac{c(d\theta)}{R(d\theta)} = \frac{c}{R}$$

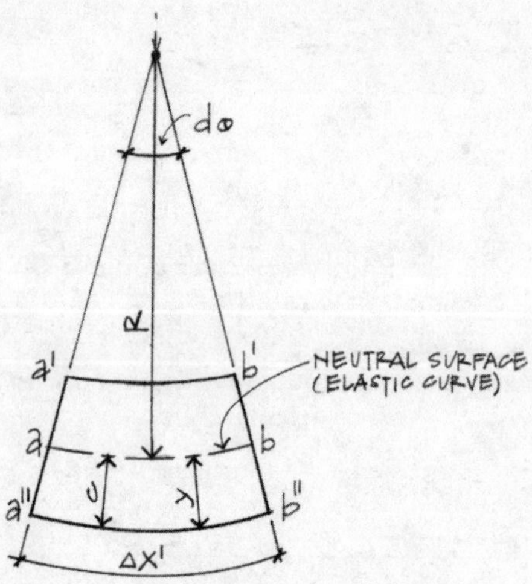

Figure 33 *Section of beam between* a-a *and* b-b.

Similarly, it can be shown that the unit strain at any distance y from the neutral surface can be written as

$$\varepsilon_y = \frac{y}{R}$$

We know that

$$\varepsilon_y = \frac{f_y}{E} \quad \text{and} \quad f_y = \frac{My}{I}; \text{so } \varepsilon_y = \frac{My}{EI}$$

Equating the two expressions for ε_y, we get

$$\frac{My}{EI} = \frac{y}{R} \text{ or } R = \frac{EI}{M} \text{ or } \frac{I}{R} = \frac{M}{EI}$$

where

R = radius of curvature
M = bending moment at section where R is desired
E = modulus of elasticity
I = moment of inertia of the beam cross-section

Because the flexure formula was used to obtain this relationship, it will be valid only for those members that meet the assumptions made in the derivation of the flexure formula. E and I will usually be constants for a given beam. The radius of curvature equation above is considered as a basic equation in the development of deflection formulas.

Deflection Formulas

Many loading patterns and support conditions occur so frequently in construction that reference manuals (e.g., AISC, AITC, etc.) and engineering handbooks tabulate the appropriate formulas for their deflections. A few of the more common cases are shown in Table 2. More often than not, the required deflection values in a beam design situation can be determined via these formulas, and one does not need to resort to deflection theory. Even when the actual loading situation does not match one of the tabulated cases, it is sufficiently accurate for most design situations to approximate the maximum deflection by using one or more of the formulas.

Computed actual deflections must be compared against the allowable deflections permitted by the building codes.

$$\Delta_{actual} \leq \Delta_{allowable}$$

Table 2 Common cases of beam loading and deflection.

Beam Load and Support	**Actual Deflection***
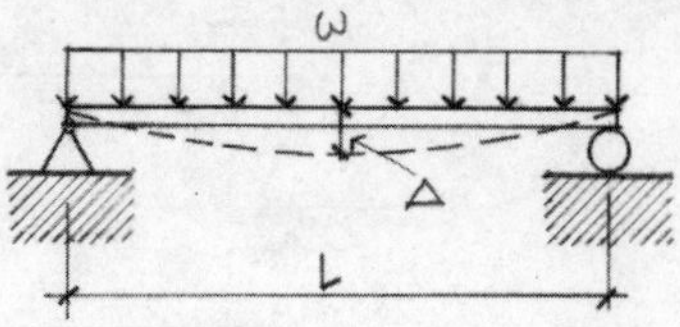 (a) Uniform load, simple span	$\Delta_{max} = \dfrac{5\omega L^4}{384EI}$ (at the centerline)
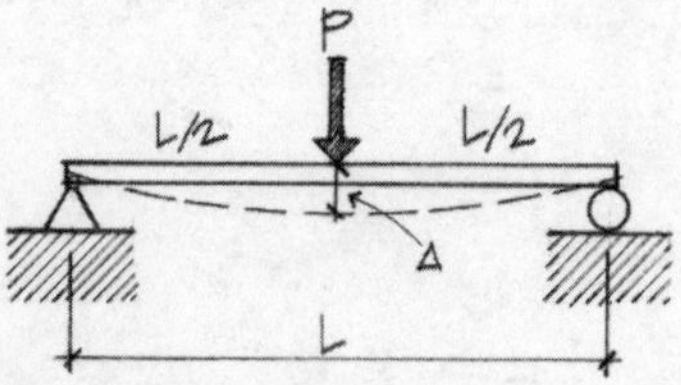 (b) Concentrated load at midspan	$\Delta_{max} = \dfrac{PL^3}{48EI}$ (at the centerline)
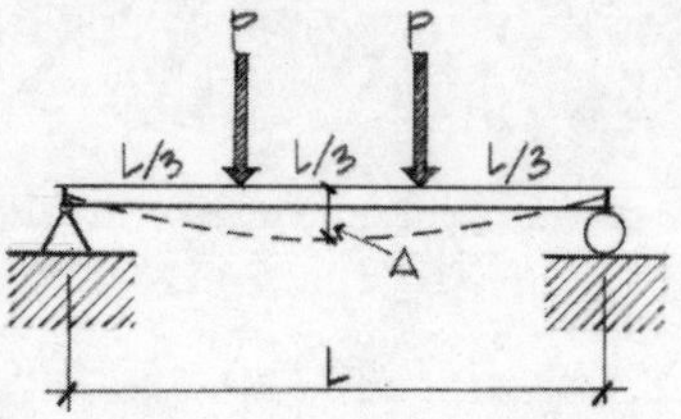 (c) Two equal concentrated loads at third points	$\Delta_{max} = \dfrac{23PL^3}{648EI} = \dfrac{PL^3}{28.2EI}$ (at the centerline)
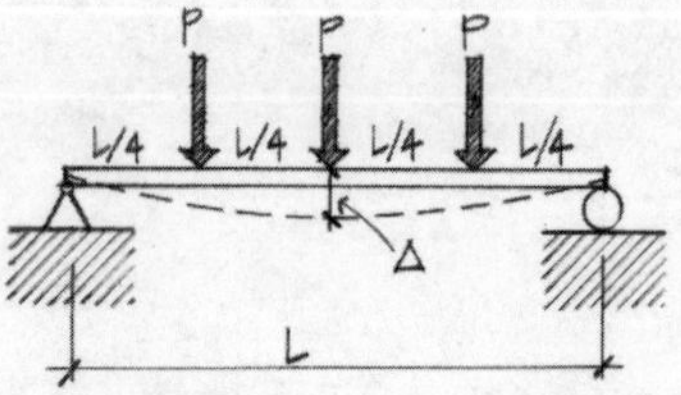 (d) Three equal concentrated loads at quarter points	$\Delta_{max} = \dfrac{PL^3}{20.1EI}$ (at the centerline)
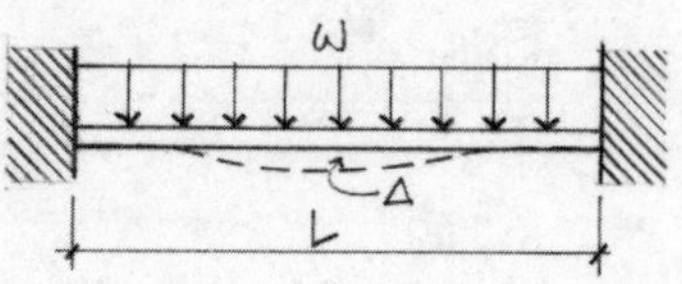 (e) Uniform load both ends fixed	$\Delta_{max} = \dfrac{\omega L^4}{384EI}$ (at the centerline)

Table 2 Continued.

Beam Load and Support	**Actual Deflection***
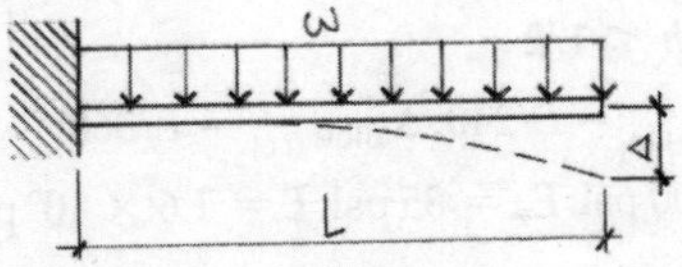 (f) Cantilever with uniform load	$\Delta_{max} = \dfrac{\omega L^4}{8EI}$ (at the free end)
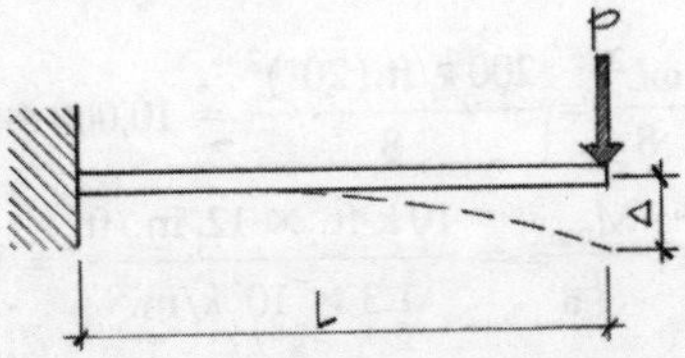 (g) Cantilever with concentrated load at the end	$\Delta_{max} = \dfrac{PL^3}{3EI}$ (at the free end)

*Because span length of beams is usually given in feet and deflections are in inches, a conversion factor must be included in all of the deflection formulas above. Multiply each deflection equation by

$$\text{conversion factor} = \text{CF} = (12\,\text{in./ft.})^3 = 1{,}728\,\text{in.}^3/\text{ft.}^3$$

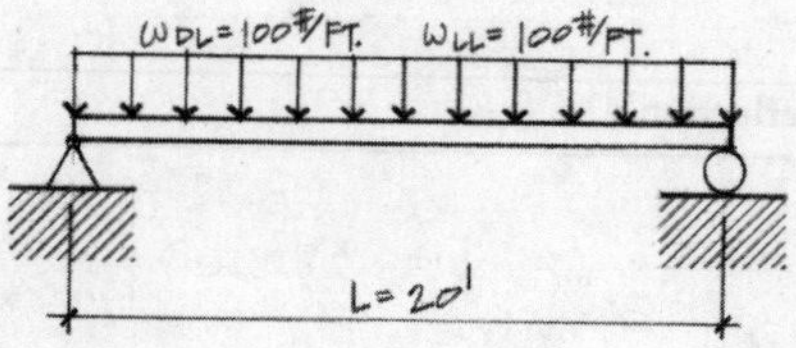

Example Problems: Deflection in Beams

14 Using DF-L No. 1, design the simply supported floor beam shown to meet bending, shear, and moment criteria.

$1/4 < b/h < 1/2$

$\Delta_{allow(DL+LL)} = L/240$; $\Delta_{allow(LL)} = L/360$

$F_b = 1{,}300$ psi; $F_v = 85$ psi; $E = 1.6 \times 10^6$ psi

Solution:

Bending

$$M_{max} = \frac{\omega L^2}{8} = \frac{200\ \#/\text{ft.}(20')^2}{8} = 10{,}000\ \#\text{-ft.}$$

$$S_{required} = \frac{M_{max}}{F_b} = \frac{10\ \text{k-ft.} \times 12.\ \text{in./ft.}}{1.3 \times 10^3\ k/\text{in.}^2} = 92.3\ \text{in.}^3$$

Shear

$$V_{max} = \frac{\omega L}{2} = \frac{200\ \#/\text{ft.}(20')}{2} = 2{,}000\#$$

$$A_{required} = \frac{1.5\,V_{max}}{F_v} = \frac{1.5 \times (2{,}000\#)}{85\ \#/\text{in.}^2} = 35.3\ \text{in.}^2$$

Deflection (Allowable)

$$\Delta_{allow(DL+LL)} = \frac{L}{240} = \frac{20' \times 12\ \text{in./ft.}}{240} = 1''$$

or

$$\Delta_{allow(LL)} = \frac{L}{360} = \frac{20' \times 12\ \text{in./ft.}}{360} = 0.67''$$

Note that the calculated $S_{required}$ and $A_{required}$ values do not account for the beam's own weight.

Try 6 × 12 S4S.

$(A = 63.25\ \text{in.}^2;\ S_x = 121.23\ \text{in.}^3;\ I_x = 697.07\ \text{in.}^4)$

Economical (efficient) beams usually have width-to-depth (b/h) ratios of $\frac{1}{4} < b/h < \frac{1}{2}$.

Check the effect of the beam's weight as it affects the bending and shear stress condition.

Bending

$$S_{add.} = \frac{M_{add}}{F_b}$$

where $M_{add.}$ = additional bending moment due to the beam's weight.

$$M_{add.} = \frac{\omega_{beam} L^2}{8}$$

Conversion for wood density of 35 pcf (Douglas fir and Southern Pine) to pounds per lineal foot (plf) of beam is

$$\omega_{beam} = 0.252 \times \text{cross-sectional area of beam}$$

$$\omega_{beam} = 0.252 \times 63.25 = 16 \text{ plf}$$

$$\therefore M_{add.} = \frac{16\ \#/\text{ft.}(20')^2}{8} = 800\ \#\text{-ft.}$$

$$S_{add.} = \frac{M_{add.}}{F_b} = \frac{800\ \#\text{ft.} \times 12\ \text{in./ft.}^2}{1{,}300\ \text{psi}} = 7.4\ \text{in.}^3$$

$$\therefore S_{total} = 92.3\ \text{in.}^3 + S_{add.} = 92.3\ \text{in.}^3 + 7.4\ \text{in.}^3$$

$$S_{total} = 99.7\ \text{in.}^3 < 121.2\ \text{in.}^3 \ \therefore \text{OK}$$

Shear

$V_{add.}$ = additional shear developed due to the beam's weight

$$\therefore V_{add.} = \frac{\omega_{beam} L}{2} = \frac{16\ \#/\text{ft.}(20')}{2} = 160\#$$

$$A_{add.} = \frac{1.5\, V_{add.}}{F_v} = \frac{1.5 \times 160\#}{85\ \text{psi}} = 2.8\ \text{in.}^2$$

$$\therefore A_{total} = 35.3\ \text{in.}^2 + A_{add.} = 35.3\ \text{in.}^2 + 2.8\ \text{in.}^2$$

$$A_{total} = 38.1\ \text{in.}^2 < 63.25\ \text{in.}^2 \ \therefore \text{OK}$$

Deflection (Actual)

$$\Delta_{actual} = \frac{5\omega_{LL} L^4}{384EI} = \frac{5(100\ \#/\text{ft.})(20')^4(1{,}728\ \text{in.}^3/\text{ft.}^3)}{384(1.6 \times 10^6\ \text{psi})(697.1\ \text{in.}^4)} = 0.32''$$

$$\Delta_{actual(LL)} = 0.32'' < \Delta_{allow(LL)} = 0.67''$$

$$\Delta_{actual} = \frac{5\omega_{total} L^4}{384EI} = \frac{5(216\ \#/\text{ft.})(20')^4(1{,}728\ \text{in.}^3/\text{ft.}^3)}{384(1.6 \times 10^6\ \text{psi})(697.1\ \text{in.}^4)} = 0.7''$$

Note: ω_{total} = *216 #/ft. includes the beam weight.*

$$\Delta_{actual(DL+LL)} = 0.7'' < \Delta_{actual(DL+LL)} = 1''$$

$\therefore$ OK Use: 6 × 12 S4S.

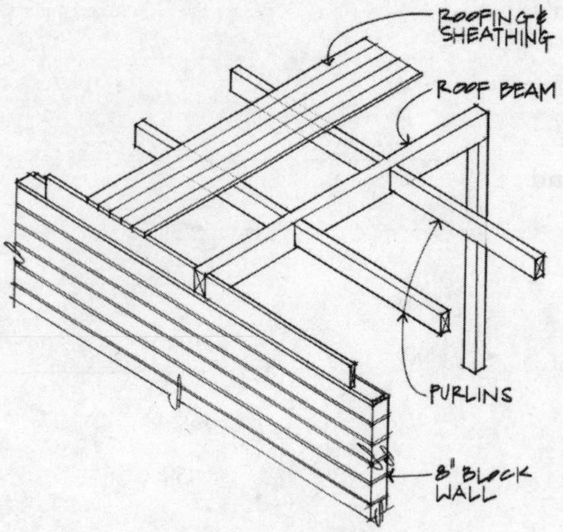

15 Design a Southern Pine No. 1 beam to carry the loads shown (roof beam, no plaster). Assume the beam is supported at each end by an eight inch block wall.

$$F_b = 1{,}550 \text{ psi}; F_v = 110 \text{ psi}; E = 1.6 \times 10^6 \text{ psi}$$

Solution:

Bending

$$S_{required} = \frac{M_{max}}{F_b} = \frac{12.8 \text{ k-ft.} \times 12 \text{ in./ft.}}{1.55 \text{ ksi}} = 99.1 \text{ in.}^3$$

Shear

$$A_{required} = \frac{1.5V_{max}}{F_v} = \frac{1.5 \times (2{,}750\,\#)}{110 \text{ psi}} = 37.5 \text{ in.}^2$$

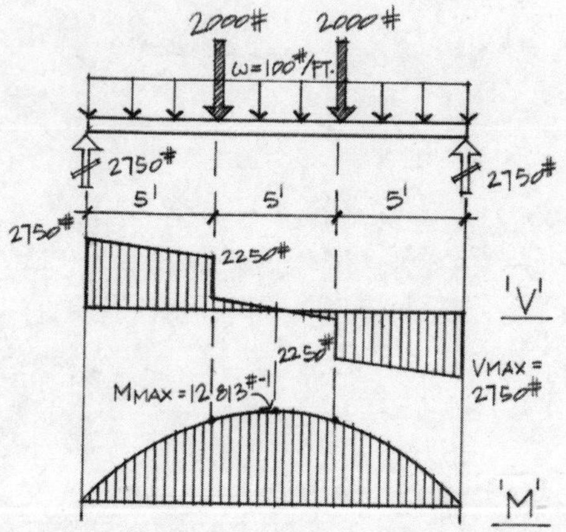

Deflection (Allowable)

$$\Delta_{allow} = \frac{L}{240} = \frac{15' \times 12 \text{ in./ft}}{240} = 0.75''$$

Try 6 × 12 S4S.

$$\left(A = 63.3 \text{ in.}^2; S_x = 121 \text{ in.}^3; I_x = 697 \text{ in.}^4\right)$$

$$\omega_{beam} \approx 0.252 \times 63.3 = 16\,\#/\text{ft.}$$

Bending

$$M_{add.} = \frac{\omega_{beam}L^2}{8} = \frac{16\,\#/\text{ft.}(15')^2}{8} = 450\,\#\text{-ft.}$$

$$S_{add.} = \frac{M_{add.}}{F_b} = \frac{450\,\#\text{-ft.} \times 12 \text{ in./ft.}}{1{,}550 \text{ psi}} = 3.5 \text{ in.}^3$$

$$S_{total} = 99.1 \text{ in.}^3 + 3.5 \text{ in.}^3 = 102.5 \text{ in.}^3 < 121 \text{ in.}^3 \quad \therefore \text{OK}$$

Note: *$S_{add.}$ is usually approximately 2% to 5% of $S_{required}$.*

Shear

$$V_{add.} = \frac{\omega_{beam}L}{2} = \frac{16\,\#/\text{ft.}(15')}{2} = 120\#$$

$$A_{add.} = \frac{1.5\,V_{add.}}{F_v} = \frac{1.5 \times 120\,\#}{110 \text{ psi}} = 1.6 \text{ in.}^2$$

$$A_{total} = 37.5 \text{ in.}^2 + 1.6 \text{ in.}^2 = 39.1 \text{ in.}^2 < 63.3 \text{ in.}^2 \quad \therefore \text{OK}$$

Actual Deflection

Using superposition (the combination, or *superimposing*, of one load condition onto another),

$$\Delta_{\text{actual}} = \frac{5\omega_{LL}L^4}{384EI} + \frac{23PL^3}{648EI} \text{ (@ centerline)}$$

$$\therefore \Delta_{\text{actual}} = \frac{5(100 + 16)(15')^4(1{,}728)}{384(1.6 \times 10^6)(697 \text{ in.}^4)} + \frac{23(2{,}000\,\#)(15')^3(1{,}728)}{684(1.6 \times 10^6)(697 \text{ in.}^4)}$$

$$\Delta_{\text{actual}} = 0.12'' + 0.35'' = 0.47'' < 0.75'' \therefore \text{OK}$$

Check the bearing stress between the beam and the block wall support.

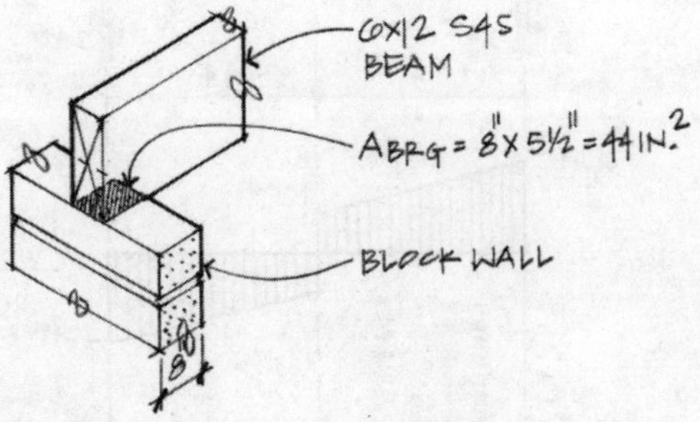

$$f_p = \frac{P}{A_{\text{bearing}}} = \frac{2{,}870\,\#}{44 \text{ in.}^2} = 65.2 \text{ psi}$$

The allowable bearing stress perpendicular to the grain for Southern Pine No. 1 is:

$$F_{c\perp} = 440 \text{ psi} \therefore \text{OK}$$

Use 6 × 12 S4S.

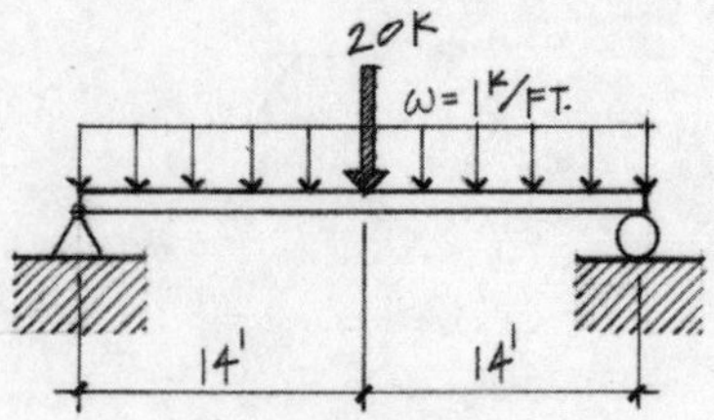

16 A steel beam (A572 Grade 50) is loaded as shown. Assuming a deflection requirement of $\Delta_{total} = L/240$ and a depth restriction of 18 inches nominal, select the most economical section.

$$F_b = 30 \text{ ksi}; F_v = 20 \text{ ksi}; E = 30 \times 10^3 \text{ ksi}$$

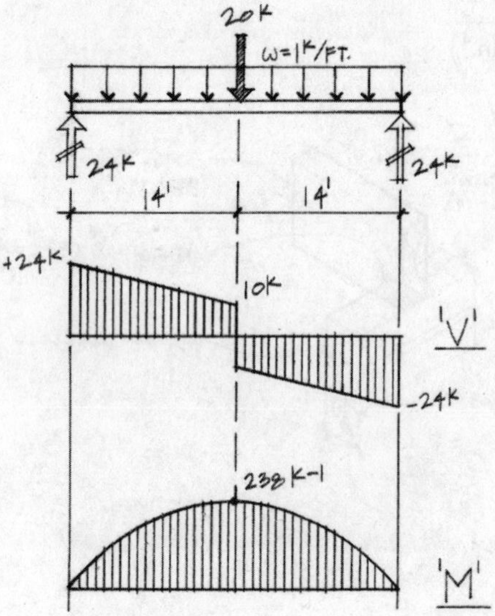

Solution:

$$V_{max} = 24 \text{ k}$$

$$M_{max} = 238 \text{ k-ft.}$$

Steel beams are usually designed for bending. Once a trial section has been selected, shear and deflection are checked.

Bending

$$S_{req'd} = \frac{M}{F_b} = \frac{238 \text{ k-ft.} \times 12 \text{ in./ft.}}{30 \text{ ksi}} = 95.2 \text{ in.}^3$$

Try W18 × 55.

$$(S_x = 98.3 \text{ in.}^3; I_x = 890 \text{ in.}^4; t_w = 0.39''; d = 18.11'')$$

$$M_{add.} = \frac{\omega_{beam}L^2}{8} = \frac{55 \#/\text{ft.}(28')^2}{8} = 5{,}390 \#\text{-ft.}$$

$$S_{add.} = \frac{M_{add.}}{F_b} = \frac{5.39 \text{ k-ft.} \times 12 \text{ in./ft.}}{30 \text{ ksi}} = 2.2 \text{ in.}^3$$

$$S_{total} = 95.2 \text{ in.}^3 + 2.2 \text{ in.}^3 = 97.4 \text{ in.}^3 < 98.3 \text{ in.}^3 \therefore \text{OK}$$

Shear Check

$$V_{add.} = \frac{\omega_{beam}L}{2} = \frac{55 \#/\text{ft.}(28')}{2} = 770 \#$$

$$f_{v_{average}} = \frac{V_{max}}{t_w d} = \frac{24{,}000\# + 770\#}{(0.39'')(18.11'')} = 3{,}510 \text{ psi}$$

$$f_{v_{average}} = 3{,}510 \text{ psi} < 20{,}000 \text{ psi} \therefore \text{OK}$$

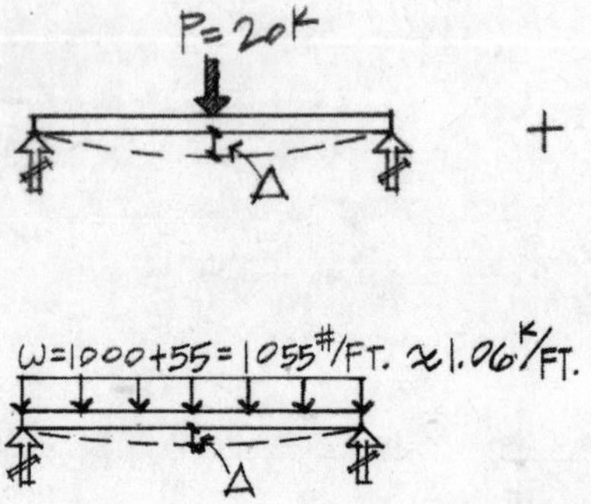

Deflection Check

$$\Delta_{allow} = \frac{L}{240} = \frac{28' \times 12 \text{ in./ft.}}{240} = 1.4''$$

$$\Delta_{actual} = \frac{PL^3}{48EI} + \frac{5\omega L^4}{384EI}$$

$$\Delta_{actual} = \frac{20 \text{ k}(28')^3 1{,}728}{48(30 \times 10^3)(890)} + \frac{5(1.06 \text{ k/ft.})(28')^4 1{,}728}{(384)(30 \times 10^3)(890)}$$

$$\Delta_{actual} = 0.59'' + 0.55'' = 1.14'' < 1.4'' \therefore \text{OK}$$

Use W18 × 55.

17 A partial plan of an office building is shown. All structural steel is A36 steel. Design a typical interior beam B1, and restrict the live load deflection to $\Delta_{LL} < L/360$. Limit depth to 14 inches. Also design the spandrel beam, restricting its total deflection to $\Delta_{LL} < L/240$. Limit depth to 18 inches.

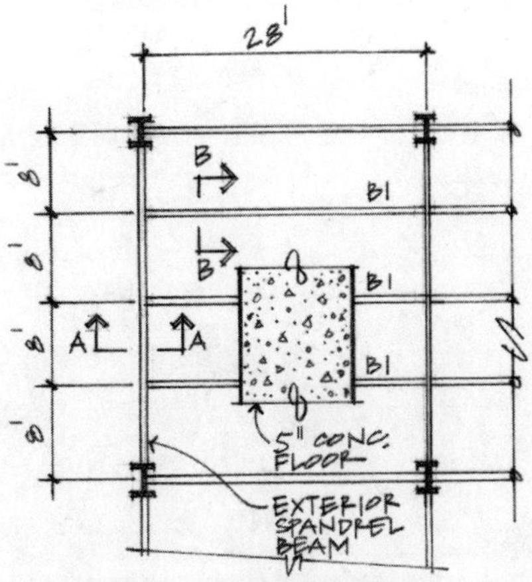

Partial floor plan (office building).

Loads:

Concrete floor:	150 pcf
1″ finish wood floor:	2.5 psf
Suspended fire-resistant ceiling:	3.0 psf
LL:	70 psf*
Curtain wall:	400 #/ft.

**Occupancy for office building with moveable partitions*

A36 steel:

$F_b = 22$ ksi

$F_v = 14.5$ ksi

$E = 29 \times 10^3$ ksi

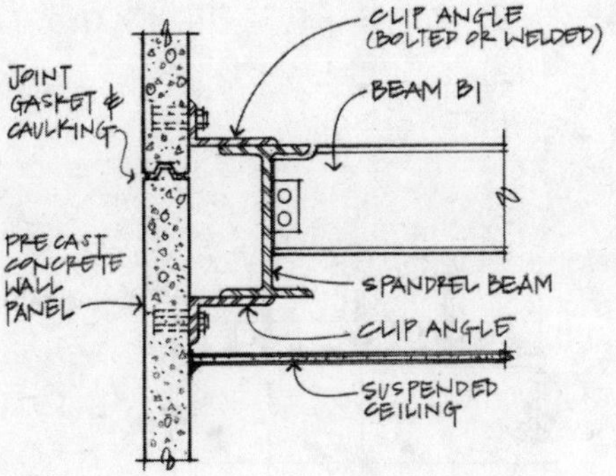

Section a-a.

Solution:

Beam B1 Design

5″ concrete floor:	62.5 psf
1″ finish wood floor:	2.5 psf
Suspended ceiling:	3.0 psf
Total DL	68 psf

Total LL = 70 psf × 8′ (tributary width) = 560 #/ft.

Total DL + LL = 138 psf × 8′ (trib. width) = 1,104 #/ft.

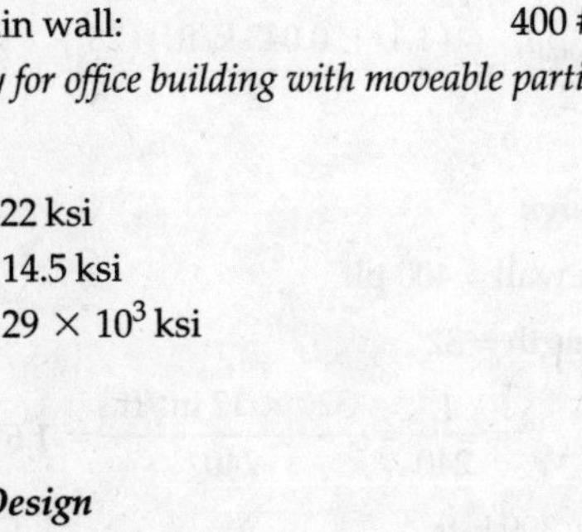

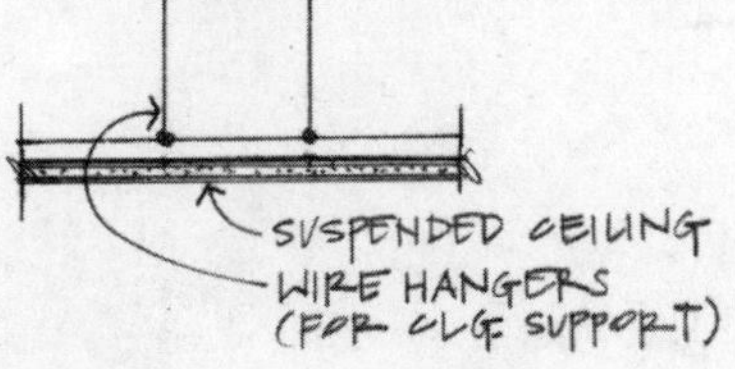

Section b-b.

$$M_{max} = \frac{\omega L^2}{8} = \frac{1.1 \text{ k/ft.} (28')^2}{8} = 108 \text{ k-ft.}$$

$$S_{required} = \frac{M_{max}}{F_b} = \frac{108 \text{ k-ft.} \times 12 \text{ in./ft.}}{22 \text{ ksi}} = 59 \text{ in.}^3$$

Try W14 × 43 ($S = 62.7$ in.^{3}; $I = 428$ in.^{4}). No check is necessary for $S_{add.}$

Deflection

$$\Delta_{allow(LL)} = \frac{L}{360} = \frac{28' \times 12\text{ in./ft.}}{22\text{ ksi}} = 0.93''$$

$$\Delta_{actual(LL)} = \frac{5\omega_{LL}L^4}{384EI} = \frac{5(0.56\text{ k/ft.})(28')(1{,}728\text{ in.}^3/\text{ft.}^3)}{384(29 \times 10^3\text{ ksi})(428\text{ in.}^4)} = 0.62''$$

$$\Delta_{actual(LL)} = 0.62'' < \Delta_{allow(LL)} = 0.93'' \therefore \text{OK}$$

Use W14 × 43.

Beam Reaction onto Spandrel Beam

$$R = \frac{\omega_{total}L}{2} = \frac{(1.1 + 0.043\text{ k/ft.})(28')}{2} = 16.1\text{ k}$$

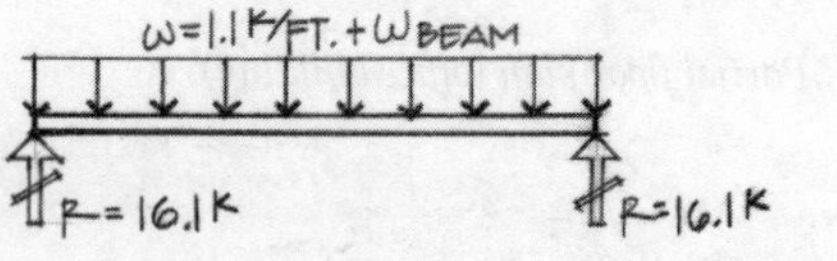

Spandrel Design

Curtain wall = 400 plf

Span length = 32′

$$\Delta_{allow(D+L)} = \frac{L}{240} = \frac{32' \times 12\text{ in./ft.}}{240} = 1.6''$$

$$M_{max} = 309\text{ k-ft.}$$

$$S_{required} = \frac{309\text{ k-ft.} \times 12\text{ in./ft.}}{22\text{ ksi}} = 168.5\text{ in.}^3$$

Try W18 × 97 $(S_x = 188\text{ in.}^3;\ I_x = 1{,}750\text{ in.}^4)$.

$$M_{add.} = \frac{0.097\text{ k/ft.}(32')^2}{8} = 12.4\text{ k-ft.}$$

$$S_{add.} = \frac{12.4\text{ k-ft.} \times 12\text{ in./ft.}}{22\text{ ksi}} = 6.8\text{ in.}^3$$

$$S_{total} = 168.5 + 6.8 = 175.3\text{ in.}^3 < 188\text{ in.}^3 \therefore \text{OK}$$

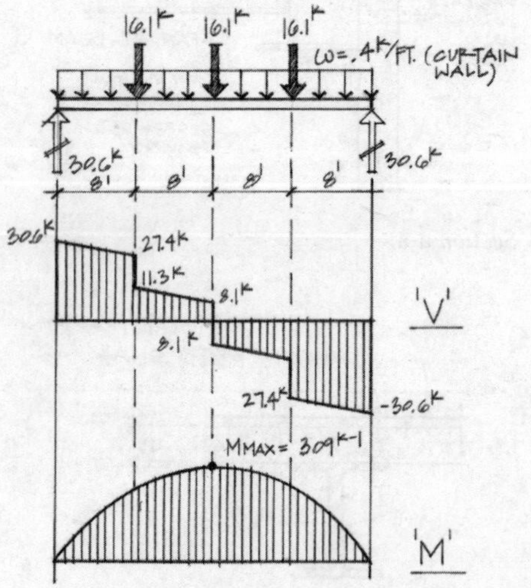

Deflection

$$\Delta_{total(DL+LL)} = \frac{5\omega L^4}{384EI} + \frac{PL^3}{20.1EI}$$

$$\Delta_{total(DL+LL)} = \frac{5(.5)(32')^4(1{,}728)}{384(29 \times 10^3)(1{,}750)} + \frac{16.1(32')^3(1{,}728)}{20.1(29 \times 10^3)(1{,}750)}$$

$$\Delta_{actual} = 0.23'' + 0.91'' = 1.14'' < \frac{L}{240} = 1.6'' \therefore \text{OK}$$

Shear Check

$$f_{v_{average}} = \frac{V}{t_w h} = \frac{30.6\text{ k} + 1.6\text{ k}}{(0.535'')(18.59'')} = 3.2\text{ ksi} < 14.5\text{ ksi} \therefore \text{OK}$$

Use W18 × 97.

18 The sun deck is to be framed using Hem-Fir No. 2 grade timber. Joists are spaced at two feet o.c. with a span length of 10 feet. One end of the joist is supported by a concrete foundation wall and the other end by a beam. The supporting beam is actually made of two beams, spliced at the center of the span. Joists and beams are to be considered as simply supported.

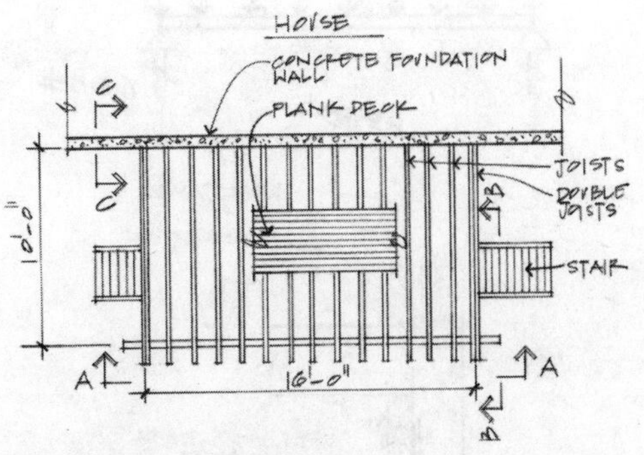

Framing plan of sun deck.

Loads:

2″ plank deck = 5 psf

LL = 60 psf

For Joists:

$\Delta_{\text{total}} < L/240$

$F_b = 1{,}150$ psi

$F_v = 75$ psi

$E = 1.4 \times 10^6$ psi

For Beams:

$\Delta_{\text{total}} < L/240$

$F_b = 1{,}000$ psi

$F_v = 75$ psi

$E = 1.4 \times 10^6$ psi

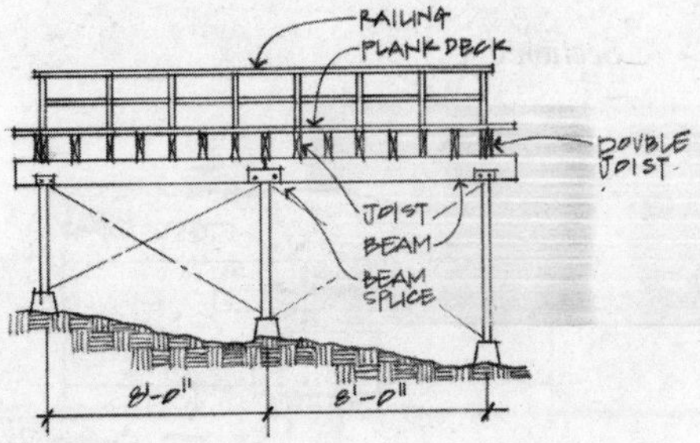

Elevation A-A.

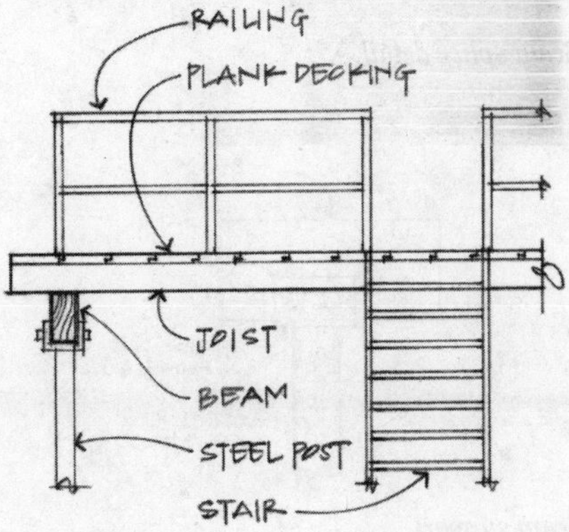

Elevation B-B.

Solution:

Joist Design

DL—2″ deck	= 5 psf
LL	= 60 psf
Total DL + LL	= 65 psf

$\omega_{DL+LL} = 65 \text{ psf} \times 2' = 130\,\#/\text{ft.}$

$$V_{max} = \frac{\omega L}{2} = \frac{130\,\#/\text{ft.}(10')}{2} = 650\,\#$$

$$M_{max} = \frac{\omega L^2}{8} = \frac{130\,\#/\text{ft.}(10')^2}{8} = 1{,}625\,\#\text{-ft.}$$

$$A_{\text{required}} = \frac{1.5\,V}{F_v} = \frac{1.5(650\#)}{75\,\#/\text{in.}^2} = 13 \text{ in.}^2$$

$$S_{\text{required}} = \frac{M}{F_b} = \frac{1{,}625\,\#\text{-ft.} \times 12 \text{ in./ft.}}{1{,}150 \text{ psi}} = 17 \text{ in.}^3$$

Try 2 × 10.

$(A = 13.88 \text{ in.}^2; S_x = 21.4 \text{ in.}^3; I_x = 98.9 \text{ in.}^4; \omega_{\text{beam}} = 3.5\,\#/\text{ft.})$

Note: *Hem-Fir has a density of 30 pcf; hence, the conversion factor is* $\omega_{\text{beam}} = 0.22 \times$ *cross-sectional area of the beam.*

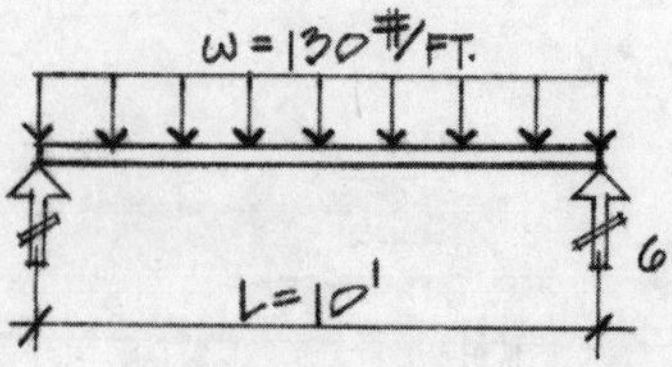

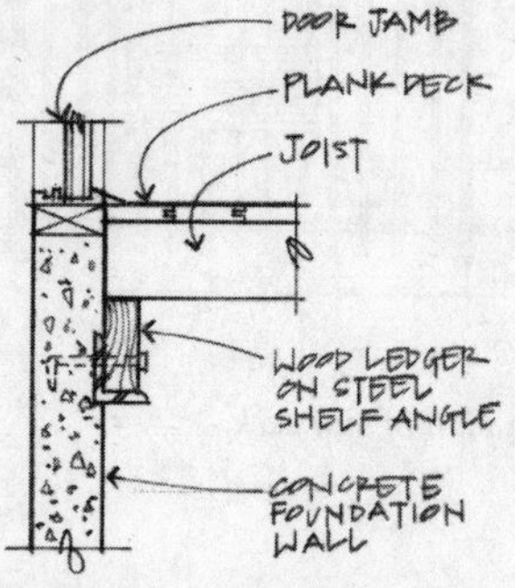

Section C-C.

Bending and Shear

$$V_{\text{add.}} = \frac{3.5\,\text{\#/ft.}\,(10')}{2} = 17.5\,\text{\#}$$

$$A_{\text{add.}} = \frac{1.5(17.5\,\text{in.}^3)}{75\,\text{psi}} = 0.35\,\text{in.}^2$$

$$A_{\text{total}} = 13.4\,\text{in.}^2 \therefore \text{OK}$$

$$M_{\text{add.}} = \frac{3.5\,\text{\#-ft.}\,(10')^2}{8} = 43.75\,\text{\#-ft.}$$

$$S_{\text{add.}} = \frac{43.75\,\text{\#-ft.} \times 12\,\text{in./ft.}}{1{,}150\,\text{psi}} = 0.5\,\text{in.}^3$$

$$S_{\text{total}} = 17.5\,\text{in.}^3 \therefore \text{OK}$$

Deflection

$$\Delta_{\text{allow(DL+LL)}} = \frac{L}{240} = \frac{10' \times 12\,\text{in./ft}}{240} = 0.5''$$

$$\Delta_{\text{actual(DL+LL)}} = \frac{5\omega L^4}{384EI} = \frac{5(130 + 3.5)(10')^4(1{,}728)}{384(1.4 \times 10^6)(98.9)}$$

$$\Delta_{\text{actual(DL+LL)}} = 0.22'' < 0.5'' \therefore \text{OK}$$

Use 2 × 10 joists at two feet o.c. (equivalent to 2 psf)

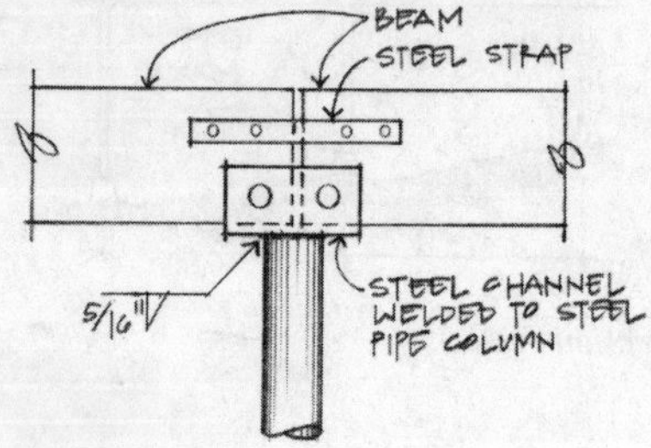

Beam splice detail.

Beam Design

Because joists are spaced uniformly and occur at a relatively close spacing, assume loads to be uniformly distributed on the beam.

Loads:

$$2''\ \text{plank deck} = 5\,\text{psf}$$

$$2 \times 10\,@\,2'\,\text{o.c.} = 2\,\text{psf}$$

$$\text{LL} = 60\,\text{psf}$$

$$\omega = 67\,\text{psf} \times 5' = 335\,\text{\#/ft.}$$

$$V_{\max} = \frac{\omega L}{2} = \frac{335\,\text{\#/ft.}\,(8')}{2} = 1{,}340\,\text{\#}$$

$$M_{\max} = \frac{\omega L^2}{8} = \frac{335\,\text{\#/ft.}\,(8')^2}{8} = 2{,}680\,\text{\#-ft.}$$

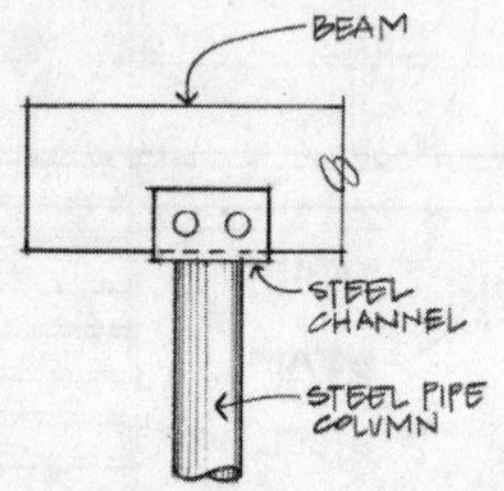

Beam support.

$$A_{\text{required}} = \frac{1.5\,V}{F_v} = \frac{1.5(1{,}340\,\#)}{75\text{ psi}} = 26.8\text{ in.}^2$$

$$S_{\text{required}} = \frac{M}{F_b} = \frac{2{,}680\,\#\text{-ft.} \times 12\text{ in./ft.}}{1{,}000\text{ psi}} = 32.2\text{ in.}^3$$

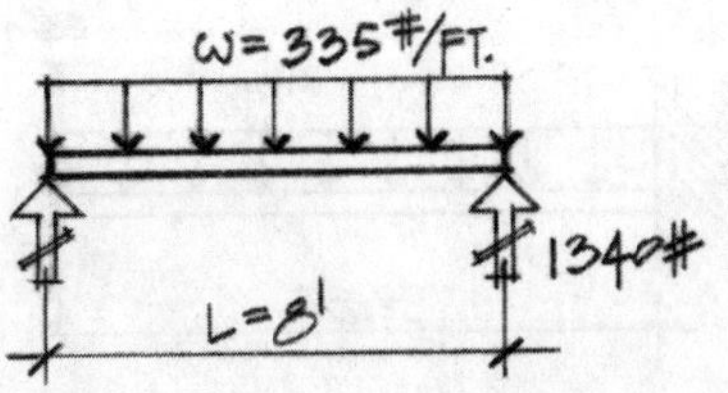

Try 4×10. ($A = 32.38\text{ in.}^2$; $S_x = 49.91\text{ in.}^3$; $I_x = 230.84\text{ in.}^4$; $\omega_{\text{beam}} = 8\,\#/\text{ft.}$)

$A_{\text{add.}}$ and $S_{\text{add.}}$ should not be critical here.

$$\Delta_{\text{allow}} = \frac{L}{240} = \frac{8' \times 12\text{ in./ft.}}{240} = 0.4''$$

$$\Delta_{\text{actual}} = \frac{5\omega L^4}{384EI} = \frac{5(335\,\#/\text{ft.})(8')^4(1{,}728)}{384(1.4 \times 10^6)(231\text{ in.}^4)}$$

$$\Delta_{\text{actual}} = 0.1'' < 0.4'' \;\therefore \text{OK}$$

Use 4×10 S4S beam.

Problems

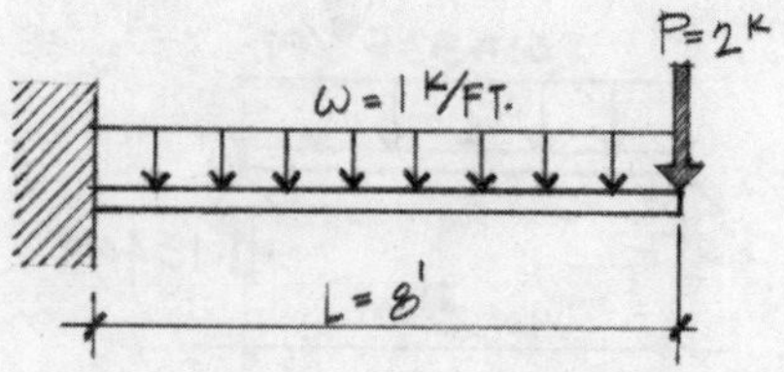

21 Assuming A36 steel, select the most economical W8 section. Check the shear stress, and determine the deflection at the free end.

$F_b = 22$ ksi

$F_v = 14.5$ ksi

$E = 29 \times 10^3$ ksi

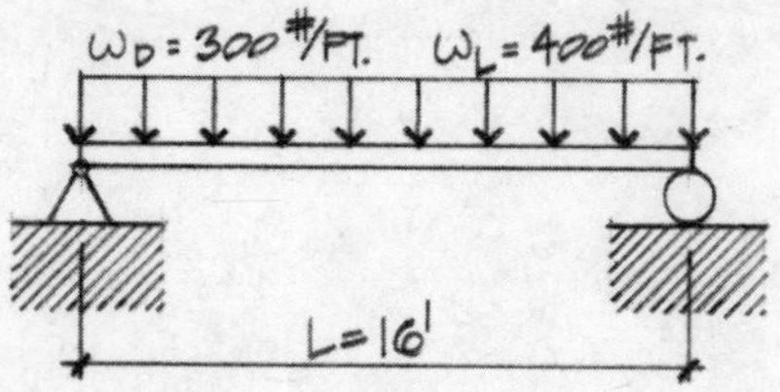

22 Design a Douglas fir–Larch No. 1 beam to support the load shown.

$F_b = 1{,}300$ psi

$F_v = 85$ psi

$E = 1.6 \times 10^6$ psi

$\Delta_{allow(LL)} = L/360$

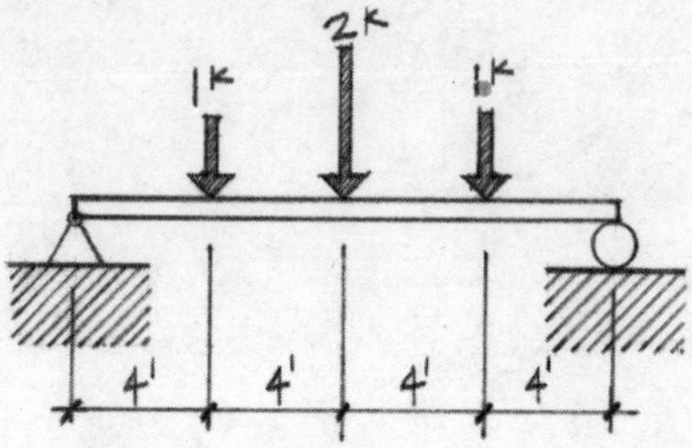

23 Design the beam shown assuming the loads are due to dead and live loads.

$\Delta_{allow(LL+DL)} = L/240$

Assuming the beam is Southern Pine No. 1 supported at both ends by girders as shown, calculate and check the bearing stress developed between the 6 ×_ beam and a 6 × 12 girder.

$F_b = 1{,}550$ psi; $F_v = 110$ psi;

$E = 1.6 \times 10^6$ psi; $F_{c\perp} = 410$ psi

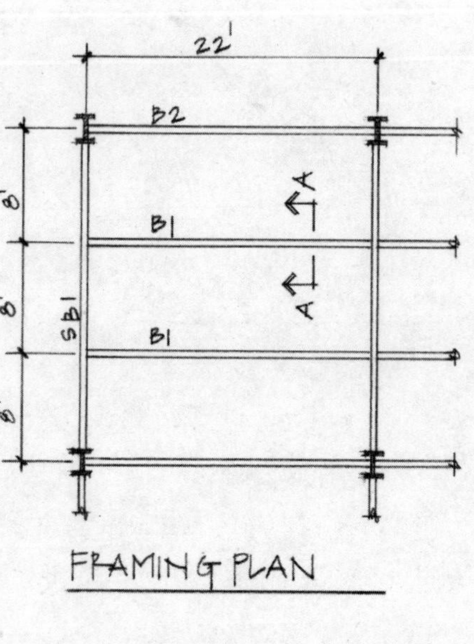

24 Design B1 and SB1 assuming A36 steel. Maximum depth for each is restricted to 16 inches" nominal.

LL	40 psf
Concrete	150 pcf
Curtain wall on spandrel beam SB1	300 plf
Suspended plaster ceiling	5 psf
Metal deck	4 psf

$\Delta_{LL} < L/360$ for B1; $\Delta_{DL+LL} < L/240$ for SB1

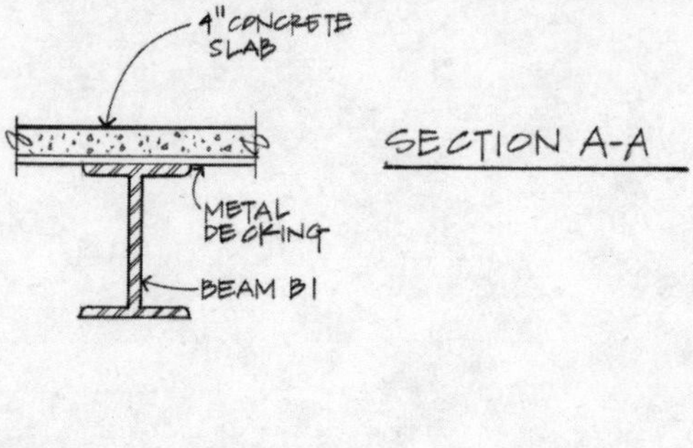

6 LATERAL BUCKLING IN BEAMS

In the previous discussion on beams, it was implied that making a beam as deep (large I_x) as possible was generally advantageous, because the I_x and S_x values are maximized. There are, however, limits on how deep a beam should be when used in the context of the building.

When a simply supported beam is subjected to a load, the top flange or surface is in compression, while the bottom flange or surface is in tension. At the compression side of the beam, there is a tendency for it to buckle (deflect sideways), just as a column can buckle under axial loading. In a cantilever or overhang beam, the buckling, or *sidesway,* will develop due to the compression on the bottom surface of the beam (Figure 34). Very narrow, deep beams are particularly susceptible to lateral buckling, even at relatively low stress levels.

To resist the tendency of a beam to displace laterally, either the compression surface needs to be braced by other framing members or the beam needs to be reproportioned to provide a larger I_y. The vast majority of beams, such as floor and roof beams in buildings, are laterally supported by the floor or roof structures attached to and supported by them.

Steel decking welded to the beams, beams with the top flange embedded in the concrete slab, or composite construction (steel beams mechanically locked to the steel decking and concrete slab) are examples of lateral support for steel beams.

Wood framing typically employs continuous support along the top compression surface through sheathing nailed at a relatively close spacing and solid blocking to provide restraint against rotation at the ends. Depending on the span of the wood beam, bridging or solid blocking is provided at intervals to resist lateral buckling.

Some roof beams that support relatively lightweight roof sheathing are not considered to be laterally supported.

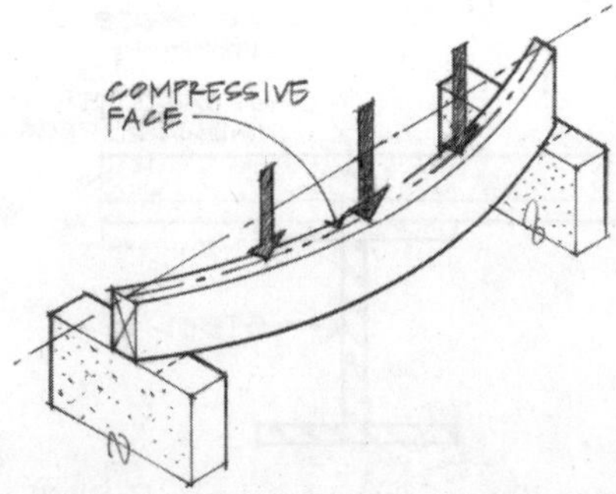

(a) Simply supported beam.

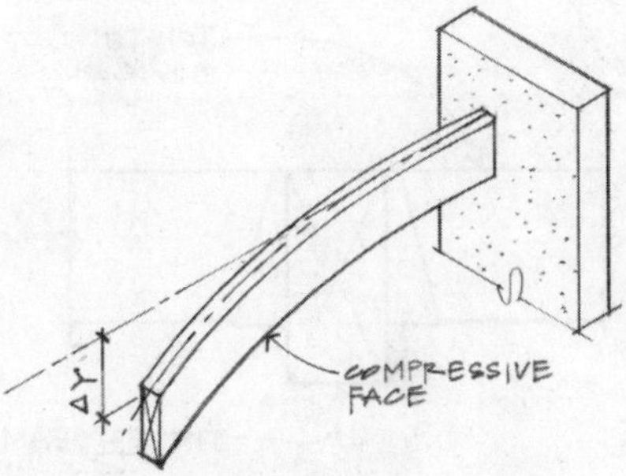

(b) Cantilever beam.

Figure 34 Lateral buckling in beams.

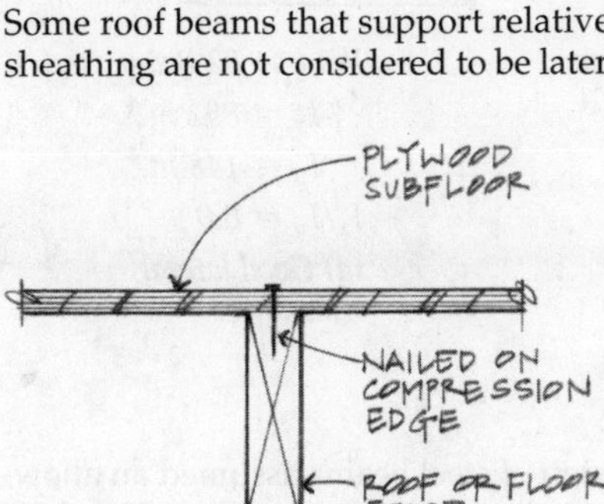

Figure 35(a) Typical wood floor joist with continuous nailing.

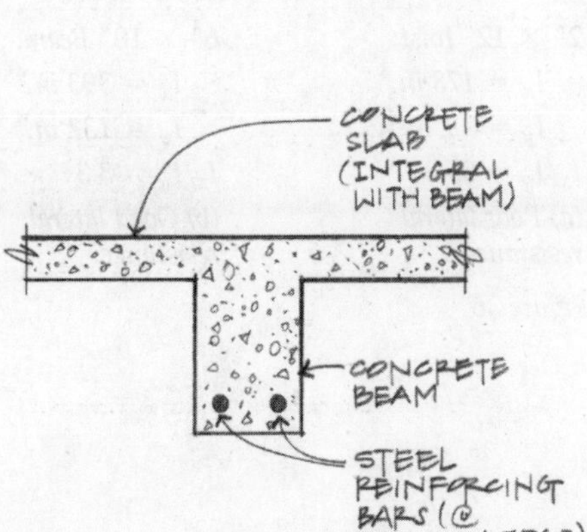

Figure 35(b) Concrete slab/beam cast monolithically.

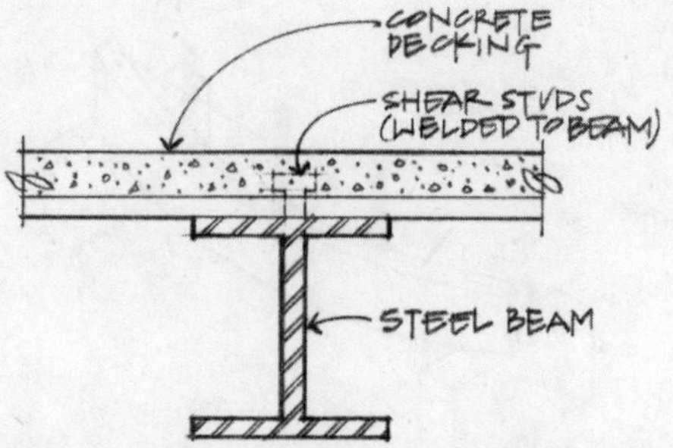

Figure 35(c) Composite concrete slab with steel beam.

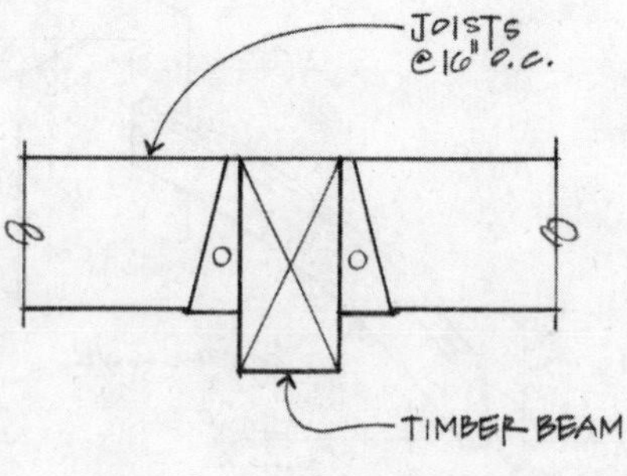

Figure 35(d) Timber beam with joist framing.

Certain beams are inherently stable against any lateral buckling tendency by virtue of their cross-sectional shapes. For example, a rectangular beam with a large width-to-depth ratio (I_y and I_x are relatively close) and loaded in the vertical plane should have no lateral stability problem (Figure 35). A wide-flange beam having a compression flange that is both wide and thick so as to provide a resistance to bending in a horizontal plane (relatively large I_y) will also have considerable resistance to buckling (Figure 36).

The problem of lateral instability in unbraced steel beams (W shapes) is amplified, because the cross-sectional dimensions are such that relatively slender elements are stressed in compression. Slender elements have large width-to-thickness ratios, and these elements are particularly susceptible to buckling.

A beam that is not laterally stiff in cross-section must be braced every so often along its compressive side to develop its full moment capacity. Sections not adequately braced or laterally supported by secondary members (Figure 34) could fail prematurely.

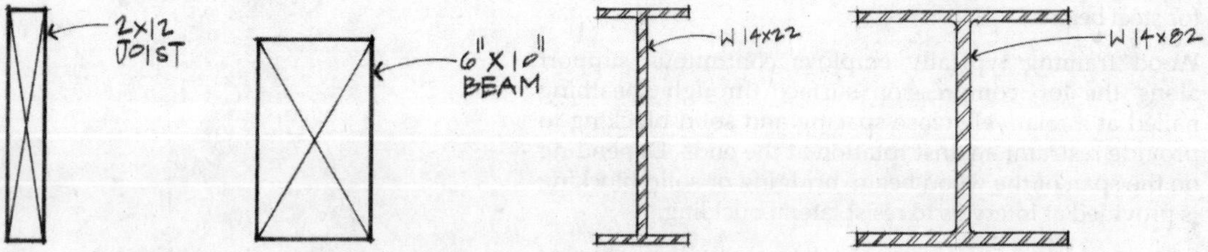

2" × 12" Joist:
$I_x = 178$ in.^{4}
$I_y = 3.2$ in.^{4}
$I_x/I_y = 55.6$
(a) Poor lateral resistance.

6" × 10" Beam:
$I_x = 393$ in.^{4}
$I_y = 132$ in.^{4}
$I_x/I_y = 3.3$
(b) Good lateral resistance.

W14 × 22 Beam:
$I_x = 199$ in.^{4}
$I_y = 7$ in.^{4}
$I_x/I_y = 28.4$
(c) Poor lateral resistance.

W14 × 82 Beam:
$I_x = 882$ in.^{4}
$I_y = 148$ in.^{4}
$I_x/I_y = 6.0$
(d) Good lateral resistance.

Figure 36

In Section 2, the design of steel beams assumed an allowable bending stress of $F_b = 0.6F_y$, where $F_b = 22$ ksi for A36 steel. Steel beams laterally supported along their compression flanges, meeting the specific requirements of the AISC, may use an allowable $F_b = 0.66F_y$, where $F_b = 24$ ksi for A36 steel. When the unsupported lengths of the compression flanges become large, allowable bending stresses may be reduced *below* the $F_b = 0.6F_y$ level.

For the purposes of preliminary sizing of steel beams in architectural practice, and in particular for this text, the allowable bending stress will be taken as

$$F_b = 0.60F_y$$

In the case of timber beams, the dimensions of the cross-sections are such that the depth-to-width ratios are relatively small. A common method of dealing with the lateral stability issue is to follow *rules of thumb* that have developed over time. These rules apply to sawn lumber beams and joists/rafters (Table 3). The beam depth-to-width ratios are based on nominal dimensions.

Table 3 Lateral bracing requirements for timber beams.

Beam Depth/ Width Ratio	Type of Lateral Bracing Required	Example
2 to 1	None	
3 to 1	The ends of the beam should be held in position	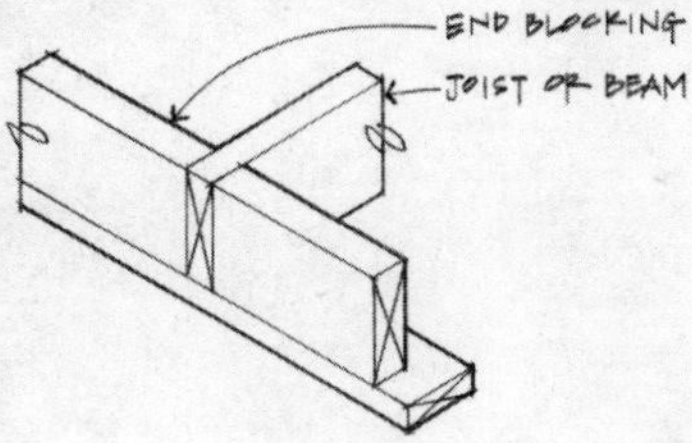
5 to 1	Hold compression edge in line (continuously)	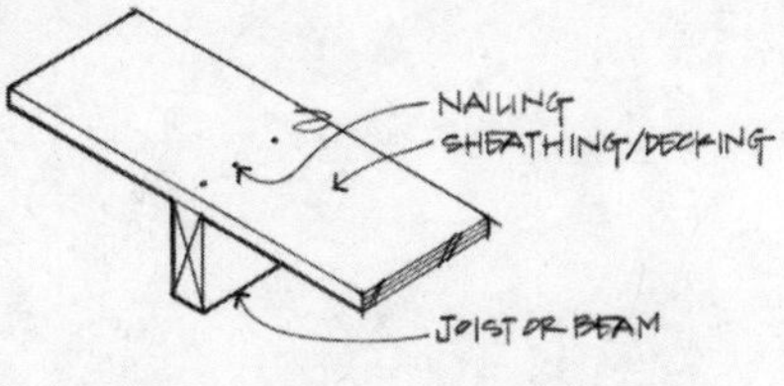
6 to 1	Diagonal bridging should be used	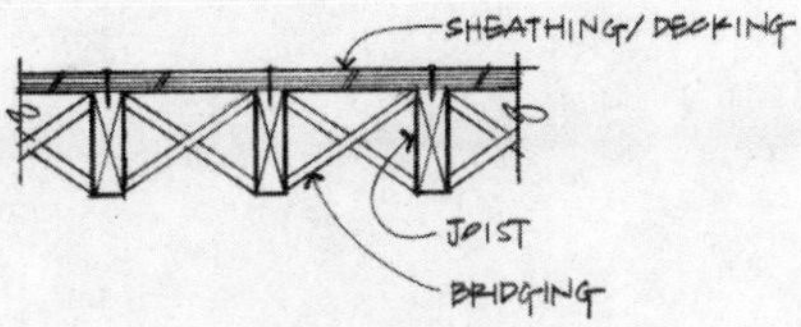
7 to 1	Both edges of the beam should be held in line	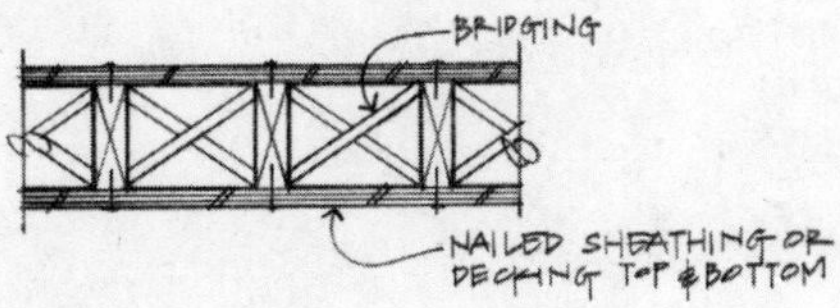

7 INTRODUCTION TO LOAD RESISTANCE FACTOR DESIGN (LRFD)

All of the previous analysis and design problems introduced in this text have been based on the allowable stresses of a member designed in timber or steel. Formerly called the *working stress* or *service load* method, the *allowable stress design*, or *ASD*, method has been the classical approach used for many years to design structures of steel, timber, and concrete. However, this methodology is slowly giving way to what is known as the *strength method*.

In concrete design, because of the complexities of analyzing composite sections using the working stress method, the ACI 318 concrete specifications have employed the *strength based method* since the 1970s.

When designing in steel and timber, a choice of design philosophies needs to be made—namely, ASD or the strength-based method, currently referred to as the *load and resistance factor design* method, or LRFD. Although LRFD is relatively new to timber design, it is now included with ASD in the current editions of the *National Design Specification for Wood Construction Manual*. In the 13th edition of the AISC's *Steel Construction Manual*, either design process is allowed.

Designing steel structures using ASD is relatively simple and has a proven track record in providing a basis for safe and reliable design. The ASD philosophy is based on keeping the member stresses below a specified percentage of the yield stress in the steel. Adequacy of the proposed design is evaluated based on specified limits set on the allowable stress, stability, and deformation.

A margin of safety, obtained by dividing the allowable stress into the failure stress, generally the yield stress for steel, constitutes the *factor of safety*. Structural elements are proportioned such that the actual computed stresses based on expected loads (both dead load and live load) are less than the allowable stresses, well within the elastic stress range. The behavior of the structure due to an overload or failure is not considered.

Also known as *strength design*, *limit state design*, or *ultimate load design*, LRFD is used to design a structure to withstand the most critical combination of *factored loads* applied to the member. *Limit state* is a condition in which a structure or a structural component is no longer fit or useful. A structural member can have several *limit states*. *Strength* limit states concern safety and relate to maximum load-carrying capacity, which may refer to moment capacity, shear capacity, buckling, or plastic hinge formation. *Serviceability* limit states relate to performance under normal conditions (unacceptable elastic deformation or drift, unacceptable vibration and permanent deformation). Essentially, ASD compares actual and allowable stresses, while LRFD compares strength to actual strength.

Load and resistance factor design for steel was initially proposed in 1978 and formally adopted by the AISC in 1986. Initially, however, the shift to LRFD was not universally embraced by the engineering profession, even though almost all universities shifted to teaching the strength method within 10 years of its introduction.

The LRFD method is believed to have a number of advantages over the allowable stress method:

- LRFD accounts for the nonlinear nature of the stress-strain diagram for materials subjected to high stress levels. It provides a better representation of the behavior of steel-composite members (Figures 37 and 38) and of members subjected to large seismic loads.
- The dead loads acting on a structure may be determined with some degree of accuracy, while live loads are less predictable. The LRFD method accounts for this by specifying higher load factors for live loads. Because the ASD method has no similar provision available, the result is a more conservative design for structures with a high ratio of dead load to live load and an inadequate safety factor for structures with a high ratio of live load to dead load.
- LRFD accounts for the variability in nominal strength of different types of members by applying different values for the resistance factor to the nominal strength. In the ASD method, achieving a uniform reliability for different members is not possible.

In the LRFD method, probability theory is used to establish an acceptable margin of safety based on the variability of anticipated loads and member strength. Failure results when the nominal strength of a member is incapable of resisting the applied forces on the member.

The third edition of the AISC's *Manual of Steel Construction: Load and Resistance Factor Design* requires that all steel structures and members be proportioned so that no *strength limit state* is exceeded when subjected to all required *factored load* combinations. In other words, the design strength of a member has to be greater than or equal to the required resistance. The required resistance is the effect (moment, shear, axial tension or compression, etc.) caused by the highest factored load combination.

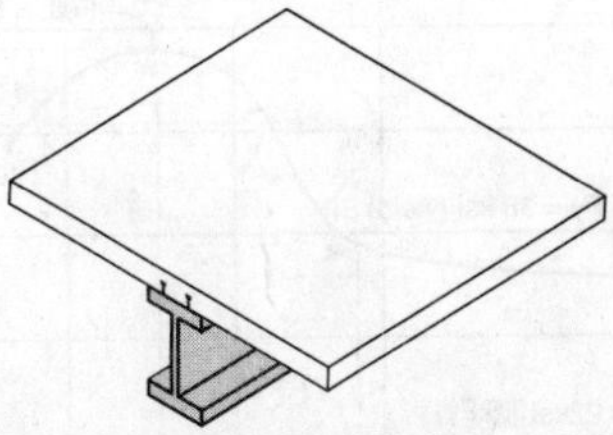

Steel beam with a solid slab and shear studs for composite action.

Figure 37 Composite beam.

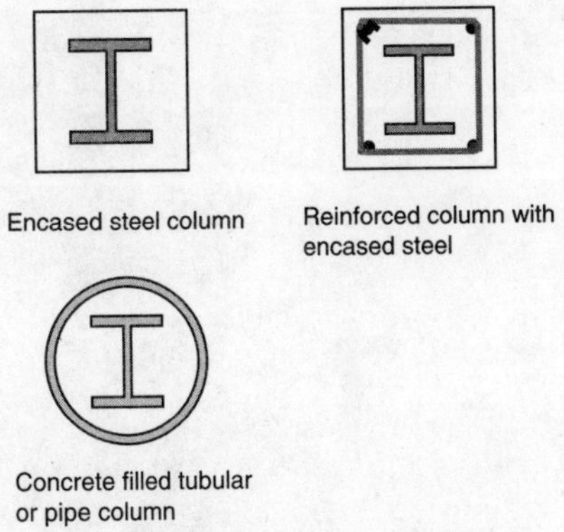

Figure 38 Composite columns.

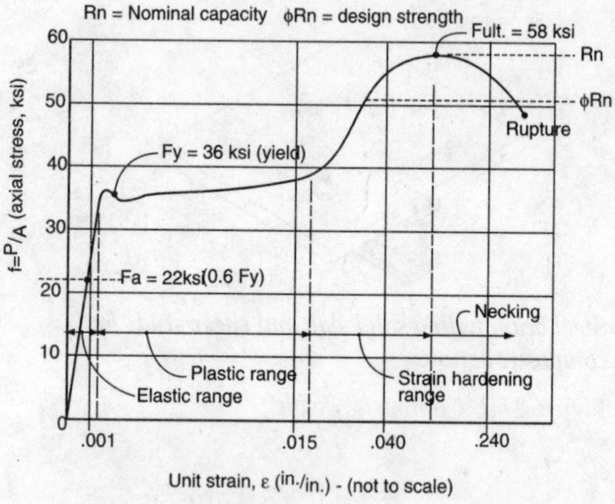

Figure 39 Stress-strain diagram for mild (A36) steel.

The general equation of the LRFD specification is

$$\Sigma\gamma_i Q_i \leq \phi R_n$$

where

γ = load factor for the type of load (dead load, live load, wind, earthquake, etc.)

i = type of load (dead load, live load, wind, etc.)

Q_i = nominal load effect

γ_i = load factor corresponding to Q_i

$\Sigma\gamma_i Q_i$ = required resistance or strength

ϕ = resistance factor corresponding to R_n

R_n = nominal resistance or strength (ultimate capacity; force, moment, shear, or stress)

ϕR_n = design strength

Nominal strength is the capacity of a structural component to resist the effects of loads, based on material strengths (yield strength or ultimate strength) (Figure 39) obtained through laboratory and field testing or derived from formulas using accepted principles of structural mechanics.

The required ultimate strength of a member ($\Sigma\gamma_i Q_i$) consists of the most critical combinations of *factored loads* applied to the member. Factored loads consist of working loads, or service loads multiplied by the appropriate load factors to account for the inherent uncertainties in the loads.

The required strength $\Sigma\gamma Q$ is defined by six load combinations. A load combination may have up to three separate parts, which can consist of (a) the factored dead load effect, (b) the 50-year maximum live load effect, and (c) a possible live load effect labeled as an *arbitrary-point-in-time*, or *APT*, value. Such APT values typically are only a fraction of their design values, because this reflects a small probability that they would occur simultaneously with the other 50-year maximum live load ad full gravity load.

Nominal loads that must be considered in design include the following:

D = dead load; includes the weight of structural elements and other permanent elements supported by the structure, such as permanent partitions

L = live load due to occupancy and movable equipment

L_r = roof live load

R = rain load; initial rainwater load or ice water load exclusive of the ponding contribution

S = snow load

W = wind load

E = earthquake load

The six load conditions for the required strength $\Sigma\gamma Q$ are as follows:

- $\Sigma\gamma Q = 1.4D$ (during construction where the predominant load is dead load)
- $\Sigma\gamma Q = 1.2D + 1.6L + 0.5$ (L_r or S or R) (when the maximum values of occupancy live loads govern the loading condition)
- $\Sigma\gamma Q = 1.2D = 1.6(L_r$ or S or $R) + (0.5L^*$ or $0.8W)$ (when the maximum values of roof live load, rainwater, or snow governs the loading condition)
- $\Sigma\gamma Q = 1.2D + 1.3W + 0.5L^* + 0.5(L_r$ or S or $R)$ (when subjected to maximum values of wind load, increasing the effects of dead load)
- $\Sigma\gamma Q = 1.2D \pm 1.0E + 0.5L^* + 0.2S$ (when subjected to maximum values of seismic load, increasing the effects of dead load)
- $\Sigma\gamma Q = 0.9D \pm (1.3W$ or $1.0E)$ (when subjected to maximum values of wind or seismic load, opposing the effects of dead load)

**Replace 0.5L with 1.0L for garages, places of public assembly, and areas where L > 100 #/ft.²*

The design strength of a member consists of the theoretical ultimate, or nominal, strength of the member R_n multiplied by the appropriate resistance factor ϕ, which accounts for the variability in the nominal strength. Resistance factor ϕ for the various stress conditions is as follows:

ϕ_b = 0.90 beams (flexure)

ϕ_v = 0.90 beams (shear)

ϕ_c = 0.85 compression members

ϕ_t = 0.90 tension members (yielding state)

ϕ_t = 0.75 tension members (fracture state)

Example Problems: LRFD Method

19 Typical W18 × 55 floor beams of an office building are spaced at 12 feet center to center supporting a superimposed dead load of 90 #/ft.^{2} and a live load of 50 #/ft.^{2}. Determine the governing load combination and the corresponding factored load.

Solution:

DL: $D = 90\text{ \#/ft.}^2 \times 12.0' + 55\text{ \#/ft.} = 1{,}135\text{ \#/ft.}$

LL: $L = 50\text{ \#/ft.}^2 \times 12.0' = 600\text{ \#/ft.}$

Two load combinations apply to this floor framing, because there is no roof live, snow, rain, or wind load, or earthquake, to consider.

$1.4D = 1.4 \times 1{,}135\text{ \#/ft.} = 1{,}589\text{ \#/ft.}$ (DL only)

$1.2D + 1.6L = 1.2 \times 1{,}135\text{ \#/ft.} + 1.6 \times 600\text{ \#/ft.}$

$= 2{,}322\text{ \#/ft.}$

The maximum factored load of 2,322 #/ft. governs the design for the floor beams.

20 A roof design supports a dead load of 65 #/ft.^{2} and a snow load of 40 #/ft.^{2} In addition, a wind pressure of 20 #/ft.^{2} (uplift or downward) must be accommodated. Determine the governing load condition.

Solution:

Six load combinations must be considered in this example.

$1.4D = 1.4 \times 65\text{ \#/ft.}^2 = 91\text{ \#/ft.}^2$

$1.2D + 1.6L + 0.5S = 1.2 \times 65\text{ \#/ft.}^2 + 0 + 0.5 \times 40\text{ \#/ft.}^2 = 98\text{ \#/ft.}^2$

$1.2D + 1.6S + 0.8W = 1.2 \times 65\text{ \#/ft.}^2 + 1.6 \times 40\text{ \#/ft.}^2 + 0.8 \times 20\text{ \# ft.}^2 = 158\text{ \#/ft.}^2$

$1.2D + 1.3W + 0.5S = 1.2 \times 65\text{ \#/ft.}^2 + 1.3 \times 20\text{ \#/ft.}^2 + 0.5 \times 40\text{ \#/ft.}^2 = 124\text{ \#/ft.}^2$

$1.2D \pm 1.0E + 0.2S = 1.2 \times 65\,\#/\text{ft.}^2 + 0 +$
$0.2 \times 40\,\#/\text{ft.}^2 = 86\,\#/\text{ft.}^2$

$0.9D \pm 1.3W = 0.9 \times 65\,\#/\text{ft.}^2 + 1.3 \times$
$20\,\#/\text{ft.}^2 = 84.5\,\#/\text{ft.}^2$

In this example, the governing load combination for the roof design is

$$1.2D + 1.6S + 0.8W = 158\,\#/\text{ft.}^2$$

Standard Structural Steels Shapes and Sections

Many grades of steel and a variety of strengths are used in building design, but certain sections may be available only in specific grades. For example, A992 is offered with $F_y = 50$ ksi but primarily in W shapes. A36 steel has a lower yield and ultimate tensile strength but is the primary source for M, S, C, L, and MC shapes as well as for plates, rods, and bars. HP piles are generally available in A572 Grade 50 and A36 Grade 36. When higher strengths are required for W sections, A572 Grade 60 or Grade 65 are specified.

Flexural Stresses

Flexural stress, or bending stress, is the primary concern in the design of beams. Flexural member strength is limited by local buckling of a cross-sectional element (the beam's web or flange), lateral-torsional buckling of the entire member, or the development of a *plastic hinge* at a particular cross-section.

Design, using the LRFD philosophy, assumes that a beam has the ability to develop yield stresses over its entire cross-section (Figure 40), which represents the *strength limit state*. The plastic design concept takes advantage of the ductile property of a material, which is characterized by its unrestricted plastic flow (Figure 41). This ability of the beam to develop a higher capacity while all fibers throughout the cross-section are yielding depends upon the individual elements of that beam (the flanges and the web) remaining stable. A beam that has this stability is referred to as being *compact* (Figure 42), and it can attain its *plastic moment capacity* (M_p) and exhibit no local buckling. This plastic moment capacity is attained when all of the beam's fibers have yielded and is, on average, 10% to 12% greater than the moment needed to produce first yield. When a beam reaches its plastic moment capacity, it

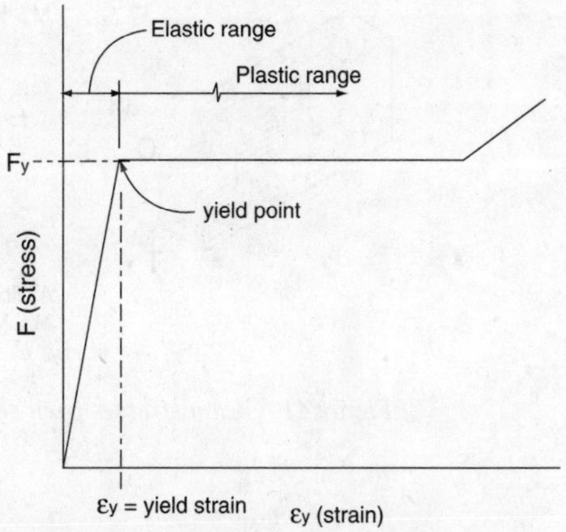

Beyond the yield point, a significant deformation occurs without an increase of stress. The behavior of the steel is inelastic or plastic. Actual failure does not occur until excessive deformation results or rupture of the material.

Figure 40 Idealized stress-strain diagram for ductile steel.

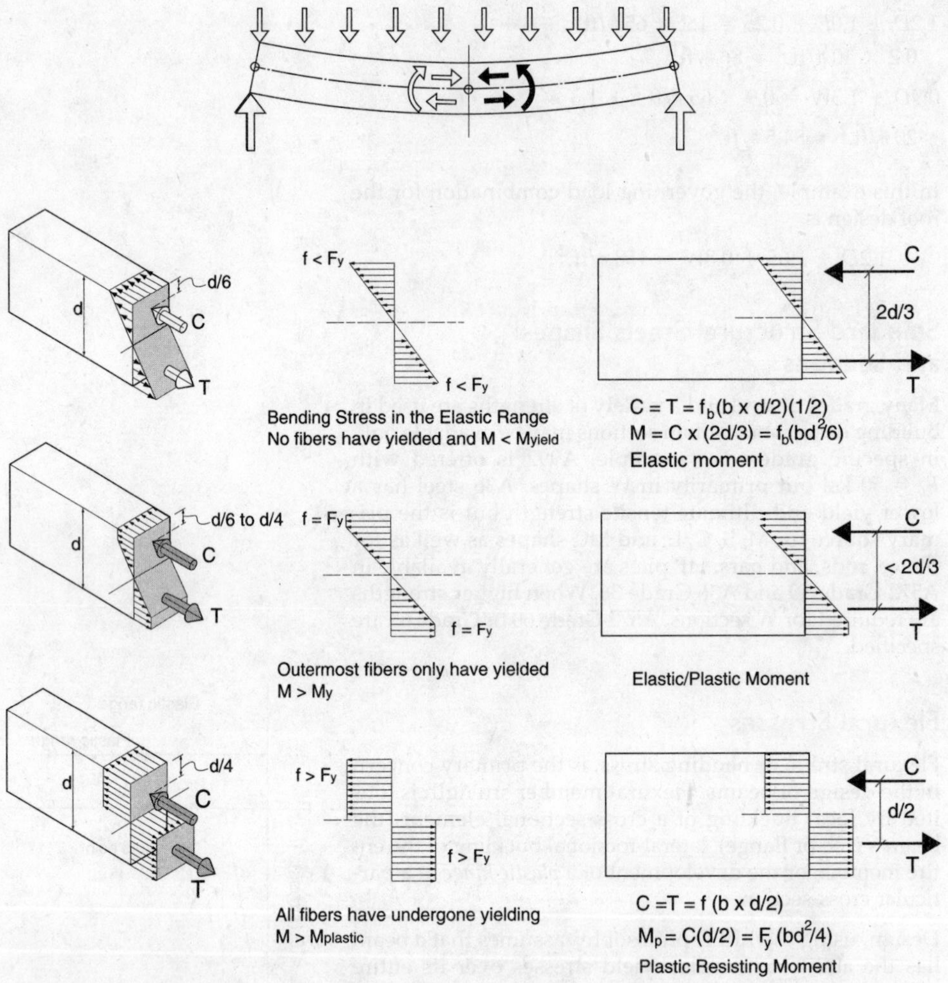

Figure 41 Beam stresses from elastic, partial yielding, and full yielding.

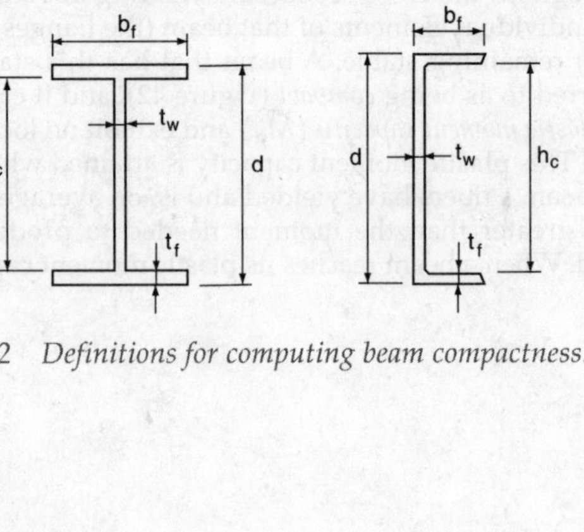

Figure 42 Definitions for computing beam compactness.

has yielded every fiber within its cross-section and develops a plastic hinge (Figure 43).

The term *plastic hinge* reflects the fact that the beam has no more rotational capacity and will most likely collapse if no moment redistribution occurs (Figure 44). The plastic hinge condition represents the absolute limit of usefulness of the cross-section. Only beams that are compact (resistant to local buckling) and adequately braced (to prevent lateral-torsional buckling) can attain this upper limit of flexural strength.

The AISC criteria for determining the compactness of a beam cross-section (see Figure 42) to prevent local buckling is expressed as

$$\frac{b_f}{2t_f} \leq \frac{65}{\sqrt{F_y}}$$

(checks for compactness of the flanges of W and other I shapes and channels)

where

b_f = flange width (in.)

t_f = flange thickness (in.)

F_y = minimum yield stress (ksi)

and as

$$\frac{h_c}{t_w} \leq \frac{640}{\sqrt{F_y}}$$

(checks for compactness of the web)

where

h_c = height of the web (in.)

t_w = web thickness (in.)

For A36 steel with $F_y = 36$ ksi,

$$\frac{b_f}{2t_f} \leq 10.8 \quad \text{and} \quad \frac{h_c}{t_w} \leq 107$$

For A572 and A992 with $F_y = 50$ ksi,

$$\frac{b_f}{2t_f} \leq 9.19 \quad \text{and} \quad \frac{h_c}{t_w} \leq 90.5$$

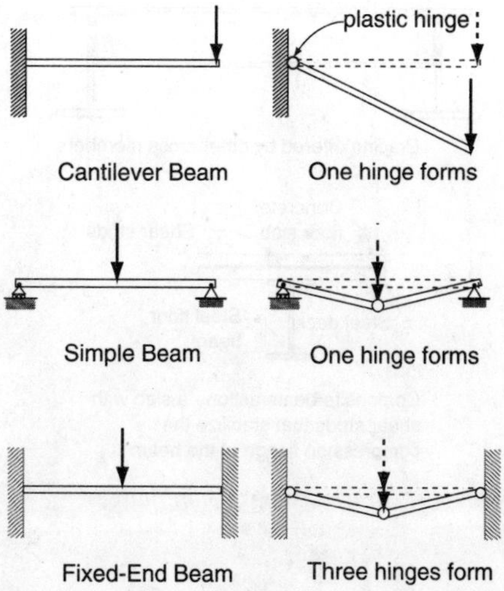

Figure 43 Instability resulting from plastic hinges.

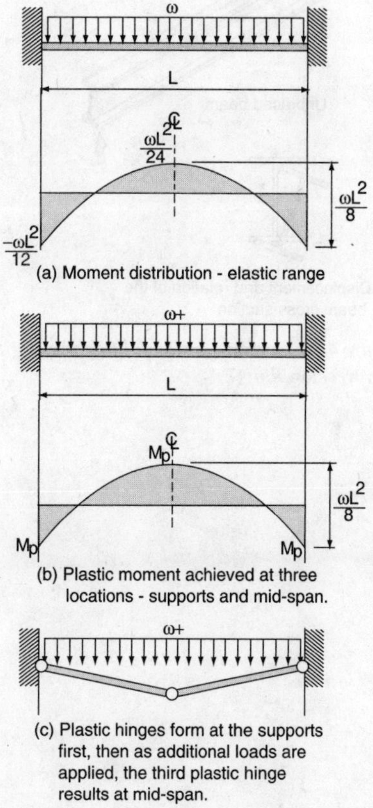

Figure 44 Plastic hinges and moment redistribution.

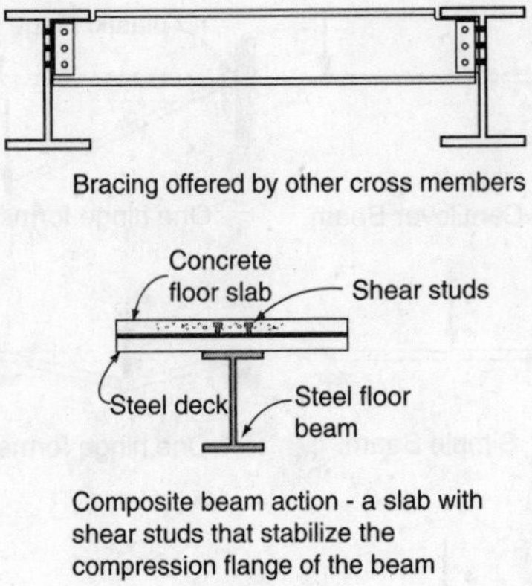

Figure 45 Braced compression flanges.

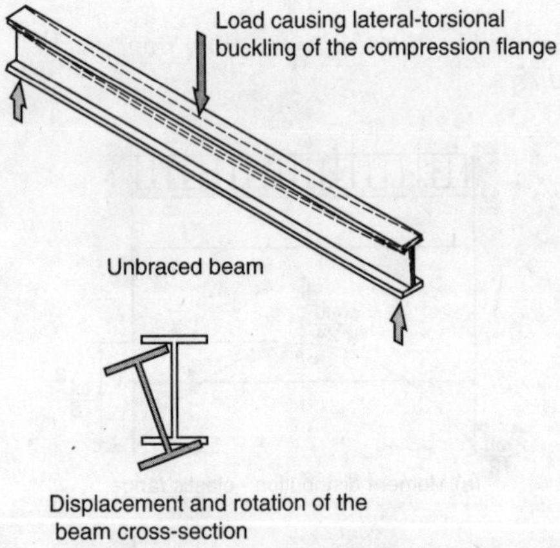

Figure 46 Lateral-torsional buckling of the compression flange.

Example Problems: Compactness

21 Check the compactness of a W10 × 45 if it is made with A992 steel ($F_y = 50$ ksi).

Solution:

From Table A3 in the Appendix,

$$b_f = 8.020''; \quad t_f = 0.620''$$
$$t_w = 0.350''; \quad h_c = 10.10'' - 2(0.620'') = 8.76''$$

Checking the compactness of the flange,

$$b_f/2t_f = 8.020''/2(0.620'') = 6.47 < 9.19$$
(flange is compact)

Check for web compactness,

$$h_c/t_w = 8.76''/0.35'' = 25.0 < 90.5 \text{ (web is compact)}$$

Lateral Support of the Compression Flange

In a compact rolled beam bending about its strong axis (x-x), the controlling factor affecting the capacity of the beam is the lateral support of the compression flange (Figure 45). Full support of the compression flange is more likely to produce a plastic hinge as its limit state. Inadequate bracing of the compression flange can result in column-type instability in beams, a type of behavior that is referred to as *lateral-torsional buckling*. The slender compression flange begins to buckle out of plane, and the beam undergoes a torsional component caused by the downward forces along the top flange (Figure 46).

Figure 45 demonstrates two common ways in which bracing of the buckling plane can be achieved, thus allowing the compression flange to be stabilized and increase the beam's ability to resist more load.

Again, referring to Figure 41, the relationships between moment and maximum (extreme fiber) stress for a given cross-section at various stages of loading are as follows: In the elastic range, before the yield point,

$$M = S(f_b)$$

At initial yielding,

$$M_y = S(F_y)$$

At full plastification (i.e., plastic hinge),

$$M_p = Z(F_y)$$

where

M = bending moment due to the applied loads (k-in.)

M_y = bending moment at initial yielding (k-in.)

M_p = plastic moment (k-in.)

S = elastic section modulus (in.^{3})

Z = plastic section modulus (in.^{3})

f_b = bending stress in the elastic range (ksi)

F_y = minimum yield stress (ksi)

Recall from Section 2 that the elastic section modulus, or the elastic section modulus, $S = I/c$, where I = moment of inertia of the cross-section about its centroidal axis (in.^{4}).

Using a rectangular beam cross-section as an example, the elastic section is given by the equation

$$S = bh^2/6 \text{ (in.}^3\text{)}$$

whereas the formula for the plastic section modulus is

$$Z = bh^2/4$$

where

b = width of the rectangular beam cross-section (in.)

h = height or depth of the beam (in.)

A comparison of the plastic moment to the moment at initial yield shows the ratio

$$M_p/M_y = (F_y)(bh^2/4)/(F_y)(bh^2/6) = 1.5$$

The ratio M_p/M_y indicates, in terms of the yield moment, the magnitude of the moment causing full yielding of the cross-section. This ratio is independent of the material properties of the member; it depends solely on the cross-sectional properties Z and S.

The ratio Z/S is defined as the *shape factor*. Shape factors of wide-flanged beams vary between 1.10 and 1.18, with the average being 1.14. Shape factors for other cross-sectional shapes are 1.70 for a round bar and 1.50 for a rectangle. As indicated earlier, the full yielding of a cross-section of a member results in a plastic hinge if no instability is present. For a simply supported beam (see Figure 43), loads higher than the ultimate load (corresponding to M_p) will cause the plastic hinge to rotate and, in turn, cause failure of the beam.

In the example of a fixed-end beam of length L, supporting a uniformly distributed load w, the greatest moment that develops is $wL^2/12$ at the ends. The elastic strength is the load magnitude that initiates yielding at these ends. Upon an increase of load intensity, plastic hinges form at the ends of the beam, while the moment increases at the center portion to maintain equilibrium with the load. This redistribution of moment continues until yielding results at the center with the formation of a third plastic hinge in the beam at midspan. A "mechanism" is then formed, and the beam can take no additional load. The result is instability and the beam fails.

Design for Bending

The most basic beam design requirement in the LRFD method is that the design moment capacity $\phi_b M_n$ must be greater than or equal to the required (factored) flexural strength M_u. The required flexural strength is generally referred to as the *ultimate moment*.

$$\phi_b M_n \geq M_u$$

where

$\phi_b = 0.90$ for bending

$M_n =$ nominal moment capacity

$M_u =$ required (factored) moment

As discussed previously, bending strength is affected by the unbraced length of the compression flange and the compactness of the member. For laterally braced *compact* sections, where the plastic moment is reached before local buckling occurs, design is based on the limit state of yielding. Therefore,

$$M_n = M_p = F_y Z_x$$

The design form of the equation for determining the required plastic section modulus Z_x from the maximum factored load moment M_u (k-ft.) is

$$Z_x = \frac{12M_u}{\phi_b F_y}$$

Issues of lateral-torsional buckling, flange local buckling, and web local buckling are beyond the scope and objectives of this text and will not be covered.

Shear Stresses

Although flexural strength usually controls the selection of rolled beams, shear strength should be checked. Shear may be critical in cases of short-span members, especially those supporting large concentrated loads. For rolled shapes, with an axis of symmetry in the plane of loading, the flange capacity to resist shear is negligible, and no web stiffeners are required. The AISC LRFD specification equations may be simplified as follows:

$$\text{For } \frac{h}{t_w} \leq \frac{418}{\sqrt{F_y}},$$

$$\sum \gamma_i R_i = V_u \leq \phi_v V_n = 0.9(0.6F_{yw}A_w)$$

where

h = the clear distance between fillets (for rolled shapes)

t_w = web thickness (in.)

d = overall depth of the rolled section (in.)

V_u = maximum shear from factored loads

ϕ_v = resistance factor for shear (0.9)

V_n = nominal shear (ultimate capacity)

F_{yw} = yield strength of the steel in the web

$A_w = t_w d$ = area of the web

Other AISC LRFD formulas are given for cases where

$$\frac{h}{t_w} \leq \frac{418}{\sqrt{F_y}}$$

but they will not be considered in this text.

Example Problems: Moment Capacity

22 Determine the moment capacity of an ASTM 992 W18 × 40 floor beam with $F_y = 50$ ksi. Assume that the beam is fully braced laterally along the compression flange (see Figure 47) with a composite concrete deck securely anchored with shear studs.

Solution:

A check must first be made to verify its compactness. For the W18 × 40,

$$d = 17.90''; \; b_f = 6.015''; \; t_f = 0.525$$

$$t_w = 0.315; \; h = 15.5''; \; Z_x = 78.4 \text{ in.}^4$$

$$\frac{b_f}{2t_f} = \frac{6.015''}{2 \times 0.525''} = 5.73 \leq 9.19 \text{ for 50 ksi steel}$$

and

$$\frac{h_c}{t_w} = \frac{15.50''}{0.315} = 49.2 \leq 90.5$$

The W18 × 40 section is compact, and the moment capacity will be equal to the plastic moment.

$$M_n = M_p = F_y Z_x = \left(50 \text{ k/in.}^2\right)\left(78.4 \text{ in.}^4\right) = 3{,}920 \text{ k-in.}$$

$$M_n = 3{,}920/12 = 327 \text{ k-ft.}$$

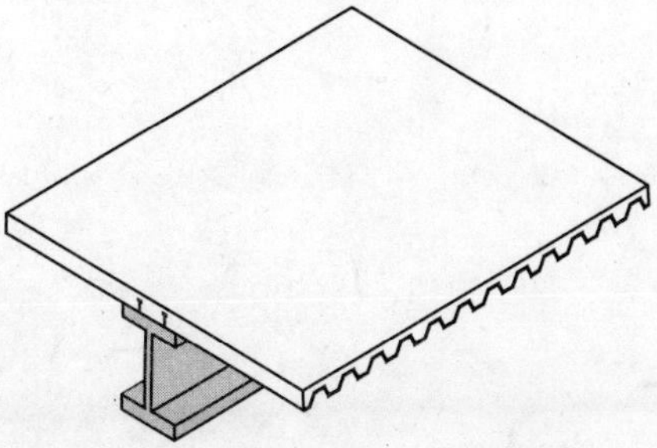

Composite beam with metal decking laid perpendicular to the beam span. Shear studs are welded to the beam flange and decking to create the composite action with the concrete slab.

Figure 47 Composite beam example.

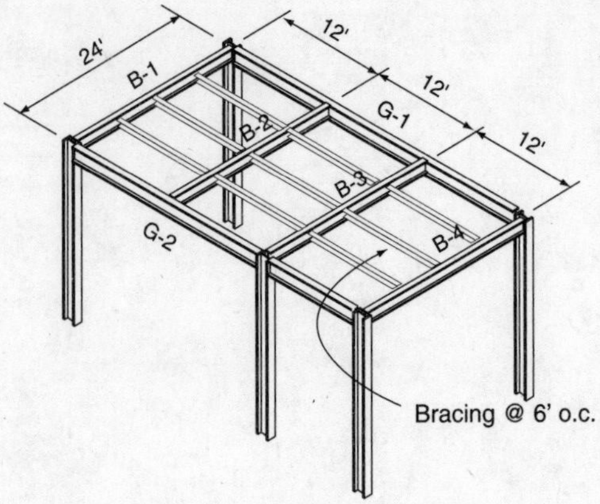

Figure 48 *Isometric view of partial steel framing arrangement.*

23 A simply supported beam (B-2) supports a uniformly distributed load and is braced at six foot intervals (see Figure 48) in addition to a composite slab that is secured to the compression flange of the beam via shear studs. Assume that the beam is made of ASTM A992 grade with $F_y = 50$ ksi.

Select the lightest W shape to safely support the following loads:

$$\text{DL} = 100 \text{ psf}; \quad \text{LL} = 75 \text{ psf}$$

Beams are spaced at 12 feet o.c.

Solution:

$$\omega_{DL} = 100\ \#/\text{ft.}^2 \times 12' = 1{,}200\ \#/\text{ft.}$$

$$\omega_{LL} = 75\ \#/\text{ft.}^2 \times 12' = 900\ \#/\text{ft.}$$

Because this example represents a floor load condition, the two factored load considerations that apply are

$$1.4D = 1.4 \times 1{,}200\ \#/\text{ft.} = 1680\ \#/\text{ft.}\ (\text{for DL only})$$

$$1.2D + 1.6L = 1.2(1{,}200\ \#/\text{ft.}) = 1.6(900\ \#/\text{ft.})$$
$$= 2{,}880\ \#/\text{ft.}$$

The factored load of 2,880 #/ft. governs the design for the floor beams.

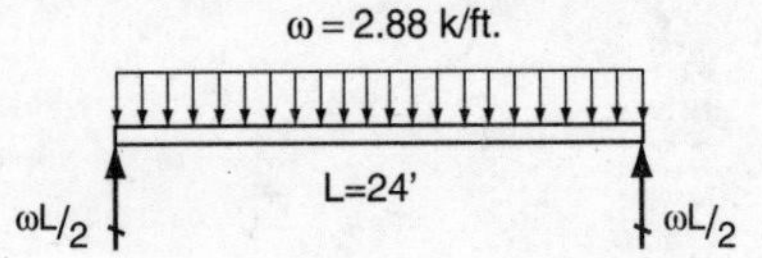

$$M_u = \frac{\omega L^2}{8} = \frac{(2.88\text{ k-ft.})(24')^2}{8} = 207.4\text{ k-ft.}$$

$$V_u = \frac{\omega L}{2} = \frac{(2.88\text{ k-ft.})(24')}{2} = 34.6\text{ k}$$

$$Z_x = \frac{12M_u}{\phi_b F_y} = \frac{12(207.4\text{ k-ft.})}{(0.90)(50\text{ k/in.}^2)} = 55.3\text{ in.}^3$$

From Tables A11(a) and A11(b) in the Appendix, select the lightest trial size.

Try W18 × 35.

$$Z_x = 66.5\text{ in.}^3, d = 17.7\text{ in.}, h = 15.5\text{ in.}$$

$$b_f = 6.00\text{ in.}, t_f = 0.425\text{ in.}, t_w = 0.30\text{ in.})$$

$$M_p = F_y Z_x = (50\text{ k-in.}^2)\left(\frac{66.5\text{ in.}^3}{12\text{ in./ft.}}\right) = 277\text{ k-ft.}$$

$$\phi M_p = (0.90)(277\text{ k-ft.}) = 249\text{ k-ft.}$$

This value can also be found directly in Table A11(b) in the Appendix.

Next, check the compactness of the beam section.

$$\frac{b_f}{2t_f} = \frac{6.00''}{2(0.425'')} = 7.06 < 9.19 \text{(the flange is compact)}$$

$$\frac{h}{t_w} = \frac{15.5''}{0.300''} = 51.7 < 90.5 \text{ (the web is compact)}$$

Shear check:

$$\frac{h}{t_w} \leq \frac{418}{\sqrt{F_y}}$$

then use

$$V_u \leq \phi_v V_n = (.90)(.6F_y t_w d)$$

$$\frac{h}{t_w} = \frac{15.5''}{0.300''} = 51.7 < \frac{418}{\sqrt{F_y}} = \frac{418}{\sqrt{50}} = 59$$

Therefore,

$$\phi_v V_n = (0.90)(0.6)(50)(0.30 \times 17.7'') = 143.4 \text{ k}$$

$$V_u = 34.6 \text{ k} < \phi_v V_n = 143.4 \text{ k}$$

$\therefore$ the beam is OK in shear

The W18 × 35 is adequate and the lightest section to use as a floor beam.

Summary

- Beams subjected to transverse loads develop internal moments, which result in bending action. Part of the beam cross-section is subjected to compressive stresses, while the remaining portion of the cross-section is in tension. The transition of stress from compression to tension occurs at the neutral axis, which corresponds to the centroidal axis of the beam's cross-section.
- Flexural stresses are directly proportional to the beam's bending moment and inversely proportional to the beam's moment of inertia relative to the neutral axis.
- Bending stresses vary from zero at the neutral axis to a maximum at the top and/or bottom fibers.
- Generally, in beam design, the maximum bending stress is used, and the equation is expressed as

$$f_b = \frac{Mc}{I} = \frac{(\text{moment}) \times (\text{distance from N.A. to extreme fiber})}{(\text{moment of inertia})}$$

- The majority of the structural shapes used in practice are standard shapes, normally available in industry. Cross-sectional properties are known and available in tables and handbooks. Therefore, the basic flexure equation can be simplified by substituting a term called the *section modulus* (S), where

$$S = \frac{I}{c}$$

- Substituting the section modulus into the flexure formula, the equation becomes

$$f_b = \frac{Mc}{I} = \frac{M}{I/C} = \frac{M}{S}$$

- Rewriting the equation into a design form, appropriate beams sizes can be selected from tables.

$$S_{\text{required}} = \frac{M_{\text{max.}}}{F_b} = \frac{\text{maximum bending moment}}{\text{allowable bending stress}}$$

- In addition to bending moment, beams are subjected to transverse (vertical) and longitudinal (horizontal) shears. At any given point along the length of the beam, the transverse shear and longitudinal shear are equal. Therefore, the shear (V) diagram can be used in the analysis or design of beams for shear.

- The general shear stress at any point on a beam is expressed as

$$f_v = \frac{VQ}{Ib} = \frac{(\text{shear force}) \times (\text{first moment } A\bar{y})}{(\text{moment of inertia}) \times (\text{width of shear plane})}$$

- Shearing stress in wide-flange, channel, and T-sections in steel are generally carried by the web. Very little shear resistance is offered by the flange; therefore, the general shear stress equation is simplified as

$$f_{v_{\text{average}}} = \frac{V}{t_w d} = \frac{(\text{shear force})}{(\text{web thickeness}) \times (\text{beam depth})}$$

  This formula gives the average unit shearing stress for the web over the full depth of the beam. Structural steel is very resistant in shear, therefore, the average shear stress formula is generally sufficient as a check.

- For solid rectangular cross-sections in timber, the general shear stress formula simplifies to

$$f_{v_{\text{maximum}}} = \frac{1.5\,V}{A} = \frac{1.5 \times (\text{shear force})}{(\text{cross-sectional area})}$$

- The maximum shear stress in a rectangular beam is 50% larger than the average stress value. Timber beams are often critical in shear, because the allowable shear stress for wood is very low.
- The third requirement for beam design is deflection. A stiffness requirement, deflection represents a change in vertical position of a beam due to the applied loads. Generally, the amount of allowable or permissible deflection is limited by building codes.
- Deflections are a function of load magnitude, beam-span length, the moment of inertia of the beam cross-section, and the beam's modulus of elasticity.
- Actual beam deflections must be compared against the allowable deflection limited by code.

$$\Delta_{actual} < \Delta_{allowable}$$

Answers to Selected Problems

1 $f = M/S = 14.2$ ksi < 22 ksi

2 $M_{max} = 4.28$ k-ft.;
$f_b = 696$ psi $< F_b = 1{,}300$ psi

4 $M_{max} = 17.2$ k-ft.; $S_{min.} = 9.38$ in.^{3}
Use W8 × 13 ($S_x = 9.91$ in.^{3})

6 (a) $M_{max} = 16.67$ k-ft.; $f = 17$ ksi
(b) $S_{req'd.} = 125$ in.^{3}; use 8 × 12 S4S

8 $M_{max} = 30.4$ k-ft.; $f_{max} = 15$ ksi;
at 4′ from the free end, $f = 1.88$ ksi

10 $M_{max} = 125.4$ k-ft.; $P = 15.7$ k

11 $V_{max} = 8.75$ k; $M_{max} = 43.75$ k-ft.
$I_x = 112.6$ in.^{4}; $f_b = 27.5$ ksi;
at the N.A.: $f_v = 1.37$ ksi;
at the web/flange: $f_v = 1.20$ ksi

12 $V_{max} = 6{,}400$ lb.; $M_{max} = 51{,}200$ lb.-ft.
Based on bending: Radius = 8.67″;
based on shear: Radius = 5.2″;
use 18″-diameter log

14 $V_{max} = 1{,}800$ lb.; $M_{max} = 7{,}200$ lb.-ft.;
$I_x = 469.9$ in.^{4}; $f_b = 1{,}170$ psi;
$f_v = 196$ psi

16 (a) Based on bending: $P = 985$ lb.
Based on shear: $P = 1{,}340$ lb.
Bending governs the design.
(b) At 4′ from the left support,
$V = 1{,}315$ lb.; $M = 5{,}250$ lb.-ft.;
$f_b = 854$ psi; $f_v = 50.2$ psi.

18 $M_{max} = 32$ k-ft.; $S_{req'd.} = 17.5$ in.^{3};
From steel tables:
Use W12 × 19 ($S_x = 21.3$ in.^{3}) or
W10 × 19 ($S_x = 18.8$ in.^{3})
Average web shear $f_v = 5.14$ ksi

20 $I_x = 1{,}965$ in.^{4}; $Q = 72$ in.^{3}; $V = 2{,}500$ lb.
$p = FI/VQ = 1.75''$ (spacing of nails)

22 $M_{max} = 22{,}400$ lb.-ft.; $S_{req'd.} = 207$ in.^{3};
$V_{max} = 5{,}600$ lb.; $A_{req'd.} = 98.8$ in.^{2};
8 × 16 S4S; $\Delta_{allow} = L/360 = 0.53''$
$\Delta_{LL} = 0.16'' < 0.53''$; ∴ 8 × 16 S4S OK

23 $V_{max} = 2{,}000$ lb.; $A_{req'd.} = 27.3$ in.^{2};
$M_{max} = 12{,}000$ lb.-ft.; $S_{req'd.} = 92.9$ in.^{3};
For a 4 × 14 S4S
$\Delta_{allow} = L/240 = 0.8''$
$\Delta_{actual} = 0.48'' < 0.8''$ ∴ OK
$f_{bearing} = 109$ psi. Use 4 × 14 S4S

24 $M_{max} = 48{,}000$ lb.-ft; $S_{req'd.} = 26.2$ in.^{3};
Try: W14 × 22; $\Delta_{allow} = 0.73''$;
$\Delta_{LL} = 0.29'' < .73''$ ∴ OK
Use W14 × 22 for beam B1.
For SB1: $M_{max} = 95.6$ k-ft.;
$S_{req'd.} = 52.1$ in.^{3}; Try W16 × 36;
$\Delta_{allow} = 1.2''$ (DL + LL);
$\Delta_{actual} = 0.78''$ (DL + LL);
$f_{v\,(ave)} = 2.7$ ksi $< F_v = 14.5$ ksi;
Use W16 × 36 for SB1.

Column Analysis and Design

Column Analysis and Design

(a) Covered walkway. Photo by Matt Bissen.

(b) Compression struts in a biplane. Photo by Chris Brown.

Figure 1 Examples of compression members.

Introduction

Columns are essentially vertical members responsible for supporting compressive loads from roofs and floors and transmitting the vertical forces to the foundations and subsoil. The structural work performed by the column is somewhat simpler than that of the beam, because the applied loads are in the same vertical orientation. Although columns are normally considered to be vertical elements, they can actually be positioned in any orientation. Columns are defined by their length dimension between support ends and can be very short (e.g., footing piers) or very long (e.g., bridge and freeway piers). They are used as major elements in trusses, building frames, and substructure supports for bridges. Loads are typically applied at member ends, producing axial compressive stresses.

Common terms used to identify column elements include *studs*, *struts*, *posts*, *piers*, *piles*, and *shafts*, as shown in Figure 1. Virtually every common construction material, including steel, timber, concrete (reinforced and prestressed), and masonry, is used for column construction. Each material possesses characteristics (material and production) that present opportunities and limitations on the shapes of cross-sections and profiles chosen. Columns are major structural components that significantly affect the building's overall performance and stability and, thus, are designed with larger safety factors than other structural components. Failure of a joist or beam may be localized and may not severely affect the building's integrity; however, failure of a strategic column may be catastrophic for a large area of the structure. Safety factors for columns adjust for the uncertainties of material irregularities, support fixity at the column ends, and take into consideration construction inaccuracies, workmanship, and unavoidable eccentric (off-axis) loading.

1 SHORT AND LONG COLUMNS—MODES OF FAILURE

The large slabs of stone used at Stonehenge were extremely massive and tended to be stabilized by their own weight. Massive stone columns continued to be used in Greek and Roman structures, but with the development of wrought iron, cast iron, steel, and reinforced concrete, columns began to take on much more slender proportions.

Column slenderness greatly influences a column's ability to carry load. Because a column is a compression member, it would be reasonable to assume that one would fail due to crushing or excessive shortening once the stress level exceeded the elastic (yield point) limit of the material. However, for most columns, failure occurs at a lower level than the column's material strength, because most columns are relatively slender (long in relation to their lateral dimension) and fail due to buckling (lateral instability). *Buckling* is the sudden, uncontrolled, lateral displacement of a column, at which point no additional load can be supported. The sideways deflection or buckle will eventually fail in bending if loads are increased. Very short, stout columns fail by crushing due to material failure; long, slender columns fail by buckling—a function of the column's dimensions and its modulus of elasticity (Figure 2).

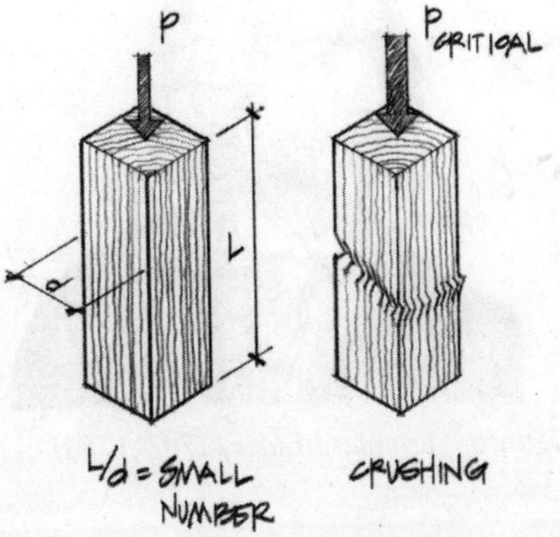

Figure 2(a) Crushing: Short column—exceed material strength.

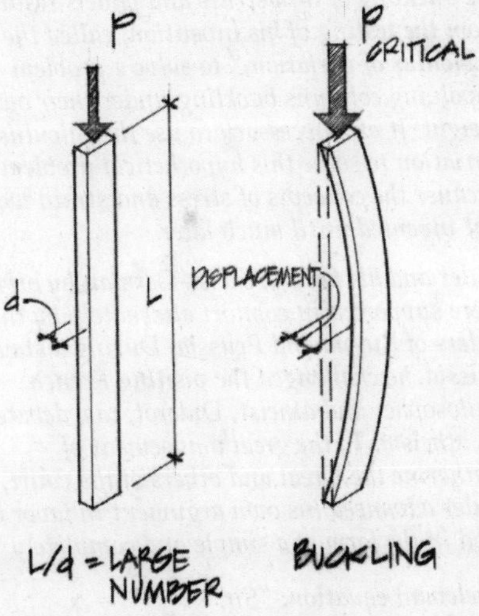

Figure 2(b) Buckling: Long column—elastic instability.

Short Columns

Stress computations for short columns are very simple and rely on a basic stress equation. If the load and column size are known, the actual compressive stress may be computed as

$$f_a = \frac{P_{actual}}{A} \leq F_a$$

where

f_a = actual compressive stress (psi or ksi)
A = cross-sectional area of column (in.^{2})
P_{actual} = actual load on the column (# or k)
F_a = allowable compressive stress per codes (psi or ksi)

This stress equation can be easily rewritten into a design form when determining the requisite short column size if the load and allowable material strength are known:

$$A_{required} = \frac{P_{actual}}{F_a}$$

where

$A_{required}$ = minimum cross-sectional area of the column

Figure 3 Leonhard Euler (1707–1783).

Known as one of the most prolific mathematicians of all time, Euler wrote profusely on every branch of the subject. His learned papers were still being published 40 years after his death. Progressively, he began to replace the geometric methods of proof used by Galileo and Newton with algebraic methods. He contributed considerably to the science of mechanics. His discovery involving the buckling of thin struts and panels resulted from the testing of his invention, called the "calculus of variation," to solve a problem involving columns buckling under their own weight. It was necessary to use the calculus of variation to solve this hypothetical problem because the concepts of stress and strain were not invented until much later.

Euler and his family, Swiss-German by origin, were supported in comfort alternately by the rulers of Russia and Prussia. During a stay in Russia, he challenged the visiting French philosopher and atheist, Diderot, to a debate on atheism. To the great amusement of Catherine the Great and others of the court, Euler advanced his own argument in favor of God in the form of a simple and completely irrelevant equation: "Sir, $\frac{a + b^n}{n} = x$, *hence God exists." All mathematics was beyond poor Diderot, and he was left speechless. Assuming that he had been shown proof, which he clearly did not understand, and feeling a fool, Diderot left Russia.*

Long Columns—Euler Buckling

The buckling phenomenon in slender columns is due to the inevitable eccentricities in loading and the likelihood of irregularities in a material's resistance to compression. Buckling could be avoided (theoretically) if the loads applied were absolutely axial and the column material was totally homogeneous with no imperfections. Obviously, this is not possible; hence, buckling is a fact of life for any slender column.

The load capacity of a slender column is directly dependent on the dimension and shape of the column as well as on the stiffness of the material (E). It is independent of the strength of the material (yield stress).

The buckling behavior of slender columns, within their elastic limit, was first investigated by a Swiss mathematician named Leonhard Euler (1707–1783) (Figure 3). Euler's equation presents the relationship between the load that causes buckling of a pinned end column and the stiffness properties of the column. The critical buckling load can be determined by the equation

$$P_{\text{critical}} = \frac{\pi^2 E I_{\min}}{L^2}$$

where

P_{critical} = critical axial load that causes buckling in the column (# or k)

E = modulus of elasticity of the column material (psi or ksi)

$I_{\min}$ = smallest moment of inertia of the column cross-section (in.^{4})

L = column length between pinned ends (in.)

Note that as the column length becomes very long, the critical load becomes very small, approaching zero as a limit. Conversely, very short column lengths require extremely large loads to cause the member to buckle. High loads result in high stresses, which cause crushing rather than buckling.

The Euler equation demonstrates the susceptibility of the column to buckling as a function of the column length squared, the stiffness of the material used (E), and the cross-sectional stiffness as measured by the moment of inertia (I) (Figure 4).

Figure 4(a) Stable equilibrium: Long column (P less than the critical load)—column stiffness keeps the member in a state of stable equilibrium.

Figure 4(b) Neutral equilibrium: Long column ($P = P_{crit.}$)—the column load equals the critical buckling load; the member is in a state of neutral equilibrium.

Figure 4(c) Unstable equilibrium: Long column ($P > P_{crit.}$)—the member buckles suddenly, changing to a state of instability.

To understand the phenomenon of buckling further, let's examine a slender column with a slight initial bow to it before loading (Figure 5).

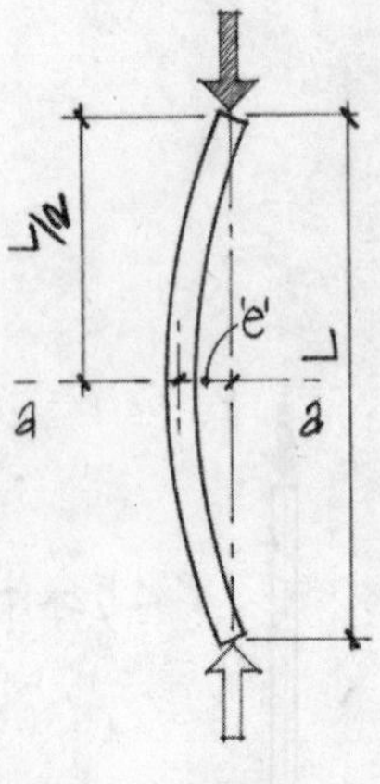

Figure 5(a) *Column with a slight bow 'e' from vertical.*

Because the load P is offset (eccentric to the central axis of the column), a moment $M = P \times e$ results in bending stresses being present in addition to the compressive stress $f = P/A$. If the load is increased, additional moment results in bending the column further and, thus, in a larger eccentricity or displacement. This moment $M' = P' \times \Delta$ results in an increased bending that causes more displacement, thus creating an even larger moment ($P - \Delta$ effect). A progressive bending moment and displacement continues until the stability of the column is compromised. The critical load at which the limit of the column's ability to resist uncontrolled, progressive displacement has been reached is referred to as *Euler's critical buckling load.*

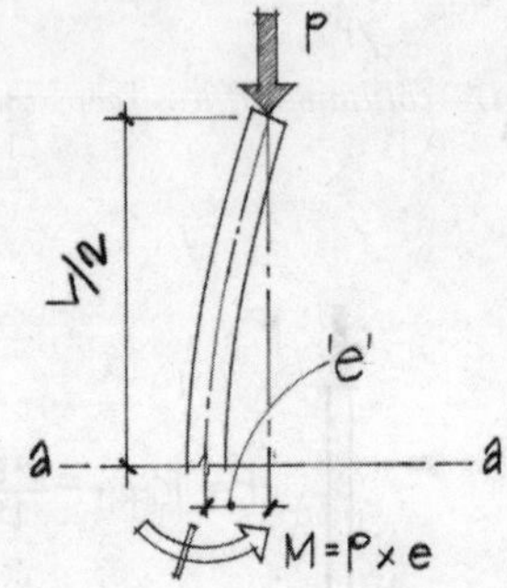

Figure 5(b) *The offset load* P *produces a moment* M = P × e.

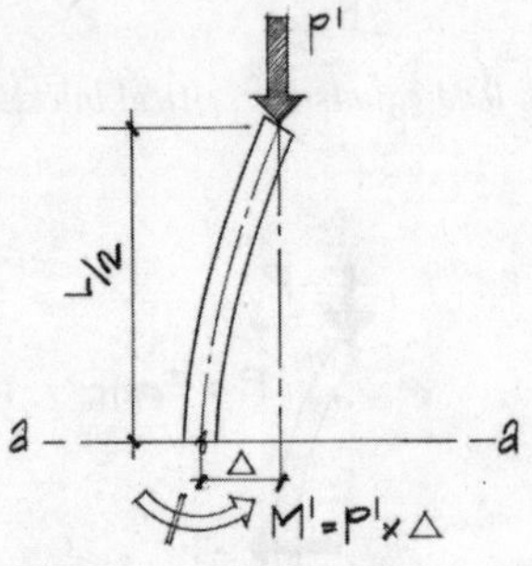

Figure 5(c) P' > P: *Increased load with an increased displacement* Δ > e.

It is important to note again that the Euler equation, which contains no safety factors, is valid only for long, slender columns that fail due to buckling and in which stresses are well within the elastic limit of the material. Short columns tend to fail by crushing at very high stress levels, well beyond the elastic range of the column material.

Slenderness Ratios

The geometric property of a cross-section is called the *radius of gyration.* This dimensional property is being recalled here in connection with the design of columns. Another useful form of the Euler equation can be developed by substituting the radius of gyration for the moment of inertia, in which

$$r = \sqrt{\frac{I}{A}}$$
$$I = Ar^2$$

where

r = radius of gyration of the column cross-section (in.)
I = least (minimum) moment of inertia (in.^{4})
A = cross-sectional area of the column (in.^{2})

The critical stress developed in a long column at buckling can be expressed as

$$f_{\text{critical}} = \frac{P_{\text{critical}}}{A} = \frac{\pi^2 E(Ar^2)}{AL^2} = \frac{\pi^2 E}{(L/r)^2}$$

Column sections with high r values are more resistant to buckling (Figure 6). Because the radius of gyration is derived from the moment of inertia, we can deduce that cross-sectional configuration is critical in generating higher r values.

The L/r term in the equation above is known as the *slenderness ratio*. The critical buckling stress of a column depends inversely on the square of the slenderness ratio. High slenderness ratios mean lower critical stresses (Figure 7) that will cause buckling; conversely, lower slenderness ratios result in higher critical stress (but still within the elastic range of the material). The slenderness ratio is a primary indicator of the mode of failure one might expect for a column under load.

As a comparison of steel column sections often found in buildings, note the difference in $r_{min.}$ values for three sections shown in Figure 8. All three sections have relatively equal cross-sectional areas but very different radii of gyration about the critical buckling axis. If all three columns were assumed as 15 feet in length and pin connected at both ends, the corresponding slenderness ratios are quite different indeed.

In general, the most efficient column sections for axial loads are those with almost equal r_x and r_y values. Circular pipe sections and square tubes are the most effective shapes, because the radii of gyration about both axes are the same $(r_x = r_y)$. For this reason, these types of sections are often used as columns for light to moderate loads. However, they are not necessarily appropriate for heavy loads and where many beam connections must be made. The practical considerations and advantages of making structural connections to easily accessible wide-flange shapes often outweigh the pure structural advantages of closed cross-sectional shapes (e.g., tubes and pipes). Special wide-flange sections are specifically manufactured to provide relatively symmetrical columns (r_x/r_y ratios approaching 1.0) with large load-carrying capability. Most of these column sections have depth and flange widths approximately equal ("boxy" configuration) and are generally in the 10, 12, and 14 inch nominal depth category.

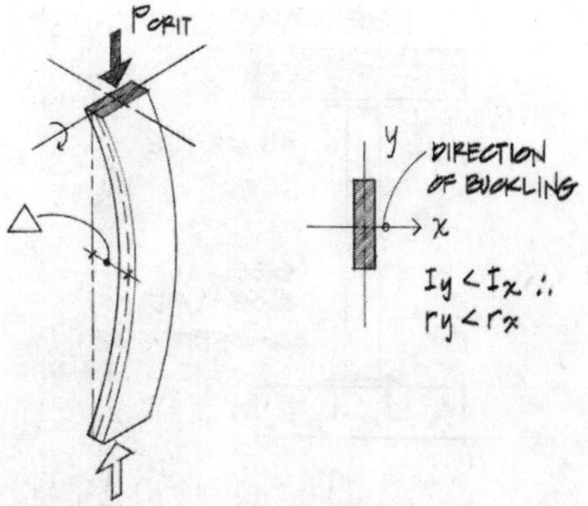

Figure 6 Column buckling about its weak axis.

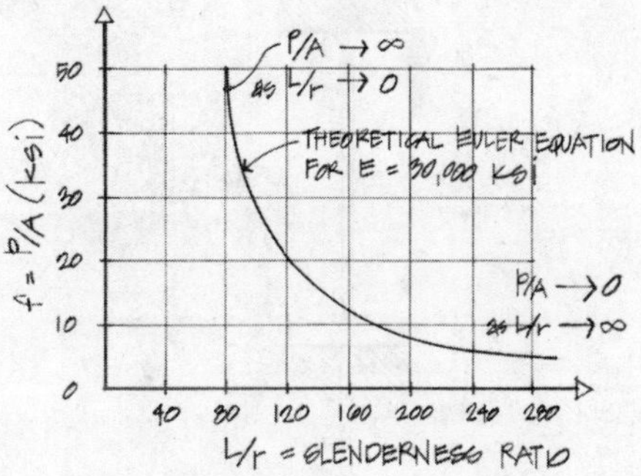

Figure 7 Buckling stress versus slenderness ratio.

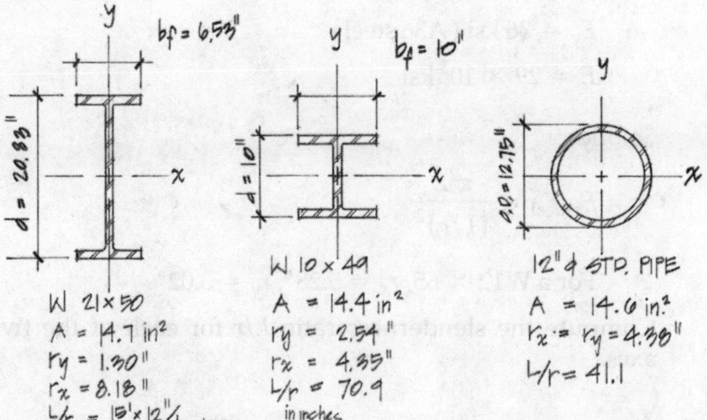

Figure 8 Comparison of steel cross-sections with equivalent areas.

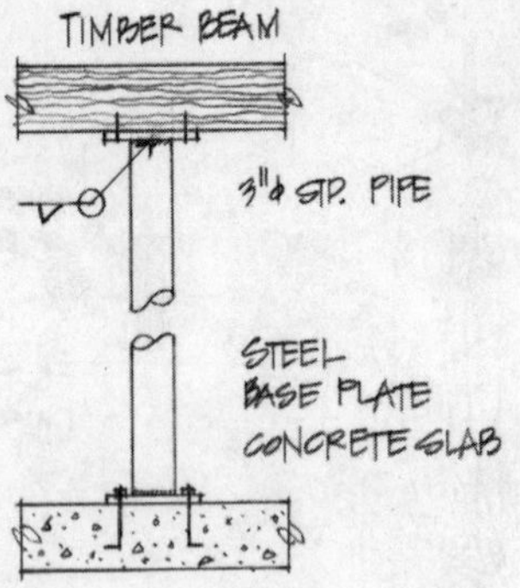

Example Problems: Short and Long Columns—Modes of Failure

1 Determine the critical buckling load for a 3″ φ standard weight steel pipe column that is 16 feet tall and pin connected. Assume that $E = 29 \times 10^6$ psi.

Solution:

From the Euler buckling equation,

$$P_{\text{critical}} = \frac{\pi^2 EI}{L^2}$$

The least (smallest) moment of inertia is normally used in the Euler equation to produce the critical buckling load. In this example, however, $I_x = I_y$ for a circular pipe:

$I = 3.02 \text{ in.}^4$ (There is no weak axis for buckling.)

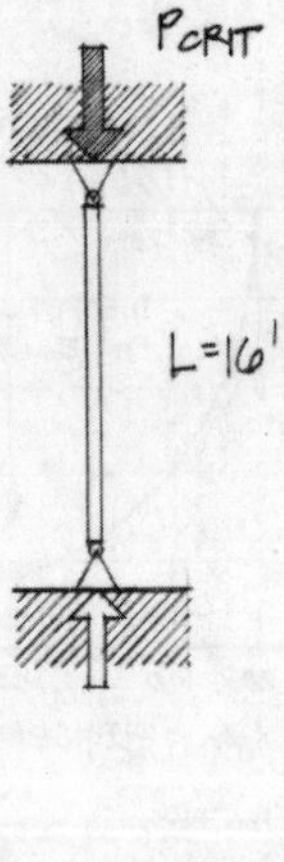

$$P_{\text{critical}} = \frac{(3.14)^2(29 \times 10^6 \text{ psi})(3.02 \text{ in.}^4)}{(16' \times 12 \text{ in./ft.})^2} = 23{,}424\#$$

The accompanying critical stress can be evaluated as

$$f_{\text{critical}} = \frac{P_{\text{critical}}}{A} = \frac{23{,}424\#}{2.23 \text{ in.}^2} = 10{,}504 \text{ psi}$$

This column buckles at a relatively low stress level.

$F_{\text{compression}} = 22$ ksi

2 Determine the critical buckling stress for a 30-foot -long W12 × 65 steel column. Assume simple pin connections at the top and bottom.

$F_y = 36$ ksi (A36 steel)

$E = 29 \times 10^3$ ksi

Solution:

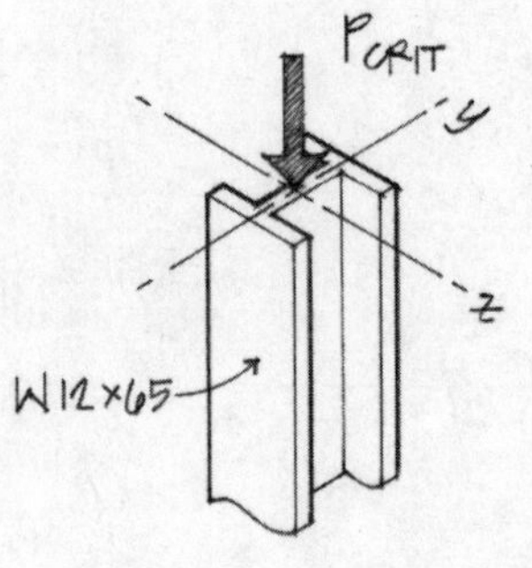

$$f_{\text{critical}} = \frac{\pi^2 E}{(L/r)^2}$$

For a W12 × 65, $r_x = 5.28''$, $r_y = 3.02''$

Compute the slenderness ratio L/r for each of the two axes.

Substitute the larger of the two values into the Euler equation, because it will yield the more critical stress value

$$\frac{L}{r_x} = \frac{30' \times 12 \text{ in./ft.}}{5.28''} = 68.2.$$

$$\frac{L}{r_y} = \frac{30' \times 12 \text{ in./ft.}}{3.02''} = 119.2 \leftarrow \text{Governs}$$

(produces a smaller stress value at buckling)

$$f_{\text{critical}} = \frac{\pi^2(29 \times 10^3 \text{ ksi})}{(119.2)^2} = 20.1 \text{ ksi}$$

The use of L/r_x would clearly yield a much larger stress value.

This indicates that the column would buckle about the y axis under a much smaller load than would be required to make it buckle the other way. In practical terms, this means that in case of overload, the column would not be able to reach the critical load necessary to make it buckle about its strong axis; it would fail at a lower load value by buckling about its weak axis. Therefore, in computing critical load and stress values, always use the greater L/r value.

2 END SUPPORT CONDITIONS AND LATERAL BRACING

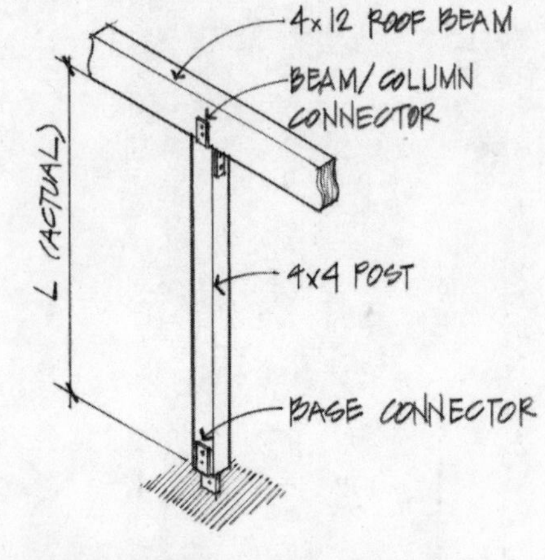

Figure 9 Effective column length versus actual length.

In the previous analysis of Euler's equation, each column was assumed to have pinned ends in which the member ends were free to rotate (but not translate) in any direction. If, therefore, a load is applied vertically until the column buckles, it will do so in one smooth curve (see Figure 8). The length of this curve is referred to as the *effective length*, or the *buckled length*. In practice, however, this is not always the case, and the length that is free to buckle is greatly influenced by its end support conditions.

The assumption of pinned ends is an important one, because a change of end conditions imposed on such a column may have a marked effect upon its load-carrying capacity. If a column is solidly connected at the top and bottom, it is unlikely to buckle under the same load assumed for a pinned end column. Restraining the ends of a column from both translation and a free-rotation condition generally increases the load-carrying capacity of a column. Allowing translation as well as rotation at the ends of a column generally reduces its load-carrying capacity.

Column design fomulas generally assume a condition in which both ends are fixed in translation but free to rotate (pin connected). When other conditions exist, the load-carrying capacity is increased or decreased, so the allowable compressive stress must be increased or decreased or the slenderness ratio increased. For example, in steel columns, a factor K is used as a multiplier for converting the actual length to an effective buckling length based on end conditions (Figure 9). The theoretical K values listed in Figure 10 are *less* conservative than the actual values often used in structural design practice.

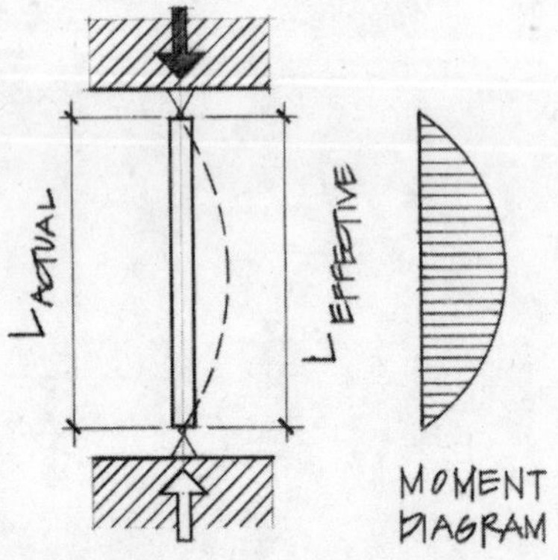

Figure 10(a) Case A—effective buckling length, both ends pinned.

Case A: Both Ends Pinned—Structure adequately braced against lateral (wind and earthquake) forces.

$$L_e = L$$

$$K = 1.0$$

$$P_{\text{critical}} = \frac{\pi^2 EI}{L^2}$$

Examples:
Timber column nailed top and bottom.

Steel column with simple clip angle connection top and bottom.

Case B: Both Ends Fixed—Structure adequately braced against lateral forces.

$L_e = 0.5L$
$K = 0.5$

$$P_{critical} = \frac{\pi^2 EI}{(0.5L)^2} = \frac{4\pi^2 EI}{L^2}$$

Examples:
Concrete column rigidly connected (monolithically cast) to large beams top and bottom.

Steel column rigidly connected (welded) to large steel beams top and bottom.

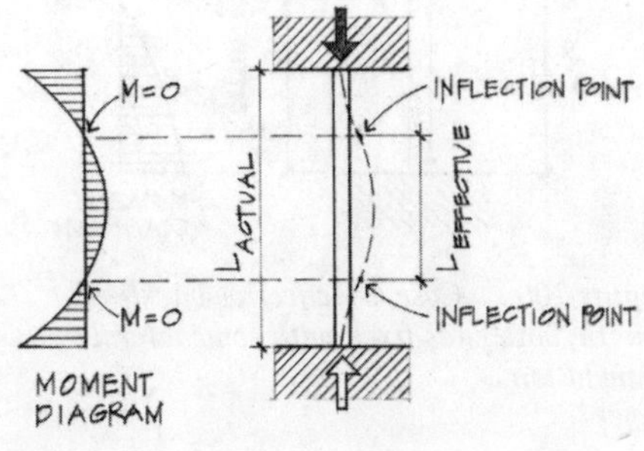

Figure 10(b) Case B—effective buckling length, both ends fixed.

Case C: One End Pinned and One End Fixed—Structure adequately braced against lateral forces.

$L_e = 0.707L$
$K = 0.7$

$$P_{critical} = \frac{\pi^2 EI}{(0.7L)^2} = \frac{2\pi^2 EI}{L^2}$$

Examples:
Concrete column rigidly connected to concrete slab at the base and attached to light-gauge roofing at the top.

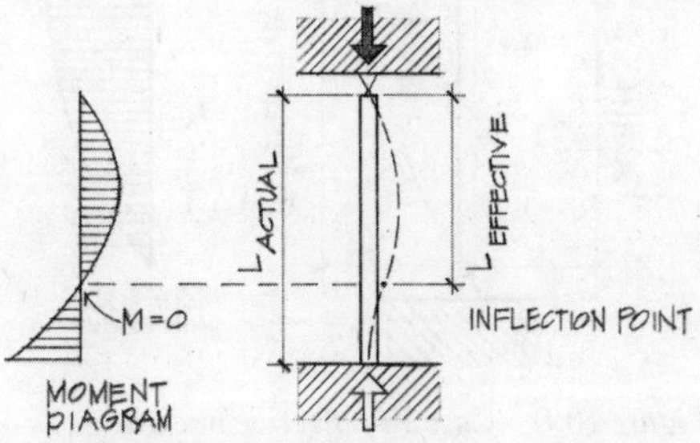

Figure 10(c) Case C—effective buckling length, one end pinned and one end fixed.

Case D: One End Free and One End Fixed—Lateral translation possible (develops eccentric column load).

$L_e = 2.0L$
$K = 2.0$

$$P_{critical} = \frac{\pi^2 EI}{(2L)^2} = \frac{\frac{1}{4}\pi^2 EI}{L^2}$$

Examples:
Water tank mounted on a simple pipe column.

Flagpole analogy.

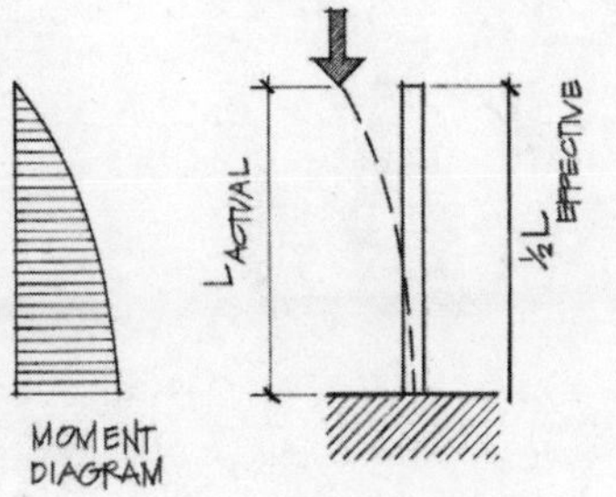

Figure 10(d) Case D—effective buckling length, one end free and one end fixed.

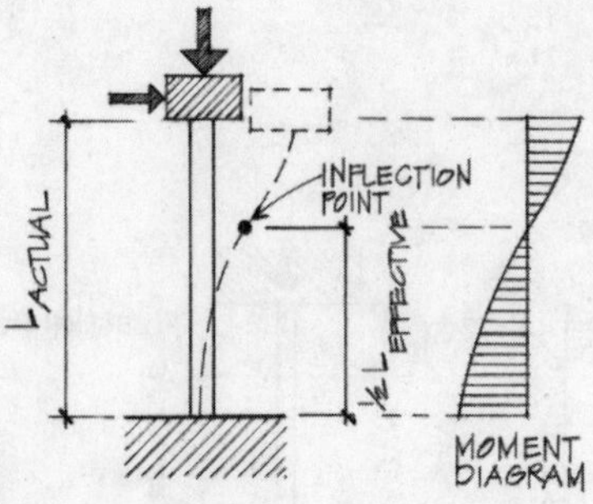

Figure 10(e) Case E—effective buckling length, both ends fixed with some lateral translation.

Case E: Both Ends Fixed with Some Lateral Translation

$L_e = 1.0L$

$K = 1.0$

$$P_{\text{critical}} = \frac{\pi^2 EI}{(L)^2}$$

Examples:
Columns in a relatively flexible rigid frame structure (concrete or steel).

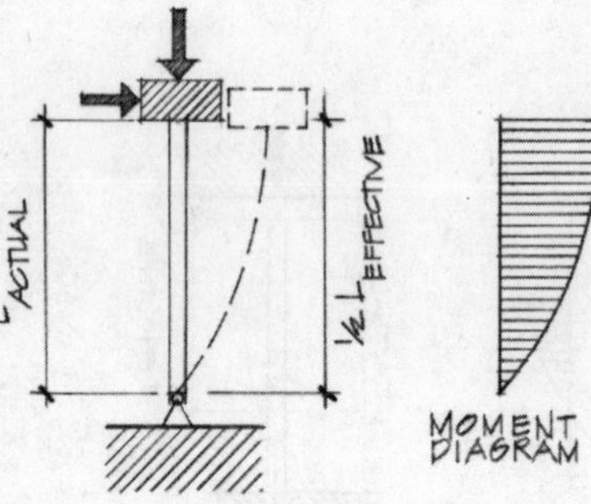

Figure 10(f) Case F—effective buckling length, base pinned, top fixed with some lateral translation.

Case F: Base Pinned, Top Fixed with Some Lateral Translation

$L_e = 2.0L$

$K = 2.0$

$$P_{\text{critical}} = \frac{\pi^2 EI}{(2L)^2} = \frac{\frac{1}{4}\pi^2 EI}{L^2}$$

Examples:
Steel column with a rigid connection to a beam above and a simple pin connection at the base. There is some flexibility in the structure, allowing column loads to be positioned eccentrically.

Intermediate Lateral Bracing

In the previous section, we found that the selection of the type of end connection used directly influenced the buckling capacity of a column. Fixed connections seem to be an obvious solution to minimizing column sizes; however, the cost associated with achieving rigid connections is high, and such connections are difficult to make. Also, timber columns are generally assumed to be pin connected, because the material strength generally precludes the construction of true rigid joints. What other methods are there to achieve an increase in column capacity without specifying larger column sizes?

A common strategy used to increase the effectiveness of a column is to introduce *lateral bracing* about the weak axis of buckling (Figure 11). Infill wall panels, window headers, girts for curtain walls, and other systems provide lateral bracing potentials that can be used to reduce the buckling length of the column. Bracing provided in one plane does not, however, provide resistance to buckling in the perpendicular plane (Figure 12). Columns must be checked in both directions to determine the critical slenderness ratio to be used in analysis or design.

Very slender sections can be used for columns if they are adequately braced or stiffened against buckling between floors, as seen in Figures 13(a)–(d).

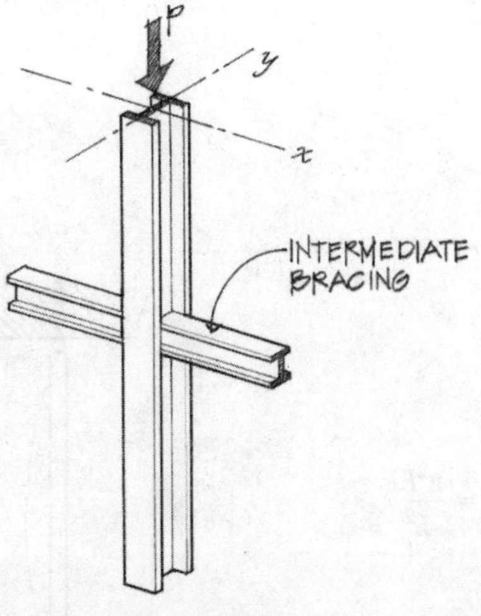

Figure 11 Wide-flange column section braced about the weak axis of buckling.

Lateral restraint provided by the bracing is for buckling resistance about the y axis only. The column is still susceptible to buckling in one smooth curve about the x axis.

Slenderness ratios must be calculated for both axes to determine which direction governs.

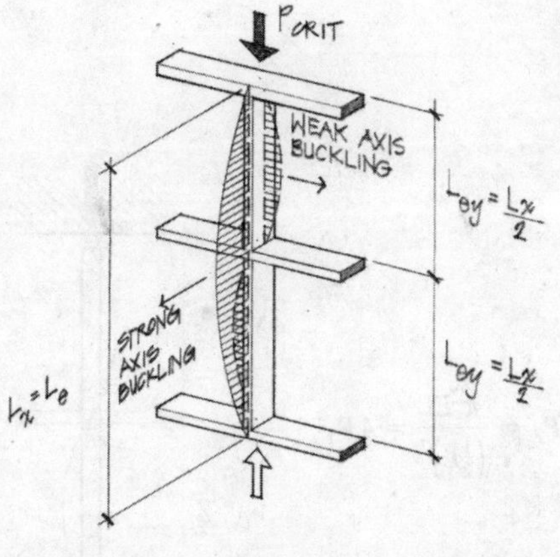

Figure 12 Rectangular timber column braced about the Y axis but free to buckle about the X axis.

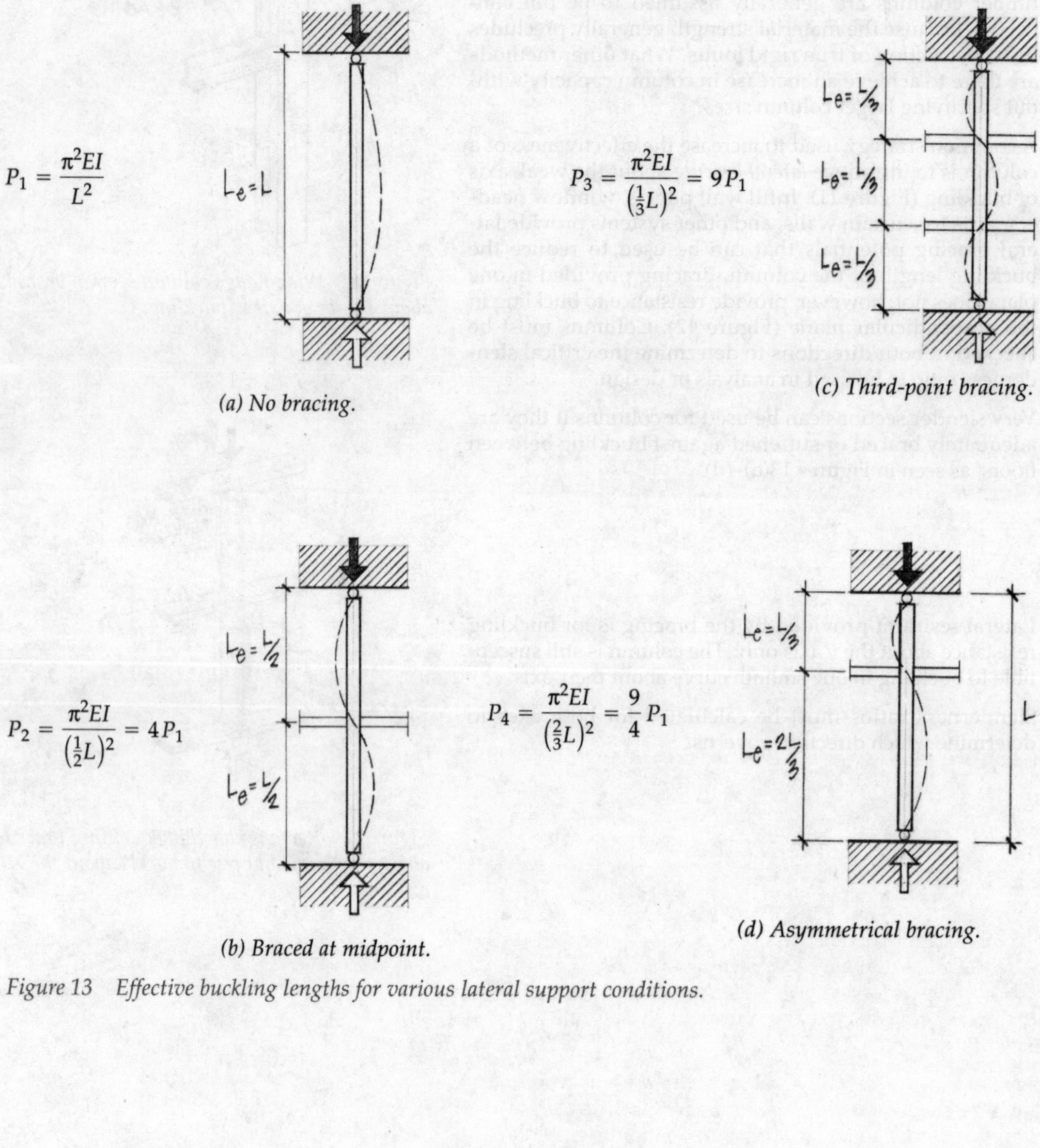

(a) No bracing.

(c) Third-point bracing.

(b) Braced at midpoint.

(d) Asymmetrical bracing.

Figure 13 Effective buckling lengths for various lateral support conditions.

Example Problems: End Support Conditions and Lateral Bracing

3 Determine the critical buckling load for a 4 × 8 S4S Douglas fir column that is 18 feet long and braced at midheight against the weak direction of buckling. $E = 1.3 \times 10^6$ psi.

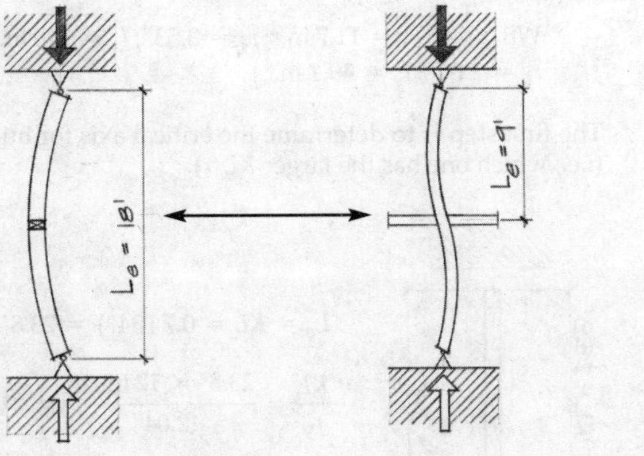

(a) Strong axis buckling. *(b) Weak axis buckling.*

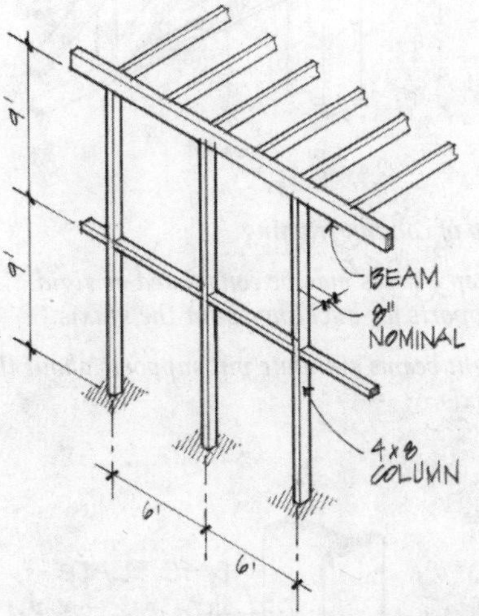

Solution:

$$4 \times 8 \text{ S4S } \left(I_x = 111.2 \text{ in.}^4; I_y = 25.9 \text{ in.}^4; A = 25.38 \text{ in.}^2\right)$$

$$r_x \sqrt{\frac{I_x}{A}} = 2.1'' \qquad r_y \sqrt{\frac{I_y}{A}} = 1.01''$$

Load causing buckling about the x axis:

$$P_{\text{critical}} = \frac{\pi^2 E I_x}{L_x^2} = \frac{3.14^2(1.3 \times 10^6 \text{ psi})(111.2 \text{ in.}^4)}{(18' \times 12 \text{ in./ft.})^2}$$
$$= 30{,}550\#$$

Load causing buckling about the y axis:

$$P_{\text{critical}} = \frac{\pi^2 E I_y}{L_y^2} = \frac{3.14^2(1.3 \times 10^6 \text{ psi})(25.9 \text{ in.}^4)}{(9' \times 12 \text{ in./ft.})^2}$$
$$= 28{,}460\#$$

Because the load required to cause the member to buckle about the weaker y axis is less than the load that is associated with buckling about the stronger x axis, the critical buckling load for the entire column is 28.46 k. In this case, the member will buckle in the direction of the least dimension.

When columns are actually tested, a difference is usually found between actual buckling loads and theoretical predictions. This is particularly true for columns near the transition between short- and long-column behavior. The result is that buckling loads are often slightly lower than predicted, particularly near the transition zone, where failure is often partly elastic and partly inelastic (crushing).

4 A W8 × 40 steel column supports trusses framed into its web, which serve to fix the weak axis and light beams that attach to the flange, simulating a pin connection about the strong axis. If the base connection is assumed as a pin, determine the critical buckling load the column is capable of supporting.

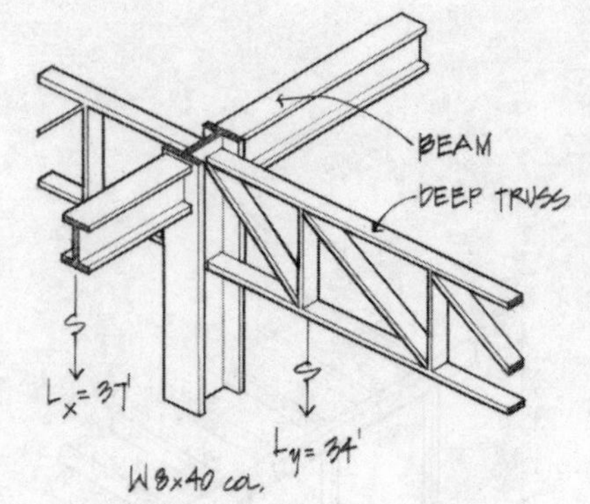

Top of column framing.

Deep trusses may be considered as rigid supports for buckling about the y axis.

Light beams simulate pin supports about the x axis.

Solution:

$$W8 \times 40 \left(A = 11.7\text{ in.}^2; r_x = 3.53''; I_x = 146\text{ in.}^4; r_y = 2.04''; I_y = 49.1\text{ in.}^4\right)$$

The first step is to determine the critical axis for buckling (i.e., which one has the larger KL/r).

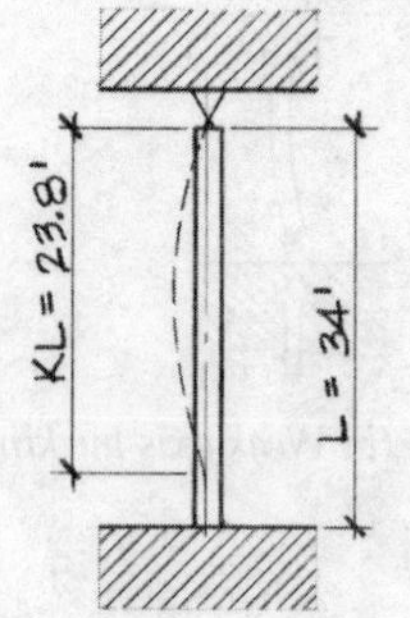

$$L_e = KL = 0.7\,(34') = 23.8'$$

$$\frac{KL}{r_y} = \frac{23.8' \times 12\text{ in./ft.}}{2.04''} = 140$$

Weak Axis

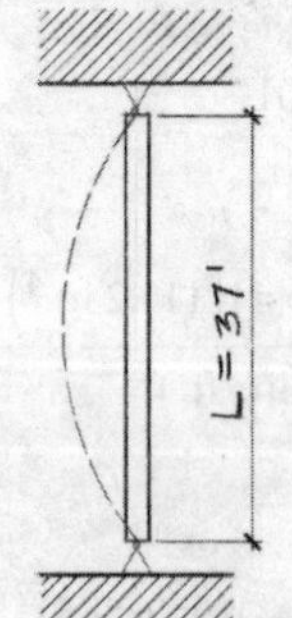

$$L_e = L; \quad K = 1.0; \quad KL = 37'$$

$$\frac{KL}{r_x} = \frac{(37' \times 12\text{ in./ft.})}{3.53''} = 125.8$$

Strong Axis

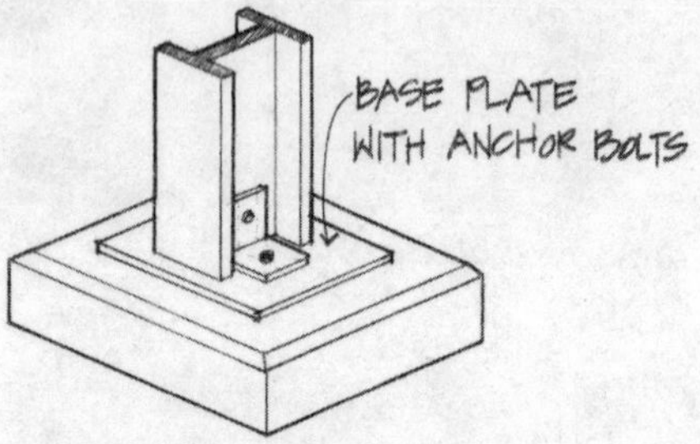

Column base connection.

The W8 × 40 (A36) steel column is connected at the base via a small base plate with two anchor bolts. This connection is assumed as a pin that allows rotation in two directions but no translation.

The weak axis for this column is critical because

$$\frac{KL}{r_y} > \frac{KL}{r_x}$$

$$P_{\text{critical}} = \frac{\pi^2 E I_y}{L_e^2} = \frac{\pi^2 E I_y}{(KL)^2} = \frac{3.14^2(29 \times 10^3\text{ ksi})(49.1\text{ in.}^4)}{(23.8 \times 12\text{ in./ft.})^2}$$

$$= 172.1\text{ k}$$

$$f_{\text{critical}} = \frac{P_{\text{critical}}}{A} = \frac{172.1\text{ k}}{11.7\text{ in.}^2} = 14.7\text{ ksi}$$

5 A rectangular steel tube is used as a 36 foot column. It has pinned ends, and its weak axis is braced at mid-height by a masonry infill wall as shown. Determine the column's critical buckling load. $E = 29 \times 10^3$ ksi.

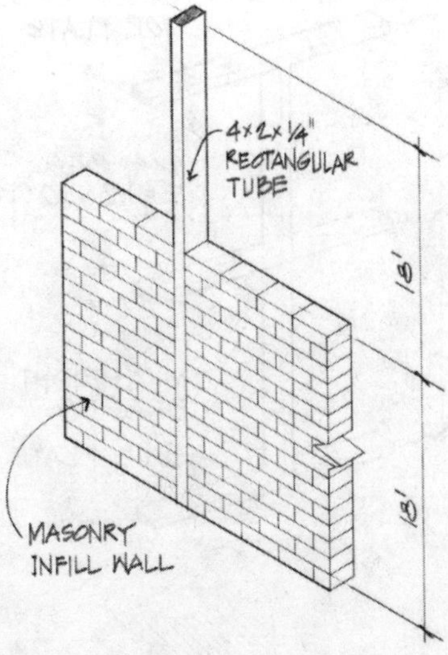

Solution:

$4'' \times 2'' \times \frac{1}{4}''$ rectangular tube

$(A = 2.59\text{ in.}^2; I_x = 4.69\text{ in.}^4; r_x = 1.35''; I_y = 1.54\text{ in.}^4;$
$r_y = 0.77'')$

Again, the first step in the solution must involve the determination of the critical slenderness ratio.

Weak Axis

$K = 0.7$

$KL = 0.7 \times 18' = 12.6' = 151.2''$

$$\frac{KL}{r_y} = \frac{151.2''}{0.77''} = 196.4$$

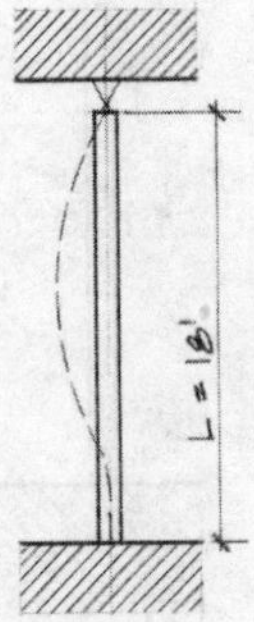

Weak axis

Strong Axis

$K = 1.0$

$KL = 1.0 \times 36' = 36' = 432''$

$$\frac{KL}{r_x} = \frac{432''}{1.35''} = 320 \leftarrow \text{Governs}$$

Because $\frac{KL}{r_x} > \frac{KL}{r_y}$, buckling is more critical about the strong axis.

$$P_{\text{critical}} = \frac{\pi^2 E I_x}{(KL_x)^2} = \frac{3.14^2(29 \times 10^3\text{ ksi})(4.69\text{ in.}^4)}{(432'')^2}$$

$$= 7.19\text{ k}$$

$$f_{\text{critical}} = \frac{P_{\text{critical}}}{A} = \frac{7.19\text{ k}}{2.59\text{ in.}^2} = 2.78\text{ ksi}$$

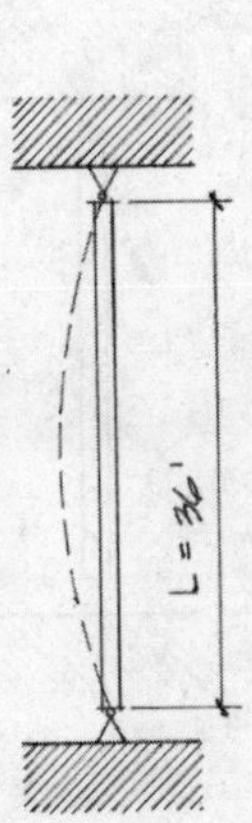

Strong axis

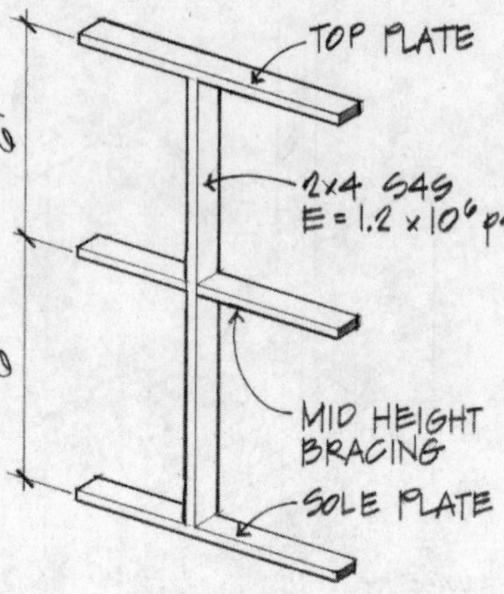

6 Determine the buckling load capacity of a 2 × 4 stud 12 feet high if blocking is provided at midheight. Assume $E = 1.2 \times 10^6$ psi.

Solution:

2×4 S4S $\left(A = 5.25\text{ in.}^2; I_x = 5.36\text{ in.}^4; I_y = 0.984\text{ in.}^4\right)$

$$r_x = \sqrt{\frac{I_x}{A}} = \sqrt{\frac{5.36}{5.25}} = 1.01''$$

$$r_y = \sqrt{\frac{I_y}{A}} = \sqrt{\frac{0.984}{5.25}} = 0.433''$$

Weak Axis

$L = 12'$

$K = 0.5$

$KL = 0.5 \times 12' = 6' = 72''$

$$\frac{KL}{r_y} = \frac{72''}{0.433''} = 166.3$$

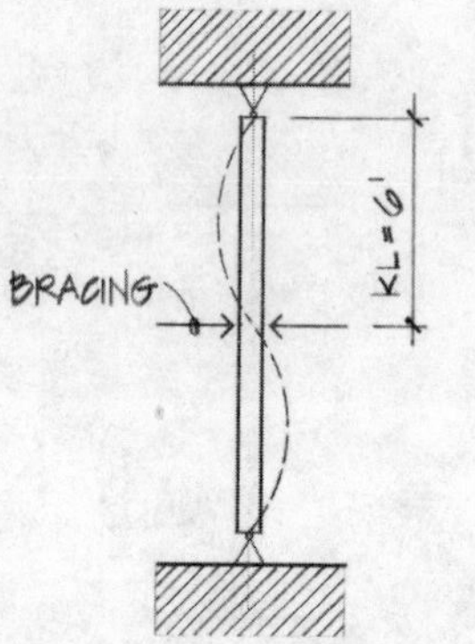

Weak axis.

Strong Axis

$L = 12'$

$K = 1.0$

$KL = 1.0 \times 12' = 12' = 144''$

$$\frac{KL}{r_x} = \frac{144''}{1.01''} = 142.6$$

The weak axis governs because $\dfrac{KL}{r_y} > \dfrac{KL}{r_x}$

$$P_{\text{critical}} = \frac{\pi^2 EI}{(KL)^2} = \frac{3.14^2\left(1.2 \times 10^6\text{ psi}\right)\left(0.984\text{ in.}^4\right)}{(72'')^2}$$

$$= 2{,}246\#$$

$$f_{\text{critical}} = \frac{P_{\text{critical}}}{A} = \frac{2{,}246\#}{5.25\text{ in.}^2} = 428\text{ psi}$$

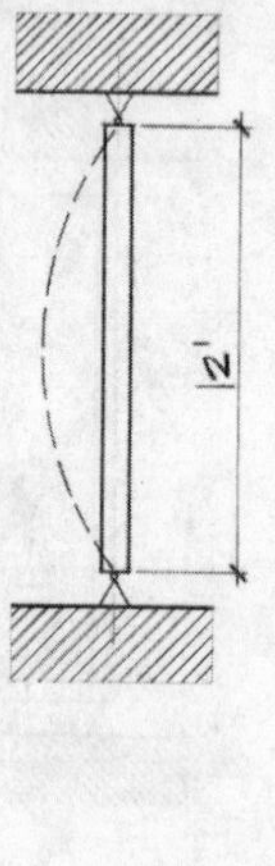

Strong axis.

Problems

1 A W8 × 31 steel column 20 feet long is pin supported at both ends. Determine the critical buckling load and stress developed in the column. $E = 29 \times 10^3$ ksi.

2 Two $3\frac{1}{2}''\phi$ standard pipe sections are strapped together to form a column as shown. If the column is pin connected at the supports and is 24 feet high, determine the critical axial load when buckling occurs. $E = 29 \times 10^6$ psi.

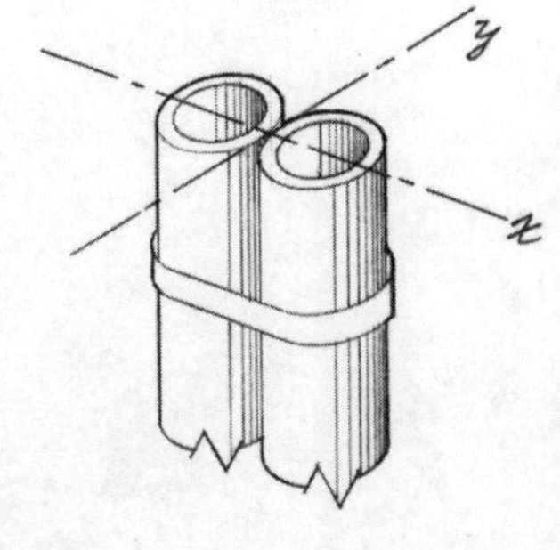

3 Determine the maximum critical length of a W10 × 54 column supporting an axial load of 250 k. $E = 29 \times 10^3$ ksi.

4 An eight-inch-diameter timber pole is fixed into a large concrete footing at grade and is completely pin connected at its upper end. How high can the pole be and still just support a load of 25 k? $E = 1.0 \times 10^6$ psi.

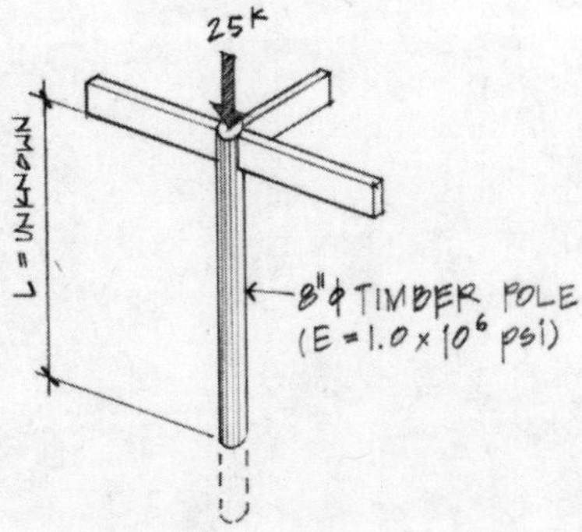

5 Determine the critical buckling load and stress of an $8'' \times 6'' \times \frac{3}{8}''$ rectangular structural tube used as a column 38 feet long, pin connected top and bottom.

6 Determine the critical buckling load and stress for the column shown.

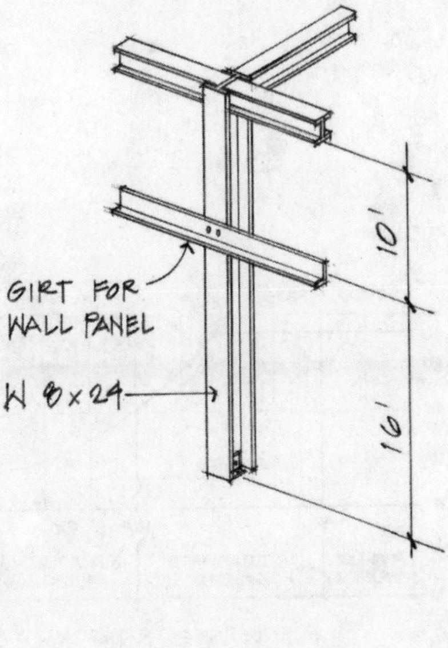

3 AXIALLY LOADED STEEL COLUMNS

Much of the discussion thus far has been limited to very short columns that crush and, on the other end of the scale, long and slender columns that buckle. Somewhere in between these two extremes lies a zone where a "short" column transitions into a "long" column. Euler's buckling equation assumes that the critical buckling stress remains within the proportional limit of the material so that the modulus of elasticity E remains valid. Substituting the proportional limit value $F_{proportional} = 31{,}000$ psi for A36 steel (close to the $F_y = 36{,}000$ psi) into Euler's equation, the minimum slenderness ratio necessary for elastic behavior is found to be

$$f_{critical} = \frac{P_{critical}}{A} = \frac{\pi^2 E}{(L/r)^2}; \quad \text{then}$$

$$\frac{\ell}{r} = \sqrt{\frac{\pi^2 E}{P/A}} = \sqrt{\frac{\pi^2(29{,}000{,}000)}{31{,}000}} = 96$$

Columns (A36 steel) with slenderness ratios below $L/r \leq 96$ generally exhibit characteristics of *inelastic buckling* or crushing.

The upper limit of KL/r for steel columns depends on good judgment and safe design and is usually established by the building code. Structural steel columns are limited to a slenderness ratio equal to

$$\boxed{\frac{KL}{r} \leq 200}$$

In reality, columns do not transition abruptly from short to long, or vice versa. A transition zone exists between the two extremes and is normally referred to as the *intermediate column range*. Intermediate columns fail by a combination of crushing (or yielding) and buckling (Figure 14).

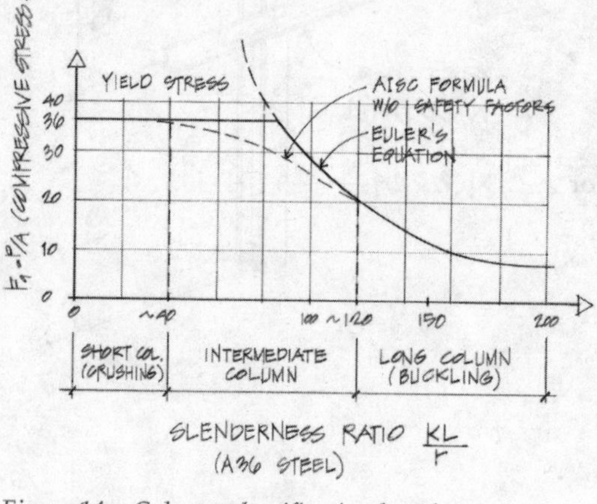

Figure 14 Column classification based on slenderness.

The initially flat portion of the curve (in the short-column range) indicates material yielding with no buckling taking place. On the far end of the curve ($K\ell/r > 120$), the compressive stresses are relatively low, and buckling is the mode of failure. In the intermediate-column range ($40 < K\ell/r < 120$), failure has aspects of both yielding and buckling.

The load-carrying ability of intermediate-length columns is influenced by both the strength and elastic properties of the column material. Empirical design formulas, based on extensive testing and research, have been developed to cover the design of columns within the limits of each column category.

Since 1961, the AISC has adopted a set of *column design formulas* that incorporate the use of a variable factor of safety, depending on slenderness, for determining allowable compressive stress. AISC formulas recognize only two slenderness categories: short/intermediate and long (Figure 15).

Slender columns are defined as those having a KL/r exceeding a value called C_c, in which:

$$C_c = \sqrt{\frac{2\pi^2 E}{F_y}}$$

where:

E = modulus of elasticity

F_y = yield stress of the steel

Mild steel (A36) with $F_y = 36$ ksi has $C_c = 126.1$; high-strength steel with $F_y = 50$ ksi has a $C_c = 107.0$.

The C_c value represents the theoretical demarcation line between inelastic and elastic behavior.

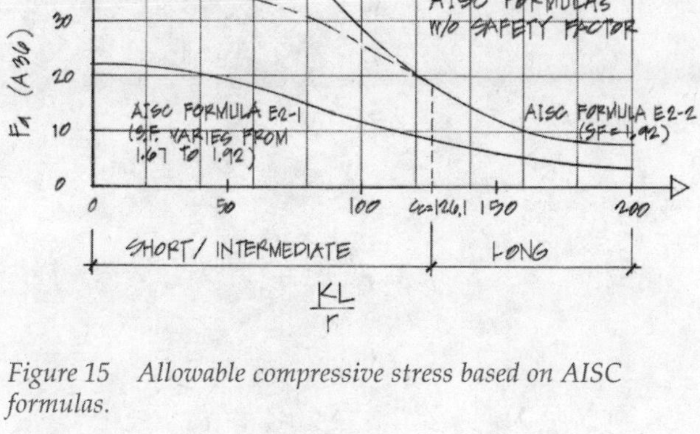

Figure 15 Allowable compressive stress based on AISC formulas.

The AISC allowable stress (F_a) formula for short/intermediate columns ($KL/r < C_c$) is expressed as

$$F_a = \frac{\left[1 - \frac{(K\ell/r)^2}{2C_c^2}\right](F_y)}{\frac{5}{3} + \frac{3(K\ell/r)}{8C_c} - \frac{(K\ell/r)^3}{8C_c^3}} \qquad \text{(AISC Eq. E2–1)}$$

where

$K\ell/r$ = the largest effective slenderness ratio of any unbraced length of column

F_a = allowable compressive stress (psi or ksi)

When axially loaded compression members have a $K\ell/r > C_c$, the allowable stress is computed as

$$F_a = \frac{12\pi^2 E}{23(K\ell/r)^2} \qquad \text{(AISC Eq. E2–2)}$$

Note that the two preceding equations represent actual design equations that can be used to size compression elements. These equations appear rather daunting, especially E2–1. Fortunately, the AISC *Manual of Steel Construction* has developed a design table for $K\ell/r$ from 1 to 200 with the respective allowable stress F_a. No computations using E2–1 and E2–2 are necessary, because the equations have been used in generating these tables (Tables 1 and 2).

In structural work, pinned ends are often assumed even if the ends of steel columns are typically restrained to some degree at the bottom by being welded to a base plate, which in turn is anchor-bolted to a concrete footing. Steel pipe columns generally have plates welded at each end and then bolted to other parts of a structure. Such restraints, however, vary greatly and are difficult to evaluate. Thus, designers rarely take advantage of the restraint to increase the allowable stress, which therefore adds to the safety factor of the design.

On the other hand, tests have indicated that in the case of fixed-end conditions, the "theoretical" $K = 0.5$ values are somewhat *nonconservative* when designing steel columns. Because true joint fixity is rarely possible, the AISC recommends the use of *recommended* K*-values* (Figure 16).

	(a)	(b)	(c)	(d)	(e)	(f)
Buckled shape of column is shown by dashed line	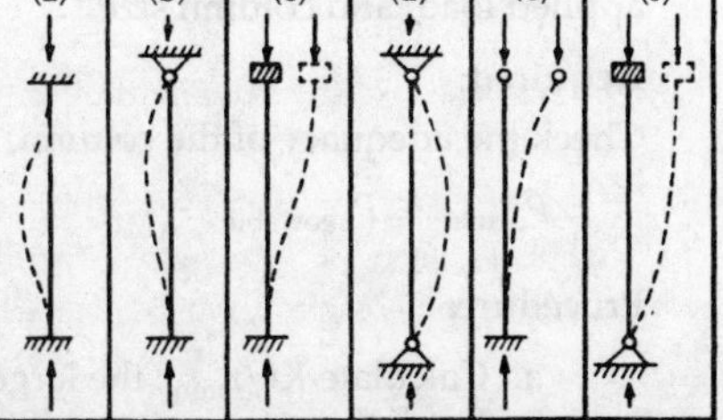					
Theoretical *K* value	0.5	0.7	1.0	1.0	2.0	2.0
Recommended design value when ideal conditions are approximated	0.65	0.80	1.2	1.0	2.10	2.0
End condition code		**Rotation fixed and translation fixed** **Rotation free and translation fixed** **Rotation fixed and translation free** **Rotation free and translation free**				

Figure 16 AISC-recommended design values for K.

Reproduced with the permission of the American Institute of Steel Construction, Chicago, Illinois; from the Manual of Steel Construction: Allowable Stress Design, *Ninth ed., Second rev. (1995).*

All examples discussed in this chapter assume that the columns are part of a braced building system. Sidesway is minimized through the use of a separate bracing system (braced frame or shearwalls), and the *K*-values for the braced columns need not exceed 1.0. In unbraced buildings, such as those utilizing rigid frames, sidesway can result in effective column lengths greater than the actual column length ($K > 1.0$). A much more involved analysis is required for columns with sidesway and, thus, will not be discussed in this text.

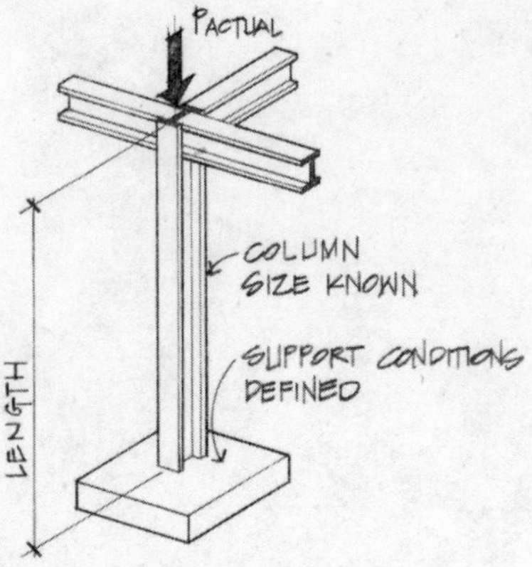

Figure 17 Analysis of steel columns.

Analysis of Steel Columns

Column analysis implies the determination of the allowable compressive stress F_a on a given column or its allowable load capacity $P_{allowable}$(Figure 17). A simple analysis procedure is outlined below.

Given:

Column length, support conditions, grade of steel (F_y), applied load, and column size.

Required:

Check the adequacy of the column. In other words, is

$$P_{actual} < P_{allowable}$$

Procedure:

a. Calculate $K\ell/r_{min.}$; the largest $K\ell/r$ governs.
b. Enter the appropriate AISC Table (Table 1 or 2 on the following pages).
c. Pick out the respective F_a.
d. Compute: $P_{allowable} = F_a \times A$

where

$A =$ cross-sectional area of the column (in.^{2})
$F_a =$ allowable compressive stress (ksi)

e. Check the column adequacy.

If

$$P_{allowable} > P_{actual}$$

then OK.

If

$$P_{allowable} < P_{actual}$$

then overstressed.

Table 1

Table C-36
Allowable Stress
For Compression Members of 36-ksi Specified Yield Stress Steel[a]

$\frac{Kl}{r}$	F_a (ksi)	$\frac{Kl}{r}$	F_a (ksi)	$\frac{Kl}{r}$	F_a (ksi)	$\frac{Kl}{r}$	F_a (ksi)	$\frac{Kl}{r}$	F_a (ksi)
1	21.56	41	19.11	81	15.24	121	10.14	161	5.76
2	21.52	42	19.03	82	15.13	122	9.99	162	5.69
3	21.48	43	18.95	83	15.02	123	9.85	163	5.62
4	21.44	44	18.86	84	14.90	124	9.70	164	5.55
5	21.39	45	18.78	85	14.79	125	9.55	165	5.49
6	21.35	46	18.70	86	14.67	126	9.41	166	5.42
7	21.30	47	18.61	87	14.56	127	9.26	167	5.35
8	21.25	48	18.53	88	14.44	128	9.11	168	5.29
9	21.21	49	18.44	89	14.32	129	8.97	169	5.23
10	21.16	50	18.35	90	14.20	130	8.84	170	5.17
11	21.10	51	18.26	91	14.09	131	8.70	171	5.11
12	21.05	52	18.17	92	13.97	132	8.57	172	5.05
13	21.00	53	18.08	93	13.84	133	8.44	173	4.99
14	20.95	54	17.99	94	13.72	134	8.32	174	4.93
15	20.89	55	17.90	95	13.60	135	8.19	175	4.88
16	20.83	56	17.81	96	13.48	136	8.07	176	4.82
17	20.78	57	17.71	97	13.35	137	7.96	177	4.77
18	20.72	58	17.62	98	13.23	138	7.84	178	4.71
19	20.66	59	17.53	99	13.10	139	7.73	179	4.66
20	20.60	60	17.43	100	12.98	140	7.62	180	4.61
21	20.54	61	17.33	101	12.85	141	7.51	181	4.56
22	20.48	62	17.24	102	12.72	142	7.41	182	4.51
23	20.41	63	17.14	103	12.59	143	7.30	183	4.46
24	20.35	64	17.04	104	12.47	144	7.20	184	4.41
25	20.28	65	16.94	105	12.33	145	7.10	185	4.36
26	20.22	66	16.84	106	12.20	146	7.01	186	4.32
27	20.15	67	16.74	107	12.07	147	6.91	187	4.27
28	20.08	68	16.64	108	11.94	148	6.82	188	4.23
29	20.01	69	16.53	109	11.81	149	6.73	189	4.18
30	19.94	70	16.43	110	11.67	150	6.64	190	4.14
31	19.87	71	16.33	111	11.54	151	6.55	191	4.09
32	19.80	72	16.22	112	11.40	152	6.46	192	4.05
33	19.73	73	16.12	113	11.26	153	6.38	193	4.01
34	19.65	74	16.01	114	11.13	154	6.30	194	3.97
35	19.58	75	15.90	115	10.99	155	6.22	195	3.93
36	19.50	76	15.79	116	10.85	156	6.14	196	3.89
37	19.42	77	15.69	117	10.71	157	6.06	197	3.85
38	19.35	78	15.58	118	10.57	158	5.98	198	3.81
39	19.27	79	15.47	119	10.43	159	5.91	199	3.77
40	19.19	80	15.36	120	10.28	160	5.83	200	3.73

[a]When element width-to-thickness ratio exceeds noncompact section limits of Sect. B5.1, see Appendix B5.
Note: C_c = 126.1

Table 2

Table C-50

Allowable Stress
For Compression Members of 50-ksi Specified Yield Stress Steel[a]

$\frac{Kl}{r}$	F_a (ksi)	$\frac{Kl}{r}$	F_a (ksi)	$\frac{Kl}{r}$	F_a (ksi)	$\frac{Kl}{r}$	F_a (ksi)	$\frac{Kl}{r}$	F_a (ksi)
1	29.94	41	25.69	81	18.81	121	10.20	161	5.76
2	29.87	42	25.55	82	18.61	122	10.03	162	5.69
3	29.80	43	25.40	83	18.41	123	9.87	163	5.62
4	29.73	44	25.26	84	18.20	124	9.71	164	5.55
5	29.66	45	25.11	85	17.99	125	9.56	165	5.49
6	29.58	46	24.96	86	17.79	126	9.41	166	5.42
7	29.50	47	24.81	87	17.58	127	9.26	167	5.35
8	29.42	48	24.66	88	17.37	128	9.11	168	5.29
9	29.34	49	24.51	89	17.15	129	8.97	169	5.23
10	29.26	50	24.35	90	16.94	130	8.84	170	5.17
11	29.17	51	24.19	91	16.72	131	8.70	171	5.11
12	29.08	52	24.04	92	16.50	132	8.57	172	5.05
13	28.99	53	23.88	93	16.29	133	8.44	173	4.99
14	28.90	54	23.72	94	16.06	134	8.32	174	4.93
15	28.80	55	23.55	95	15.84	135	8.19	175	4.88
16	28.71	56	23.39	96	15.62	136	8.07	176	4.82
17	28.61	57	23.22	97	15.39	137	7.96	177	4.77
18	28.51	58	23.06	98	15.17	138	7.84	178	4.71
19	28.40	59	22.89	99	14.94	139	7.73	179	4.66
20	28.30	60	22.72	100	14.71	140	7.62	180	4.61
21	28.19	61	22.55	101	14.47	141	7.51	181	4.56
22	28.08	62	22.37	102	14.24	142	7.41	182	4.51
23	27.97	63	22.20	103	14.00	143	7.30	183	4.46
24	27.86	64	22.02	104	13.77	144	7.20	184	4.41
25	27.75	65	21.85	105	13.53	145	7.10	185	4.36
26	27.63	66	21.67	106	13.29	146	7.01	186	4.32
27	27.52	67	21.49	107	13.04	147	6.91	187	4.27
28	27.40	68	21.31	108	12.80	148	6.82	188	4.23
29	27.28	69	21.12	109	12.57	149	6.73	189	4.18
30	27.15	70	20.94	110	12.34	150	6.64	190	4.14
31	27.03	71	20.75	111	12.12	151	6.55	191	4.09
32	26.90	72	20.56	112	11.90	152	6.46	192	4.05
33	26.77	73	20.38	113	11.69	153	6.38	193	4.01
34	26.64	74	20.10	114	11.49	154	6.30	194	3.97
35	26.51	75	19.99	115	11.29	155	6.22	195	3.93
36	26.38	76	19.80	116	11.10	156	6.14	196	3.89
37	26.25	77	19.61	117	10.91	157	6.06	197	3.85
38	26.11	78	19.41	118	10.72	158	5.98	198	3.81
39	25.97	79	19.21	119	10.55	159	5.91	199	3.77
40	25.83	80	19.01	120	10.37	160	5.83	200	3.73

[a]When element width-to-thickness ratio exceeds noncompact section limits of Sect. B5.1, see Appendix B5.
Note: C_c = 107.0

Example Problems: Axially Loaded Steel Columns

7 A W12 × 53 ($F_y = 36$ ksi) column is to be used as a primary support in a building. If the unbraced height of the column is 16 feet with both ends assumed as pin connected, compute the allowable load on the column.

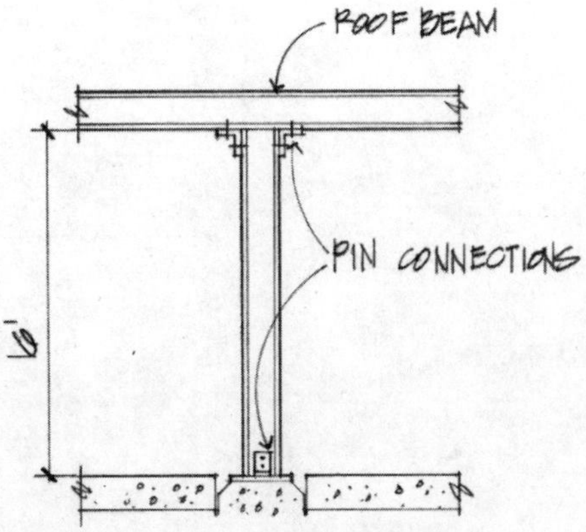

Solution:

Enter the AISC section properties table (Appendix Table A3), and extract the data for the W12 × 53 column.

W12 × 53: $A = 15.6 \text{ in.}^2$;

$r_x = 5.23 \text{ in.}, r_y = 2.48 \text{ in.}$

Because the column is assumed to be pin connected at both ends and for both directions (axes) of buckling, the least radius of gyration (r_y) will yield the more critical (larger) slenderness ratio.

The critical slenderness ratio is then computed as

$$\frac{K\ell}{r_y} = \frac{(1.0)(16' \times 12 \text{ in./ft.})}{2.48''} = 77.42$$

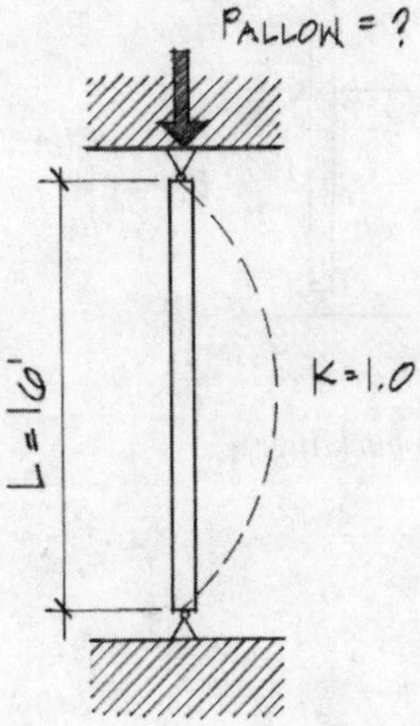

To determine the allowable compressive stress F_a, enter Table 1 with the critical slenderness ratio.

	$K\ell/r$	F_a
	77	15.69 ksi
$KL/r = 77.42 \rightarrow$	Interpolating	15.64 ksi
	78	15.58 ksi

The allowable capacity of the W12 × 53 is computed as:

$$P_{\text{allowable}} = F_a \times A = 15.64 \text{ k/in.}^2 \times 15.6 \text{ in.}^2 = 244 \text{ k}$$

8 A 24-foot-tall steel column (W14 × 82) with $F_y = 50$ ksi has pins at both ends. Its weak axis is braced at midheight, but the column is free to buckle the full 24 feet in the strong direction. Determine the safe load capacity for this column.

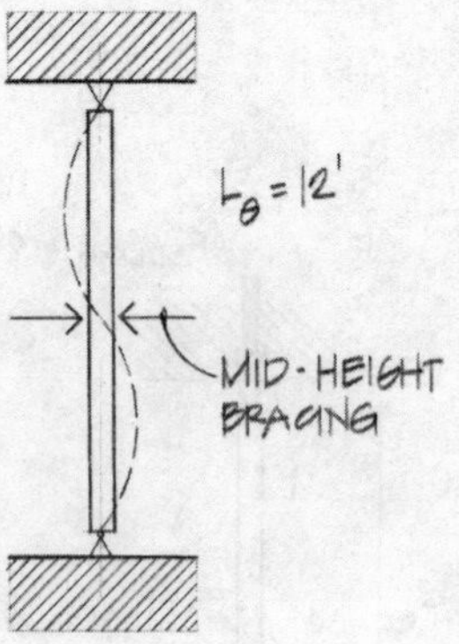

Weak axis buckling.

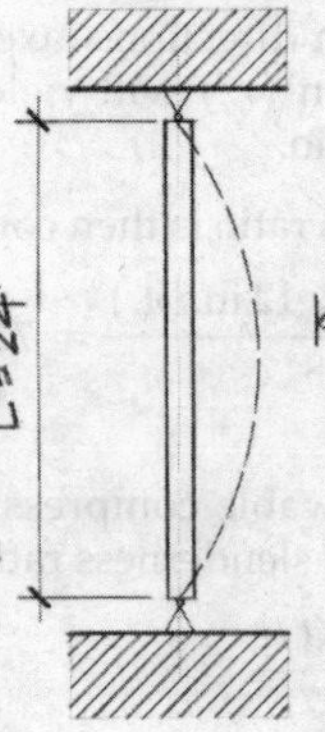

Strong axis buckling.

Solution:

Properties of the W14 × 82:

$$A = 24.1 \text{ in.}^2$$
$$r_x = 6.05''$$
$$r_y = 2.48''$$

Compute the slenderness ratio about both axes to determine the critical direction for buckling.

$$\frac{K\ell}{r_x} = \frac{24' \times 12 \text{ in./ft.}}{6.05''} = 47.6$$

$$\frac{K\ell}{r_y} = \frac{12' \times 12 \text{ in./ft.}}{2.48''} = 58.1$$

The larger slenderness ratio governs; therefore, the weak axis (y) buckling is used in determining F_a.

From Table 2,

Interpolating for $K\ell/r = 58.1$; $F_a = 23.04$ ksi

$$\therefore P_{\text{allowable}} = F_a \times A = 23.04 \text{ k/in.}^2 \times 24.1 \text{ in.}^2 = 555 \text{ k}$$

9 A 4″ϕ standard weight steel pipe (F_y = 50 ksi) supports a roof framing system as shown. The timber beam-to-column connection is considered to be a pin, while the base of the column is rigidly embedded into the concrete. If the load from the roof is 35 k, is the column adequate?

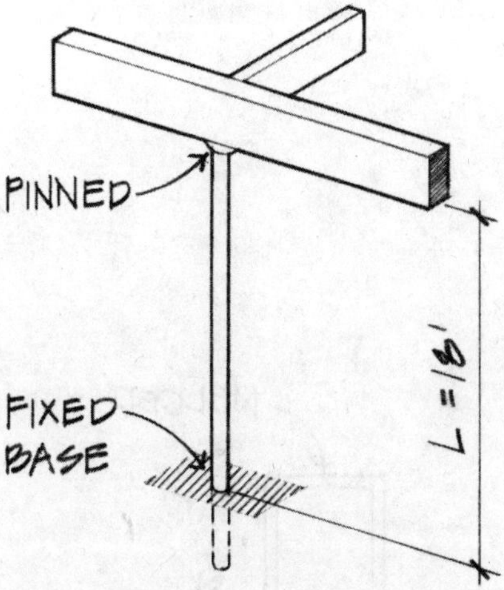

Solution:

Four-inch″-diameter standard weight pipe:

$$A = 3.17\text{ in.}^2$$
$$r = 1.51\text{ in.}$$

Although the theoretical K is 0.7 for the support condition shown, the AISC-recommended value for use in design is

$$K = 0.80$$

$$K\ell/r = \frac{0.80 \times (18' \times 12\text{ in./ft.})}{1.51''} = 114.43$$

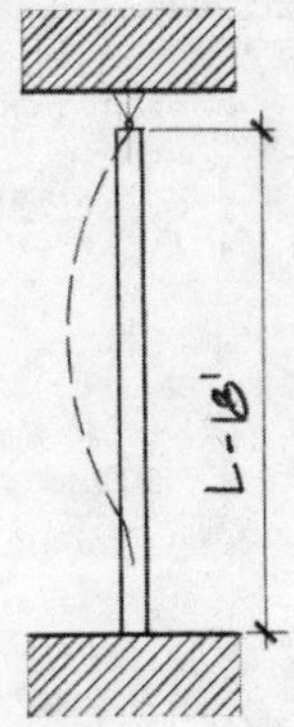

Using Table 2,

$$F_a = 11.4\text{ ksi}$$

$$P_a = 11.4\text{ k/in.}^2 \times 3.17\text{ in.}^2 = 36.14\text{ k} > 35\text{ k}$$

The column is adequate.

Problems

7 Determine the allowable load capacity ($P_{allowable}$) for an $F_y = 36$ ksi steel column, W12 × 65, when $L = 18'$ and

a. the base and top are both fixed.
b. the base is fixed and the top is pinned.
c. both the top and bottom are pinned.

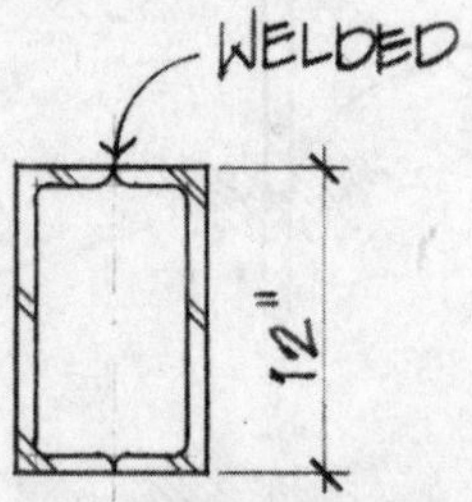

8 Two C12 × 20.7 channel sections are welded together to form a closed box section. If $L = 20'$ and the top and bottom are pinned, determine the allowable axial load capacity P_a. Assume $F_y = 36$ ksi.

9 An angle $5'' \times 3\frac{1}{2}'' \times \frac{1}{2}''$ is used as a compression member in a truss. If $L = 7'$, determine the allowable axial load for an $F_y = 36$ ksi.

10 Determine the maximum allowable height of an A36 column (5″ϕ standard steel pipe) if the applied load is 60 k. Assume the top to be pin connected and the base to be fixed.

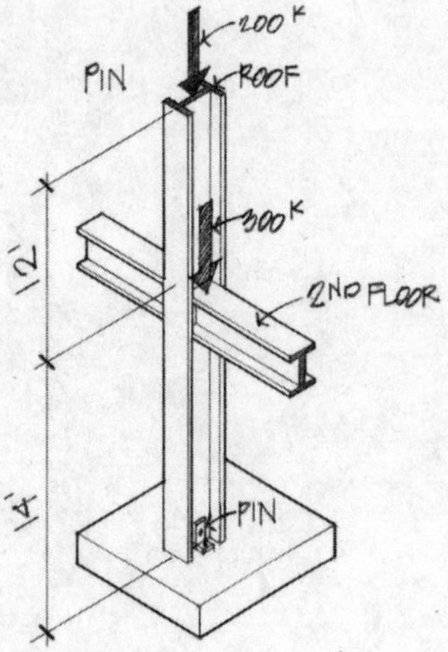

11 A two-story, continuous W12 × 106 column of A36 steel supports a roof load of 200 k and an intermediate (second floor) load of 300 k. Assume the top and bottom have pin connections. Is the column section shown adequate?

Note: *Assume the second-floor load to be applied at the top of the column—this will result in a somewhat conservative answer. The concept of intermediate loads is much more complicated and will not be discussed further in this text.*

Design of Steel Columns

The design of axially loaded steel columns (in other words, the selection of an appropriate column size) is usually accomplished by using specialized column tables, such as those contained in the ninth edition of the AISC's *Manual of Steel Construction: Allowable Stress Design*. *Structural design* varies from *analysis* in that each problem has several possible answers. For example, the selection of a column size is justly dependent on strength and safety requirements, but other issues (architectural as well as constructional) may influence the final selection.

Because the AISC Column Design Tables are assumed not to be available (it would require the purchase of the AISC manual), steel column design will involve an iterative, trial-and-error process. This methodology appears to be long and tedious, but in fact, very few cycles are usually necessary to zoom in on a solution.

An earlier discussion of efficient column cross-sections for axial loads (see Figure 8) suggested the use of circular or "boxier" wide-flange members. Along with spatial and constructional concerns, relative maximum or minimum sizes may already be specified by the architect, thus limiting the array of choices that would otherwise be available. This in no way limits the design possibilities; in fact, it helps guide the structural design and choices made by the engineer. Smaller-scale steel structures may use 8 and 10 inch nominal size wide-flange columns, while larger buildings with heavier loads will often use 12 and 14 inch nominal sizes. These sections are the "boxier" or square sizes, with the depth and flange width of the cross-section being approximately equal.

One trial-and-error procedure may be outlined as follows (Figure 18):

Given:

Column length, support conditions, grade of steel (F_y), applied load (P_{actual}).

Required:

Column size to safely support the load.

Procedure:

a. Guess at a size. But where does one begin? If it were a smaller-scale building, try a square W8 or W10 in the middle of the weight grouping. A similar estimate using larger sections is appropriate for heavier loads.

b. Once the *trial size* has been selected, cross-sectional properties are known. Compute the critical slenderness ratio, taking into account the end conditions and intermediate bracing.

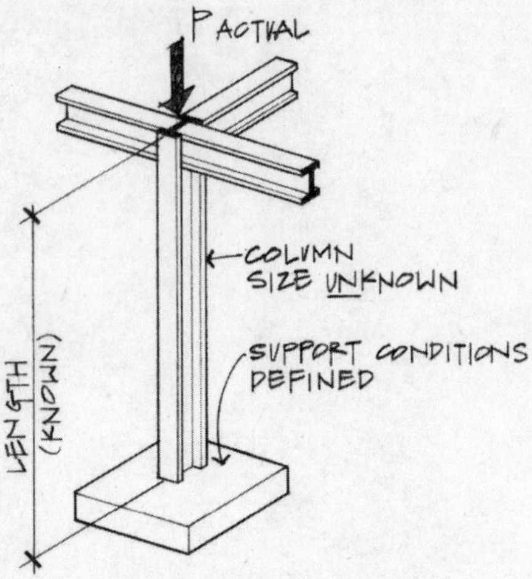

Figure 18 Design of steel columns.

c. Using the larger $K\ell/r$ value, enter Table 1 or 2. Obtain the respective F_a.

d. Calculate the $P_{allowable} = F_a \times A$ of the trial section.

e. Check to see if $P_{allowable} > P_{actual}$. If $P_{allowable} < P_{actual}$, then the column is overstressed, and a larger section should be selected next. If the trial section is much too strong, cycle again with a smaller size. One way to check the relative efficiency of the cross-section is to examine its percentage of stress level.

$$\% \text{ of stress} = \frac{P_{actual}}{P_{allowable}} \times 100\%$$

A percentage of stress in the 90% to 100% level is very efficient.

f. Repeat this process until an adequate but efficient section is obtained.

Note: *Steps (b) through (e) are essentially the procedure used previously in the analysis of steel columns.*

Example Problems: Design of Steel Columns

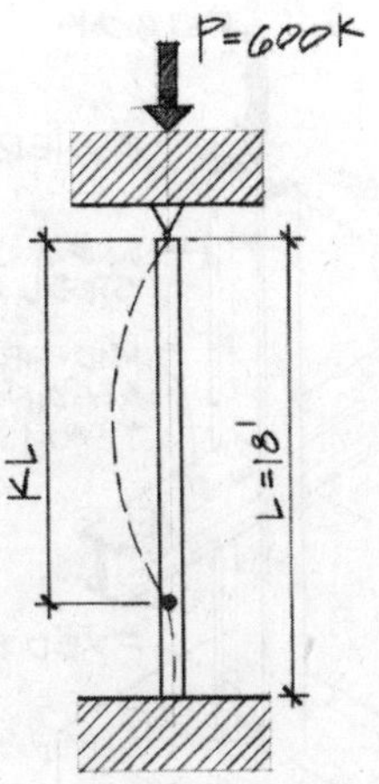

10 Select the most economical W12 shape column 18 feet in height to support an axial load of 600 k using A572 Grade 50 steel. Assume that the column is hinged at the top but fixed at the base.

Solution:

As a first guess in this trial-and-error process, try W12 × 96 (about the middle of the available "boxier" sections).

$$W12 \times 96 \; (A = 28.2\text{ in.}^2, r_x = 5.44'', r_y = 3.09'')$$

Compute $(K\ell/r)$ critical:

$$\frac{K\ell}{r_x} = \frac{(0.80)(18' \times 12\text{ in./ft.})}{5.44''} = 31.8$$

$$\frac{K\ell}{r_y} = \frac{(0.80)(18' \times 12\text{ in./ft.})}{3.09} = 55.9$$

The larger slenderness is critical; therefore, use

$$K\ell/r = 55.9$$

Enter Table 2, and obtain the respective F_a:

$$F_a = 23.41\text{ ksi}$$

$$P_{\text{allowable}} = F_a \times A$$

$$P_{\text{allowable}} = 23.41\text{ k/in.}^2 \times 28.2\text{ in.}^2 = 660\text{ k} > 600\text{ k}$$

$$\%\,\text{stress} = \frac{P_{\text{actual}}}{P_{\text{allowable}}} \times 100\% = \frac{600\text{ k}}{660\text{ k}} \times 100\% = 91\%$$

This selection is quite efficient and still a bit understressed. Therefore, use W12 × 96.

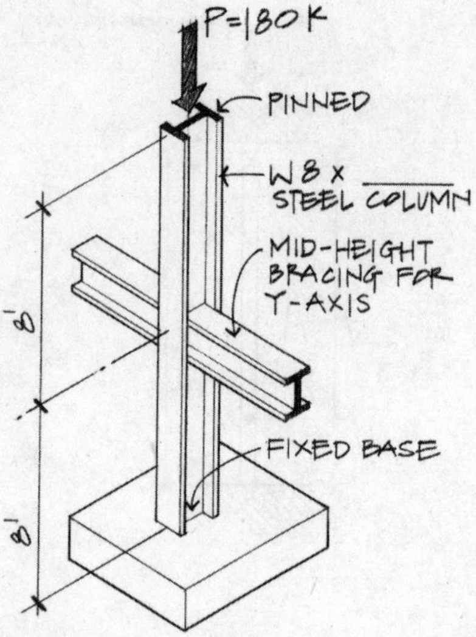

11 Select the most economical W8 shape column, 16 feet long, with $P = 180$ k. Assume that lateral bracing is provided at midheight in the weak axis of buckling and that the top and bottom are pin connected. $F_y = 36$ ksi.

Solution:

Again, we need to begin by guessing at a size and then checking the adequacy of the selection.

Try W8 × 35.

$$\text{W8} \times 35 \left(A = 10.3\text{ in.}^2; r_x = 3.51''; r_y = 2.03''\right)$$

Determine the critical slenderness ratio:

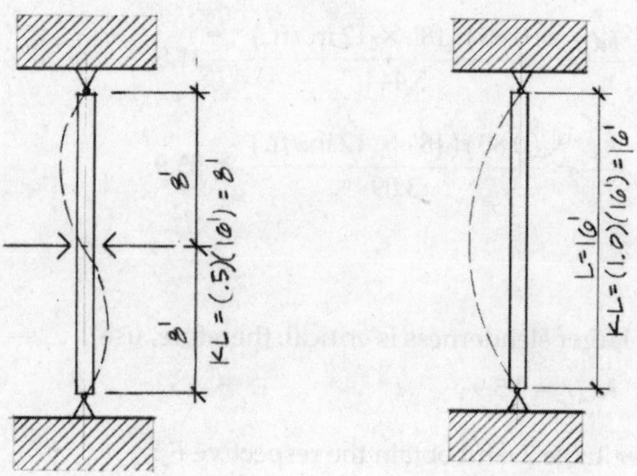

Weak axis. *Strong axis.*

$$\frac{K\ell}{r_y} = \frac{(0.80)(18' \times 12\text{ in./ft.})}{3.09} = 55.9$$

$$\frac{K\ell}{r_x} = \frac{(0.80)(18' \times 12\text{ in./ft.})}{5.44''} = 31.8$$

Buckling about the strong axis is more critical in this example because of the lateral bracing provided for the weak axis. Therefore, the F_a value is obtained from Table 1 based on $K\ell/r = 54.7$.

$$F_a = 17.93\text{ ksi}$$

$$P_{\text{allowable}} = F_a \times A = (17.93\text{ ksi}) \times \left(10.3\text{ in.}^2\right) = 184.7\text{ k}$$

$$P_{\text{allowable}} = 184.7\text{ k} > P_{\text{actual}} = 180\text{ k}$$

$$\%\text{ stress} = \frac{180\text{ k}}{184.7\text{ k}} \times 100\% = 97.5\%$$

(very efficient selection)

Therefore, use W8 × 35.

12 A four-story building has a structural steel beam-girder-column framing system. Columns are spaced at 20 feet o.c. in one direction and 30 feet o.c. in the perpendicular direction. An interior column supports a typical tributary floor area of 600 square feet.

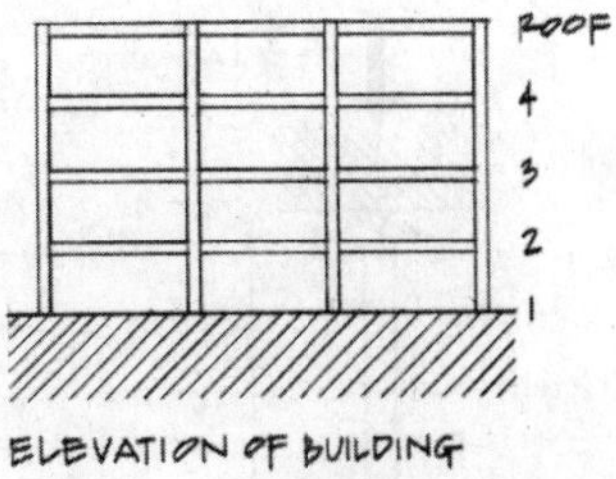

For a preliminary design, find an economical W10 or W12 section for an interior first-floor column. Assume that the columns have unsupported lengths of 14 feet and $K = 1.0$. $F_y = 36$ ksi.

Roof Loads: DL = 80 psf
SL = 30 psf

Floor Loads: DL = 100 psf
LL = 70 psf

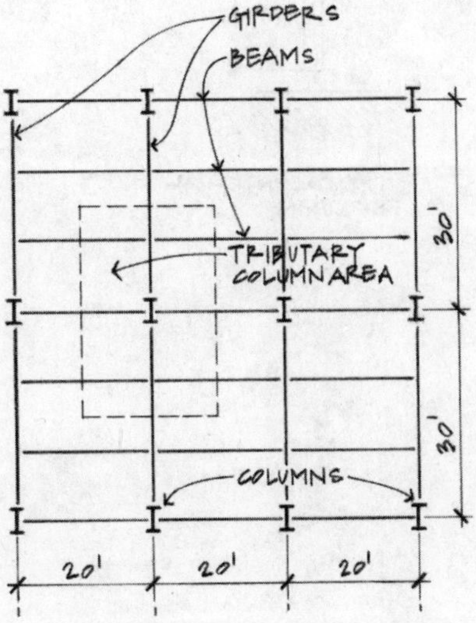

Floor Plan.

Solution:

Total roof loads: DL + SL = 80 + 30 =

$$(110\,\text{psf}) \times (600\,\text{ft.}^2) = 66{,}000\# = 66\,\text{k}$$

Total floor loads: DL + LL = 100 + 70 =

$$(170\,\text{psf}) \times (600\,\text{ft.}^2) = 102{,}000\# = 102\,\text{k per floor}$$

The load at the top of the interior first-floor column is a result of the roof plus three floor loads.

Total load on the first-floor column = P_{actual}

$$P_{\text{actual}} = 66\,\text{k}\,(\text{roof}) + 3(102\,\text{k})\,(\text{floors}) = 372\,\text{k}$$

Try W10 × 60.

$$\text{W10} \times 60\ (A = 17.6\,\text{in.}^2;\ r_y = 2.57')$$

The assumption being made is that the y axis is the critical buckling direction, because no weak axis bracing is provided.

$$\frac{K\ell}{r_y} = \frac{(1.0)(14' \times 12\,\text{in./ft.})}{2.57''} = 65.4$$

$$\therefore F_a = 16.9\,\text{ksi}$$

$$P_a = 16.9\,\text{ksi} \times 17.6\,\text{in.}^2 = 297.4\,\text{k} < 372\,\text{k}$$

Therefore, this column section is overstressed. Select a larger section.

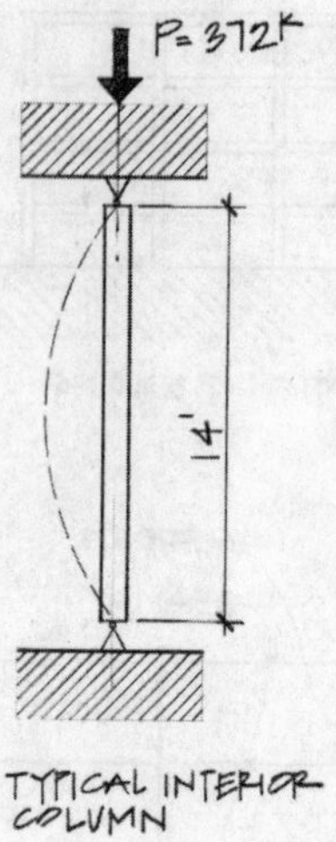

Try W10 × 77.

$$W10 \times 77\ (A = 22.6\ \text{in.}^2, r_y = 2.60'')$$

$$\frac{K\ell}{r_y} = \frac{(1.0)(14' \times 12\ \text{in./ft.})}{2.60''} = 64.6$$

$$\therefore\ F_a = 16.98\ \text{ksi}$$

$$P_a = 16.98\ \text{ksi} \times 22.6\ \text{in.}^2 = 383.7\ \text{k}$$

$$P_a = 383.7\ \text{k} > 372\ \text{k}\ \therefore\ \text{OK}$$

$$\%\ \text{stress} = \frac{372}{383.7} \times 100\% = 97\%$$

Use W10 × 77.

A column design using a W12 section can be carried out using an identical procedure. The resulting W12 size would be

$$W12 \times 72\ (P_a = 377\ \text{k})$$

Both of these sections are adequate for stress and efficient in material. However, the W12 × 72 is more economical, because it is 5 pounds per foot less in weight. The final decision on selection will undoubtedly involve issues concerning dimensional coordination and construction.

Problems

Note: *The following column design problems assume pinned ends top and bottom and* $F_y = 36$ *ksi.*

12 Select the most economical steel pipe column (standard weight) to support a load of 30 k and a length of 20 feet.

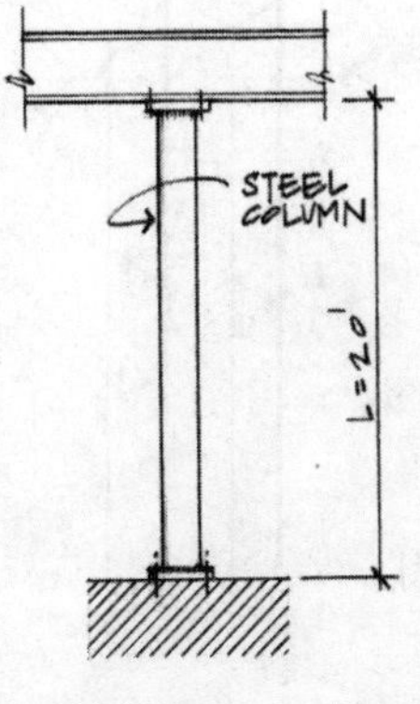

13 What is the most economical W8 column for Problem 12?

14 Select an appropriate steel column section 24 feet long, braced at midheight about the weak axis, that supports a load of 350 k. Use a W14 section. (See Example Problem 11.)

15 A six-story building has a structural steel beam-column frame that is appropriately fireproofed. The columns are spaced 20 feet o.c. in one direction and 25 feet o.c. in the perpendicular direction. A typical interior column supports a tributary floor area of 500 square feet. The governing building code specifies that the frame must be designed to withstand the dead weight of the structure plus a roof snow load of 40 psf and a live load on each floor of 125 psf. The dead weight of the roof is estimated to be 80 psf, and each floor is 100 psf. The unsupported length of the ground-floor column is 20 feet, and the columns at the other floor levels are 16 feet. Design a typical interior third-floor column and the first-floor column using the most economical W12 section at each level.

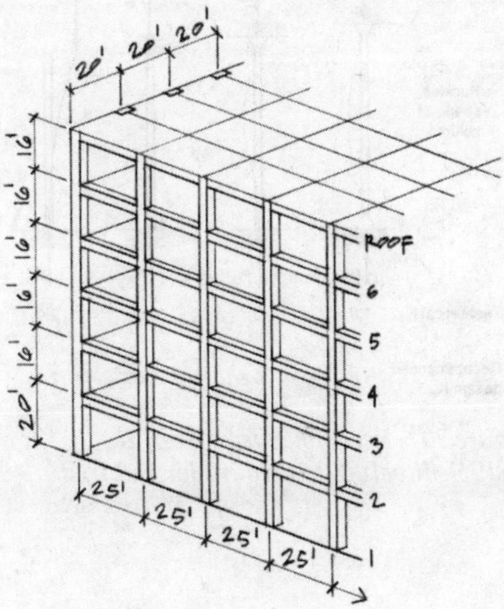

4 AXIALLY LOADED WOOD COLUMNS

Wood columns are commonly found supporting beams and girders, which in turn support tributary areas of roof and floor loads. Other structural members, such as bridge piers, compression chords of a truss, or the studs in a load-bearing wall, subjected to compression are also designed using the same methods utilized for building columns.

As discussed in Section 1, long columns will tend to buckle under critical load, while short columns will fail by the crushing of fibers. For wood columns, the ratio of the column length to its width is just as important as it is for steel columns. However, in wood columns, the slenderness ratio is defined as the laterally unsupported length in inches divided by the least (minimum) dimension of the column (Figure 19).

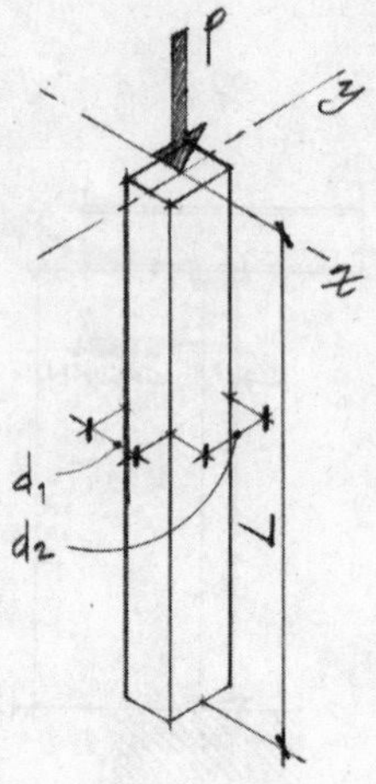

Figure 19 Slenderness ratio of wood columns.

$$\text{slenderness ratio} = \frac{L}{d_{\text{min.}}} = \frac{L}{d_1}$$

where
$d_1 < d_2$

Wood columns are restricted to a maximum slenderness ratio:

$$\frac{L}{d} \leq 50$$

which is approximately the same as the $\frac{KL}{r_{\text{min.}}} \leq 200$ used for steel columns.

A larger L/d ratio indicates a greater instability and a tendency for the column to buckle under lower axial load.

The effective length of steel columns was determined by applying a K factor (see Figure 16) to the unsupported length of the column to adjust for end fixity. Similar effective length factors, called K_e in wood columns, are used to adjust for the various end conditions. In fact, the recommended design K_e values are identical to those of steel columns except for a column with a pinned base and rigid top connection, susceptible to some sidesway (Figure 20).

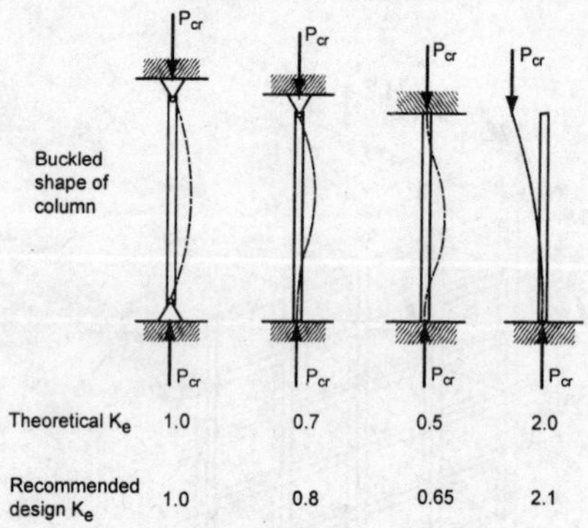

Figure 20 Recommended design K_e coefficient values to account for end fixity.

Most wood construction is detailed such that translation (sidesway) is restrained but the ends of the column are free to rotate (i.e., pin connection). The K_e value is generally taken as 1.0, and the effective length is equal to the actual unsupported length. Even if some fixity may exist in the top or bottom connection, it is difficult to evaluate the degree of fixity to assume in design. Therefore, $K_e = 1.0$ is an acceptable assumption that is usually a bit conservative in some connection conditions.

Wood columns can be solid members of rectangular, round [Figure 21(a)], or other shapes, or spaced columns built up from two or more individual solid members separated by blocking [Figure 21(b)].

Because the majority of all wood columns in buildings are solid rectangular sections, the analysis and design methods examined in this section will be limited to these types. A more thorough treatment for the design of wood elements is usually covered in advanced structures courses.

In 1992, the American Forest and Paper Association, in its *National Design Specification for Wood Construction* (NDS–91), approved a new standard and incorporated a new methodology and equations for the design of wood elements and connections. Previous categorizing of wood columns into the short-, intermediate-, or long-column range resulted in three different equations for each respective slenderness range. The NDS–91 now utilizes a single equation, providing a continuous curve over the entire range of slenderness ratios (Figure 22).

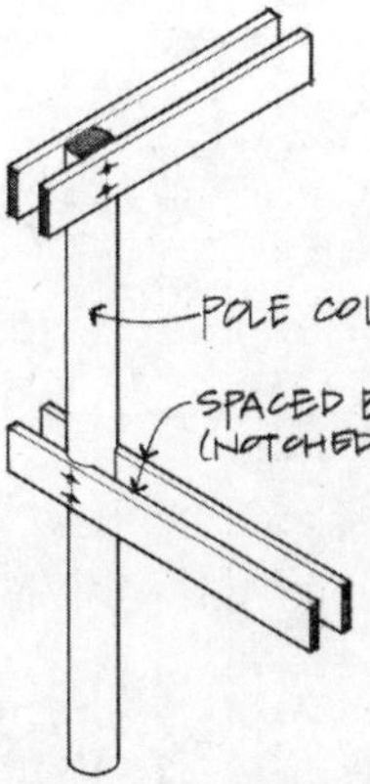

Figure 21(a) An example of a pole column.

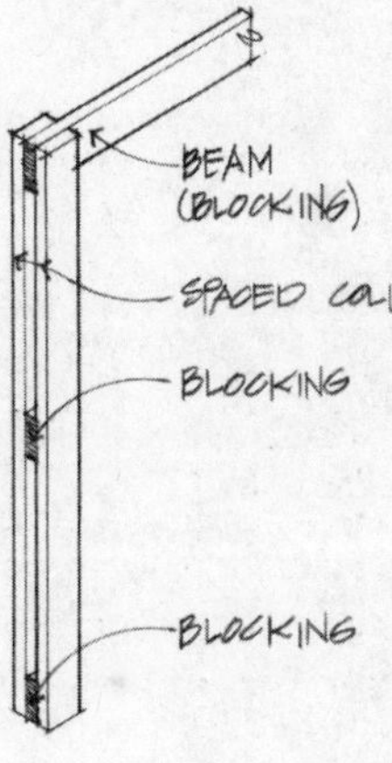

Figure 21(b) An example of a spaced column.

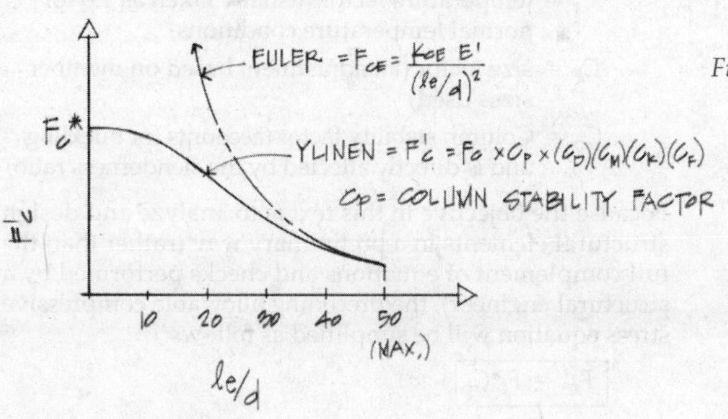

Figure 22 Ylinen column curve—allowable stress versus slenderness ratio.

The allowable compressive stress for an axially loaded wood column of known size is expressed as

$$f_c = \frac{P}{A} \leq F_c'$$

where

f_c = actual compressive stress parallel to grain
P = axial compressive force in the member
A = cross-sectional area of the column
F_c' = allowable compressive stress parallel to grain

To obtain the allowable compressive stress F_c', many adjustments to the tabulated base stress are necessary.

The NDS–91 defines the F_c' as

$$F_c' = F_c(C_D)(C_M)(C_t)(C_F)(C_p)$$

where:

F_c' = allowable compressive stress parallel to grain
F_c = tabulated compressive stress parallel to grain (found in building code tables, NDS tables, and wood design handbooks)
C_D = load duration factor (defined later in this section)
C_M = wet service factor (accounts for moisture content in the wood)
= 1.0 for dry service conditions as in most covered structures, dry service condition defined as:
moisture content $\leq$ 19% for sawn lumber
moisture content $\leq$ 16% for glu-lams
C_t = temperature factor (usually taken as 1.0 for normal temperature conditions)
C_F = size factor (an adjustment based on member sizes used)
C_p = Column stability factor (accounts for buckling and is directly affected by the slenderness ratio)

Because the objective in this text is to analyze and design structural elements in a preliminary way (rather than the full complement of equations and checks performed by a structural engineer), the preceding allowable compressive stress equation will be simplified as follows:

$$F_c' = F_c^* C_p$$

where

$$F_c^* = F_c(C_D)(C_M)(C_t)(C_F) \cong F_c C_D$$

(for preliminary column design)

This simplification assumes C_M, C_t, and C_F are all equal to 1.0, which is generally the case for a majority of wood columns.

Now a word about the load duration factor C_D. Wood has a unique structural property in which it can support higher stresses if the applied loads are for a short period of time. All tabulated stress values contained in building codes, NDS, or wood design manuals apply to "normal" load duration and dry service conditions. The C_D value adjusts tabulated stresses to allowable values based on the duration (time) of loading. "Normal" duration is taken as 10 years, and $C_D = 1.0$. Short-duration loading from wind, earthquake, snow, or impact allows C_D values higher than 1.0 but less than 2.0 (Figure 23).

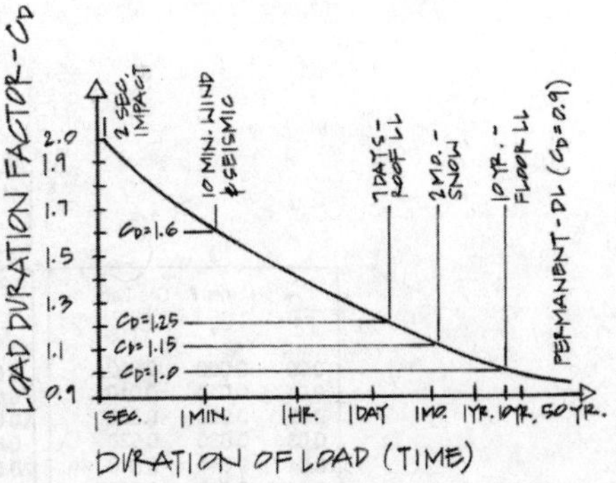

Figure 23 Madison curve for load duration factors.

The column stability factor C_p multiplied by F_c essentially defines the column curve (equation) as shown in Figure 22. This equation, originally developed by Ylinen, explains the behavior of wood columns as the interaction of two modes of failure: buckling and crushing.

$$C_p = \frac{1 + (F_{cE}/F_c{}^*)}{2c} - \sqrt{\left[\frac{1 + (F_{cE}/F_c{}^*)}{2c}\right]^2 - \frac{F_{cE}/F_c^*}{c}}$$

where

F_{cE} = Euler critical buckling stress for columns

$$= \frac{K_{cE}E'}{(\ell_e/d)^2} \cong \frac{K_{cE}E}{(\ell_e/d)^2}$$

$F_c{}^* \cong F_c C_D$

E' = modulus of elasticity associated with the axis of column buckling

c = buckling and crushing interaction factor for columns

= 0.9 for glu-lam columns

= 0.8 for sawn lumber columns

K_{cE} = 0.30 for visually graded lumber

= 0.418 for glu-lams

The column stability factor C_p is directly affected by the Euler buckling stress value F_{cE}, which in turn is inversely proportional to the square of a column's slenderness ratio. A table, to simplify the computations for preliminary column analysis/design, could be created by inputting slenderness ratios between 1 and 50, which results in F_{cE} values for sawn and glu-lam members. Then, if various F_{cE} values were divided by $F_c{}^*$, generating ratios of a $(F_{cE}/F_c{}^*)$, a computer could easily calculate corresponding C_p values.

Table 3 was created for this purpose and eliminates the necessity of laborious computations for C_p.

Table 3

Column Stability Factor C_p

"C_p" | $F_c' = C_p \cdot F_c^*$ | $F_{CE} = \frac{30\,E}{(l/d)^2}$ for sawn posts | $F_{CE} = \frac{418\,E}{(l/d)^2}$ for Glu-Lam posts

F_{CE}/F_c^*	Sawn C_p	Glu-Lam C_p	F_{CE}/F_c^*	Sawn C_p	Glu-Lam C_p	F_{CE}/F_c^*	Sawn C_p	Glu-Lam C_p	F_{CE}/F_c^*	Sawn C_p	Glu-Lam C_p
0.00	0.000	0.000	0.60	0.500	0.538	1.20	0.750	0.822	2.40	0.894	0.940
0.01	0.010	0.010	0.61	0.506	0.545	1.22	0.755	0.826	2.45	0.897	0.941
0.02	0.020	0.320	0.62	0.512	0.552	1.24	0.760	0.831	2.50	0.899	0.943
0.03	0.030	0.030	0.63	0.518	0.559	1.26	0.764	0.836	2.55	0.901	0.944
0.04	0.040	0.040	0.64	0.524	0.566	1.28	0.769	0.840	2.60	0.904	0.946
0.05	0.049	0.050	0.65	0.530	0.573	1.30	0.773	0.844	2.65	0.906	0.947
0.06	0.059	0.060	0.66	0.536	0.580	1.32	0.777	0.848	2.70	0.908	0.949
0.07	0.069	0.069	0.67	0.542	0.587	1.34	0.781	0.852	2.75	0.910	0.950
0.08	0.079	0.079	0.68	0.548	0.593	1.36	0.785	0.855	2.80	0.912	0.951
0.09	0.088	0.089	0.69	0.553	0.600	1.38	0.789	0.859	2.85	0.914	0.952
0.10	0.098	0.099	0.70	0.559	0.607	1.40	0.793	0.862	2.90	0.916	0.953
0.11	0.107	0.109	0.71	0.564	0.613	1.42	0.796	0.865	2.95	0.917	0.954
0.12	0.117	0.118	0.72	0.569	0.619	1.44	0.800	0.868	3.00	0.919	0.955
0.13	0.126	0.128	0.73	0.575	0.626	1.46	0.803	0.871	3.05	0.920	0.956
0.14	0.136	0.138	0.74	0.580	0.632	1.48	0.807	0.874	3.10	0.922	0.957
0.15	0.145	0.147	0.75	0.585	0.638	1.50	0.810	0.877	3.15	0.923	0.958
0.16	0.154	0.157	0.76	0.590	0.644	1.52	0.813	0.879	3.20	0.925	0.959
0.17	0.164	0.167	0.77	0.595	0.650	1.54	0.816	0.882	3.25	0.926	0.960
0.18	0.173	0.176	0.78	0.600	0.655	1.56	0.819	0.884	3.30	0.927	0.961
0.19	0.182	0.186	0.79	0.605	0.661	1.58	0.822	0.887	3.35	0.929	0.961
0.20	0.191	0.195	0.80	0.610	0.667	1.60	0.825	0.889	3.40	0.930	0.962
0.21	0.200	0.205	0.81	0.614	0.672	1.62	0.827	0.891	3.45	0.931	0.963
0.22	0.209	0.214	0.82	0.619	0.678	1.64	0.830	0.893	3.50	0.932	0.963
0.23	0.218	0.224	0.83	0.623	0.683	1.66	0.832	0.895	3.55	0.933	0.964
0.24	0.227	0.233	0.84	0.628	0.688	1.68	0.835	0.897	3.60	0.934	0.965
0.25	0.235	0.242	0.85	0.632	0.693	1.70	0.837	0.899	3.65	0.936	0.965
0.26	0.244	0.252	0.86	0.637	0.698	1.72	0.840	0.901	3.70	0.937	0.966
0.27	0.253	0.261	0.87	0.641	0.703	1.74	0.842	0.903	3.75	0.938	0.966
0.28	0.261	0.270	0.88	0.645	0.708	1.76	0.844	0.904	3.80	0.938	0.967
0.29	0.270	0.279	0.89	0.649	0.713	1.78	0.846	0.906	3.85	0.939	0.968
0.30	0.278	0.288	0.90	0.653	0.718	1.80	0.849	0.908	3.90	0.940	0.968
0.31	0.287	0.297	0.91	0.658	0.722	1.82	0.851	0.909	3.95	0.941	0.969
0.32	0.295	0.306	0.92	0.661	0.727	1.84	0.853	0.911	4.00	0.942	0.969
0.33	0.304	0.315	0.93	0.665	0.731	1.86	0.855	0.912	4.05	0.943	0.969
0.34	0.312	0.324	0.94	0.669	0.735	1.88	0.857	0.914	4.10	0.944	0.970
0.35	0.320	0.333	0.95	0.673	0.740	1.90	0.858	0.915	4.15	0.944	0.970
0.36	0.328	0.342	0.96	0.677	0.744	1.92	0.860	0.916	4.20	0.945	0.971
0.37	0.336	0.351	0.97	0.680	0.748	1.94	0.862	0.918	4.25	0.946	0.971
0.38	0.344	0.360	0.98	0.684	0.752	1.96	0.864	0.919	4.30	0.947	0.972
0.39	0.352	0.368	0.99	0.688	0.756	1.98	0.866	0.920	4.35	0.947	0.972
0.40	0.360	0.377	1.00	0.691	0.760	2.00	0.867	0.921	4.40	0.948	0.972
0.41	0.367	0.386	1.01	0.694	0.764	2.02	0.869	0.922	4.45	0.949	0.973
0.42	0.375	0.394	1.02	0.698	0.767	2.04	0.870	0.924	4.50	0.949	0.973
0.43	0.383	0.403	1.03	0.701	0.771	2.06	0.872	0.925	4.55	0.950	0.974
0.44	0.390	0.411	1.04	0.704	0.774	2.08	0.874	0.926	4.60	0.950	0.974
0.45	0.398	0.420	1.05	0.708	0.778	2.10	0.875	0.927	4.65	0.951	0.974
0.46	0.405	0.428	1.06	0.711	0.781	2.12	0.876	0.928	4.70	0.952	0.975
0.47	0.412	0.436	1.07	0.714	0.784	2.14	0.878	0.929	4.75	0.952	0.975
0.48	0.419	0.444	1.08	0.717	0.788	2.16	0.879	0.930	4.80	0.953	0.975
0.49	0.427	0.453	1.09	0.720	0.791	2.18	0.881	0.931	4.85	0.953	0.975
0.50	0.434	0.461	1.10	0.723	0.794	2.20	0.882	0.932	4.90	0.954	0.976
0.51	0.441	0.469	1.11	0.726	0.797	2.22	0.883	0.932	5.00	0.955	0.976
0.52	0.448	0.477	1.12	0.729	0.800	2.24	0.885	0.933	6.00	0.963	0.981
0.53	0.454	0.484	1.13	0.731	0.803	2.26	0.886	0.934	8.00	0.973	0.986
0.54	0.461	0.492	1.14	0.734	0.806	2.28	0.887	0.935	10.00	0.979	0.989
0.55	0.468	0.500	1.15	0.737	0.809	2.30	0.888	0.936	20.00	0.990	0.995
0.56	0.474	0.508	1.16	0.740	0.811	2.32	0.889	0.937	40.00	0.995	0.997
0.57	0.481	0.515	1.17	0.742	0.814	2.34	0.891	0.937	60.00	0.997	0.998
0.58	0.487	0.523	1.18	0.745	0.817	2.36	0.892	0.938	100.00	0.998	0.999
0.59	0.494	0.530	1.19	0.747	0.819	2.38	0.893	0.939	200.00	0.999	0.999

Table developed and permission for use granted by Professor Ed Lebert, Department of Architecture, University of Washington.

Analysis of Wood Columns

A simple procedure can be adopted for checking the adequacy or capacity of wooden columns (Figure 24). This methodology is for approximate analysis and assumes the simplifications discussed in the previous section.

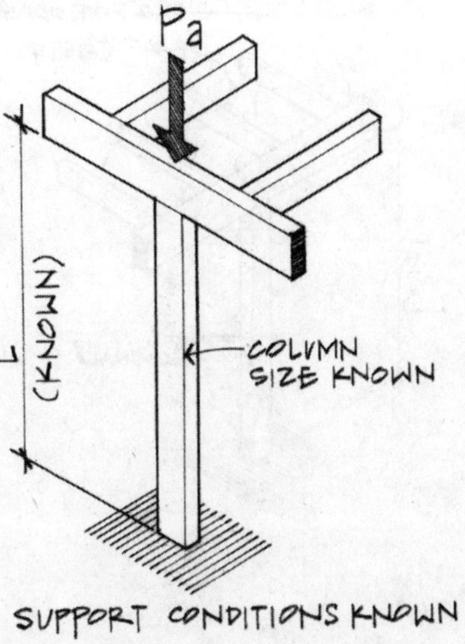

Figure 24 Checking the capacity of wooden columns.

Given:

Column size, column length, grade and species of lumber, and end conditions.

Required:

The allowable capacity of a column or the adequacy of a given column.

Procedure:

a. Calculate the $(\ell_e/d)_{min.}$
b. Obtain F'_c (allowable compressive stress)

where

$$F_c' = F_c(C_D)(C_M)(C_t)(C_F)(C_p)$$

or

$$F_c' = F_c^* C_p$$

Compute:

$$F_{cE} = \frac{K_{cE}E}{(\ell_e/d)^2}$$

$$K_{cE} = 0.3 \text{ (sawn lumber)}$$

$$K_{cE} = 0.418 \text{ (glu-lams)}$$

$$c = 0.8 \text{ (sawn lumber)}$$

$$c = 0.9 \text{ (glu-lams)}$$

c. Compute $F_c^* \cong F_c C_D$
d. Calculate the ratio $\dfrac{F_{cE}}{F_c^*}$
e. Enter Table 3; obtain respective C_p
f. Calculate: $F_c' = F_c^* C_p$

$$\therefore P_{allowable} = F_c' \times A \leq P_{actual}$$

where

A = cross-sectional area of the column

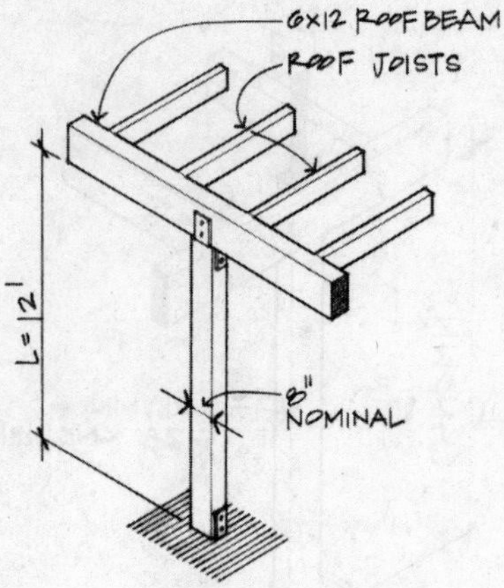

Example Problems: Analysis of Wood Columns

13 A 6 × 8 Douglas fir No. 1 post supports a roof load of 20 k. Check the adequacy of the column assuming pin support conditions at the top and bottom. Use $F_c = 1{,}000$ psi and $E = 1.6 \times 10^6$ psi.

Solution:

6 × 8 S4S Douglas fir No. 1 $\left(A = 41.25 \text{ in.}^2\right)$

$$\frac{\ell_e}{d} = \frac{12' \times 12 \text{ in./ft.}}{5.5''} = 26.2$$

$$F_{cE} = \frac{0.3E}{(\ell_e/d)^2} = \frac{0.3\left(1.6 \times 10^6\right)}{(26.2)^2} = 699 \text{ psi}$$

$$F_c{}^* \cong F_c C_D$$

Load duration factor for snow is $C_D = 1.15$

(15% increase in stress above "normal" condition)

$$\therefore\ F_c{}^* = (1{,}000 \text{ psi})(1.15) = 1{,}150 \text{ psi}$$

The column stability factor C_p can be obtained from Table 3 by entering the ratio

$$\frac{F_{cE}}{F_c{}^*} = \frac{699 \text{ psi}}{1{,}150 \text{ psi}} = 0.61$$

$$\therefore\ C_p = 0.506$$

$$F_c{}' = F_c{}^* C_p = (1{,}150 \text{ psi}) \times (.506) = 582 \text{ psi}$$

Then,

$$P_{\text{allowable}} = P_a = F_c{}' \times A = (582 \text{ psi}) \times \left(41.25 \text{ in.}^2\right) = 24{,}000\,\#$$

$$P_a = 24 \text{ k} > P_{\text{actual}} = 20 \text{ k}$$

The column is adequate.

14 An 18-foot-tall 6 × 8 Southern Pine column supports a roof load (dead load plus a seven-day live load) equal to 16 k. The weak axis of buckling is braced at a point nine feet, six inches from the bottom support. Determine the adequacy of the column.

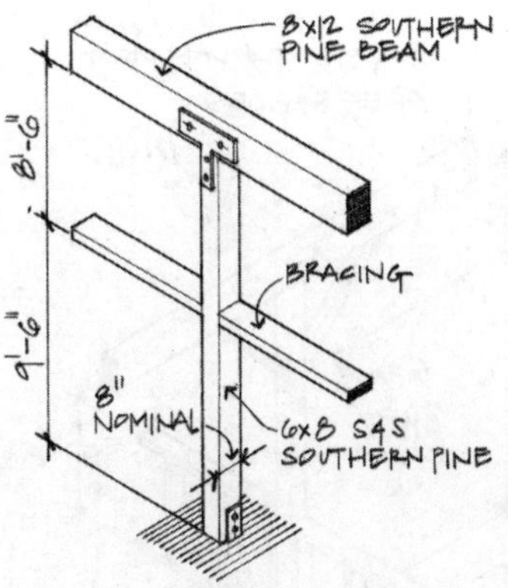

Solution:

6 × 8 S4S Southern Pine Post: ($A = 41.25$ in.^{2}; $F_c = 975$ psi; $E = 1.6 \times 10^6$ psi)

Check the slenderness ratio about the weak axis:

$$\frac{\ell_e}{d} = \frac{(9.5' \times 12 \text{ in./ft.})}{5.5''} = 20.7$$

The slenderness ratio about the strong axis is

$$\frac{\ell_e}{d} = \frac{(18' \times 12 \text{ in./ft.})}{7.5''} = 28.8$$

This value governs.

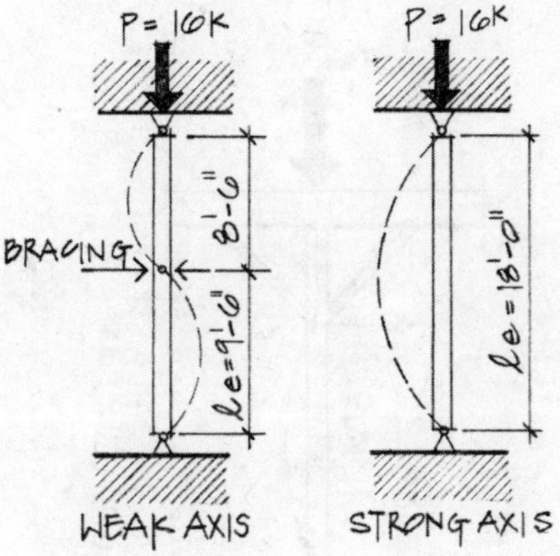

$$F_{cE} = \frac{0.3E}{(\ell_e/d)^2} = \frac{0.3(1.6 \times 10^6 \text{ psi})}{(28.8)^2} = 579 \text{ psi}$$

$$F_c^* \cong F_c C_D$$

where

$C_D = 1.25$ for 7-day-duration load

$$\therefore F_c^* = 975 \text{ psi} \times 1.25 = 1{,}219 \text{ psi}$$

$$\frac{F_{cE}}{F_c^*} = \frac{579 \text{ psi}}{1{,}219 \text{ psi}} = 0.47$$

From Table 3, $C_p = 0.412$.

$$\therefore F_c' = F_c^* C_p = 1{,}219 \text{ psi} \times 0.412 = 502 \text{ psi}$$

$$P_a = F_c' \times A = (502 \text{ psi}) \times (41.25 \text{ in.}^2) = 20{,}700\ \#$$

$P_a = 20.7\text{ k} > P_{actual} = 16$ kips

$\therefore$ *OK*

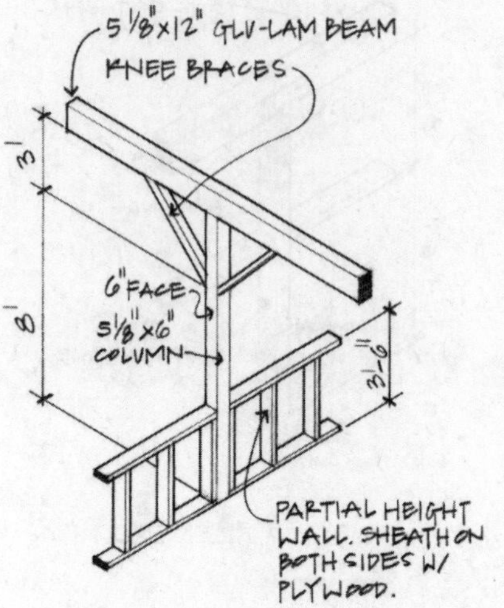

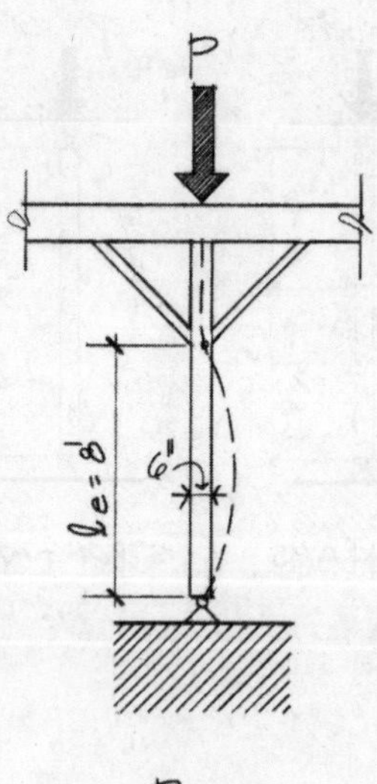

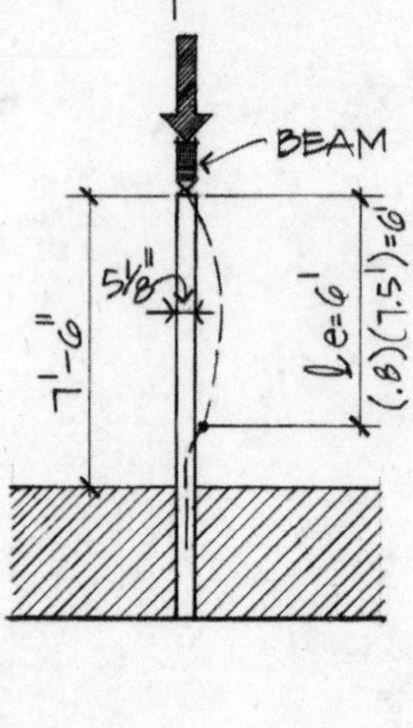

15 An 11-foot-tall Douglas fir glu-lam column is used to support a roof load (dead load plus snow) as shown. A partial-height wall braces the $5\frac{1}{8}''$ direction, and knee braces from the beam support the six inch face. Determine the capacity of the column.

Solution:

$5\frac{1}{8}'' \times 6''$ glu-lam post: ($A = 30.8 \text{ in.}^2$; $F_c = 1650$ psi; $E = 1.8 \times 10^6$ psi)

Buckling in the plane of the 6″ dimension:

$$\frac{\ell_e}{d} = \frac{8' \times 12 \text{ in./ft.}}{6''} = 16 \Leftarrow \text{Governs}$$

In the $5\frac{1}{8}''$ direction:

$$\frac{\ell_e}{d} = \frac{8' \times 12 \text{ in./ft.}}{6''} = 16 \Leftarrow \text{Governs}$$

Comparing the buckling condition in both directions, the 6″ direction is more critical and, therefore, governs.

$$F_{cE} = \frac{0.418E}{(\ell_e/d)^2} = \frac{0.418 \times \left(1.8 \times 10^6 \text{ psi}\right)}{(16)^2}$$

$$= 2{,}939 \text{ psi}$$

$$F_c^* \cong F_c C_D = 1{,}650 \text{ psi} \times (1.15) = 1{,}898 \text{ psi}$$

$$\frac{F_{cE}}{F_c} = \frac{2{,}939 \text{ psi}}{1{,}898 \text{ psi}} = 1.55$$

From Table 3, $C_p = 0.883$.

$$\therefore F_c' = F_c^* Cp = 1{,}898 \text{ psi} \times (0.883) = 1{,}581 \text{ psi}$$

$$P_a = F_c' \times A = 1{,}581 \text{ psi} \times \left(30.8 \text{ in.}^2\right) = 48{,}700\ \#$$

Design of Wood Columns

Column design in wood is a *trial-and-error process* (Figure 25). Start by making a quick estimate on size (try out your intuition), and check out the adequacy or inadequacy by following the analysis procedure given in the previous section. Axially loaded wood columns without midheight bracing are generally square in cross-section or, in some cases, just slightly rectangular. Fortunately, there are fewer possible wood sections to choose from compared with the wide array of sizes available in steel.

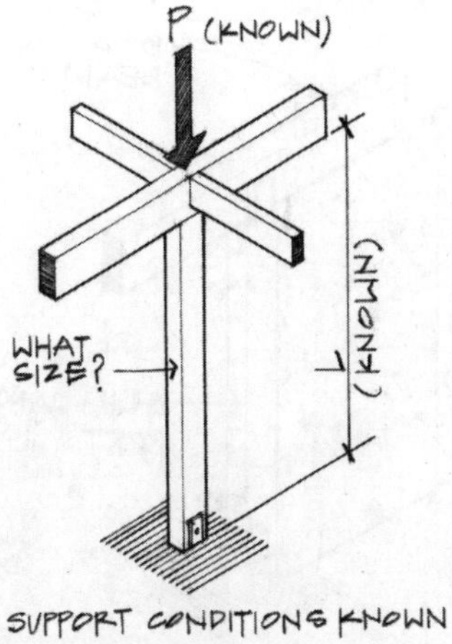

Figure 25 *Column design in wood.*

One design procedure using the trial-and-error method could be the following:

Given:

Column length, column load, grade and species of lumber to be used, and end conditions.

Required:

An economical column size.

Procedure:

a. Guess at a trial size; unless the column's weak axis is braced, try to select a square or almost square cross-section.
b. Follow the same steps used in the analysis procedure of the previous section.
c. If $P_{allowable} \geq P_{actual}$, then OK.
d. If $P_{allowable} \leq P_{actual}$, pick a larger size and cycle through the analysis procedure again.

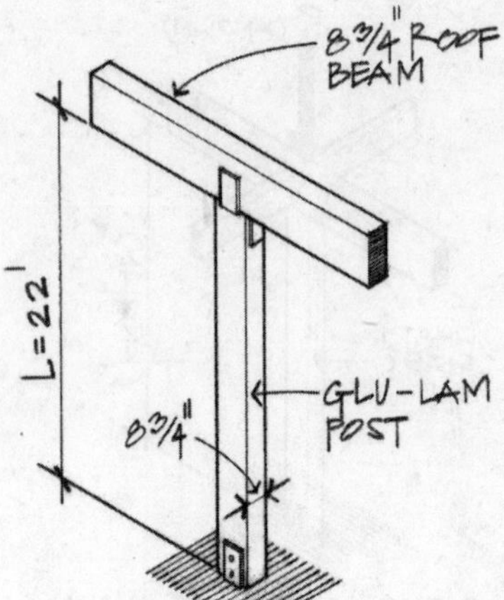

Example Problems: Design of Wood Columns

16 A 22-foot-tall glu-lam column is required to support a roof load (including snow) of 40 k. Assuming $8\frac{3}{4}''$ in one dimension (to match the beam width above), determine the minimum column size if the top and bottom are pin supported.

Select from the following sizes:

$8\frac{3}{4}'' \times 9'' \left(A = 78.75 \text{ in.}^2\right)$

$8\frac{3}{4}'' \times 1010\frac{1}{2}'' \left(A = 91.88 \text{ in.}^2\right)$

$8\frac{3}{4}'' \times 12'' \left(A = 105.0 \text{ in.}^2\right)$

Solution:

Glu-lam column: $(F_c = 1{,}650 \text{ psi}, E = 1.8 \times 10^6 \text{ psi})$

Try $8\frac{3}{4}'' \times 10\frac{1}{2}''$

$8\frac{3}{4}'' \times 10\frac{1}{2}'' \left(A = 91.9 \text{ in.}^2\right)$

$$\frac{\ell_e}{d_{\text{min.}}} = \frac{22 \times 12}{8.75} = 30.2 < 50 \quad \text{(max. slenderness ratio)}$$

$$F_{cE} = \frac{0.418E}{(\ell_e/d)^2} = \frac{0.418\left(1.8 \times 10^6\right)}{(30.2)^2} = 825 \text{ psi}$$

$$F_c{}^* \cong F_c C_D = 1{,}650 \text{ psi}(1.15) = 1{,}898 \text{ psi}$$

$$\frac{F_{cE}}{F_c{}^*} = \frac{825}{1{,}898} = 0.43$$

From Table 3, $C_p = 0.403$

$$F_c{}' = F_c{}^* C_p = 1{,}898(.403) = 765 \text{ psi}$$

$$P_a = F_c{}' \times A = 765 \text{ psi}(91.9 \text{ in.}^2) = 70{,}300\,\# > 40{,}000\,\#$$

Cycle again, trying a smaller, more economical section.

Try $8\frac{3}{4}'' \times 9''$.

$8\frac{3}{4}'' \times 9'' (A = 78.8 \text{ in.}^2)$

Because the critical dimension is still $8\frac{3}{4}''$, the values for F_{cE}, $F^*{}_c$, and $F'{}_c$ all remain the same as in trial 1. The only change that affects the capability of the column is the available cross-sectional area.

$$\therefore P_a = F_c{}'A = (765 \text{ psi})(78.8 \text{ in.}^2) = 60{,}300\,\#$$

$$P_a = 60.3 \text{ k} > 40 \text{ k}$$

Use $8\frac{3}{4}'' \times 9''$ glu-lam section.

Problems

16 A 6 × 6 S4S Southern Pine (Dense No. 1) column is used to support headers that carry loads from roof joists. Determine the capacity of the column assuming pin connections at the top and bottom. Assume a seven-day-duration roof live load.

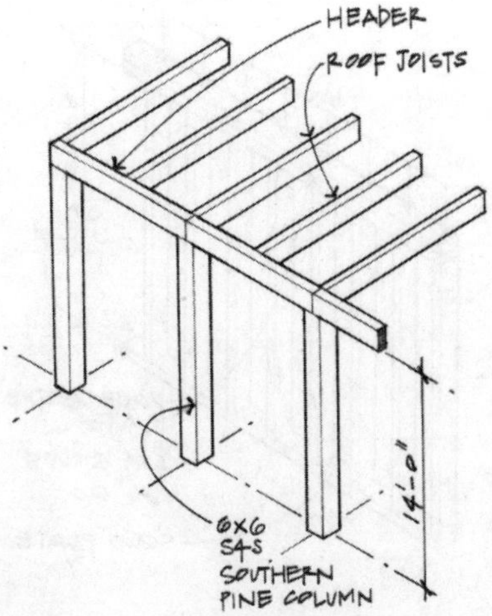

17 An 8 × 8 S4S first-floor column supports a load of $P_1 = 20$ k from roof and floors above and an additional second-floor load $P_2 = 12$ k. Determine the adequacy of the column assuming a "normal" load duration.

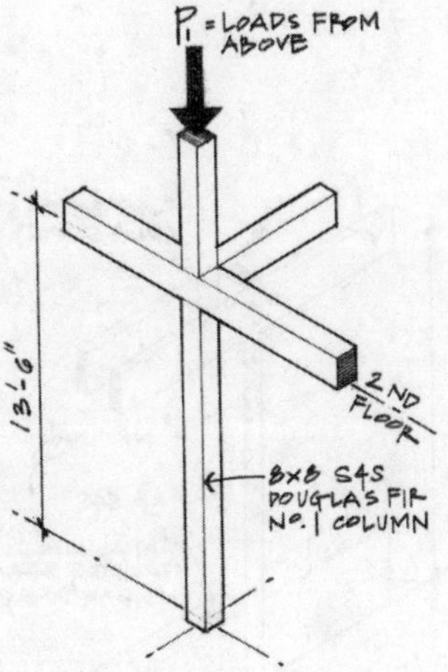

18 Determine the axial load capacity of a $6\frac{3}{4}'' \times 10\frac{1}{2}''$ glu-lam column $\left(A = 70.88 \text{ in.}^2\right)$ assuming lateral bracing about the weak axis at the midheight level. Assume pin connections top and bottom in both directions of buckling $\left(F_c = 1{,}650 \text{ psi}; E = 1.8 \times 10^6 \text{ psi}\right)$.

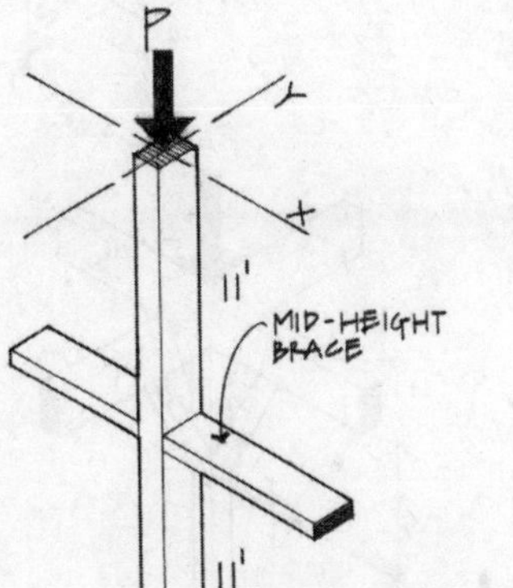

19 An interior bearing wall in the basement of a residence utilizes 2 × 4 S4S studs spaced at 16 inches o.c. to support the floor load above. Sheathing is provided on both sides of the wall and serves to prevent buckling about the weak axis of the member. Determine the permissible load ω (in pounds per lineal foot) assuming Hem-Fir (joist/planks). Then, using the ω value computed, determine the bearing stress that develops between the stud and sole plate.

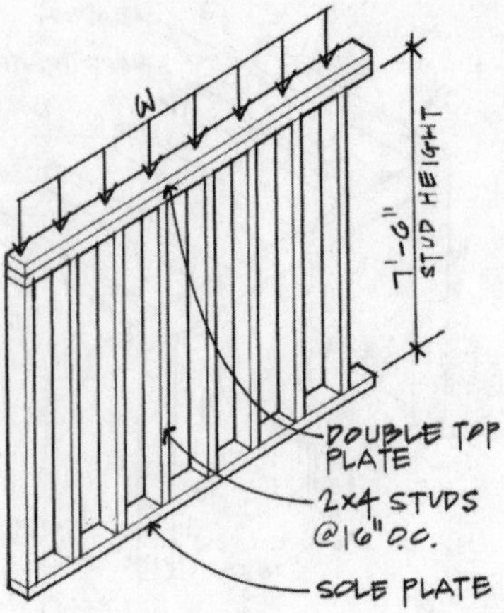

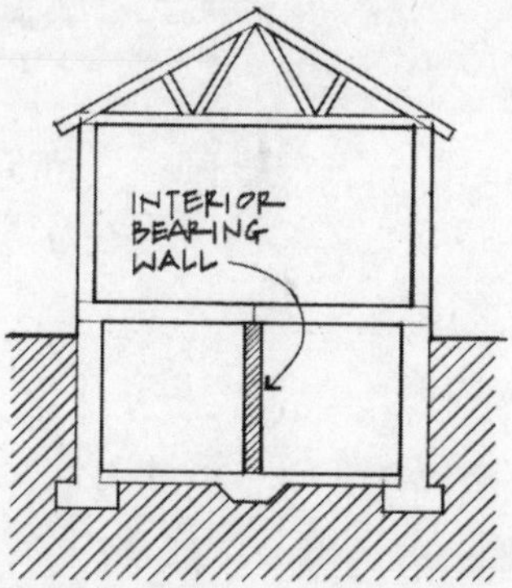

20 A 4 × 8 S4S Douglas fir column supports a roof beam as shown. The beam-column connection is considered to be a pin. The lower end is pinned for buckling about the strong axis but is fixed in the weak axis by the partial wall that measures 2 feet in height. Determine the tributary area that can be supported by this column if DL = 20 psf and SL = 30 psf.

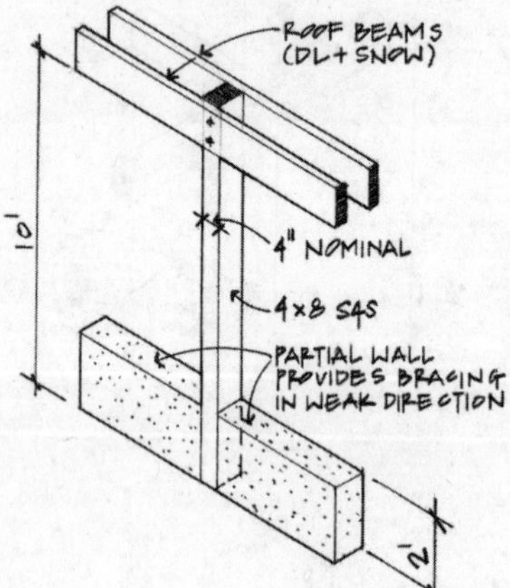

21 Determine the minimum size column (Southen Pine Dense No. 1) required to support an axial load of $P = 25$ k assuming an effective column length $\ell_e = 16'$.

22 An interior glu-lam column supports a roof load of $P = 15$ k. The total column height is 24 feet, but knee-bracing from the beams reduces the unsupported height to 18 feet. Assuming $6\frac{3}{4}''$ in on dimension, determine the minimum size required. Use $F_c = 1{,}650$ psi and $E = 1.8 \times 10^6$ psi.

Select a size from the following:

$6\frac{3}{4}'' \times 7\frac{1}{2}''$ $(A = 50.63 \text{ in.}^2)$

$6\frac{3}{4}'' \times 9''$ $(A = 60.75 \text{ in.}^2)$

$6\frac{3}{4}'' \times 10\frac{1}{2}''$ $(A = 70.88 \text{ in.}^2)$

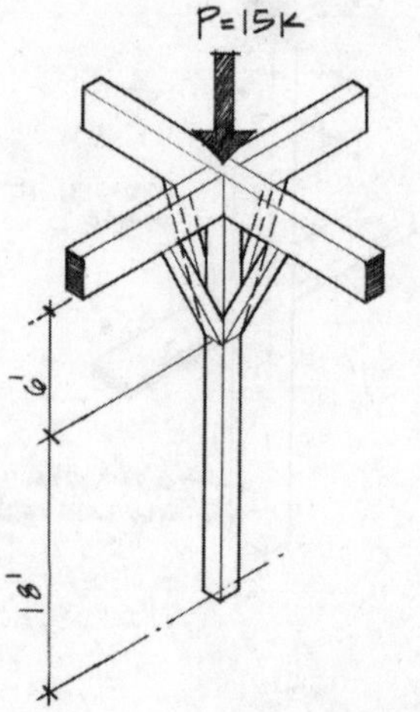

5 COLUMNS SUBJECTED TO COMBINED LOADING OR ECCENTRICITY

So far, the previous sections have assumed compression members subjected to concentric loading (loads acting through the centroid of the column section). The study of axially loaded columns (Figure 26) was essential to the understanding of the primary issue of slenderness and its relationship to failure modes involving crushing and buckling. In practice, however, concentric loading is rarely the case. This section will introduce the idea of eccentricity (Figure 27) and/or side loading (Figure 28) and their effect on column behavior.

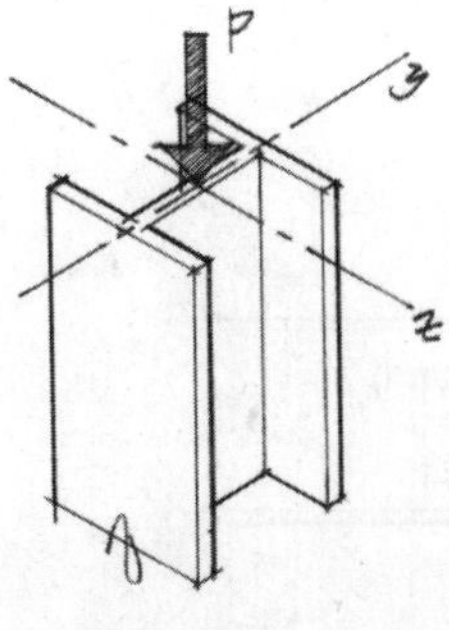

Figure 26 Concentrically (axially) loaded column.

Many columns are subjected to bending in combination with axial compression loads. Nonuniform bearing, misalignment of the framing, or even the crookedness of a member will cause a load to miss the centroid of the column cross-section. Compression members carrying bending moment due to eccentricity or side loading in addition to compression are referred to as *beam columns* (Figure 29).

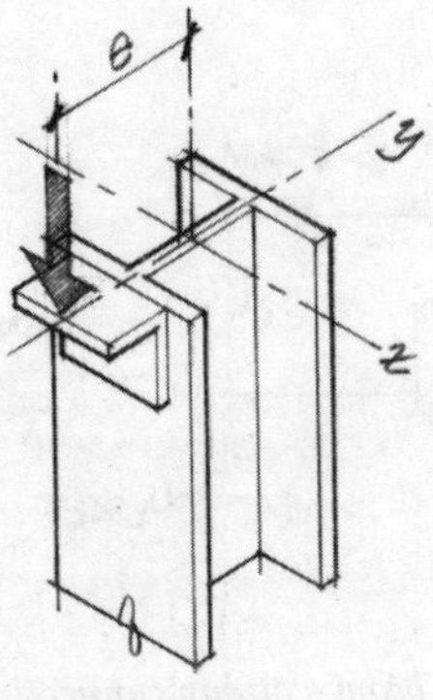

Figure 27 Eccentrically loaded column.

An assumption that was made for axially loaded columns was the relative uniformity of the stress distribution over the cross-sectional area, as shown in Figure 30(a). Bending stress, which involves tension and compression stresses, must be added algebraically to the compressive stresses from gravity loading. If a beam is very flexible and the column is very rigid, the eccentricity effect will be small, because most of the bending stress will be absorbed by the beam. Relatively small eccentricities alter the final stress distribution, but the cross-section will remain in compression, although nonuniform, as shown in Figure 30(b). On the other hand, if a rigid beam is connected to a less rigid column, a considerably large eccentricity will be transmitted to the column. When large eccentricities exist, tensile stresses may develop over part of the cross-section, as shown in Figure 30(c).

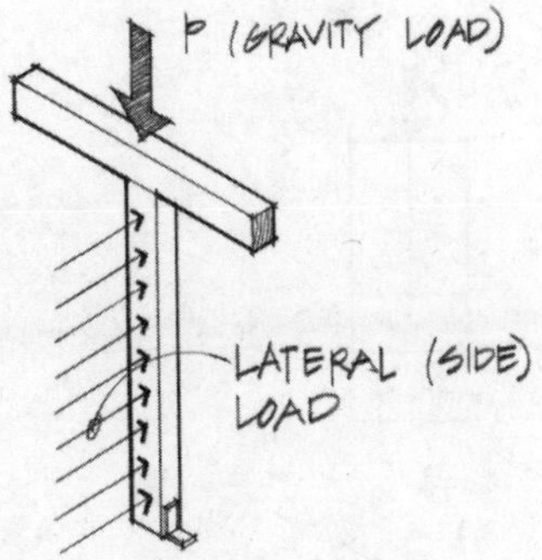

Figure 28 Column with compression plus side load.

The tension stresses that developed in masonry construction of the past were formerly of great concern, but they have little significance for the building systems and materials used today. Timber, steel, prestressed concrete, and reinforced concrete all possess good tensile capability.

The masonry construction of the Gothic cathedrals required a keen awareness of the resultant force (from the flying buttress and the vertical pier) remaining within a zone (the *middle third*) of the cross-section to avoid developing tensile stresses. The area within the third point of each face of the pier is called the *kern* area (Figure 31).

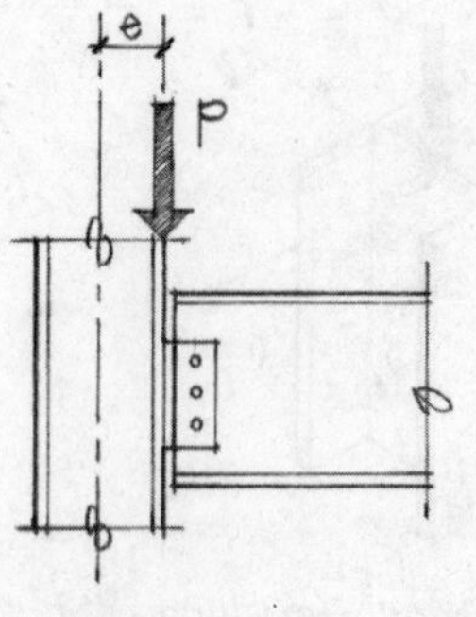

(a) *Framed beam (shear) connection.*
e = *Eccentricity;* M = P × e

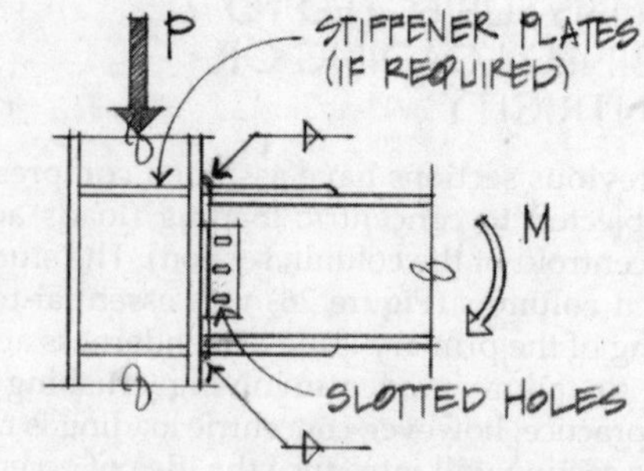

(b) *Moment connection (rigid frame).*
M = *Moment due to beam bending*

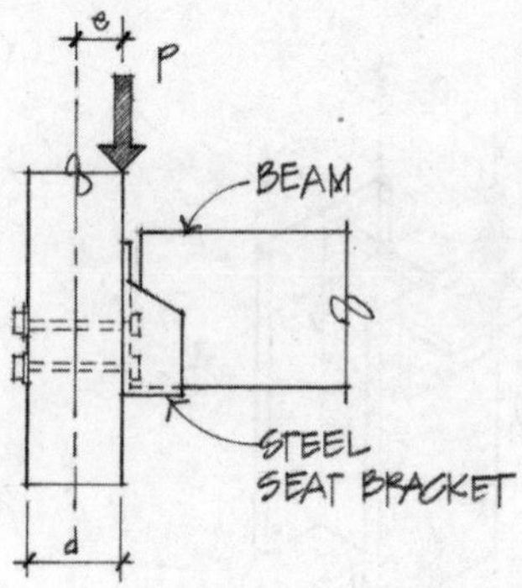

(c) *Timber beam–column connection.*
e = d/2 = *eccentricity;* M = P × e

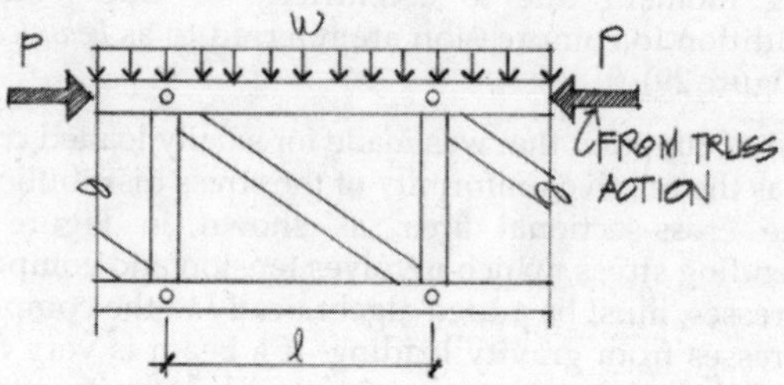

(d) *Upper chord of a truss—compression plus bending.*

$$M = \frac{\omega l^2}{8}$$

Figure 29 Examples of beam-column action.

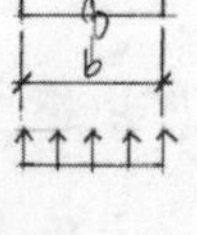

(a) *Axially loaded—*
uniform compressive stress.

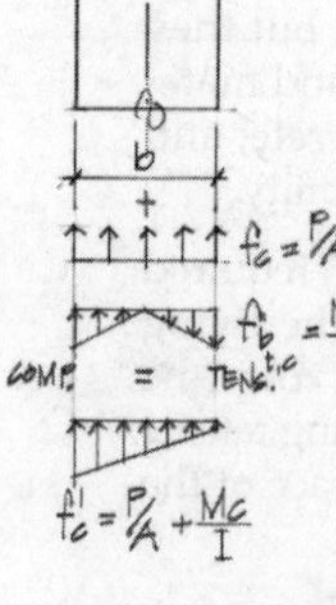

(b) *Small eccentricity—*
linearly varying stress.

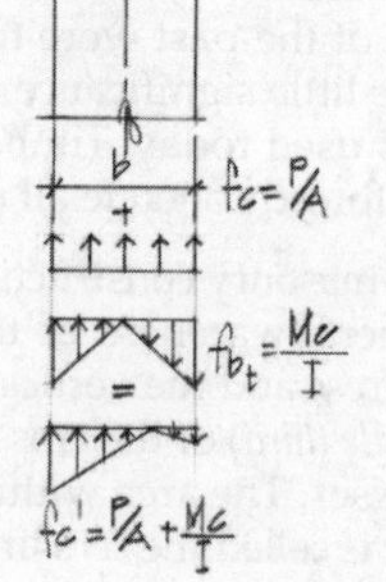

(c) *Large eccentricity—tensile*
stress on part of cross-section.

Figure 30 Stress distribution for eccentrically loaded rectangular columns.

Beam columns are evaluated using an interaction equation that incorporates the bending stress with the compressive stress. The general interaction equation is expressed as

$$\boxed{\frac{f_a}{F_a} + \frac{f_b}{F_b} \le 1.} \quad \text{(interaction equation)}$$

where

$f_a = P/A$ [the actual compressive (axial) stress]

F_a = allowable compressive stress [based on $K\ell/r$ (steel) or ℓ_e/d (timber)]

$f_b = \dfrac{Mc}{I} = \dfrac{M}{S}$ (actual bending stress)

$M = P \times e$ for eccentrically loaded members

M = bending moment due to side load or rigid frame action

F_b = allowable bending stress (values from tables)

If a member is subjected to axial compression and bending about both the x and y axes, the interaction formula is adapted to incorporate the biaxial bending (Figure 32). Therefore, the most generalized form of the equation is

$$\boxed{\frac{f_a}{F_a} + \frac{f_{bx}}{F_{bx}} + \frac{f_{by}}{F_{by}} \le 1.0} \quad \text{(for biaxial bending)}$$

where:

$f_{bx} = \dfrac{M}{S_x}$ = actual bending stress about the x axis

$f_{by} = \dfrac{M}{S_y}$ = actual bending stress about the y axis

When both bending and axial forces act on a member, the magnitude of the axial stress is expressed as a certain percentage of the allowable axial stress, and the bending stress will be a certain fraction of the allowable bending stress. The sum of these two percentages cannot exceed unity (100% stress). The interaction curve shown in Figure 33 illustrates the theoretical combining of the axial compressive and bending stresses.

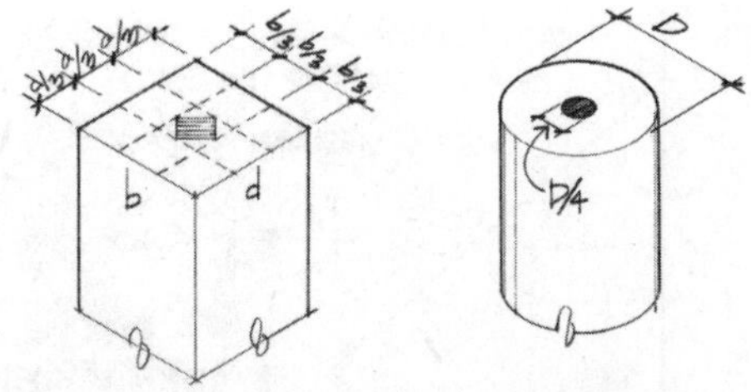

Figure 31 Kern areas for two cross-sections.

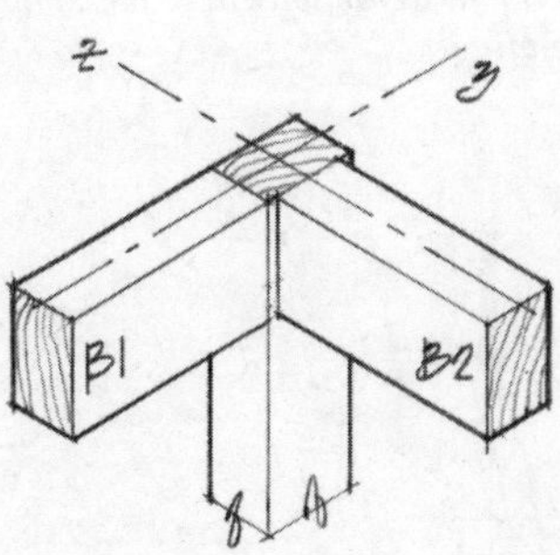

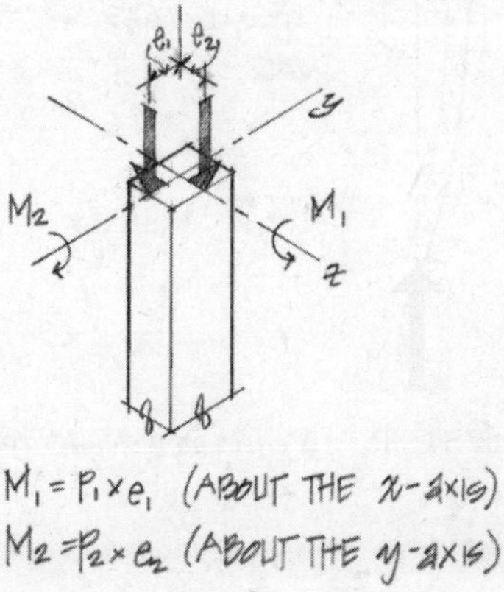

Figure 32 Example of biaxial bending due to two eccentric loads.

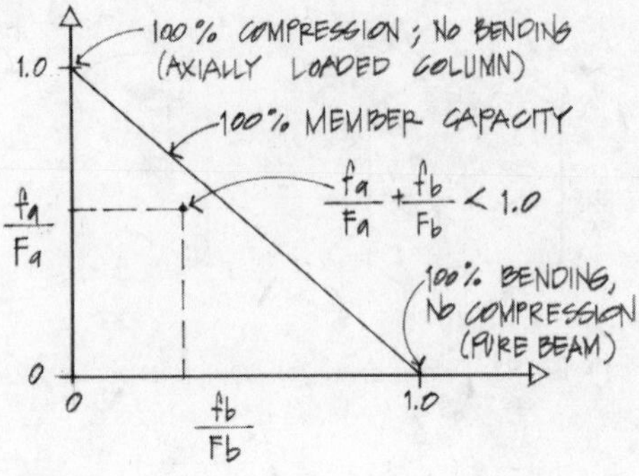

Figure 33 Interaction curve for compression and bending.

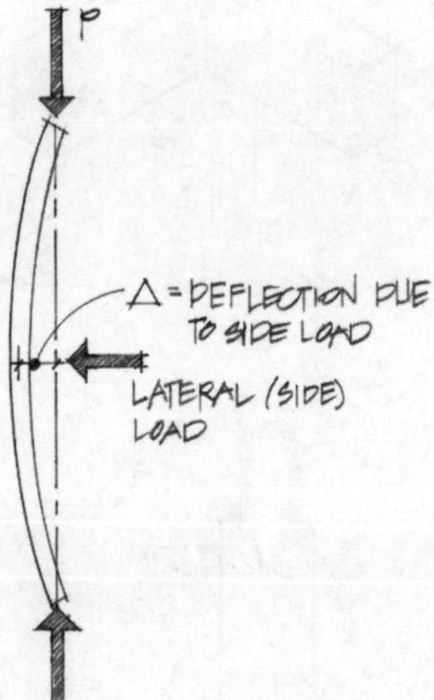

Figure 34 P – Δ *effect on a slender column.*

Bending moments in columns, whether they result from lateral forces, applied moments, or eccentricity of the end loads, can cause a member to deflect laterally, resulting in additional bending moment due to the $P - \Delta$ effect (see Figure 5). In Figure 33, a slender column deflects an amount Δ due to a side load. However, the lateral displacement generates an eccentricity for the load P, which results in the creation of additional moment at the midheight of the column equal to $P \times \Delta$ (known as a *second-order bending moment* and also as a *moment magnification*). Slender columns are particularly sensitive to this $P - \Delta$ effect and must be accounted for in the interaction equation (Figure 34).

The AISC (steel) and NDS (timber) manuals have introduced a magnification factor to incorporate the $P - \Delta$ effect, which results from the initial bending moment. A generalized representation for both steel and wood is

$$\frac{f_a}{F_a} + \frac{f_b(\text{magnification factor})}{F_b} \le 1.0$$

The actual analysis/design equation for steel as specified by the AISC is expressed as

$$\frac{f_a}{F_a} + \frac{C_{Mx} f_{bx}}{\left(1 - \frac{f_a}{F'_{ex}}\right)F_{bx}} + \frac{C_{My} f_{by}}{\left(1 - \frac{f_a}{F'_{ey}}\right)F_{by}}$$

where

$$\frac{1}{1 - f_a/F_e'} = \text{magnification factor to account for } P - \Delta$$

$$F_e' = \frac{12\pi^2 E}{23(K\ell/r)^2} = \text{Euler's formula with a safety factor}$$

C_M = modification factor, which accounts for loading and end conditions

An equivalent equation specified by the NDS for analyzing and designing wood columns subjected to compression and uniaxial bending is

$$\frac{f_c}{f_c'} + \frac{f_{bx}}{f'_{bx}[\ - (f_c/F_{cEx})]} \leq 1.0$$

where

$$\frac{f_c}{F_c'} = \text{equivalent of the steel ratio for compression}$$

$$f_c = \frac{P}{A} = \text{actual compressive stress}$$

$$F_c' = F_c C_D C_M C_t C_F C_p = \text{allowable compressive stress}$$

$$f_{bx} = \frac{M}{S_x} = \text{bending stress about the } x \text{ axis}$$

$$F_{bx}' = \text{allowable bending stress about the } x \text{ axis}$$

$$\frac{1}{[1 - f_c/F_{cEx}]} = \text{magnification factor for } P - \Delta \text{ effect}$$

Analyzing and designing beam columns using the AISC and NDS equations are more appropriately done in follow-up courses dealing specifically with steel and wood design. Oversimplification of the preceding equations does not necessarily result in appropriate approximations, even for preliminary design purposes. This text does not include problems involving the use of the interaction equation.

Summary

- Column slenderness greatly influences a column's ability to support load. Short, stout columns fail by crushing due to material failure, while long, slender columns fail by buckling. Buckling (elastic instability) is the sudden, uncontrolled lateral displacement of a column.
- Short columns are evaluated based on the basic stress equation:

$$f_a = \frac{P_{actual}}{A} = \frac{\text{(actual load)}}{\text{(cross-sectional area)}} \leq F_a \text{ (allowable compressive stress)}$$

- The critical buckling load of a slender column was predicted by Leonhard Euler.

$$P_{critical} = \frac{\pi^2 EI_{min}}{L^2} = \frac{\pi^2\text{(modulus of electricity)(smallest moment of intertia)}}{\text{(column length between pinned ends)}}$$

  As the column length increases, the critical load decreases. Euler's equation contains no safety factor. $P_{critical}$ represents the actual failure load.

- The length of a column between pinned ends divided by the column's least radius of gyration is known as the slenderness ratio.

$$\text{slenderness ratio} = \frac{L}{r_{min.}}$$

  High slenderness ratios mean lower critical stresses that result in buckling. Column sections with high radii of gyration r are more resistant to buckling.

- Euler's buckling equation assumes pinned ends. If a column support at the top and/or bottom is restrained from rotation, the load-carrying capacity of a column increases.
- The slenderness ratio of a column is adjusted by a K factor to incorporate the end support conditions.

$$\text{slenderness ratio} = \frac{KL}{r}$$

  where K is the multiplier for converting the actual length to an effective buckling length based on end conditions.

- A column's effectiveness can be increased by the introduction of lateral bracing about the weak axis. Lateral bracing reduces the effective buckling length of a column, thereby resulting in a higher load capacity.

- Structural steel columns are classified as short, intermediate, and long. The two AISC allowable compressive stress formulas recognize only two slenderness categories—short/intermediate and long.
- Short columns are expressed as a function of slenderness and the yield strength of the steel.
- The long column formula is a modified version of the Euler buckling formula with a safety factor incorporated.
- The slenderness of rectangular timber columns is evaluated by

$$\text{slenderness ratio} = \frac{L}{d_{min.}} = \frac{(\text{column length})}{(\text{minimum column dimension})}$$

- Most wood construction assumes that the ends are pinned and free to rotate ($K = 1$).
- The analysis and design of wood columns generally follow the provisions established by the *National Design Specification for Wood Construction* manual.
- Many columns used in actual buildings are subjected to bending in combination with axial compressive loads. The general condition of stress is expressed as

$$\frac{f_a}{F_a} + \frac{f_b}{F_b} \leq 1.0 \text{ (interaction formula)}$$

$$\frac{(\text{actual compressive stress})}{(\text{allowable compressive stress})} + \frac{(\text{actual bending stress})}{(\text{allowable bending stress})} \leq 1.0$$

Answers to Selected Problems

1 $P_{critical} = 184.2$ k; $f_{critical} = 20.2$ ksi

3 $L = 28.6'$

5 $KL/r_y = 193.2$; $P_{cr} = 73.64$ k; $f_{cr} = 7.7$ ksi

7 (a) $KL/r_y = 46.5$; $P_a = 356$ k
(b) $KL/r_y = 57.2$; $P_a = 339$ k
(c) $KL/r_y = 71.5$; $P_a = 311$ k

9 $KL/r_z = 111.25$; $F_a = 11.5$ ksi; $P_a = 46$ k

11 Weak axis: $KL/r_y = 54$; $P_a = 561.3$ k;
Strong axis: $KL/r_x = 57$; $P_a = 553$ k

13 W8 × 24; $KL/r = 149$; $P_a = 47.6$ k

15 Roof load = 60 k; floor load = 112.5 k
$P_{actual} = 397.5$ k (3rd-floor column)
W12 × 79 ($P_a = 397.6$ k)
$P_{actual} = 622.5$ k.(1st-floor column)
W12 × 136 ($P_a = 630$ k)

16 $L_e/d = 30.5$; $F_c = 459.5$ psi; $P_a = 13.9$ k

18 Strong axis controls the design;
$L_e/d = 25.15$; $F_c = 1{,}021$ psi; $P_a = 72.4$ k

20 Weak axis: $L_e/d = 21.9$ (governs)
Strong axis: $L_e/d = 16.6$;
$P_a = 17.54$ k; $A_{trib.} = 350.8$ ft.^{2}

21 Use 8 × 8; $P_a = 32$ k > 25 k

Structural Connections

Structural Connections

Figure 1 Sir Humphrey Davy (1778–1829).

The colleague and, in some ways, the rival of Thomas Young, Davy was appointed Professor of Chemistry at the Royal Institute at the age of 24 in the same year that Young was appointed. Davy, in contrast to Young, exhibited a dynamic and captivating public personality in his lectures, which garnered both money and publicity for the Institute. Davy was extremely prolific in his work, isolating himself and conducting extensive research. He discovered the exhilarating and anesthetic effects of nitrous oxide (laughing gas) as well as pioneering in the field of electrical engineering. One of the major contributions to the modern world of construction was his development of arc welding in the early 1800s. Davy remained at the Institute for the duration of his professional career and prospered. He eventually was knighted and became Sir Humphrey. He also served as president of the Royal Society.

Introduction

An examination was made of the load paths through a structural assemblage, beginning with the roof, floors, walls, and columns and eventually tracing the loads to the foundation. Forces and support reactions were obtained for each structural element through the use of FBDs and the equations of equilibrium. Later, the construction of load, shear, and moment diagrams enabled us to determine the critical shears and moments used in the design of bending members, which include joists, rafters, beams, and girders. Beam and girder reactions were then used in the design of timber and steel columns.

Individual structural members were designed as isolated elements, assuming that the transfer of loads from one member to the next was assured. In reality, however, all structural assemblages are interconnected, and individual members work in combination with other members through physical connections. Structural members must be joined in such a way that permits the safe transfer of loads from one member to another. Many of the structural failures in buildings and bridges occur in the connection of members and not in the members themselves. The techniques used by carpenters, welders, and iron workers in making a specific joint can create situations that are not amenable to mathematical computations. An improperly installed bolt, undersized or improper strength rating of the bolts, bolt holes that are too large, welds made with improper penetration of the weld material, improper tightening of a bolt, and so on can all lead to unsatisfactory structural attachments. To preclude such bad joints—or at least limit the number of them that occur—various standard codes are in effect. Timber design, including its connections, is overseen by the AITC and the NDS by the American Forest and Paper Association. In steel design, the AISC's *Manual of Steel Construction* and the specifications of the American Welding Society (AWS) are the most comprehensive and most widely used in industry.

1 STEEL BOLTED CONNECTIONS

Bolts used in building connections are generally subjected to forces that cause tension, shear, or a combination of the two. Typical connections subjecting fasteners to axial shear are splices used in trusses, beam-lap splices, and gussets (Figure 2). Brackets and web shear splices are typical eccentric shear connections (Figures 3 and 4). Bolts in tension are common in hanger connections (Figure 5). Typical beam-to-column moment connections are examples of combined tension and shear forces (Figure 6).

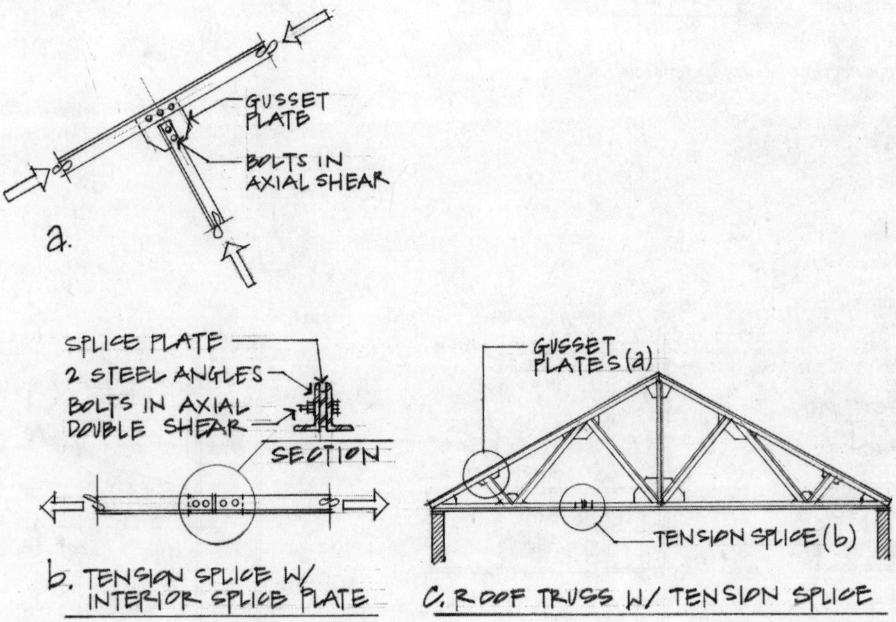

Figure 2 Roof truss with a tension splice—axial shear.

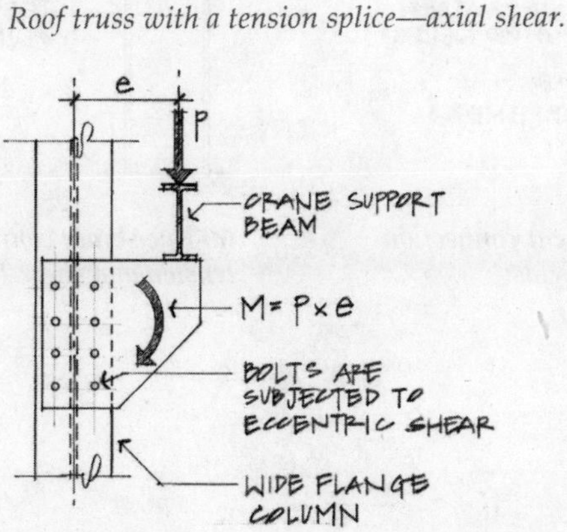

Figure 3 Bracket connection, mill building—eccentric shear.

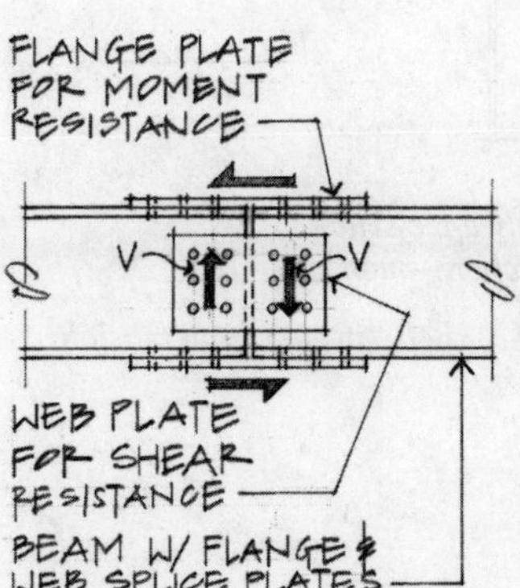

Figure 4 Beam splice—eccentric shear.

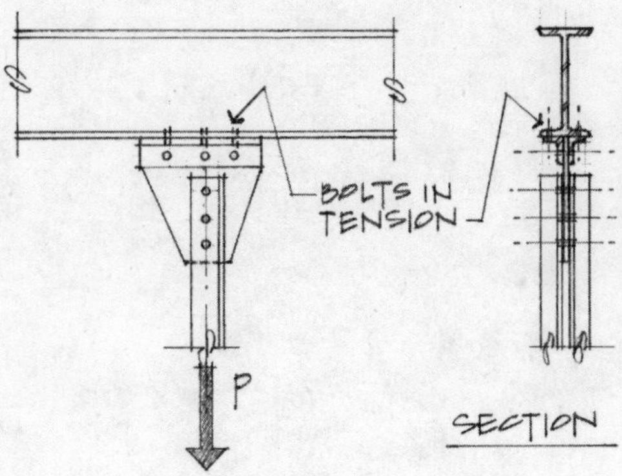

Figure 5 Hanger connection—bolts in tension.

The connection shown in Figure 6(a) is no longer recommended because of its difficulty in fabrication and expense. Welding has simplified the moment connection considerably, as shown in Figure 6(b). Many moment connections today utilize a combination of shop welding with field bolting to simplify the erection process as well as keep cost down.

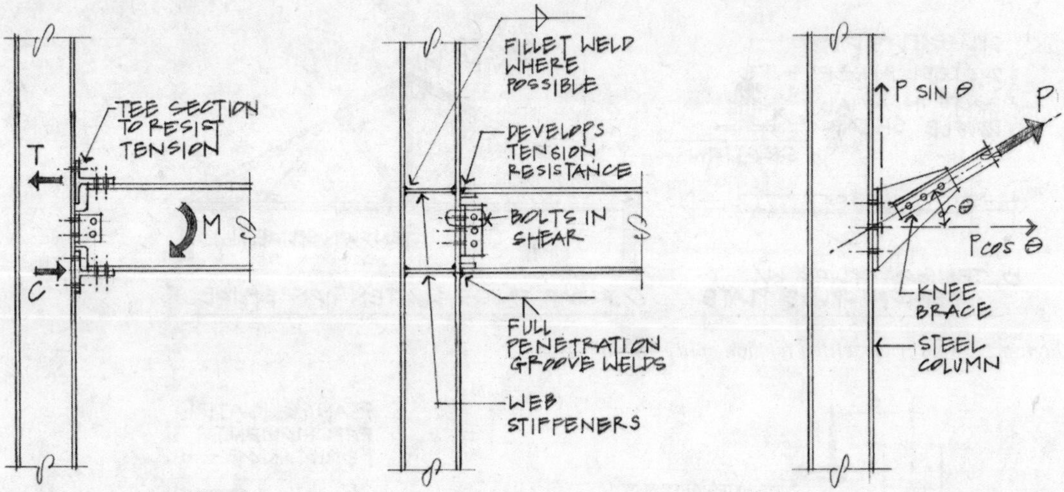

(a) Bolted tee-stub connection—moment.

(b) Typical moment connection with bolts and welds.

(c) Knee brace connection in tension and shear.

Figure 6 Bolts in shear and tension.

Failure of Bolted Connections

The choice of suitable design stresses for bolted joints is not a simple task. Consideration must be given both to the possible modes of failure of a given joint and to the behavior of materials under such loading. In addition, the methods of fabricating a particular joint may induce latent local stresses or physical conditions that could cause the joint to fail. However, the design of a bolted joint in many cases is a comparatively simple matter, and the computations are generally not very involved.

In designing a bolted joint properly, one must anticipate and control the maximum stresses developed at critical sections. Because it is to be expected that failure will occur at one of these critical sections, any knowledge as to where these sections may be located provides information for a successful design. Several common critical stress conditions develop in all joints, each of which is capable of producing failure. Shown in Figures 7 through 12 are the five basic types of failure:

1. Shear of the bolt (Figures 7 and 8).
2. Bearing failure (crushing) of the connected members against the bolt (Figure 9).
3. Tension failure of the connected member material (Figure 10).
4. End tear-out of the connected member (Figure 11).
5. Block shear, a condition that can occur when the top flange of the beam is coped to intersect with a girder (Figure 12).

Bolted joints are usually categorized by the type and complexity of the joint. The most commonly encountered bolted joints are the lap joint and the butt joint, shown schematically in Figures 7 and 8.

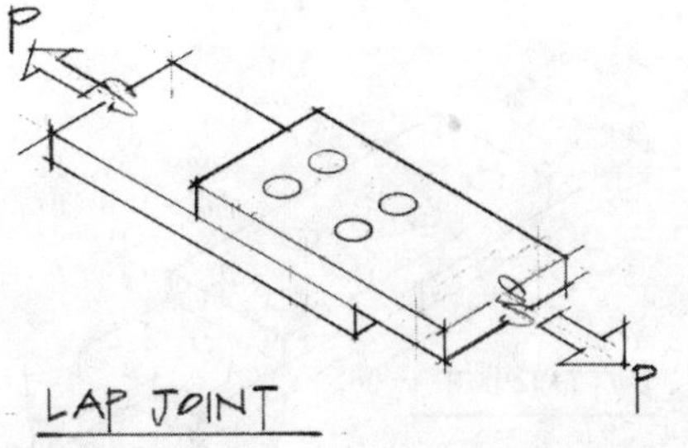

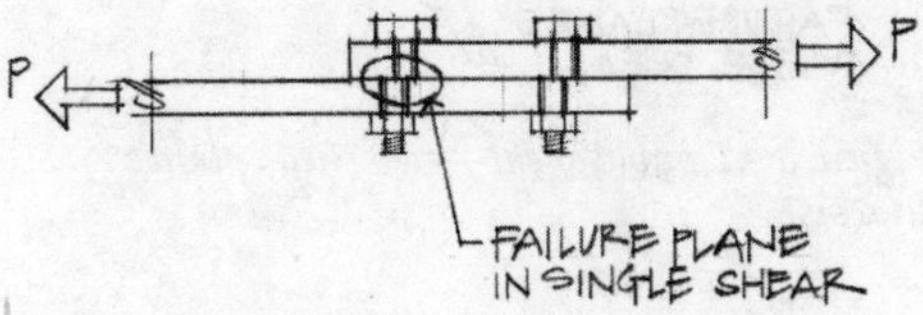

Figure 7 Shear failure—single shear (one shear surface).

Shear failure

The resisting shear stress developed is only an average shear stress. Shear stresses are not uniform on the bolt cross-section but are assumed so for design.

Single shear:

$$\underset{\text{(ave)}}{f_v} = \frac{P}{n \times A} \leq F_v$$

where:

f_v = average shear stress (psi or ksi)
P = load on the plate or connection (# of kips)
A = cross-sectional area of bolt $\left(\text{in.}^2\right)$
F_v = Allowable shear stress of bolt (psi or ksi)
n = number of bolts

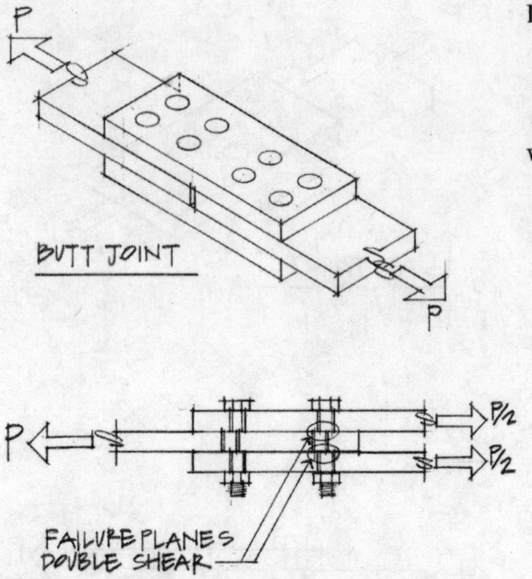

Figure 8 Double shear—two shear planes to resist.

Double shear:

$$f_{v\,(ave)} = \frac{P}{2A \times n} \leq F_v$$

where

f_v = average shear stress (ksi or psi)
P = loads on the plate or connection (# or kips)
$2A$ = two cross-sectional areas per bolt (in.^{2})
F_v = Allowable shear stress (ksi or psi)
n = number of bolts

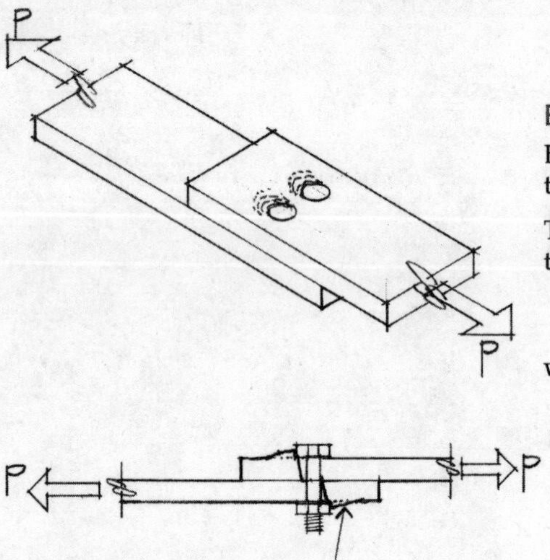

Figure 9 Bearing failure.

Bearing failure (Figure 9)

Bearing failure involves the connecting members and not the bolt itself.

The contact surface of the bolt pushing on the plate is taken as

$$A_p = n \times t \times d$$

where

A_p = bearing area of plate (in.^{2})
t = plate thickness (in.)
d = bolt diameter (in.)
n = number of bolts in bearing

The *average* bearing stress developed between the bolt and plate can be expressed as

$$f_{p\,(ave)} = \frac{P}{A_p} \le F_p$$

where

f_p = average bearing stress (psi or ksi)
A_p = bearing area (in.^{2})
P = applied load (# or kips)
F_p = allowable bearing stress (psi or ksi)
$F_p = 1.2F_u$
F_u = ultimate stress (psi or ksi)

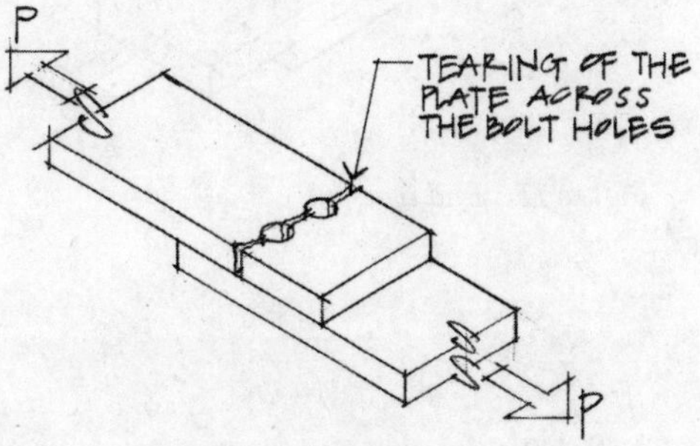

Tensile failure

The shaded area in Figure 10 represents the amount of material left across the tear to resist the applied load after deducting the void left by the bolt hole:

$$A_{net} = (b - n \times D)t$$

where

A_{net} = net plate area resisting tension (in.^{2})
b = plate width (in.)
D = diameter of a standard size bolt hole. (D = bolt diameter + $\frac{1}{16}''$)
t = plate thickness (in.)
n = number of bolts in a row

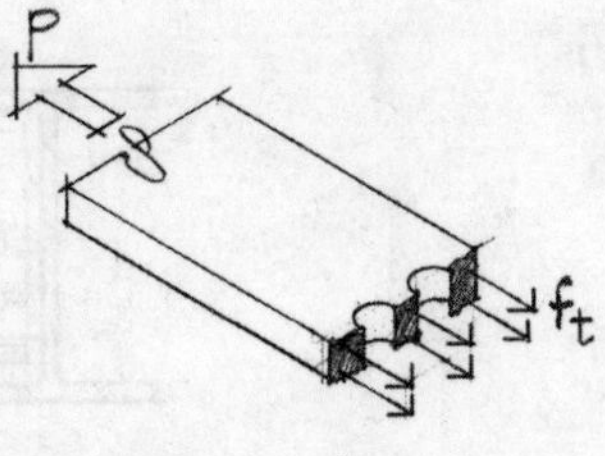

Figure 10 Tensile failure.

The average net tension in the plate across the first line of bolts is expressed as

$$f_{t\,(net)} = \frac{P}{A_{net}} \le F_t$$

where

f_t = average tension stress across the net area of the member (psi or ksi)

P = applied load (# or kips)

F_t = allowable tensile stress across the net area

$F_t = 0.5F_u$

F_u = ultimate tensile stress (psi or ksi)

End tear-out (Figure 11) and *block shear* (Figure 12) are possible failure modes when high, allowable fastener values are used in conjunction with relatively thin material. However, failure is less likely to occur because of the design specifications requiring ample edge and end distances and minimum bolt spacing.

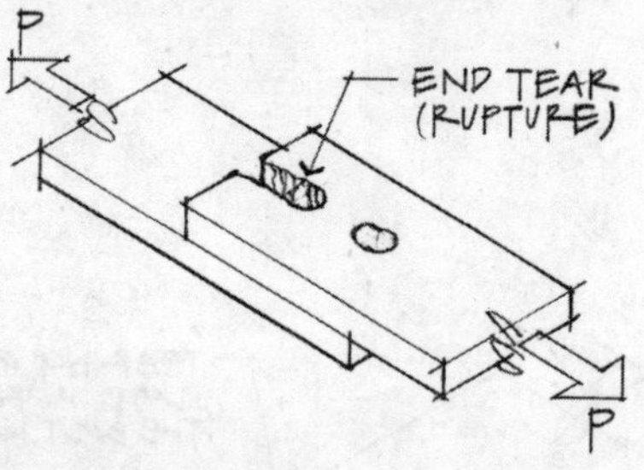

Figure 11 End tear-out.

Figure 13 illustrates, for preliminary design purposes, the minimum pitch and edge distances specified by the AISC to avoid these failure modes. The AISC specifies an absolute minimum pitch and gage (center-to-center) spacing of $2\frac{2}{3}$ times the bolt diameter (d), with $3d$ being the preferred spacing. In some cases, a dimension of three inches is used for all sizes of bolts up to one inch in diameter. Shear and bearing failures, the result of excessive stresses on the bolts, are avoided by providing a sufficient number of fasteners to keep the stresses within the allowable limits.

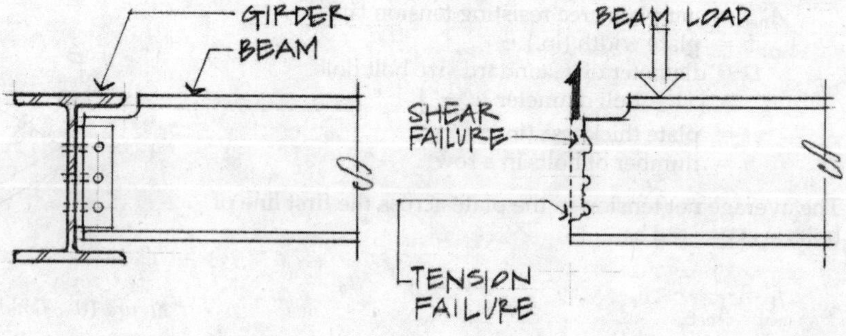

Figure 12 Block shear—tension failure at the end connections along the perimeter of a group of bolts.

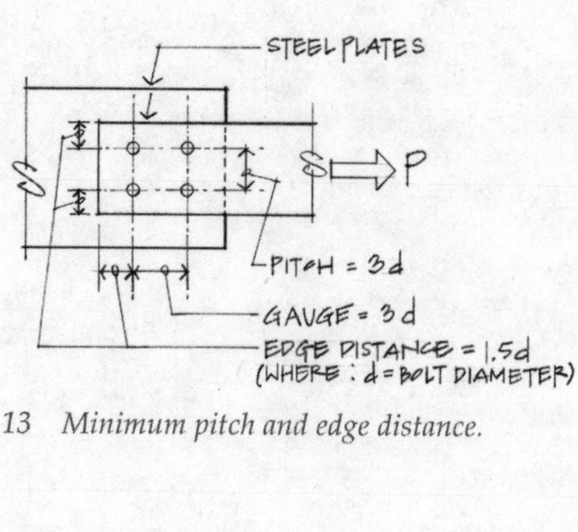

Figure 13 Minimum pitch and edge distance.

Design Stresses for Bolts

Bolting has replaced riveting as a means of structurally connecting members, because it is quieter, simpler, and can be performed more quickly with smaller crews, resulting in lower labor costs. Possibly the most common construction methodology today is to utilize shop welding in combination with field bolting.

Three primary types of bolts are used in steel construction today. *Common bolts*, also known as *rough bolts* or *unfinished bolts*, are designated as American Society of Testing Materials (ASTM) A307 and are suitable for use in light-steel-frame structures where vibration and impact do not have to be considered. Also, unfinished bolts are not permitted under some building codes in the construction of buildings exceeding certain height limits. Where these conditions exist, nuts may become loose, impairing the strength of the connection.

Figure 14 ASTM A490 tension-control bolt with the fluted tip that twists off at the proper tightness. Available in A325 and A490 for high-strength bolting. Image reprinted with permission, courtesy of the LeJeune Bolt Company.

The two other types of bolts, designated as ASTM A325 and A490, are *high-strength bolts* are the most widely used fasteners for structural steel connections made in the field (Figure 14). High-strength bolts are identified on the top of the head with the legend A325 or A490 and the manufacturer's mark. Bolts are available in a variety of sizes, from $\frac{5}{8}''$ to $1\frac{1}{2}''$ in diameter. However, the most typically used sizes in building construction are $\frac{3}{4}''$ and $\frac{7}{8}''$. Larger-diameter bolts generally require special equipment as well as increased spacing and edge distances for proper bolt placement. Allowable AISC shear capacities are listed in Table 1, and AISC allowable bearing values are contained in Table 2.

Figure 15 shows two plates held together by a high-strength bolt with a nut and two washers. When a high-strength bolt is tightened, a very high tensile force T develops in the bolt, thus tightly clamping the connected parts together. It is the resulting friction force S that resists the applied load; unlike unfinished bolts, there is no actual shear or bearing stress. When the joint load P exceeds the magnitude S, slip occurs. If there is slip between the plates, the edges of the plates are brought in contact with the shank of the bolt, thereby producing bearing and shearing stresses in the bolt. If there is no slip, the load P is transmitted from one plate to the other by the frictional resistance.

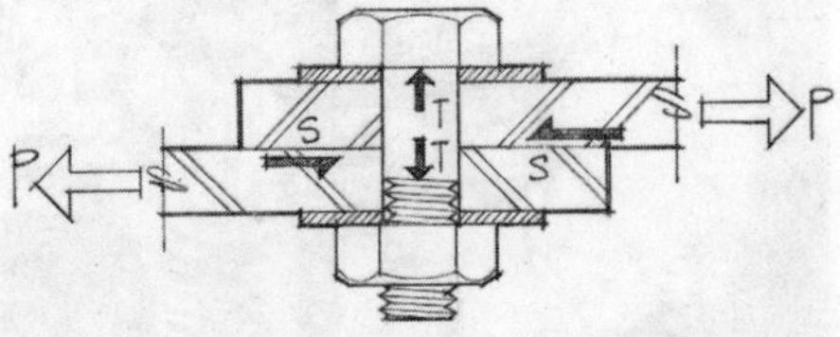

Figure 15 High-strength bolt in single shear.

Theoretically, the bolt's shank and the surfaces of the plates through which it passes are not in contact at all, because the holes are punched slightly larger than the bolt. Even when a connection of this type is subjected to vibration, the high residual tensile stress prevents loosening.

Mechanically fastened connections that transmit load by means of shear in their fasteners are categorized as either *slip-critical* (SC) or *bearing-type* (N or X). Slip-critical connections, also formerly referred to as *friction-type connections*, depend upon sufficiently high clamping force to prevent slip of the connected parts under anticipated service conditions.

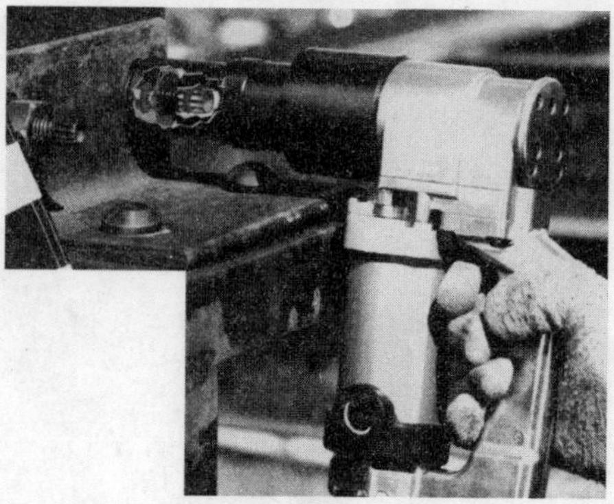

Figure 16 *Tension-control wrench. Image reprinted with permission. Courtesy of the LeJeune Bolt Company.*

Bearing-type connections are based on the contact (bearing) between the bolt(s) and the sides of the holes to transfer the load from one connected element to another.

Before tension is applied to high-strength bolts through tightening, the joint surfaces adjacent to bolt heads, nuts, or washers must be free of scale, burrs, dirt, and other foreign material.

Tightening of high-strength bolts in slip-critical connections is accomplished by special torque or impact wrenches to a tension equal to 70% of the specified minimum tensile strength of the bolt. The Research Council on Structural Connections provides four methods of controlling bolt tension: (a) the calibrated wrench, (b) the twist-off-type tension-control bolt, (c) the direct tension indicator, and (d) the turn-of-nut method, which requires specified additional nut rotation after the bolts are "snug tight." Snug tight is defined as the full effort of an iron worker with an ordinary spud wrench that brings the connected plies into firm contact. When bolts are not fully tensioned, the connections are designed as bearing-type connections, where a small amount of movement (slippage) is expected (Figures 16 and 17).

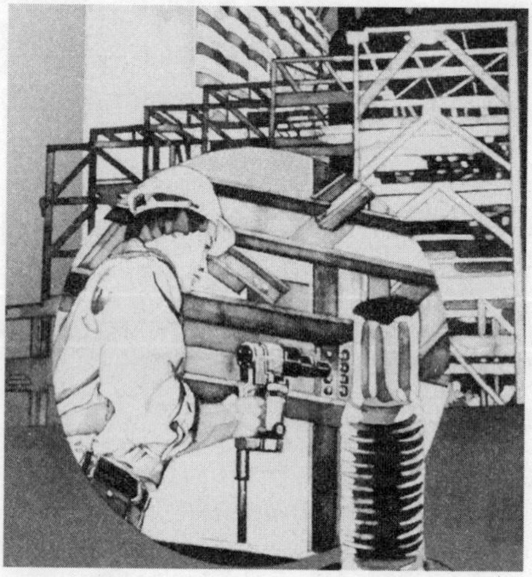

Figure 17 *"Snugging" the bolts and nuts with a tension-control wrench. Image reprinted with permission. Courtesy of the LeJeune Bolt Company.*

The high clamping force produced by the properly tightened A325 and A490 bolts is sufficient to assure that slippage between the connected parts will not occur at full allowable stress in slip-critical connections and probably will not occur at working loads in bearing-type connections. The allowable stress in bearing-type connections is based on a factor of safety of 2.0 or more, which over a long period of observation has been found to be adequate. This safety factor is higher than that used for the design of the connected member.

The allowable shear stresses for A325 and A490 bolts used in standard round holes are as follows:

A325-SC	F_v = 17 ksi (slip-critical connection, standard round hole).
A325-N	F_v = 21 ksi (bearing-type connection with threads included in shear plane).
A325-X	F_v = 30 ksi (bearing-type connection with threads excluded from shear plane).
A490-SC	F_v = 22 ksi (slip-critical connection, standard round hole).
A490-N	F_v = 28 ksi (bearing-type connection with threads included in shear plane).
A490-X	F_v = 40 ksi (bearing-type connection with threads excluded from shear plane).

See Table 1 for the allowable AISC shear stress of other bolts.

The efficiency of threaded fasteners in resisting shear in bearing-type connections is reduced when the bolt threads extend into the shear plane(s) between the connected plates (Figures 18 and 19). Allowable shear stress values remain the same for slip-critical connections that have bolt threads included in the shear planes.

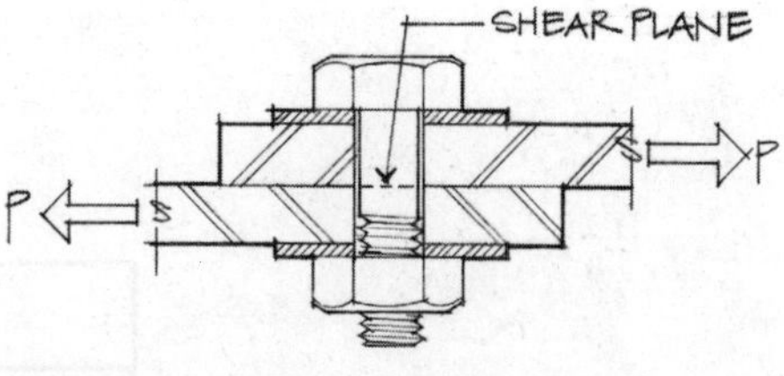

Figure 18 *Threads excluded from the shear plane.*

ASTM A325 and A490 high-strength bolts are purposefully proportioned and produced so that the threads can be excluded from the shear planes when it is desirable.

Several types of holes are typically used for bolted connections (Figure 20): (a) standard round holes, (b) oversized holes, (c) short-slotted holes, and (d) long-slotted holes.

Standard round holes are made $\frac{1}{16}''$ larger than the diameter of the bolt. In steel-to-steel structural connections, standard round holes can be used in many joint applications and, in some cases, are preferred. For example, standard round holes are commonly used in girder and beam connections to columns as a means of controlling the center-to-center dimension between columns and to facilitate the alignment of the column to a plumb position. Oversized and slotted holes are typically used in the field to reduce the fit-up and assembly time during erection.

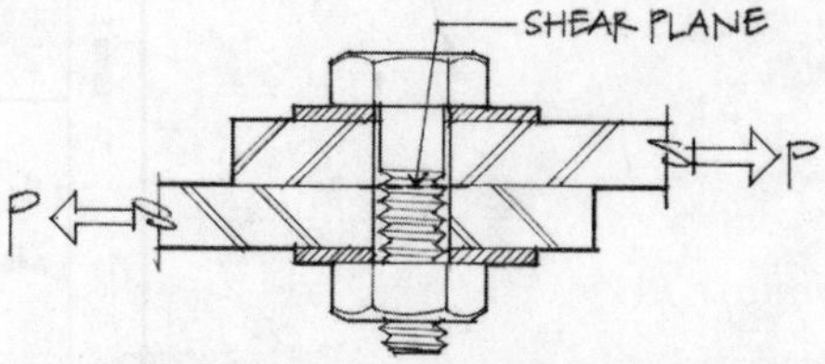

Figure 19 *Shear plane passing through threads.*

Oversized holes have nominal diameters up to $\frac{3}{16}''$ larger than bolts $\frac{7}{8}''$ and less in diameter, while bolts with a 1″ diameter will have a hole $\frac{1}{4}''$ larger. Oversize holes are permitted in slip-critical connections only.

Short-slotted holes are $\frac{1}{16}''$ wider than the bolt diameter and have a length that does not exceed the oversize hole dimensions by more than $\frac{1}{16}''$. This type of hole can be used in either bearing-type or slip-critical connections, but if used in bearing-type connections, the slots must be perpendicular to the direction of load.

Long-slotted holes are $\frac{1}{16}''$ wider than the bolt diameter and have a length not exceeding $2\frac{1}{2}$ times the bolt diameter. This type of connection may be used in slip-critical connections without regard for the load direction. However, in bearing-type connections, the load must be perpendicular to the slot direction. Slotted holes are particularly useful where some amount of field adjustment is necessary. Long-slotted holes can only be used in one of the connected members at a joint; the other member must use a standard round hole or be welded.

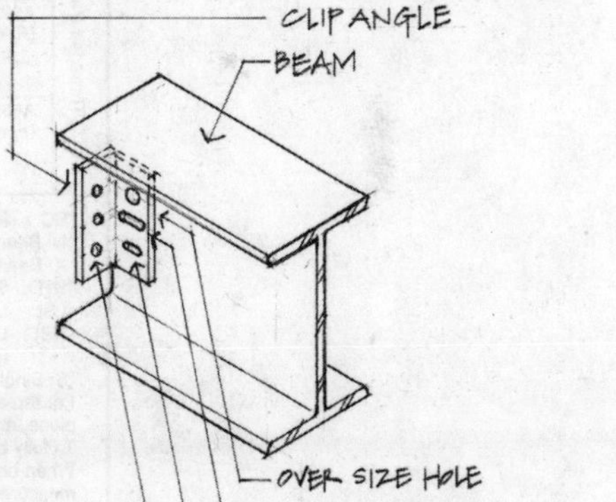

Figure 20 *Typically used hole types.*

Allowable shear stress values for bolts in slip-critical connections remain unchanged for the oversized and short-slotted holes. However, allowable shear stress values decrease when using long-slotted holes for loads applied perpendicular to the slot, and an even larger reduction occurs for loads applied parallel to the slot.

Table 1

BOLTS, THREADED PARTS AND RIVETS
Shear
Allowable load in kips

TABLE SHEAR

	ASTM Designation	Connection Type[a]	Hole Type[b]	F_V ksi	Loading[c]	Nominal Diameter d, in.							
						5/8	3/4	7/8	1	1 1/8	1 1/4	1 3/8	1 1/2
						Area (Based on Nominal Diameter) in.^{2}							
						.3068	.4418	.6013	.7854	.9940	1.227	1.485	1.767
Bolts	A307	—	STD NSL	10.0	S	3.1	4.4	6.0	7.9	9.9	12.3	14.8	17.7
					D	6.1	8.8	12.0	15.7	19.9	24.5	29.7	35.3
	A325	SC[a] Class A	STD	17.0	S	5.22	7.51	10.2	13.4	16.9	20.9	25.2	30.0
					D	10.4	15.0	20.4	26.7	33.8	41.7	50.5	60.1
			OVS, SSL	15.0	S	4.60	6.63	9.02	11.8	14.9	18.4	22.3	26.5
					D	9.20	13.3	18.0	23.6	29.8	36.8	44.6	53.0
			LSL	12.0	S	3.68	5.30	7.22	9.42	11.9	14.7	17.8	21.2
					D	7.36	10.6	14.4	18.8	23.9	29.4	35.6	42.4
		N	STD, NSL	21.0	S	6.4	9.3	12.6	16.5	20.9	25.8	31.2	37.1
					D	12.9	18.6	25.3	33.0	41.7	51.5	62.4	74.2
		X	STD, NSL	30.0	S	9.2	13.3	18.0	23.6	29.8	36.8	44.5	53.0
					D	18.4	26.5	36.1	47.1	59.6	73.6	89.1	106.0
	A490	SC[a] Class A	STD	21.0	S	6.44	9.28	12.6	16.5	20.9	25.8	31.2	37.1
					D	12.9	18.6	25.3	33.0	41.7	51.5	62.4	74.2
			OVS, SSL	18.0	S	5.52	7.95	10.8	14.1	17.9	22.1	26.7	31.8
					D	11.0	15.9	21.6	28.3	35.8	44.2	53.5	63.6
			LSL	15.0	S	4.60	6.63	9.02	11.8	14.9	18.4	22.3	26.5
					D	9.20	13.3	18.0	23.6	29.8	36.8	44.6	53.0
		N	STD, NSL	28.0	S	8.6	12.4	16.8	22.0	27.8	34.4	41.6	49.5
					D	17.2	24.7	33.7	44.0	55.7	68.7	83.2	99.0
		X	STD, NSL	40.0	S	12.3	17.7	24.1	31.4	39.8	49.1	59.4	70.7
					D	24.5	35.3	48.1	62.8	79.5	98.2	119.0	141.0
Rivets	A502-1	—	STD	17.5	S	5.4	7.7	10.5	13.7	17.4	21.5	26.0	30.9
					D	10.7	15.5	21.0	27.5	34.8	42.9	52.0	61.8
	A502-2 A502-3	—	STD	22.0	S	6.7	9.7	13.2	17.3	21.9	27.0	32.7	38.9
					D	13.5	19.4	26.5	34.6	43.7	54.0	65.3	77.7
Threaded Parts	A36 (F_u=58 ksi)	N	STD	9.9	S	3.0	4.4	6.0	7.8	9.8	12.1	14.7	17.5
					D	6.1	8.7	11.9	15.6	19.7	24.3	29.4	35.0
		X	STD	12.8	S	3.9	5.7	7.7	10.1	12.7	15.7	19.0	22.6
					D	7.9	11.3	15.4	20.1	25.4	31.4	38.0	45.2
	A572, Gr. 50 (F_u=65 ksi)	N	STD	11.1	S	3.4	4.9	6.7	8.7	11.0	13.6	16.5	19.6
					D	6.8	9.8	13.3	17.4	22.1	27.2	33.0	39.2
		X	STD	14.3	S	4.4	6.3	8.6	11.2	14.2	17.5	21.2	25.3
					D	8.8	12.6	17.2	22.5	28.4	35.1	42.5	50.5
	A588 (F_u=70 ksi)	N	STD	11.9	S	3.7	5.3	7.2	9.3	11.8	14.6	17.7	21.0
					D	7.3	10.5	14.3	18.7	23.7	29.2	35.3	42.1
		X	STD	15.4	S	4.7	6.8	9.3	12.1	15.3	18.9	22.9	27.2
					D	9.4	13.6	18.5	24.2	30.6	37.8	45.7	54.4

[a]SC = Slip critical connection.
N: Bearing-type connection with threads *included* in shear plane.
X: Bearing-type connection with threads *excluded* from shear plane.
[b]STD: Standard round holes (d + 1/16 in.) OVS: Oversize round holes
LSL: Long-slotted holes normal to load direction SSL: Short-slotted holes
NSL: Long-or short-slotted hole normal to load direction (required in bearing-type connection).
[c]S: Single shear D: Double shear.
For threaded parts of materials not listed, use $F_v = 0.17F_u$ when threads are included in a shear plane, and $F_v = 0.22F_u$ when threads are excluded from a shear plane.
To fully pretension bolts 1 1/8-in. dia. and greater, special impact wrenches may be required.
When bearing-type connections used to splice tension members have a fastener pattern whose length, measured parallel to the line of force, exceeds 50 in., tabulated values shall be reduced by 20%. See AISC ASD Commentary Sect. J3.4.

Table 2

BOLTS AND THREADED PARTS
Bearing
Allowable loads in kips

TABLE BEARING
Slip-critical and Bearing-type Connections

Material Thickness	F_u = 58 ksi Bolt dia.			F_u = 65 ksi Bolt dia.			F_u = 70 ksi Bolt dia.			F_u = 100 ksi Bolt dia.		
	3/4	7/8	1	3/4	7/8	1	3/4	7/8	1	3/4	7/8	1
1/8	6.5	7.6	8.7	7.3	8.5	9.8	7.9	9.2	10.5	11.3	13.1	15.0
3/16	9.8	11.4	13.1	11.0	12.8	14.6	11.8	13.8	15.8	16.9	19.7	22.5
1/4	13.1	15.2	17.4	14.6	17.1	19.5	15.8	18.4	21.0	22.5	26.3	30.0
5/16	16.3	19.0	21.8	18.3	21.3	24.4	19.7	23.0	26.3	28.1	32.8	37.5
3/8	19.6	22.8	26.1	21.9	25.6	29.3	23.6	27.6	31.5	33.8	39.4	45.0
7/16	22.8	26.6	30.5	25.6	29.9	34.1	27.6	32.2	36.8		45.9	52.5
1/2	26.1	30.5	34.8	29.3	34.1	39.0	31.5	36.8	42.0			60.0
9/16	29.4	34.3	39.2	32.9	38.4	43.9		41.3	47.3			
5/8	32.6	38.1	43.5		42.7	48.8		45.9	52.5			
11/16		41.9	47.9		46.9	53.6			57.8			
3/4		45.7	52.2			58.5						
13/16			56.6									
7/8			60.9									
15/16												
1	52.2	60.9	69.6	58.5	68.3	78.0	63.0	73.5	84.0	90.0	105.0	120.0

Notes:
This table is applicable to all mechanical fasteners in both slip-critical and bearing-type connections utilizing standard holes. Standard holes shall have a diameter nominally 1/16-in. larger than the nominal bolt diameter (d + 1/16 in.).
Tabulated bearing values are based on $F_p = 1.2\ F_u$.
F_u = specified minimum tensile strength of the connected part.
In connections transmitting axial force whose length between extreme fasteners measured parallel to the line of force exceeds 50 in., tabulated values shall be reduced 20%.
Connections using high-strength bolts in slotted holes with the load applied in a direction other than approximately normal (between 80 and 100 degrees) to the axis of the hole and connections with bolts in oversize holes shall be designed for resistance against slip at working load in accordance with AISC ASD Specification Sect. J3.8.
Tabulated values apply when the distance l parallel to the line of force from the center of the bolt to the edge of the connected part is not less than 1½ d and the distance from the center of a bolt to the center of an adjacent bolt is not less than $3d$. See AISC ASD Commentary J3.8.
Under certain conditions, values greater than the tabulated values may be justified under Specification Sect. J3.7.
Values are limited to the double-shear bearing capacity of A490-X bolts.
Values for decimal thicknesses may be obtained by multiplying the decimal value of the unlisted thickness by the value given for a 1-in. thickness.

Example Problems

1 Determine the allowable load capacity of the connection shown in Figure 21 if $\frac{7}{8}''\phi$ A307 unfinished bolts are used with standard-size round holes. Assume the plates are A36 steel.

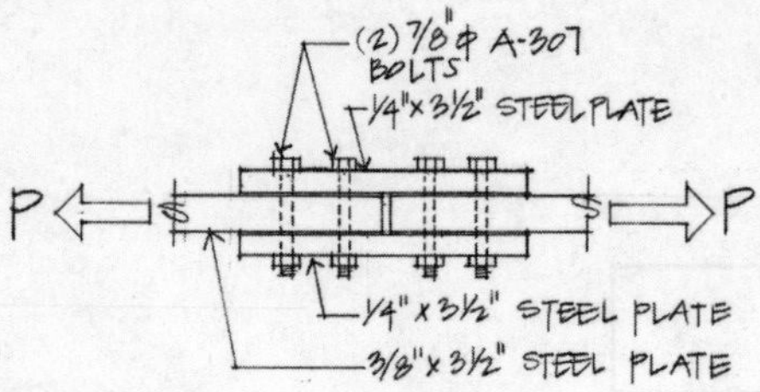

Figure 21 Typical butt splice.

Solution:

Three possible failure modes could occur in this typical butt splice condition. Shear, bearing, and net tension will be checked to determine the critical condition that governs the connection capacity.

Shear—Double Shear

Take a section cut through the connection at the butt splice, and draw an FBD for one-half of the assembly. The bolts pass through three plates and are thus subjected to double shear. The general equation for determining the shear capacity of this connection is

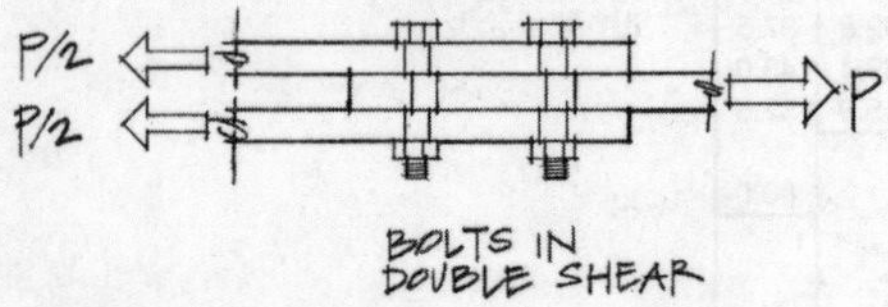

Bolts in double shear.

$$P_v = F_v \times A_v$$

where

$$F_v = 10\,\text{ksi (see Table 1)}$$

$$A_v = 2\,\text{bolts} \times \underset{\text{double shear}}{2} \times \left(\pi \times \frac{d^2}{4}\right)$$

$$A_v = 2 \times 2 \times \left[\pi \times \frac{\left(\frac{7}{8}\right)^2}{4}\right] = 2.41\,\text{in.}^2$$

$$P_v = F_v \times A_v = 10\,\text{k/in.}^2 \times 24.1\,\text{in.}^2 = 24.1\,\text{k}$$

Another way of obtaining the same result but minimizing some of the computations is to use Table .1, where the actual load capacities of commonly used bolt sizes and grades are given for both single and double shear.

$$\therefore P_v = 2\,\text{bolts} \times 12\,\text{k/bolt} = 24\,\text{k} \quad \text{(in double shear)}$$

Bearing

Unfinished bolts are checked for bearing in which, assuming standard round holes, the allowable stress is taken as

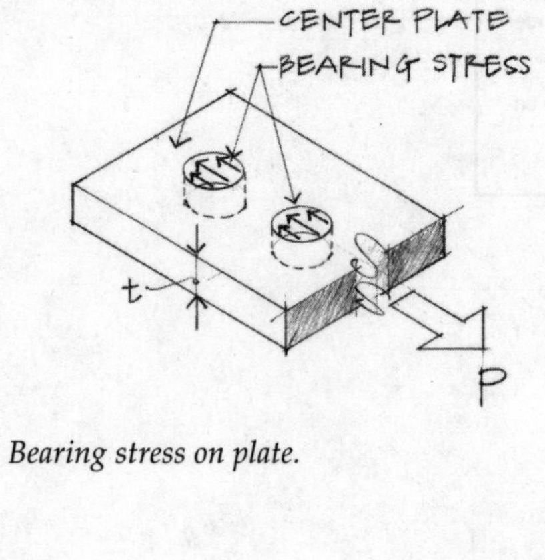

Bearing stress on plate.

$$F_p = 1.2F_u$$

where

$$F_u = 58\,\text{ksi for A36 steel}$$

$$F_p = 1.2 \times (58\,\text{ksi}) = 69.6\,\text{ksi}$$

The center plate is critical.

$$\therefore P_p = 2\text{ bolts} \times \left(\tfrac{3}{8}'' \times \tfrac{7}{8}''\right) \times 69.6\text{ k/in.}^2 = 45.7\text{ k}$$

Or, using the AISC allowable bearing in Table 2,

$$P_p = 2\text{ bolts} \times 22.8\text{ k/bolt} = 45.6\text{ k}$$

Remember that bearing failure is in the plate material being connected and not in the connector (bolt).

Net Tension—At Connection

Net tension results in the tearing of the plate due to insufficient material (cross-section) to resist the tension stress. The number and placement of bolts in a row across the connection greatly influences the susceptibility of the plate to net tension failure.

$$F_t = 0.5F_u = 0.5(58\text{ ksi})29\text{ ksi}$$

$$A_{net} = \left(\tfrac{3}{8}''\right) \times \left(3\tfrac{1}{2}'' - \tfrac{15}{16}''\right) = 0.96\text{ in.}^2$$

$$P_t = 0.96\text{ in.}^2 \times 29\text{ k/in.}^2 = 27.8\text{ k}$$

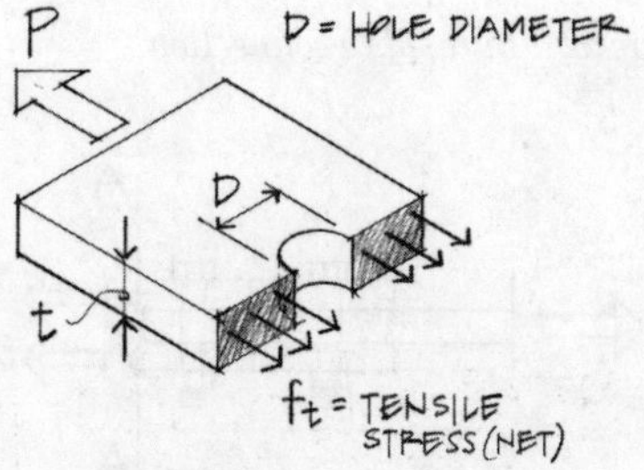

Net tension stress.

Tension on the gross area of the plate (in a region beyond the connection):

$$A_{gross} = \left(\tfrac{3}{8}''\right) \times \left(3\tfrac{1}{2}''\right) = 1.31\text{ in.}^2$$

$$P_t = F_t \times A_{gross}$$

and

$$F_t = 0.6F_y = 0.6(36\text{ ksi}) = 22\text{ ksi}$$

$$\therefore \underset{(gros)}{P_t} = 1.31\text{ in.}^2 \times 22\text{ k/in.}^2 = 28.2\text{ k}$$

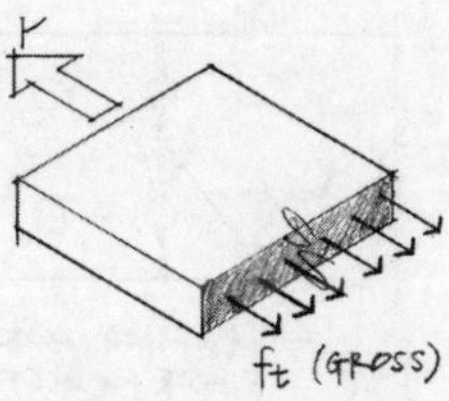

Tension stress on the gross area of bar.

Because the shear check resulted in the smallest allowable value, it governs the capacity of the connection.

$$\therefore P_{allowable} = 24\text{ k}$$

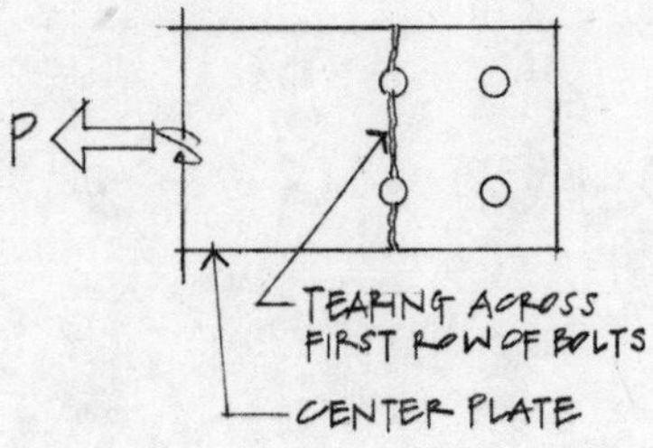

Figure 22 *Butt splice connection.*

2 The butt splice shown in Figure 22 uses two $8 \times \frac{3}{8}''$ plates to "sandwich" in the $8 \times \frac{1}{2}''$ plates being joined. Four $\frac{7}{8}''\phi$ A325-SC bolts are used on both sides of the splice. Assuming A36 steel and standard round holes, determine the allowable capacity of the connection.

Solution:

Shear, bearing, and net tension will be checked to determine the critical condition that governs the capacity of the connection.

Shear: Using the AISC allowable shear in Table 1,

$$P_v = 20.4 \text{ k/bolt} \times 4 \text{ bolts} = 81.6 \text{ k (double shear)}$$

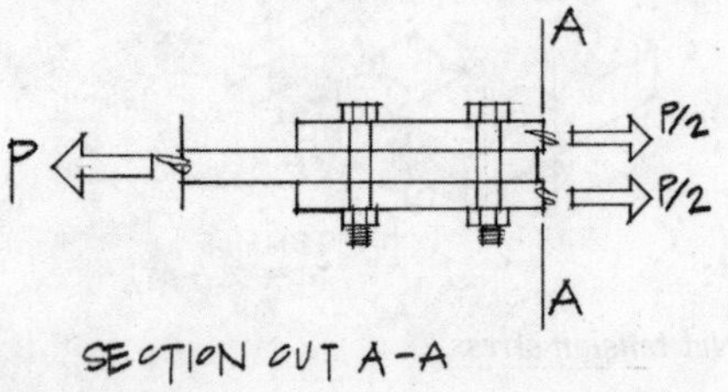

Section cut A–A.

Bearing: Use the AISC allowable bearing value found in Table 2.

The thinner material with the largest proportional load governs; therefore, the $\frac{1}{2}''$ center plate governs. Assume the bolts are at a 3*d* spacing, center to center.

$$P_b = 30.5 \text{ k/bolt} \times 4 \text{ bolts} = 122 \text{ k}$$

Tension: The center plate is critical, because its thickness is less than the combined thickness of the two outer plates.

$$\text{Hole diameter} = (\text{bolt diameter}) + \frac{1}{16}'' = \frac{7}{8}'' + \frac{1}{16}''$$
$$= \frac{15}{16}''$$

$$P_t = F_t \times A_{net}$$

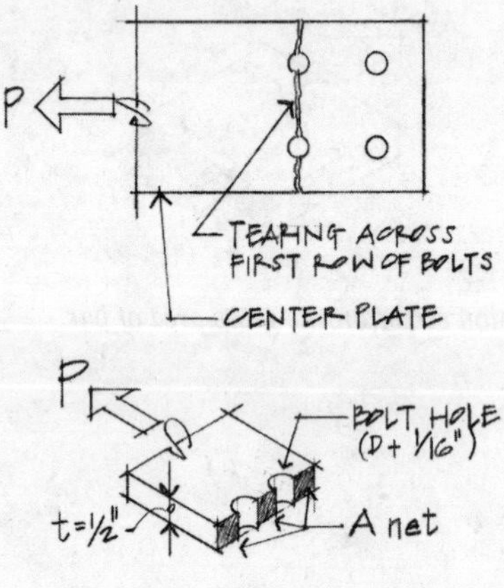

where

$$F_t = 0.5\,F_u = 0.5(58 \text{ ksi}) = 29 \text{ ksi}$$
$$P_t = 29 \text{ k/in.}^2 \times 3.06 \text{ in.}^2 = 88.7 \text{ k}$$

The maximum connection capacity is governed by shear.

$$P_{allow} = 81.6 \text{ k}$$

3 A simple truss connection is accomplished using A325-N bolts in standard round holes. Determine the size of the bolts required for the load condition shown in Figure 23.

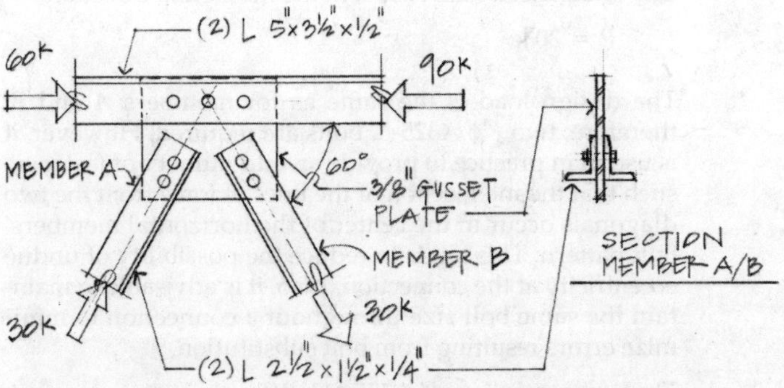

Figure 23 Typical truss connection with gusset plate.

Solution:

Each truss member will be examined individually to determine the minimum number of bolts required. Shear and bearing will be checked in each design. However, no net tension computation will be made, because the double angles and gusset plate have large cross-sectional areas.

Diagonal Members A and B

Shear: Double shear, two bolts:

$$\frac{30\text{ k}}{2\text{ bolts}} = 15\text{ k/bolt}$$

Using Table 1,

$$2 - \tfrac{3}{4}''\phi\text{ A325-N } (P_v = 2 \times 18.6\text{ k/bolt} = 37.2\text{ k})$$

Bearing: The $\frac{3}{8}''$ gusset plate is critical in bearing.

$$A_{\text{bolt}} = \frac{15\text{ k/bolt}}{F_p} = \frac{15\text{ k}}{69.6\text{ k/in.}^2} = 0.216\text{ in.}^2$$

Bearing area:

$$A_p = d \times t = 0.216\text{ in.}^2$$

$$d = \frac{0.216\text{ in.}^2}{\frac{3}{8}''.} = 0.576\text{ in.}$$

Two $\frac{5}{8}''\phi$ bolts are necessary for bearing.

Shear governs the design; therefore, use two $\frac{3}{4}''\phi$ bolts.

Horizontal Member C

The unbalanced load is 30 k in the horizontal direction.

$$P = 30\,\text{k}$$

The design load is the same as for members *A* and *B*; therefore, two $\frac{3}{4}''\phi$ A325-N bolts are required. However, it is useful in practice to provide an odd number of fasteners such that the intersection of the lines of force from the two diagonals occur in the center of the horizontal members' bolt pattern. This tends to reduce the possibility of undue eccentricity at the connection. Also, it is advisable to maintain the same bolt size throughout a connection to minimize errors resulting from bolt substitution.

Therefore, use three $\frac{3}{4}''$ A325-N bolts.

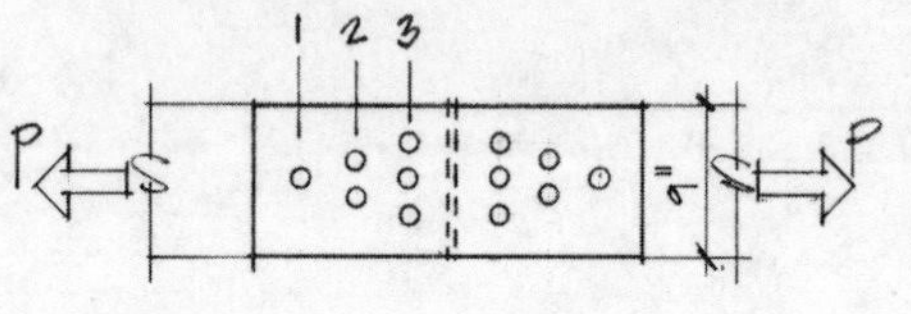

Figure 24 A typical bolt pattern.

4 For the three-row bolted butt joint shown in Figure 24, determine the load that can be carried based on shear, bearing, and tension. Assume A325-SC bolts in standard round holes.

Solution:

Shear: Six $\frac{3}{4}''\phi$ bolts in double shear (see Table 1):

$$P_v = 6\text{ bolts} \times 15\,\text{k/bolt} = 90\,\text{k}$$

Bearing: The center plate is critical in bearing. Using Table 2,

$$P_p = 6\text{ bolts} \times 26.1\,\text{k/bolt} = 156.6\,\text{k}$$

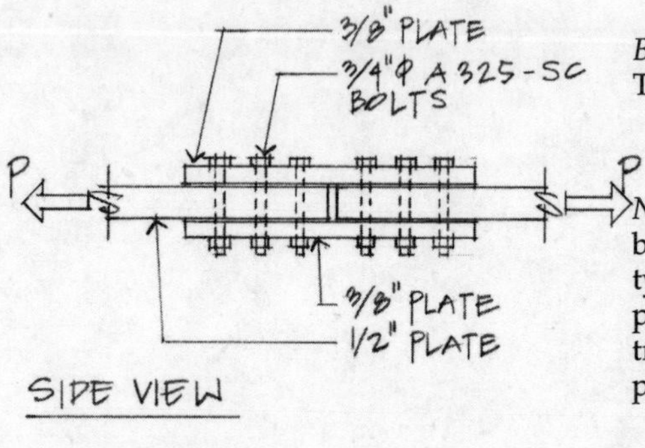

Net Tension: The tension capability of the plate (center) will be checked across the three rows of bolts. This particular type of bolt arrangement is sometimes used to reduce the possibility of net tension failure. The idea is to have the load transfer through the rows of bolts, diminishing the force progressively for each subsequent row of bolts.

Section 1

$F_t = 29\text{ ksi}$

Hole diameter $D = \frac{3}{4}'' + \frac{1}{16}'' = 0.8125''$

$A_{net} = \frac{1}{2}'' \times (9'' - 0.813'') = 4.1\text{ in.}^2$
(across one bolt)

$P_{t_1} = F_t \times A_{net} = 29\text{ k/in.}^2 \times 4.1\text{ in.}^2$

Section 2

The bolt across section 1 reduces the total tensile load occurring at section 2. Therefore, the tensile capacity of section 2 will include the shear contribution of one bolt from section 1.

$A_{net} = \frac{1}{2}'' \times (9'' - 2 \times 0.813'') = 3.69\text{ in.}^2$
(across two bolts)

$P_{t_2} = (29\text{ k/in.}^2 \times 3.69\text{ in.}^2) + \underset{\text{(1 bolt in shear)}}{15\text{ k}} = 92\text{ k}$

Section 3

This section will include the shear contribution of bolts in sections 1 and 2. The net area of the plate across the row of bolts at section 3 is

$A_{net} = \frac{1}{2}'' \times (9'' - 3 \times 0.813'') = 3.28\text{ in.}^2$

$P_{t_3} = 29\text{ k/in.}^2 \times 3.28\text{ in.}^2 + 3(15\text{ k}) = 140.1\text{ k}$

Based on examining the conditions of shear, bearing, and net tension across three different sections, the capacity of the connection is governed by shear:

$P_{allow} = P_v = 90\text{ k}$

Problems

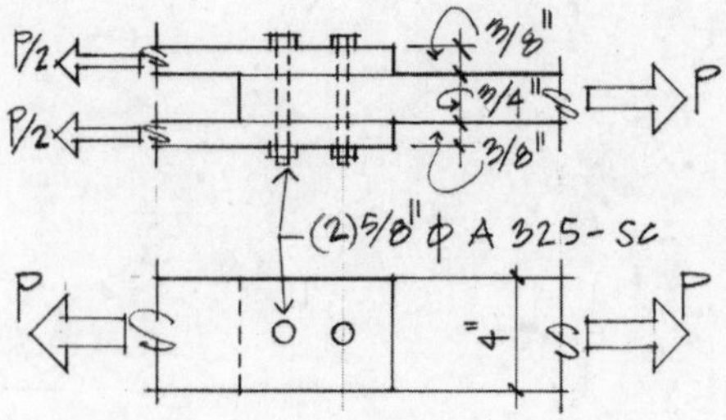

1 Determine the allowable load P permitted for this double shear joint connection assuming A36 steel and A325-SC bolts in standard round holes.

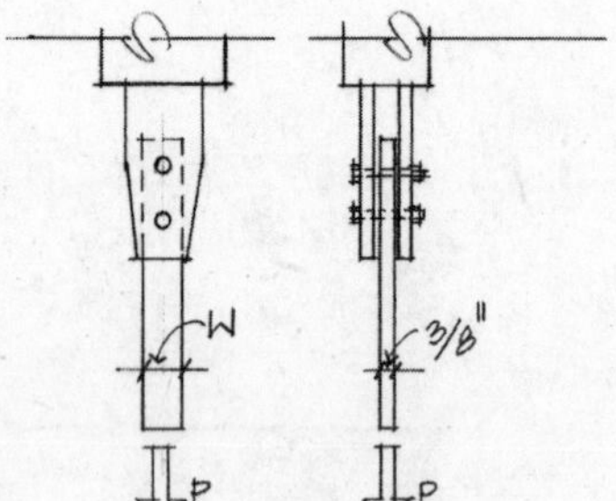

2 The vertical steel bar shown is $\frac{3}{8}''$ thick and must be designed to withstand a tensile load $P = 28$ k. Two A325-X bolts will be used. Assuming A36 material and standard round holes, calculate the following:

a. The required diameter d of the bolts.

b. The required width W of the bar.

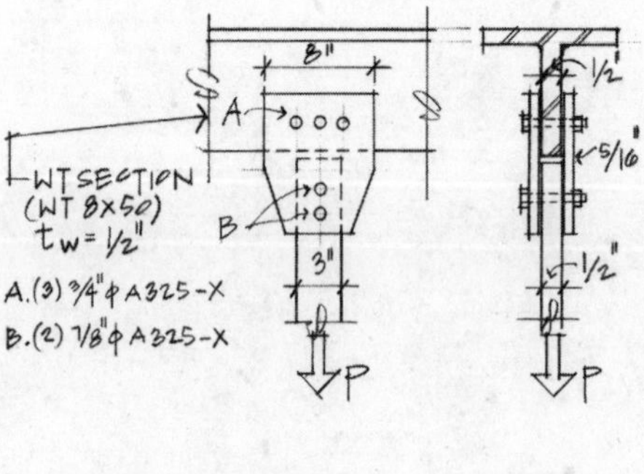

3 A connection of the type shown uses three $\frac{3}{4}''\phi$ A325-X (STD) bolts in the upper connection and two $\frac{7}{8}''\phi$ A325-X (STD) bolts in the three inch bar. What is the maximum load P that this connection can support?

***Note:** This is an academic exercise. Generally, it is not advisable to use different-sized bolts in the same connection.*

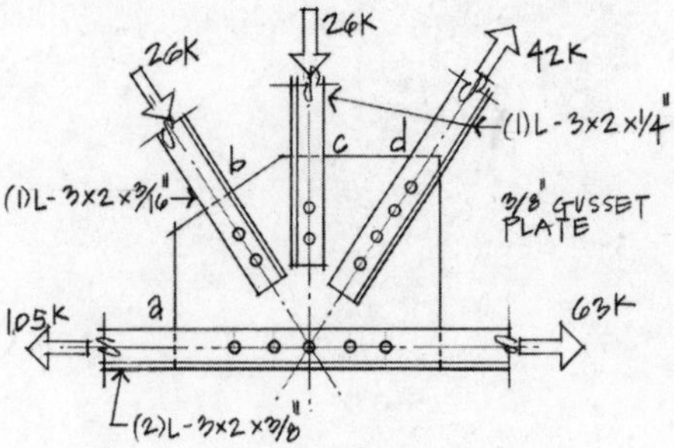

4 Determine the number of bolts necessary for each member framing into the truss joint shown. Bolts are $\frac{3}{4}''\phi$ A325-X (NSL), and members are A36 steel.

5 Determine the capacity of this butt splice based on shear, bearing, and net tension. The plates are made of A36 steel, and the four bolts on each side of the splice are A325-SC with standard round holes.

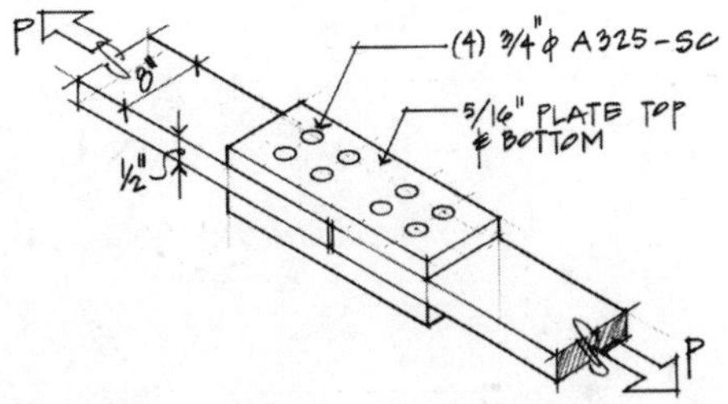

6 A suspension bridge over a river uses a system of linked bars connected as shown for the main suspension system. Assuming A36 steel and A490-X bolts, determine the maximum load P that the system can carry. Check for shear, bearing, and net tension at the bolt and tension of the member.

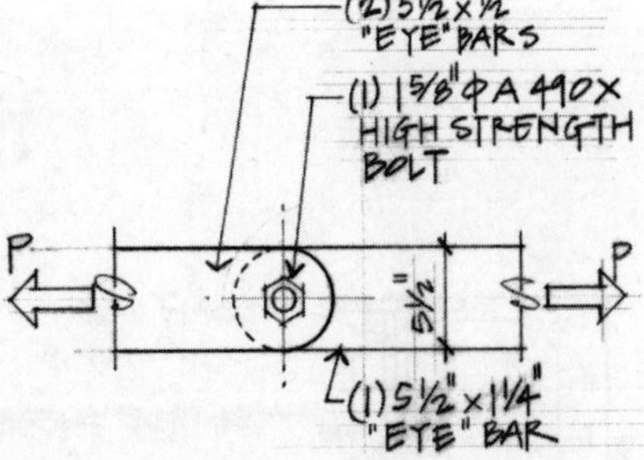

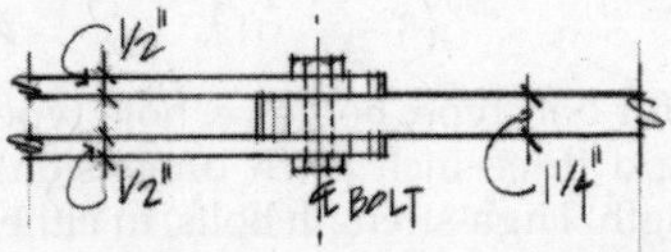

Standard Framed Beam Connections

Standard AISC tables are available to cover the design of a vast majority of typical structural connections where filler beams frame into girders or girders frame into columns (Figures 25 and 26). This type of standard shear connection consists of two clip angles placed back to back on either side of the beam or girder web.

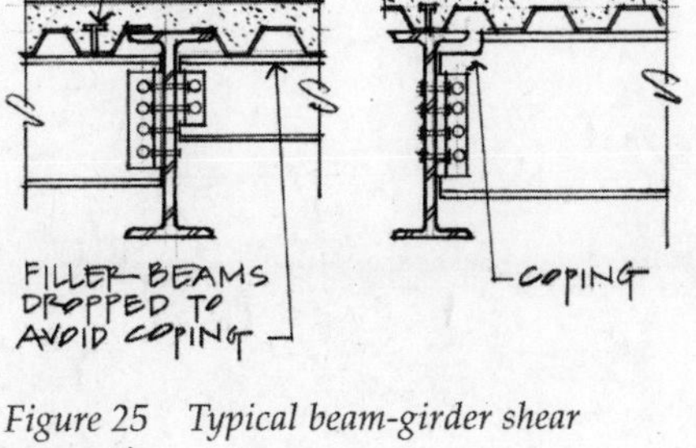

Figure 25 Typical beam-girder shear connection.

When a beam frames into a girder such that the upper surfaces of the top flanges are at the same elevation, the term *flush top* is used. To accomplish this, it is necessary to cut away a portion of the upper flange as shown in the illustration on the right in Figure 25. This is known as *coping*, or *blocking*, and for economy, it should be avoided whenever possible.

Framed beam connections are generally designed for shear, bearing, and web tear-out or block shear (for beams with the top flange coped). A sample AISC table is shown in Table 3 for use in designing slip-critical and bearing-type connections based on shear capacity for standard-size holes. Other AISC tables (not included in this text) are used to check the bearing and web tear-out capacities.

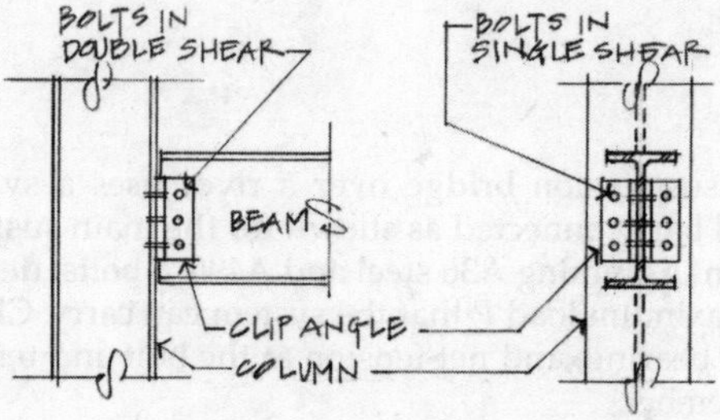

Figure 26 Standard framed beam-column connection.

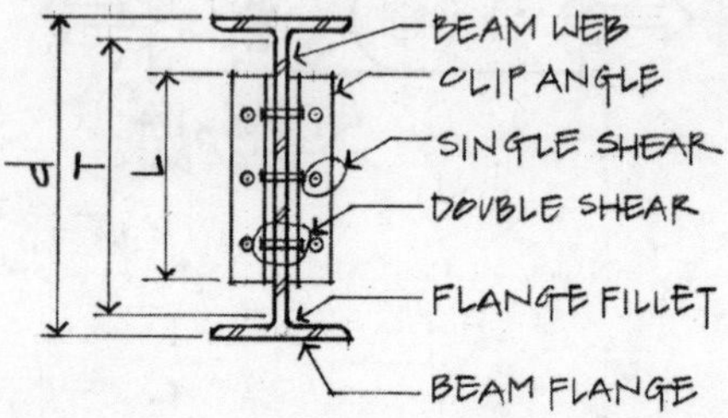

Figure 27 Beam cross-section with clip angles.

Table 3 has provisions for bolt type, bolt size, hole type, number of bolts (using a three inch pitch dimension), angle thickness, and length. High-strength bolts, in either slip-critical or bearing-type connections, assume a double shear condition through the beam web and a single shear attachment to the column flange or girder web. Clip angle thickness and length are dependent on the fastener size, the magnitude of the applied load, and space limitation within the beam's flanges. Angles must be able to fit between the clearance of top and bottom flange fillets (Figure 27). Angle lengths are generally at least one-half of the beam's depth to provide some resistance to end rotation at the beam's end.

Table 3 .

FRAMED BEAM CONNECTIONS
Bolted
TABLE Allowable loads in kips

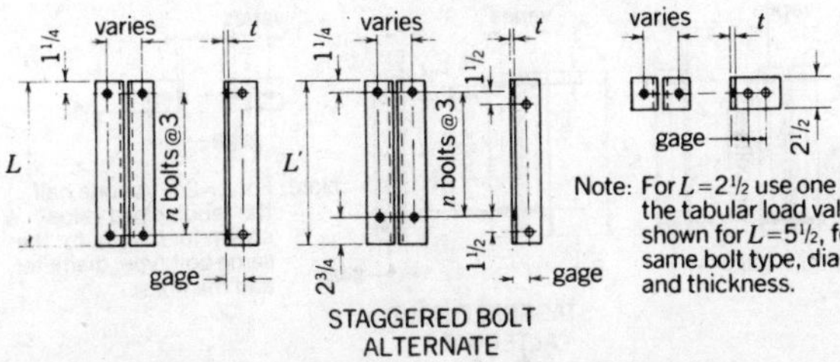

Note: For $L = 2^1/_2$ use one half the tabular load value shown for $L = 5^1/_2$, for the same bolt type, diameter, and thickness.

TABLE Bolt Shear[a]

For A307 bolts in standard or slotted holes and for A325 and A490 bolts in slip-critical connections with standard holes and Class A, clean mill scale surface condition.

Bolt Type			A307			A325-SC			A490-SC		
F_v, Ksi			10.0			17.0			21.0		
Bolt Dia., *d* In.			¾	⅞	1	¾	⅞	1	¾	⅞	1
Angle Thickness *t*, In.			¼	¼	¼	¼	5/16	½	5/16	½	⅝
L In.	*L'* In.	*n*									
29½	31	10	88.4	120	157	150	204	267	186	253	330
26½	28	9	79.5	108	141	135	184	240	167	227	297
23½	25	8	70.7	96.2	126	120	164	214	148	202	264
20½	22	7	61.9	84.2	110	105	143	187	130	177	231
17½	19	6	53.0	72.2	94.2	90.1	123	160	111	152	198
14½	16	5	44.2	60.1	78.5	75.1	102	134	92.8	126	165
11½	13	4	35.3	48.1	62.8	60.1	81.8	107	74.2	101	132
8½	10	3	26.5	36.1	47.1[b]	45.1	61.3	80.1	55.7	75.8	99.0
5½	7	2	17.7	24.1	31.4[b]	30.0	40.9	53.4	37.1	50.5	66.0

Note:
For slip-critical connections with oversize or slotted holes, see Table II-B.

Notes:

[a]Tabulated load values are based on double shear of bolts unless noted. See RCSC Specification for other surface conditions.

[b]Capacity shown is based on double shear of the bolts; however, for length *L*, net shear on the angle thickness specified is critical. See Table II-C.

Table 3 Continued.

FRAMED BEAM CONNECTIONS
Bolted
TABLE Allowable loads in kips

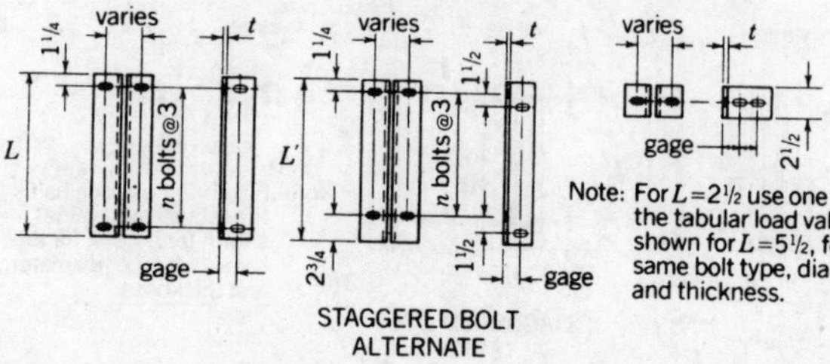

Note: For $L=2\frac{1}{2}$ use one half the tabular load value shown for $L=5\frac{1}{2}$, for the same bolt type, diameter, and thickness.

TABLE Bolt Shear[a]

For bolts in **bearing-type** connections with standard or slotted holes.

Bolt Type			A325-N			A490-N			A325-X			A490-X		
F_v, Ksi			21.0			28.0			30.0			40.0		
Bolt Dia., *d* In.			¾	⅞	1	¾	⅞	1	¾	⅞	1	¾	⅞	1
Angle Thickness *t*, In.			5⁄16	⅜	⅝	⅜	½	⅝	⅜	⅝	⅝	½	⅝	⅝
L In.	*L′* In.	*n*												
29½	31	10	186	253	330	247	337	440[b]	265	361	[c]	353	481	[c]
26½	28	9	167	227	297	223	303	396[b]	239	325	[c]	318	433	[c]
23½	25	8	148	202	264	198	269	352[b]	212	289	[c]	283	385	[c]
20½	22	7	130	177	231	173	236	308[b]	186	253	[c]	247	337	[c]
17½	19	6	111	152	198	148	202	264[b]	159	216	283	212	289	377
14½	16	5	92.8	126	165	124	168	220[b]	133	180	236	177	242	314
11½	13	4	74.2	101	132	99.0	135	176[b]	106	144	188	141	192	251
8½	10	3	55.7	75.8[b]	99.0	74.2	101[b]	132[b]	79.5[b]	108	141	106[b]	144	188
5½	7	2	37.1	50.5[b]	66.0	49.5	67.3[b]	88.0[b]	53.0[b]	72.2	94	70.7[b]	96	126

[a]Tabulated load values are based on double shear of bolts unless noted. See RCSC Specification for other surface conditions.

[b]Capacity shown is based on double shear of the bolts; however, for length *L*, net shear on the angle thickness specified is critical. See Table II-C.

[c]Capacity is governed by net shear on angles for lengths *L* and *L′*. See Table II-C.

Example Problems

5 Using the AISC framed beam connection bolt shear in Table 3, determine the shear adequacy of the connection shown in Figure 28. What thickness and angle length are required?

End beam reaction = 60 k.

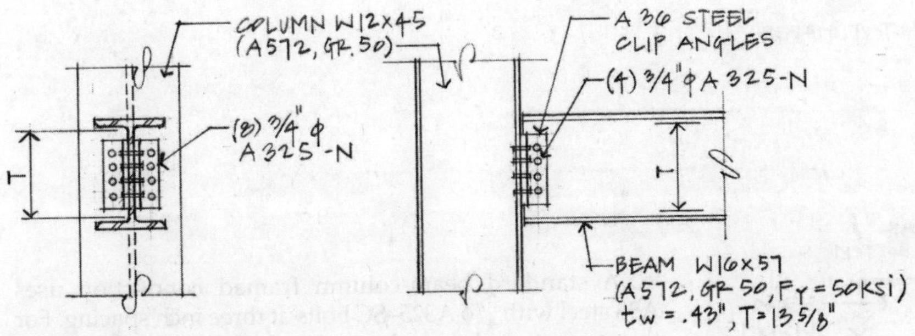

Figure 28 Typical beam-column connection.

Solution:

Enter a bolt diameter of $\frac{3}{4}''\phi$ (from Table 3), A325-N type fasteners, and $n = 4$ bolts in double shear through the beam web.

The shear allowable = 74.2 k > 60 k.

The connection is adequate in shear.

Angles are $\frac{5}{16}''$ thick and have a length of $L = 11\frac{1}{2}''$. Because the angles are less than the clear dimension T between the flange fillets, there should not be a problem of fit.

6 Determine the number of bolts required for the connection in Figure 29 based on shear if the end reaction is 120 k. What is the required angle thickness and length? Does the angle fit within the flanges?

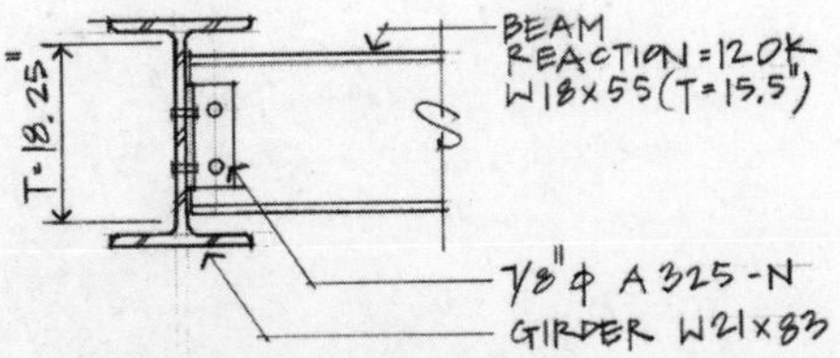

Figure 29 Typical beam-girder shear connection.

Solution:

From Table 3, this connection requires five $\frac{7}{8}''\phi$ A325-N bolts through the beam web and ten $\frac{7}{8}''\phi$ bolts through the girder web.

Shear capacity = 126 k > 120 k.

Angles are $\frac{3}{8}''$ thick and $14\frac{1}{2}''$ long.

Because $T = 15.5''$ is greater than $L = 14.5''$, the connection angles should fit adequately between the flanges.

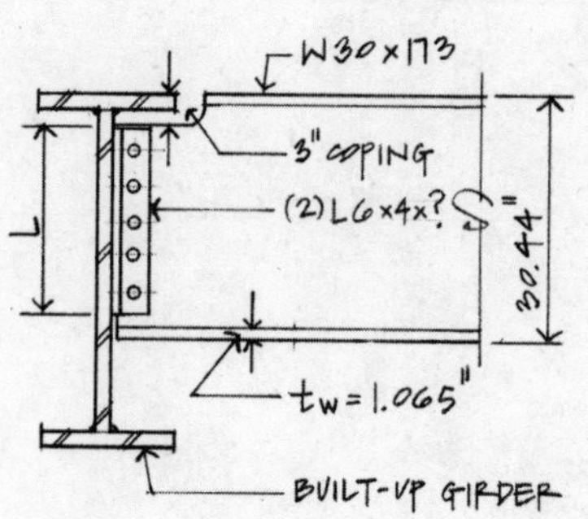

Problems

7 A beam-to-girder connection is bolted using two clip angles and five A490-X bolts as shown. The beam reaction is equal to 210 kips. Assuming A36 steel and three inch bolt spacing, determine the bolt diameter required, the clip angle thickness, and the angle length.

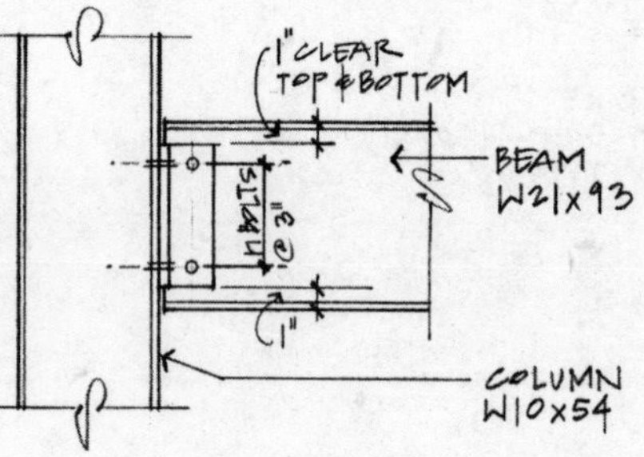

8 A standard beam-column framed connection uses A36 steel with $\frac{3}{4}$"ϕ A325–SC bolts at three inch spacing. For the connection shown, determine the following:

a. The maximum allowable shear capacity for the connection.

b. The number of bolts required.

c. The length L of the clip angle.

2 WELDED CONNECTIONS

Welding, as ordinarily considered for structural use, may be defined as a method of joining metals by fusion without the application of pressure. The metal at the joint, together with additional metal supplied in the form of filler metal (from an electrode), is melted, forming a small pool or crater. Upon cooling, the weld and base metal form a continuous and almost homogeneous joint. Many welding processes are recognized by the AWS, but for structural steel used in building construction, arc welding is the method generally used. For this text, the term *welding* refers to arc welding, in which the fusion process occurs by the generation of heat from an electric arc. Arc welding was first made possible by the discovery of the electric arc by Sir Humphrey Davy (see Figure 1 at the beginning of the chapter) early in the 19th century. He also developed the methodology of starting and maintaining an electric arc.

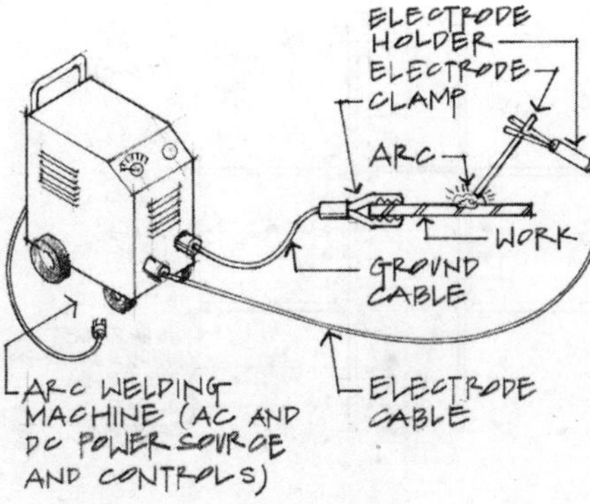

Figure 30 The welding circuit.

Electric arc welding requires a power source connected in a circuit that includes a ground cable to the piece being welded and, on the electrode cable, the electrode holder and electrode (Figure 30).

A sustained arc is formed between the work to be welded and the electrode in a gap, completing the electrical circuit. The resistance from the air or gas in the gap transforms the electrical energy into heat at extremely high temperatures (approximately 6,500°F at the electrode tip). Intense heat is generated by the arc in which the base metal and electrode filler metal liquefy (at a temperature in excess of 3,000°F) into a pool (called a *crater*). As the molten metal cools and solidifies, the metals are joined into a metallurgically solid, homogeneous piece.

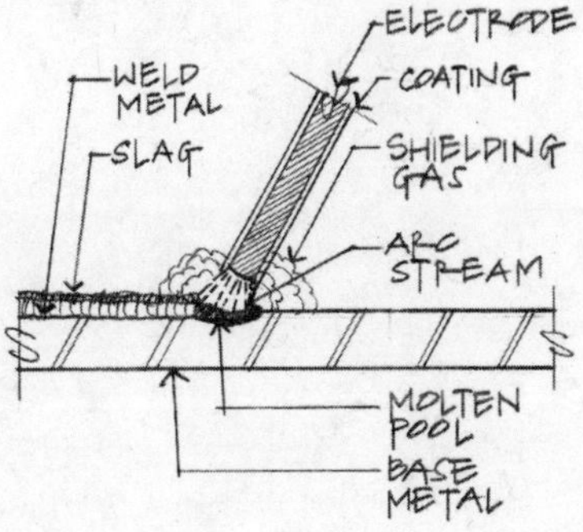

Figure 31 Shielded metal arc welding.

Shielded metal arc welding (Figure 31) is used to control the oxidation of the molten pool to prevent porosity in the metal (causing embrittlement) and to control the melting of the rod for more effective penetrative power.

Shielding in manual arc welding is generally accomplished through the use of a chemical coating on the electrode, while automatic welding frequently uses a powdered flux to submerge the arc and protect the molten metal from air.

In recent years, great advances have been made in automatic and semiautomatic welding processes so that manual welding today is generally limited to short welds and field welding (welding done at the site). A very common practice for making a structural connection is to shop weld a connecting device—clip angles, bearing plates, and so on—to one member and then fasten through bolting to a connecting member in the field.

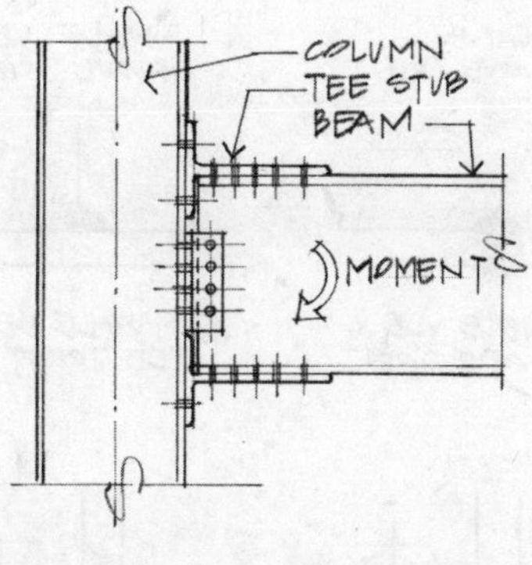

Figure 32 Bolted tee-stub moment connection—not recommended for new construction.

In some instances, such as in moment-resisting connections, fully welded joints are a reasonable option. Because welded members can be attached together for moment capability without using connecting plates or angles (Figures 32 and 33), the welded connection is usually simpler, is more compact, and requires a smaller crew.

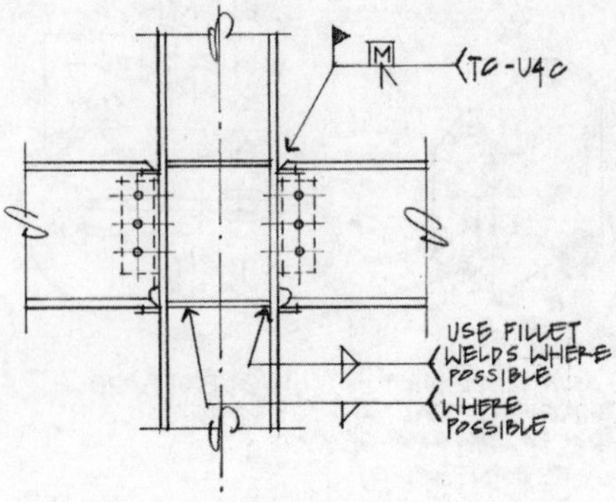

Figure 33 Typical welded moment connection.

Holes for bolts are avoided; therefore, the gross section rather than the net section is used to determine the cross-sectional area of members in tension.

On occasion, problems will arise in the application of welding to structural connections. The selection of a wrong electrode, use of an improper amperage/voltage setting on the welding machine, too rapid a cooling rate of the weld, and development of internal stresses from differential cooling are some of the factors affecting proper weldments. In the past, these considerations were primarily the concern of the welder. However, with the inception of better methods and standardization, much of this responsibility has now been shifted from the welder to the AWS welding code. Seriously flawed work has been substantially eliminated by requiring each welder to pass rigid qualification tests and submit his or her work to the careful scrutiny of a trained inspector. To further test the safety of welded joints, ultrasonic testing and magnetic particle inspection are occasionally used to locate internal flaws.

Designers of structural connections, whether bolted or welded, should always be aware of the actual conditions during the erection procedure to facilitate that process and to provide for an economical solution. A wide variety of connection types and combinations are possible, and an experienced designer is most desirable in determining a practical and economical connection.

Types of Welded Joints

There are various types of welded joints in common use. The selection of the appropriate type is a function of the magnitude of the load at the joint, the direction of the applied load, the configuration of the joint, the difficulty of the joint preparation, and the cost of erection. Fillet welds (Figure 34) and groove (butt) welds (Figure 35) are the two most commonly used weld types in building construction.

Figure 35 Typical groove (butt) welds.

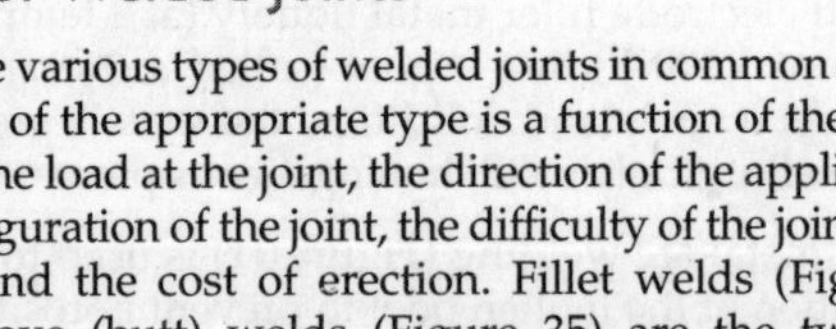

Figure 34 Typical fillet welds.

On occasion, plug and slot welds (Figure 36) are used for special circumstances. The following discussion will be limited to load-carrying fillet and groove welds. Common symbols used for designating the type of weld is shown in Table 4. Appropriate weld symbols are indicated for fillet and groove welds in Figures 34 and 35.

Fillet welds and groove welds differ primarily from the manner in which the stress transfer takes place. Groove welds are normally in direct tension or compression (Figure 37), whereas fillet welds are generally subjected to shear as well as tension or compression (Figure 38).

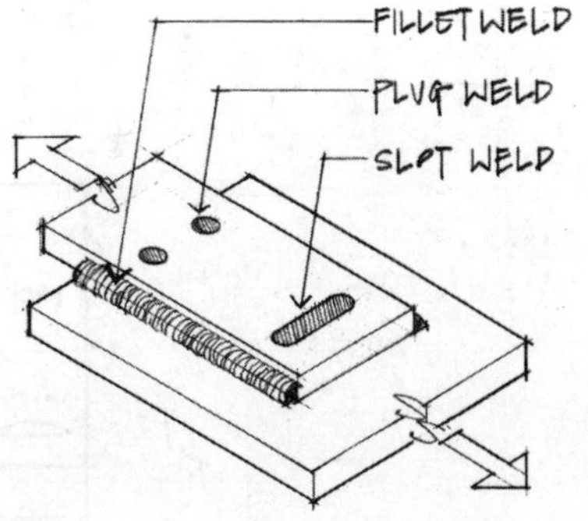

Figure 36 Plug and slot welds.

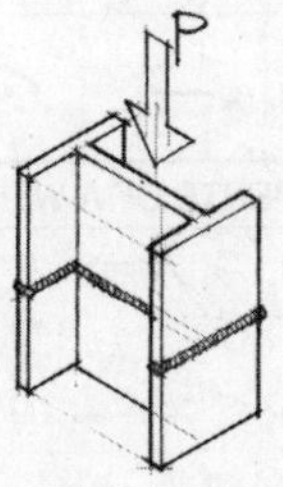

Figure 37(b) Full- or partial-penetration groove welds develop full compressive capability of the section.

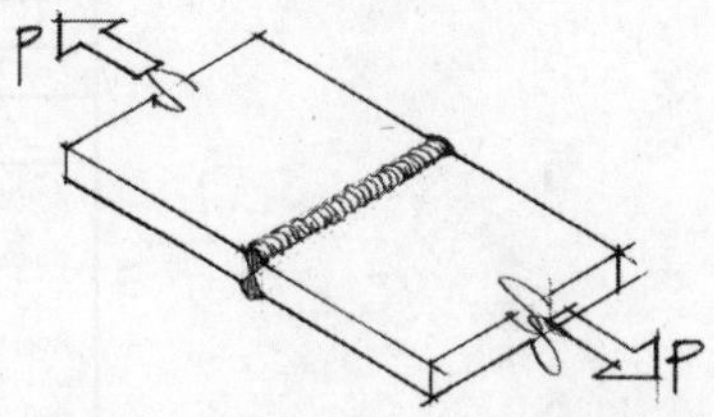

Figure 37(a) Full-penetration groove weld develops the full tensile capability of the plate.

The strength of a full-penetration groove weld is proportional to its cross-sectional area and the strength of the filler metal. Because the filler metal from the electrode exceeds the strength of typical A36 steel base metal, the groove weld is stronger than the base material in shear, tension, and compression. The strength for full-penetration groove welds is conservatively assumed to be equal to that of the base material. In other words, a groove weld of the same cross-section as the connected members is assumed to be 100% efficient in transferring stress. If a groove weld were made with an incomplete penetration, its strength would have to be reduced in accordance with the welding code used.

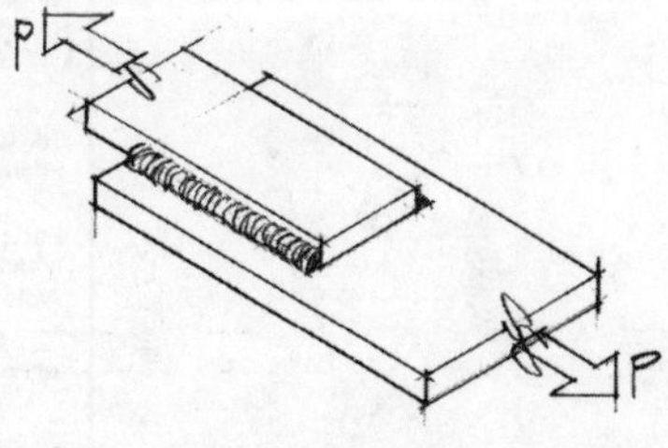

Figure 38(a) Fillet welds resist in shear.

Groove welds are generally used for structural assemblies in which full-strength welds are mandatory. They require relatively large amounts of weld metal and can sometimes experience problems during the welding process. Groove welds also require the cutting of structural members to more or less exact lengths for the ends to butt, and they necessitate extensive edge preparation. As a result, groove welds are more expensive to produce than fillet welds.

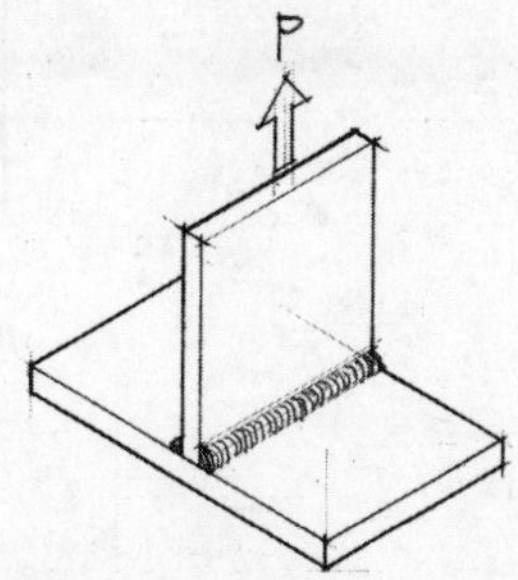

Figure 38(b) Fillet weld resists tension through shear across throat.

Table 4

WELDED JOINTS
Standard symbols

BASIC WELD SYMBOLS

BACK	FILLET	PLUG OR SLOT	Groove or Butt						
			SQUARE	V	BEVEL	U	J	FLARE V	FLARE BEVEL

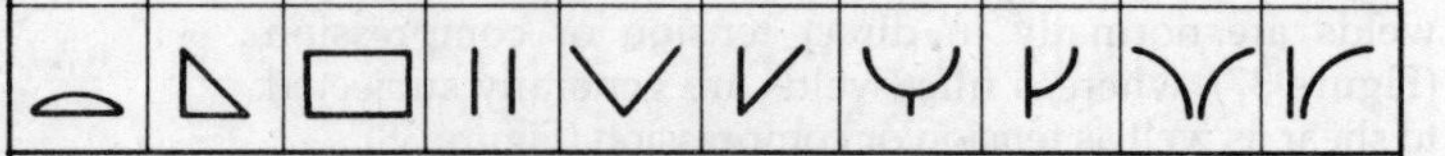

SUPPLEMENTARY WELD SYMBOLS

BACKING	SPACER	WELD ALL AROUND	FIELD WELD	CONTOUR		For other basic and supplementary weld symbols, see AWS A2.4-86
				FLUSH	CONVEX	

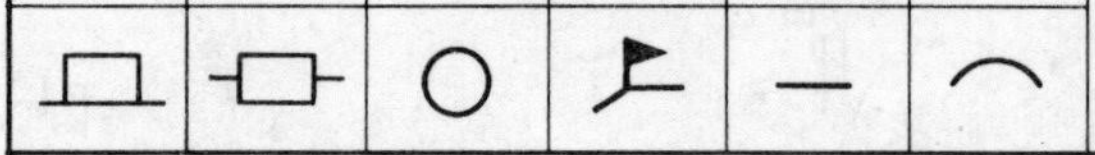

STANDARD LOCATION OF ELEMENTS OF A WELDING SYMBOL

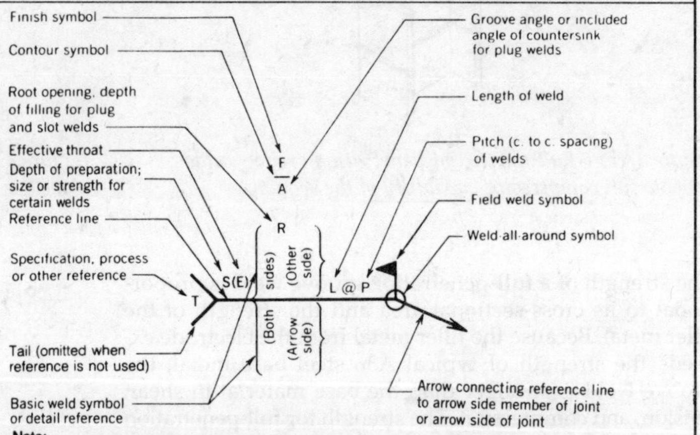

Note:

Size, weld symbol, length of weld and spacing must read in that order from left to right along the reference line. Neither orientation of reference line nor location of the arrow alters this rule.

The perpendicular leg of 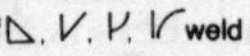 **weld symbols must be at left.**

Arrow and Other Side welds are of the same size unless otherwise shown. Dimensions of fillet welds must be shown on both the Arrow Side and the Other Side Symbol.

Flag of field-weld symbol shall be placed above and at right angle to reference line of junction with the arrow.

Symbols apply between abrupt changes in direction of welding unless governed by the "all around" symbol or otherwise dimensioned.

These symbols do not explicitly provide for the case that frequently occurs in structural work, where duplicate material (such as stiffeners) occurs on the far side of a web or gusset plate. The fabricating industry has adopted this convention: that when the billing of the detail material discloses the existence of a member on the far side as well as on the near side, the welding shown for the near side shall be duplicated on the far side.

The fillet weld is one of the most commonly used welds. It is the weld by which steel fabricators join plate material to make built-up beams and girders and, more frequently, to join beams to columns or to girders. Even though groove welds possess greater strength than fillet welds, most structural connections are joined by fillet welding. Fillet welds allow for greater fit-up tolerances and generally require no edge preparation before welding. The ultimate strength of a fillet weld is dependent upon the direction of the applied load, which is parallel (longitudinal) or transverse to the weld.

Experiments have shown that the ends of a fillet weld, lying parallel to the line of action of the load, carry higher unit stresses than the midportion of the weld, as illustrated in Figure 39. Also, when an end weld is combined with longitudinal welds, the unit stress in the end (transverse) weld will be approximately 30% higher than those in the side (longitudinal) welds; however, this fact is not recognized by most design specifications.

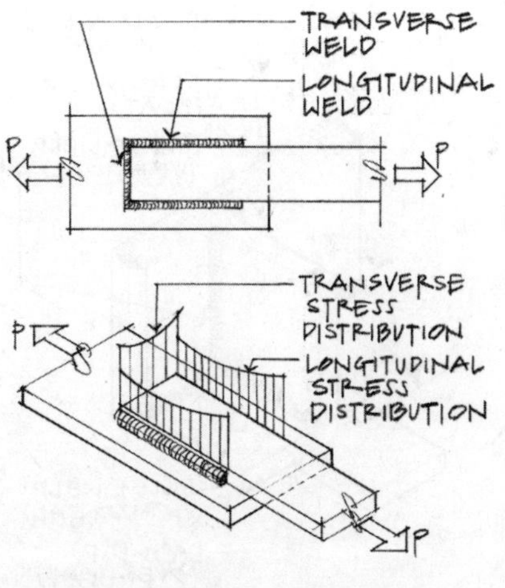

Figure 39 Longitudinal and transverse stresses in fillet welds.

In fillet welds, with a theoretically triangular cross-section, the critical stress is assumed to be acting on the *minimum throat area,* regardless of the direction of the applied load. The *throat* of a fillet weld (Figure 40) is measured from the root (inside vertex of the triangle) to the theoretical face of the weld. The throat is equal to the product of the theoretical throat T and the weld length. Shear, bending, and axial forces all cause shear stresses (across the throat) in fillet welds.

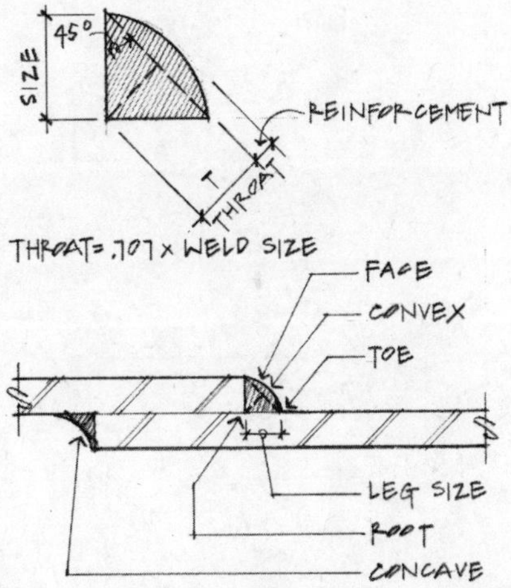

Figure 40 Parts of a fillet weld.

Fillet welds are generally specified with equal legs, and the length of these legs is conveniently used to represent the size of the weld. The effective throat T thickness of an equal-leg 45° fillet weld is considered as

$$T = 0.707 \times \text{weld size}$$

The compatible and most commonly used electrodes for welding A36 steel are the E60XX and E70XX, where the prefix E denotes *electrode* and the first two digits indicate the ultimate tensile strength in thousands of pounds per square inch. For example, an E70XX electrode has an ultimate tensile capacity of 70 ksi. The next-to-last digit indicates the weld position (Figure 41) in which the electrode is capable of making satisfactory welds. For example,

E701X	All positions
E702X	Flat position and horizontal fillets

Fillet weld strength is based on the allowable shear stress for the weld metal across the effective throat area. The AISC specifications limit the allowable shear stress on the effective area to 30% of the nominal tensile strength of the weld metal. Therefore, for A36 steel and E60XX and E70XX electrodes,

$$F_v = 0.30 \times 60\text{ ksi} = 18\text{ ksi} \quad \text{(E60XX)}$$

$$F_v = 0.30 \times 70\text{ ksi} = 21\text{ ksi} \quad \text{(E70XX)}$$

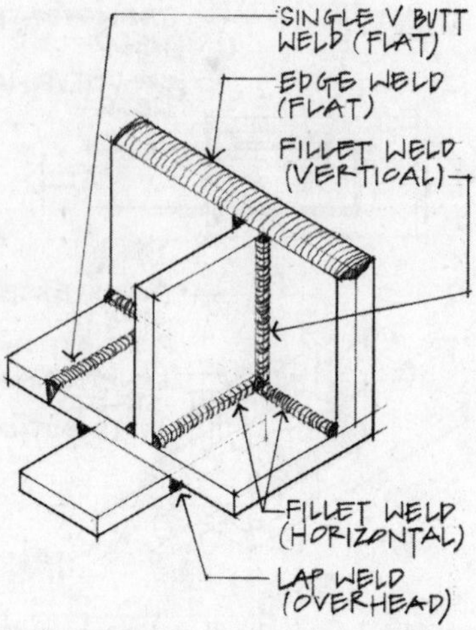

Figure 41 Types of welds based on weld position.

Weld strengths per inch of weld for any size equal-leg weld can be found by multiplying the weld size by 0.707 times the allowable shear stress.

Throat dimension: $T = 0.707 \times$ weld size

Throat area: $A_{\text{throat}} = T \times$ length of weld

For a 1″ weld: $A_{\text{throat}} = T \times 1''$

weld strength per inch = throat area $(A_t) \times$ allowable shear stress (F_v)

Table 5 is included for quicker computations involving fillet welds.

Table 5 Allowable strength of fillet welds per inch of weld

Weld Size (in.)	E70XX (k/in.)
$\frac{3}{16}''$	2.78
$\frac{1}{4}''$	3.71
$\frac{5}{16}''$	4.64
$\frac{3}{8}''$	5.57
$\frac{7}{16}''$	6.49
$\frac{1}{2}''$	7.42
$\frac{5}{8}''$	9.27
$\frac{3}{4}''$	11.13

In addition to fillet weld strength based on the size and length of the weld, other welding code provisions are addressed fully in the AISC's *Manual of Steel Construction Allowable Stress Design* and the structural code of the AWS. Some of the other code items are the following:

- The maximum size of a fillet weld applied to a square edge of a plate or section $\frac{1}{4}''$ or more in thickness should be $\frac{1}{16}''$ less than the nominal thickness of the edge. Along edges of material less than $\frac{1}{4}''$ thick, the maximum size may be equal to the thickness of the material.

- The minimum size of a fillet weld is dependent on the thicker of two members being welded but cannot exceed the thickness of the thinner member. The minimum size of fillet welds is $\frac{1}{8}''$ for material with a thickness of $\frac{1}{4}''$ or less, $\frac{3}{16}''$ for a material thickness over $\frac{1}{4}''$ to $\frac{1}{2}''$, $\frac{1}{4}''$ for material thickness over $\frac{1}{2}''$ to $\frac{3}{4}''$, and $\frac{5}{16}''$ for material thickness over $\frac{3}{4}''$.
- The minimum effective length of fillet welds should be four times the nominal size, or else the weld size is to be taken as $\frac{1}{4}''$ of its effective length.
- If two or more welds are parallel to each other, the length must be at least equal to the perpendicular distance between them (Figure 42).
- The minimum length of intermittent fillet welds should be not less than four times the weld size, with a minimum of $1\frac{1}{2}''$.
- Side or end fillet welds terminating at the ends or sides should be returned, if practical, around the corners for a distance not less than two times the nominal weld size (Figure 43). Added strength is given to fillet welds with end returns.

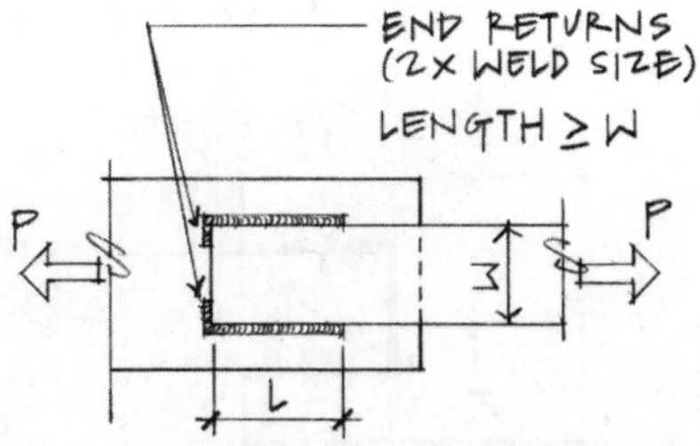

Figure 42 Minimum length for parallel welds.

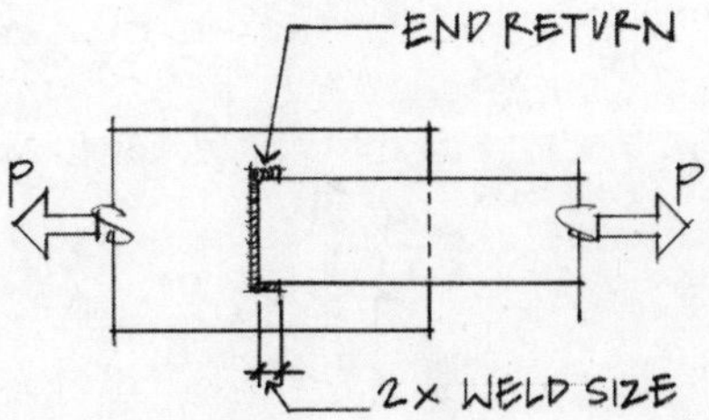

Figure 43 End returns for fillet welds.

Cost concerns also dictate to a large extent the size of the fillet weld to be used. Weld metal volume has a direct correlation to the labor costs involved in depositing the weld. The most economical weld minimizes weld metal volume and, at the same time, reduces the heat input and the associated shrinkage and distortion of the joint. Minimizing the weld metal also minimizes the potential for weld defects. Fillet weld sizes should be kept to $\frac{5}{16}''$ or less, because the $\frac{5}{16}''$ weld is the largest weld size that can be deposited in one pass with the shielded metal arc process in the horizontal and flat positions. Larger fillet welds generally require two or more passes.

In practice, it is also advisable to maintain the same-size fillet throughout the connection. A change of fillet size necessitates a change of welding rods and, therefore, slows the work and may cause errors.

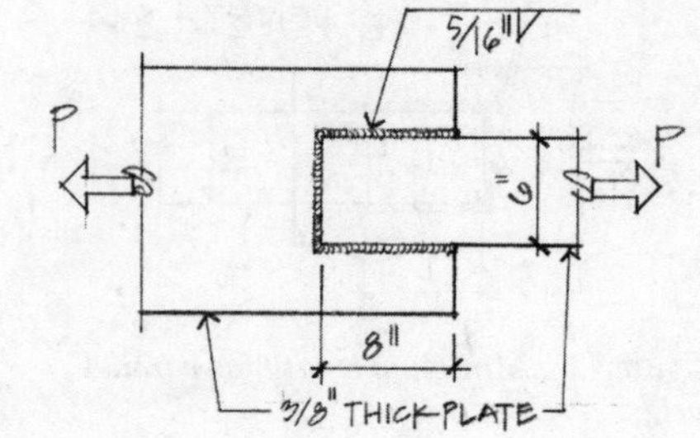

Figure 44 Plate fillet welded on three sides.

Example Problems

7 Determine the capacity of the connection in Figure 44 assuming A36 steel with E70XX electrodes.

Solution:

Capacity of weld:

For a $\frac{5}{16}''$ fillet weld, $S = 3.98$ k/in.

Weld length = 22″

Weld capacity = 22″ × 3.98 k/in. = 87.6 k

Capacity of plate:

$F_{t_{allow}} = 0.6F_y = 22$ ksi

plate capacity $= \frac{3}{8}'' \times 6'' \times 22\,\text{k/in.}^2 = 49.5$ k

$\therefore$ plate capacity governs, $P_{allow} = 49.5$ k

The weld size used is obviously too strong. To what size, then, can the weld be reduced so that the weld strength is more compatible to the plate capacity? To make the weld capacity ≈ plate capacity,

$$22'' \times (\text{weld capacity per in.}) = 49.5\text{ k}$$

$$\text{weld capacity per inch} = \frac{49.5\text{ k}}{22\text{ in.}} = 2.25\text{ k/in.}$$

From Table 5, use $\frac{3}{16}''$ weld ($S = 2.78$ k/in.).
Minimum size fillet $= \frac{3}{16}''$ based on a $\frac{3}{8}''$ thick plate.

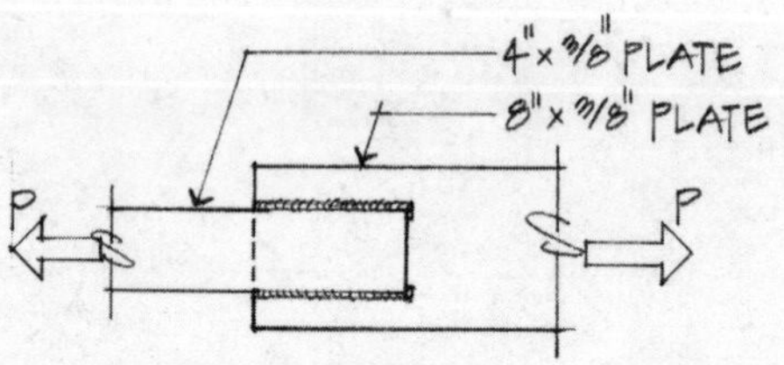

Figure 45 Parallel fillet welds.

8 Determine the size and length of longitudinal fillet welds that will develop the strength of the smaller plate (Figure 45). Assume A36 steel with E70XX electrodes.

Solution:

plate capacity $= 4'' \times \frac{3}{8}'' \times 22\,\text{k/in.}^2 = 33$ k

Maximum weld size (limited by the plate thickness):

weld size $= \frac{3}{8}'' - \frac{1}{16}'' = \frac{5}{16}''$

Note: *This is good, because this weld size can be deposited in one pass.*

Allowable weld strength: $S = 4.64$ k/in.

$$\text{total weld length required} = \frac{33\text{ k}}{4.64\text{ k/in.}} = 7.1\text{ in.}$$

Rounding upward to the nearest $\frac{1}{4}''$, use a total of $7\frac{1}{4}''$ of $\frac{5}{16}''$ weld or $\frac{5}{16}'' \times 3\frac{5}{8}''$ on each side.

Note: *The AWS specifies that the weld length on each side of the plate for parallel welds should not be less than the perpendicular distance between the welds. This requirement is to ensure full development of the plate capacity.*

$\therefore$ Use 4″ minimum of weld length on each side of the plate.

A smaller weld size can be tried because more weld length is required.

Try:

$\frac{1}{4}''$ weld with $S = 3.71$ k/in.

$$\text{total weld length required} = \frac{33\text{ k}}{3.71\text{ k/in.}} = 8.9\text{ in.}$$

$\therefore$ Use $\frac{1}{4}'' \times 4\frac{1}{2}''$ weld on each side.

9 Determine the capacity of the full-penetration groove weld shown in Figure 46. Assume A36 steel with E70XX electrodes.

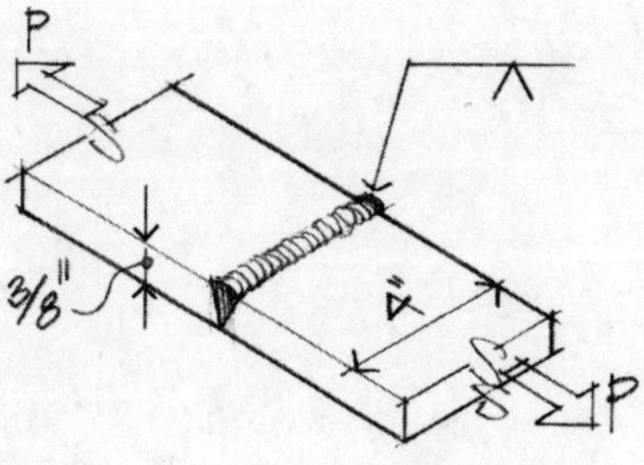

Figure 46 Transverse full-penetration groove weld.

Solution:

Full-penetration groove welds carry the full capacity of the plate.

$$\therefore P_t = \tfrac{3}{8}'' \times 4'' \times 22\text{ k/in.}^2 = 33\text{ k}$$

Eccentricity in Welded Joints

One of the most common examples of eccentrically loaded welded joints is that of a structural angle welded to a gusset plate as shown in Figure 47. The load P in the angle is presumed to act along its centroidal axis. Consequently, because an angle is an asymmetrical cross-section, the welds marked L_1 and L_2 are made unequal in length so that their stresses will be proportional in accordance with the distributed area of the angle.

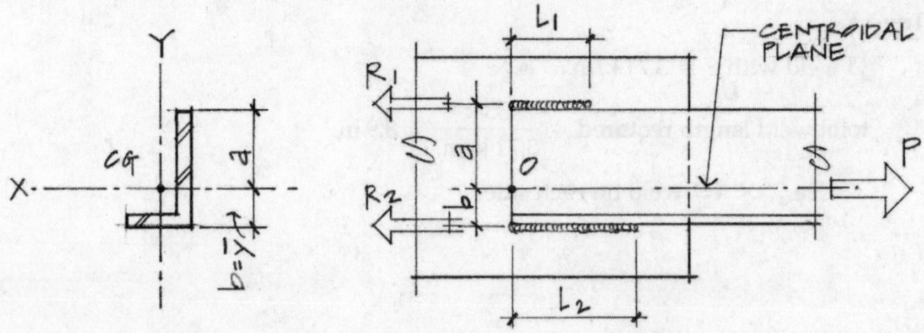

Figure 47 Angle welded to a gusset plate.

Writing the equations of equilibrium for the applied force and weld resistance R_1 and R_2,

$$[\Sigma F_x = 0]\ R_1 + R_2 = P$$

or

$$S_1L_1 + S_2L_2 = P$$

If the strength of the weld (Table 5) is defined as S,

$$[\Sigma M_0 = 0]\ R_1 \times a = R_2 \times b$$

or

$$S_1L_1a = S_2L_2b$$

and if the weld size is constant,

$$S_1 = S_2$$

where

$$L_1 = \frac{L_2b}{a}$$

Example Problem

10 An $L3 \times 2 \times \frac{5}{16}''$ angle (A36 steel) is attached to a large gusset plate by $\frac{1}{4}''$ fillet welds s shown in Figure 48. Determine the lengths L_1 and L_2 to support a tensile load of 30 k. Assume the angle to be subjected to repeated stress variations (minimize eccentricity).

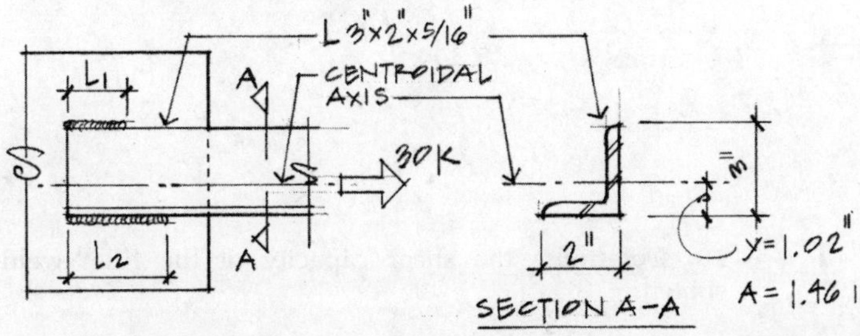

Figure 48 Welded connection of angle iron and gusset plate.

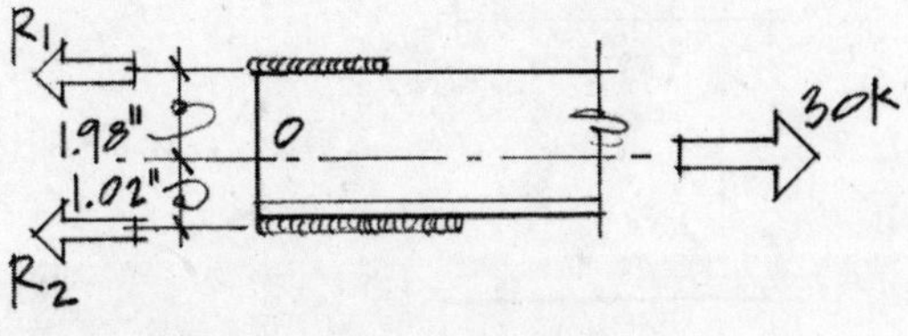

FDB of the angle iron welds.

$$[\Sigma F_x = 0] R_1 + R_2 = 30\text{ k}$$

$$[\Sigma M_0 = 0] R_1(1.98'') = R_2(1.02'')$$

$$R_1 = \frac{1.02R_2}{1.98} = 0.515R_2$$

Substituting:

$$0.515R_2 + R_2 = 30\text{ k}$$

$$R_2 = 19.8\text{ k and } R_1 = 10.2\text{ k}$$

For $\frac{1}{4}''$ fillet welds (E70 electrode),

Weld strength: $S = 4.64$ k/in.

$R_1 = S \times L_1 = 3.71$ k/in. (L_1)

Use: $\frac{1}{4}'' \times 2\frac{3}{4}''$ weld.

$R_2 = S \times L_2 = 3.71$ k/in. (L_2)

Use: $\frac{1}{4}'' \times 5\frac{3}{8}''$ weld.

Check the tensile capacity of the angle:

$P_t = A \times F_t = 1.46\text{ in.}^2 \times 22\text{ k/in.}^2 = 32.1\text{ k} > 30\text{ k}$

$\therefore$ OK

Problems

Assume in each problem that the base metal is A36 steel and that the electrodes are E70XX.

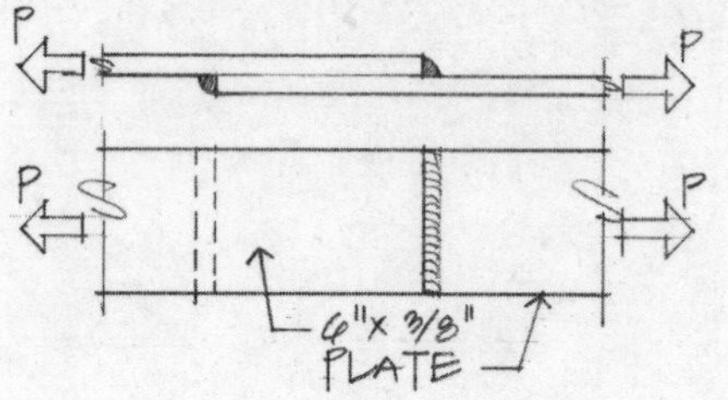

9 Determine the maximum load-carrying capacity of this lap joint.

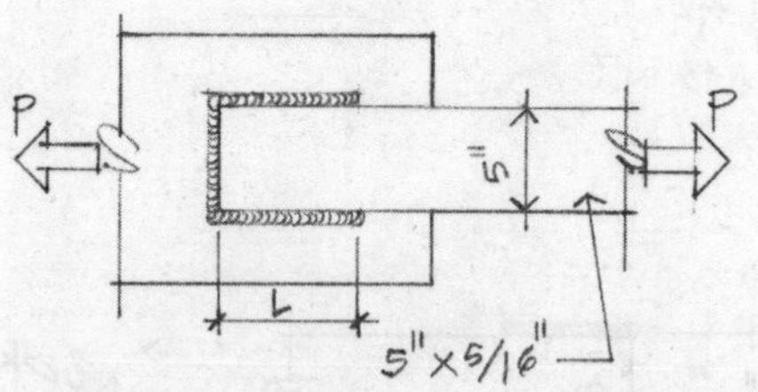

10 Determine the shear capacity of the fillet weld shown.

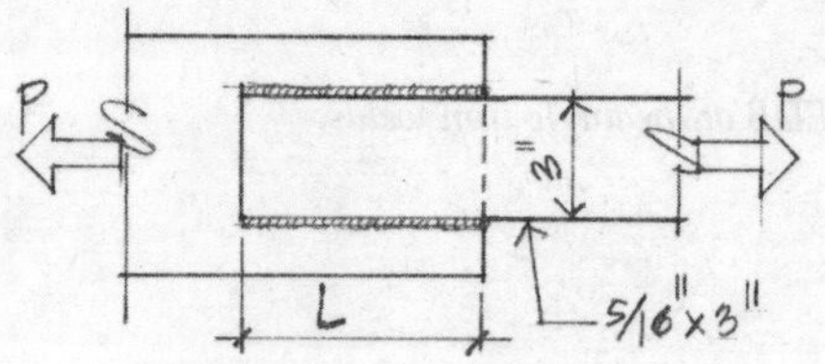

11 What length L is required to develop the full capacity of the plate?

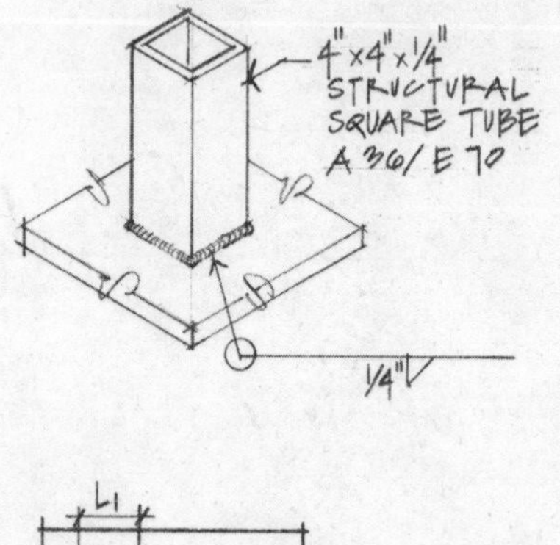

12 Determine the capacity of the $\frac{1}{4}''$ fillet weld connection shown. What would the capacity of the connection be if a full-penetration groove weld were used instead?

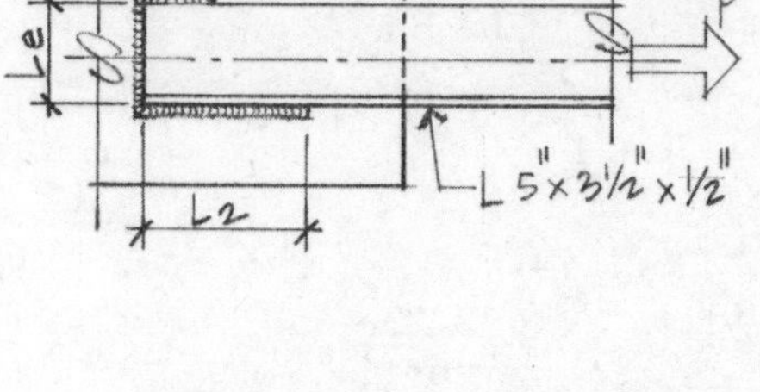

13 Compute the length and size of the fillet weld needed to develop the full tensile strength of the angle. Use a full-transverse fillet weld on the end and balanced welds on the sides (for minimizing eccentricity).

3 COMMON FRAMING DETAILS IN STEEL

Structural analysis theory assumes that connections between beams and columns or between columns and foundations are rigid (fixed), allowing no relative rotation between connected elements or true pins, hinged with no moment resistance. In reality, structural design deals with connections that fit neither of these assumptions fully. Most connections exhibit some degree of moment resistance and a varying degree of rotational joint resistance.

The true behavior of the connection (i.e., moment and rotational characteristics) affects the strength and stability of the individual connected elements and the stability of the entire building structure. Proper detailing of the connections to provide a continuous load path through the interconnected elements is essential in assuring that the resisting forces will develop in the physical connection to provide overall structural stability. Consideration of a lateral resisting strategy for a structural framework should occur in the early planning stages of a project. Selection of a lateral resisting system greatly influences the design of individual members and their connections.

The three basic lateral resisting systems for steel-framed structures are the rigid frame (Figure 49), the braced frame (Figure 50), and the shearwall system. Rigid frame systems require the use of rigid, moment resisting connections, while braced frames are generally designed as pin connections. Material and labor costs are generally much lower in pin connections as compared to rigid, moment connections.

© Aardvark/Alamy

Figure 49 Exposed rigid frame for lateral stability.

© Caro/Alamy

Figure 50 Concentric bracing in lower two floors and eccentric bracing in upper two stories.

Examples of Connection Details

It is particularly useful, when studying structural steel framing, to examine some of the standard or typical details of connections used in the preparation of structural drawings. The accompanying drawings in Figures 51 through Figure 55 show standard details, in a very basic and general form, that are frequently employed in detail drawings of steel buildings. Selected details are referenced to the hypothetical structure shown in Figure 51. The example structure assumes a lateral strategy that utilizes a rigid frame system working in conjunction with a centrally located, concrete shear core. Lateral stability is achieved through the use of a braced frame-shearwall system in the perpendicular direction. To illustrate the various types of connections employed with the different types of bracing, a composite braced frame has been created. This is not a type of braced frame system that one would normally see in an actual building frame.

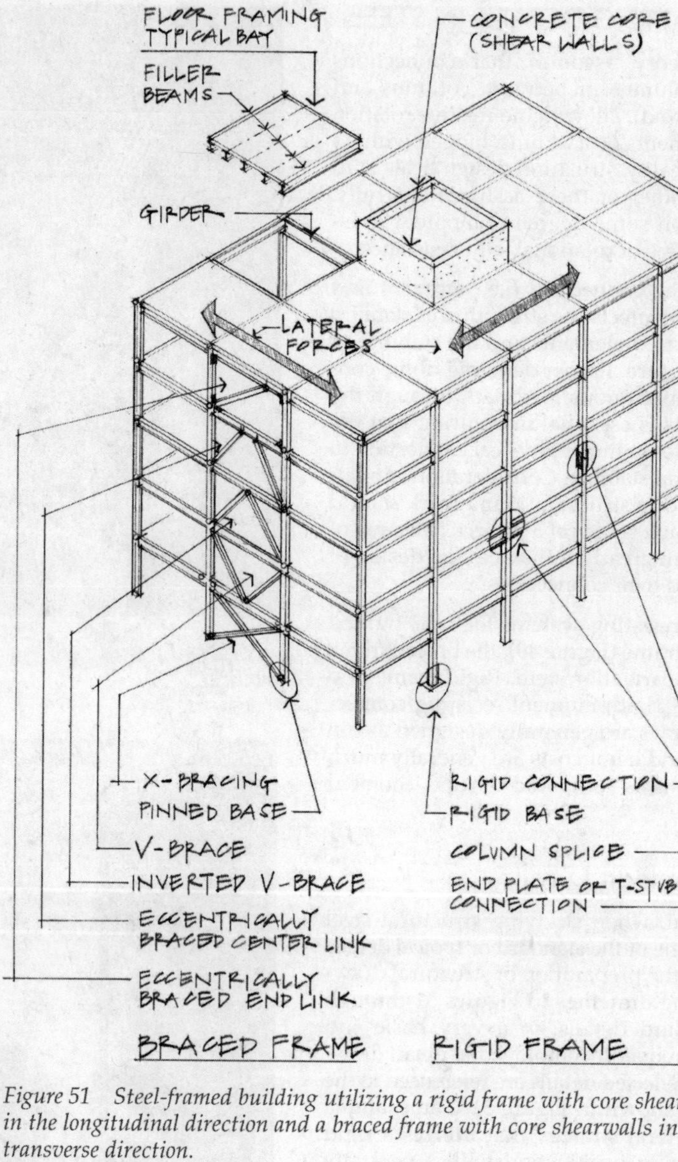

Figure 51 Steel-framed building utilizing a rigid frame with core shearwalls in the longitudinal direction and a braced frame with core shearwalls in the transverse direction.

Rigid Frames

Rigid frames are constructed with beam and columns rigidly attached using moment-resisting connections. The rigid frame derives its strength to resist gravity and lateral loads from the moment interaction between beams and columns (as shown in Figure 52). Beam-column connections maintain their relative 90° orientation to each other under load, even if the connection assembly rotates as a unit.

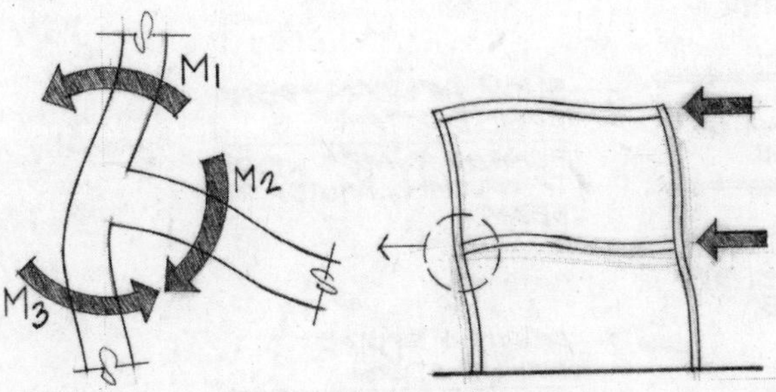

Figure 52 Rigid frame with beam-column interaction.

Columns, beams, girders, and joints are responsible for transferring the horizontal, vertical, and rotational (moment) forces throughout the rigid frame. Because bending moments are shared by both beams and columns, member sizes are generally heavier than would be found in braced frame systems. Stability of the structure is maintained by the usually high stiffness (I_x) required in the column and beam or girder. Therefore, members are typically oriented to take advantage of its strong axis.

Beam-column connections often consist of a shear connection for gravity loads acting in combination with field-welded beam flanges for moment resistance (Figure 53).

Compared with braced frames or shearwall structures, rigid frames have the advantage of providing unobstructed space. However, under high seismic loading, the large deformations encountered may cause distress to the architectural finishes. Rigid frame systems are effective for low- to medium-rise buildings.

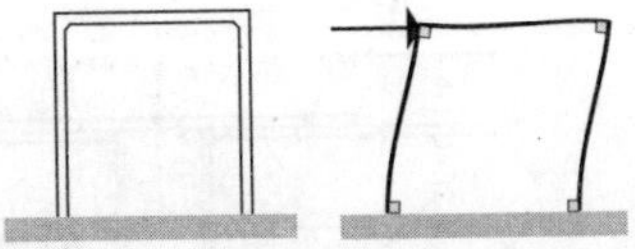

Rigid frame - beam/column and support

Rigid beam/column connection and rigid bases. All members share in resisting the lateral force through bending.

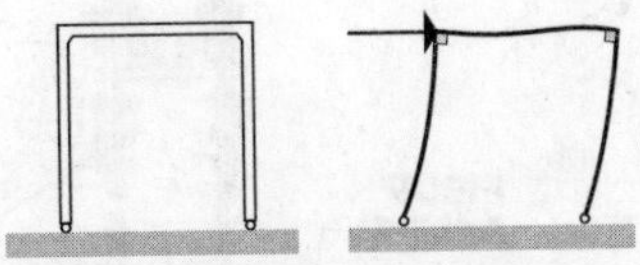

Two-hinged frame - pinned base

Most frames assume pin connections at the base since footings are susceptible to some degree of rotation.

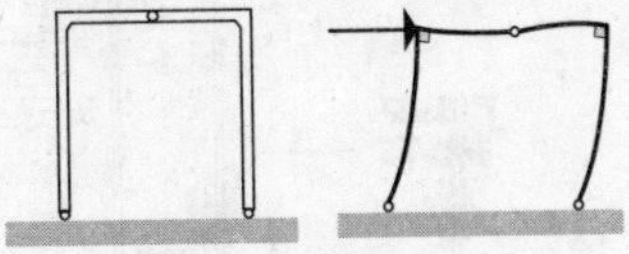

Three-hinged frame

Three-hinged frame; one hinge at the beam's mid-span

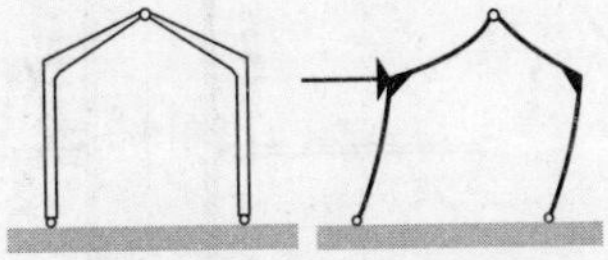

Three-hinged frame pitched roof

Rigid frame with a pitched roof. Large bending moments develop at the haunch (pitched-rafter and column joint).

Figure 53 Examples of single-bay, single-story rigid frames.

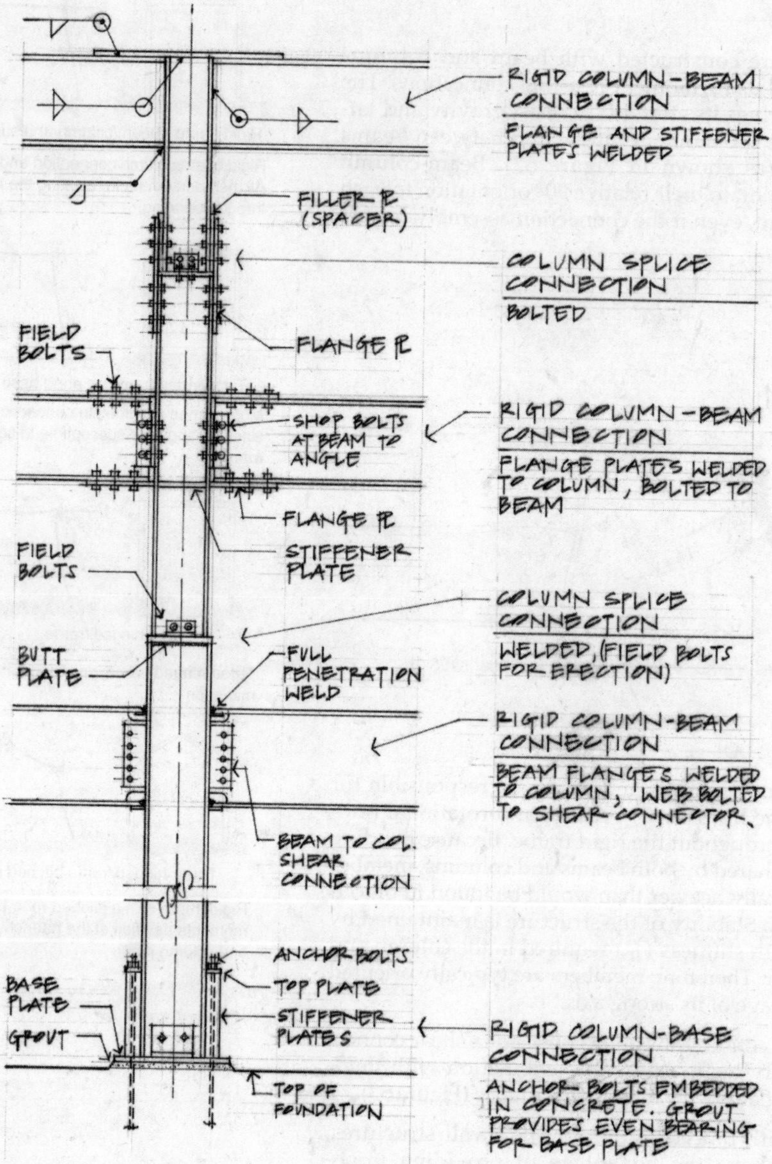

Figure 54 Common rigid connection details for beam-column, column splice, and column-foundation.

Braced Frames

Braced frames found in use today include X-bracing, K-bracing (Vee or inverted Vee), and eccentric bracing. Two basic categories of braced frames are the concentrically and eccentrically braced frames. Diagonal bracing, X-bracing, and K- or Vee-bracing are classified as concentrically braced. The members of a concentrically braced frame act as a vertical truss system, and diagonal members are generally assumed to act primarily in tension and sometimes compression. Diagonal tension X-bracing is typically analyzed as having only tension forces. This design assumption utilizes only one-half of the members to resist lateral loads, while the adjacent member within the same panel is assumed to be negligible in resisting compressive stress. K-bracing is used in design circumstances when access through the bracing plane is required. The inverted Vee (K-bracing) allows clearance for doorways, corridors, and rooms.

Bracing members in eccentrically braced frames, as shown in Figure 55(a) and 55(b), are connected to the beam so as to form a short "link beam" between the brace and the column or between two opposing braces. Link beams act as a "fuse" to prevent other elements in the frame from being overstressed. In low-to-moderate ground shaking, an eccentrically braced frame performs as a braced frame rather than as a moment frame. Therefore, the structure experiences smaller lateral displacements, minor architectural damage, and no structural damage. In major earthquakes, the link beam (Figures 56 and 57) is specifically designed to yield, thereby absorbing large quantities of seismic energy and preventing buckling of the other bracing members. Braced frames are more cost effective when compared to rigid frames.

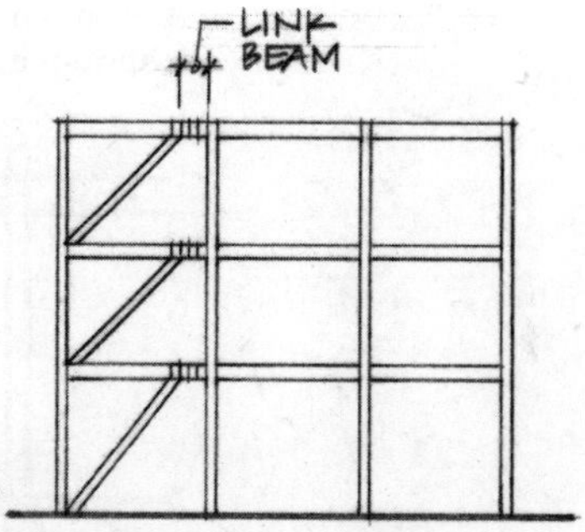

Figure 55(a) Diagonal eccentric brace.

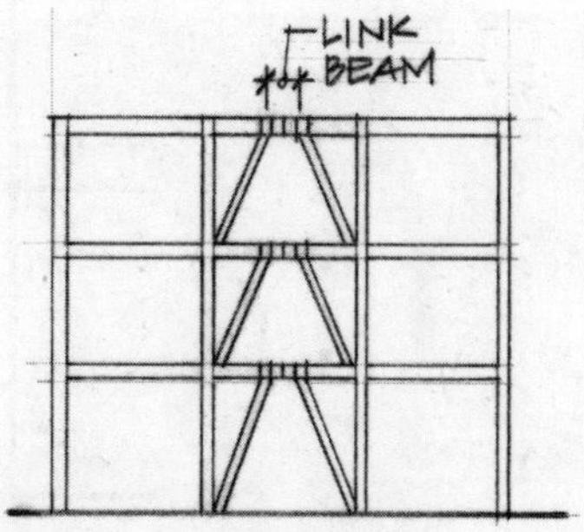

Figure 55(b) Eccentric K-brace.

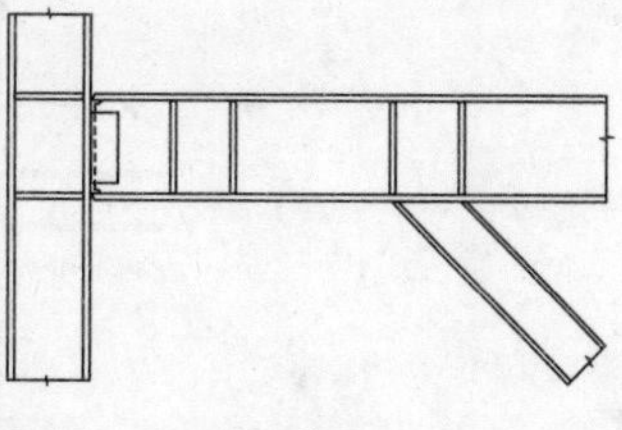

Figure 56(a) Detail of an eccentrically braced frame connection.

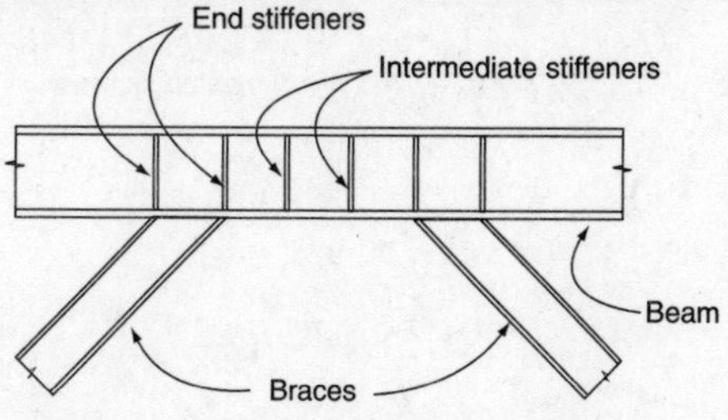

Figure 56(b) Link beam detail.

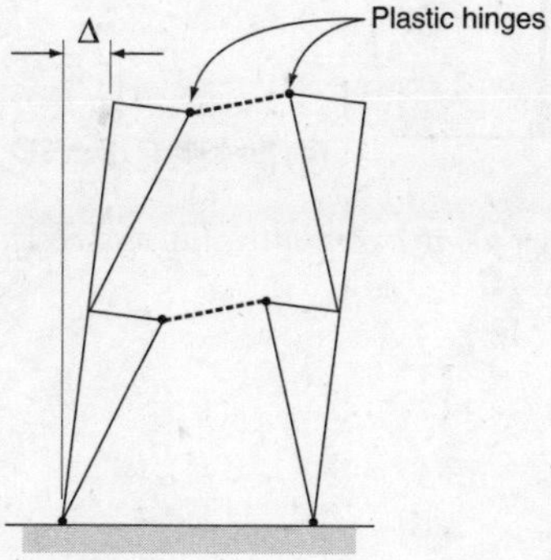

Figure 57 Link beam rotation.

A summary of the various lateral resisting systems in steel is shown in Figure 58.

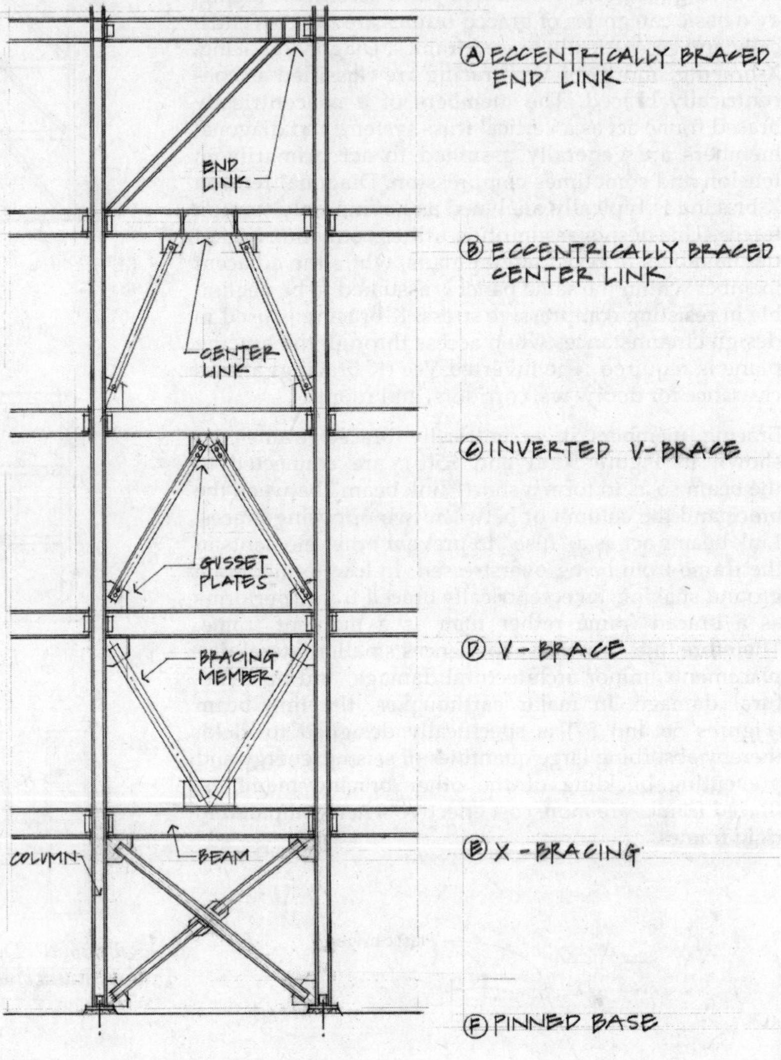

Figure 58 Lateral resisting strategy using a concentrically and eccentrically braced frame.

Summary

- Five basic types of failure that can cause a critical stress condition at a joint are
  - Shear of the bolt.
  - Bearing failure of the connected members against the bolt.
  - Tension failure of the connected member material.
  - End tear-out of the connected member.
  - Block shear.
- There are three primary types of bolts used in steel construction currently:
  - ASTM A307 unfinished bolt—used in light steel frame structures where vibration and impact are not critical.
  - ASTM A325 and A490 high-strength bolts—the most widely used fasteners of steel construction.
- Mechanically fastened high-strength connections that transmit load by means of shear in their fasteners are categorized as either slip-critical (SC) or bearing-type (N or X).
- Slip-critical connections depend upon sufficiently high clamping force to prevent slip of the connected parts under service conditions.
- Bearing-type connections are based on the contact (bearing) between the bolt(s) and the sides of the holes to transfer load from one connected member to another.
- Standard AISC tables are used to cover the design of a vast majority of typical structural connections where filler beams frame into girders or girders into columns.
- The various types of welded joints commonly use a fillet weld or a groove (butt) weld.
- Fillet welds resist load in shear. The critical shear stress is assumed to be acting on the minimum throat area of the weld. The throat of a fillet weld is measured from the root to the theoretical face of the weld.
- The strength of a full-penetration groove weld is proportional to its cross-sectional area and the strength of the filler metal. In general, a groove weld is assumed equal to the strength of the base material being welded.

Answers to Selected Problems

1 Shear: $P_v = 20.8$ k (governs)
Bearing: $P_p = 65.2$ k
Net tension: $P_t = 71.9$ k
Plate tension: $P = 66$ k

3 Group A:
Shear: $P_v = 79.5$k
Bearing: $P_p = 78.3$ k
Net tension: $P_t = 115.5$ k
Group B:
Shear: $P_v = 72.2$ k
Bearing: $P_p = 61$ k
Net tension: $P_t = 29.9$ k (governs)
Plate capacity in tension: $P = 33$k

4 Member A: 3 bolts; Member B: 3 bolts; Member C: 2 bolts: Member D: 4 bolts

6 Shear: $P_v = 119$ k
Bearing: $P_p = 95.7$ k
Net tension: $P_t = 117.8$ k (governs)

(a) $P_y = 90.1$ k
(b) $6\frac{3}{4}''$ A325-SC
(c) $L = 17\frac{1}{2}''$

9 Plate capacity: $P_t = 49.5$ k
Using $\frac{5}{16}''$ weld size:
Weld capacity = 55.7 k
Length of weld = 12″

11 Assuming the maximum weld size of $\frac{5}{16}''$ is used: $L = 5.6''$

12 Fillet weld: $P = 59.4$ k
Full-penetration groove weld: $P_t = 79$ k

13 Using the minimum size fillet weld of $\frac{3}{16}''$:
$L_1 = 8.01''$
$L_2 = 18.64''$

Structure, Construction, and Architecture

Structure, Construction, and Architecture

Building Case Study: REI Flagship Store, Seattle, WA

Architects: Mithun Partners, Inc.

Structural Engineers: RSP-EQE

General Contractor: Gall Landau Young

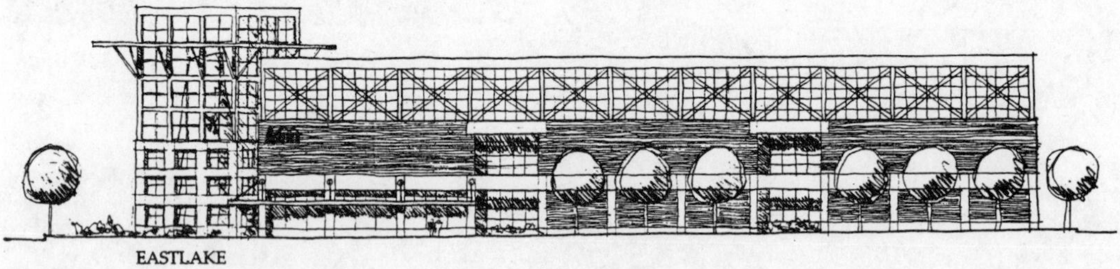

Figure 1 *East elevation, design sketch. Courtesy of Mithun Partners, Inc.*

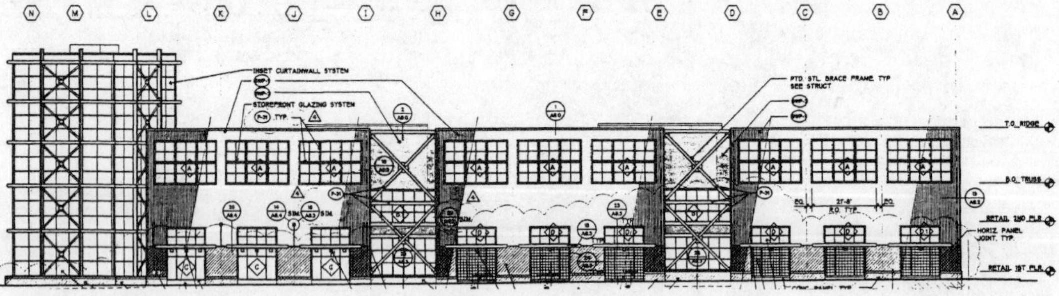

Figure 2 *East elevation, construction drawing. Courtesy of Mithun Partners, Inc.*

Figure 3 *East elevation, photograph of the completed building. Photograph by Robert Pisano.*

Introduction

It is difficult to separate precisely the contributions of the engineers, architects, and contractors to the success of a building project. The process of design and construction varies with each owner, site, design, and construction team. Most building projects begin with a client program outlining the functional and spatial requirements, which is then interpreted and prioritized by the architect, who coordinates architectural design work with the work of other consultants on the project. The architect and structural engineer must satisfy a wide range of factors in determining the most appropriate structural system.

Figure 4 The original store was housed in a converted warehouse with exposed heavy-timber framing. The rugged, functional character of the building was consistent with the nature of REI products. Photo courtesy of Mithun Partners, Inc.

I INITIATION OF PROJECT—PREDESIGN

REI Outgrows Capitol Hill Store and Site

Recreation Equipment, Inc., or REI, has been making and selling outdoor gear and clothing in Seattle since 1938. The design of the REI flagship store began with an analysis of REI's former converted warehouse building and site in Seattle's Capitol Hill neighborhood. A program document was prepared that outlined functional and space requirements for the store. The need for additional retail space, structural improvements for seismic safety, handicapped accessibility (elevators in particular), expanded loading, and parking would require difficult and costly renovation of the existing building as well as acquisition of additional site area. After evaluating several locations, a site in the Cascade neighborhood was selected and purchased for the relocation of the store.

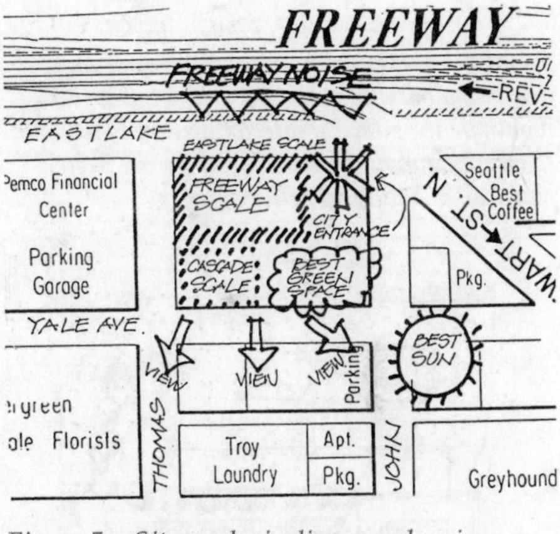

Figure 5 Site analysis diagram showing adjacent buildings and roads in relation to solar orientation. Sketch courtesy of Mithun Partners, Inc.

The general contractor (Gall Landau Young) was engaged before the selection of the architect and engineering consultants. The collaboration of the design team and general contractor helped ensure that issues of constructability—schedule, cost, and availability of materials—were considered from the very beginning of the design process.

The selected site was a full city block—approximately 90,400 square feet—and was occupied by several existing buildings and paved parking areas. The size, configuration, and poor condition of the existing buildings made them unsuitable for adaptation and renovation. The neighborhood was a varied mix of industrial, commercial, and residential buildings just outside the downtown core and adjacent to a noisy interstate freeway. Soil conditions were typical for the area: compacted glacial till, with no unusual groundwater problems.

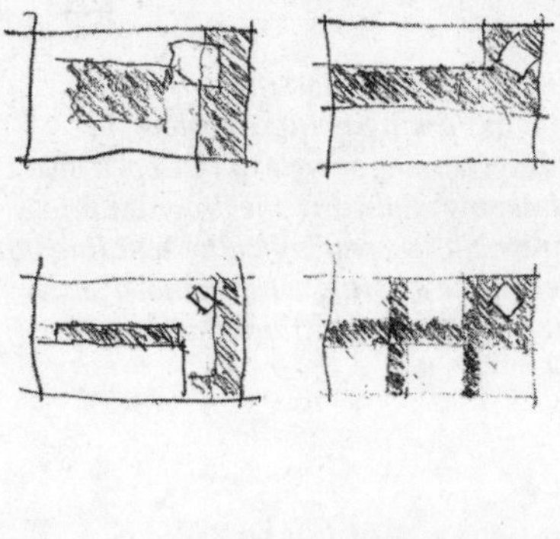

Figure 6 Early site plan diagrams studying building and open space placement on the site. Sketch courtesy of Mithun Partners, Inc.

2 DESIGN PROCESS

The Owner's Program and Requirements

REI members were fond of the old warehouse store, and it was decided that the new store should reflect the feel and character of the former store. In addition to the 98,000 square feet of retail sales space, a 250-seat meeting room, a 100-seat delicatessen, administrative offices, a rental-repair shop, and a multistory rock-climbing structure were desired. In addition, city zoning regulations required 160,000 square feet of parking for 467 cars, loading docks for large trucks, and some small landscaped areas.

Because of their commitment to environmental quality, REI requested that the building respond to the region and climate, conserving both energy and materials. By exposing the structural elements and mechanical systems, material and labor (money) that would be needed to conceal and finish the spaces would be conserved. Expressing the structural and mechanical systems contributed significantly to the functional, no-nonsense character of the building. It also required a greater design and coordination effort to make presentable the systems that are typically hidden.

Building code requirements limit the area and height of buildings based on their occupancy or use and their type of construction. Generally, larger buildings are allowed if more expensive, fire-resistive construction is employed.

After analyzing the site, program, and building code requirements, several options were developed and evaluated.

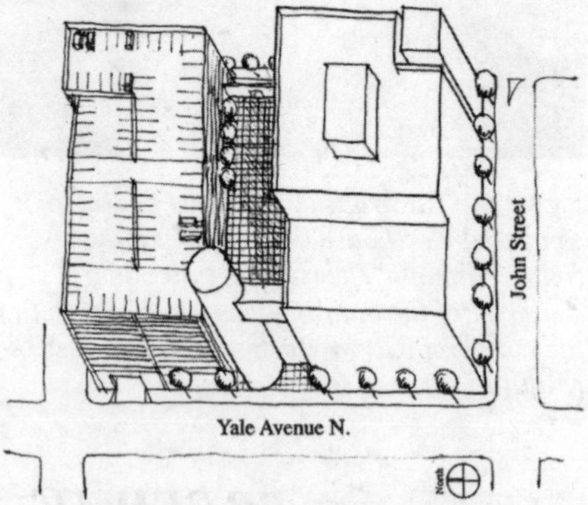

Figure 8 Design massing sketches, option 4. The bulky parking structure and retail block dominate the site. An interior atrium is required to admit daylight into the lower floors. Sketch courtesy of Mithun Partners, Inc.

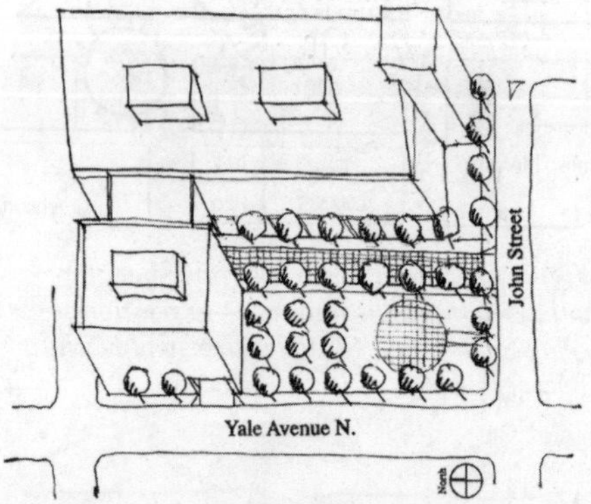

Figure 9 Design massing sketches, option 5. Parking is tucked below the building, leaving more exterior open space for landscaping. Splitting the program into separate blocks creates smaller buildings that better fit the existing neighborhood scale. Sketch courtesy of Mithun Partners, Inc.

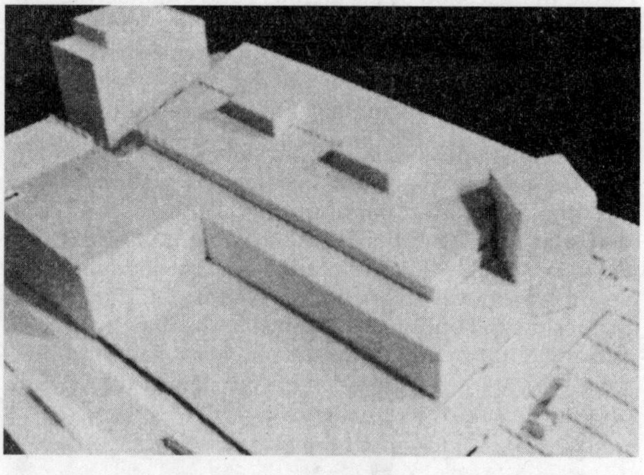

Figure 7 Photograph of massing model, option 5, used to study the exterior massing and form of the building. Photo courtesy of Mithun Partners, Inc.

Option 4 split the project into two parts, an eight-level parking garage and a three-level retail building on the south part of the site. The large parking structure with cars on the rooftop and bulky retail building were inconsistent with the scale of the existing neighborhood and would have required visitors to enter the building via elevators. In addition, the large retail floors required a costly atrium to bring adequate natural light to the interior. This alternative was abandoned in favor of option 5.

The parking structure was largely screened from view by placing most of the parking below grade under the retail building on the uphill part of the site. By working with the existing slope, excavation was limited, and a larger, more usable outdoor space for landscaping was provided on the sunny south portion of the site. Breaking the retail building into two parts, a two-level warehouse-like building along the freeway edge protected the interior of the block from traffic noise, and a four-story concrete building at the northwest corner broke the project into smaller components more appropriate to the character of the neighborhood.

A large, welcoming entry porch was created on the pedestrian-oriented west side of the building, and a 85-foot-tall glass enclosure for the 65-foot-high climbing pinnacle was added to the southeast corner, visible from the freeway.

Figure 10 Schematic design sketch of option 5 as seen from Eastlake Avenue. Sketch courtesy of Mithun Partners, Inc.

Figure 11 Presentation model showing the entry space at the southwest corner. Most of the large-scale decisions about the building form and site plan have been established at this point. Photo courtesy of Mithun Partners, Inc.

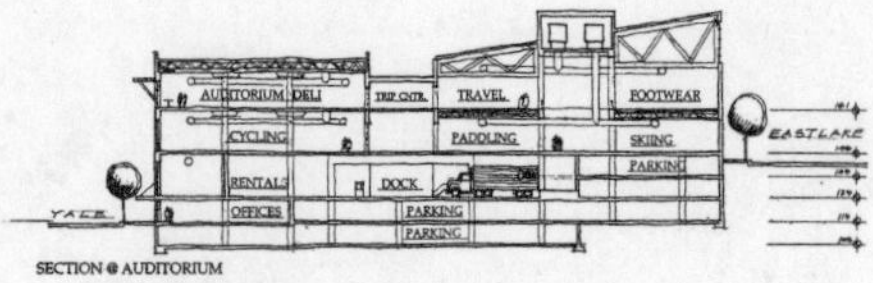

Figure 12(a) Building section—schematic design sketch.

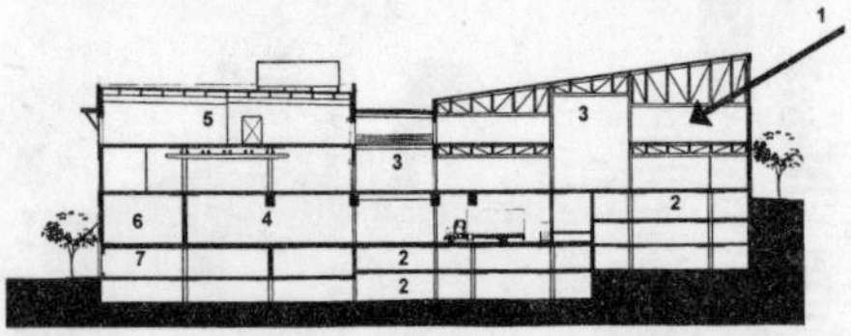

Figure 12(b) Building section—design development drawing. Further development and refinements of the spaces and structural system resulted in a change from bowstring trusses to glu-lam beams at the Yale Street portion (at the left side of the drawings). Drawings courtesy of Mithun Partners, Inc.

3 SCHEMATIC DESIGN

The selected design was further refined and tested to more carefully fit the program to the site. Circulation (the movement of people and cars in and out of the site) and building horizontally as well as vertically, were worked out in plans and section drawings. The below-grade parking levels provided integral concrete retaining walls and a substantial foundation for the building.

The main sales areas were designed as large open spaces to recall the character of the original warehouse store. Studies for bringing natural light into the main sales area suggested that the roof be sloped to allow east light to enter high above the wall in the mornings, when heat gain would be less problematic. The roof slope also created a larger-scale protective wall on the freeway side of the building and a lower, pedestrian-scale wall on the landscaped entry side. The entry porch protected the west side from prevailing rains and the late afternoon sun. Rainwater from the large shed roof would be collected on the west side of the building and used to supplement and recharge a waterfall within the landscaped courtyard.

Mechanical equipment for heating and cooling the building was located centrally on the rooftop to distribute the conditioned air more economically.

Figure 13 A photograph of the entry elevator/stair tower and front porch illustrates how early design ideas shown in Figure 11 were finally designed and built. Photograph by Robert Pisano.

The architects researched the Seattle and Uniform Building Code requirements and determined that based on occupancy/use, floor area, and height, the project should be separated into three buildings (Figure 14). Although the three buildings were contiguous spatially, they would be separated by fire-resistive walls or floors. Each building was a different construction type, with specific fire-resistive standards for structural elements and walls.

- **Building 1.** A three-level parking garage located primarily below grade and using the most fire-resistive construction (Type I). Structural elements must be noncombustible: steel, iron, concrete, or masonry.
- **Building 2.** A two-level retail structure located above the parking levels and containing the main sales areas. Construction type is III-N (or nonrated), which allows structural elements to be of any material, including wood.
- **Building 3.** A two-level structure above the parking garage containing some retail and storage, a small auditorium, a restaurant, and office space. Construction is Type III–1 hour, requiring structural elements to be protected by a one-hour fire-rated assembly. Sprayed-on fireproofing or gypsum wallboard are commonly used to protect structural elements. The city of Seattle also allows for heavy-timber construction to qualify as Type III–1 hour.

Cost estimates and construction feasibility studies were provided by the building contractor at critical points throughout the design process.

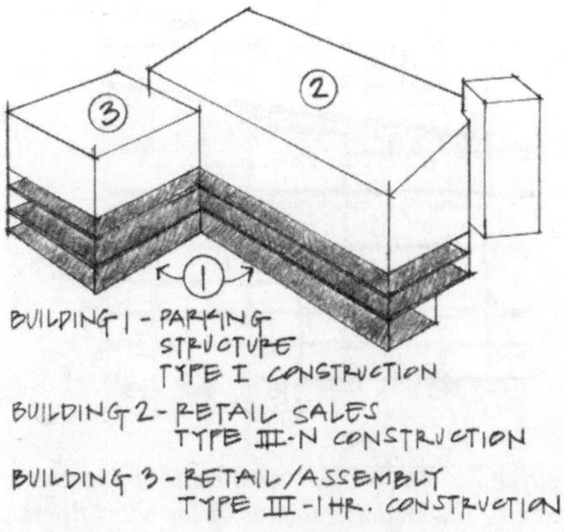

Figure 14 Building code diagram.

Figure 15 Board-formed reinforced concrete is used for the four-hour fire-resistive exterior bearing walls at Building 3 (located at the northwest corner of the site). The texture of the rough-sawn form boards helps establish an industrial character and provides a durable weather enclosure. Photo courtesy of Mithun Partners, Inc.

Figure 16 Photograph of parking garage posttensioned concrete slab at the drop support and column (also illustrated in Figure 19). Photo courtesy of Mithun Partners, Inc.

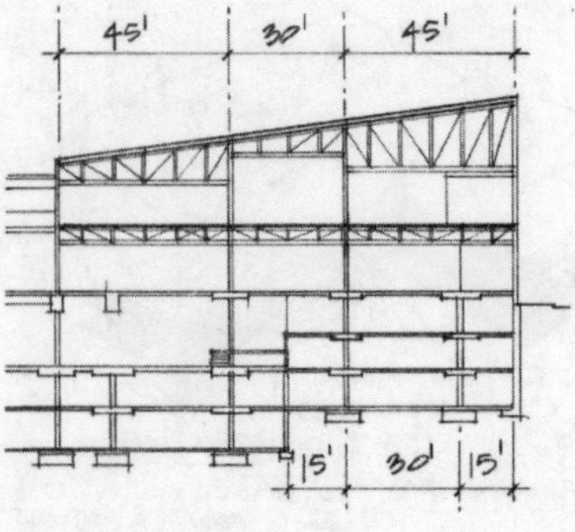

Figure 17 Partial east-west building section showing the structural bays of the sales floors aligned above the parking levels. Drawing courtesy of Mithun Partners, Inc.

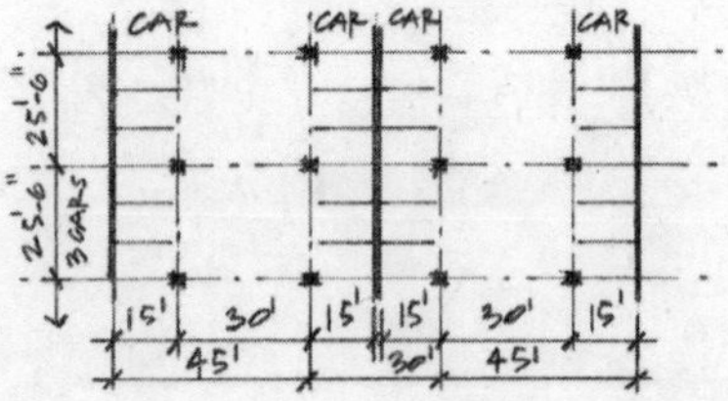

Figure 18 Plan diagram of parking space requirements and dimensions of structural bays. Drawing courtesy of Mithun Partners, Inc.

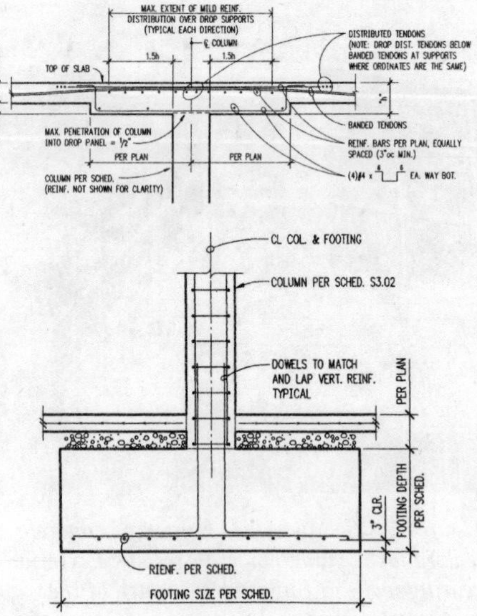

Figure 19 Structural details of posttensioned concrete slab at column and detail of conventionally reinforced column at footing. Drawings courtesy of Mithun Partners, Inc.

4 DESIGN DEVELOPMENT AND CONSTRUCTION DOCUMENTS

In the course of schematic design, the organization and approximate spacing of the structural bays were coordinated with the parking layout. Columns, bearing walls, and shearwalls were carefully located to use space on the parking levels efficiently. Because the retail sales floors could be arranged more flexibly, the vertical structure at those levels could align with columns and bearing walls at the parking levels below with a minimum of transfer beams or unusable space. The three structural bays helped organize spaces on the sales floors—locating circulation and stairs in the center two-story bay, with display areas in the side bays.

While the vertical load trace analysis generally proceeds from the top down (beginning with the roof loads and ending at the foundation), the layout of the structural bays was developed from the bottom up, helping to keep the vertical load path as direct as possible.

The architects and structural engineers based the selection of materials for structural elements and enclosure assemblies on several criteria:

- Building code requirements for fire resistance.
- Structural properties, performance, and efficiency.
- Resistance to weathering or decay; longevity.
- Appearance, aesthetics, or character.
- Cost and availability, including skilled construction labor.
- Resource efficiency.

Parking Garage and Building 3

Reinforced concrete is an economical and durable material and was therefore used for the parking garage. Located below ground, concrete was used for retaining walls on the freeway side. The concrete ceiling/floor provided a horizontal fire separation and satisfied the Type I fire-resistive construction requirement for structural elements.

Posttensioned reinforced concrete slabs were used for their efficient span-to-depth ratio. The slabs were only $6\frac{1}{2}''$ thick, spanning 30 feet in some locations. Drop panels at column-slab connections reinforced the slab against "punching shear" stresses and provided additional depth for bending stresses over the columns. By reducing the vertical dimension (depth) of the parking structure, costs were saved on excavation, shoring, and vertical structure.

Conventionally reinforced concrete was used for columns, bearing walls, shearwalls, retaining walls, and footings. All concrete utilized recycled fly ash in the mix, a waste by-product of coal-generating power plants.

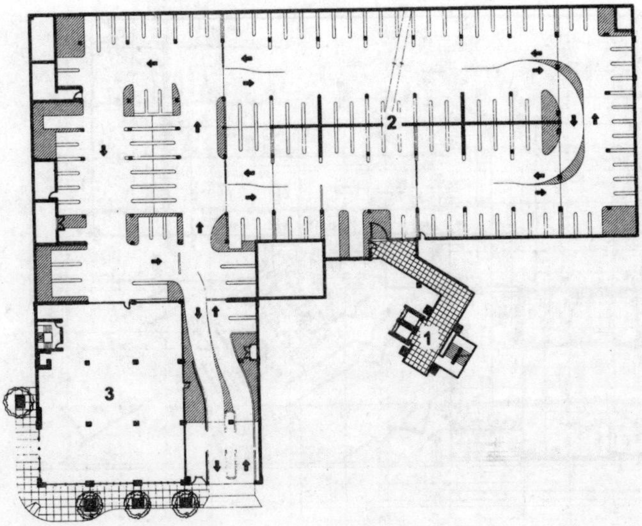

Figure 20 *Plan at the basement parking level. Drawing courtesy of Mithun Partners, Inc.*

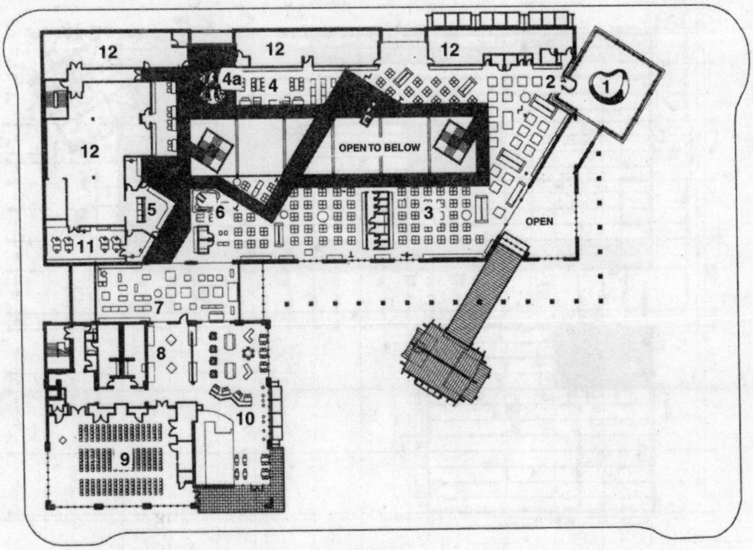

Figure 21 *Plan at upper retail level. The path of movement through the building and the arrangement of sales areas relate to, but are not determined by, the structural grid. Drawing courtesy of Mithun Partners, Inc.*

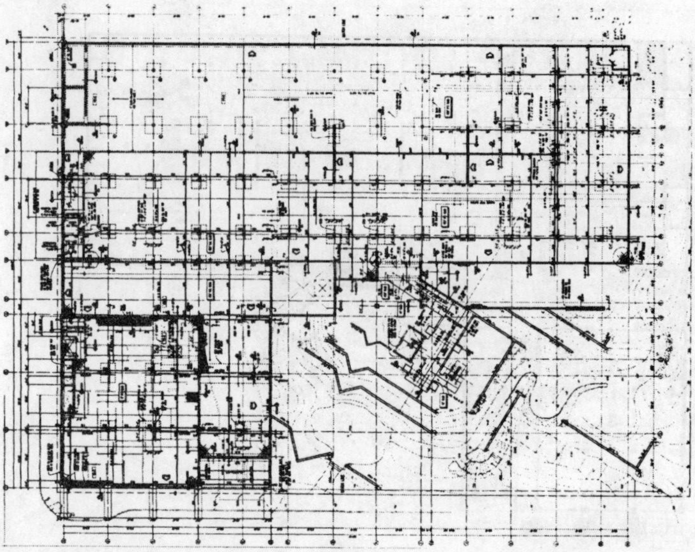

Figure 22 *Structural plan at parking level. Concrete footings, columns, and shearwalls are arranged in a regular spacing to accommodate car parking and maneuvering. Drawing courtesy of Mithun Partners, Inc.*

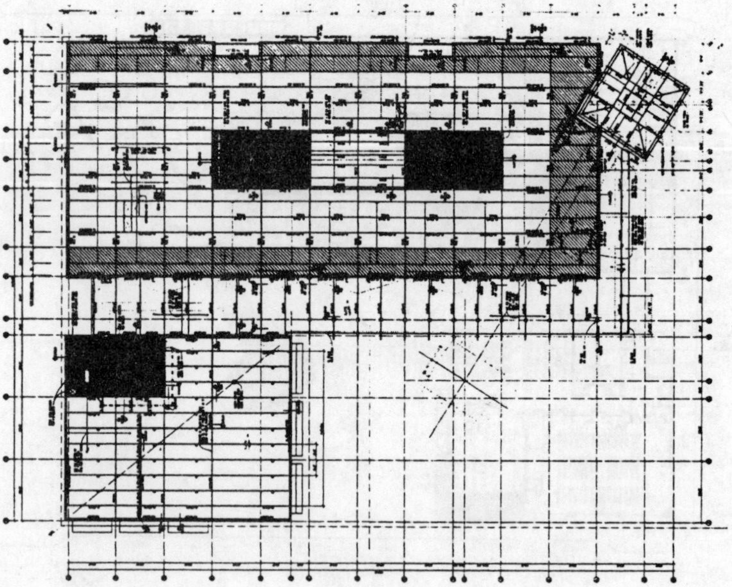

Figure 23 *Roof framing plan. The structural grid established at the parking level is apparent at the roof framing. The shaded areas at the roof edge indicate shear panels in the roof diaphragm. Drawing courtesy of Mithun Partners, Inc.*

Retail Sales Floors

Since there were no fire-resistive requirements for structural elements in Building 2, housing the retail sales floors, wood was selected as an economical structural material that would also evoke the warmer character of the original store. The bays and spanning requirements of the primary structure for the roof and floor were effectively established by the column locations in the parking levels below.

The use of heavy timbers, common in early American warehouse construction, was considered. Today, however, the availability of quality timbers is mostly limited to recycled material from old and abandoned structures, and costs are relatively high. Steel beams or trusses and glu-laminated timbers are more cost-effective and could span the required bays efficiently, but these were not as appropriate in scale or character. Ultimately, trusses made with glu-lam chords and compression members as well as steel tension members and connections were developed. The trusses spanned east-west a distance of 45 feet.

The architects, contractors, and structural engineers discussed the idea of using a very common and economical industrial roof system. Following these discussions, the structural engineers developed a modified "Berkeley" system. Partly prefabricated onsite, $\frac{5}{8}''$ plywood decking was nailed to $2'' \times 6''$ joists spaced 24 inches o.c. Joists were eight feet long and spanned between glu-lam beams. The dimensions took advantage of the $4' \times 8'$ modular dimensions of the plywood sheathing.

The $3\frac{1}{8}'' \times 18''$ glu-lam purlins spanned 25 feet, 6 inches between the trusses. The eight foot spacing of the glu-lam beams established the spacing of truss panel points. Because of the sloping top chord, the truss panels changed proportion, and the diagonal tension members were not acting as efficiently as they could. To maintain a consistent appearance and construction detail, the tension rods were sized for the worst case and remained the same diameter, even as the loads varied.

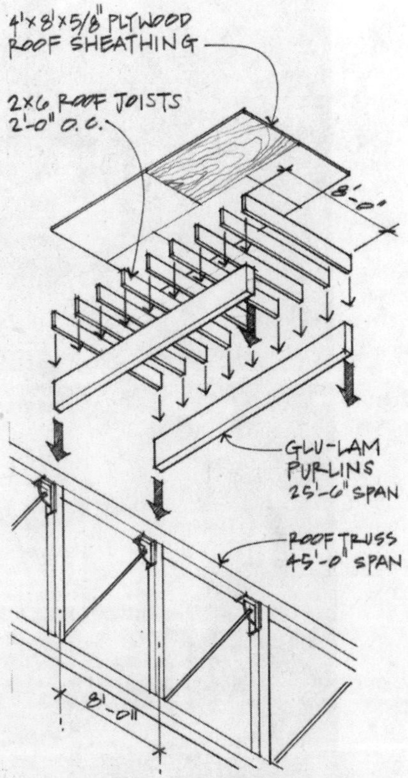

Figure 24 Diagram of the modified "Berkeley" system roof structure.

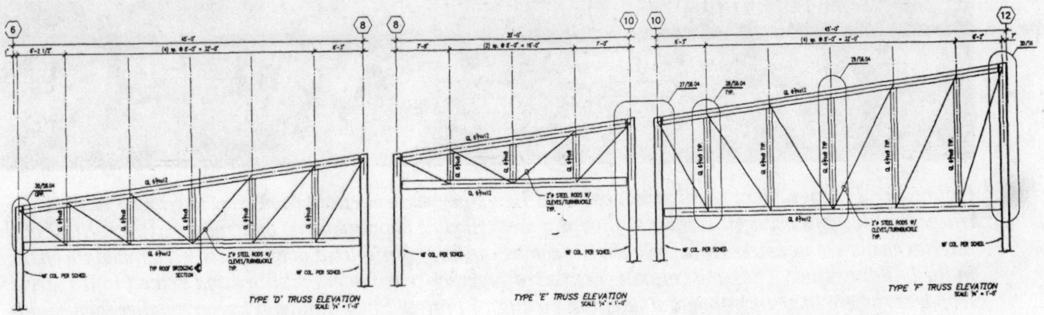

Figure 25 Construction drawing—elevation of the roof trusses. Glu-lam beams frame onto the truss at panel points eight feet o.c. Drawing courtesy of Mithun Partners, Inc.

Figure 26 Photograph of retail sales areas and two-story central circulation bay. The roof and floor trusses easily span between columns, allowing more flexible arrangements of display fixtures. Most of the interior walls are nonstructural, so even the rooms can be reconfigured over time to accommodate changes in the building's use. Four-log columns are bolted together to support the stairs and extend to the steel roof deck, where they are supported laterally by angled braces. Even though fewer or smaller logs could adequately support the stair, several large logs were used to keep the support visually in scale with the height of the space. Photograph by Robert Pisano.

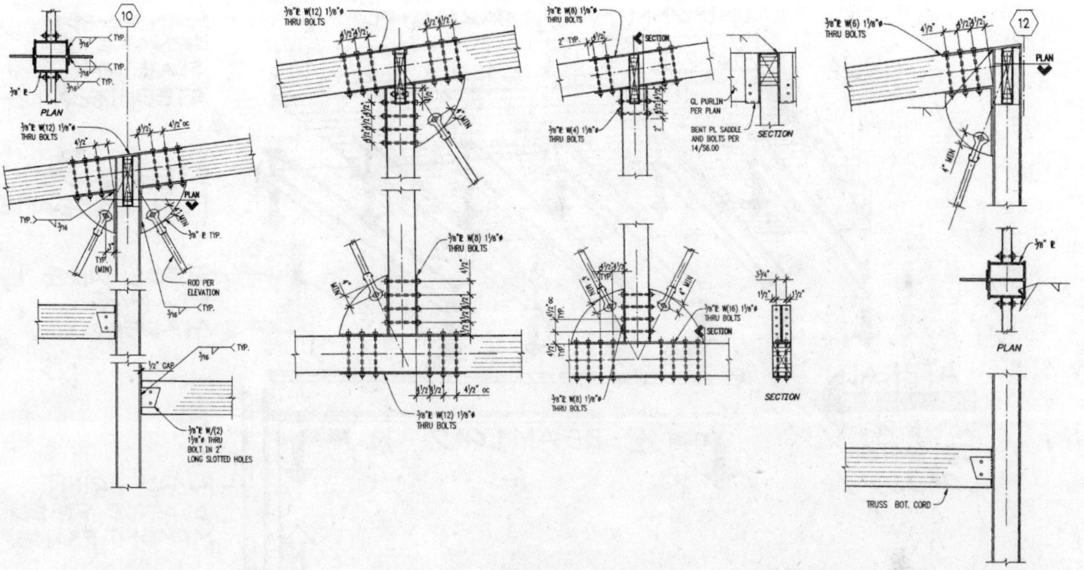

Figure 27 Construction drawings detailing the connections at roof truss joints. A steel gusset plate, drilled to accept the clevis pin/tension rod, is welded to a bent plate, which in turn is bolted through the glu-lam truss member. Another steel plate on the opposite side acts as a large washer. Drawings courtesy of Mithun Partners, Inc.

The floor was framed in much the same way as the roof, but because of the greater live loads (75 psf), the floor sheathing was $1\frac{1}{8}''$-thick plywood on 3×8 S4S joists spaced 32 inches o.c. These spanned eight feet between $5\frac{1}{8}'' \times 21''$ glu-lam beams, which in turn were supported by floor trusses at panel points.

Figure 28 Photograph of the connection detail at a roof truss. Photograph courtesy of Mithun Partners, Inc.

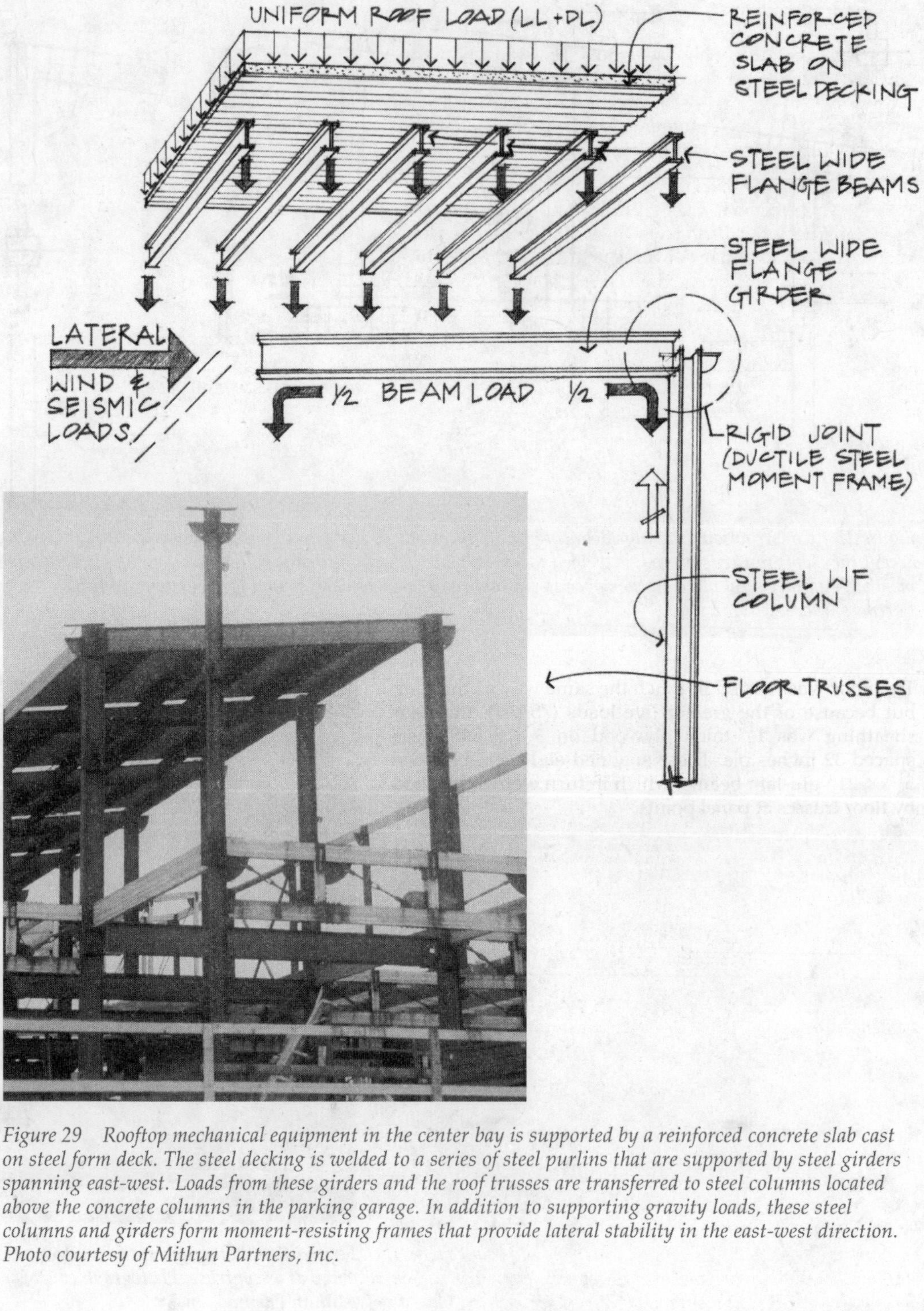

Figure 29 Rooftop mechanical equipment in the center bay is supported by a reinforced concrete slab cast on steel form deck. The steel decking is welded to a series of steel purlins that are supported by steel girders spanning east-west. Loads from these girders and the roof trusses are transferred to steel columns located above the concrete columns in the parking garage. In addition to supporting gravity loads, these steel columns and girders form moment-resisting frames that provide lateral stability in the east-west direction. Photo courtesy of Mithun Partners, Inc.

Lateral Loads

Seattle is in a relatively high seismic zone. In addition, the large wall areas of the store accumulated significant wind loads. Forces in the east-west direction were resisted by a series of ductile steel moment-resisting frames, which were tied to the roof and floor diaphragms at the trusses.

Shearwalls or cross-braced frames would have restricted north-south movement through the building, dividing the space into a series of small bays. Steel moment frames had several distinct advantages over concrete: partial prefabrication, easier and faster erection, connection compatibility with the wood and steel trusses, lighter weight, and smaller size.

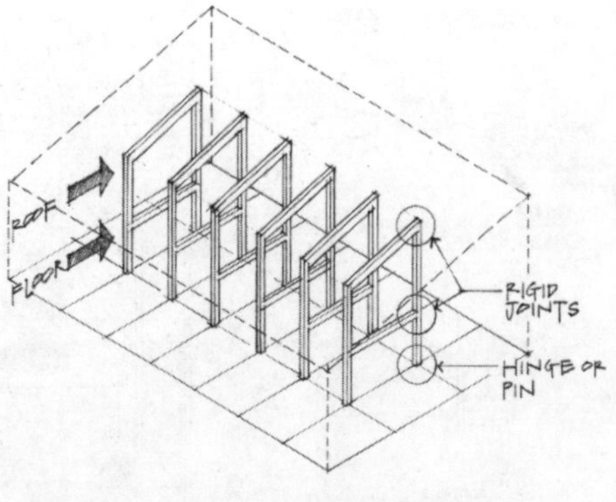

Figure 30 Diagram of the east-west lateral load bracing system consisting of ductile steel moment-resisting frames.

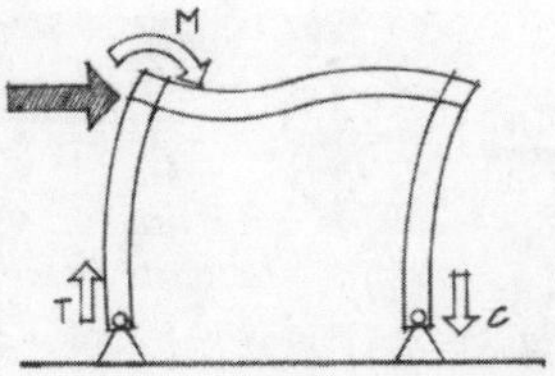

Figure 31 Seven ductile steel moment-resisting frames form the two-story center bay of the retail building. The frames are anchored to concrete columns that extend through the parking structure to concrete footings. Photograph by Robert Pisano.

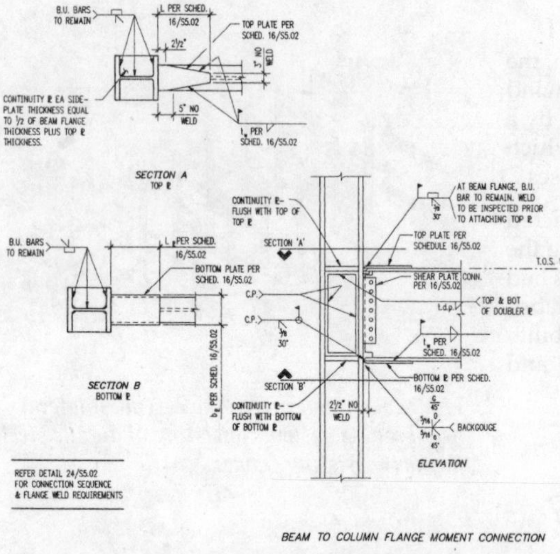

Figure 32 Construction details at moment-resisting column-beam connection. Steel stiffener plates and angles are added to resist local bending of the column at the flanges. Courtesy of Mithun Partners, Inc.

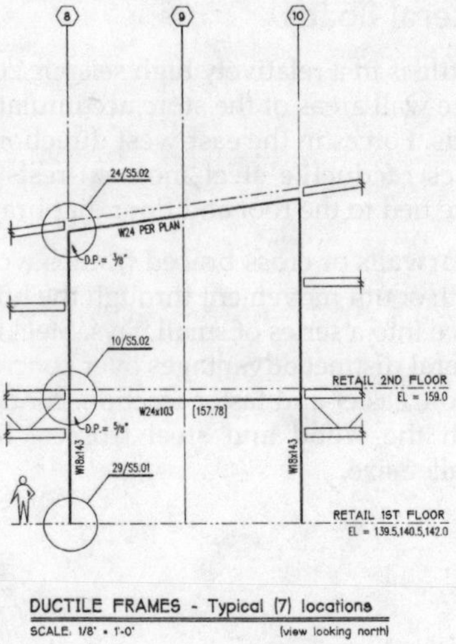

Figure 34 Construction drawing of a typical ductile frame. Courtesy of Mithun Partners, Inc.

Figure 33 Photograph of moment-resisting column-beam connection at first-floor truss. Additional steel plates were welded to the top and bottom flanges of the beams, preventing structural failure in an earthquake. Study of the Northridge, CA, earthquake led to the development of this detail, which exceeds current seismic code requirements in Seattle. Photo courtesy of Mithun Partners, Inc.

North-south lateral loads were resisted through plywood roof and floor diaphragms, which were collected and directed into steel diagonal braced frames in the exterior walls. The diagonal cross-braces were very effective, and only two bays on the east and west walls were required. These braces were exposed on the exterior of the east elevation, and windows were located there to further reveal their presence.

The exposed portion of the diagonal braces on the east elevation were designed to appear symmetrical top and bottom, matching the bracing on the climbing pinnacle tower. Behind the metal siding, the diagonal braces extended to the floor framing and diaphragm.

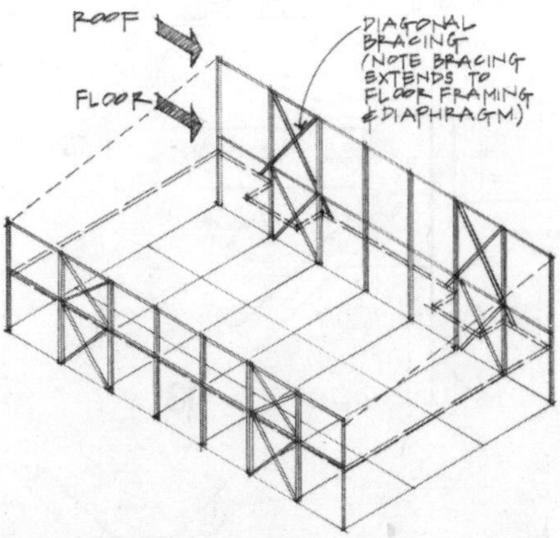

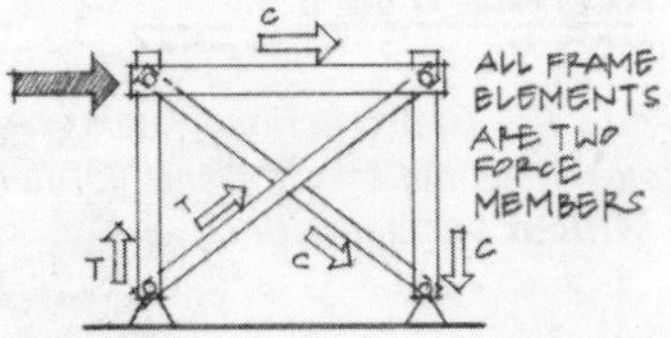

Figure 35 Diagram of the diagonal bracing system at the east and west walls of the retail building. Drawings courtesy of Mithun Partners, Inc.

Figure 36 Photograph of the diagonal bracing system meeting the building envelope. The structural bays are further defined by setting the wall back, using a lighter-color siding, and placing windows behind the braced frame. Photo courtesy of Mithun Partners, Inc.

Figure 37 Photograph of the diagonal braces at the east elevation. The braces do not align with the second floor diaphragm; instead, they extend to the floor concealed behind the exterior siding. Photograph by Robert Pisano.

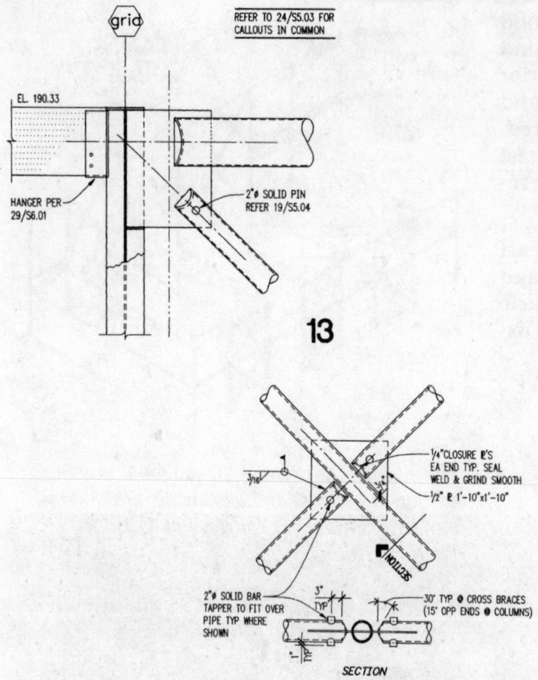

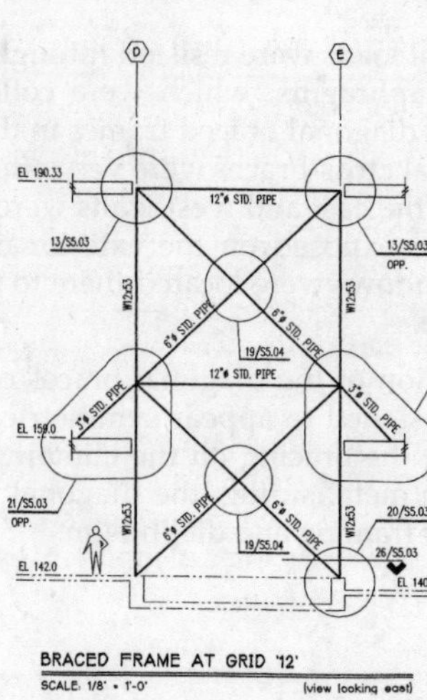

Figure 38 Construction drawings—elevation of a typical diagonal braced frame. Drawings courtesy of Mithun Partners, Inc.

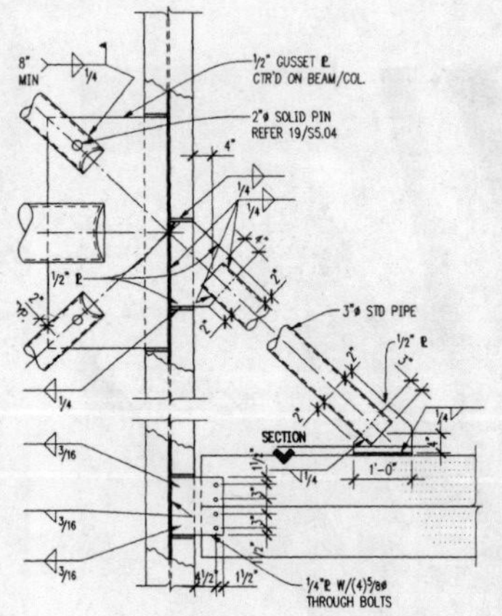

Figure 39 Construction drawings at diagonal braced frame. The concentric section of the steel pipe efficiently resists axial tension and compression loads. Drawings courtesy of Mithun Partners, Inc.

5 INTEGRATION OF BUILDING SYSTEMS

All building systems—lighting, heating and cooling, ventilation, plumbing, fire sprinklers, and electrical—have a rational basis that governs their arrangement. It is generally more elegant and cost-effective to coordinate these systems, thus avoiding conflict and compromise in their performance. This is especially the case where structure is exposed and dropped ceiling spaces are not available to conceal duct and pipe runs.

After the spaces and systems had been roughly arranged in schematic design, the architects and engineers worked through several generations of plans and sections to refine the size and location of system components and resolve any conflicts between systems.

Figure 40 Roof drains are located on either side of the glu-lam roof beam at the entry porch. Steel downspouts are supported by the column in the wall. Photo by author.

Figure 41 Mechanical supply and return air ducts, lighting fixtures, and the fire sprinkler system are coordinated with the structural elements and spatial requirements. The open webs of the roof and floor trusses allow space for these other systems to run perpendicular to the framing. Photo courtesy of Mithun Partners, Inc.

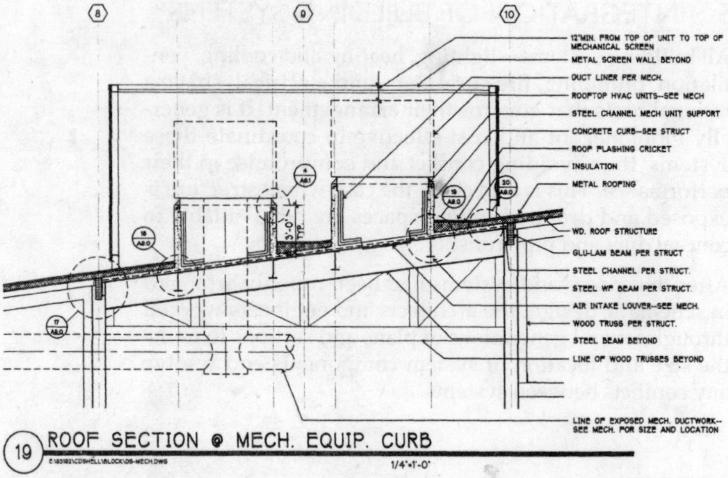

Figure 42 Section at rooftop mechanical equipment shows structural frame in relation to air handler and ductwork. Drawing courtesy of Mithun Partners, Inc.

Figure 43 The middle bay of the retail sales building provides a central distribution location for the ventilation ducts. Photo courtesy of Mithun Partners, Inc.

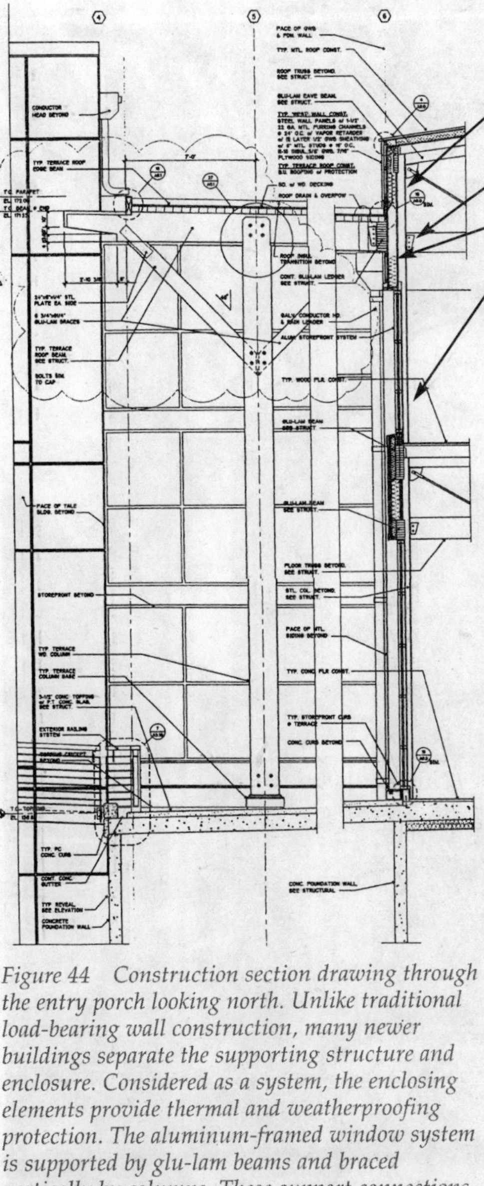

Glu-lam beam at eave provides lateral support for roof edge and top of wall framing.

Roof and floor trusses bear directly on steel columns.

Glu-lam ledger beam supports porch roof beams.

Aluminum window system is supported vertically by metal wall studs and horizontally by glu-lam beams.

Figure 44 Construction section drawing through the entry porch looking north. Unlike traditional load-bearing wall construction, many newer buildings separate the supporting structure and enclosure. Considered as a system, the enclosing elements provide thermal and weatherproofing protection. The aluminum-framed window system is supported by glu-lam beams and braced vertically by columns. These support connections must be carefully detailed to accommodate the deflection and displacement of the primary structure under load without loading the enclosing elements. Differential thermal expansion of the structural frame and skin must also be considered.

An elevation of the secondary wall framing (inset drawing) was provided by the structural engineers to describe the location, size, and connection of beams to columns and wall framing. Drawings courtesy of Mithun Partners, Inc.

Photograph of the entry wall on grid line 6 under construction. Steel columns and glu-lam beams support the light-gauge steel stud framing. Photo courtesy of Mithun Partners, Inc.

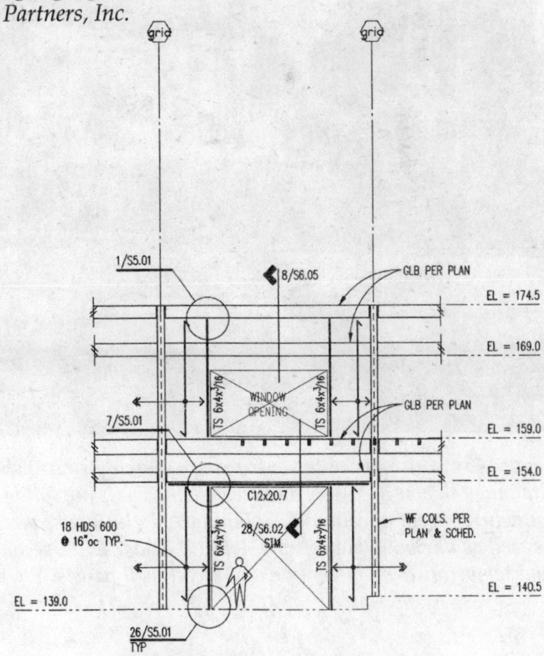

Figure 45 This view of the entry porch (looking south) shows the wall and roof structure described in the drawings shown in Figure 44. Because the walls are not load bearing, windows and doors can be located anywhere except at columns. Columns and glu-lam beams are required to support the actual weight of the wall as well as the wind and seismic (lateral) loads. These secondary structural members are protected from weather and temperature by insulation and metal wall panels. Photograph by Robert Pisano.

Details and Connections

Connections must be carefully designed to transfer loads predictably, particularly when the load path is redirected or changed. The structural action (tension, compression, bending, torsion, shear) of each assembly ultimately determines the behavior of the structural framework. In the REI building, pin or hinge joints would be used to prevent the transfer of bending moments at a connection by accommodating controlled movement or rotation. At the entry stair tower, construction materials would be clearly identifiable, with each connection visible and directly contributing to the rugged utilitarian character of the building.

(a)

(b)

Figure 46 The shed roof framing at the entry stair tower (a) is supported by a small wide-flange beam and two steel pipe columns (b) triangulated in a "V." A cast-in-place concrete wall carries the column loads to the foundation and ground.

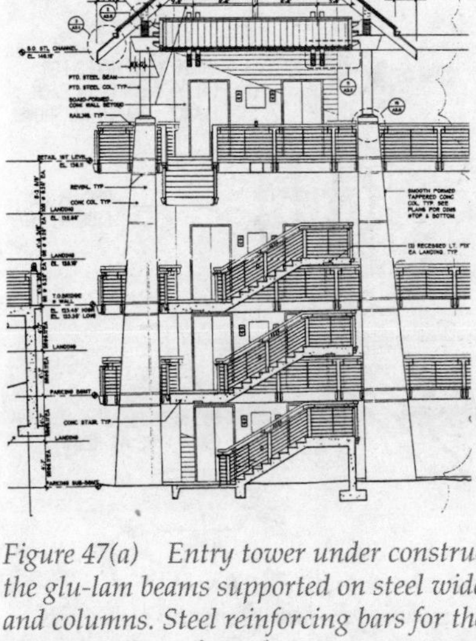

Figure 47(a) Entry tower under construction shows the glu-lam beams supported on steel wide-flange beams and columns. Steel reinforcing bars for the concrete stairs cantilever from the concrete supporting wall.

Figure 47(b) By examining the roof support at the south end of the entry stair tower, one can see how the theoretical principles of statics and strength of materials are applied. The section is cut through the roof behind the steel pipe "V." The 4" × 6" purlins run perpendicular to two pairs of glu-lam beams, which are shown at the section cut. Photographs and drawings on this page are courtesy of Mithun Partners, Inc.

Figure 48 The W10 × steel beam has stiffener plates welded to the web and flanges to prevent local failure as loads and stresses increase at the connection. Photo by author.

Bent steel plate connectors were welded to the top to the steel wide-flange beam to accept the sloping glu-lam beams. The $\frac{5}{8} \times 6''$lag screws through the bottom bearing plate into the beams and two through bolts at the side plates completed the connection. A short W6 × 20 section welded to the top of the beam acted as a spacer and connector. These were predrilled and welded to the W10 × steel beam in the fabrication shop. Bolt holes in the glu-lams and purlins were shop drilled to speed onsite erection.

The four-inch-diameter steel pipe acted as both column and lateral brace. A steel kerf plate, cut to the required angle, was welded in a slot cut in the pipe. This common steel connection enabled increased welding at the joint, and provided a $\frac{3}{4}''$-thick steel bearing plate for the beam. The prefabricated beam and diagonal support were field bolted. Slotted bolt holes allowed some assembly tolerance and thermal movement of the beam.

Careful preparation and review of shop drawings ensured that the assembly would act as intended and that the parts would fit together efficiently onsite. In construction, important details consider the properties, shape, and physical dimensions of the materials to be joined as well as the tools and tradespeople needed to assemble them.

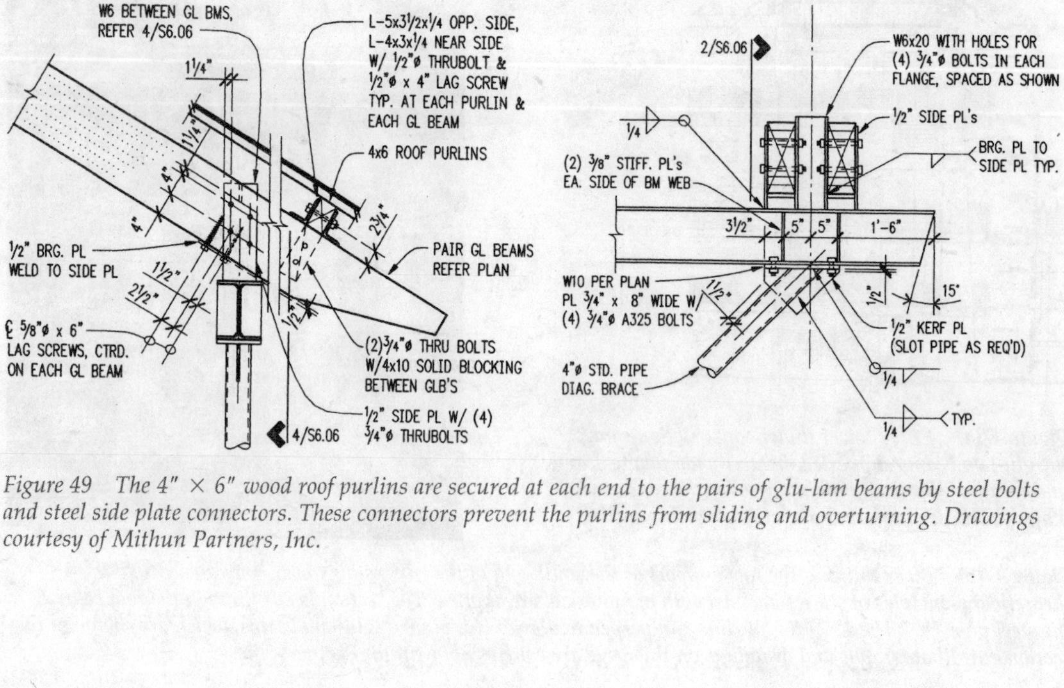

Figure 49 The 4" × 6" wood roof purlins are secured at each end to the pairs of glu-lam beams by steel bolts and steel side plate connectors. These connectors prevent the purlins from sliding and overturning. Drawings courtesy of Mithun Partners, Inc.

6 CONSTRUCTION SEQUENCE

Building proceeds from the ground up. Sitework, demolition, clearing, excavation, shoring, and grading prepared the site for foundations. While concrete foundations and substructure were being completed onsite, many components of the structural frame were prefabricated in shops and trucked to the site as needed. This overlapping of construction saved time and money. Large stationary tools and equipment allowed closer tolerances in shop fabrication—cutting, drilling, and welding. In Seattle, rainy winter weather made shop fabrication even more attractive.

Some parts of the structure, like the glu-lam and steel trusses, were prefabricated and set in place by crane. The steel moment frames were too large to truck to the site, so they were partly prefabricated. Erection bolts were used to secure members temporarily while site welding was completed.

Figure 50 Site casting is used to achieve monolithic, moment-resisting joints in concrete. The general contractor is responsible for the engineering of formwork and scaffolding required for large and complex pours. Photo courtesy of Mithun Partners, Inc.

Figure 51 Erection sequence of the climbing tower braced frames. Portions of the four frames were shop-fabricated and shipped to the site, where they were assembled and welded, each on top of the other. The frames, corner columns, and corner struts were then erected in one weekend so that the mobile crane would not interfere with freeway commuters. Photos courtesy of Mithun Partners, Inc.

7 CONCLUSION

The REI building, like most successful building projects, involved the effort of many design and construction professionals working together in the spirit of collaboration. The early decision to expose and express the structural system required collaboration from the earliest design sketches. The architects, structural engineers, and builders, while not always agreeing on the same course of action, nevertheless understood and appreciated one another's expertise. This creative conflict, managed constructively, resulted in a project greater than the sum of the individuals.

The structural engineers for this project did not simply calculate loads, stresses, and deflections to ensure that the architect's design would stand up. At the same time, the architects did not simply conceive of a sculptural or spatial form without regard for basic principles of structural soundness, order, and stability. Structural design is rarely, if ever, entirely rational or pure. Engineers rely on professional experience and intuition as well as the analytical methods and formulas developed over the course of engineering history.

The structural system as a whole must be configured. Assumptions about probable loads and load paths must be made and tested by calculation to ensure the stability of a structure. Each member and connection must be designed to act as intended, resisting loads and stress concentrations. The effects of time and weather must be anticipated to accommodate movement and prevent corrosion or premature failure.

After a building is finally constructed and loaded, it is very difficult to determine if it is behaving exactly as designed. Loads may not be distributed or concentrated as anticipated, and under some conditions, structural members may be acting in compression rather than tension. Therefore, building codes and good engineering practice provide adequate safety factors and redundancy.

The REI building demonstrates that good structural design and architecture are possible without overly expressive, exotic, or untested configurations and materials. It is possible to utilize time-tested engineering principles and materials in an imaginative and appropriate way to achieve a successful building.

Figure 52 Photograph of the climbing pinnacle and enclosing tower. Photo courtesy of Mithun Partners, Inc.

Figure 53 One of two interior stair structures. Photograph by Robert Pisano.

Definition of Terms

Measurement	U.S. Units	Metric (S.I.)
a measure of length	inch (in. or ″)	millimeter (mm)
	feet (ft. or ′)	meter (m)
a measure of area	square inches (in.^{2})	square millimeters (mm^2)
	square feet (ft.^{2})	square meters (m^2)
a measure of mass	pound mass (lbm)	kilogram (kg)
a measure of force	pound (lb. or #)	newton (N)
	kilopound = 1,000 lb. (k)	kilonewton = 1,000 N (kN)
a measure of stress (force/area)	psi (lb./in.^{2} or #/in.^{2})	pascal (N/m^2)
	ksi (k/in.^{2})	
a measure of pressure	psf (lb./ft.^{2} or #/ft.^{2})	kilopascal = 1,000 Pa
moment (force × distance)	pound-feet (lb.-ft. or #-ft.)	newton-meter (N-m)
	kip-feet (k-ft.)	kilonewton-meter (kN-m)
a load distributed over length	ω (lb./ft., #/ft., or plf)	ω (kN/m)
density (weight/volume)	γ (lb./ft.^{3} or #/ft.^{3})	γ (kN/m^3)

force = (mass) × (acceleration); acceleration due to gravity: 32.17 ft./sec.^{2} = 9.807 m/sec.^{2}

Conversions

1 m = 39.37 in.	1 ft. = 0.3048 m
1 m^2 = 10.76 ft.^{2}	1 ft.^{2} = 92.9×10^{-3} m^2
1 kg = 2.205 lb.-mass	1 lbm = 0.4536 kg
1 kN = 224.8 lb.-force	1 lb. = 4.448 N
1 kPa = 20.89 lb./ft.^{2}	1 lb./ft.^{2} = 47.88 Pa
1 MPa = 145 lb./in.^{2}	1 lb./in.^{2} = 6.895 kPa
1 kg/m = 0.672 lbm/ft.	1 lbm/ft. = 1.488 kg/m
1 kN/m = 68.52 lb./ft.	1 lb./ft = 14.59 N/m

Prefix	Symbol	Factor
giga-	G	10^9 or 1,000,000,000
mega-	M	10^6 or 1,000,000
kilo-	k	10^3 or 1,000
milli-	m	10^{-3} or 0.001

Index

Page references followed by "f" indicate illustrated figures or photographs; followed by "t" indicates a table.

C

Y

Z